PHYSICAL CHEMISTRY

WALTER J. MOORE

PROFESSOR OF CHEMISTRY
INDIANA UNIVERSITY

PHYSICAL CHEMISTRY

PRENTICE-HALL, INC.
ENGLEWOOD CLIFFS, N. J.

THIRD EDITION

PRENTICE-HALL CHEMISTRY SERIES

PRENTICE-HALL INTERNATIONAL, INC.
LONDON • TOKYO • SYDNEY • PARIS
PRENTICE-HALL OF CANADA, LTD.
PRENTICE-HALL DE MEXICO, S.A.

Third printing...... September, 1963

LIBRARY OF CONGRESS CATALOG CARD NUMBER 62-10559

PRINTED IN THE UNITED STATES OF AMERICA

66594-C

PREFACE

I have written this book to introduce physical chemistry to university students. One physical chemist defined his subject as the study of anything in science that is interesting. This enthusiasm, though understandable, is a bit excessive. On the other hand, many interesting scientific fields do involve considerable physical chemistry. This is true not only of pure chemistry, but also of interdisciplinary fields such as medical research, molecular biology, nuclear engineering and geochemistry.

This third edition is, in many respects, a new book. The arrangement of the chapters has been changed so as to bring the subjects of chemical kinetics and electrochemistry into an earlier part of the course. The present arrangement fairly consistently places first the facts of experimental chemistry. The interpretations in terms of the fine structure of matter then follow inductively. I do not mean to imply by this sequence that electrons are any less real than steam engines. I do believe, however, that the logical structure of thermodynamics has an architectural beauty, which deserves a little time to be contemplated without distractions. On the other hand, the teacher who wishes to start with elementary particles and work his way upward to steam engines can rearrange the order without serious difficulty, bringing Chapters 7, 11, 12, 13, and 14 to the fore.

Students who study this text will find a previous acquaintance with basic physics and elementary mathematics (including calculus) to be helpful, and even necessary. Yet, a student who plans to do research should begin his study of physical chemistry as soon as possible. He must expect, therefore, to learn some of the mathematics and physics as he goes along. Students should not shy away from physical chemistry because of its mathematical format. Even some practising physical chemists have problems in this regard. Einstein once remarked that the trouble with chemistry is that it is too difficult for chemists. Nevertheless, with clear thinking, hard work, critical experiments, wild experiments, and good luck, some progress has been made. There are even a few physical chemists (mostly statistical mechanicians) who have achieved a degree of mathematical elegance.

The advice of Paul Klee to students of art seems applicable also to the work of the physical chemist: "We construct and keep on constructing, yet intuition is still a good thing. You can do a good deal without it, but not everything. Where intuition is combined with exact research it speeds up the progress of research. Exactitude winged by intuition is at times best. But because exact research is exact research, it gets ahead even without intuition. It can be logical; it can construct. It can build bridges boldly from one thing to another. It can maintain order in the midst of turmoil."*

Some of my scientific friends generously spent valuable hours to give good advice and correction concerning many points in the manuscript. The mistakes that remain were all put there by the author and by the publisher afterwards. I wish especially to thank the following colleagues: Walter Kauzmann, Ken Pitzer, Bob Parr, Frank Ellison, Gilbert Mains, Jacques Fresco, Ralph Seifert, Harrison Shull, André de Bethune, Ward Schaap, Michael Kasha, Jim Arnold, Dick Curtis, Charles Tanford, John Arents, Martin Gouterman, Ed Hughes, Russ Bonham, S. P. McGlynn, Austin Taylor, Walter Stockmayer and Robert Scott. Scientists and publishers in many parts of the world kindly provided illustrative material. Acknowledgments are made with the pictures in the text. Marcia Haag prepared the manuscript for the publisher; my wife, Patricia, compiled the index. Anton Siqueira was in charge of the production for Prentice-Hall, Inc. and Theodore Lortscher drew the figures.

In this edition, the problems have been divided into two sections by a thin double line. The student who crosses this line does so at his own risk. The problems above the line are believed to provide straightforward illustrations of the text material without any pitfalls. A number of problems were taken from the collection of R. Krishnamurthy, and Derek Klemperer provided an interesting set used at the University of Melbourne. Dudley Herschbach earned the gratitude of the author (if not of the students) by contributing an entire set of problems from his course in molecular structure at Berkeley.

Comments and criticisms from users of this edition will be received with thanks.

W. J. MOORE

*"Exakte Versuche im Bereiche der Kunst" (1928). Translated by Paul Manheim in *The Thinking Eye* (New York: Wittenborn, 1961).

CONTENTS

1. THE DESCRIPTION OF PHYSICOCHEMICAL SYSTEMS, 1

2. THE FIRST LAW OF THERMODYNAMICS, 35

3. THE SECOND LAW OF THERMODYNAMICS, 69

15. CHEMICAL STATISTICS, 617

16. THE SOLID STATE, 645

17. THE LIQUID STATE, 703

18. PHYSICAL CHEMISTRY OF SURFACES, 727

1 THE DESCRIPTION OF PHYSICOCHEMICAL SYSTEMS

The essential components of the scientific method are experiment and theory. Experiments are planned observations of the physical world. A theory seeks to correlate observables with ideals. These ideals have often taken the form of simplified models, which, in turn, are based on everyday experience. We have, for example, the little billiard balls of the kinetic theory of gases, the miniature hooks and springs of chemical bonds, and the microcosmic solar systems of atomic theory.

As man's investigation of the universe progressed to the almost infinitely large distances of interstellar space or to the almost infinitesimal magnitudes of atomic structures, he began to realize that these other worlds could not be adequately described in terms of the bricks and mortar and plumbing of terrestrial architecture. Thus a straight line might be the shortest distance between two points on a blackboard, but not between Sirius and Aldebaran. We can ask whether Graham Greene is in London, but we cannot ask whether electron A is at point B.

Intensive research into the ultimate nature of our universe thus changes the meanings we attach to such words as "explanation" or "understanding." Originally they signified a representation of the strange in terms of the commonplace; nowadays, scientific explanation tends more to be a description of the relatively familiar in terms of the unfamiliar, light in terms of photons, matter in terms of waves. Yet, in our search for understanding, we still consider it important to "get a physical picture" of the process behind the mathematical treatment of a theory.

1. PHYSICAL CHEMISTRY

There are probably two equally logical approaches to the study of a branch of scientific knowledge such as physical chemistry. We may adopt a synthetic approach and, beginning with the structure and behavior of matter in its finest known states of subdivision, gradually progress from electrons to atoms to molecules to states of aggregation and chemical reactions. Alternatively, we may adopt an analytical treatment and, starting with matter or chemicals as we find them in the laboratory, gradually work our way back to finer states of subdivision as we require them to explain our experimental results. This latter method follows more closely the historical development, although a strict adherence to history is impossible in a broad subject whose different branches have progressed at very different rates.

Two main problems have occupied most of the efforts of physical chemists: the question of the position of chemical equilibrium, which is the principal problem of chemical thermodynamics; and the question of the rate of chemical reactions, which is the field of chemical kinetics. Since these problems are ultimately concerned with the interactions of molecules, their final solution should be implicit in the mechanics of molecules and molecular aggregates. Therefore molecular structure is an important part of physical chemistry. The discipline that allows us to bring our knowledge of molecular structure to bear on the problems of equilibrium and kinetics is found in the study of statistical mechanics.

We shall begin our study of physical chemistry with thermodynamics, which is based on concepts common to the everyday world. We shall follow quite closely the historical development of the subject, since more knowledge can be gained by watching the construction of something than by inspecting the polished final product.

2. MECHANICS: FORCE

The first thing that may be said of thermodynamics is that the word itself is evidently derived from *dynamics*, which is a branch of mechanics dealing with matter in motion.

Mechanics was founded on the work of Isaac Newton (1642–1727), and usually begins with a statement of the well known equation

$$f = ma$$

with

$$a = dv/dt = d^2r/dt^2 \tag{1.1}$$

The equation states the proportionality between a vector quantity f, called the force applied to a particle of matter, and the acceleration a of the particle, a vector in the same direction, with a proportionality factor m, called the *mass*. (A vector is a quantity that has a definite direction as well as a definite magnitude.) Equation (1.1) may also be written

$$f = \frac{d(mv)}{dt} \tag{1.2}$$

where the product of mass and velocity is called the *momentum*.

With mass in grams, time in seconds, and displacement r in centimeters (cgs system), the unit force is the *dyne*. With mass in kilograms, time in seconds and displacement in meters (mks system), the unit force is the *newton*.

Mass might be introduced in Newton's *Law of Gravitation*,

$$f = \frac{\mu m_1 m_2}{r_{12}^2}$$

which states that there is an attractive force between two masses proportional to their product and inversely proportional to the square of their separation. If this gravitational mass is to be the same as the inertial mass of Eq. (1.1), the proportionality constant

$$\mu = 6.66 \times 10^{-8} \text{ cm}^3 \text{ sec}^{-2} \text{ g}^{-1}$$

The weight of a body, W, is the force with which it is attracted towards the earth, and, naturally, may vary slightly at various points on the earth's surface, owing to the slight variation of r_{12} with latitude and elevation, and of the effective mass of the earth with subterranean density.
Thus

$$W = mg$$

At New York City, $g = 980.267$ cm per sec^2; at Spitzbergen, $g = 982.899$; at Panama, $g = 978.243$.

In practice, the mass of a body is measured by comparing its weight by means of a balance with that of known standards $(m_1/m_2 = W_1/W_2)$.

3. MECHANICAL WORK

In mechanics, if the point of application of a force f moves, the force is said to *do work*. The amount of work done by a force f whose point of application moves a distance dr along the direction of the force is

$$dw = f\,dr \tag{1.3}$$

If the direction of motion of the point of application is not the same as the direction of the force, but at an angle θ to it, we have the situation shown in Fig. 1.1. The component of f in the direction of motion is $f \cos \theta$, and the element of work is

$$dw = f \cos \theta \, dr \tag{1.4}$$

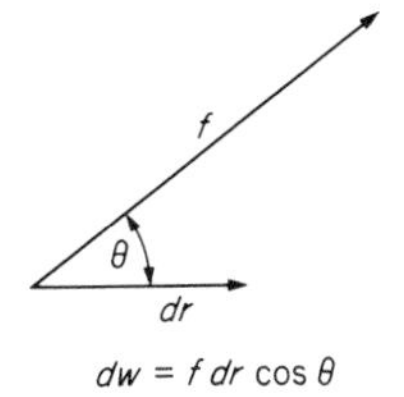

FIG. 1.1 Definition of differential element of work.

For the case of a force constant in direction and in magnitude, Eq. (1.3) can be integrated to give

$$w = \int_{r_0}^{r_1} f\,dr = f(r_1 - r_0)$$

An example is the force acting on a body of mass m in the earth's gravitational field. Over distances which are short when compared to the diameter of the earth, this $f = mg$. To lift a body against earth's gravitational attraction we must apply to it an external force equal to mg. What is the work done on a mass of 1 kg when it is lifted a distance of one meter?

$$w = mgr_1 = (1)(980.7 \times 10^{-2})(1) \text{ kg m sec}^{-2} \text{ m} = 980.7 \times 10^{-2} \text{ kg m}^2 \text{ sec}^{-2}$$
$$= 9.807 \text{ newton meter} = 9.807 \text{ joule}$$

An application of Eq. (1.3) in which the force is not a constant is in the stretching of a perfectly elastic spring. In accord with the law of Hooke, 1660, *ut tensio sic vis:* the restoring force is directly proportional to the extension,

$$f = -\kappa r \tag{1.5}$$

where κ is called the *force constant* of the spring. Hence the work dw done on the spring to extend it by dr is

$$dw = \kappa r \, dr$$

Suppose the spring is stretched by a distance r_1,

$$w = \int_0^{r_1} \kappa r \, dr = \frac{\kappa}{2} r_1^2$$

The work done *on* the spring is taken by convention to be positive.

4. MECHANICAL ENERGY

In 1644, René Descartes declared that in the beginning God imparted to the universe a certain amount of motion in the form of vortices, and this motion endured eternally and could be neither increased nor decreased. For almost a century after the death of Descartes, a great controversy raged between his followers and those of Leibniz on the question of whether motion was conserved. As often happens, lack of a precise definition of the terms used prevented a meeting of minds. The word *motion* then usually designated what we now call *momentum*. In fact the momentum in any given direction is conserved in collisions between elastic bodies.

In 1669 Huygens discovered that if he multiplied each mass m by the square of its velocity v^2, the sum of these products was conserved in all collisions between elastic bodies. Leibniz called mv^2 the *vis viva*. In 1735 Jean Bernoulli asked himself what happened to the *vis viva* in an inelastic collision. He concluded that some of it was lost into some kind of *vis mortua*. In all mechanical systems operating without friction the sum of *vis viva* and *vis mortua* was conserved at a constant value. In 1742, this idea was also clearly expressed by Gabrielle du Châtelet, Voltaire's mistress, who said that although it was difficult to follow the course of the *vis viva* in an inelastic collision, it must nevertheless be conserved in some way.

The first to use the word "energy" appears to have been d'Alembert in the French *Encyclopédie* of 1785. "There is in a body in movement an effort or *énergie*, which is not at all in a body at rest." In 1787 Thomas Young called the *vis viva* the "actual energy" and the *vis mortua* the "potential energy." The name "kinetic energy" for $\frac{1}{2} mv^2$ was introduced much later by William Thomson.

We can give these developments a mathematical formulation starting with Eq. (1.3). Let us consider a body at position r_0 and apply to it a force $f(r)$ that depends only on its position. In the absence of any other forces, the work done on the body in a finite displacement from r_0 to r_1 is

$$w = \int_{r_0}^{r_1} f(r)\, dr \tag{1.6}$$

The integral over distance can be transformed to an integral over time:

$$w = \int_{t_0}^{t_1} f(r) \frac{dr}{dt}\, dt = \int_{t_0}^{t_1} f(r)\, v\, dt$$

Introducing Newton's Law of Force, Eq. (1.1), we obtain

$$w = \int_{t_0}^{t_1} m \frac{dv}{dt} v\, dt = m \int_{v_0}^{v_1} v\, dv$$

$$w = \tfrac{1}{2}mv_1^2 - \tfrac{1}{2}mv_0^2 \tag{1.7}$$

The kinetic energy is defined by

$$T = \tfrac{1}{2}mv^2$$

Hence,

$$w = \int_{r_0}^{r_1} f(r)\, dr = T_1 - T_0 \tag{1.8}$$

The work done on the body equals the difference between its kinetic energies in the final and the initial states.

Since the force in Eq. (1.8) is a function of r alone, the integral defines another function of r which we can write thus:

$$f(r)\, dr = -dU(r)$$

or

$$f(r) = -dU(r)/dr \tag{1.9}$$

Thus, Eq. (1.8) becomes

$$\int_{r_0}^{r_1} f(r)\, dr = U(r_0) - U(r_1) = T_1 - T_0$$

or

$$U_0 + T_0 = U_1 + T_1 \tag{1.10}$$

The new function $U(r)$ is the *potential energy*. The sum of the potential and the kinetic energies, $U + T$, is the total mechanical energy of the body and this sum evidently remains constant during the motion. Equation (1.10) has the form typical of an *equation of conservation*. It is a statement of the mechanical principle of the *conservation of energy*. For example, the gain in kinetic energy of a body falling in a vacuum is exactly balanced by an equal loss in potential energy.

If a force depends on velocity as well as position, the situation is more complex. This would be the case if a body falls, not in a vacuum, but in a viscous fluid like air or water. The higher the velocity, the greater is the frictional or viscous resistance opposed to the gravitational force. We can no longer write $f(r) = -dU/dr$, and we can no longer obtain an equation such as (1.10), because the mechanical energy is no longer conserved. From the dawn of history it has been known that the frictional dissipation of energy is attended by the evolution of something called *heat.* We shall see later how it became possible to include heat among the ways of transforming energy, and in this way to obtain a new and more inclusive principle of the conservation of energy.

It may be noted that whereas the kinetic energy T is zero for a body at rest, there is no naturally defined zero of potential energy. Only differences in potential energy can be measured. Sometimes, however, a zero of potential energy is chosen *by convention;* an example is the choice $U(r) = 0$ for the gravitational potential energy when two bodies are an infinite distance apart.

5. EQUILIBRIUM

The ordinary subjects for chemical experimentation are not individual particles of any sort but more complex *systems,* which may contain solids, liquids and gases. A *system* is a part of the world isolated from the rest of the world by definite boundaries. The experiments that we perform on a system are said to measure its *properties,* these being the attributes that enable us to describe it with all requisite completeness. This complete description is said to define the *state* of the system.

The idea of predictability enters here. Having once measured the properties of a system, we expect to be able to predict the behavior of a second system with the same set of properties from our knowledge of the behavior of the original. This is, in general, possible only when the system has attained a state called *equilibrium.* A system is said to have attained a state of equilibrium when it shows no further tendency to change its properties with time.

A simple mechanical illustration will clarify the concept of equilibrium. Fig. 1.2(a) shows three different equilibrium positions of a box resting on a table. In both positions A and C, the center of gravity of the box is lower than in any slightly displaced position, and if the box is tilted slightly it will tend to return spontaneously to its original equilibrium position. The gravitational potential energy of the box in positions A or C is at a minimum, and both positions represent *stable equilibrium* states. Yet it is apparent that position C is more stable than position A, and a certain large tilt of A will suffice to push it over into C. In position A therefore, the box is said to be in *metastable equilibrium.*

Position B is also an equilibrium position, but it is a state of *unstable equilibrium,* as anyone who has tried to balance a chair on two legs will agree. The center of gravity of the box in B is higher than in any slightly displaced position, and the tiniest tilt will send the box into either position A or C. The potential

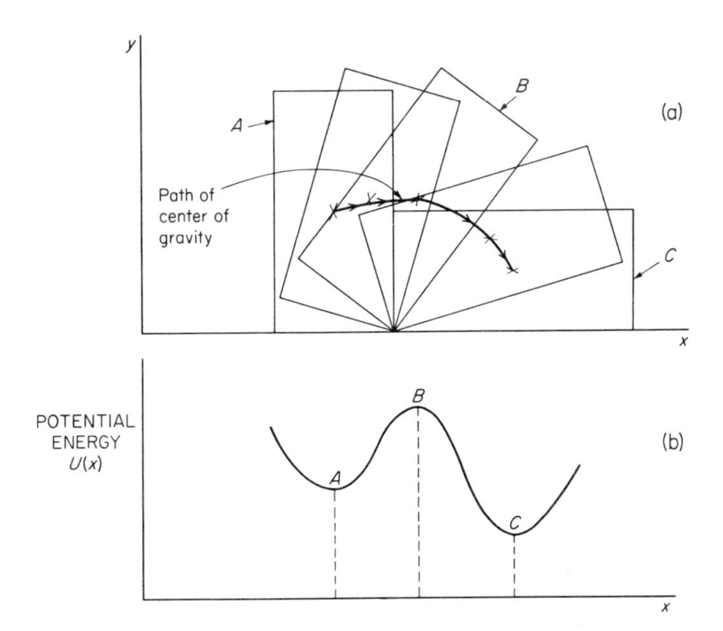

FIG. 1.2 An illustration of mechanical equilibrium.

energy at a position of unstable equilibrium is a maximum, and such a position could be realized only in the absence of any disturbing forces.

These relations may be presented in more mathematical form by plotting in Fig. 1.2(b) the potential energy of the system as a function of the horizontal position of the center of gravity in Fig. 1.2(a). Positions of stable equilibrium are seen to be minima in the curve, and the position of unstable equilibrium is represented by a maximum. Positions of stable and unstable equilibrium alternate in this way in any system. For an equilibrium position, the slope dU/dr of the curve for U vs. displacement is equal to zero, and one may write the equilibrium condition as

$$\left(\frac{dU}{dr}\right)_{r=r_0} = 0$$

Although these considerations have been presented in terms of a simple mechanical model, similar principles will be found to apply in the more complex physicochemical systems that we shall study. In addition to purely mechanical changes, such systems may undergo temperature changes, changes of state of aggregation, and chemical reactions. The problem of thermodynamics is to discover or invent new functions that will play the role in these more general systems that the potential energy plays in mechanics.

6. THE THERMAL PROPERTIES OF MATTER

In order to specify precisely the state of a substance studied in the laboratory, we must give the numerical values of certain of its measured properties. Since there are equations that give relations between properties, it is not necessary to specify the values of each and every property in order to define exactly the state of a substance. In fact, if we ignore external fields of force (gravitational, electromagnetic) and take a gas or a liquid as the substance under consideration,* the exact specification of its state requires the values of only a few quantities. At present, we shall confine the problem to individual, pure substances, for which no composition variables are needed. To specify the state of a pure gas or liquid, we may first of all state the mass m of the substance. Then, there are three variables, any two of which may be specified. These are the pressure P, the volume V, and the temperature θ. If any two of these are fixed, the value of the third will also be fixed, because of the existence of a relation between the variables. In other words, of the three variables of state, P, V, θ, only two are independent variables. Note particularly that we may describe the state of the substance entirely in terms of the two mechanical variables, P and V, and not use the thermal variable θ at all.

The use of the pressure P as a variable to describe the state of a substance requires some care. In Fig. 1.3, consider a fluid contained in a cylinder with a frictionless piston. We can calculate the pressure on the fluid by dividing the force on the piston by its area. (P = force/area.) At equilibrium, this pressure will be uniform throughout the fluid, so that on any imaginary unit area in the fluid there will be a force P. A pressure is thus a stress that is uniform in all directions.

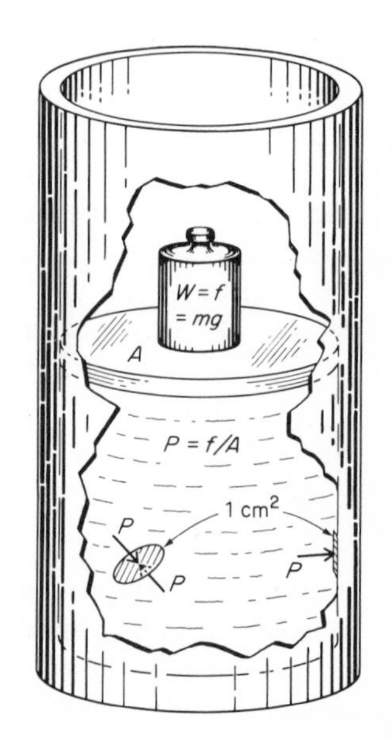

FIG. 1.3 Definition of pressure in a fluid, neglecting gravitational field in the fluid.

In this analysis, we neglect the effect of the weight of the fluid itself. If we included the weight, there would be an extra force per unit area, increasing with the depth of the fluid and equal to the weight of the column of fluid above the given section. In the subsequent analysis this effect of the weight will be neglected and we shall consider the pressure of a volume of fluid to be the same throughout. This simplification is what we mean by "ignoring the gravitational field."

If the fluid is not in equilibrium, we can still speak of the external pressure P_{ex} on the piston, but this is clearly not a property of the state of the fluid itself. Until equilibrium is restored, the pressure may vary from point to point in the fluid and we cannot define its state by a single pressure P.

The properties of a system can be classified as *extensive* or *intensive*. Extensive properties are additive; their value for the whole system is equal to the sum of their values for the individual parts. Sometimes they are called *capacity*

---

* The properties of solids may depend in a rather complicated way on *direction*.

factors. Examples are the volume and the mass. Intensive properties, or *intensity factors,* are not additive. Examples are temperature and pressure. The temperature of any small part of a system in equilibrium is the same as the temperature of the whole.

Before we use the temperature θ as a physical quantity, we should consider how it can be measured quantitatively. The concept of *temperature* evolved from sensual perceptions of hotness and coldness. It was found that these perceptions could be correlated with the readings of *thermometers* based on the volume changes of liquids. In 1631, the French physician Jean Rey used a glass bulb having a stem partly filled with water to follow the progress of fevers in his patients. In 1641, Ferdinand II, Grand Duke of Tuscany and founder of the Accademia del Cimento of Florence, invented an alcohol-in-glass *thermoscope* to which a scale was added by marking equal divisions between the volumes at "coldest winter cold" and "hottest summer heat." A calibration based on two fixed points was introduced in 1688 by Dalencé, who chose the melting point of snow as $-10°$ and the melting point of butter as $+10°$. In 1694 Renaldi took the boiling point of water as the upper fixed point and the melting point of ice as the lower. To make the specification of these fixed points exact, we must add the requirements that the pressure is maintained at one atmosphere, and that the water in equilibrium with ice is saturated with air. Apparently Elvius, a Swede, in 1710, first suggested assigning the values 0° and 100° to these two points. They define the *centigrade scale,* officially called the *Celsius scale,* after a Swedish astronomer who used a similar system.

7. TEMPERATURE AS A MECHANICAL PROPERTY

The existence of a temperature function can be based on the fact that whenever two bodies are separately brought to equilibrium with a third body, they are then found to be in equilibrium with each other.

We can specify the state of each body by specifying its pressure P and volume V. If we so prefer, we may choose one body (1) and call it a *thermometer,* and use some property of the state of this body (P_1, V_1) to define a temperature scale. When any second body (2) is brought into equilibrium with the *thermometer,* the equilibrium value of $\theta_1(P_1, V_1)$ measures its temperature.

$$\theta_2 = \theta_1(P_1, V_1) \tag{1.11}$$

Note that the temperature defined and measured in this way is defined entirely in terms of the mechanical properties of pressure and volume, which suffice to define the state of the body. We have left our sensory perceptions of hotness and coldness and reduced the concept of temperature to a mechanical concept.

A simple example of Eq. (1.11) is a liquid thermometer, in which P_1 is kept constant and the volume V_1 is used to measure the temperatures. In other cases, electrical, magnetic, or optical properties can be used to define the temperature scale, since in every case the property θ_1 can be expressed as a function of the state of the body, fixed by specifying P_1 and V_1.

8. THE SPRING OF THE AIR AND BOYLE'S LAW

The mercury barometer was invented in 1643 by Evangelista Torricelli, a mathematician who studied with Galileo in Florence. The height of the column under atmospheric pressure may vary from day to day over a range of several centimeters of mercury, but a standard atmosphere has been *defined* equal to 76.00 cm Hg at 0°C, 45° latitude and sea level. The unit of pressure in the cgs system is dyne cm^{-2}. To convert 76.00 cm Hg to cgs units, we multiply by the density of mercury at 0°C to determine the mass of a mercury column of one square centimeter cross section, and then multiply by the acceleration due to gravity, 980.665 cm sec^{-2}, to obtain the force in dynes at the base of the mercury column. Thus,

$$1 \text{ atm} = 76.00 \text{ cm Hg} = 76.00 \times 13.5950 \times 980.665 = 1.01324 \times 10^6 \text{ dyne cm}^{-2}$$

Another unit of pressure is the *bar* = 10^6 dyne cm^{-2}, slightly less than 1 atm. The millibar is 10^{-3}, and the microbar is 10^{-6} bar or 1 dyne cm^{-2}.

Robert Boyle and his contemporaries often referred to the pressure of a gas as the "spring of the air." They knew that a volume of gas behaved mechanically like a spring. If you compress it in a cylinder with a piston, the piston recoils when the force on it is released. Boyle tried to explain the springiness of the air in terms of the corpuscular theories popular in his day. "Imagine the air," said he, "to be such a heap of little bodies, lying one upon another, as may be resembled to a fleece of wool. For this . . . consists of many slender and flexible hairs, each of which may indeed, like a little spring, be still endeavoring to stretch itself out again." In other words, Boyle supposed that the corpuscles of air were in close contact with each other, and that when air was compressed, the individual corpuscles were compressed like springs. This conclusion was, of course, incorrect.

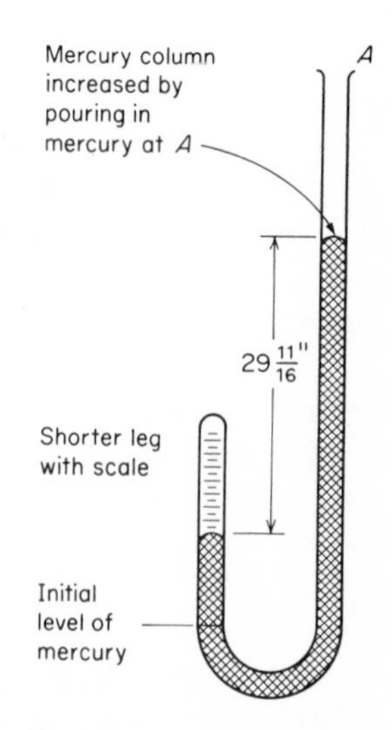

FIG. 1.4 Boyle's J-tube, showing experiment in which the volume of gas was halved when the pressure was doubled.

In 1660 Boyle published the first edition of his book *New Experiments, Physico-Mechanical, Touching the Spring of the Air, and its Effects,* in which he described observations made with a new vacuum pump he had constructed. He found that when the air surrounding the reservoir of a Torricellian barometer was evacuated, the mercury column fell. This experiment seemed to him to prove conclusively that the column was held up by the air pressure. Nevertheless, two attacks on Boyle's work were immediately published, one by Thomas Hobbes, the famous political philosopher and author of *Leviathan*, and the other by a devout Aristotelian, Franciscus Linus. Hobbes based his criticism on the "philosophical impossibility of a vacuum." ("A vacuum is nothing, and what is nothing cannot exist.") Linus claimed that the mercury column was held up by an invisible thread, which fastened itself to the upper end of the tube. This theory seemed quite reasonable, he said, for anyone could easily feel the pull of the thread by covering the end of the barometer tube with his finger.

In answer to these objections, Boyle included an appendix in the second edition of his book, published in 1662, in which he described an important new experiment. He used essentially the apparatus shown in Fig. 1.4. By addition of mercury to the open end of the J-shaped tube, the pressure could be increased on the gas in the closed end. Boyle observed that as the pressure increased, the volume of the gas proportionately decreased. The temperature of the gas was almost constant during these measurements. In modern terms we would therefore state Boyle's result thus: *At constant temperature, the volume of a given sample of gas varies inversely as the pressure.* In mathematical terms, this becomes $P \propto 1/V$ or $P = C/V$ where C is a constant of proportionality. This is equivalent to

$$PV = C \text{ (at constant } \theta) \tag{1.12}$$

Equation (1.12) is known as *Boyle's Law.* It is followed quite closely by many gases at moderate pressures, but the real behavior of gases may deviate greatly, especially at higher pressures.

9. THE LAW OF GAY-LUSSAC

The first detailed experiments on the variation with temperature of the volumes of gases at constant pressures were those published by Joseph Gay-Lussac from 1802 to 1808. Working with the "permanent gases" such as nitrogen, oxygen and hydrogen, he found that the different gases all showed the same dependence of V on θ.

His results can be put into mathematical form as follows. A gas temperature scale is defined by assuming that the volume V varies linearly with the temperature θ. If V_0 is the volume of a sample of gas at 0°C, we have

$$V = V_0(1 + \alpha\theta) \tag{1.13}$$

The coefficient α is called the *thermal expansivity* or *coefficient of thermal expansion.* Gay-Lussac found α approximately equal to 1/267, but in 1847, Regnault obtained the value $\alpha = 1/273$ with an improved experimental procedure. Thus, Eq. (1.13) may be written as,

$$V = V_0\left(1 + \frac{\theta}{273}\right)$$

This relation is called the *Law of Gay-Lussac.* It states that a gas expands by 1/273 of its volume at 0°C for each degree rise in temperature at constant pressure.

Careful measurements revealed that real gases do not obey exactly the Laws of Boyle and Gay-Lussac. The variations are least when a gas is at high temperature and low pressure. Furthermore, the deviations vary from gas to gas; for example, helium obeys closely, whereas carbon dioxide is relatively disobedient. It is useful to introduce the concept of the *ideal gas*, a gas that follows these laws exactly. Since gases at low pressures, i.e., low densities, obey the gas laws most closely, we can often obtain the properties of *ideal gases* by extrapolation to zero pressure of measurements on real gases.

Figure 1.5 shows the results of measurements of α on different gases at successively lower pressures. Note that the scale is greatly expanded so that the

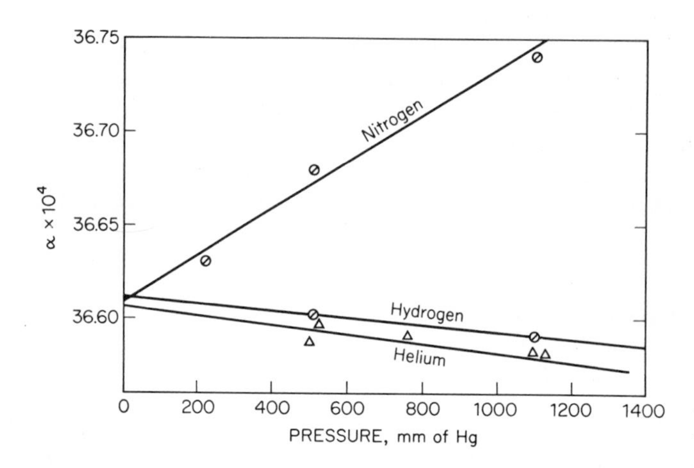

FIG. 1.5 Extrapolation of thermal expansion coefficients to zero pressure.

maximum differences shown do not exceed about 0.5 per cent. Within experimental uncertainty, the value found by extrapolation to zero pressure is the same for all these gases. This is the value of α for an ideal gas. The consensus of the best measurements gives

$$\alpha = 36.610 \times 10^{-4} \text{ deg}^{-1}$$

or

$$1/\alpha = 273.15° \pm .02° = T_0$$

Thus, the Law of Gay-Lussac for an ideal gas may be written

$$V = V_0\left(1 + \frac{\theta}{T_0}\right) \tag{1.14}$$

It is now possible and most convenient to define a new temperature scale with the temperature denoted by T and called the *absolute temperature*. Temperatures on this scale are called *degrees Kelvin*, °K. Thus

$$T = \theta + T_0$$

In terms of T, the Law of Gay-Lussac, Eq. (1.14), becomes

$$V = V_0[1 + (T - T_0)/T_0]$$

$$V = V_0 T/T_0 \tag{1.15}$$

As extensive work was done in the region of very low temperatures, from 0°K to 20°K, it became clear that there were serious inconveniences involved in the definition of a temperature scale based on two fixed points. The difficulty was that despite the most earnest attempts it was evidently impossible to obtain a measurement of the ice point accurate to within better than a few hundredths of a degree. Many years of the most careful work by skilled scientists in this field yielded results from 273.13°K to 273.17°K.

Therefore, in 1954, the Tenth Conference of the International Committee on Weights and Measures, meeting in Paris, decided to define a temperature scale with only one fixed point, and with an arbitrary choice of a universal constant for the temperature at this point. The point chosen was the *triple point of water*, the point at which water, ice and water vapor are simultaneously in equilibrium (see Fig. 4.1 on p. 102). They chose 273.16°K for the value at this point. The value of the ice point then became 273.15°K. The advantage of this definition is that it removes the great uncertainty from reports of low temperature measurements. Suppose, for example, a measurement was carried out at 5.13°K. Depending on the value preferred for the ice point in different laboratories, this figure might have been recorded in the old system as anywhere from 5.13° to 5.17°, a variation of almost 1 per cent. With the new system, the value reported is unequivocal, since it is taken with reference to a fixed arbitrary point. Under the new system, of course, the boiling point of water becomes simply another experimental point to be measured with the maximum possible accuracy, but not fixed by convention.

10. EQUATION OF STATE OF AN IDEAL GAS

Any two of the three variables P, V, and T suffice to specify the state of a given mass of gas and to fix the value of the third variable. In Eq. (1.12) we have an expression for the variation of P with V at constant T and in Eq. (1.15) an expression for the variation of V with T at constant P.

$$PV = \text{constant} \quad (\text{constant } T)$$

$$V/T = \text{constant} \quad (\text{constant } P)$$

We can readily combine these two relations to give

$$\frac{PV}{T} = \text{constant} \tag{1.16}$$

It is evident that this expression contains both the other two as special cases.

The next problem is the evaluation of the constant in Eq. (1.16). The equation states that the product PV divided by T is always the same for each specified state of the gas; hence, if we know these values for any one state we can derive the value of the constant. Let us take this reference state to be an ideal gas at 1 atm pressure and 273.15°K. The volume under these conditions is 22 414 cc per mole. If we have n moles of gas, therefore, the constant in Eq. (1.16) can be written

$$\frac{(1 \text{ atm})(n)(22\,414 \text{ cc})}{273.15°\text{K}} = 82.057n \frac{\text{cc atm}}{\text{deg}}$$

Thus, Eq. (1.16) becomes

$$\frac{PV}{T} = 82.057n = nR$$

The constant R is called the *gas constant per mole.* We often write Eq. (1.16) as

$$PV = nRT \tag{1.17}$$

Equation (1.17) is called the *equation of state of an ideal gas* and is one of the most useful relations in physical chemistry.

We first obtained the gas constant R in units of cc atm deg^{-1}. Note that cc atm has the dimensions of energy. Some convenient values of R in various units are summarized in Table 1.1.

TABLE 1.1 Values of the Ideal Gas Constant R in Various Units

UNITS	R
joules °K^{-1} mole^{-1}	8.31431
calories °K^{-1} mole^{-1}	1.98717
cc atm °K^{-1} mole^{-1}	82.0575
liter atm °K^{-1} mole^{-1}	0.0820575

Equation (1.17) allows us to calculate the molecular weight M of a gas from measurements of its density. If a mass of gas m is weighed in a gas density bulb of volume V, the density $\rho = m/V$. The number of moles $n = m/M$. Therefore, from Eq. (1.17),

$$M = RT\rho/P$$

11. THE EQUATION OF STATE AND *PVT* RELATIONSHIPS

If P and V are chosen as independent variables, the temperature of a pure substance is some function of P and V. Thus,

$$T = f(P, V) \tag{1.18}$$

For any fixed value of T, this equation defines an *isotherm* of the substance under consideration. The state of a substance in thermal equilibrium can be fixed by specifying any two of the three variables, pressure, volume and temperature. The third variable can then be found by solving the equation (1.18). Equation (1.18) is the general form of the *equation of state.*

Geometrically considered, the state of a pure fluid in equilibrium can be represented by a point on a three-dimensional surface, described by the variables

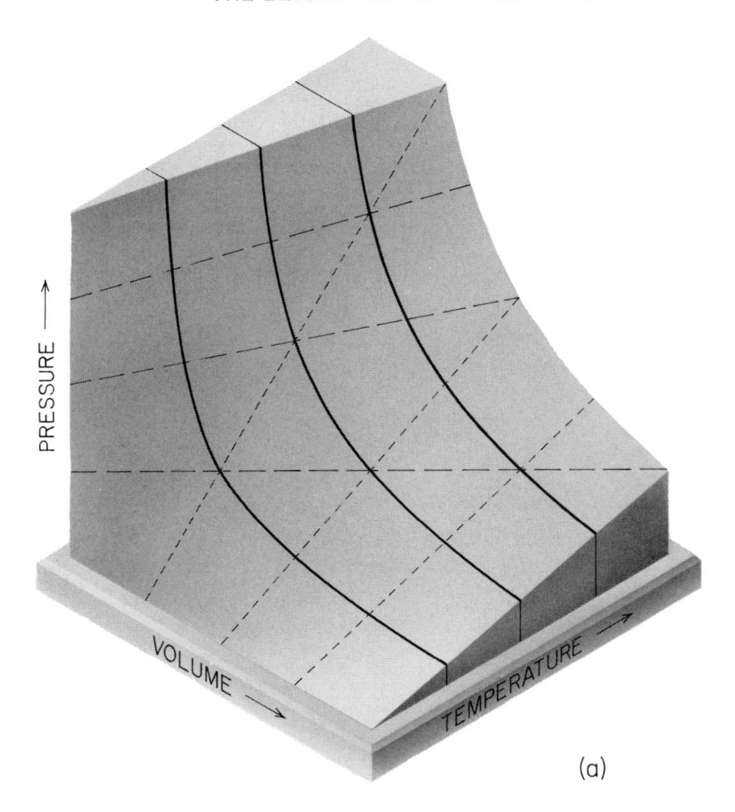

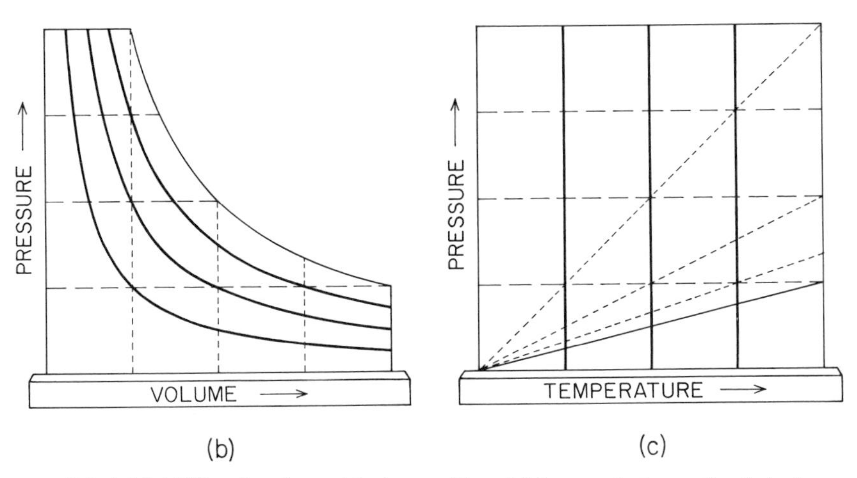

FIG. 1.6 (a) *PVT* surface for an ideal gas. The solid lines are isotherms, the dashed lines are isobars, and the dotted lines are isometrics. (b) Projection of the *PVT* surface on *PV* plane, showing isotherms. (c) Projection of the *PVT* surface on the *PT* plane, showing isometrics. [After F. W. Sears, *An Introduction to Thermodynamics* (Cambridge, Mass.: Addison-Wesley, 1950)].

P, V, and T. Fig. 1.6(a) shows such a PVT surface for an ideal gas. The isothermal lines connecting points at constant temperature are shown in Fig. 1.6(b), projected on the PV plane. The projection of lines of constant volume on the PT plane gives the *isochores* or *isometrics* shown in Fig. 1.6(c). Of course for a nonideal gas these would not be straight lines. Constant pressure lines are called *isobars*.

The slope of an isobaric curve gives the rate of change of volume with temperature at the constant pressure chosen. This slope is therefore written $(\partial V/\partial T)_P$. It is a partial derivative since V is a function of the two variables T and P. The change in V with T relative to a standard $V = V_0$, usually chosen to be the volume at 0°C and 1 atm pressure, is α the *thermal expansivity*.

$$\alpha = \frac{1}{V_0}\left(\frac{\partial V}{\partial T}\right)_P \tag{1.19}$$

Note that α has the dimensions of T^{-1}.

In a similar way, the slope of an isothermal curve gives the variation of volume with pressure at constant temperature. We define β, the compressibility of a substance, as

$$\beta = \frac{-1}{V_0}\left(\frac{\partial V}{\partial P}\right)_T \tag{1.20}$$

The negative sign is introduced because an increase in pressure decreases the volume, so that $(\partial V/\partial P)_T$ is negative. The dimensions of β are those of P^{-1}.

Since the volume is a function of both T and P, a differential change in volume can be written,*

$$dV = \left(\frac{\partial V}{\partial T}\right)_P dT + \left(\frac{\partial V}{\partial P}\right)_T dP \tag{1.21}$$

Equation (1.21) allows us to derive an interesting relation between the partial differential coefficients. For a condition of constant volume, V = constant, $dV = 0$, and

$$0 = \left(\frac{\partial V}{\partial T}\right)_P dT + \left(\frac{\partial V}{\partial P}\right)_T dP$$

Hence

$$\left(\frac{\partial P}{\partial T}\right)_V = \frac{-(\partial V/\partial T)_P}{(\partial V/\partial P)_T} = \frac{\alpha}{\beta} \tag{1.22}$$

The variation of P with T for any substance can therefore be readily calculated if we know α and β. An interesting example is suggested by a common laboratory accident, the breaking of a mercury-in-glass thermometer by overheating. If a thermometer is exactly filled with mercury at 50°C, what pressure will be developed within the thermometer if it is heated to 52°C? For mercury,

* W. A. Granville, P. F. Smith, W. R. Longley, *Elements of Calculus* (Boston: Ginn and Co., 1957), page 445. The total change in a function of several independent variables is the sum of the changes that would be caused by changing each variable separately. This is true because a change in one variable does not influence the change in another independent variable.

$\alpha = 1.8 \times 10^{-4}$ deg^{-1}, $\beta = 3.9 \times 10^{-6}$ atm^{-1}. Therefore, $(\partial P/\partial T)_V = \alpha/\beta =$ 46 atm per deg. For $\Delta T = 2°$, $\Delta P = 92$ atm. It is apparent why even a little overheating will break the usual thermometer.

12. *PVT* BEHAVIOR OF REAL GASES

The pressure, volume, temperature (PVT) relationships for gases, liquids, and solids would preferably all be succinctly summarized in the form of equations of state of the general type of Eq. (1.18). Only in the case of gases has there been much progress in the development of these state equations. They are obtained not only by correlation of empirical PVT data, but also from theoretical considerations based on atomic and molecular structure. These theories are farthest advanced for gases, but more recent developments in the theory of liquids and solids give promise that suitable state equations may eventually be available in these fields also.

The ideal gas equation $PV = nRT$ describes the PVT behavior of real gases only to a first approximation. A convenient way of showing the deviations from ideality is to write for the real gas:

$$PV = znRT \tag{1.23}$$

The factor z is called the *compressibility factor*. It is equal to PV/nRT. For an ideal gas $z = 1$, and departure from ideality will be measured by the deviation of the compressibility factor from unity. The extent of deviations from ideality depends on the temperature and pressure, so z is a function of T and P. Some compressibility-factor curves are shown in Fig. 1.7; these are determined from experimental measurements of the volumes of the substances at different pressures. (The data for NH_3 and C_2H_4 at high pressures pertain to the liquid substances.)

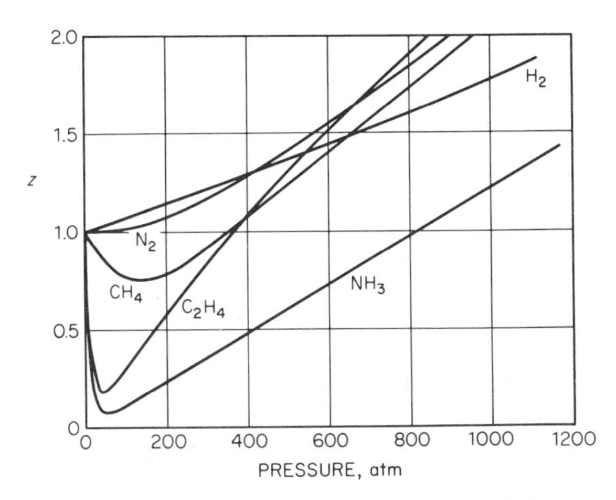

FIG. 1.7 Compressibility factors $z = PV/nRT$.

13. LAW OF CORRESPONDING STATES

Let us consider a liquid at some temperature and pressure at which it is in equilibrium with its vapor. This equilibrium pressure is called the *vapor pressure* of the liquid. The liquid will be more dense than the vapor, and if we have a sample of the substance in a closed transparent tube, we can see a meniscus between the liquid and the vapor. As the temperature is raised, the density of the liquid decreases while the density of the vapor increases (as the vapor pressure increases). Eventually a temperature is reached at which these densities become identical and the meniscus separating liquid from vapor disappears. Above this temperature, there is no distinction between the liquid and the gaseous states, and we speak of the substance simply as a *fluid*.

The temperature at which the meniscus disappears is called the *critical temperature* T_c of the substance. The vapor pressure at T_c is called the *critical pressure*. The volume occupied by the substance at T_c and P_c is its *critical volume* V_c. These *critical constants* for various substances are collected in Table 1.2.

TABLE 1.2 CRITICAL POINT DATA AND VAN DER WAALS CONSTANTS

Formula	T_c (°K)	P_c (atm)	V_c (cc/mole)	a (l² atm/mole²)	b (cc/mole)
He	5.3	2.26	57.6	0.0341	23.7
H_2	33.3	12.8	65.0	0.244	26.6
N_2	126.1	33.5	90.0	1.39	39.1
CO	134.0	35.0	90.0	1.49	39.9
O_2	153.4	49.7	74.4	1.36	31.8
C_2H_4	282.9	50.9	127.5	4.47	57.1
CO_2	304.2	73.0	95.7	3.59	42.7
NH_3	405.6	111.5	72.4	4.17	37.1
H_2O	647.2	217.7	45.0	5.46	30.5
Hg	1823.0	200.0	45.0	8.09	17.0

The ratios of P, V and T to the critical values P_c, V_c and T_c are called the *reduced* pressure, volume and temperature. These reduced variables may be written

$$P_R = \frac{P}{P_c} \qquad V_R = \frac{V}{V_c} \qquad T_R = \frac{T}{T_c} \tag{1.24}$$

To a fairly good approximation, especially at moderate pressures, all gases obey the same equation of state when described in terms of the reduced variables, P_R, V_R and T_R instead of P, V and T. If two different gases have identical values for two reduced variables, they therefore have approximately identical values for the third. They are then said to be in *corresponding states*, and this approximation is called the *Law of Corresponding States*. This is equivalent to saying that the compressibility factor z is the same function of the reduced variables for all gases. This rule is illustrated in Fig. 1.8 for a number of different gases, where $z = PV/nRT$ is plotted at various reduced temperatures, against the reduced pressure. The fit is quite good at these rather low pressures.

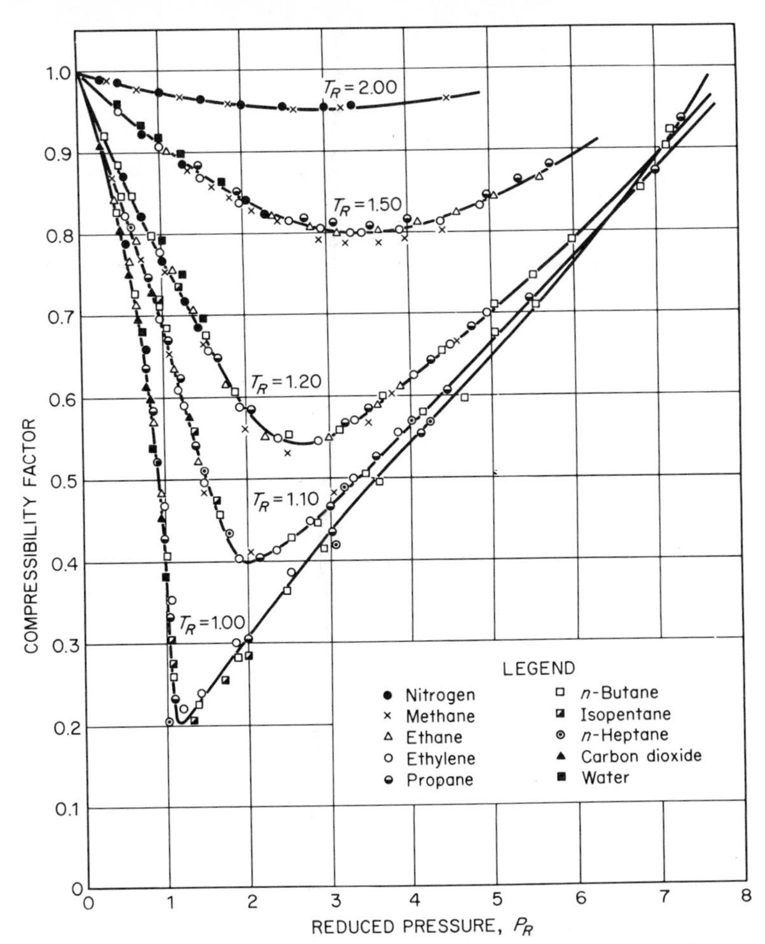

FIG. 1.8 Compressibility factor as function of reduced state variables. [Gouq-Jen Su, *Ind. Eng. Chem.*, **38**, 803 (1946)].

14. EQUATIONS OF STATE FOR GASES

If the equation of state is written in terms of reduced variables such as $F(P_R, V_R) = T_R$, it is evident that it contains at least two independent constants, characteristic of the gas in question, for example P_c and V_c. Many equations of state, proposed on semi-empirical grounds, serve to represent the PVT data more accurately than does the ideal gas equation. Several of the best known of these also contain two added constants. For example,

The equation of van der Waals: $$\left(P + \frac{n^2a}{V^2}\right)(V - nb) = nRT \tag{1.25}$$

The equation of D. Berthelot: $$\left(P + \frac{n^2A}{TV^2}\right)(V - nB) = nRT \tag{1.26}$$

The van der Waals equation provides a reasonably good representation of the PVT data of gases in the range of moderate deviations from ideality.

For example, consider the following values in liter atm of the PV product for one mole of carbon dioxide at 40°C, observed experimentally and as calculated from the van der Waals' equation. We have written $\overline{V} = V/n$ for the volume per mole.

P, atm	1	10	50	100	200	500	1100
$P\overline{V}$, obs.	25.57	24.49	19.00	6.93	10.50	22.00	40.00
$P\overline{V}$, calc.	25.60	24.71	19.75	8.89	14.10	29.70	54.20

The constants a and b are evaluated by fitting the equation to experimental PVT measurements, or from the critical constants of the gas. Some values for

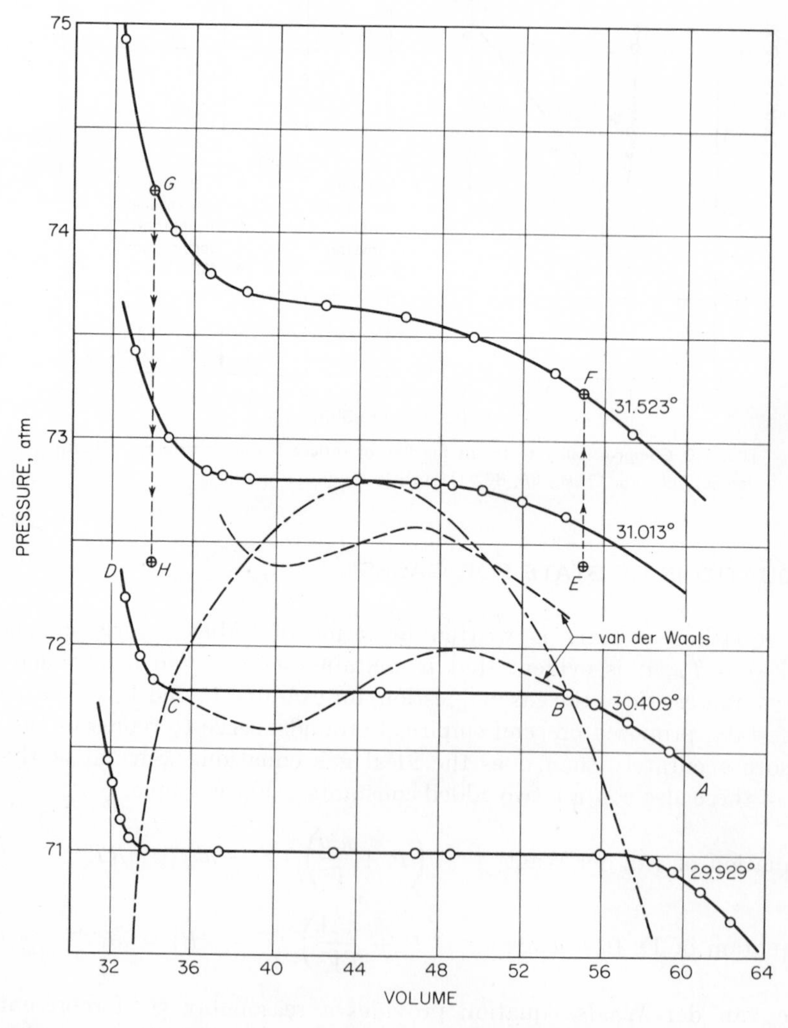

FIG. 1.9 Isotherms of carbon dioxide near the critical point.

van der Waals' a and b are included in Table 1.2. Berthelot's equation is somewhat better than van der Waals' at pressures not much above one atmosphere, and is preferred for general use in this range.

The way in which the constants in these equations are evaluated from critical data will now be described, with the van der Waals equation as an example.

15. THE CRITICAL REGION

The behavior of a gas in the neighborhood of its critical region was first studied by Thomas Andrews in 1869 in a classic series of measurements on carbon dioxide. Results of recent determinations by A. Michels of these PV isotherms around the critical temperature of 31.01°C are shown in Fig. 1.9.

Consider the isotherm at 30.4°C, which is below T_c. As the vapor is compressed, the PV curve first follows AB, which is approximately a Boyle's Law isotherm. When the point B is reached, a meniscus appears and liquid begins to form. Further compression then occurs at constant pressure until the point C is reached, at which all the vapor has been converted into liquid. The curve CD is the isotherm of liquid carbon dioxide, its steepness indicating the low compressibility of the liquid.

As isotherms are taken at successively higher temperatures, the points of discontinuity B and C are observed to approach each other gradually, until at 31.01°C they coalesce, and no appearance of a second phase is observable. This isotherm corresponds to the critical temperature of carbon dioxide. Isotherms above this temperature exhibit no formation of a second phase no matter how great the applied pressure.

Above the critical temperature there is no reason to draw any distinction between liquid and vapor, since there is a complete *continuity of states.* This may be demonstrated by following the path $EFGH$. The vapor at point E, at a temperature below T_c, is warmed at constant volume to point F, above T_c. It is then compressed along the isotherm FG, and finally cooled at constant volume along GH. At the point H, below T_c, the carbon dioxide exists as a liquid, but at no point along this path are two phases, liquid and vapor, simultaneously present. One must conclude that the transformation from vapor to liquid occurs smoothly and continuously.

16. THE VAN DER WAALS EQUATION AND LIQUEFACTION OF GASES

Van der Waals' equation provides a reasonably accurate representation of the PVT data of gases under conditions that deviate only moderately from ideality. When we apply the equation to gases in states which depart greatly from ideality, we do not obtain a quantitative representation of the data, but we still get an interesting qualitative picture. A typical example is shown in Fig. 1.9, where the van der Waals isotherms, drawn as dashed lines, are compared with the experimental isotherms for carbon dioxide in the neighborhood of the critical point. The van der Waals equation provides an adequate representation of the isotherms for the homogeneous vapor and even for the homogeneous liquid.

As might be expected, the equation cannot represent the discontinuities arising during liquefaction. Instead of the experimental straight line, it exhibits a maximum and a minimum within the two-phase region. We note that as the temperature gradually approaches the critical temperature, the maximum and the minimum gradually approach each other. At the critical point itself they have merged to become a point of inflection in the PV curve. The analytical condition for a maximum is that $(\partial P/\partial V)_T = 0$ and $(\partial^2 P/\partial V^2)_T < 0$; for a minimum, $(\partial P/\partial V)_T = 0$ and $(\partial^2 P/\partial V^2) > 0$. At the point of inflection, both the first and the second derivatives vanish, $(\partial P/\partial V)_T = 0 = (\partial^2 P/\partial V^2)_T$.

According to van der Waals' equation, therefore, the following three equations must be satisfied simultaneously at the critical point ($T = T_c$, $V = V_c$, $P = P_c$) for one mole of gas, $n = 1$:

$$P_c = \frac{RT_c}{V_c - b} - \frac{a}{V_c^2}$$

$$\left(\frac{\partial P}{\partial V}\right)_T = 0 = \frac{-RT_c}{(V_c - b)^2} + \frac{2a}{V_c^3}$$

$$\left(\frac{\partial^2 P}{\partial V^2}\right)_T = 0 = \frac{2RT_c}{(V_c - b)^3} - \frac{6a}{V_c^4}$$

When these equations are solved for the critical constants we find

$$T_c = \frac{8a}{27bR} \qquad V_c = 3b \qquad P_c = \frac{a}{27b^2} \tag{1.27}$$

Values for the van der Waals constants and for R can be calculated from these equations. We prefer, however, to consider R as a universal constant, and to obtain the best fit by adjusting a and b only. Then Eq. (1.27) would yield the relation $P_cV_c/T_c = 3R/8$ for all gases.

In terms of the reduced variables of state, P_R, V_R and T_R, one obtains from Eq. (1.27):

$$P = \frac{a}{27b^2} P_R \qquad V = 3bV_R \qquad T = \frac{8a}{27Rb} T_R$$

The van der Waals equation then reduces to

$$\left(P_R + \frac{3}{V_R^2}\right)\left(V_R - \frac{1}{3}\right) = \frac{8}{3} T_R \tag{1.28}$$

A reduced equation of state similar to Eq. (1.28) can be obtained from an equation of state containing no more than three arbitrary constants, such as a, b, and R, provided it has an algebraic form capable of giving a point of inflection. Berthelot's equation is often used in the following form, applicable at pressures of the order of one atmosphere:

$$P_R V_R = nR'T_R \left[1 + \frac{9}{128} \frac{P_R}{T_R} \left(1 - \frac{6}{T_R^2} \right) \right] \tag{1.29}$$

where $R' = R(T_c/P_c V_c)$.

17. OTHER EQUATIONS OF STATE

In order to represent the behavior of gases with greater accuracy, especially at high pressures or near their condensation temperatures, it is necessary to use expressions having more than two adjustable parameters. Typical of such expressions is a *virial equation* similar to that given by Kammerlingh-Onnes in 1901.

$$P\overline{V} = A + BP + CP^2 + DP^3 + \ldots \tag{1.30}$$

Here A, B, C, etc., which are functions of temperature, are called the first, second, third, etc. *virial coefficients*. If $\overline{V}$ is the molar volume, it is evident that $A = RT$. Figure 1.10 shows the second virial coefficients B of several gases

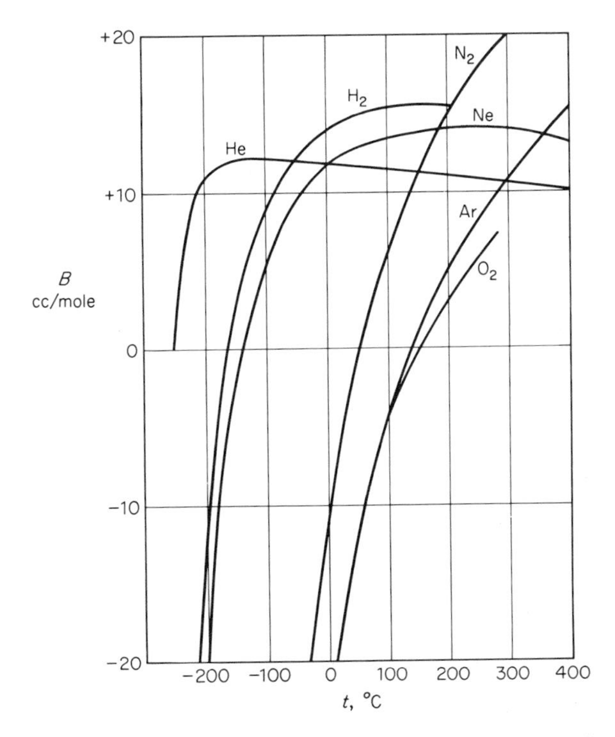

FIG. 1.10 The second virial coefficients B of several gases as functions of temperature.

over a range of temperature. This B is an important property in theoretical calculations on imperfect gases.*

The virial equation can be extended to as many terms as are needed to represent the experimental PVT data to any desired accuracy.

For gases at low pressures, a useful equation of state is obtained by setting equal to zero all the coefficients beyond the second. Thus,

$$P\overline{V} = RT + BP \tag{1.31}$$

One of the best of the empirical equations is that proposed by Beattie and Bridgeman.† It contains five constants in addition to R, and fits the PVT data over a wide range of pressures and temperatures, even near the critical point, to within 0.5 per cent. An equation with eight constants has been described that even reproduces the isotherms in the liquid region quite well.††

18. THE CONCEPTS OF HEAT AND HEAT CAPACITY

The experimental observations that led to the concept of *temperature* also led to that of *heat*, but for a long time students did not clearly distinguish between these two concepts, often using the same name for both, *calor* or *caloric*.

The beautiful work of Joseph Black on *calorimetry*, the measurement of heat changes, was published in 1803, four years after his death. In his *Lectures on the Elements of Chemistry*, he pointed out the distinction between the intensive factor, *temperature*, and the extensive factor, *quantity of heat*. Black showed that equilibrium required an equality of *temperature*, and did not imply that there was an equal "quantity of heat" in different bodies.

He then proceeded to investigate the capacity for heat or the amount of heat needed to increase the temperature of different bodies by a given number of degrees. "It was formerly a supposition that the quantities of heat required to increase the heat of different bodies by the same number of degrees were directly in proportion to the quantity of matter in each. . . . But very soon after I began to think on this subject (Anno 1760) I perceived that this opinion was a mistake, and that the quantities of heat which different kinds of matter must receive to reduce them to an equilibrium with one another, or to raise their temperatures by an equal number of degrees, are not in proportion to the quantity of matter of each, but in proportions widely different from this, and for which no general principle or reason can yet be assigned."

In explaining his experiments, Black assumed that heat behaved as a substance, which could flow from one body to another but whose total amount must always remain constant. This idea of heat as a substance was generally accepted

* See, for example, T. L. Hill, *Introduction to Statistical Thermodynamics*, (Reading, Mass.: Addison-Wesley, 1960), Ch. 15.

† J. A. Beattie and O. C. Bridgeman, *Proc. Am. Acad. Arts Sci.*, *63*, 229–308 (1928).

†† M. Benedict, G. W. Webb, L. C. Rubin, *J. Chem. Phys. 10*, 747 (1942).

at that time. Lavoisier even listed *caloric* in his "Table of the Chemical Elements." In the particular kind of experiment often done in *calorimetry,* heat does in fact behave much like a weightless fluid, but this behavior is the consequence of certain special conditions. Consider a typical experiment: A piece of metal of mass m_2 and temperature T_2 is introduced into an insulated vessel containing a mass m_1 of water at temperature T_1. We impose the following conditions: (1) the system is completely isolated from its surroundings, (2) any change in the container itself can be neglected, (3) there is no change such as vaporization, melting or solution in either substance and no chemical reaction. Under these strict conditions, the system finally reaches a new temperature T, somewhere between T_1 and T_2, and the temperatures are related by an equation of the form

$$c_2m_2(T_2 - T) = c_1m_1(T - T_1) \tag{1.32}$$

Here c_2 is the *specific heat* of the metal and $c_2m_2 = C_2$ is the *heat capacity* of the mass of metal used. The corresponding quantities for the water are c_1 and $c_1m_1 = C_1$. The specific heat is the heat capacity per unit mass.

Equation (1.32) has the form of an equation of conservation like Eq. (1.10). Under the restrictive conditions of this experiment it is permissible to consider that heat is conserved, and flows from the hotter to the colder substance until their temperatures are equal. The flow of heat is

$$q = C_2(T_2 - T) = C_1(T - T_1) \tag{1.33}$$

A more exact definition of heat will be given in the next chapter.

The *unit of heat* was originally defined in terms of such an experiment in calorimetry. The *gram calorie* was the heat that must be absorbed by one gram of water to raise its temperature 1°C. It followed that the specific heat of water was 1 calorie per °C.

More careful experiments showed that the specific heat was itself a function of the temperature. It therefore became necessary to redefine the calorie by specifying the range over which it was measured. The standard was taken to be the *15° calorie,* probably because of the lack of central heating in European laboratories. This is the heat required to raise the temperature of a gram of water from 14.5° to 15.5°C. Finally another change in the definition of the calorie was found to be desirable. Electrical measurements are capable of greater precision than calorimetric measurements. The Ninth International Conference on Weights and Measures (1948) therefore recommended that the *joule (volt coulomb)* be used as the unit of heat. The *calorie,* however, is still popular among chemists, and the National Bureau of Standards uses a *defined calorie* equal to exactly 4.1840 joules.

The specific heat, being a function of temperature, should be defined precisely only in terms of a differential heat flow dq and temperature change dT. Thus, in the limit, Eq. (1.33) becomes

$$dq = C\,dT, \qquad \text{or} \qquad C = \frac{dq}{dT} \tag{1.34}$$

19. WORK IN CHANGES OF VOLUME

In our discussion of the transfer of heat, so far we have carefully restricted our attention to the simple case in which the system is isolated and is not allowed to interact mechanically with its surroundings. If this restriction does not apply, the system may either do work on its surroundings or have work done on itself. Thus, in certain cases, only a part of the heat added to a substance causes its temperature to rise, the remainder being used in the work of expanding the substance. The amount of heat that must be added to produce a certain temperature change depends on the exact process by which the change is effected.

A differential element of work was defined in Eq. (1.3) as $dw = f\,dr$, the product of a force and the displacement of its point of application when both have the same direction. Figure 1.3 showed a simple thermodynamic system, a fluid confined in a cylinder with a movable piston that is assumed to be frictionless. The external pressure on the piston of area A is $P_{ex} = f/A$. If the piston is displaced a distance dr in the direction of the force f, the change in volume of the fluid $dV = -A\,dr$. Therefore the element of work is written

$$dw = (f/A)\,A\,dr = -P_{ex}\,dV \tag{1.35}$$

In accord with our sign convention, work done *on* the system is positive since dV is negative for a compression.

Note that the calculation of the work requires that we know the *external pressure* P_{ex} on the system. It does not require that the system be in equilibrium with this external pressure. If the pressure is *kept constant* during a finite compression from V_1 to V_2, we can calculate the work done on the fluid by integrating Eq. (1.35).

$$w = \int_{V_1}^{V_2} -P_{ex}\,dV = -P_{ex}\int_{V_1}^{V_2} dV = -P_{ex}\,(V_2 - V_1) = -P_{ex}\,\Delta V \tag{1.36}$$

If a finite change in volume is carried out in such a way that the external pressure is known at each successive state of expansion or compression, we can plot the process on a graph of P_{ex} vs. volume V. Such a plot is called an *indicator diagram;* an example is shown in (a), Fig. 1.11. The work done by the system is equal to the area under the curve.

It is evident that the work done in going from point A to point B in the P_{ex}-V diagram, or from one state to another, depends upon the particular path that is traversed. Consider, for example, two alternate paths from A to B in (b), Fig. 1.11. More work will be done in going by the path ADB than by the path ACB, as is evident from the greater area under curve ADB. If we proceed from state A to state B by path ADB and return to A along BCA, we shall have completed a *cyclic process.* The net work done by the system during this cycle is seen to be equal to the difference between the areas under the two paths, which is the shaded area in (b), Fig. 1.11.

If each successive point along the P_{ex}-V curve is an equilibrium state of the system, we have the very special case that P_{ex} always equals P, the pressure of

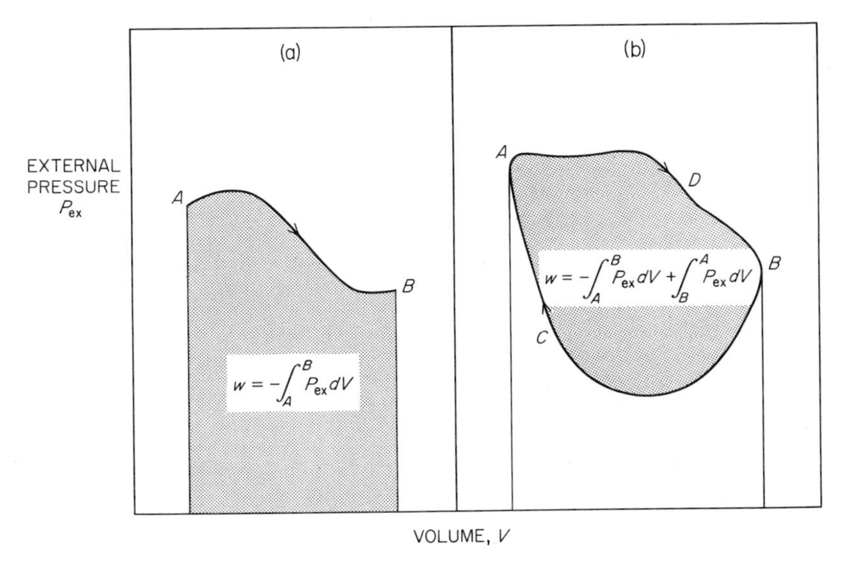

FIG. 1.11 Indicator diagrams for *PV* work. (a) A general process from A to B. (b) A cyclic process ADBCA.

the fluid itself. The indicator curve then becomes an equilibrium PV curve for the system. Such a case is shown in Fig. 1.12. Only when equilibrium is maintained can the work be calculated from functions of the state of the substance itself, P and V.

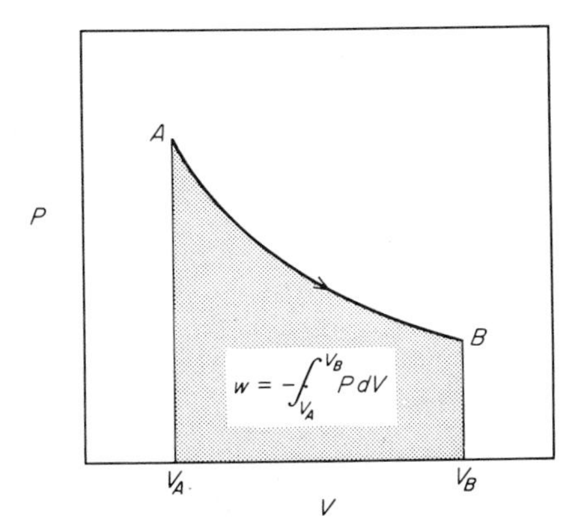

FIG. 1.12 Indicator diagram for the work done on a system consisting of a fluid in equilibrium, with external pressure $P_{ex} = P$.

20. GENERAL CONCEPT OF WORK

In the mechanical systems described, the work was always formulated as the product of two terms, an intensive factor, which is a generalized force, and an extensive factor, which is a generalized displacement. Such a formulation applies also to nonmechanical work.

In physical chemistry, we are often interested in changes carried out in electrical cells. We shall postpone a detailed description of such systems until Chapter 10, but mention now that in the case of electrical work, the generalized force becomes the electromotive force (emf) or electrical pressure E, and the generalized displacement becomes the charge transported Q. Similarly, in the magnetic case the intensive factor is the magnetic field H and the extensive factor is the magnetic moment M. We can thus summarize the various examples of work in Table 1.3. Work done on a system is taken as *positive*, $w > 0$.

TABLE 1.3 EXAMPLES OF WORK

Intensive Factor	*Extensive Factor*	*Element of Work dw*
Tension f	Distance l	$f\,dl$
Surface Tension γ	Area A	$\gamma\,dA$
Pressure P	Volume V	$-P\,dV$
Electromotive Force E	Charge Q	$E\,dQ$
Magnetic Field H	Magnetic Moment M	$H\,dM$

21. REVERSIBLE PROCESSES

The path followed in the PV diagram of Fig. 1.12 belongs to a special class, of great importance in thermodynamic arguments. It is called a *reversible path.* A reversible path is one connecting intermediate states all of which are equilibrium states. A process carried out along such an equilibrium path is called a *reversible process.*

In order, for example, to expand a gas reversibly, the pressure on the piston must be released so slowly, in the limit infinitely slowly, that at every instant the pressure everywhere within the gas volume is exactly the same and is just equal to the opposing pressure on the piston. Only in this case can the state of the gas be represented by the variables of state, P and V.* In geometric terms, the state is represented by a point in the PV plane. The line joining such points is a line joining points of equilibrium.

Consider the situation if the piston were drawn back suddenly. Gas would rush in to fill the space, pressure differences would be set up throughout the gas volume, and even a state of turbulence might ensue. The state of the gas under such conditions could no longer be represented by the two variables, P and V. Indeed an enormous number of variables would be required, corresponding to the many different pressures at different points throughout the gas volume. Such a rapid expansion is a typical *irreversible process;* the intermediate states are no longer equilibrium states.

Reversible processes are never realizable in actuality since they must be carried out infinitely slowly. All processes which occur naturally are therefore irreversible. The reversible path is the limiting path that is reached as we carry out an irreversible process under conditions that approach more and more closely to equilibrium conditions. We can define a reversible path exactly and calculate the work done in moving along it, even though we can never carry out an actual change reversibly. The conditions for reversibility can, however, be closely approximated in certain experiments.

* We can represent an irreversible path on the indicator diagram by plotting P_{ex} vs. V. Only in the reversible case does $P_{ex} = P$, the state property of the substance itself.

22. REVERSIBLE WORK

In Fig. 1.12, the change from A to B can be carried out along different reversible paths, of which only one is drawn. These different paths are possible because the volume V is a function of the temperature T, as well as of the pressure P. If one particular temperature is chosen and held constant throughout the process, only one reversible path is possible. Under such an *isothermal condition* the work obtained from the system in going from A to B via a path that is reversible is the *maximum work* possible for the particular temperature in question. This is true because in the reversible case the expansion takes place against the maximum possible opposing force, which is one exactly in equilibrium with the driving force. If the opposing force, e.g., pressure on a piston, were any greater, the process would occur in the reverse direction; instead of expanding and doing work the gas in the cylinder would have work done upon it and would be compressed. Conversely, if we compress the system from B to A at a particular constant temperature, the work done on the system will be a minimum if the reversible path is followed.

PROBLEMS

1. An evacuated glass bulb weighs 37.9365 g. Filled with dry air at 1 atm pressure and 25°C, it weighs 38.0739 g. Filled with a mixture of methane and ethane, it weighs 38.0347 g. Calculate the percentage of methane in the gas mixture. [*Ans.* 66.8 mole %]

2. An oil bath maintained at 50°C loses heat to its surroundings at the rate of 1000 calories per minute. Its temperature is maintained by an electrically heated coil with a resistance of 50 ohms operated on a 110-volt line. A thermoregulator switches the current on and off. What percentage of the time will the current be turned on? [*Ans.* 28.8%]

3. Calculate the work done in accelerating a 2000 kg car from rest to a speed of 50 km per hr, neglecting friction. [*Ans.* 1.93×10^5 joule]

4. A lead bullet is fired at a wooden plank. At what speed must it be traveling to melt on impact, if its initial temperature is 25° and heating of the plank is neglected? The melting point of lead is 327° and its specific heat is 0.030 cal $\text{deg}^{-1}\,\text{g}^{-1}$. The heat of fusion of lead is 1.24 kcal/g atom. [*Ans.* 3.54×10^4 cm sec^{-1}]

5. What is the average power production in watts of a man who burns 2500 kcal of food in a day? [*Ans.* 121 watt]

6. Calculate the pressure exerted by 10 g of nitrogen in a closed 1-liter vessel at 25°C, using: (a) the ideal gas equation; (b) van der Waals' equation. [*Ans.* (a) 8.73 atm, and (b) 8.68 atm]

7. The density of solid aluminum at 20°C is 2.70 g per cc; of the liquid at 660°C, 2.38 g per cc. Calculate the work done on the surroundings when 10 kg of Al are heated under atmospheric pressure from 20° to 660°C. [*Ans.* 50.2 joule]

8. Two identical calorimeters are prepared, containing equal volumes of water at 20°C. A 5-g piece of Al at 40°C is dropped into calorimeter A and 5-g piece of alloy at 40°C into B. The equilibrium temperature in A is 22°C; in B, 21.5°C. Take the specific heat of water to be independent of temperature and equal to 4.18 joule deg^{-1}. If the specific heat of Al is 0.887 joule deg^{-1}, estimate the specific heat of the alloy.

9. What is the gravitational force in dynes between two masses of one gram one cm apart? What is the gravitational force between two neutrons 10^{-13} cm apart?

10. The density of gaseous HBr at 0°C and 1 atm is 3.6444 g l^{-1}. What volume would be occupied by one mole of HBr under these conditions?

11. Calculate the volume of one mole of an ideal gas at: (a) 0°C and 1 atm; (b) 25°C and 1 atm; (c) 100°C and 1 atm.

12. Calculate the density of UF_6 gas at its boiling point 56°C and 1 atm pressure.

13. Calculate the pressure at which one mole of CO_2 occupies a volume of one liter at 20°C, using: (a) ideal gas law; (b) van der Waals' equation.

14. Calculate the work done on the surroundings when one mole of water: (a) freezes at 0°C; (b) boils at 100°C. Compare these values with the corresponding latent heats.

15. What weights of H_2, O_2, and N_2 are in 10 l of a mixture measured at 18°C and 750 mm Hg, the volumetric composition of which is: H_2 10%; O_2 15%; N_2 75%. [*Ans.* 0.0828 g; 1.987 g; 8.684 g]

16. The critical temperature of CO is -141°C; the critical pressure is 35.9 atm. Calculate van der Waals' constants a (in units of dyne cm^4 $mole^{-2}$) and b (cc $mole^{-1}$). One mole of CO at 27.5°C occupies 137.69 cc. If it obeys van der Waals' equation, what is its pressure in dyne cm^{-2}? [*Ans.* $a = 1.398 \times 10^{12}$, $b = 37.71$; $P = 17.63 \times 10^7$ dyne cm^{-2}]

17. One mole of a gas AB occupies 40 l at 400°K, but the gas dissociates according to $AB \rightleftarrows A + B$, and the degree of dissociation is 10%. Calculate the total pressure.

18. 15 cc of a gaseous hydrocarbon was mixed with 100 cc of oxygen in a eudiometer. After explosion, a potassium hydroxide solution absorbed 45 cc of the gas from the residue, the remaining 25 cc being oxygen. What was the formula of the hydrocarbon? [*Ans.* C_3H_8]

19. A mixture of 32 cc of methane, hydrogen, and nitrogen was exploded with 61 cc of oxygen. The residual gases measured 34.5 cc, but 24.1 cc of this was absorbed by a caustic soda solution. Find the percentages of the three gases in the mixture. [*Ans.* 75% CH_4; 21% H_2; 4% N_2]

20. A barometer gives false readings because a small amount of air has been trapped above the mercury column. At a pressure of 755 mm, it reads 748; at 740 mm, it reads 736. (a) If the barometer tube has a cross-sectional area of 1 sq cm, what is the volume of the space above the mercury when the barometer reads 748? (b) Suppose that this space is made to be 200 cc and the same amount of air has collected above the mercury. What will be the percentage error when the true barometric pressure is 755 mm? Compare the percentage error found in (b) with the error found for the volume calculated in (a). This should suggest why some barometers are made with a large amount of dead space above the mercury. Assume that all the pressure readings mentioned above were taken at 27°C.

---

21. The coefficient of thermal expansion of ethanol is given by $\alpha = 1.0414 \times 10^{-3} + 1.5672 \times 10^{-6}t + 5.148 \times 10^{-8}t^2$, where t is the centigrade temperature. If 0° and 50° are taken as fixed points on a centigrade scale, what will be the reading of the alcohol thermometer when an ideal gas thermometer reads 30°C? [*Ans.* 28.85°C]

22. Evaluate the constants a' and b' in Dieterici's equation $[P(V - b')e^{a'/RTV} = RT]$ in terms of the critical constants P_c, V_c, T_c of a gas. [*Ans.* $a' = 2RT_cV_c$; $b' = V_c/2$]

23. Show that

$$\left(\frac{\partial P}{\partial V}\right)_T = -\frac{(\partial P/\partial T)_V}{(\partial V/\partial T)_P}$$

24. Derive an expression for the coefficient of thermal expansion α for a gas that follows: (a) the ideal gas law; (b) the van der Waals equation.

$$\left[Ans.\ \alpha = 1/T;\ \alpha = R\left(PV - \frac{a}{V} + \frac{2ab}{V^2}\right)^{-1}\right]$$

25. The gas densities (g per liter) of CO_2 and SO_2 at 0°C and 1 atm are 1.9769 and 2.9269, respectively. Calculate the molar volumes of the gases and compare them with the values given by Berthelot's equation. [*Ans.* (a) CO_2 = 22 262 obs., 22 260 calc.; (b) SO_2 = 21 890 obs., 21 969 calc.]

26. One mole of an ideal gas at 25°C is held in a cylinder by a piston at a pressure of 100 atm. The piston pressure is released in three stages: first to 50 atm; then to 20 atm; and finally to 10 atm. Calculate the work done by the gas during these irreversible isothermal expansions and compare it with the work done in an isothermal reversible expansion from 100 to 10 atm at 25°C. [*Ans.* 3965, 5710 joules]

27. A kilogram of ammonia is compressed from 1000 liters to 100 liters at a constant temperature of 50°C. Calculate the minimum work that must be expended, assuming: (a) ideal gas; (b) van der Waals' equation. [*Ans.* (a) 3.64×10^5 joule; (b) 3.53×10^5 joule]

28. Calculate the work needed to remove a 100 kg mass from the gravitational field of the earth. Neglecting friction, estimate the initial velocity with which this 100 kg mass would need to leave the surface of the earth.

29. Calculate the work expended in bringing two electric charges of one coulomb each from infinite separation to a distance of: (a) 1 mm (b) 10^{-8} cm of each other.

30. An elastic sphere of mass 1 kg with a kinetic energy of 1 joule strikes another such sphere of mass 1 g, which is initially at rest. What is the maximum energy E_m that can be transferred from the moving to the stationary sphere? What is the E_m if the moving sphere has a mass of 1 g and energy of 1 joule, whereas the stationary sphere has a mass of 1 kg?

31. A 100 watt electric motor is used to open a door held shut by a spring. If it is necessary to move the door spring 10 cm in 10 sec, what is the force constant of the spring (neglect friction)?

32. It is sometimes necessary to correct weighings to vacuum readings by allowing for the buoyancy of air. Suppose you use brass weights (density $\rho = 8.4$ g cm^{-3}) to weigh exactly 10 g of aluminum ($\rho = 2.70$ g cm^{-3}) at 25°C and 750 mm. What is the *in vacuo* weight?

33. One liter of pure N_2 at 0°C weighs 1.25050 g at 1 atm and 0.125002 g at 0.1 atm. Calculate an accurate molecular weight of nitrogen from these data.

34. From a porcelain bulb of volume 197.8 cc, 169.1 cc of air measured at 10°C were expelled on heating from 12°C to t°C. The pressure was always 747 mm. Neglecting expansion of the bulb, calculate t. [*Ans.* $t = 1777$°C]

35. Show that the maximum work that can be done by one mole of gas in expanding at constant temperature T from V_1 to V_2 is $w_{\max} = RT \ln (V_2/V_1)$.

36. One mole of gas occupies 20 cc at 310°K. Suppose the gas obeys van der Waals' equation with $a = 0.0260$ l^2 atm mole^{-2} and $b = 0$. What is the maximum work in joules that the gas will do in expanding to 200 cc at constant temperature?

37. The Boyle temperature of a gas is the temperature at which the PV product neither rises nor falls as the pressure is increased from zero. Show that the Boyle temperature, as predicted by the van der Waals equation, is $T_B = a/Rb$. From this equation estimate the Boyle temperatures of H_2, N_2, CO_2.

38. Calculate the volume of a balloon with a lifting power of 400 kg at 20°C and 1 atm, if the ballon is filled with (a) hydrogen, (b) helium. Calculate the volume of the helium balloon in the stratosphere at −60°C and 0.1 atm. Assume that air is 80% N_2 and 20% O_2. [*Ans.* (a) 359 m^3; (b) 388 m^3; (c) 2820 m^3]

39. The gas N_2O_4 dissociates partially into NO_2. A flask filled with this gas mixture at 50°C and 500 mm Hg total pressure weighed 71.981 g. When evacuated, the flask weighed 71.217 g, and when filled with water at 25°C (density 0.997 g ml^{-1}), it weighed 555.9 g. What fraction of the N_2O_4 molecules was dissociated?

40. At 0°C, the density of nitric oxide at various pressures was found to be:

P (atm)	1.0000	0.8000	0.5000	0.3000
ρ(g l^{-1})	1.3402	1.0719	0.66973	0.40174

Calculate (ρ/P) at each pressure, and hence determine an exact value for the atomic weight of nitrogen. [*Ans.* 14.007]

2 THE FIRST LAW OF THERMODYNAMICS

The First Law of Thermodynamics is an extension of the principle of the conservation of mechanical energy. This extension became natural when it was realized that work could be converted into heat, the expenditure of a fixed amount of work always giving rise to the production of the same amount of heat. To give the law an analytical formulation, it was only necessary to define a new energy function that included the heat.

1. HISTORY OF THE FIRST LAW

The first quantitative experiments were carried out by Benjamin Thompson, a native of Woburn, Massachusetts, who became Count Rumford of The Holy Roman Empire. Commissioned by the King of Bavaria to supervise the boring of cannon at the Munich Arsenal, he became impressed by the tremendous generation of heat during this operation. He suggested (1798) that the heat arose from the mechanical energy expended, and was able to estimate the amount of heat produced by a horse working for an hour; in modern units his value would be 0.183 calorie per joule. Contemporary critics of these experiments said that heat was evolved because metal in the form of fine turnings had a lower heat capacity than bulk metal. Rumford then substituted a blunt borer, producing just as much heat with very few turnings. The advocates of the caloric hypothesis thereupon claimed that the heat arose from the action of air on the metallic surfaces. In 1799, Humphry Davy provided further support for Thompson's theory by rubbing together two pieces of ice by clockwork in a vacuum and noting their rapid melting, showing that, even in the absence of air, this latent heat could be provided by mechanical work.

Nevertheless, the time was not scientifically ripe for a mechanical theory of heat until the work of Dalton and others provided an atomic theory of matter, and gradually an understanding of heat in terms of molecular motion.

By about 1840, the law of conservation of energy was accepted in purely mechanical systems, the interconversion of heat and work was well established, and it was understood that heat was simply a form of motion of the smallest particles composing a substance. Yet the generalization of the conservation of energy to include heat changes had not yet been clearly made.

Thus we turn to the work of Julius Robert Mayer, one of the most curious figures in the history of science. He was born in 1814, the son of an apothecary in Heilbronn. He was always a mediocre student, but entered Tübingen University in 1832 to study medicine, and obtained a good grounding in chemistry under Gmelin. He took his degree in 1838, presenting a short dissertation on the effect of santonin on worms in children. Nothing in his academic career suggested that he was about to make a great contribution to science.

Wishing to see the world, he signed as ship's doctor on the three-master *Java*, and sailed from Rotterdam in February, 1840. He spent the long voyage in idleness, lulled by the balmy off-shore breezes; according to Ostwald, in this manner he stored up the psychic energy which was to burst forth suddenly soon after he landed. According to Mayer's own story, his train of thought began abruptly on the dock at Surabaya, when several of the sailors needed to be bled. The venous blood was such a bright red that at first he thought he had opened an artery. The local physicians told him, however, that this color was typical of blood in the tropics, since the consumption of oxygen required to maintain the body temperature was less than in colder regions. Mayer began to think along these lines. Since the animal heat was created by the oxidation of nutriments, the question arose of what happened if in addition to warmth the body also produced work. From an identical quantity of food, sometimes more and sometimes less heat could be obtained. If a fixed total yield of energy from food is obtainable, then one must conclude that work and heat are interchangeable quantities of the same kind. By burning the same amount of food the animal body can produce different proportions of heat and of work, but the sum of the two must be constant. Mayer spent his days on shipboard working feverishly on his theory. He became a man obsessed with one great idea, his whole life dedicated to it.

Actually Mayer was thoroughly confused about the distinctions between the concepts of force, momentum, work and energy, and the first paper that he wrote was not published by the editor of the journal to whom he submitted it. Poggendorf filed it away without even deigning to answer Mayer's letters. By the beginning of 1842, Mayer had straightened out his ideas and he could equate heat to kinetic energy and potential energy. In March, 1842, Liebig accepted his paper for the *Annalen der Chemie und Pharmazie.*

"From application of established theorems on the warmth and volume relations of gases, one finds . . . that the fall of a weight from a height of about 365 meters corresponds to the warming of an equal weight of water from 0 to 1°C." This figure relates mechanical units of energy to thermal units. The conversion factor is called the mechanical equivalent of heat J. Hence,

$$w = Jq \tag{2.1}$$

In modern units J is usually given as joules per calorie. To lift a weight of 1 gram to a height of 365 meters requires $365 \times 10^2 \times 981$ ergs of work, or 3.58

joules. To raise the temperature of 1 gram of water from 0 to 1°C requires 1.0087 calorie. The value of J calculated by Mayer is therefore 3.56 joule/calorie. The accepted modern figure is 4.184. Mayer was able to state the principle of the conservation of energy, the First Law of Thermodynamics, in general terms, and to give one rather rough numerical example of its application. The exact evaluation of J and the proof that it is a constant independent of the method of measurement was accomplished by Joule.

2. THE WORK OF JOULE

Although Mayer was the philosophic father of the First Law, Joule's beautifully precise experiments firmly established the Law on an experimental or inductive foundation. James Prescott Joule was born in 1818 near Manchester, the son of a wealthy brewer. He studied as a pupil of John Dalton. When he was 20 he began his independent researches in a laboratory provided by his father adjacent to the brewery. In later years he managed the business with good success, in addition to carrying on his intensive work in experimental chemistry and physics.

In 1840 he published his work on the heating effects of the electric current and established the following law: "When a current of voltaic electricity is propagated along a metallic conductor, the heat evolved in a given time is proportional to the resistance of the conductor multiplied by the square of the electric intensity [current]". Thus,

$$q = I^2R/J \tag{2.2}$$

This *Joulean heat,* as it is now called, can be considered as the frictional heat caused by the motion of the carriers of the electric current.

In a long series of most careful experiments Joule proceeded to measure the conversion of work into heat in various ways, by electrical heating, by compression of gases, by forcing liquids through fine tubes, and by the rotation of paddle wheels in water and mercury. These studies culminated in his great paper "On the Mechanical Equivalent of Heat" read before the Royal Society in 1849. After all corrections, he obtained the final result that 772 foot pounds of work would produce the heat required to warm 1 lb. of water 1°F. In our units, this corresponds to $J = 4.154$ joules per calorie.

3. FORMULATION OF THE FIRST LAW

The philosophical argument of Mayer and the experimental work of Joule led to a definite acceptance of the conservation of energy. Hermann von Helmholtz placed the principle on a better mathematical basis in his work *Über die Erhaltung der Kraft* (1847) which clearly stated the conservation of energy as a principle of universal validity and as one of the fundamental laws applicable to all natural phenomena.

We can use the principle to *define* a function E called the *internal energy.* Suppose any closed system* undergoes a process in which it passes from a state A to a state B. If the only interaction with its surroundings is in the form of transfers of heat q to the system, or the performance of work w on the system, the change in E will be

$$\Delta E = E_B - E_A = q + w \tag{2.3}$$

Now the First Law of Thermodynamics states that this energy difference ΔE depends only on the initial and final states and in no way on the path followed between them. Both q and w can have many different values, depending on exactly how the system passes from A to B, but their sum $q + w = \Delta E$ is invariable and independent of the path. If this were not true, it would be possible by passing from A to B along one path and then returning from B to A along another to obtain a net change in the energy of the closed system in contradiction to the principle of conservation of energy, the First Law of Thermodynamics. Therefore we can say that Eq. (2.3) is a mathematical expression of the First Law.

For a differential change, Eq. (2.3) becomes

$$dE = dq + dw \tag{2.4}$$

The energy function is undetermined to the extent of an arbitrary additive constant; it has been defined only in terms of the difference in energy between one state and another. Sometimes, as a matter of convenience, we may adopt a conventional standard state for a system, and set its energy in this state equal to zero. For example, we might choose the state of the system at 0°K and 1 atm pressure as our standard. Then the energy E in any other state would be the change in energy in going from the standard state to the state in question.

The First Law has often been stated in terms of the universal human experience that it is impossible to construct a perpetual motion machine, that is, a machine that produces useful work or energy from nothing. To see how this experience is embodied in the First Law, consider a cyclic process from state A to B and back to A again. If perpetual motion were ever possible, it would sometimes be possible to obtain a net increase in energy $\Delta E > 0$ by such a cycle. That this is impossible can be ascertained from Eq. (2.3), which indicates that for any such cycle $\Delta E = (E_B - E_A) + (E_A - E_B) = 0$. A more general way of expressing this fact is to say that for any cyclic process the integral of dE vanishes:

$$\oint dE = 0 \tag{2.5}$$

4. THE NATURE OF INTERNAL ENERGY

On page 8 we restricted the systems under consideration to those in a state of rest in the absence of gravitational or electromagnetic fields. With these re-

* A *closed system* is a system into or out of which there is no transfer of *mass*.

strictions, changes in the internal energy E include changes in the potential energy of the system, and in the energy transferred as heat. The potential energy changes may be considered to include also the energy changes caused by the rearrangements of molecular configurations that take place during changes in state of aggregation, or in chemical reactions.

If the system is moving, the kinetic energy is added to E. If the restriction on electromagnetic fields is removed, the definition of E is expanded to include the electromagnetic energy. Similarly, if gravitational effects are of interest, as in centrifugal operations, the energy of the gravitational field must be included in or added to E before applying the First Law.

In anticipation of future discussions, it may be mentioned that the interconversion of mass and energy can be readily measured in nuclear reactions. The First Law should, therefore, become a law of the conservation of mass-energy. The changes in mass theoretically associated with the energy changes in chemical reactions are so small that they lie just outside the range of our present methods of measurement.* Thus they need not be considered in ordinary chemical thermodynamics.

5. A MECHANICAL DEFINITION OF HEAT

Before continuing, we shall give a better definition of heat. Figure 2.1 shows a system I separated from its surroundings II by an *adiabatic wall*. This is defined as a wall that separates two systems so that they are prevented from coming to thermal equilibrium with each other. Such a definition does not require the concept of heat flow, and as shown in Sec. 1.7 thermal equilibrium can be defined even without reference to temperature.

The pressure on System I is increased and it is compressed from its initial state A to a new equilibrium state B; the adiabatic work done on the system is w_{ad}. The first law of thermodynamics can be stated in this form: when a system changes from state A to state B, the adiabatic work depends only on the initial and final states and can be set equal to the increase in a state function E, the internal energy. This statement follows at once from the impossibility of a perpetual motion machine. Thus we can write

$$\Delta E = E_B - E_A = w_{ad} \tag{2.6}$$

* The change in energy corresponding to a change in mass of Δm is $\Delta E = c^2 \Delta m$ where c is the speed of light. The most exothermic chemical reaction for a given mass of reactants is the recombination of two hydrogen atoms ($2H \rightarrow H_2$) which has $\Delta E = -103$ kcal/mole or $103 \times 10^3 \times 4.184 \times 10^7 \times (1/2) = 2.16 \times 10^{12}$ ergs/gram H. The decrease in mass on recombination of 2H would be $2.16 \times 10^{12}/(3 \times 10^{10})^2 = 2.4 \times 10^{-9}$ gram/gram of H. This is too small a change to be detected by present methods of weighing.

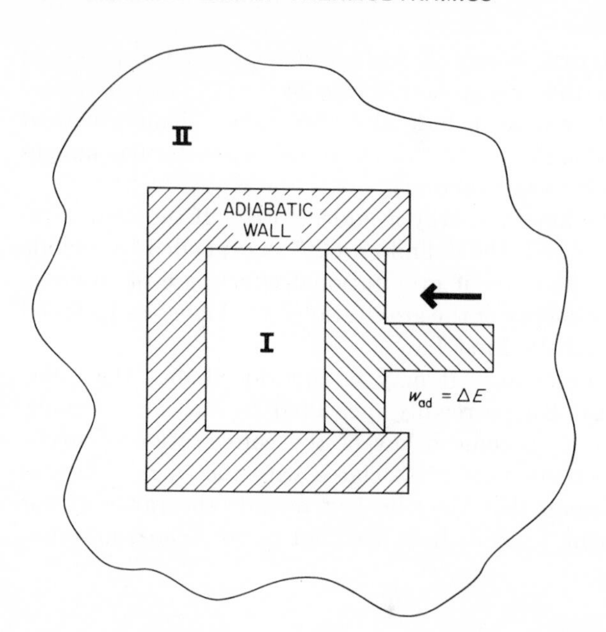

FIG. 2.1 A system I separated from environment II by an adiabatic wall

Now suppose the system to be again in state A, and replace the adiabatic wall by a *diathermic wall,* one that allows separated systems to come to equilibrium. The system is brought from state A to state B by one of an infinite number of possible nonadiabatic paths. The work done on the system is w. The difference $w_{\text{ad}} - w$ is *defined* as the heat q transferred to the system in the change from A to B.

$$q = w_{\text{ad}} - w \tag{2.7}$$

Or, from Eq. (2.6)

$$q = \Delta E - w$$

Thus the heat q transferred in a given process can be defined as the difference between the work done on the system along an adiabatic path from A to B and the work done along the given path from A to B. Although the concept of *heat* followed quite a different line in its historical development, this definition in terms of work gives a certain logical satisfaction.

6. PROPERTIES OF EXACT DIFFERENTIALS

We have seen in Sec. 1.19 that the work done by a system in going from one state to another is a function of the path between the states, and that $\oint dw$ is not in general equal to zero. The reason was readily apparent when the reversible process was considered. Then $\int_A^B dw = \int_A^B -P\,dV$. The differential expression $P\,dV$ cannot be integrated when only the initial and final states are known, since P is a function not only of the volume V but also of the temperature T, and this temperature may also change along the path of integration. On the other hand, $\int_A^B dE$ can always be carried out, giving $E_B - E_A$ since E is a function of the state of the system alone,* and is not dependent on the path by which that state is reached or on the previous history of the system.

Mathematically, therefore, we distinguish two classes of differential expressions. Those such as dE, dV or dT are called *exact differentials* since they are obtained by differentiation of some state function such as E, V or T. Those such as dq or dw are *inexact differentials*, since they cannot be obtained by differentiation of a function of the state of the system alone. Conversely, dq or dw cannot be integrated to yield a q or w. The First Law states that although dq and dw are not exact differentials, their sum $dE = dq + dw$ is an exact differential.

The following statements are mathematically equivalent:

(1) The function E is a function of the state of a system.
(2) The differential dE is an exact differential.
(3) The integral of dE about a closed path $\oint dE$ is equal to zero.

As an important corollary of the fact that it is an exact differential, dE can be written

$$dE = \left(\frac{\partial E}{\partial x}\right)_y dx + \left(\frac{\partial E}{\partial y}\right)_x dy \tag{2.8}$$

where x and y are any other variables of state of the system, for instance any two of P, T, V. Thus, for example,

$$dE = \left(\frac{\partial E}{\partial V}\right)_T dV + \left(\frac{\partial E}{\partial T}\right)_V dT \tag{2.9}$$

A further useful property of exact differential expressions is the *Euler reciprocity relation.* If an exact differential is written $dE = M\,dV + N\,dT$, then

$$\left(\frac{\partial M}{\partial T}\right)_V = \left(\frac{\partial N}{\partial V}\right)_T \tag{2.10}$$

This can be seen immediately from the typical case of Eq. (2.9), whence Eq. (2.10) becomes $(\partial^2 E/\partial V \partial T) = (\partial^2 E/\partial T \partial V)$, which is true since the order of differentiation is immaterial.

7. ADIABATIC AND ISOTHERMAL PROCESSES

Two kinds of process occur frequently both in laboratory experiments and in thermodynamic arguments. An *isothermal process* is one that occurs at constant temperature, T = constant, $dT = 0$. To approach isothermal conditions, reactions are often carried out in thermostats. In an *adiabatic process*, heat is neither added to nor taken from the system; i.e., $q = 0$. For a differential adiabatic process, $dq = 0$, and therefore from Eq. (2.4) $dE = dw$. For an adia-

* There is nothing esoteric in the concept of a state function. Temperature T, volume V, and pressure P, are all state functions like energy E.

batic reversible change in volume, $dE = -P\,dV$.* Adiabatic conditions can be approached by careful thermal insulation of the system. High vacuum is the best insulator against heat conduction. Highly polished walls minimize heat loss by radiation. These principles are combined in Dewar vessels of various types.

8. THE HEAT CONTENT OR ENTHALPY

No mechanical work is done during a process carried out at constant volume; since $V =$ constant, $dV = 0$, $w = 0$. It follows that the increase in energy equals the heat absorbed at constant volume.

$$\Delta E = q_V \tag{2.11}$$

If pressure is held constant, as for example in experiments carried out under atmospheric pressure, and no work is done except $P\,\Delta V$ work,

$$\Delta E = E_2 - E_1 = q + w = q - P(V_2 - V_1)$$

or

$$(E_2 + PV_2) - (E_1 + PV_1) = q_P$$

where q_P is the heat absorbed at constant pressure. We now define a new function, called the *enthalpy* or *heat content*† by

$$H = E + PV \tag{2.12}$$

Then

$$\Delta H = H_2 - H_1 = q_P \tag{2.13}$$

The increase in enthalpy equals the heat absorbed at constant pressure when no work is done other than $P\,\Delta V$ work.

It will be noted that the enthalpy H, like the energy E or the temperature T, is a function of the state of the system alone, and is independent of the path by which that state is reached. This fact follows from the definition in Eq. (2.12), since E, P and V are all state functions.

9. HEAT CAPACITIES

Heat capacities may be measured either at constant volume or at constant pressure. From the definitions in Eqs. (1.34), (2.11) and (2.13):

$$\text{heat capacity at constant volume: } C_V = \frac{dq_V}{dT} = \left(\frac{\partial E}{\partial T}\right)_V \tag{2.14}$$

$$\text{heat capacity at constant pressure: } C_P = \frac{dq_P}{dT} = \left(\frac{\partial H}{\partial T}\right)_P \tag{2.15}$$

---

* For an adiabatic irreversible change, $dE = -P_{ex}\,dV$.

† Note carefully that *heat content* H and *heat capacity* dq/dT are two entirely different functions. The similarity in nomenclature is unfortunate, and the term *enthalpy* is therefore preferable to *heat content*.

The symbols $\overline{C}_V$ and $\overline{C}_P$ are used to represent the heat capacities per mole. Thus $C_V = n\overline{C}_V$ and $C_P = n\overline{C}_P$.

The heat capacity at constant pressure C_P is usually* larger than that at constant volume C_V, because at constant pressure part of the heat added to a substance may be used in the work of expanding it, whereas at constant volume all of the added heat produces a rise in temperature. An important equation for the difference $C_P - C_V$ can be obtained as follows:

$$C_P - C_V = \left(\frac{\partial H}{\partial T}\right)_P - \left(\frac{\partial E}{\partial T}\right)_V = \left(\frac{\partial E}{\partial T}\right)_P + P\left(\frac{\partial V}{\partial T}\right)_P - \left(\frac{\partial E}{\partial T}\right)_V \tag{2.16}$$

Since

$$dE = \left(\frac{\partial E}{\partial V}\right)_T dV + \left(\frac{\partial E}{\partial T}\right)_V dT$$

$$\left(\frac{\partial E}{\partial T}\right)_P = \left(\frac{\partial E}{\partial V}\right)_T \left(\frac{\partial V}{\partial T}\right)_P + \left(\frac{\partial E}{\partial T}\right)_V$$

Substituting this value in Eq. (2.16), we find

$$C_P - C_V = \left[P + \left(\frac{\partial E}{\partial V}\right)_T\right]\left(\frac{\partial V}{\partial T}\right)_P \tag{2.17}$$

The term $P\,(\partial V/\partial T)_P$ may be seen to represent the contribution to the heat capacity C_P caused by the change in volume of the system against the *external pressure* P. The other term $(\partial E/\partial V)_T\,(\partial V/\partial T)_P$ is the contribution from the energy required for the change in volume against the internal cohesive or repulsive forces of the substance, represented by a change of the energy with volume at constant temperature. The term $(\partial E/\partial V)_T$ is called the *internal pressure*.† In the case of liquids and solids, which have strong cohesive forces, this term is large. In the case of gases, on the other hand, the term $(\partial E/\partial V)_T$ is usually small compared to P. In fact, the first attempts to measure $(\partial E/\partial V)_T$ for gases failed to detect it at all. These experiments were carried out by Joule in 1843.

10. THE JOULE EXPERIMENT

Joule's drawing of his apparatus is reproduced in Fig. 2.2 and he described the experiment as follows:††

> *I provided another copper receiver (E) which had a capacity of 134 cubic inches . . . I had a piece D attached, in the center of which there was a bore $\frac{1}{8}$ of an inch in diameter, which could be closed perfectly by means of a proper stopcock. . . . Having*

* Substances usually expand with increase of temperature at constant pressure, but in exceptional cases there may be a contraction, for example, water between 1 and 4°C.

† Note that just as $\partial E/\partial r$, the derivative of the energy with respect to a displacement, is a force, the derivative with respect to volume, $\partial E/\partial V$, is a force per unit area or a pressure.

†† *Phil. Mag.*, 1843, p. 263.

filled the receiver R with about 22 atmospheres of dry air and having exhausted the receiver E by means of an air pump, I screwed them together and put them into a tin can containing 16½ lb. of water. The water was first thoroughly stirred, and its temperature taken by the same delicate thermometer which was made use of in the former experiments on mechanical equivalent of heat. The stopcock was then opened by means of a proper key, and the air allowed to pass from the full into the empty receiver until equilibrium was established between the two. Lastly, the water was again stirred and its temperature carefully noted.

Joule then presented a table of experimental data, showing that there was no measurable temperature change, and arrived at the conclusion that "no change of temperature occurs when air is allowed to expand in such a manner as not to develop mechanical power" (i.e., so as to do no external work).

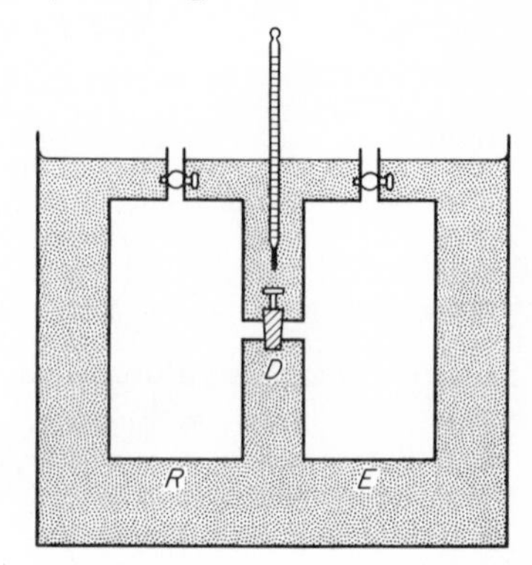

FIG. 2.2 The Joule experiment.

The expansion in Joule's experiment, with the air rushing from R into the evacuated vessel E, is a typical irreversible process. Inequalities of temperature and pressure arise throughout the system, but eventually an equilibrium state is reached. There has been no change in the internal energy of the gas since no work was done by or on it, and it has exchanged no heat with the surrounding water (otherwise the temperature of the water would have changed). Therefore $dE = 0$. Experimentally it is found that $dT = 0$. It may therefore be concluded that the internal energy must depend only on the temperature and not on the volume. In mathematical terms, since

$$dE = \left(\frac{\partial E}{\partial V}\right)_T dV + \left(\frac{\partial E}{\partial T}\right)_V dT = 0$$

$$\left(\frac{\partial E}{\partial V}\right)_T = -C_V \left(\frac{\partial T}{\partial V}\right)_E$$

Then, $$\left(\frac{\partial E}{\partial V}\right)_T \text{ must} = 0, \qquad \text{if} \left(\frac{\partial T}{\partial V}\right)_E = 0.$$

Joule's experiment, however, was not capable of detecting small effects since the heat capacity of his water calorimeter was extremely large compared to that of the gas used.

11. THE JOULE-THOMSON EXPERIMENT

William Thomson (Kelvin) suggested a better procedure, and working with Joule, carried out a series of experiments between 1852 and 1862. Their apparatus is shown schematically in Fig. 2.3. The principle involved throttling the

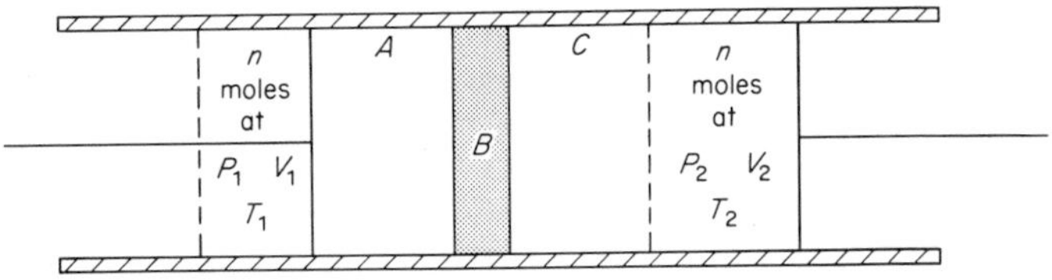

FIG. 2.3 Schematic representation of the Joule-Thomson experiment.

gas flow from the high pressure side A to the low pressure side C by interposing a porous plug B. In their first trials, this plug consisted of a silk handkerchief; in later work, porous meerschaum was used. In this way, by the time the gas emerges into C, it has already reached equilibrium and its temperature can be measured directly. The entire system is thermally insulated, so that the process is an adiabatic one, and $q = 0$.

Suppose that the fore pressure in A is P_1, the back pressure in C is P_2, and the volumes of gas at these pressures are V_1 and V_2, respectively. The work done *on* the gas in forcing it through the plug is then P_1V_1, and the work done *by* the gas in expanding on the other side is P_2V_2. The net work done on the gas is therefore $w = P_1V_1 - P_2V_2$.

It follows that a Joule-Thomson expansion occurs at constant enthalpy, since

$$\Delta E = E_2 - E_1 = q + w = 0 + w$$

$$E_2 - E_1 = P_1V_1 - P_2V_2$$

$$E_2 + P_2V_2 = E_1 + P_1V_1$$

$$H_2 = H_1$$

The Joule-Thomson coefficient, μ, is defined as the change of temperature with pressure at constant enthalpy,

$$\mu = \left(\frac{\partial T}{\partial P}\right)_H \tag{2.18}$$

This quantity is measured directly from the temperature change ΔT of the gas as it undergoes a pressure drop ΔP through the porous plug. Some experimental values of the J.-T. coefficients, which are functions of temperature and pressure, are collected in Table 2.1 for a typical gas.

A positive μ corresponds to cooling on expansion, a negative μ, to warming. Most gases at room temperatures are cooled by a J.-T. expansion. Hydrogen, however, is warmed if its initial temperature is above $-80°C$, but if it is first cooled below $-80°C$ it can then be cooled further by a J.-T. effect. The temperature $-80°C$ at which $\mu = 0$ is called the *Joule-Thomson inversion temperature for hydrogen*. Inversion temperatures for other gases, except helium, lie considerably higher. The Joule-Thomson expansion provides one of the most important methods for liquefying gases.

TABLE 2.1 JOULE-THOMSON COEFFICIENTS FOR CARBON DIOXIDE*
μ (°K per atm)

Temperature (°K)	Pressure (atm)						
	0	1	10	40	60	80	100
220	2.2855	2.3035					
250	1.6885	1.6954	1.7570				
275	1.3455	1.3455	1.3470				
300	1.1070	1.1045	1.0840	1.0175	0.9675		
325	0.9425	0.9375	0.9075	0.8025	0.7230	0.6165	0.5220
350	0.8195	0.8150	0.7850	0.6780	0.6020	0.5210	0.4340
380	0.7080	0.7045	0.6780	0.5835	0.5165	0.4505	0.3855
400	0.6475	0.6440	0.6210	0.5375	0.4790	0.4225	0.3635

* From John H. Perry, *Chemical Engineers' Handbook* (New York: McGraw-Hill, 1941). Rearranged from *International Critical Tables*, vol. 5, where further data may be found.

12. APPLICATION OF THE FIRST LAW TO IDEAL GASES

An analysis of the theory of the Joule-Thomson experiment must be postponed until the Second Law of Thermodynamics has been studied in the next chapter. It may be said, however, that the porous-plug experiments showed that Joule's original conclusion that $(\partial E/\partial V)_T = 0$ for all gases was too broad. A real gas may have a considerable internal pressure, showing the existence of cohesive forces, and its energy depends on its volume as well as on its temperature.

An *ideal gas* may now be defined in thermodynamic terms as follows:*

(1) The internal pressure $(\partial E/\partial V)_T = 0$.

(2) The gas follows the equation of state, $PV = nRT$.

It follows from Eq. (2.9) that the energy of an ideal gas is a function of its temperature alone. For an ideal gas,

$$dE = (\partial E/\partial T)_V \, dT = C_V \, dT, \qquad C_V = dE/dT$$

The heat capacity of an ideal gas also depends only on its temperature. These conclusions greatly simplify the thermodynamics of ideal gases, so that many discussions are carried on in terms of the ideal-gas model. Some examples follow.

Difference in heat capacities: When Eq. (2.17) is applied to an ideal gas, it becomes

$$C_P - C_V = P\left(\frac{\partial V}{\partial T}\right)_P$$

Then, since

$$PV = nRT$$

$$\left(\frac{\partial V}{\partial T}\right)_P = \frac{nR}{P}$$

* After a thermodynamic definition of temperature is obtained from the Second Law of Thermodynamics, we can derive (1) from (2), or derive (2) from (1) and Boyle's Law. Thus (2) in itself completely defines an ideal gas.

and

$$C_P - C_V = nR \tag{2.19}$$

Temperature changes: Since $dE = C_V\,dT$ for an ideal gas,*

$$\Delta E = E_2 - E_1 = \int_{T_1}^{T_2} C_V\,dT \tag{2.20}$$

Likewise for an ideal gas,*

$$dH = C_P\,dT$$

$$\Delta H = H_2 - H_1 = \int_{T_1}^{T_2} C_P\,dT \tag{2.21}$$

Isothermal reversible volume or pressure change: For an isothermal change in an ideal gas, the internal energy remains constant. Since $dT = 0$ and $(\partial E/\partial V)_T = 0$,

$$dE = dq - P\,dV = \left(\frac{\partial E}{\partial T}\right)_V dT + \left(\frac{\partial E}{\partial V}\right)_T dV = 0$$

Hence,

$$dq = -dw = P\,dV$$

Since

$$P = \frac{nRT}{V}$$

$$\int_1^2 dq = \int_1^2 -dw = \int_1^2 nRT\,\frac{dV}{V}$$

or,

$$q = -w = nRT \ln \frac{V_2}{V_1} = nRT \ln \frac{P_1}{P_2} \tag{2.22}$$

Since the volume change is carried out reversibly, P always has its equilibrium value nRT/V, and the work $-w$ in Eq. (2.22) is the maximum work done in an expansion, or the minimum work needed to effect a compression. The equation tells us that the work required to compress a gas from 10 atm to 100 atm is just the same as that required to compress it from 1 atm to 10 atm.

Reversible adiabatic expansion: In this case, $dq = 0$, and $dE = dw = -P\,dV$. From Eq. (2.20),

$$dw = C_V\,dT \tag{2.23}$$

For a finite change,

$$w = \int_1^2 C_V\,dT \tag{2.24}$$

We may write Eq. (2.23) as $C_V\,dT + P\,dV = 0$, whence,

$$C_V\,\frac{dT}{T} + nR\,\frac{dV}{V} = 0 \tag{2.25}$$

---

* For any substance, at constant volume, $dE = C_V\,dT$, and at constant pressure, $dH = C_P\,dT$. For an ideal gas, E and H are functions only of T and these relations hold even if V and P are not constant.

Integrating between T_1 and T_2, and V_1 and V_2, the initial and final temperatures and volumes, we have

$$C_V \ln \frac{T_2}{T_1} + nR \ln \frac{V_2}{V_1} = 0 \tag{2.26}$$

This integration assumes that C_V is a constant, not a function of T.

We may substitute for nR from Eq. (2.19) and using the conventional symbol γ for the heat capacity ratio C_P/C_V we find

$$(\gamma - 1) \ln \frac{V_2}{V_1} + \ln \frac{T_2}{T_1} = 0$$

Therefore,

$$\frac{T_1}{T_2} = \left(\frac{V_2}{V_1}\right)^{\gamma-1} \tag{2.27}$$

Since, for an ideal gas, $\dfrac{T_1}{T_2} = \dfrac{P_1V_1}{P_2V_2}$, we have

$$P_1V_1^{\gamma} = P_2V_2^{\gamma} \tag{2.28}$$

It has been shown, therefore, that for a reversible adiabatic expansion of an ideal gas (with constant C_V)

$$PV^{\gamma} = \text{constant} \tag{2.29}$$

We recall that for an isothermal expansion, PV = constant.

These equations are plotted in Fig. 2.4. A given pressure fall produces a lesser volume increase in the adiabatic case, because the temperature also falls during the adiabatic expansion.

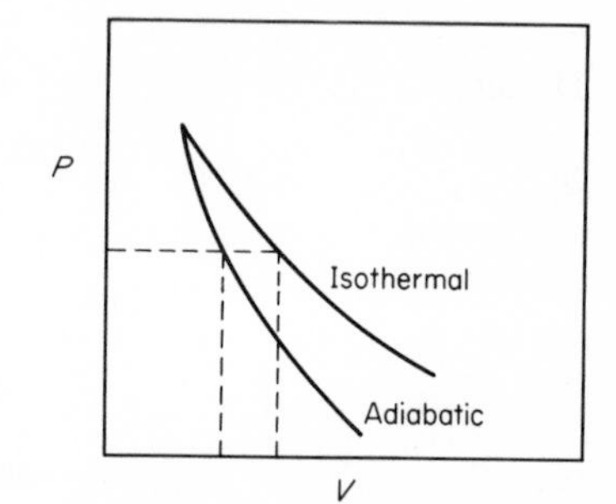

FIG. 2.4 Isothermal and adiabatic reversible expansions.

13. EXAMPLES OF IDEAL-GAS CALCULATIONS

Let us take 10 liters of gas at 0°C and 10 atm. We therefore have 100/22.414 = 4.461 moles. We shall calculate the final volume and the work done in three different expansions to a final pressure of 1 atm. Let us assume that we have a monatomic gas such as neon. The molar heat capacity is then $\overline{C}_V = \frac{3}{2}R$, independent of temperature.

Isothermal reversible expansion: In this case the final volume

$$V_2 = P_1V_1/P_2 = (10)(10)/(1) = 100 \text{ liters.}$$

The work done by the gas in expanding equals the heat absorbed by the gas from its environment. From Eq. (2.22),

$$-w = q = nRT \ln \frac{V_2}{V_1}$$

$$= (4.461)(8.314)(273.2)(2.303) \log (10)$$

$$= 23\,285 \text{ joules}$$

Adiabatic reversible expansion: The final volume is calculated from Eq. (2.28), with

$$\gamma = \frac{C_P}{C_V} = \frac{\frac{3}{2}R + R}{\frac{3}{2}R} = \frac{5}{3}$$

Thus, $$V_2 = \left(\frac{P_1}{P_2}\right)^{1/\gamma} V_1, \qquad V_2 = (10)^{3/5} \times 10 = 39.81 \text{ liters.}$$

The final temperature is obtained from $P_2V_2 = nRT_2$:

$$T_2 = \frac{P_2V_2}{nR} = \frac{(1)(39.81)}{(4.461)(0.08205)} = 108.8°\text{K}.$$

For an adiabatic process, $q = 0$, and $\Delta E = q + w = w$. Also, since C_V is constant, Eq. (2.20) gives

$$\Delta E = nC_V\,\Delta T = n\frac{3R}{2}(T_2 - T_1) = -9141 \text{ joules.}$$

The work *done by* the gas on expansion is therefore 9141 joules.

Irreversible adiabatic expansion: Suppose the pressure is suddenly released to 1 atm and the gas expands adiabatically against this constant pressure. Since this is not a reversible expansion, Eq. (2.28) cannot be applied. Since $q = 0$, $\Delta E = w$. The value of ΔE depends only on the initial and final states:

$$\Delta E = w = C_V(T_2 - T_1)$$

Also, for an expansion at constant pressure, we have from Eq. (1.36),

$$-w = P_2(V_2 - V_1) = P_2\left(\frac{nRT_2}{P_2} - \frac{nRT_1}{P_1}\right)$$

Equating the two expressions for w, we obtain

$$-C_V(T_2 - T_1) = P_2\left(\frac{nRT_2}{P_2} - \frac{nRT_1}{P_1}\right)$$

The only unknown is T_2.

$$-\tfrac{3}{2}nR(T_2 - 273.2) = 1\left(\frac{nRT_2}{1} - \frac{nR\,273.2}{10}\right)$$

$$T_2 = 174.8°\text{K}$$

Then,

$$\Delta E = w = \tfrac{3}{2}nR(174.8 - 273.2)$$

$$\Delta E = -5474 \text{ joules}$$

Note that there is considerably less cooling of the gas and less work done by the gas in the irreversible adiabatic expansion than in the reversible expansion.

14. THERMOCHEMISTRY — HEATS OF REACTION

Thermochemistry is the study of the heat effects that accompany chemical reactions, the formation of solutions, and changes in state of aggregation like melting or vaporization. Physicochemical changes are classified as *endothermic*, accompanied by the absorption of heat, or *exothermic*, accompanied by the evolution of heat. An example of an exothermic reaction is the burning of hydrogen.

$$H_2 + \tfrac{1}{2}O_2 \longrightarrow H_2O \text{ (gas)} \qquad \Delta H = -57\,780 \text{ cal at } 18°\text{C}$$

The heat is given off *from the system* and therefore is written with a negative sign. A typical endothermic reaction would be the decomposition of water vapor,

$$H_2O \text{ (gas)} \longrightarrow H_2 + \tfrac{1}{2}O_2 \qquad \Delta H = 57\,780 \text{ cal at } 18°\text{C}$$

Like any other transfer of heat, the heat of a chemical reaction depends upon the conditions that hold during the process by which it is carried out. There are two particular conditions that are important because they lead to heats of reaction equal to changes in thermodynamic functions.

The first such condition is that of *constant volume*. If the volume of a system is held constant, no work is done on the system,* and Eq. (2.3) for the First Law of Thermodynamics becomes

$$\Delta E = q_V \tag{2.30}$$

Thus the heat of reaction measured at constant volume is exactly equal to the change in internal energy ΔE of the reaction system. This condition is excellently approximated when the reaction is carried out in a bomb calorimeter.

The other important special condition is that of *constant pressure*. During the course of an experiment under ordinary bench-top conditions, the pressure is effectively constant. Many calorimeters operate at this constant atmospheric pressure. From Eq. (2.13),

$$\Delta H = q_P \tag{2.31}$$

The heat of reaction measured at constant pressure is exactly equal to the change in enthalpy ΔH of the reaction system.

It is often necessary to use data obtained with a bomb calorimeter, which give ΔE, in order to calculate ΔH. From the definition of H in Eq. (2.12)

$$\Delta H = \Delta E + \Delta(PV) \tag{2.32}$$

By $\Delta(PV)$ we mean the sum of the PV for each of the products of the reaction less the sum of the PV for each of the reactants. If all the reactants and products are liquids or solids, these PV values change only slightly during the reaction, and $\Delta(PV)$ is usually so small compared to ΔH or ΔE that it may be neglected.

* It is assumed that no work except "PV work" would be possible in the experimental arrangement used.

In this case, $q_P = q_V$.* For reactions in which gases occur in the reaction equation, the value of $\Delta(PV)$ depends on the change in the number of moles of gas as a result of reaction. From the ideal gas equation we can write

$$\Delta(PV) = \Delta n\, RT$$

Therefore, from Eq. (2.32)

$$\Delta H = \Delta E + \Delta n\, RT \tag{2.33}$$

By Δn we mean the number of moles of gaseous products minus the number of moles of gaseous reactants.

Consider as an example the reaction,

$$SO_2 + \tfrac{1}{2}O_2 \longrightarrow SO_3$$

The ΔE for this reaction as measured in a bomb calorimeter was $-23\,190$ cal at 298°K. What is the ΔH? The $\Delta n = 1 - 1 - \frac{1}{2} = -\frac{1}{2}$.
Therefore,

$$\Delta H = \Delta E - \tfrac{1}{2}RT$$

$$\Delta H = -23\,190 - \tfrac{1}{2}(1.9872)\,(298) = -23\,486 \text{ cal}$$

To specify the heat of reaction it is necessary to write the exact chemical equation for the reaction and to specify the states of all reactants and products, noting particularly the constant temperature at which the measurement is made. Since most reactions are studied under conditions of essentially constant pressure, ΔH is usually the heat of reaction stated. Two examples follow:

$$CO_2 \text{ (1 atm)} + H_2 \text{ (1 atm)} \longrightarrow CO \text{ (1 atm)} + H_2O \text{ (g, 1 atm)}, \; \Delta H_{298} = 9838 \text{ cal}$$

$$AgBr + \tfrac{1}{2}Cl_2 \text{ (1 atm)} \longrightarrow AgCl \text{ (c)} + \tfrac{1}{2}Br_2, \; \Delta H_{298} = -6582 \text{ cal}$$

As an immediate consequence of the First Law, ΔE or ΔH for any chemical reaction is independent of the path, that is, independent of any intermediate reactions that may occur. This principle, first established experimentally by G. H. Hess (1840), is called *The Law of Constant Heat Summation.* It is often possible, therefore, to calculate the heat of a reaction from measurements on quite different reactions. For example,

$$(1)\quad COCl_2 + H_2S \longrightarrow 2HCl + COS \qquad \Delta H_{298} = -18\,811 \text{ cal}$$

$$(2)\quad COS + H_2S \longrightarrow H_2O \text{ (g)} + CS_2 \text{ (l)} \qquad \Delta H_{298} = 817 \text{ cal}$$

$$(3)\quad COCl_2 + 2H_2S \longrightarrow 2HCl + H_2O \text{ (g)} + CS_2 \text{ (l)} \qquad \Delta H_{298} = -17\,994 \text{ cal}$$

* Note, however, that we cannot carry out a reaction at constant P, T and constant V, T and at the same time require that the initial and final P, V, T be the same in the two cases. Thus Eq. (2.32) becomes, in the general case,

$$q_P = \Delta E_P + P\,\Delta V$$

or

$$\Delta H_V = q_V + V\,\Delta P$$

depending on whether a condition of constant P or of constant V is chosen.

15. HEATS OF FORMATION

A convenient standard state for a substance is the state in which it is stable at 25°C and 1 atm pressure, for example, oxygen as O_2 (g), sulfur as S (rhombic crystal), mercury as Hg (l), and so on. By convention, the enthalpies of the chemical elements in these standard states are set equal to zero. The standard enthalpy of any compound is then the heat of the reaction by which it is formed from its elements, the reactants and products all being in the standard state at 25°C and 1 atm. For example,

$$(1)\ S + O_2 \longrightarrow SO_2 \qquad \Delta H^\circ_{298} = -\ 70\,960 \text{ cal}$$

$$(2)\ 2Al + \tfrac{3}{2}O_2 \longrightarrow Al_2O_3 \qquad \Delta H^\circ_{298} = -399\,090 \text{ cal}$$

The superscript zero indicates we are writing a *standard* heat of formation with reactants and products at 1 atm; the absolute temperature is written as a subscript. Thermochemical data are conveniently tabulated as heats of formation. A few examples, selected from a recent compilation of the National Bureau of Standards* are given in Table 2.2. The standard heat of any reaction at 25°C

TABLE 2.2 STANDARD HEATS OF FORMATION AT 25°C

Compound	State	$\Delta H^\circ_{298.15}$ (kcal/mole)	Compound	State	$\Delta H^\circ_{298.15}$ (kcal/mole)
H_2O	g	−57.7979	H_2S	g	−4.815
H_2O	l	−68.3174	H_2SO_4	l	−193.91
H_2O_2	g	−31.83	SO_2	g	−70.96
HF	g	−64.2	SO_3	g	−94.45
HCl	g	−22.063	CO	g	−26.4157
HBr	g	−8.66	CO_2	g	−94.0518
HI	g	+6.20	$SOCl_2$	l	−49.2
HIO_3	c	−57.03	S_2Cl_2	g	−5.70

is then readily found as the difference between the standard heats of formation of the products and of the reactants.

Many of our thermochemical data have been obtained from measurements of heats of combustion. If the heats of formation of all its combustion products are known, the heat of formation of a compound can be calculated from its heat of combustion. For example,

$$(1)\ C_2H_6 + \tfrac{7}{2}O_2 \longrightarrow 2CO_2 + 3H_2O\ (l) \qquad \Delta H^\circ_{298} = -372.87 \text{ kcal}$$

$$(2)\ C\ (\text{graphite}) + O_2 \longrightarrow CO_2 \qquad \Delta H^\circ_{298} = -\ 94.05 \text{ kcal}$$

$$(3)\ H_2 + \tfrac{1}{2}O_2 \longrightarrow H_2O\ (l) \qquad \Delta H^\circ_{298} = -\ 68.32 \text{ kcal}$$

$$(4)\ 2C + 3H_2 \longrightarrow C_2H_6 \qquad \Delta H^\circ_{298} = -\ 20.19 \text{ kcal}$$

* The Bureau publishes a comprehensive collection of thermodynamic data, copies of which are to be deposited in every scientific library (*Selected Values of Chemical Thermodynamic Properties*).

The data in Table 2.3 were obtained from heats of combustion by F. D. Rossini and his coworkers at the National Bureau of Standards. The standard state of carbon has been taken to be graphite.

TABLE 2.3 HEATS OF FORMATION OF GASEOUS HYDROCARBONS

Substance	*Formula*	ΔH°_{298} (cal/mole)
Paraffins:		
Methane	CH_4	−17 865 ± 74
Ethane	C_2H_6	−20 191 ± 108
Propane	C_3H_8	−24 750 ± 124
n-Butane	C_4H_{10}	−29 715 ± 153
Isobutane	C_4H_{10}	−31 350 ± 132
n-Pentane	C_5H_{12}	−34 739 ± 213
2-Methylbutane	C_5H_{12}	−36 671 ± 153
Tetramethylmethane	C_5H_{12}	−39 410 ± 227
Monolefines:		
Ethylene	C_2H_4	12 556 ± 67
Propylene	C_3H_6	4956 ± 110
1-Butene	C_4H_8	383 ± 180
cis-2-Butene	C_4H_8	−1388 ± 180
trans-2-Butene	C_4H_8	−2338 ± 180
2-Methylpropene	C_4H_8	−3205 ± 165
1-Pentene	C_5H_{10}	−4644 ± 300
Diolefines:		
Allene	C_3H_4	46 046 ± 260
1,3-Butadiene	C_4H_6	26 865 ± 240
1,3-Pentadiene	C_5H_8	18 885 ± 300
1,4-Pentadiene	C_5H_8	25 565 ± 300
Acetylenes:		
Acetylene	C_2H_2	54 228 ± 235
Methylacetylene	C_3H_4	44 309 ± 240
Dimethylacetylene	C_4H_6	35 221 ± 355

When changes in state of aggregation occur, the appropriate latent heat must be added. For example,

$$\text{S (rhombic)} + O_2 \longrightarrow SO_2 \qquad \Delta H^\circ_{298} = -70.96 \text{ kcal}$$

$$\text{S (rhombic)} \longrightarrow \text{S (monoclinic)} \qquad \Delta H^\circ_{298} = 0.07 \text{ kcal}$$

$$\text{S (monoclinic)} + O_2 \longrightarrow SO_2 \qquad \Delta H^\circ_{298} = -71.03 \text{ kcal}$$

16. EXPERIMENTAL CALORIMETRY*

One of the landmarks in the development of thermochemistry was the publication in 1780 by Lavoisier and Laplace of their memoir *Sur la Chaleur*. They de-

* Descriptions of the experimental equipment and procedures can be found in the publications of the Thermodynamics Section at the National Bureau of Standards: *J. Res. of N.B.S. 6*, 1(1931); *13*, 469 (1934); *27*, 289 (1941). The best general account of experimental calorimetry is the article by J. M. Sturtevant in *Physical Methods of Organic Chemistry*, (3rd edition), vol. 1, pt. 1, 523–654. (ed. A. Weissberger, New York: Interscience, 1959).

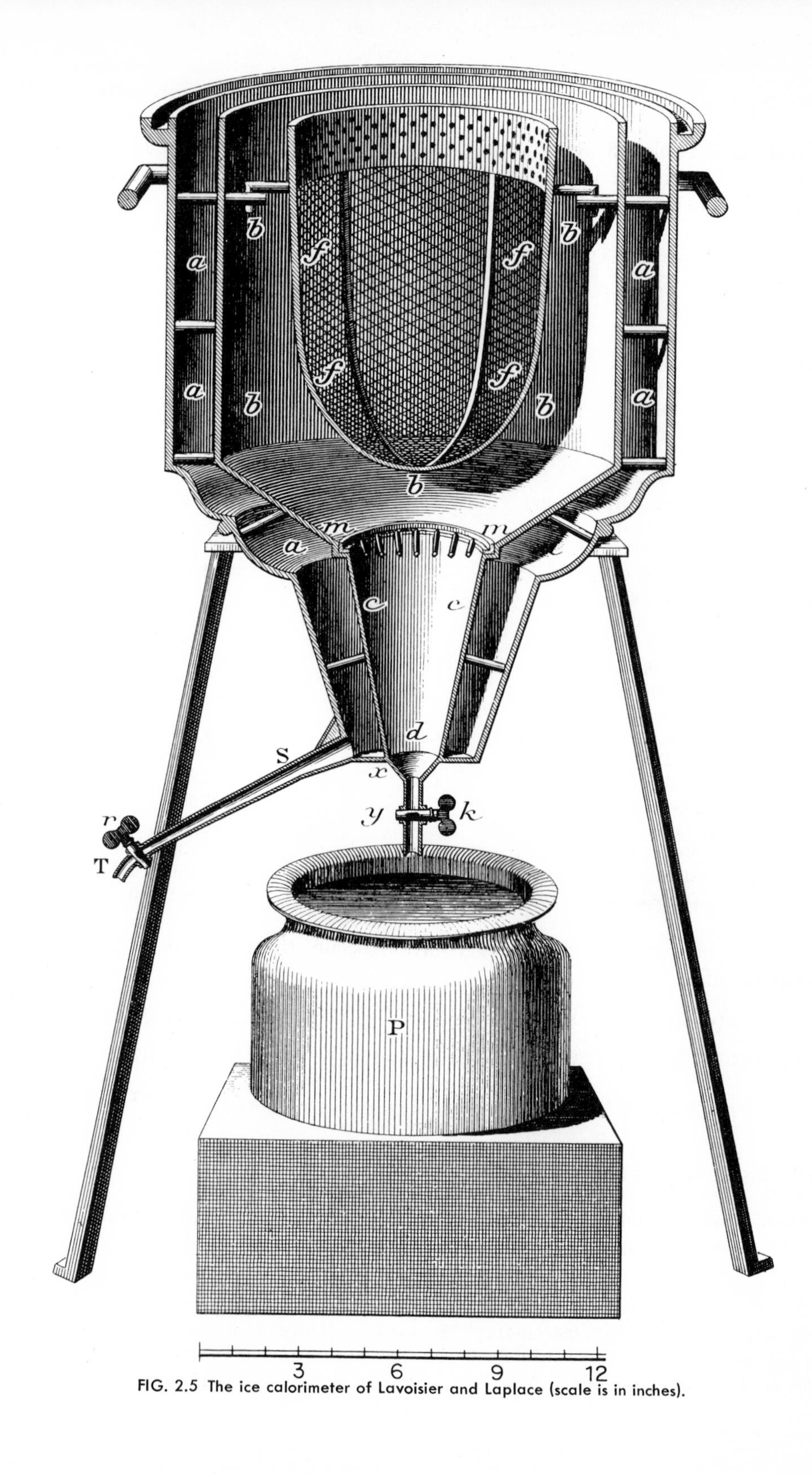

FIG. 2.5 The ice calorimeter of Lavoisier and Laplace (scale is in inches).

scribed the use of an ice calorimeter in which the heat liberated was measured by the mass of ice melted. They measured the heat of combustion of carbon, finding that "one ounce of carbon in burning melts six pounds and two ounces of ice." This result corresponds to a heat of combustion of −98 850 calories per mole, as compared to the best modern value of −94 052. The calorimeter is shown in Fig. 2.5. It was filled with ice in the regions bbb and aaa, the outer layer of ice preventing heat transfer into the calorimeter. Lavoisier and Laplace also measured the heat evolved by a guinea pig placed in the calorimeter and compared it with the amount of "dephlogisticated air" (oxygen) consumed by the animal. They concluded that "respiration is thus a combustion, to be sure very slow, but otherwise perfectly similar to that of carbon; it takes place in the interior of the lungs, without emitting visible light, because the matter of the fire on becoming free is soon absorbed by the humidity of these organs. The heat developed in the combustion is transferred to the blood which traverses the lungs, and from this is spread throughout all the animal system."

The field of calorimetry has always been one of the most precise and exacting parts of physical chemistry, and a prodigious amount of experimental ingenuity has been devoted to the design and construction of calorimeters. The measurement of the heat of a reaction consists essentially of (1) the careful determination of the amount of chemical reaction that produces a definite change in the calorimeter, (2) the measurement of the amount of electrical energy needed to produce exactly the same change in the calorimeter. The change in question is usually a temperature change. (A notable exception is an ice calorimeter like that of Lavoisier and Laplace.) Electrical energy is almost always used because it can be measured with the highest precision. If a potential difference E in absolute volts is impressed across a resistance R in absolute ohms for a time of t seconds, the energy dissipated is E^2t/R absolute joules or $E^2t/4.1840R$ defined calories. The measurement of the heat capacity of a substance consists of the determination of the input of electrical energy and the resultant rise in temperature.

A calorimeter enclosed entirely in a jacket maintained at a constant temperature is called an *isothermal calorimeter*. The part of the heat which is exchanged with the isothermal jacket is calculated from the laws of heat transfer. The remainder of the heat is measured by the change in temperature of the calorimeter.

A calorimeter designed so that it exchanges no heat with its environment is called an *adiabatic calorimeter*. The adiabatic condition can be approximated closely by automatically maintaining the temperature of the jacket as nearly as possible equal to that of the calorimeter.

A schematic diagram of a calorimeter designed by the National Bureau of Standards for the measurement of heats of combustion is shown in Fig. 2.6. This calorimeter uses a combustion bomb of the type invented by Berthelot in 1881. The sample is burned completely in oxygen under a pressure of 25 atm or more. The calorimeter is operated under isothermal conditions, the temperature of the jacket being maintained constant within 0.005°C by means of a special thermoregulator. The temperature of the calorimeter itself is measured with a platinum resistance thermometer.

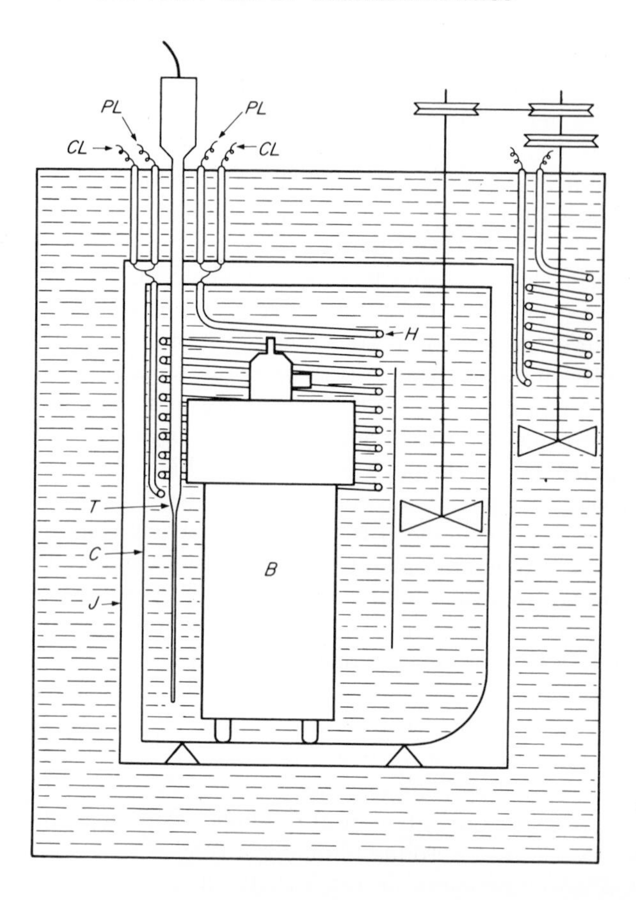

FIG. 2.6 Bomb calorimeter used at National Bureau of Standards. (B, bomb; H, heater; C, calorimeter vessel; T, resistance thermometer; J, jacket; PL, potential leads; CL, current leads.

To determine the heat of combustion of a substance, we place a weighed quantity in a platinum cup. Volatile substances are first sealed in glass ampoules. The top is screwed down and the bomb is filled with oxygen. When an iron wire in the bomb is electrically heated, it glows and ignites the substance.

Most of the available data on the heats of formation of organic substances have been obtained in bombs of this type. It is estimated that the limit of accuracy with the present apparatus and technique is two parts in ten thousand. Measurements with the bomb calorimeter yield ΔE values which are converted to ΔH by means of Eq. (2.32). The ΔH values in Table 2.3 were obtained from heats of combustion measured in this way.

An important thermochemical problem in recent years has been the difference in the energies of various organic compounds, especially the hydrocarbons. It is evident that extremely precise work is necessary to evaluate such differences from data on the heats of combustion. For example, the enthalpies of the five isomers of hexane differ by one to five kcal per mole, and the heats of combustion of the hexanes are around 1000 kcal per mole; even a 0.1 per cent uncertainty in the heats of combustion would lead to about a fifty per cent uncertainty in the enthalpy differences. For unsaturated hydrocarbons information about such small differences in energy can be obtained by measurement of their heats of hydrogenation. This method has been developed to a high precision by G. B. Kistiakowsky and his coworkers at Harvard.*

It is evident that in calorimetric experiments — for example, in the determination of a heat of combustion — the chemical reaction studied may actually occur at an elevated temperature. We measure, however, the net temperature rise after equilibrium has been reached and this usually amounts to only a few degrees owing to the high heat capacity of the calorimeter. Since ΔE and ΔH depend only on the initial and final states, we actually measure them, therefore, at about 25°C even though temperatures of over 2000°C may have been attained during the combustion process.

17. BOND ENERGIES

Ever since the time of van't Hoff, the chemist has sought to express the structures and properties of molecules in terms of the bonds between the atoms. In many cases, to a good approximation, it is possible to express the heat of formation of a molecule as an additive property of the bonds forming the molecule. This formulation has led to the concept of *bond energy*. We might define bond energy as the ΔH or ΔE required to form a bond between two atoms in a molecule.

To be precise, the bond energy for a given type of bond will depend upon the particular molecule in which it occurs and its exact situation in the molecule. Consider, for example, the molecule CH_4 and imagine that the H atoms are removed from it one at a time.

$$(1)\ CH_4 \longrightarrow CH_3 + H$$

$$(2)\ CH_3 \longrightarrow CH_2 + H$$

$$(3)\ CH_2 \longrightarrow CH + H$$

$$(4)\ CH \longrightarrow C + H$$

If we could determine ΔE for each of these reactions, they would give the energy of the CH bond in these four different cases. Actually it is difficult to obtain such data. The approximate values are (1) 101, (2) 87, (3) 92, and (4) 80 kcal/mole.

For many purposes a much simpler kind of information would be adequate. Thus the four C-H bonds in methane are certainly all equivalent and if we could imagine the carbon atom reacting with four hydrogen atoms to form methane, we could set one quarter of this overall heat of reaction equal to the average energy of a C-H bond. The reaction in question would be

$$C + 4H \longrightarrow CH_4$$

In order to calculate bond energies we do not consider the ordinary standard heats of formation of the molecules from the elements in their standard states,

---

* *J. Am. Chem. Soc.*, *57*, 876 (1935).

but the heats of formation of the molecules from the atoms. If we know the heats of atomization for all the elements, we can use these data to calculate the bond energies from the ordinary standard heats of formation. In most cases, it is not too difficult to obtain the heats of formation of the elements as monatomic gases. In the case of the metals, the ΔH in question is simply the heat of sublimation to the monatomic form. For example,

$$\text{Mg (c)} \longrightarrow \text{Mg (g)} \qquad \Delta H^\circ_{298} = 35.90 \text{ kcal}$$

$$\text{Ag (c)} \longrightarrow \text{Ag (g)} \qquad \Delta H^\circ_{298} = 69.12 \text{ kcal}$$

In other cases, the heats of atomization can be obtained from the dissociation energies of diatomic gases. For example,

$$Br_2 \text{ (g)} \longrightarrow 2\,\text{Br (g)} \qquad \Delta H^\circ_{298} = 53.42 \text{ kcal}$$

or,

$$\tfrac{1}{2}Br_2 \text{ (g)} \longrightarrow \text{Br (g)} \qquad = 26.71 \text{ kcal}$$

$$O_2 \text{ (g)} \longrightarrow 2\,\text{O (g)} \qquad \Delta H^\circ_{298} = 118.318 \text{ kcal}$$

or,

$$\tfrac{1}{2}O_2 \text{ (g)} \longrightarrow \text{O (g)} \qquad = 59.159 \text{ kcal}$$

In a few cases, however, it has proved to be exceedingly difficult to obtain the heats of atomization. The most notorious case is also the most important one, since all the bond energies of the organic molecules depend upon it, namely, the heat of sublimation of graphite.

$$\text{C (crystal, graphite)} \longrightarrow \text{C (gas)}$$

Even today not all scientists are agreed on the correct value for the heat of sublimation of graphite, but the most reasonable value appears to be

$$\Delta H^\circ_{298} = 171.7 \text{ kcal}$$

The standard enthalpies of formation for the elements in the form of monatomic gases (heats of atomization) are given in Table 2.4.

TABLE 2.4 STANDARD HEATS OF ATOMIZATION OF ELEMENTS

Element	ΔH°_{298} (kcal)	Element	ΔH°_{298} (kcal)
H	52.089	N	85.566
O	59.159	P	75.18
F	32.25	C	171.698
Cl	29.012	Si	88.04
Br	26.71	Hg	14.54
I	25.482	Ni	101.61
S	53.25	Fe	96.68

With these data, it is possible to calculate bond energies from standard heats of formation. Consider, for example, the application of thermochemical data to determine the energy of the O-H bond in water.

$$H_2 \longrightarrow 2\text{H} \qquad \Delta H = 104.2 \text{ kcal (spectroscopic)}$$

$$O_2 \longrightarrow 2O \qquad \Delta H = 118.3 \text{ kcal (spectroscopic)}$$

$$H_2 + \tfrac{1}{2}O_2 \longrightarrow H_2O \qquad \Delta H = -57.8 \text{ kcal (calorimetric)}$$

Therefore,

$$2H + O \longrightarrow H_2O \qquad \Delta H = -221.1 \text{ kcal}$$

This is the ΔH for the formation of two O-H bonds, so that the strength of the O-H bond in water can be taken as $221/2 = 110.5$ kcal.

The main sources of data for the determination of bond energies are molecular spectroscopy, thermochemistry, and electron-impact studies. The electron-impact method employs a mass spectrometer; the energy of the electrons in the ion source is gradually increased until the molecule is broken into fragments by the electrons striking it.

Some bond energies taken from a recent compilation are collected in Table 2.5.

TABLE 2.5 SINGLE BOND ENERGIES (kcal/mole)

	F	O	N	Cl	Br	I	C	H	Si
Si	128	89	...	66	73	51	68	81	43
H	135	110	84	103	87	71	99	104	
C	102	81	62	77	64	56	80		
I	...	...	...	51	43	36			
Br	61	...	...	52	46				
Cl	61	49	37	58					
N	56	...	32						
O	44	33							
F	37								

Electronegativity ←

Electronegativity ↓

It is necessary to distinguish the bond energies of the single bonds from those of double and triple bonds. It is not always possible to define exactly the type of bond, and in such cases large departures from the average bond energy may be found. Also the bond energy will vary with the polarity of the bond, covalent bonds and ionic bonds tending to differ.

It should be emphasized, therefore, that although the concept of bond energy has been useful, it cannot be a substitute for accurate calorimetric data when these are available. In some cases, however, when no data are at hand, it is possible to estimate the heat of formation or the heat of combustion of a compound quite well from a table of bond energies. Also, of course, it is a major theoretical problem to calculate the bond energies from the configurations of the nuclei and electrons in the molecules.

18. HEATS OF SOLUTION

In many chemical reactions, one or more of the reactants are in solution, and the investigation of heats of solution is an important branch of thermochemistry. It is necessary to distinguish the *integral heat of solution* and the *differential heat of solution.* The distinction between these two terms can best be understood by means of a practical example.

If one mole of alcohol (C_2H_5OH) is dissolved in nine moles of water, the final solution contains 10 mole per cent alcohol. The heat absorbed is the integral heat of solution per mole of alcohol to form a solution of this final composition. If the mole of alcohol is dissolved in four moles of water, the integral heat of solution has a different value, corresponding to the formation of a 20 mole per cent solution. The difference between any two integral heats of solution yields a value for the integral *heat of dilution.* The example can be written in the form of thermochemical equations as follows:

$$(1)\ C_2H_5OH + 9H_2O \longrightarrow C_2H_5OH\ (10\text{ mole }\%\text{ solution}) \qquad \Delta H^\circ_{298} = -1678\text{ cal}$$

$$(2)\ C_2H_5OH + 4H_2O \longrightarrow C_2H_5OH\ (20\text{ mole }\%\text{ solution}) \qquad \Delta H^\circ_{298} = -898\text{ cal}$$

$$(3)\ C_2H_5OH\ (20\%) + 5H_2O \longrightarrow C_2H_5OH\ (10\text{ mole }\%) \qquad \Delta H^\circ_{298} = -780\text{ cal}$$

The heat of dilution from 20 to 10 mole % amounts to -780 cal per mole.

The heat evolved ($-\Delta H$) when a mole of alcohol is dissolved in water depends upon the final concentration of the solution. If we plot the measured integral heat of solution against the number of moles of water per one mole of alcohol (n_w/n_a), we obtain the curve in Fig. 2.7. As the solution becomes more and more dilute, n_w/n_a approaches infinity. The asymptotic value of the heat of solution is called the *heat of solution to infinite dilution,* ΔH^∞. For alcohol in water at 25°C, $\Delta H^\infty = -3350$ cal. The values of ΔH of solution become quite constant with increasing dilution, so that values measured in dilute solutions are usually close to ΔH^∞. We often find literature values for which the dilution is not specified. These are written, for aqueous solution, simply as in the following example:

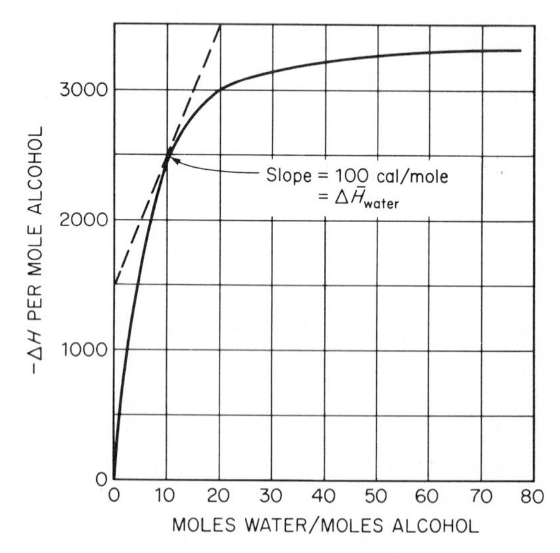

FIG. 2.7 Integral heat of solution of ethyl alcohol in water at 0°C.

$$NaCl + \text{aqua} \longrightarrow NaCl\ (aq) \qquad \Delta H^\infty_{298} = 930\text{ cal}$$

In the absence of more detailed information, such values may be taken to give approximately the ΔH to infinite dilution.

The integral solution heats provide an average ΔH over a range of concentrations. For example, if alcohol is added to water to make a 50 mole per cent solution, the first alcohol added gives a heat essentially that for the solute dissolving in pure water, whereas the last alcohol is added to a solution of about 50 per cent concentration. It is often necessary to know what the ΔH would be for the solution of solute in a solution of definite fixed concentration. Let us imagine a colossal volume of solution of definite composition and add one more mole of solute to it. We can then suppose that this addition causes no detectable change in the concentration. The heat absorbed in this kind of solution process is the *differential heat of solution.**

19. TEMPERATURE DEPENDENCE OF REACTION HEATS

Sometimes the ΔH of a reaction is measured at one temperature and we need to know its value at another. Such a situation is shown in schematic form as follows:

$$\begin{array}{lccccl} T_2 \ldots & & \text{REACTANTS} & \xrightarrow[\Delta H_{T_2}]{} & \text{PRODUCTS} & \\ & C_P^{\text{re}}\,(T_2 - T_1) & \uparrow & & \uparrow & C_P^{\text{pr}}\,(T_2 - T_1) \\ T_1 \ldots & & \text{REACTANTS} & \xrightarrow[\Delta H_{T_1}]{} & \text{PRODUCTS} & \end{array}$$

In this diagram it is assumed that the heat capacities C_P are constant over the temperature range. C_P^{re} means the sum of the heat capacities for all the re-

---

* The relation between the integral and differential heats of solution can be shown as follows. The integral ΔH depends on the numbers of moles of each of the two components, n_1 and n_2.

$$\Delta H = \Delta H(n_1, n_2)$$

Hence, for a change at constant T and P,

$$d(\Delta H) = \left(\frac{\partial \Delta H}{\partial n_1}\right) dn_1 + \left(\frac{\partial \Delta H}{\partial n_2}\right) dn_2 \tag{a}$$

The partial derivative

$$\left(\frac{\partial \Delta H}{\partial n_1}\right) = \Delta \overline{H}_1 \tag{b}$$

is the differential heat of solution of component 1, for example, the solvent. Similarly

$$\left(\frac{\partial \Delta H}{\partial n_2}\right) = \Delta \overline{H}_2$$

is the differential heat of solution of component 2, for example, the solute. Thus, Eq. (a) becomes

$$d(\Delta H) = \Delta \overline{H}_1\, dn_1 + \Delta \overline{H}_2\, dn_2 \tag{c}$$

Integrating at constant composition, we have

$$\Delta H = \Delta \overline{H}_1 n_1 + \Delta \overline{H}_2 n_2 \tag{d}$$

From Eq. (b) we see that the slope of the curve in Fig. 2.7 gives the differential heat of solution of water in the solution $\Delta \overline{H}_1$. Knowing $\Delta \overline{H}_1$ and ΔH, we can get $\Delta \overline{H}_2$ from Eq. (d). Other methods of evaluating $\Delta \overline{H}_1$ and $\Delta \overline{H}_2$ will be found in Chapter 5.

actants in the stoichiometric equation for the reaction; and similarly for C_P^{pr}. From the First Law it is evident that

$$\Delta H_{T_1} + C_P^{\text{pr}}(T_2 - T_1) = C_P^{\text{re}}(T_2 - T_1) + \Delta H_{T_2}$$

or that

$$\Delta H_{T_2} - \Delta H_{T_1} = (C_P^{\text{pr}} - C_P^{\text{re}})(T_2 - T_1) \tag{2.34}$$

If we write the difference $C_P^{\text{pr}} - C_P^{\text{re}}$ as ΔC_P, Eq. (2.34) becomes

$$\frac{\Delta H_{T_2} - \Delta H_{T_1}}{T_2 - T_1} = \Delta C_P \tag{2.35}$$

In the limit as $T_2 - T_1$ becomes very small, this could be written in the differential form,

$$\frac{d(\Delta H)}{dT} = \Delta C_P \tag{2.36}$$

These equations were first obtained by G. R. Kirchhoff in 1858. They show that the rate of change of the heat of reaction with the temperature is equal to the difference in heat capacities of products and reactants.

There is one oversimplification in the treatment given, since actually the heat capacities themselves vary with the temperature. Often, however, it is sufficiently accurate to use the average value of the heat capacity over the range of temperature considered.

As an example of the use of Eq. (2.35) consider the reaction

$$H_2O\ (g) \longrightarrow H_2 + \tfrac{1}{2}O_2 \qquad \Delta H^\circ = 57\ 780 \text{ at } 18°C$$

What would be the ΔH° at 25°C? The C_P values are

$$\overline{C}_P(H_2O) = 8.02,\ \overline{C}_P(H_2) = 6.89,\ \overline{C}_P(O_2) = 6.96 \text{ cal deg}^{-1}\text{ mole}^{-1}$$

Hence,

$$\Delta C_P = \overline{C}_P(H_2) + \tfrac{1}{2}\overline{C}_P(O_2) - \overline{C}_P(H_2O) = 6.89 + \tfrac{1}{2}(6.96) - 8.02 = 2.35$$

From Eq. (2.35),

$$\frac{\Delta H^\circ_{298} - 57\ 780}{298 - 291} = 2.35$$

Thus

$$\Delta H^\circ_{298} = 57\ 796$$

To integrate Eq. (2.36) more exactly, we require expressions for the heat capacities of reactants and products over the temperature range of interest.

The experimental heat-capacity data can be represented by a power series:

$$\overline{C}_P = a + bT + cT^2 + \dots \tag{2.37}$$

Examples of such heat-capacity equations are given in Table 2.6. These three-term equations fit the experimental data to within about 0.5 per cent over a temperature range from 0°C to 1250°C. When the series expression for ΔC_P is substituted* in Eq. (2.36), the integration can be carried out analytically. Thus

* For a typical reaction,

$$\tfrac{1}{2}N_2 + \tfrac{3}{2}H_2 \rightarrow NH_3\text{: } \Delta C_P = \overline{C}_{P\,NH_3} - \tfrac{1}{2}\overline{C}_{P\,N_2} - \tfrac{3}{2}\overline{C}_{P\,H_2}$$

TABLE 2.6 HEAT CAPACITY OF GASES (273–1500°K)*
$C_P = a + bT + cT^2$ (C_P in calories per deg per mole)

Gas	a	$b \times 10^3$	$c \times 10^7$
H_2	6.9469	−0.1999	4.808
O_2	6.148	3.102	−9.23
Cl_2	7.5755	2.4244	−0.650
Br_2	8.4228	0.9739	−3.555
N_2	6.524	1.250	−0.01
CO	6.420	1.665	−1.96
HCl	6.7319	0.4352	3.697
HBr	6.5776	0.9549	1.581
H_2O	7.256	2.298	2.83
CO_2	6.214	10.396	−35.45
Benzene	−0.283	77.936	−262.96
n-Hexane	7.313	104.906	−323.97
CH_4	3.381	18.044	−43.00

* H. M. Spencer, *J. Am. Chem. Soc.*, *67*, 1858 (1945). Spencer and Justice, *ibid.*, *56*, 2311 (1934).

at constant pressure, for the standard enthalpy change,

$$d(\Delta H^\circ) = \Delta C_P\, dT = (A + BT + CT^2 + \ldots)\, dT$$

$$\Delta H_T^\circ = \Delta H_0^\circ + AT + \tfrac{1}{2}BT^2 + \tfrac{1}{3}CT^3 + \ldots \tag{2.38}$$

Here ΔH_0° is the constant of integration.* Any one measurement of ΔH° at a known temperature T makes it possible to evaluate the constant ΔH_0° in Eq. (2.38). Then the ΔH° at any other temperature can be calculated from the equation.

Recently rather extensive enthalpy tables have become available, which give $(H_T - H_0)$ as a function of T over a wide range of temperatures. The use of these tables makes direct reference to the heat capacities unnecessary.

20. CHEMICAL AFFINITY

Much of the earlier work on the heats of reaction was done by Julius Thomsen and Marcellin Berthelot, in the latter part of the nineteenth century. They were inspired to carry out a vast program of thermochemical measurements by the conviction that the heat of reaction was the quantitative measure of the *chemical affinity* of the reactants. In the words of Berthelot, in his *Essai de Mécanique chimique* (1878):

"Every chemical change accomplished without the intervention of an external energy tends toward the production of the body or the system of bodies that sets free the most heat."

* If the heat-capacity equations are valid to 0°K, we may note that at $T = 0$, $\Delta H^\circ = \Delta H_0^\circ$, so that the integration constant can be interpreted as the enthalpy change in the reaction at 0°K.

Although, as Ostwald remarked in an unusually sarcastic vein, priority for this erroneous principle does not rest with Berthelot, "what undoubtedly belongs to Berthelot are the numerous methods which he found to explain the cases in which the so-called principle is in contradiction with the facts. In particular, in the assumption of partial decomposition or dissociation of one or several of the reacting substances he discovered a never failing method for calculating an overall evolution of heat in cases where the experimental observation showed directly that there was an absorption of heat."

Thus the principle of Thomsen and Berthelot is incorrect: it would imply that no endothermic reaction could occur spontaneously and it fails to consider the reversibility of most chemical reactions. In order to understand the true nature of chemical affinity and the driving force in chemical reactions, it is necessary to go beyond the First Law of Thermodynamics, and to include the results of the Second Law. In the next chapter we shall see how this has been done.

PROBLEMS

1. The pressure on one kilogram of silver is increased at a constant temperature of 20°C from 0 to 500 atm. The density at 1 atm is 10.5 g cm^{-3} and the compressibility is constant (1×10^{-6} atm^{-1}). Calculate the work of compression. [*Ans.* 11.9 cc atm]

2. When tungsten carbide WC was burnt with excess oxygen in a bomb calorimeter, it was found that ΔE (300°K) = -284.76 kcal for the reaction

$$WC(s) + \tfrac{5}{2}O_2(g) \longrightarrow WO_3(s) + CO_2(g)$$

   What would be the ΔH at 300°K? What is the heat of formation of WC if the heats of combustion ΔH of pure C and pure W under these conditions are -94.05 and -195.70 kcal respectively?

3. Derive the expression $(\partial E/\partial T)_P = C_P - P(\partial V/\partial T)_P$. Show that $(\partial H/\partial V)_T = 0$ and $(\partial C_V/\partial V)_T = 0$ for an ideal gas.

4. One step in the manufacture of CCl_4 involves the reaction

$$CS_2(l) + 3Cl_2(g) \longrightarrow CCl_4(l) + S_2Cl_2(l)$$

   which takes place in a water-cooled reactor at 25°C. The standard molar enthalpies at this temperature are $CS_2(l)$ 21 kcal, $CCl_4(l)$ -33.3 kcal, $S_2Cl_2(l)$ -14.4 kcal. How many kg of cooling water at 10°C must pass through the coils in the reactor for each kg of Cl_2 reacting to keep the temperature at 25°C? [*Ans.* At least 21.5 kg]

5. Ammonia at 27°C and 1 atm is passed at a rate of 41 ml s^{-1} into an apparatus where it flows over an electrically heated wire of resistance 100 ohm. When the heating current is 50 ma, the gas leaves the apparatus at 31.09°C. Calculate $\overline{C}_P$ and $\overline{C}_V$ for ammonia. [*Ans.* 8.77, 6.78 cal deg^{-1} $mole^{-1}$]

6. The ΔH°_{298} for combustion of hydrogen, benzene, and cyclohexane are -57.80, -757.52, and -881.67 kcal mole^{-1}, respectively. Calculate the ΔH°_{298} for the reaction

$$C_6H_6(g) + 3H_2(g) \longrightarrow C_6H_{12}(g)$$

Calculate the ΔH for this reaction at 125°C, given: $C_6H_6(g)$, $\overline{C}_P = 2.8 + 0.059\ T$; $C_6H_{12}(g)$, $\overline{C}_P = 2.6 + 0.096\ T$; $H_2(g)$, $\overline{C}_P = 6.9$ (over the range of T from 290 to 400°K). [*Ans.* -49.25, -50.05 kcal]

7. When 1 mole of HCl(g) at 18°C is dissolved in 900 g of water in a calorimeter vessel at 18°C, the temperature of the calorimeter and its contents rises to 35°C and no heat is exchanged with the surroundings. The water equivalent of the calorimeter vessel and measuring instruments is 170 g, and the specific heat of the solution is 0.900 cal g^{-1} deg^{-1}. Calculate ΔH for the solution of HCl(g) in 900 g of water at 18°C.

8. The heat of combustion of cyanamide, $CH_2N_2(c) + \frac{3}{2}O_2 \rightarrow CO_2 + H_2O(l) + N_2$ is $\Delta H^\circ_{298} = -177.20$ kcal. Calculate the standard enthalpy of formation for this compound.

9. An average man produces about 2500 kcal of heat a day through metabolic activity. If a man was a closed system of mass 70 kg with the heat capacity of water, what would be the temperature rise in a day? Man is actually an open system, and the main mechanism of heat loss is evaporation of water. How much water would he need to evaporate in a day to maintain constant temperature: the ΔH (vaporization) of water at 37°C is 575 cal g^{-1}?

10. An important reaction in muscular activity is the oxidation of lactic to pyruvic acid. Calculate the ΔH for the reaction, given that the ΔH (18°C) of combustion is -279.1 kcal mole^{-1} for pyruvic acid (liq) and -326 kcal mole^{-1} for lactic acid (solid).

11. Calculate ΔE and ΔH when 100 liters of helium at STP are heated to 100°C in a closed container. Assume gas is ideal with $C_V = \frac{3}{2}R$. [*Ans.* 1330, 2216 cal]

12. One mole of ideal gas at 25°C is expanded adiabatically and reversibly from 20 atm to 1 atm. What is the final temperature of the gas, assuming $C_V = \frac{3}{2}R$? [*Ans.* 90°K]

13. 100 g of nitrogen at 25°C are held by a piston under 30 atm pressure. The pressure is suddenly released to 10 atm and the gas adiabatically expands. If $\overline{C}_V$ for nitrogen $= 4.95$ cal per deg, calculate the final temperature of the gas. What are ΔE and ΔH for the change? Assume gas is ideal. [*Ans.* 241°K; $\Delta E = -1010$, $\Delta H = -1415$ cal.]

14. Using the heat-capacity equation in Table 2.6, calculate the heat required to raise the temperature of one mole of HBr from 0° to 500°C. [*Ans.* 3560 cal]

15. In a laboratory experiment in calorimetry, 100 cc of 0.500 N acetic acid are mixed with 100 cc of 0.500 N sodium hydroxide in a calorimeter. The temperature rises from 25° to 27.55°C. The effective heat capacity of the calorimeter is 36 cal per deg. The specific heat of 0.250 N sodium acetate solution is 0.963 cal deg^{-1} g^{-1} and its density is 1.034 g cm^{-3}. Calculate the heat of neutralization of acetic acid per mole. [*Ans.* 11 990 cal at 25°C]

16. Assuming ideal gas behavior, calculate the values of ΔE°_{298} for $SO_3(g)$, $H_2O(g)$, and HCl(g) from the ΔH°_{298} values in Table 2.2. [*Ans.* −94.15; −57.50; −22.06 kcal]

17. From the heats of formation in Table 2.3, calculate ΔH°_{298} for the following cracking reactions

$$C_2H_6 + H_2 \longrightarrow 2CH_4$$

$$n-C_4H_{10} + 3H_2 \longrightarrow 4CH_4$$

$$iso-C_4H_{10} + 3H_2 \longrightarrow 4CH_4$$

[*Ans.* −15 540, −41 745, −40 110 cal]

18. Calculate the heat evolved when iron rusts to form one mole of Fe_2O_3, using the following data at 18°C and 1 atm constant pressure. The heat absorbed when one g-atom of iron is dissolved in dilute HCl to give dilute aqueous $FeCl_3$ plus hydrogen gas is −11 400 cal $mole^{-1}$. The heat absorbed when one mole of Fe_2O_3 is dissolved in dilute HCl to give $2FeCl_3$ (dilute aqueous) is −37 260 cal $mole^{-1}$. The heat of formation of liquid water is −68 390 cal $mole^{-1}$.

---

19. The enthalpy of formation of the solid solution of NaCl and NaBr at 25°C is given in cal $mole^{-1}$ as

$$\Delta \overline{H} = 1433\, X_{NaBr} - 1616\, X^2_{NaBr} + 183\, X^3_{NaBr}$$

[M. A. Fineman and W. E. Wallace, *J. Am. Chem. Soc. 70*, 4165 (1948)] where X_{NaBr} is the mole fraction of NaBr in the solution. Calculate: (a) the ΔH when 0.5 mole of NaBr and 0.5 mole of NaCl form a solid solution; (b) the differential heat of solution of NaCl and NaBr in the 50 mole per cent solution.

20. The integral heat of solution of m moles of NaCl in 1000 g H_2O at 25°C is given in calories by

$$\Delta H = 923\, m + 476\, m^{3/2} - 726\, m^2 + 243.5\, m^{5/2}$$

Calculate: (a) the ΔH per mole of NaCl to form a one molal solution; (b) the ΔH per mole of NaCl to infinite dilution; (c) the ΔH of dilution of a 1 molal solution to 0.1 molal (per mole of NaCl); (d) the differential heat of solution at 1 molal.

21. Show that

$$\mu_{JT} = -\frac{1}{C_P}\left(\frac{\partial H}{\partial P}\right)_T$$

If the Joule-Thomson coefficient is $\mu_{JT} = 1.084$ deg per atm and the heat capacity $C_P = 8.75$ cal per mole deg, calculate the change in enthalpy ΔH when 50 g of CO_2 at 25°C and 1 atm pressure are isothermally compressed to 10 atm pressure. What would the value be for an ideal gas? [*Ans.* -97 cal; 0]

22. When *n*-hexane is passed over a chromia catalyst at 500°C, benzene is formed: $C_6H_{14}(g) \rightarrow C_6H_6(g) + 4H_2$, $\Delta H^\circ_{298} = 59.78$ kcal per mole. Calculate ΔH° for the reaction at 500°C (Table 2.6). [*Ans.* 63.39 kcal]

23. Show that $(\partial E/\partial P)_V = \beta C_V/\alpha$.

24. Derive a general expression for ΔH° of the water gas reaction ($H_2 + CO_2 \rightarrow H_2O + CO$) as a function of temperature. Use it to calculate ΔH° at 500°K and 1000°K. [*Ans.* $\Delta H^\circ = 9933 + 0.515T - 3.117 \times 10^{-3}T^2 + 10.50 \times 10^{-7}T^3$; $\Delta H^\circ_{500} = 9540$; $\Delta H^\circ_{1000} = 8380$]

25. If a compound is burned under adiabatic conditions so that all the heat evolved is utilized in heating the product gases, the maximum temperature attained is called the *adiabatic flame temperature.* Calculate this temperature for the burning of ethane with twice the amount of air (80 per cent N_2, 20 per cent O_2) needed for complete combustion to CO_2 and H_2O. Use heat capacities in Table 2.6, but neglect the terms cT^2. [*Ans.* 1460°K]

26. From the bond energies in Table 2.5, calculate the heat of formation of C_2H_6, C_2H_5OH, and C_2H_5SH. The experimental values are -20.23, -56.63, and -11.04 kcal mole^{-1} at 25°C.

27. The coefficient of thermal expansion of bromine is 1.038×10^{-3} deg^{-1}, its density at 20°C is 3.119 g cm^{-3}, and its heat capacity is 17.2 cal deg^{-1} mole^{-1}. Calculate q, w, ΔE, and ΔH when one mole of Br_2 is heated from 0° to 30°C at a pressure of 1 atm.

28. When H_2 and Cl_2 were combined in a constant-pressure calorimeter at essentially one atm and 30°C, it was found that the formation of 0.1527 moles of HCl was accompanied by a rise in temperature of 0.9116°C. In the same apparatus, under substantially the same conditions, it was found that the expenditure of 15 418 joules of electrical energy caused a rise in temperature of 1.0000°C. What is the heat of formation of HCl at 30°C? Assuming ideal gas behavior, what is q_V for the above process?

29. Calculate ΔH for the combustion of CO to CO_2 at the temperature of a blast furnace (approximately 1400°C). The heat-capacity data are given in Table 2.6, and ΔH at 18°C is $-67\,610$ cal mole^{-1}.

3 THE SECOND LAW OF THERMODYNAMICS

Science owes more to the steam engine than the steam engine owes to Science.

L. J. HENDERSON (1917)

The experiments of Joule showed clearly that heat was not a "substance" conserved in physical processes, since it could be generated by mechanical work. The reverse transformation, the conversion of heat into work, had been of greater interest to the practical engineer ever since the development of the steam engine by James Watt in 1769. Such an engine operates essentially as follows: A source of heat (e.g., a coal or wood fire) is used to heat a "working substance" (e.g., steam), causing it to expand through an appropriate valve into a cylinder fitted with a piston. The expansion drives the piston forward, and by suitable coupling mechanical work can be obtained from the engine. The working substance is cooled by the expansion, and this cooled working substance is withdrawn from the cylinder through a valve. A flywheel arrangement returns the piston to its original position, in readiness for another expansion stroke. In simplest terms, therefore, any such heat engine withdraws heat from a heat source, or hot reservoir, converts some of this heat into work, and discards the remainder to a heat sink or cold reservoir. In practice frictional losses of work occur in the various moving components of the engine.

1. THE EFFICIENCY OF HEAT ENGINES

The first theoretical discussions of these engines were expressed in terms of the caloric hypothesis. The principal problem was to understand the factors governing the *efficiency* e of the engine, which was measured by the ratio of useful work output $-w$ to the heat input q_2.

$$e = \frac{-w}{q_2} \tag{3.1}$$

A remarkable advance toward the solution of this problem was made in 1824 by a young French engineer, Sadi Carnot, in a monograph, *Réflexions sur la Puissance motrice du Feu.*

2. THE CARNOT CYCLE

The Carnot cycle represents the operation of an idealized engine in which heat is transferred from a hot reservoir at temperature t_2, is partly converted into work, and partly discarded to a cold reservoir at temperature t_1 [Fig. 3.1(a)]. The working substance through which these operations are carried out is returned at the end to the same state that it initially occupied, so that the entire process constitutes a complete cycle. We have written the temperatures as t_1 and t_2 to indicate that they are empirical temperatures, measured on any convenient scale whatsoever. The various steps in the cycle are carried out reversibly.

To make the operation more definite, we may consider the working substance to be a gas (not ideal) and we may represent the cyclic process by the indicator diagram of Fig. 3.1(b). The steps in the working of the engine for one complete cycle are then: [The sign convention is based on the engine (gas) as the system.]

(1) Withdrawal of heat $= q_2$ from a hot reservoir at temperature t_2 by the isothermal reversible expansion of the gas from V_1 to V_2. Work done on gas $= w_1$.

(2) Adiabatic reversible expansion from V_2 to V_3, during which $q = 0$, work done on gas $= w_2$ and gas cools from t_2 to t_1.

(3) Isothermal reversible compression at t_1 from V_3 to V_4. Work done on the gas $= w_3$. Heat $= -q_1$ taken from the gas and absorbed by the cold reservoir at t_1.

(4) Adiabatic reversible compression from V_4 to V_1, gas warming from t_1 to t_2. Work done on gas $= w_4$, $q = 0$.

The First Law of Thermodynamics requires that for the cyclic process

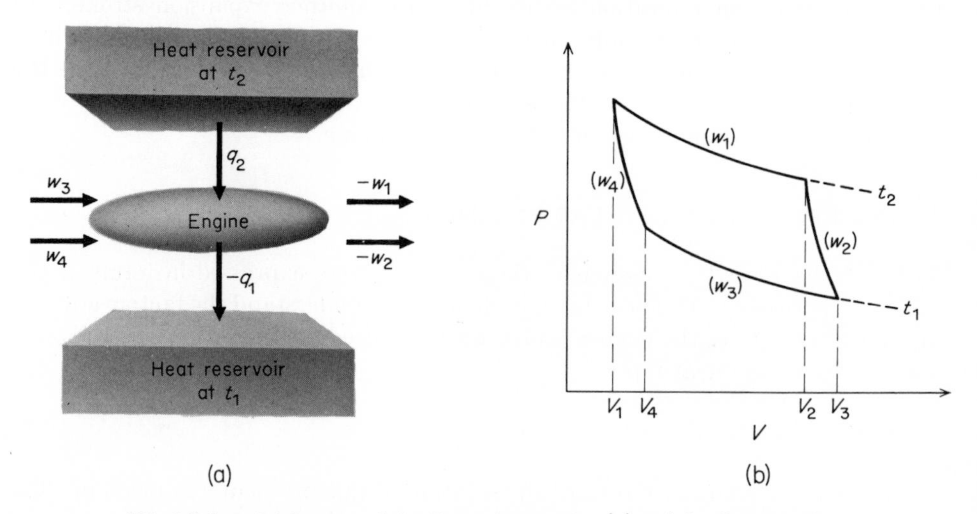

FIG. 3.1 Essential features of the Carnot heat engine (a) and the Carnot cycle for its operation shown on the indicator diagram (b).

$\Delta E = 0$. Now ΔE is the sum of all the heat added to the gas, $q = q_2 + q_1$, plus the sum of all the work done on the gas, $w = w_1 + w_2 + w_3 + w_4$.

$$\Delta E = q + w = q_2 + q_1 + w = 0$$

The net work done by the engine is equal, therefore, to the heat taken from the hot reservoir less the heat that is returned to the cold reservoir: $-w = q_2 + q_1$. The efficiency of the engine is

$$e = \frac{-w}{q_2} = \frac{q_2 + q_1}{q_2} \tag{3.2}$$

Since every step in this cycle is carried out reversibly, the maximum possible work is obtained for the particular working substance and temperatures considered.*

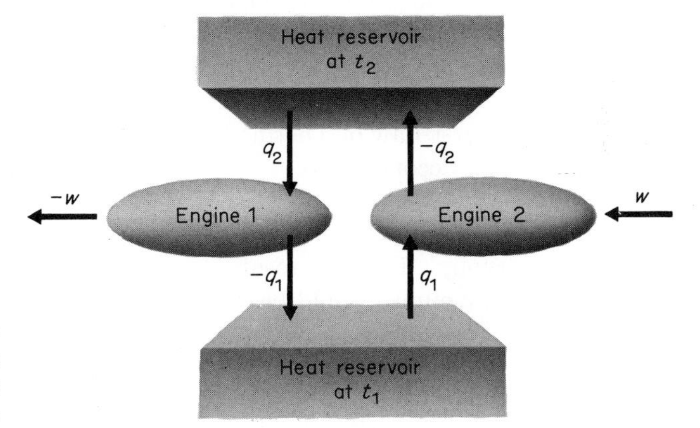

FIG. 3.2 Diagram to represent Engine 1 operating in forward direction and Engine 2 in reverse (as a heat pump).

Consider now another engine operating, for example, with a different working substance. Let us assume that this second engine, working between the same two empirical temperatures t_2 and t_1, is more efficient than engine 1; that is, it can deliver a greater amount of work, $-w' > -w$, from the same amount of heat q_2 taken from the hot reservoir. (See Fig. 3.2.) It could accomplish this only by discarding less heat, $-q_1' < -q_1$, to the cold reservoir.

Let us now imagine that after the completion of a cycle by this supposedly more efficient engine, the original engine is run in reverse. It therefore acts as a *heat pump*. Since the original Carnot cycle is reversible, all the heat and work terms are changed in sign but not in magnitude. The heat pump takes in q_1 of heat from the cold reservoir; by the expenditure of work w provided from an external source, it delivers $-q_2$ of heat to the hot reservoir.

For the first process (engine 2) $\quad -w' = q_2 + q_1'$

For the second process (engine 1) $\quad w + q_1 = -q_2$

Therefore, the final result is: $\quad -w' + w = -q_1 + q_1'$

* In the isothermal steps, the maximum work is obtained on expansion and the minimum work done in compression of the gas (cf. p. 47). In the adiabatic steps $\Delta E = w$, and the work terms are constant (but not necessarily equal) once the initial and final states are fixed.

Since $w' < w$, and $q_1' > q_1$, the net result of the combined operation of these two engines is that an amount of heat, $q'' = q_1' - q_1$, has been abstracted from a heat reservoir at constant temperature t_1 and an amount of work $w'' = w - w'$ has been obtained from it, without any other change whatsoever taking place.

In this result there is nothing contrary to the First Law of Thermodynamics, for energy has been neither created nor destroyed. The work done would be equivalent to the heat extracted from the reservoir. Nevertheless, in all of human history, nobody has ever observed the isothermal conversion of heat into work without any concomitant change in the system. Think what it would imply. It would not be necessary for a ship to carry fuel: this wonderful device would enable it to use a small fraction of the immense thermal energy of the ocean to turn its propellers and run its dynamos. Such a continuous extraction of useful work from the heat of the environment has been called "perpetual motion of the second kind," whereas the production of work from nothing at all was called "perpetual motion of the first kind." The impossibility of the latter is postulated by the First Law of Thermodynamics; the impossibility of the former is postulated by the Second Law.

If the supposedly more efficient Carnot engine delivered the same amount of work $-w$ as the original engine, it would need to withdraw less heat $q_2' < q_2$ from the hot reservoir. Then the result of running engine 2 forward and engine 1 in reverse, as a heat pump, would be

$$\begin{array}{lr} (2) & -w = q_2' + q_1' \\ (1) & w + q_1 = -q_2 \\ \hline \text{Final result:} & q_2 - q_2' = q_1' - q_1 = q \end{array}$$

This amounts to the transfer of heat q from the cold reservoir at t_1 to the hot reservoir at t_2 without any other change in the system.

There is nothing in this conclusion contrary to the First Law, but it is even more obviously contrary to human experience than is perpetual motion of the second kind. We know that heat always flows from the hotter to the colder region. If we place a hot body and a cold body together, the hot one never grows hotter while the cold one becomes colder. We know in fact that considerable work must be expended to refrigerate something, to pump heat out of it. Heat never flows uphill, i.e., against a temperature gradient, of its own accord.

3. THE SECOND LAW OF THERMODYNAMICS

This Second Law may be expressed precisely in various equivalent forms. For example,

The principle of Thomson: It is impossible by a cyclic process to take heat from a reservoir and convert it into work without, in the same operation, transferring heat from a hot to a cold reservoir.

The principle of Clausius: "Die Wärme kann nicht von selbst aus einem kälteren in einen wärmeren Körper übergehen." (It is impossible by a cyclic process to transfer heat from a colder to a warmer reservoir without net changes in other bodies.)

Returning to Carnot's cycle, we have seen that the supposition that one reversible cycle may exist that is more efficient than another has led to results contradicting human experience as embodied in the Second Law of Thermodynamics. We therefore conclude that *all reversible Carnot cycles operating between the same initial and final temperatures must have the same efficiency.* Since the cycles are reversible, this efficiency is the maximum possible. It is completely independent of the working substance and is a function only of the working temperatures:

$$e = f(t_1, t_2)$$

4. THE THERMODYNAMIC TEMPERATURE SCALE

The principle of Clausius may be translated more literally as "heat never flows spontaneously [i.e., without the expenditure of work] from a colder to a hotter body." This statement contains essentially a definition of temperature, and we may recall that the temperature concept was first introduced as a result of the observation that all bodies gradually reach a state of thermal equilibrium.

William Thomson (Kelvin) was the first to use the Second Law to define a *thermodynamic temperature scale*, which is completely independent of any thermometric substance. The Carnot theorem on the efficiency of a reversible cycle may be written: Efficiency (independent of working substance) $= (q_2 + q_1)/q_2 = f'(t_1, t_2)$, or $1 + q_1/q_2 = f'(t_1, t_2)$. Therefore,

$$\frac{q_1}{q_2} = f(t_1, t_2) \tag{3.3}$$

We have written $f'(t_1, t_2)$ and $f(t_1, t_2) = f' - 1$ to indicate unspecified functions of t_1 and t_2.

Consider two Carnot cycles such that: $q_1/q_2 = f(t_1, t_2)$; $q_2/q_3 = f(t_2, t_3)$. They must be equivalent to a third cycle, operating between t_1 and t_3, with $q_1/q_3 = f(t_1, t_3)$. Therefore,

$$\frac{q_1}{q_2} = \frac{f(t_1, t_3)}{f(t_2, t_3)} = f(t_1, t_2)$$

But, if this condition is satisfied, we can write: $f(t_1, t_3) = F(t_1)/F(t_3)$ and $f(t_2, t_3) = F(t_2)/F(t_3)$. That is, the efficiency function, $f(t_1, t_2)$, is the quotient of a function of t_1 alone and a function of t_2 alone. It follows that

$$\frac{q_1}{q_2} = \frac{F(t_1)}{F(t_2)} \tag{3.4}$$

Kelvin decided to use Eq. (3.4) as the basis of a *thermodynamic temperature scale.* He took the functions $F(t_1)$ and $F(t_2)$ to have the simplest possible form. Thus a temperature ratio on the Kelvin scale was defined as equal to the ratio of the heat absorbed to the heat rejected in the working of a reversible Carnot cycle.

$$\frac{q_2}{-q_1} = \frac{T_2}{T_1} \tag{3.5}$$

The efficiency of the cycle, Eq. (3.2), then becomes

$$e = \frac{q_2 + q_1}{q_2} = \frac{T_2 - T_1}{T_2} \tag{3.6}$$

The zero point of the thermodynamic scale is physically fixed as the temperature of the cold reservoir at which the efficiency becomes equal to unity, i.e., the heat engine becomes perfectly efficient. From Eq. (3.6), in the limit as $T_1 \to 0$, $e \to 1$.

The efficiency calculated from Eq. (3.6) is the *maximum thermal efficiency* that can be approached by a heat engine. Since it is calculated for a reversible Carnot cycle, it represents an ideal, which actual irreversible cycles can never achieve. Thus with a heat source at 120°C and a sink at 20°C, the maximum thermal efficiency is $100/393 = 25.4$ per cent. If the heat source is at 220° and the sink still at 20°, the efficiency is raised to $200/493 = 40.6$ per cent. It is easy to see why the trend in power plant design has been to higher temperatures for the heat source. In practice, the efficiency of steam engines seldom exceeds 80 per cent of the theoretical value. Steam turbines generally can operate somewhat closer to their maximum thermal efficiencies, since they have fewer moving parts and consequently lower frictional losses.

5. APPLICATION TO IDEAL GASES

Temperature on the Kelvin, or thermodynamic, scale has been denoted by the symbol T, which is the same symbol used previously for the absolute ideal gas scale. It can be shown that these scales are indeed numerically the same by running a Carnot cycle with an ideal gas as the working substance.

Applying Eqs. (2.22) and (2.24) to the four steps, we have

(1) Isothermal expansion: $-w_1 = q_2 = RT_2 \ln (V_2/V_1)$

(2) Adiabatic expansion: $-w_2 = \int_{T_1}^{T_2} C_V\, dT;\; q = 0$

(3) Isothermal compression: $w_3 = -q_1 = -RT_1 \ln (V_4/V_3)$

(4) Adiabatic compression: $w_4 = \int_{T_1}^{T_2} C_V\, dT;\; q = 0$

By summation of these terms, the total work obtained is

$$-w = -w_1 - w_2 - w_3 - w_4 = RT_2 \ln V_2/V_1 + RT_1 \ln V_4/V_3.$$

Since, from Eqs. (2.22) and (3.5), $V_2/V_1 = V_3/V_4$,

$$-w = R(T_2 - T_1) \ln (V_2/V_1)$$

$$e = \frac{-w}{q_2} = \frac{T_2 - T_1}{T_2}$$

Comparison with Eq. (3.6) completes the proof of the identity of the ideal gas and thermodynamic temperature scales.

6. ENTROPY

Equation (3.6) for a reversible Carnot cycle operating between T_2 and T_1 irrespective of the working substance may be rewritten

$$\frac{q_2}{T_2} + \frac{q_1}{T_1} = 0 \tag{3.7}$$

It can be shown that *any cyclic process can be broken down into a number of Carnot cycles.* Consider the perfectly general ABA of Fig. 3.3. The area of the figure has been divided into a number of Carnot cycles by the cross-hatched system of isothermals and adiabatics. The outside boundaries of these little cycles form the heavy zigzag curve which follows quite closely the path of the general cycle ABA. The inside portions of the little Carnot cycles cancel out, since each section is traversed once in the forward direction and once in the reverse direction. For example, consider the isotherm xy which belongs to an expansion in the small cycle β, and to a compression in the small cycle α, all the work and heat terms arising from it thereby being canceled.

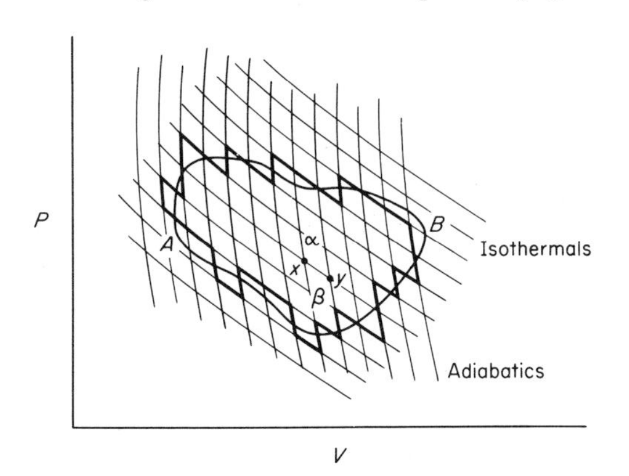

FIG. 3.3 Representation of a general cycle as a series of Carnot cycles.

If Eq. (3.7) is now applied to all these little Carnot cycles, we have for the zigzag segments $\sum q/T = 0$. As the Carnot cycles are made smaller and smaller, the boundary curve approaches more and more closely to that for the general cyclic process ABA. In the limit, for differential Carnot cycles, the area enclosed by the crooked boundary becomes identical with the area of the cycle ABA. We can then replace the summation of finite terms by the integration of differentials and obtain*

$$\text{(reversible)} \quad \oint \frac{dq}{T} = 0 \tag{3.8}$$

* See P. S. Epstein, *Textbook of Thermodynamics* (New York: Wiley, 1938), p. 57.

This equation holds true for any *reversible* cyclic process whatsoever.

It may be recalled (p. 41) that the vanishing of the cyclic integral means that the integrand is a perfect differential of some function of the state of the system. A new state function is thus defined by

$$dS = \frac{dq}{T} \quad \text{(for a reversible process)} \tag{3.9}$$

Hence,

$$\oint dS = \int_A^B dS + \int_B^A dS = S_B - S_A + S_A - S_B = 0$$

The function S was first introduced by Clausius in 1850, and is called the *entropy*. Equation (3.9) indicates that when the inexact differential expression dq is multiplied by $1/T$, it becomes an exact differential; $1/T$ is called an *integrating factor*. The integral $\int_A^B dq_{\text{rev}}$ is dependent on the path, whereas $\int_A^B dq_{\text{rev}}/T$ is independent of the path. This, in itself, is an alternative statement of the Second Law of Thermodynamics.

It is interesting to consider the TS diagram in Fig. 3.4, which is analogous to the PV diagram of Fig. 3.1. In the PV case, the area under the curve is a measure of the work done in traversing the indicated path. In the TS diagram, the area under the curve is a measure of the heat added to the system. Temperature and pressure are intensity factors; entropy and volume are capacity factors. The products $P\,dV$ and $T\,dS$ both have the dimensions of energy.

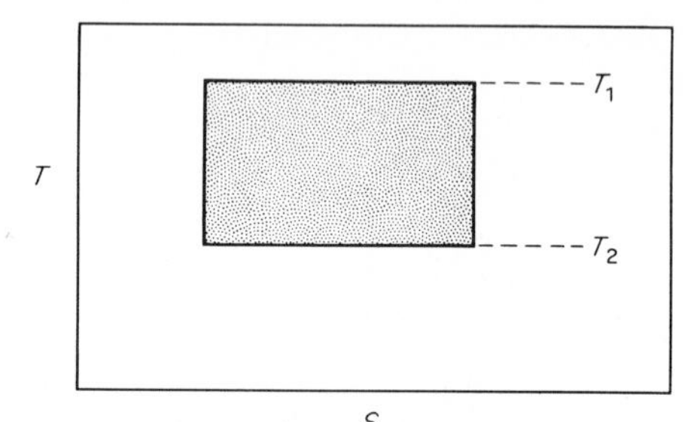

FIG. 3.4 Carnot cycle on a TS diagram.

7. THE INEQUALITY OF CLAUSIUS

Equation (3.8) was obtained for a reversible cycle. Clausius showed that for a cycle into which irreversibility enters at any stage, the integral of dq/T is always less than zero.

$$\text{(irreversible)} \quad \oint \frac{dq}{T} < 0 \tag{3.10}$$

The proof is based on the fact that the efficiency of an irreversible Carnot cycle is always less than that of a reversible cycle operating between the same two temperatures. In the reversible cycle, the isothermal expansion yields the maximum work and the isothermal compression requires the minimum work, so that the efficiency is highest for the reversible case. For the irreversible case, we therefore conclude from Eq. (3.6) that

$$\frac{q_2 + q_1}{q_2} < \frac{T_2 - T_1}{T_2}$$

Then, instead of Eq. (3.7), we find

$$\frac{q_2}{T_2} + \frac{q_1}{T_1} < 0$$

This relation is extended to the general cycle, by following the argument based on Fig. (3.3). Instead of Eq. (3.8), which applies to the reversible case, we obtain the inequality of Clausius, given by Eq. (3.10).

8. ENTROPY CHANGES IN AN IDEAL GAS

The calculation of entropy changes in an ideal gas is particularly simple because in this case $(\partial E/\partial V)_T = 0$, and energy terms due to cohesive forces need not be considered at any point. For a reversible process in an ideal gas, the First Law requires that

$$dq = dE + P\,dV = C_V\,dT + nRT\,dV/V$$

Therefore,

$$dS = \frac{dq}{T} = \frac{C_V\,dT}{T} + \frac{nR\,dV}{V} \tag{3.11}$$

On integration,

$$\Delta S = S_2 - S_1 = \int_1^2 C_V\,d\ln T + \int_1^2 nR\,d\ln V$$

If C_V is independent of temperature,

$$\Delta S = C_V \ln\frac{T_2}{T_1} + nR\ln\frac{V_2}{V_1} \tag{3.12}$$

For the special case of a temperature change at constant volume, the increase in entropy with increase in temperature is therefore

$$\Delta S = C_V \ln\frac{T_2}{T_1} \tag{3.13}$$

If the temperature of one mole of ideal gas with $\overline{C}_V = 3$ is doubled, the entropy is increased by $3 \ln 2 = 2.08$ cal deg^{-1}.

For the case of an isothermal expansion, the entropy increase becomes

$$\Delta S = nR\ln\frac{V_2}{V_1} = nR\ln\frac{P_1}{P_2} \tag{3.14}$$

If one mole of ideal gas is expanded to twice its original volume, its entropy is increased by $R \ln 2 = 1.38$ cal deg^{-1}.

9. ENTROPY CHANGES IN ISOLATED SYSTEMS

The change in entropy in going from a state A to a state B is always the same, irrespective of the path between A and B, since the entropy is a function of the state of the system alone. It makes no difference whether the path is reversible or irreversible. Only in case the path is reversible, however, is the entropy change given by $\int dq/T$:

$$\Delta S = S_B - S_A = \int_A^B \frac{dq}{T} \quad \text{(reversible)} \tag{3.15}$$

In order to evaluate the entropy change for an irreversible process, it is necessary to devise a reversible method for going from the same initial to the same final state, and then to apply Eq. (3.15).

In any completely isolated system we are restricted to adiabatic processes since no heat can either enter or leave such a system.* For a *reversible* process in an isolated system, therefore, $dq = 0$ and $dS = dq/T = 0$, or $S =$ constant. If one part of the system increases in entropy, the remaining part must decrease by an exactly equal amount.

A fundamental example of an irreversible process is the transfer of heat from a hot to a colder body. We can make use of an ideal gas to carry out the transfer reversibly, and thereby calculate the entropy change. The gas is placed in thermal contact with the hot body at T_2 and expanded reversibly and isothermally until it takes up heat equal to q. To simplify the argument, it is assumed that the bodies have heat capacities so large that changes in their temperatures on adding or withdrawing heat q are negligible. The gas is then removed from contact with the hot reservoir and allowed to expand reversibly and adiabatically until its temperature falls to T_1. Next it is placed in contact with the colder body at T_1 and compressed isothermally until it gives up heat equal to q.

The hot reservoir has now lost entropy $= q/T_2$, whereas the cold reservoir has gained entropy $= q/T_1$. The net entropy change of the reservoirs has therefore been $\Delta S = q/T_1 - q/T_2$. Since $T_2 > T_1$, $\Delta S > 0$, and the entropy has increased. The entropy of the ideal gas, however, has decreased by an exactly equal amount, so that for the entire isolated system of ideal gas plus heat reservoirs, $\Delta S = 0$ for the reversible process. If the heat transfer had been carried out irreversibly, for example by placing the two bodies in direct thermal contact and allowing heat q to flow along the finite temperature gradient thus established, there would have been no compensating entropy decrease. The entropy of the isolated system would have increased during the irreversible process, by the amount $\Delta S = q/T_1 - q/T_2$.

We shall now prove that *the entropy of an isolated system always increases during an irreversible process.* The proof of this theorem is based on the inequal-

---

* The completely isolated system is, of course, a figment of imagination. Perhaps our whole universe might be considered as an isolated system, but no small section of it can be rigorously isolated. As usual, the precision and sensitivity of our experiment must be allowed to determine how the system is to be defined.

ity of Clausius. Consider in Fig. 3.5 a perfectly general irreversible process in an isolated system, leading from state A to state B. It is represented by the dashed line. Next consider that the system is returned to its initial state A by a reversible path represented by the solid line from B to A. During this reversible process, the system need not be isolated, and can exchange heat and work with its environment. Since the entire cycle is in part irreversible, Eq. (3.10) applies, and

$$\oint \frac{dq}{T} < 0$$

Writing the cycle in terms of its two sections, we obtain

$$\int_A^B \frac{dq_{\text{irrev}}}{T} + \int_B^A \frac{dq_{\text{rev}}}{T} < 0 \tag{3.16}$$

The first integral is equal to zero, since during the process $A \rightarrow B$ the system is by hypothesis isolated and therefore no transfer of heat is possible. The second integral, from Eq. (3.15), is equal to $S_A - S_B$. Therefore, Eq. (3.16) becomes

$$S_A - S_B < 0 \quad \text{or} \quad S_B - S_A > 0$$

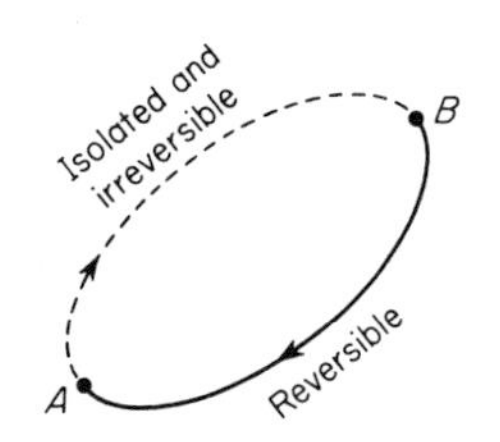

FIG. 3.5 A cyclic process.

We have therefore proved that the entropy of the final state B is always greater than that of the initial state A, if A passes to B by an irreversible process in an isolated system.

Since all naturally occurring processes are irreversible, any change that actually occurs spontaneously in nature is accompanied by a net increase in entropy. This conclusion led Clausius to his famous concise statement of the laws of thermodynamics. "The energy of the universe is a constant; the entropy of the universe tends always towards a maximum."

If there is any conceivable process by which the entropy can increase, i.e., for which $dS > 0$, a system will be subject to a spontaneous change. It is a necessary and sufficient condition for equilibrium that for any process

$$dS = 0$$

This condition, however, is extremely general in that it applies to all conceivable changes taking place in all the systems in the world considered together.

This increasing tendency of the entropy has also been expressed as a principle of the degradation of energy, by which it becomes less available for useful work. Thus temperature differences tend to become leveled out, fuel supplies become exhausted, and work is frittered away into heat by frictional losses. Interesting philosophical discussions have arisen from the entropy concept, notably the suggestion of Eddington that, because of its continuously increasing character, "entropy is time's arrow;" that is, the constantly increasing entropy of the universe is the physical basis of our concept of time. Entropy will be displayed in yet another aspect when we discuss its statistical interpretation.

10. CHANGE OF ENTROPY IN CHANGES OF STATE OF AGGREGATION

As an example of a change in state of aggregation we may take the melting of a solid. At a fixed pressure, the melting point is a definite temperature T_f at which solid and liquid are in equilibrium. In order to change some of the solid to liquid, heat must be added to the system. As long as both solid and liquid are present, this added heat does not change the temperature of the system, but is absorbed by the system as the *latent heat of fusion* λ_f of the solid. Since the change occurs at constant pressure, the latent heat, by Eq. (2.13), equals the difference in enthalpy between liquid and solid. Per mole of substance,

$$\lambda_f = \Delta\overline{H}_f = \overline{H}_{\text{liquid}} - \overline{H}_{\text{solid}}$$

At the melting point, liquid and solid exist together in equilibrium. The addition of a little heat would melt some of the solid, the removal of a little heat would solidify some of the liquid, but the equilibrium between solid and liquid would be maintained. The latent heat at the melting point is necessarily a *reversible heat,* because the process of melting follows a path consisting of successive equilibrium states. We can therefore evaluate the entropy of fusion ΔS_f at the melting point by a direct application of the relation $\Delta S = q_{\text{rev}}/T$, which applies to any reversible isothermal process.

$$S_{\text{liquid}} - S_{\text{solid}} = \Delta S_f = \frac{\Delta H_f}{T_f} \tag{3.17}$$

For example,* ΔH_f for ice is 1430 cal per mole, so that $\Delta S_f = 1430/273.2 = 5.23$ cal deg^{-1} mole^{-1}.

By an exactly similar argument the entropy of vaporization ΔS_v, the latent heat of vaporization ΔH_v, and the boiling point T_b are related by

$$S_{\text{vapor}} - S_{\text{liquid}} = \Delta S_v = \frac{\Delta H_v}{T_b} \tag{3.18}$$

A similar equation holds for a change from one form of a polymorphic solid to another, if the change occurs at a T and P at which the two forms are in equilibrium, and if there is a latent heat associated with the transformation. For example, grey tin and white tin are in equilibrium at 13°C and 1 atm, and $\lambda = 500$ cal. Then $\Delta S_t = 500/286 = 1.75$ cal deg^{-1} mole^{-1}.

11. ENTROPY AND EQUILIBRIUM

Now that the entropy function has been defined and a method outlined for the evaluation of entropy changes, we have gained a powerful tool for our attack on

* Further typical data are shown in Table 17.1.

the fundamental problem of physicochemical equilibrium. In our introductory chapter, the position of equilibrium in purely mechanical systems was shown to be the position of minimum potential energy. What is the criterion for equilibrium in a thermodynamic system?

Any spontaneously occurring change in an isolated system is accompanied by an increase in entropy. From the First Law of Thermodynamics we know that energy can be neither created nor destroyed, so that the internal energy of an isolated system must be constant. The only way such a system could gain or lose energy would be by some interaction with its surroundings, but the absence of any such interaction is just what we mean when we say that the system is *isolated* — no work is done on it; no heat flows across its boundaries. A sufficient condition for a system to be *isolated* is that it have a constant energy and volume. The first sentence of this paragraph can thus be rephrased: In a system at constant E and V, any spontaneous change is accompanied by an increase in entropy.

Now a system is said to be at equilibrium when it has no further tendency to change its properties. The entropy of an isolated system will increase until no further spontaneous changes can occur. When the entropy reaches its maximum, the system no longer changes; the equilibrium has been attained. A criterion for *thermodynamic equilibrium* is therefore the following: *In a system at constant energy and volume, the entropy is a maximum. At constant E and V, the S is a maximum.*

If instead of a system at constant E and V, a system at constant S and V is considered, the equilibrium criterion takes the following form: *At constant S and V, the E is a minimum.* This is just the condition applicable in ordinary mechanics, in which thermal effects are excluded.

The drive, or perhaps better the drift, of physicochemical systems toward equilibrium is therefore compounded of two factors. One is the tendency toward minimum energy, the bottom of the potential energy curve. The other is the tendency toward maximum entropy. Only if E is held constant can S achieve its maximum; only if S is held constant can E achieve its minimum. What happens when E and S are forced to strike a compromise?

12. THE FREE ENERGY AND WORK FUNCTIONS

Chemical reactions are rarely studied under conditions of constant entropy or constant energy. Usually the physical chemist places his systems in thermostats and investigates them under conditions of approximately constant temperature and pressure. Sometimes changes at constant volume and temperature are followed, for example, in bomb calorimeters. It is most desirable, therefore, to obtain criteria for thermodynamic equilibrium that will be applicable under these practical conditions.*

* We call a system under these conditions a *closed system*, since no mass can be transferred across the boundary of the system, but transfer of energy is allowed.

Let us first consider the conditions for equilibrium at constant temperature. The First Law of Thermodynamics for a differential change in the energy is $dE = dq + dw$. For a change at constant temperature along a reversible path, $dq = T\,dS$ and

$$dE = T\,dS + dw_{\text{rev}} \tag{3.19}$$

In other words, if the system is in a state such that any differential change in the energy satisfies this equation, it is in a state of equilibrium. This is so because a reversible path traverses a succession of equilibrium states; if a system is somewhere on such a path, it must be in an equilibrium state. At constant temperature, $T\,dS = d\,(TS)$, so that Eq. (3.19) can be written

$$d(E - TS) = dw_{\text{rev}}$$

We define a new function A, called the *work function*, by

$$A = E - TS \tag{3.20}$$

Hence,

$$dA = dw_{\text{rev}} \quad (\text{constant } T) \tag{3.21}$$

The change in the work function A equals the work done on the system along an isothermal reversible path. In any naturally occurring process, which is always more or less irreversible, the work done on the system must exceed the reversible work, so that

$$dA < dw_{\text{irrev}} \quad (\text{constant } T) \tag{3.22}$$

A particular case of Eq. (3.21) is $dw_{\text{rev}} = -P\,dV$, in which the only kind of work done is "PV work," associated with the expansion or compression of the system. If a condition of constant volume is imposed in this case, $dw_{\text{rev}} = -P\,dV = 0$. Thus *at constant T and V, when only PV work is permitted, $dA = 0$, or A is a minimum, at equilibrium.* We can see that A must be a minimum rather than a maximum from the defining equation (3.20), since E tends to decrease and S tends to increase as a system approaches equilibrium.

Now let us find the conditions for equilibrium when temperature and pressure are held constant. This is an important case since so many chemical processes are studied in thermostats under conditions of effectively constant atmospheric pressure. We recall that the enthalpy H was useful in expressing heats of reaction at constant pressure, so let us try dH instead of dE in our analysis of the equilibrium condition.

$$H = E + PV$$

$$dH = dE + P\,dV + V\,dP$$

We substitute for dE the expression in the equilibrium condition of Eq. (3.19), and obtain, at constant T,

$$dH = T\,dS + dw_{\text{rev}} + P\,dV + V\,dP$$

Or, at constant T and P,

$$d(H - TS) = P\,dV + dw_{\text{rev}}$$

We define a new function, G, called the *free energy*,* by

$$G = H - TS = A + PV \tag{3.23}$$

Thus,

$$dG = P\,dV + dw_{\text{rev}} \tag{3.24}$$

If the work is restricted to PV work, $dw_{\text{rev}} = -P\,dV$ and

$$dG = 0 \tag{3.25}$$

Thus, *at constant T and P, when only PV work is permitted, the condition of equilibrium is that G be a minimum.* This is probably the equilibrium condition most useful under ordinary laboratory conditions.

Thus we have obtained an answer to the question of how the drive toward maximum entropy and the drive toward minimum energy reach a compromise as a system tends toward equilibrium.

If other kinds of work, electrical work, for example, are considered, we can define a differential of the *net work* as

$$dw_{\text{net}} = dw + P\,dV$$

so that

$$dG = dw_{\text{net}} \quad \text{(reversible)} \tag{3.26}$$

The change in the free energy equals the net work done on the system in a reversible process at *constant temperature and pressure.*

13. MAXIMUM WORK

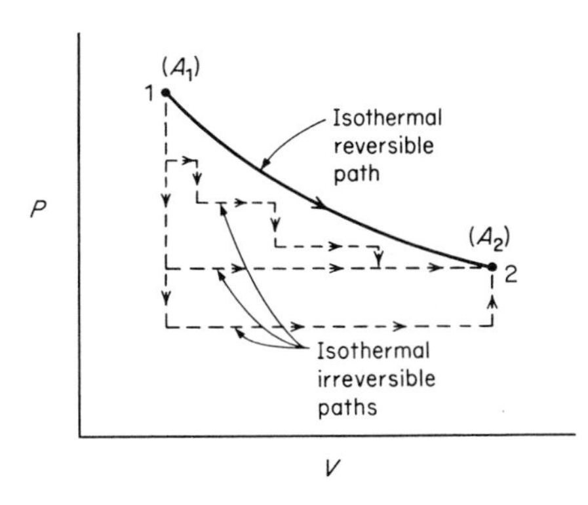

FIG. 3.6 Isothermal paths traversed by a system between state (1) and state (2).

Consider in Fig. 3.6 a system that changes from state 1 to state 2 via different processes at constant temperature. There are infinitely many of these isothermal paths that the system might traverse between states 1 and 2. Only one, however, is a reversible path. Since A is a state function, $\Delta A = A_2 - A_1$ does not depend on the path. Also, from Eq. (3.20), for the isothermal change,

$$A_2 - A_1 = E_2 - E_1 - TS_2 + TS_1$$

or

$$\text{(constant } T\text{)} \quad \Delta A = \Delta E - T\,\Delta S \tag{3.27}$$

From Eq. (3.21), for the *isothermal reversible path*, $\Delta A = w_{\text{rev}}$, the reversible work done on the system. The maximum work that can be done by the system on its surroundings in the change from 1 to 2 is $-\Delta A = -w_{\text{rev}}$.

* Sometimes A is called the *Helmholtz free energy* and G the *Gibbs free energy*.

Let us consider, for example, that the change in question is the oxidation of one mole of 2, 2, 4, trimethylpentane ("iso-octane") at 25°C and 1 atm.

$$C_8H_{18}\,(g) + 12\tfrac{1}{2}O_2 \longrightarrow 8CO_2 + 9H_2O\,(g)$$

We can find the ΔE for the reaction by measuring the heat of combustion in a bomb calorimeter. It is actually $\Delta E_{298} = -5\,109\,000$ joule. The ΔS can be found by calorimetric methods to be described later; it is in fact $\Delta S_{298} = +421.5$ joule deg^{-1}. Thus, from Eq. (3.27),

$$\Delta A_{298} = -5\,109\,000 - 298(421.5) = -5\,234\,600 \text{ joule}$$

This is the ΔA for the change, irrespective, of course, of how it was carried out. It tells us that 5 234 600 joules is the maximum work that could possibly be obtained from the oxidation of one mole of "isooctane" at 25°C and 1 atm. Note that this work is actually greater than $-\Delta E$ for the change, simply because the ΔS for the change is positive. There is no contradiction of thermodynamics here, since the system is not isolated. When ΔS is negative for a change, the $-w_{\text{rev}} = -\Delta A$ will be less than the $-\Delta E$.

If we burned the octane in a calorimeter, we would obtain no work at all, $w = 0$. If we burned it in an internal combustion engine, we would obtain some work, perhaps as much as 1 000 000 joules, not much compared to $-w_{\text{rev}}$ but better than nothing. If we knew how to do it, we might burn the octane in a fuel cell, and obtain considerably more useful work, perhaps as much as 3 000 000 joules. There would, however, be no practical way to obtain $-w_{\text{rev}} = 5\,234\,600$ joules, since to approach the reversible condition we should need to eliminate all frictional losses and to carry out the process in the cell infinitely slowly, with an opposing emf always almost equal to the driving force. Nevertheless, it is helpful to know that $-\Delta A$ is the upper limit for the work that might conceivably be obtained. It is most important to remember that ΔA is determined by both ΔE and ΔS for the isothermal change in accord with Eq. (3.27).

14. CHANGES IN FREE ENERGY

The change in free energy of the system in an *isothermal* process leading from state 1 to state 2 is given from Eq. (3.23) as

$$G_2 - G_1 = H_2 - H_1 - T(S_2 - S_1)$$

$$(\text{constant } T) \quad \Delta G = \Delta H - T\,\Delta S \tag{3.28}$$

If we consider a process at constant pressure, from Eq. (3.23),

$$(\text{constant } P) \quad \Delta G = \Delta A + P\,\Delta V$$

The work done on the system by its surroundings when its volume changes by ΔV at constant pressure is $-P\,\Delta V$. Provided the external pressure is kept constant, this term is fixed, no matter how the change occurs, reversibly or irreversibly.

Let us compute the ΔG for the burning of the octane. From the reaction equation,

$$P\Delta V = \Delta n\, RT = (17 - 13.5)\, RT = 3.5\, RT$$

$$= (3.5)(8.314)(298) = 8680 \text{ joule}$$

Since

$$\Delta A = -5\,234\,600 \text{ joule}$$

$$\Delta G = -5\,225\,900 \text{ joule}$$

The maximum net work obtainable from the combustion of one mole of the octane at 298°K would therefore be 5 225 900 joule.

15. PRESSURE DEPENDENCE OF FREE ENERGY

From Eq. (3.23),

$$G = H - TS = E + PV - TS.$$

Differentiating, we obtain

$$dG = dE + P\,dV + V\,dP - T\,dS - S\,dT$$

Since

$$dE = T\,dS - P\,dV$$

$$dG = V\,dP - S\,dT \tag{3.29}$$

Therefore,

$$\left(\frac{\partial G}{\partial P}\right)_T = V \tag{3.30}$$

For an isothermal change from state (1) to state (2),

$$G_2 - G_1 = \Delta G = \int_1^2 dG = \int_1^2 V\,dP \tag{3.31}$$

In order to integrate this equation, the variation of V with P must be known for the substance being studied. Then if the free energy is known at one pressure, it can be calculated for any other pressure. If a suitable equation of state is available, it can be solved for V as a function of P, and Eq. (3.31) can be integrated after substituting this $f(P)$ for V. In the simple case of the ideal gas, $V = nRT/P$, and

$$G_2 - G_1 = \Delta G = nRT \ln P_2/P_1 \tag{3.32}$$

This gives the change in free energy on compression or expansion. For example, if one mole of an ideal gas is compressed isothermally at 300°K to twice its original pressure, its free energy is increased by $1.987 \times 300 \ln 2 = 413$ calories.

16. TEMPERATURE DEPENDENCE OF FREE ENERGY

From Eq. (3.29) at constant pressure,

$$\left(\frac{\partial G}{\partial T}\right)_P = -S \tag{3.33}$$

To integrate this equation, we must know S as a function of temperature. This question is considered in the next section. An alternative expression can be obtained by combining Eq. (3.33) with Eq. (3.23):

$$\left(\frac{\partial G}{\partial T}\right)_P = \frac{G - H}{T} \tag{3.34}$$

The relation between G and H as functions of T is shown in Fig. 3.7.

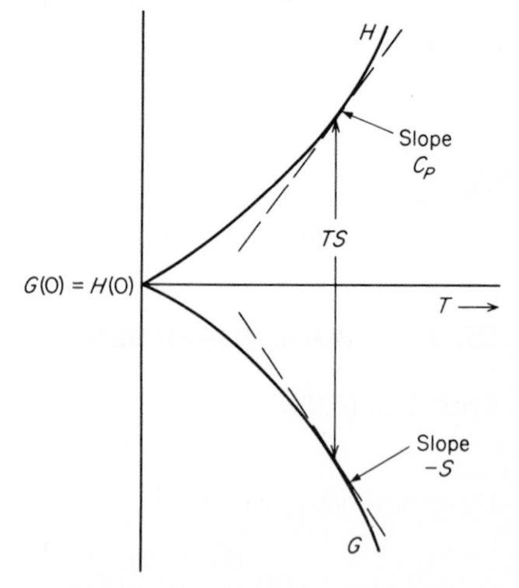

FIG. 3.7 Variation of free energy G and enthalpy H of a pure substance with T at constant P.

For isothermal changes in a system, the variation of ΔG with temperature* is then

$$\left(\frac{\partial \Delta G}{\partial T}\right)_P = -\Delta S = \frac{\Delta G - \Delta H}{T} \tag{3.35}$$

This is called the *Gibbs-Helmholtz equation.* It permits us to calculate the change in enthalpy ΔH from a knowledge of ΔG and the temperature coefficient of ΔG. Since

$$\frac{d}{dT}\left(\frac{\Delta G}{T}\right) = \frac{1}{T}\frac{d(\Delta G)}{dT} - \frac{\Delta G}{T^2}$$

the Gibbs-Helmholtz equation can be written in the alternative forms:

$$\left[\frac{\partial}{\partial T}\left(\frac{\Delta G}{T}\right)\right]_P = \frac{-\Delta H}{T^2}$$

or (3.36)

$$\left[\frac{\partial(\Delta G/T)}{\partial(1/T)}\right]_P = \Delta H$$

Thus the slope of the plot of $\Delta G/T$ vs. $1/T$ is ΔH, the change in enthalpy. Applications of these equations to chemical reactions will be considered in the next chapter. They are especially important because many chemical processes are carried out in thermostats under practically constant atmospheric pressure.

17. VARIATION OF ENTROPY WITH TEMPERATURE AND PRESSURE

Besides its usefulness in the formulation of equilibrium conditions, the free-energy function can be used to derive important relations between the other

* For example, the free energy change ΔG of a chemical reaction might be studied at a series of different constant temperatures, always under the same constant pressure. The equation predicts how the observed ΔG depends on the temperature at which the reaction is studied.

thermodynamic variables. Consider, for example, the mathematical identity,

$$\frac{\partial}{\partial P}\left(\frac{\partial G}{\partial T}\right)_P = \frac{\partial}{\partial T}\left(\frac{\partial G}{\partial P}\right)_T$$

By virtue of Eqs. (3.30) and (3.33), this identity yields an expression for the pressure coefficient of the entropy:*

$$\left(\frac{\partial S}{\partial P}\right)_T = -\left(\frac{\partial V}{\partial T}\right)_P \tag{3.37}$$

Thus at constant temperature, $dS = -(\partial V/\partial T)_P\, dP$, so that

$$\Delta S = -\int_{P_1}^{P_2}\left(\frac{\partial V}{\partial T}\right)_P dP = -\int_{P_1}^{P_2} \alpha V_0\, dP \tag{3.38}$$

To evaluate this integral, the equation of state or other PVT data must be available. For an ideal gas, $(\partial V/\partial T)_P = nR/P$. In this case Eq. (3.37) becomes $dS = -nR\, d\,(\ln P)$, or $\Delta S = nR \ln (P_1/P_2) = nR \ln (V_2/V_1)$, as already shown in Section 3.8.

The temperature variation of the entropy can be calculated as follows: At constant pressure,

$$dS = \frac{dq}{T} = \frac{dH}{T} = \frac{C_P\, dT}{T} \tag{3.39}$$

At constant volume,

$$dS = \frac{dq}{T} = \frac{dE}{T} = \frac{C_V\, dT}{T} \tag{3.40}$$

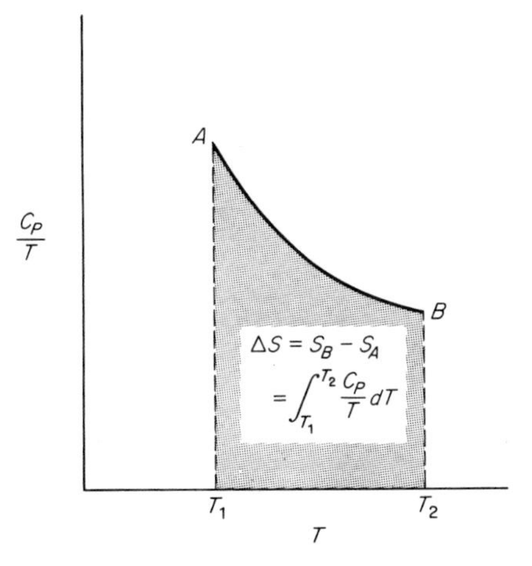

FIG. 3.8 Graphical evaluation of the entropy change with temperature.

Thus at constant pressure,

$$S = \int C_P\, d \ln T + \text{constant}$$

$$S = \int \frac{C_P}{T}\, dT + \text{constant}; \quad \Delta S = \int_{T_1}^{T_2} \frac{C_P}{T}\, dT \tag{3.41}$$

When C_P is known as a function of T, the entropy change is evaluated by the integration in Eq. (3.41). This integration is often conveniently carried out graphically, as in Fig. 3.8; if C_P/T is plotted against T, the area under the curve between T_1 and T_2 is a measure of the entropy change. If a change of phase occurs, the corresponding $\Delta S = \Delta H_t/T$ must be included.

* Alternatively, apply Euler's rule to Eq. (3.29).

18. THE CALCULATION OF THERMODYNAMIC RELATIONS

One great utility of thermodynamics is that it enables us by means of a few paper-and-pencil operations to avoid many difficult laboratory experiments. The general aim is to reduce the body of thermodynamic data to relations in terms of readily measurable functions. Thus the coefficients $(\partial V/\partial T)_P$, $(\partial P/\partial T)_V$, and $(\partial V/\partial P)_T$ can usually be measured by straightforward experiments. The results are often expressed implicitly in the equation of state for the substance, of the general form $f(P, V, T) = 0$. The heat capacity at constant pressure C_P is usually measured directly and C_V can then be calculated from it and the equation of state. Thermodynamics itself does not provide any theoretical interpretation of heat capacities, the magnitudes of which depend on the structures and constitutions of the substance considered.

The basic thermodynamic relations may be reduced to a few fundamental equations:

$$(1)\quad H = E + PV$$

$$(2)\quad A = E - TS$$

$$(3)\quad G = E + PV - TS$$

$$(4)\quad dE = T\,dS - P\,dV$$

$$(5)\quad dH = T\,dS + V\,dP$$

$$(6)\quad dA = -S\,dT - P\,dV$$

$$(7)\quad dG = -S\,dT + V\,dP$$

Since dA and dG are perfect differentials, they obey the Euler condition, Eq. (2.10), and therefore, from (6) and (7),

$$(8)\quad (\partial S/\partial V)_T = (\partial P/\partial T)_V$$

$$(9)\quad (\partial S/\partial P)_T = -(\partial V/\partial T)_P$$

By the definition of the heat capacities,

$$(10)\quad C_P = (dq/dT)_P = T(\partial S/\partial T)_P$$

$$(11)\quad C_V = (dq/dT)_V = T(\partial S/\partial T)_V$$

These eleven equations are the starting point for the evaluation of all others.*

The relation $dE = T\,dS - P\,dV$ may be considered as a convenient expression of the combined First and Second Laws of Thermodynamics. By differentiating it with respect to volume at constant temperature, $(\partial E/\partial V)_T = T(\partial S/\partial V)_T - P$. Then, since $(\partial S/\partial V)_T = (\partial P/\partial T)_V$,

$$\left(\frac{\partial E}{\partial V}\right)_T + P = T\left(\frac{\partial P}{\partial T}\right)_V \tag{3.42}$$

This equation has often been called a *thermodynamic equation of state*, since it

* A. Tobolsky, *J. Chem. Phys.*, *10*, 644 (1942), gives a useful general method.

provides a relationship among P, T, V, and the energy E, which is valid for all substances. To be sure, all thermodynamic equations are in a sense equations of state, since they are relations between state variables, but equations like Eq. (3.42) are particularly useful because they are closely related to the ordinary PVT data.

It is now possible by means of Eq. (3.42) to prove the statement in the previous chapter that a gas that obeys the equation $PV = nRT$ has a zero internal pressure, $(\partial E/\partial V)_T$. For such a gas

$$T(\partial P/\partial T)_V = nRT/V = P$$

so that

$$(\partial E/\partial V)_T = P - P = 0.$$

With the help of Eq. (3.42) we can also get a useful expression for $C_P - C_V$. Eq. (2.17) becomes

$$C_P - C_V = \left[P + \left(\frac{\partial E}{\partial V}\right)_T\right]\left(\frac{\partial V}{\partial T}\right)_P = T\left(\frac{\partial P}{\partial T}\right)_V\left(\frac{\partial V}{\partial T}\right)_P$$

Then, from Eq. (1.22),

$$C_P - C_V = \alpha^2 V_0 T/\beta \tag{3.43}$$

An equation similar to Eq. (3.42) can be obtained in terms of the enthalpy instead of the energy:

$$\left(\frac{\partial H}{\partial P}\right)_T - V = -T\left(\frac{\partial V}{\partial T}\right)_P \tag{3.44}$$

An important application of this equation is the theoretical discussion of the Joule-Thomson experiment. Since

$$\mu = \left(\frac{\partial T}{\partial P}\right)_H = -\frac{1}{C_P}\left(\frac{\partial H}{\partial P}\right)_T$$

it follows from Eq. (3.44) that

$$\mu = \frac{T(\partial V/\partial T)_P - V}{C_P} \tag{3.45}$$

It is apparent that the Joule-Thomson effect can be either a warming or a cooling of the substance, depending on the relative magnitudes of the two terms in the numerator of Eq. (3.45). In general, a gas will have one or more *inversion points* at which the sign of the coefficient changes as it passes through zero. The condition for an inversion point is that

$$T\left(\frac{\partial V}{\partial T}\right)_P = \alpha V_0 T = V$$

For an ideal gas this is always true (Law of Gay-Lussac) so that μ is always zero in this case. For other equations of state, it is possible to derive μ from Eq. (3.45) without direct measurement, if C_P data are available. These considerations are most important in the design of equipment for the liquefaction of gases.

PROBLEMS

1. A steam engine operates between 140° and 30°C. What is the minimum amount of heat that must be withdrawn from the hot reservoir to obtain 1000 joules of work? [*Ans.* 3750 joules]

2. Compare the maximum thermal efficiencies of heat engines operating with: (a) steam between 130° and 40°C; (b) mercury vapor between 380° and 50°C. [*Ans.* 22.3%; 50.5%]

3. One mole of an ideal gas is heated at constant pressure from 25° to 300°C. Calculate the entropy change ΔS, if $C_V = \frac{3}{2}R$. [*Ans.* 3.26 cal deg^{-1}]

4. Find the molar increase in E, H, S, A, and G in expanding one liter of an ideal gas at 25°C to 100 liters at the same temperature. [*Ans.* $\Delta E = 0$, $\Delta H = 0$, $\Delta S = 9.15$ cal deg^{-1} mole^{-1}; $\Delta A = \Delta G = -2729$ cal mole^{-1}]

5. At −5°C, the vapor pressure of ice is 3.012 mm, whereas the vapor pressure of supercooled liquid water is 3.163 mm. Calculate the ΔG per mole for the transition water → ice at −5°C. [*Ans.* −26.08 cal]

6. The following data are available for water: latent heat of vaporization 9630 cal per mole; latent heat of fusion 1435 cal per mole. Molar heat capacities: solid, $C_P = 0.50 + 0.03\,T$; liquid, $C_P = 18$; vapor, $C_P = 7.256 + 2.30 \times 10^{-3}T + 2.83 \times 10^{-7}T^2$. Calculate ΔS when one mole of water at 100°K is heated at constant P of 1 atm to 500°K. [*Ans.* 44.85 dal deg^{-1}]

7. Calculate the ΔS per liter of solution when pure N_2, H_2, and NH_3 gases are mixed to form a solution having the final composition 15 per cent N_2, 55 per cent H_2, and 30 per cent NH_3 (at STP). [*Ans.* 0.086 cal deg^{-1}]

8. For each of the following processes, state which of the quantities ΔE, ΔH, ΔS, ΔG, or ΔA are equal to zero.

   (a) An ideal gas is taken around a Carnot cycle.
   (b) H_2 and O_2 react to form H_2O in a thermally isolated bomb.
   (c) A nonideal gas is adiabatically expanded through a throttling valve.
   (d) Liquid water is vaporized at 100°C and 1 atm pressure.

   [*Ans.* (a) all; (b) ΔE; (c) ΔH; (d) ΔG]

9. Derive the expression $(\partial H/\partial P)_T = T(\partial S/\partial P)_T + V$.

10. Evaluate the following coefficients for an ideal gas: $(\partial^2 P/\partial T^2)_V$; $(\partial E/\partial P)_T$; $(\partial P/\partial V)_S$. $\left[\textit{Ans.}\ 0; 0; -\gamma \frac{P}{V}\right]$

11. Suppose that $\Delta H°$ for a reaction is constant between T_1 and T_2. What can you say about $\Delta S°$ for this reaction?

12. Calculate the ΔS° when 0.5 mole of liquid water at 0°C is mixed with 0.5 mole of liquid water at 100°C. Assume $C_P = 18$ cal deg^{-1} mole^{-1} over the whole range of temperatures.

13. Calculate the ΔS of vaporization of the following liquids at their normal boiling points: benzene; water; nitrogen; ether; *n*-pentane. [You will need data on T_B and ΔH_{vap} from handbooks.]

14. Assuming that the density of mercury remains constant at 13.5 g ml^{-1} at 25°C, calculate ΔG of one mole of mercury when pressure is increased from 1 to 101 atm.

15. In the transition

$$CaCO_3 \text{ (aragonite)} \longrightarrow CaCO_3 \text{ (calcite)}$$

$\Delta \overline{G}^\circ_{298} = -190$ cal, $\Delta \overline{V} = 2.75$ ml. At what pressure would aragonite become the stable form at 25°C?

16. In regions with cheap electric power, heat pumps can be used for space heating in winter and cooling in summer. Assuming ideal thermodynamic efficiency for the pump, compare the cost of keeping a room at 70°F in winter with the outside temperature 50°F, with the cost of keeping it at 70°F in summer with outside temperature 90°F.

17. A mole of steam is condensed at 100°C, the water is cooled to 0°C and frozen to ice. What is the difference in the entropies of the steam and the ice? The heats of vaporization and fusion are 540 cal g^{-1} and 80 cal g^{-1}, respectively. Use the average heat capacity of liquid water, 1 cal g^{-1} deg^{-1}.

18. An electric current of 10 amp flows through a resistor of 20 ohms, which is kept at the constant temperature of 10°C by running water. In one sec, what is the entropy change of the resistor and the entropy change of the water?

19. An electric current of 10 amp flows through a thermally insulated resistor of 20 ohms, initially at a temperature of 10°C, for one sec. If the resistor has a mass of 5 g and $C_P = 0.20$ cal g^{-1} deg^{-1}, what is the entropy change of the resistor and the entropy change of its surroundings?

20. One mole of an ideal gas is expanded adiabatically, but completely irreversibly, from a volume V_1 to a volume V_2; no work is done. Does the temperature of the gas change? (a) What is the ΔS of the gas and the ΔS of its surroundings? (b) If the expansion were performed reversibly and isothermally, what would be the ΔS of the gas and of its surroundings?

21. One mole of an ideal gas in contact with a heat reservoir at 25°C expands isothermally from 100 atm to 1 atm pressure. Make a table showing the ΔS for the gas, for the heat reservoir, and for the two systems combined, if in the expansion: (a) 2730 cal of work is done; (b) 1000 cal of work is done; (c) no work is done.

22. Consider the T-S diagram for a given ideal gas. Show that: (a) any two isobaric lines have the same slope at the same temperature; (b) any two isovolumic lines have the same slope at the same temperature; (c) the slope of an isovolumic is greater than that of an isobaric at the same temperature and that the ratio of the slopes at the same temperature is C_P/C_V.

23. (a) One mole of an ideal gas in 22.4 l is expanded isothermally and reversibly at 0°C to a volume of 224 l. Calculate w, q, ΔE, ΔH, ΔA, ΔG, and ΔS. (b) One mole of an ideal gas in 22.4 l is allowed to expand irreversibly into an evacuated vessel such that the final volume is 224 l. Calculate w, q, ΔE, ΔH, ΔA, ΔG, and ΔS for the gas. (c) Calculate ΔS for the gas plus its surroundings in (a) and in (b).

---

24. The velocity of sound in a gas is related to the mechanical properties of the gas by the expression

$$c^2 = (\partial P/\partial \rho)_S$$

where c = velocity of sound; P = pressure; ρ = density; S = entropy. Show that $c^2 = \gamma RT/M$ for an ideal gas and $c^2 = \frac{\gamma}{M}\left[RT\left(\frac{V}{V-b}\right)^2 - \frac{2a}{V}\right]$ for a van der Waals gas, where $\gamma = C_P/C_V$ and M is the molecular weight.

25. A cooling system is designed to maintain a refrigerator at -20°C in a room at ambient temperature of 25°C. The heat transfer into the refrigerator is estimated as 10^4 joules per min. If the refrigerating unit is assumed to operate at 50 per cent of its reversible efficiency, estimate the power (in watts) required to operate the unit. [*Ans.* 59.3 watt]

26. Prove that it is impossible for two reversible adiabatics on a P-V diagram to intersect.

27. Ten grams of carbon monoxide at 0°C are adiabatically and reversibly compressed from 1 atm to 20 atm. Calculate ΔE, ΔH, and ΔS for the change in the gas. Assume $C_V = 4.95$ cal per deg mole and ideal gas behavior. Would it be possible to calculate ΔG from the data provided? [*Ans.* 656, 920 cal; $\Delta S = 0$; No]

28. One mole of an ideal gas, initially at 100°C and 10 atm, is adiabatically expanded against a constant pressure of 5 atm until equilibrium is reattained. If $C_V = 4.50 + 0.005T$, calculate ΔE, ΔH, ΔS for the change in the gas. [*Ans.* -281, -371 cal; 0.318 cal/deg]

29. Calculate ΔS when 10 g of ice at 0°C are added to 50 g of water at 40°C in an isolated system. The latent heat of fusion of ice is 79.7 cal per g; the specific heat of water is 1 cal per g deg. [*Ans.* 0.34 cal/deg]

30. Prove that a gas that obeys Boyle's Law and has zero internal pressure follows the equation of state, $PV = nRT$.

31. Derive

$$\left(\frac{\partial C_P}{\partial P}\right)_T = -T\left(\frac{\partial^2 V}{\partial T^2}\right)_P$$

32. Derive expressions for: (a) $(\partial A/\partial P)_T$ in terms of P and V; (b) $(\partial G/\partial T)_P$ in terms of A and T. [*Ans.* $-P(\partial V/\partial P)_T$, $(\partial A/\partial T)_V$]

33. Bridgman obtained the following volumes for methanol under high pressure, relative to a volume = 1 at 0°C and 1 kg per cm²:

P, kg cm²	1	500	1000	2000	3000	4000	5000
Vol. at 20°	1.0238	0.9823	0.9530	0.9087	0.8792	0.8551	0.8354
Vol. at 50°	1.0610	1.0096	0.9763	0.9271	0.8947	0.8687	0.8476

Use these data to estimate the ΔS when 1 mole of methanol at 35°C and 1 kg per cm² pressure is compressed isothermally to 5000 kg per cm². [*Ans.* -2.90 cal deg^{-1}]

34. Consider the state of a metal bar of mass m to be specified by its length l, temperature T, and the tension along the bar σ. Derive the equations

$$\sigma = T\left(\frac{\partial \sigma}{\partial T}\right)_l + \left(\frac{\partial E}{\partial l}\right)_T$$

35. The reversible work expended to produce in a sample of ferromagnetic material a moment M by application of a magnetic field H is, $-H \cdot dM$. Show that

$$C_H - C_M = -T\left(\frac{\partial M}{\partial T}\right)_H\left(\frac{\partial H}{\partial T}\right)_M$$

where C_H and C_M are the heat capacities at constant field and constant moment.

36. Derive an expression for the Joule-Thomson coefficient of a gas obeying the equation of state $P(\overline{V} - b) = RT$.

37. Draw a Carnot cycle for an ideal gas with the coordinates: (a) E, S; (b) T, P; (c) H, T.

38. One mole of H_2 at 100°C is compressed adiabatically and reversibly from 1 atm to 10 atm. Assume ideal gas behavior and $C_P = 6.9$ cal deg^{-1} mole^{-1}, $\overline{S}^\circ_{298} = 49$ cal deg^{-1}. Calculate ΔE, ΔH, ΔS, ΔG and ΔA for the change.

39. Show that for a van der Waals gas, $(\partial E/\partial V)_T = a/V^2$.

4 CHANGES OF STATE

Thermodynamics can be used to study the equilibrium conditions for changes such as the melting of ice, the solution of sugar, the vaporization of benzene, or the transformation of monoclinic to rhombic sulfur. Certain fundamental principles are applicable to all such phenomena, which are examples of changes in state of aggregation or *phase changes*.

1. PHASES

The word *phase* is derived from the Greek φάσις, meaning appearance. If a system is "uniform throughout, not only in chemical composition, but also in physical state,"* it is said to be *homogeneous*, or to consist of only *one phase*. Examples are a volume of air, a noggin of rum, or a cake of ice. Mere difference in shape or in degree of subdivision is not enough to determine a new phase. Thus a mass of cracked ice is still only one phase.†

A system consisting of more than one phase is called *heterogeneous*. Each physically or chemically different, homogeneous, and mechanically separable part of a system constitutes a distinct phase. Thus water with cracked ice in it is a two-phase system. The contents of a flask of liquid benzene in contact with benzene vapor and air is a two-phase system; if we add a spoonful of sugar (practically insoluble in benzene) we obtain a three-phase system: a solid, a liquid, and a vapor phase.

In systems consisting entirely of gases, only one phase can exist at equilibrium, since all gases are miscible in all proportions (unless, of course, a chemical reaction intervenes, e.g., $NH_3 + HCl$). With liquids, depending on their mutual miscibility, one, two, or more phases can arise. Many different solid phases can coexist.

---

* J. Willard Gibbs.

† This is because we are assuming, at this state in our analysis, that a variable surface area has no appreciable effect on the properties of a substance.

2. COMPONENTS

The composition of a system can be completely described in terms of the "components" that are present in it. The ordinary meaning of the word "component" is somewhat restricted in this technical usage. We wish to impose a requirement of economy on our description of the system. This is done by using the *minimum* number of chemically distinct constituents necessary to describe the composition of each phase in the system. The constituents so chosen are the *components*. If the concentrations of the components are stated for each phase, then the concentrations in each phase of any and all substances present in the system are uniquely fixed. This definition may be expressed more elegantly by saying that the components are those constituents whose concentrations may be *independently varied* in the various phases.

A more practical way of defining the *number of components* is to set it equal to the total number of different chemical constituents in the system minus the number of distinct chemical reactions that can occur in the system between these constituents. We mean by a *distinct chemical reaction* one that cannot be written simply as a sequence of other reactions in the system.

Consider, for example, the system consisting of calcium carbonate, calcium oxide and carbon dioxide. There are three distinct chemical constituents, $CaCO_3$, CaO and CO_2. One reaction occurs between them: $CaCO_3 \rightarrow CaO + CO_2$. Hence the number of components $c = 3 - 1 = 2$.

A more complex example is the system formed from NaCl, KBr and H_2O. Suppose that we can isolate from this system also the constituents KCl, NaBr, $NaBr \cdot H_2O$, $KBr \cdot H_2O$ and $NaCl \cdot H_2O$. The possible distinct chemical reactions between these constituents are:

$$NaCl + KBr \longrightarrow NaBr + KCl$$

$$NaCl + H_2O \longrightarrow NaCl \cdot H_2O$$

$$KBr + H_2O \longrightarrow KBr \cdot H_2O$$

$$NaBr + H_2O \longrightarrow NaBr \cdot H_2O$$

Therefore, the number of components, $c = 8 - 4 = 4$.

A chemical reaction included in calculating the number of components must be one that actually occurs in the system, and not simply a *possible* reaction that does not occur because of the absence of a suitable catalyst or other condition necessary to give it a measurable rate. Thus a mixture of water vapor, hydrogen and oxygen would be a three component system if conditions were such that the reaction $H_2 + \frac{1}{2}O_2 \rightarrow H_2O$ did not actually occur. If, however, a suitable catalyst was present, or if the temperature was high enough for reaction, the system would become one with $c = 3 - 1 = 2$ components.

Careful examination of each individual system is necessary in order to decide the best choice of components. It is generally wise to choose as components those constituents that cannot be converted into one another by reactions occurring within the system. Thus $CaCO_3$ and CaO would be a possible choice for the $CaCO_3 \rightleftharpoons CaO + CO_2$ system, but a poor choice because the concentration of CO_2 would have to be expressed by negative quantities. While the *identity* of the components is subject to some degree of choice, the *number* of components is always definitely fixed for any given case.

3. DEGREES OF FREEDOM

For the complete description of a system, the numerical values of certain variables must be reported. These variables are chosen from among the state functions of the system, such as pressure, temperature, volume, energy, entropy, and the concentrations of the various components in the different phases. Values for all of the possible variables need not be explicitly stated, for a knowledge of some of them definitely determines the values of the others. For any complete description, however, at least one capacity factor is required, since otherwise the mass of the system is undetermined, and we are not able, for example, to distinguish between a system containing a ton of water and one containing a few drops.

An important feature of equilibria between phases is that they are independent of the actual amounts of the phases that may be present.* Thus the vapor pressure of water above liquid water in no way depends on the volume of the vessel or on whether a few milliliters or many liters of water are in equilibrium with the vapor phase. Similarly, the concentration of a saturated solution of salt in water is a fixed and definite quantity, regardless of whether a large or a small excess of undissolved salt is present.

In discussing phase equilibria, we therefore need not consider the capacity factors, which express the masses of the phases. We consider only the intensity factors, such as temperature, pressure, and concentrations. Of these variables a certain number may be independently varied, but the rest are fixed by the values chosen for the independent variables and by the thermodynamic requirements for equilibrium. The number of the intensive state variables that can be independently varied without changing the number of phases is called the *number of degrees of freedom* of the system, or sometimes, the *variance*.

For example, the state of a certain amount of a pure gas may be specified completely by any two of the variables, pressure, temperature, and density. If any two of these are known, the third can be calculated. This is therefore a system with two degrees of freedom, or a bivariant system.

In the system "water — water vapor," only one variable need be specified to determine the state. At any given temperature, the pressure of vapor in equilibrium with liquid water is fixed in value. This system has one degree of freedom, or is said to be *univariant*.

---

* This statement is proved in the next Section. It is true as long as variations in surface area are not considered. (See Chapter 19.)

4. GENERAL EQUILIBRIUM THEORY: THE CHEMICAL POTENTIAL

Under conditions of constant temperature and pressure, any change in the system proceeds from a state of higher free energy G_1 to a state of lower free energy G_2. For this reason, it became natural to think of the free energy G as a thermodynamic potential, and to think of any change in a system as a passage from a state of higher to a state of lower potential. Of course, the choice of G as the potential function is due to the choice of the condition of constant T and P. At constant T and V, the suitable potential function would be A; at constant T and S, it would be H; and so on.

If a system contains more than one component in a given phase, we cannot specify its state without some specification of the *composition* of that phase. In addition to P, V, and T, we need to introduce new variables which are measures of the amounts of the different chemical constituents in the system. As usual, the *mole* will be chosen as the chemical measure, with the symbols $n_1, n_2, n_3 \ldots n_i$ representing the number of moles of component $1, 2, 3 \ldots i$ in the particular phase we are considering.

It then follows that each thermodynamic function depends on these n_i's as well as on P, V, T. Thus $E = E(V, T, n_i)$; $G = G(P, T, n_i)$, etc. Consequently, a complete differential, for example of the free energy, becomes

$$dG = \left(\frac{\partial G}{\partial T}\right)_{P,n_i} dT + \left(\frac{\partial G}{\partial P}\right)_{T,n_i} dP + \sum_i \left(\frac{\partial G}{\partial n_i}\right)_{T,P,n_j} dn_i \tag{4.1}$$

From Eq. (3.29), $dG = -S\,dT + V\,dP$ for any system of constant composition, i.e., when all the $dn_i = 0$. Therefore, Eq. (4.1) becomes

$$dG = -S\,dT + V\,dP + \sum \left(\frac{\partial G}{\partial n_i}\right)_{T,P,n_j} dn_i \tag{4.2}$$

The coefficient $(\partial G/\partial n_i)_{T,P,n_j}$ was introduced by Gibbs, who called it the *chemical potential*, and gave it the special symbol μ_i. Hence,

$$\mu_i = \left(\frac{\partial G}{\partial n_i}\right)_{T,P,n_j} \tag{4.3}$$

It is the change in the free energy of the system [phase] with a change in the number of moles of component i, the temperature, the pressure, and the number of moles of all other components being kept constant. The chemical potentials therefore measure how the free energy of a phase depends on any changes in its composition.

Equation (4.2) can now be written

$$dG = -S\,dT + V\,dP + \sum \mu_i\,dn_i \tag{4.4}$$

An equation like Eq. (4.4), which includes the variation of a thermodynamic function with the number of moles of the different components, is said to apply to an *open system*. We can change the amount of any component i in an open system by adding or removing dn_i of this component. At constant temperature and pressure, Eq. (4.4) becomes

$$\text{(constant } T, P) \qquad dG = \sum \mu_i \, dn_i \tag{4.5}$$

An equation like this would apply to each phase of a system of several phases, and the transfers of mass dn_i might occur from one phase to another. If we consider the phase to be *closed*, so that no transfer of mass across its boundaries is allowed, Eq. (3.25) applies, and we have

$$\text{(constant } T, P, \text{ closed phase)} \quad \sum \mu_i \, dn_i = 0 \tag{4.6}$$

We might, however, consider the entire system of several phases to be closed. We then have the relation

$$\sum_i \mu_i^\alpha \, dn_i^\alpha + \sum_i \mu_i^\beta \, dn_i^\beta + \sum_i \mu_i^\gamma \, dn_i^\gamma + \ldots = 0 \tag{4.7}$$

where $\alpha, \beta, \gamma \ldots$ represent the several phases. We can still transfer components across the phase boundaries in this system, but no mass can enter or leave the system as a whole.

We shall explore other aspects and applications of the chemical potential in the next chapter on solutions. Now we shall use the new function μ to follow the derivation given by Gibbs of the *phase rule*, the fundamental equation governing equilibria between phases.

5. CONDITIONS FOR EQUILIBRIUM BETWEEN PHASES

In a system containing several phases, certain thermodynamic requirements for the existence of equilibrium may be derived.

For thermal equilibrium it is necessary that the temperatures of all the phases be the same. Otherwise, heat would flow from one phase to another. This intuitively recognized condition may be proved by considering two phases α and β at temperatures T^α and T^β. The condition for equilibrium at constant volume and composition is given on p. 79 as $dS = 0$. Let S^α and S^β be the entropies of the two phases, and suppose there were a transfer of heat δq from α to β at equilibrium. Then,

$$dS = dS^\alpha + dS^\beta = 0 \quad \text{or} \quad -\frac{\delta q}{T^\alpha} + \frac{\delta q}{T^\beta} = 0$$

Whence,

$$T^\alpha = T^\beta \tag{4.8}$$

For mechanical equilibrium it is necessary that the pressures of all the phases be the same. Otherwise, one phase would increase in volume at the expense of another. This condition may be derived from the equilibrium condition at constant overall volume and temperature, $dA = 0$. Suppose one phase expanded into another by δV. Then,

$$dA = P^\alpha \, \delta V - P^\beta \, \delta V = 0$$

or

$$P^\alpha = P^\beta \tag{4.9}$$

In addition to the conditions given by Eqs. (4.8) and (4.9), a condition is needed that expresses the requirements of chemical equilibrium. Let us consider the system with phases α and β maintained at constant temperature and pressure, and denote by n_i^α, n_i^β, the number of moles of some particular component i in the two phases. From Eq. (3.25) the equilibrium condition $dG = 0$ becomes

$$dG = dG^\alpha + dG^\beta = 0 \tag{4.10}$$

Suppose that a process occurred by which δn_i moles of component i were taken from phase α and added to phase β. (This process might be a chemical reaction or a change in aggregation state.) Then, by virtue of Eq. (4.7), Eq. (4.10) becomes

$$dG = -\mu_i^\alpha\,\delta n_i + \mu_i^\beta\,\delta n_i = 0$$

or

$$\mu_i^\alpha = \mu_i^\beta \tag{4.11}$$

This is the general condition for equilibrium with respect to transport of matter between phases in a closed system, including chemical equilibrium between phases. For any component i in the system, the value of the chemical potential μ_i must be the same in every phase, when the system is in equilibrium at constant T and P.

An important symmetry between the various equilibrium conditions is apparent in the following summary.

Capacity Factor	*Intensity Factor*	*Equilibrium Condition*
S	T	$T^\alpha = T^\beta$
V	P	$P^\alpha = P^\beta$
n_i	μ_i	$\mu_i^\alpha = \mu_i^\beta$

6. THE PHASE RULE

Between 1875 and 1876, Josiah Willard Gibbs, Professor of Mathematical Physics at Yale University, published in the *Transactions of the Connecticut Academy of Sciences* a series of papers entitled "On the Equilibrium of Heterogeneous Substances." With brilliant beauty and precision, Gibbs disclosed in these papers the basic science of heterogeneous equilibrium.

The Gibbs phase rule provides a general relationship among the degrees of freedom of a system f, the number of phases p, and the number of components c. This relationship always is

$$f = c - p + 2 \tag{4.12}$$

The derivation proceeds as follows:

The number of degrees of freedom is equal to the number of intensive variables required to describe a system, minus the number that cannot be independently varied. The state of a system containing p phases and c components is specified at equilibrium if we specify the temperature, the pressure, and the amounts of each component in each phase. The total variables required in order to do this are therefore $pc + 2$.

Let n_i^α denote the number of moles of a component i in a phase α. Since the size of the system, or the actual amount of material in any phase, does not affect the equilibrium, we are really interested in the relative amounts of the components in the different phases and not in their absolute amounts. Therefore, instead of the mole numbers n_i^α, the mole fractions X_i^α should be used. These are given by

$$X_i^\alpha = \frac{n_i^\alpha}{\sum_i n_i^\alpha} \tag{4.13}$$

For each phase, the sum of the mole fractions equals unity.

$$X_1 + X_2 + X_3 + \ldots + X_c = 1$$

or

$$\sum X_i = 1 \tag{4.14}$$

If all but one mole fraction are specified, that one can be calculated from Eq. (4.14). If there are p phases, there are p equations similar to Eq. (4.14), and therefore p mole fractions that need not be specified since they can be calculated. The total number of independent variables to be specified is thus $pc + 2 - p$ or $p(c - 1) + 2$.

At equilibrium, the Eqs. (4.11) impose a set of further restraints on the system by requiring that the chemical potentials of each component be the same in every phase. These conditions are expressed by a set of equations such as:

$$\begin{aligned} \mu_1^\alpha &= \mu_1^\beta = \mu_1^\gamma = \ldots \\ \mu_2^\alpha &= \mu_2^\beta = \mu_2^\gamma = \ldots \\ &\vdots \\ \mu_c^\alpha &= \mu_c^\beta = \mu_c^\gamma = \ldots \end{aligned} \tag{4.15}$$

Each equality sign in this set of equations signifies a condition imposed on the system, decreasing its variance by one. Inspection shows that there are therefore $c(p - 1)$ of these conditions.

The degrees of freedom equal the total required variables minus the restraining conditions. Therefore

$$f = p(c - 1) + 2 - c(p - 1)$$

$$f = c - p + 2 \tag{4.16}$$

7. SYSTEMS OF ONE COMPONENT — WATER

In the remainder of this chapter, systems of one component will be considered. These systems comprise the study of the conditions of equilibrium in changes in the state of aggregation of pure substances.

From the phase rule, when $c = 1$, $f = 3 - p$, and three different cases are possible:

$p = 1, f = 2$ bivariant system

$p = 2, f = 1$ univariant system

$p = 3, f = 0$ invariant system

Since the maximum number of degrees of freedom is two, any one-component system can be represented by a two-dimensional diagram. The most convenient variables are the pressure and the temperature.

The water system is shown in Fig. 4.1. The diagram is divided into three areas, the fields of existence of ice, liquid, and vapor. Within these single-phase areas, the system is bivariant, and pressure and temperature can be independently varied.

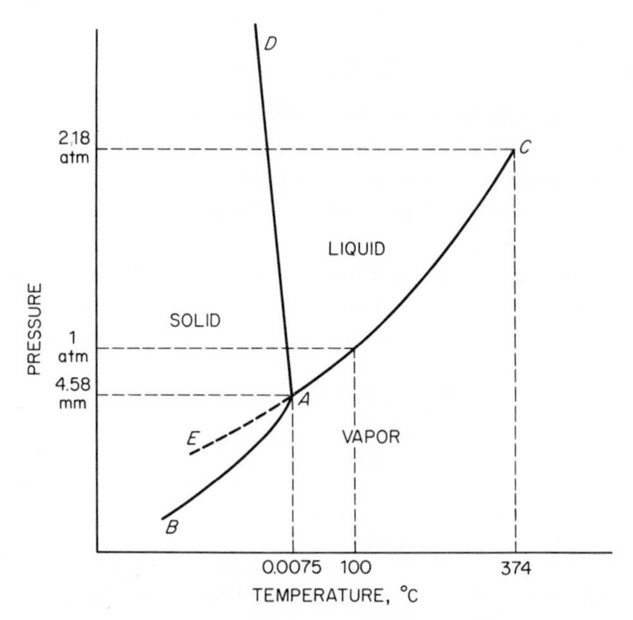

FIG. 4.1 The water system — schematic. (Not drawn to scale.)

Separating the areas are lines connecting the points at which two phases can coexist at equilibrium. Thus the curve AC dividing the liquid from the vapor region is the familiar vapor-pressure curve of liquid water. At any given temperature there is one and only one pressure at which water vapor is in equilibrium with liquid water. The system is univariant, having one degree of freedom. The curve AC has a natural upper limit at the point C, which is the critical point, beyond which the liquid phase is no longer distinguishable from the vapor phase.

Similarly, the curve AB is the sublimation-pressure curve of ice, giving the pressure of water vapor in equilibrium with solid ice, and dividing the ice region from the vapor region.

The curve AD divides the solid-ice region from the liquid-water region. It shows how the melting temperature of ice or the freezing temperature of water varies with the pressure. It is still an open question whether such curves, at sufficiently high pressures, ever have a natural upper limit beyond which solid and liquid are indistinguishable.

These three curves intersect at a point A, at which solid, liquid, and vapor are simultaneously at equilibrium. This point, at 273.16°K and 4.579 mm pressure, is called a *triple point*. Since three phases coexist, the system is invariant. There are no degrees of freedom and neither pressure nor temperature can be altered even slightly without causing the disappearance of one of the phases.

It should be noted that this triple point is not the same as the ordinary melting point of ice, which is the temperature at which ice and water are in equilibrium under an applied pressure of 1 atm or 760 mm of air. This temperature is 273.15°K.

Liquid water may be cooled below its freezing point without solidifying. In AE we have drawn the vapor-pressure curve of this *supercooled* water, which is a continuous extension of curve AC. It is shown as a dotted line on the diagram since it represents a *metastable* system. Note that the metastable vapor pressure of supercooled water is higher than the vapor pressure of ice.

The slope of the curve AD, the melting-point curve, is worth remarking. It shows that the melting point of ice is decreased by increasing pressure. This is a rather unusual behavior; only bismuth and antimony among common substances behave similarly. These substances expand on freezing. Therefore the Le Chatelier principle demands that increasing the pressure should lower the melting point. The popularity of ice skating and the flow of glaciers are among the consequences of the peculiar slope of the melting-point curve for ice. For most substances, the density of the solid is greater than that of the liquid, and by Le Chatelier's principle, increase in pressure raises the melting point.

8. THE CLAPEYRON-CLAUSIUS EQUATION

Two fundamental theoretical equations govern the domain of phase equilibrium. The first is the Gibbs phase rule, which determines the general pattern of the phase diagram. The second is the Clapeyron-Clausius equation, which determines the slopes of the lines in the diagram. First proposed by the French engineer Clapeyron in 1834, it was placed on a firm thermodynamic basis by Clausius, some thirty years later.

From Eq. (4.11) the condition for equilibrium of a component i between two phases, α and β, is $\mu_i^\alpha = \mu_i^\beta$. For a system of one component, the chemical potential μ is identical with the free energy per mole $\overline{G}$, so that $\overline{G}^\alpha = \overline{G}^\beta$ at equilibrium. Consider two different equilibrium states, at slightly separated temperatures and pressures:

$$(1)\quad T,\ P,\ \overline{G}^\alpha = \overline{G}^\beta$$

$$(2)\quad T + dT,\ P + dP,\ \overline{G}^\alpha + d\overline{G}^\alpha = \overline{G}^\beta + d\overline{G}^\beta$$

It follows that $d\overline{G}^\alpha = d\overline{G}^\beta$. The change in G with T and P is given by Eq. (3.29),

$$d\overline{G} = \overline{V}\,dP - \overline{S}\,dT$$

Therefore,

$$\overline{V}^\alpha\,dP - \overline{S}^\alpha\,dT = \overline{V}^\beta\,dP - \overline{S}^\beta\,dT,$$

or

$$\frac{dP}{dT} = \frac{\overline{S}^\beta - \overline{S}^\alpha}{\overline{V}^\beta - \overline{V}^\alpha} = \frac{\Delta\overline{S}}{\Delta\overline{V}} \tag{4.17}$$

If the latent heat of the phase transformation is λ, $\Delta\overline{S}$ is simply λ/T where T is the temperature at which the phase change is occurring. The Clapeyron-Clausius equation is thus obtained as

$$\frac{dP}{dT} = \frac{\lambda}{T\,\Delta\overline{V}} \tag{4.18}$$

This equation applies to any change of state (fusion, vaporization, sublimation, and changes between crystalline forms) provided the appropriate latent heat is employed.

In order to integrate the equation exactly, it would be necessary to know both λ and $\overline{V}$ as functions of temperature and pressure.* The latter corresponds to a knowledge of the densities of the two phases over the desired temperature range. In most calculations over short temperature ranges, however, both λ and $\overline{V}$ may be taken as constants.

In the case of the change "liquid → vapor," Eq. (4.18) becomes

$$\frac{dP}{dT} = \frac{\lambda_{\text{vap}}}{T_b(\overline{V}_g - \overline{V}_l)} \tag{4.19}$$

Several good approximations can be made in this equation. If we neglect the volume of the liquid compared to that of the vapor, and assume ideal gas behavior for the latter, we obtain

$$\frac{d\ln P}{dT} = \frac{\lambda_{\text{vap}}}{RT^2} \tag{4.20}$$

A similar equation would be a good approximation for the sublimation curve.

As we showed for Eq. (3.36), we may also write Eq. (4.20) as

$$\frac{d\ln P}{d(1/T)} = -\frac{\lambda}{R} \tag{4.21}$$

If the logarithm of the vapor pressure is plotted against $1/T$, the slope of the curve at any point multiplied by $-R$ yields a value for the heat of vaporization. In many cases, since λ is effectively constant over short temperature ranges, the curve is a straight line. This fact is useful to remember in extrapolating vapor-pressure data.

---

* A good discussion of the temperature variation of λ is given by E. A. Guggenheim in *Modern Thermodynamics* (London: Methuen, 1933), p. 57. The variation with pressure of λ and $\overline{V}$ is much less than that with temperature.

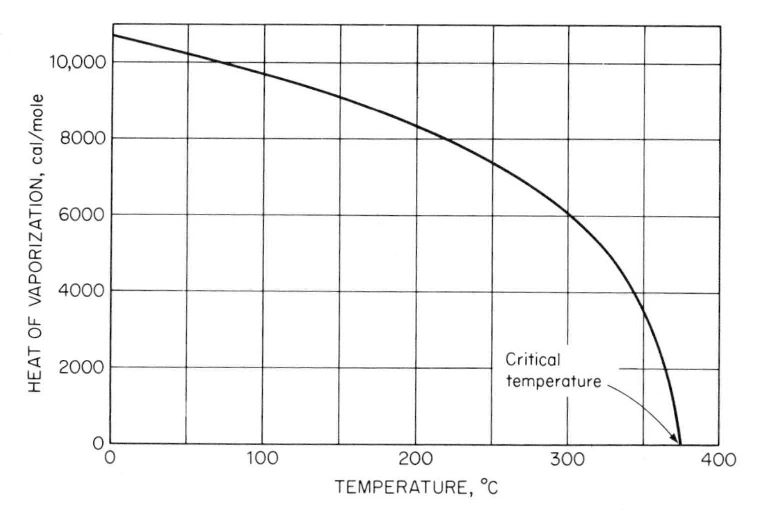

FIG. 4.2 The heat of vaporization of water as a function of temperature.

Over any extended range of temperature the latent heat of vaporization varies considerably. It must decrease with increasing temperature and approach zero at the critical point. Fig. 4.2 shows how the latent heat of vaporization of water varies with temperature.

When λ is taken as constant, the integrated form of Eq. (4.20) is

$$\ln \frac{P_2}{P_1} = -\frac{\lambda}{R}\left(\frac{1}{T_2} - \frac{1}{T_1}\right) \tag{4.22}$$

An approximate value for λ_{vap} can often be obtained from *Trouton's Rule* (1884):

$$\frac{\lambda_{\text{vap}}}{T_b} \approx 22 \text{ cal deg}^{-1} \text{ mole}^{-1}$$

The rule is followed fairly well by many nonpolar liquids. It is equivalent to the statement that the entropy of vaporization is approximately the same for all such liquids.

9. VAPOR PRESSURE AND EXTERNAL PRESSURE

Let us consider the effect of an increased hydrostatic pressure on the vapor pressure of a liquid. Let us suppose that an external hydrostatic pressure P_e is imposed on a liquid of molar volume $\overline{V}_l$. Let the vapor pressure be P, and the molar volume of the vapor $\overline{V}_g$. At equilibrium at constant temperature,

$$dG_{\text{vap}} = dG_{\text{liq}} \quad \text{or} \quad \overline{V}_g\, dP = \overline{V}_l\, dP_e$$

Hence,

$$\frac{dP}{dP_e} = \frac{\overline{V}_l}{\overline{V}_g} \tag{4.23}$$

This is sometimes called the *Gibbs equation.* If the vapor is an ideal gas, it becomes

$$RT\frac{d\ln P}{dP_e} = \overline{V}_l$$

Since the molar volume of the liquid does not vary greatly with pressure, we may integrate this equation, assuming constant $\overline{V}_l$.

$$\ln\frac{P_1}{P_2} = \frac{\overline{V}_l(P_{e1} - P_{e2})}{RT} \tag{4.24}$$

In theory, we can measure the vapor pressure of a liquid under an applied hydrostatic pressure in only two ways: (1) with an atmosphere of "inert" gas; (2) with an ideal membrane semipermeable to the vapor. In practice, the inert gas may dissolve in the liquid, in which case the application of the Gibbs equation to the problem is dubious. The second way is treated in the theory of osmotic pressure.

As an example of the use of Eq. (4.24), let us estimate the vapor pressure of mercury under an external pressure of 1000 atm at 100°C. The density is 13.352 g cm^{-3}; hence

$$\overline{V}_l = M/\rho = 200.61/13.352 = 15.025 \text{ cm}^3,$$

and

$$\ln\frac{P_1}{P_2} = \frac{15.025(1000 - 1)}{82.05 \times 373.2} = 0.4902$$

Therefore $P_1/P_2 = 1.633$. The vapor pressure at 1 atm is 0.273 mm, so that the calculated vapor pressure at 1000 atm is 0.455 mm.

10. EXPERIMENTAL MEASUREMENT OF VAPOR PRESSURE

One of the most convenient static methods is the *isoteniscope* shown in Fig. 4.3. The bulb and short attached U-tube are filled with the liquid to be studied, which is allowed to boil vigorously until all air is removed from the sample side of the

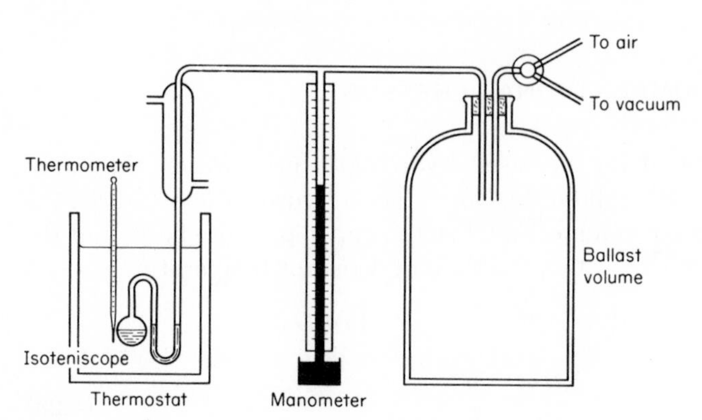

FIG. 4.3 Vapor pressure measurement with isoteniscope of Smith and Menzies.

U-tube. At each temperature the external pressure is adjusted until the arms of the differential U-tube manometer are level, and the pressure and temperature are then recorded.

The *gas-saturation* method was used extensively by Ramsay and Young. An inert gas is passed through the liquid maintained in a thermostat. The volume of gas used is measured, and its final vapor content or the loss in weight of the substance being studied is determined. If care is taken to ensure saturation of the flowing gas, the vapor pressure of the liquid may readily be calculated.

Some experimentally measured vapor pressures are collected in Table 4.1.

TABLE 4.1 TYPICAL VAPOR PRESSURE DATA*

	Vapor Pressure in Millimeters of Mercury						
Temp. °C	CCl_4	C_2H_5OH	n-C_7H_{16}	$C_6H_5 \cdot CH_3$	H_2O	D_2O	Hg(mm × 10^4)
0	....	12.2	11.45	6.9	4.579	3.65	1.898
10	....	23.6	20.5	13.0	9.209	7.79	4.971
20	91	43.9	35.5	22.3	17.535	15.2	12.20
30	143.0	78.8	58.35	36.7	31.824	28.0	28.01
40	215.8	135.3	92.05	59.1	55.324	49.3	61.18
50	317.1	222.2	140.9	92.6	92.51	83.6	127.2
60	450.8	352.7	208.9	139.5	149.38	136.6	252.6
70	622.3	542.5	302.3	202.4	233.7	216.1	482.3
80	843	812.6	426.6	289.7	355.1	331.6	886.5
90	1122	1187	588.8	404.6	525.76	495.5	1576
100	1463	1690	795.2	557.2	760.00	722.2	2713

* T. E. Jordan, *Vapor Pressure of Organic Compounds*, (New York: Interscience, 1954).

11. SOLID-SOLID TRANSFORMATIONS – THE SULFUR SYSTEM

Sulfur provides the classic example of a one-component system displaying a solid-solid transformation. The phenomenon of *polymorphism*, discovered by Mitscherlich in 1821, is the occurrence of the same chemical substance in two or more different crystalline forms. In the case of elements, it is called *allotropy*.

Sulfur occurs in a low-temperature rhombic form and a high-temperature monoclinic form. The phase diagram for the system is shown in Fig. 4.4. The pressure scale in this diagram has been made logarithmic in order to bring the interesting low-pressure regions into prominence.

The curve AB is the vapor-pressure curve of solid rhombic sulfur. At point B it intersects the vapor-pressure curve of monoclinic sulfur BE, and also the transformation curve for rhombic–monoclinic sulfur, BD. This intersection determines the triple point B, at which rhombic and monoclinic sulfur and sulfur vapor coexist. Since there are three phases and one component, $f = c - p + 2 = 3 - 3 = 0$, and point B is an invariant point. It occurs at 0.01 mm pressure and 95.5°C.

The density of monoclinic sulfur is less than that of rhombic sulfur, and therefore the transition temperature ($S_r \rightarrow S_m$) increases with increasing pressure.

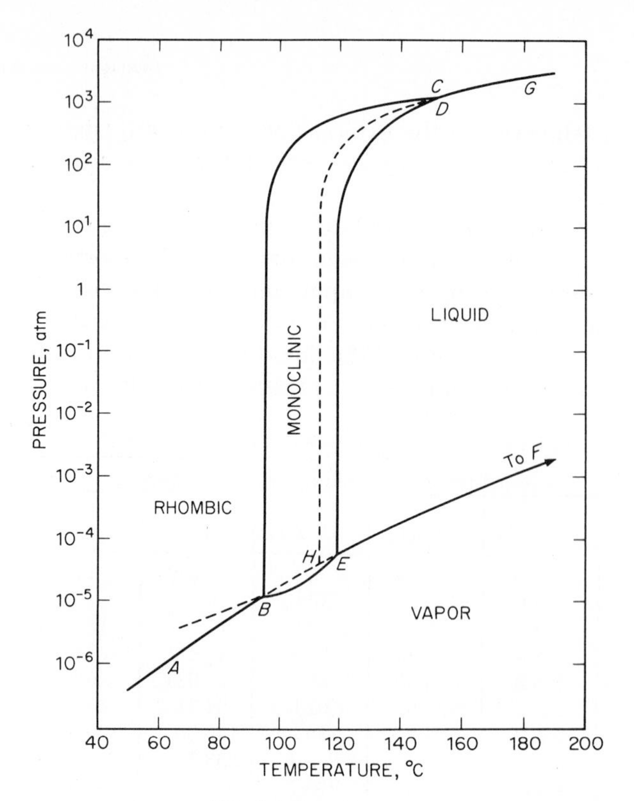

FIG. 4.4 The sulfur system.

Monoclinic sulfur melts under its own vapor pressure of 0.025 mm at 120°C' the point E on the diagram. From E to the critical point F there extends the vapor-pressure curve of liquid sulfur EF. Also from E, there extends the curve ED, the melting-point curve of monoclinic sulfur. The density of liquid sulfur is less than that of the monoclinic solid, the usual situation in a solid-liquid transformation, and hence ED slopes to the right as shown. The point E is a triple point, $S_m - S_{\text{liq}} - S_{\text{vap}}$.

The slope of BD is greater than that of ED, so that these curves intersect at D, forming a third triple point on the diagram, $S_r - S_m - S_{\text{liq}}$. This occurs at 155° and 1290 atm. At pressures higher than this, rhombic sulfur is again the stable solid form, and DG is the melting-point curve of rhombic sulfur in this high-pressure region. The range of stable existence of monoclinic sulfur is confined to the totally enclosed area BED.

Besides the stable equilibria represented by the solid lines, a number of metastable equilibria are easily observed. If rhombic sulfur is heated quite rapidly, it will pass by the transition point B without change and finally melt to liquid sulfur at 114°C (point H). The curve EH is the metastable vapor pressure curve of supercooled liquid sulfur. Extending from H to D is the metastable rhombic melting-point curve. Point H is a metastable triple point, $S_r - S_{\text{liq}} - S_{\text{vap}}$.

All these metastable equilbria are quite easily studied because of the sluggishness that characterizes the rate of attainment of equilibrium between solid phases.

12. SECOND-ORDER TRANSITIONS

The usual change of state (solid to liquid, liquid to vapor, etc.) is called a *first-order transition.* At the transition temperature T_t at constant pressure, the free energies of the two forms are equal, but there is a discontinuous change in the slope of the G vs. T curve for the substance at T_t. Since $(\partial G/\partial T)_P = -S$, there is therefore a break in the S vs. T curve, the value of ΔS at T_t being related to the observed latent heat for the transition by $\Delta \overline{S} = \lambda/T_t$. There is also a discontinuous change ΔV in volume, since the densities of the two forms are not the same.

A number of transitions have been studied in which no latent heat or density change can be detected. Examples are the transformations of certain metals from ferromagnetic to paramagnetic solids at their Curie points, the transitions of some metals at low temperatures to a condition of electric superconductivity, and the transition observed in helium from one liquid form to another.* In these cases, there is a change in slope, but no discontinuity, in the S vs. T curve at T_t. As a result, there is a break ΔC_P in the heat-capacity curve, since $C_P = T(\partial S/\partial T)_P$. Such a change is called a *second-order transition.*

13. THE HELIUM SYSTEM

The phase diagram for helium is shown in Fig. 4.5(a). This is the only known system in which two liquid phases exist for a single pure substance. Liquid Helium-II has many unusual and remarkable properties. It has been called a *superfluid* because of its extremely low viscosity. It is hard to keep it in any container for it can run spontaneously up the sides and escape.

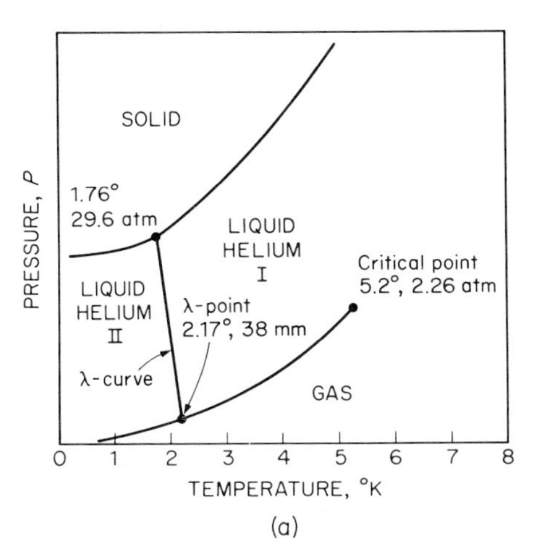

FIG. 4.5(a) Phase diagram of helium (schematic).

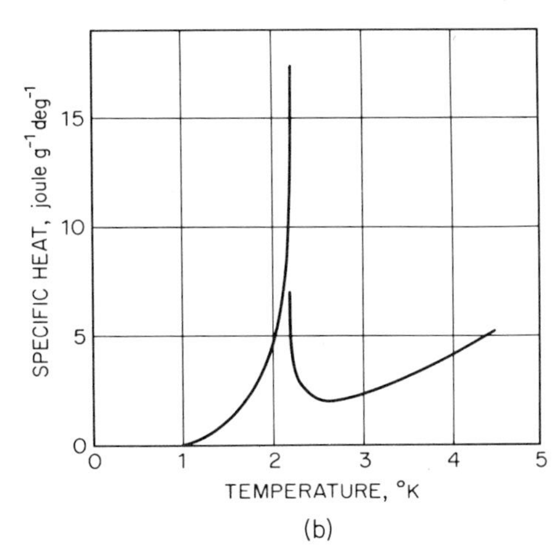

FIG. 4.5(b) Specific heat of liquid helium.

* W. H. Keesom, *Helium* (Amsterdam: Elsevier, 1942).

FIG. 4.6 A tetrahedral-anvil apparatus which can attain 130 000 atm at 3000°C. (H. Tracy Hall, Brigham Young University).

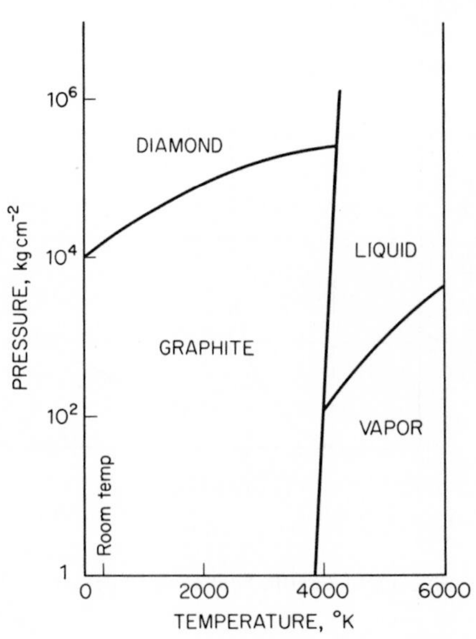

FIG. 4.7 The phase diagram of carbon.

There is no solid-liquid-vapor triple point in the helium system. There is a solid-liquid I-liquid II triple point at 1.8°K and 30 atm, and a liquid II-liquid I-vapor triple point at 2.17°K and 0.05 atm. The transition from liquid He-I to liquid He-II is a typical second-order transition. There is no latent heat, but there is a discontinuity in the C_P vs. T curve. This is shown in Fig. 4.5(b). The resemblance of the curve to the Greek letter lambda led to the name λ-*point transition* for this kind of behavior.

14. HIGH-PRESSURE STUDIES

It is only a truism that our attitude toward the physical world is conditioned by the scale of magnitudes provided in our terrestrial environment. We tend, for example, to classify pressures or temperatures as high or low by comparing them with the fifteen pounds per square inch and 70°F of a spring day in the laboratory, despite the fact that almost all the matter in the universe exists under conditions very different from these. Even at the center of the earth, by no means a large astronomical body, the pressure is around 1 200 000 atm, and substances at this pressure have properties quite unlike those to which we are accustomed. At the center of a comparatively small star, like our sun, the pressure would be around ten billion atmospheres.

The pioneer work of Gustav Tammann on high-pressure measurements was greatly extended by P. W. Bridgman and his associates at Harvard. Pressures up to 400 000 atm were achieved and methods developed for measuring the properties of substances at 100 000 atm.* The attainment of such pressures was made possible by the construction of pressure vessels of alloys such as Carboloy. In the multiple-chamber technique, the container for the substance to be studied is enclosed in another vessel, and pressure is applied both inside and outside the inner container, usually by means of hydraulic presses. Thus, although the absolute pressure in the inner vessel may be 100 000 atm, the pressure differential that its walls must sustain is only 50 000 atm.

An effective arrangement of a high pressure press is the *tetrahedral anvil* designed by Tracy Hall, shown in Fig. 4.6. Diamonds can be made on a routine basis by compressing graphite at an elevated temperature in such a device. The carbon system is shown in Fig. 4.7. Without catalytic action it was estimated that pressures of 200 000 atm and temperatures of about 4000°C would be required to transform graphite into diamond. No containers could withstand these conditions. By the use of metallic catalysts such as tantalum and cobalt a rapid transformation was achieved at about 70 000 atm and 2000°C. Fig. 4.8 shows synthetic diamonds covered by catalyst in a graphite matrix.

High-pressure measurements on water yielded some of the most interesting results, which are shown in the phase diagram of Fig. 4.9. The melting point

* For details see P. W. Bridgman, *The Physics of High Pressures* (London: Bell and Co., 1949), and his review article, *Rev. Mod. Phys.*, *18*, 1 (1946).

of ordinary ice (ice I) falls on compression, until a value of −22.0°C is reached at 2040 atm. Further increase in pressure results in the transformation of ice I into a new modification, ice III, whose melting point increases with pressure. Altogether six different polymorphic forms of ice have been found. There are

FIG. 4.8 Synthetic diamonds in a graphite matrix. (General Electric Research Laboratories)

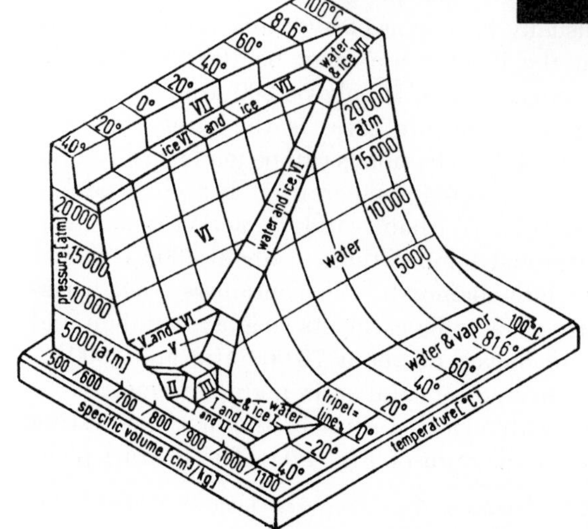

FIG. 4.9 Water system at high pressures, showing various forms of ice.

Constructed by Verwiebe from measurements of Bridgman. [Zemansky, *Heat and Thermodynamics,* New York, McGraw-Hill, 1957].

five triple points shown on the water diagram. Ice VII is an extreme high-pressure form not shown on the diagram; at a pressure of around 20 000 atm, liquid water freezes to ice VII at about 100°C. Ice IV is not shown. Its existence was indicated by the work of Tammann, but it was not confirmed by Bridgman.

PROBLEMS

1. From the following data, roughly sketch the phase diagram for carbon dioxide: (a) critical point at 31°C and 73 atm; (b) triple point (solid-liquid-vapor) at −57°C and 5.3 atm; (c) solid is denser than liquid at the triple point. Label all regions on the diagram.

2. Roughly sketch the phase diagram of acetic acid, from the data: (a) The low-pressure α form melts at 16.6°C under its own vapor pressure of 9.1 mm; (b) there is a high-pressure β form that is denser than the α, but both α and β are denser than the liquid; (c) the normal boiling point of liquid is 118°C; (d) phases α, β, and liquid are in equilibrium at 55°C and 2000 atm.

3. The density ρ of ice at 1 atm and 0°C is 0.917 g per cc. Water under the same conditions has $\rho = 0.9998$. Estimate the melting point of ice under a pressure of 400 atm, assuming that ρ for both ice and water are practically constant over the temperature and pressure range. [*Ans.* −3°C]

4. Estimate the vapor pressure of mercury at 25°C, assuming that the liquid obeys Trouton's rule. The normal boiling point is 356.9°C. [*Ans.* 0.0033 mm]

5. The vapor pressure of solid iodine is 0.25 mm and its density 4.93 at 20°C. Assuming the Gibbs equation to hold, calculate the vapor pressure of iodine under a 1000-atm argon pressure. [*Ans.* 2.1 mm]

6. In a determination of the vapor pressure of ethyl acetate by the gas-saturation method, 100 liters of nitrogen (STP) were passed through a saturator containing ethyl acetate at 0°C, which lost a weight of 12.8 g. Calculate the vapor pressure at 0°C. [*Ans.* 25 mm]

7. From the following data, sketch the low-temperature phase diagram of nitrogen. There are three crystal forms, α, β, and γ, which coexist at a triple point at 4650 atm and 44.5°K. At the triple point, the volume changes ΔV in cc/mole are $\alpha \rightarrow \gamma$, 0.165; $\beta \rightarrow \gamma$, 0.208; $\beta \rightarrow \alpha$, 0.043. At 1 atm and 36°K, $\beta \rightarrow \alpha$ with a $\Delta V = 0.22$.

8. If the free energy $\overline{G}^\circ$ of graphite at 25°C and 1 atm is taken as zero, the $\overline{G}^\circ$ of diamond = 685 cal mole^{-1} under the same conditions. The entropies

are $\overline{S}^\circ_{298}$ (diamond) $= 0.583$ cal deg^{-1} and $\overline{S}^\circ_{298}$ (graphite) $= 1.361$. What is the possibility of converting graphite to diamond by change of temperature alone? Assume the S do not depend on T.

9. The melting points and volume changes on fusion are found for CCl_4. At 1 atm, -22.6°C, 0.0258 cc g^{-1}; at 1000 atm, $+15.3$°C, .0199 cc g^{-1}; at 2000 atm, 48.9°C, 0.0163 cc g^{-1}. Estimate the latent heat of fusion of CCl_4 at 1000 atm.

10. The vapor pressure of water at 20°C is 17.54 torr (mm Hg). What is ΔG°_{298} for the change $H_2O(l) \rightarrow H_2O(g)$?

11. The vapor pressure of ice is 4.58 torr at 0°C and 1.95 torr at -10°C. What is the average latent heat of sublimation of ice over this range of T?

12. The following data are given for Cl_2. Calculate the ΔH of vaporization of Cl_2 at 10°C. If Cl_2 were assumed to behave as an ideal gas, how would it change your result?

T°C	0°	10°	20°
P atm	3.65	4.96	6.57
ρ (liq)	1.468	1.438	1.408
ρ (gas)	0.0128	0.0175	0.0226

13. The entropy of saturated water at 100°C is 0.31 cal/gm-deg and that of saturated steam at 100°C is 1.76 cal/gm-deg. (a) What is the heat of vaporization at 100°C? (b) The enthalpy of saturated steam at 100°C is 640 cal/gm. From (a) calculate the enthalpy of saturated water at 100°C. (c) Calculate the Gibbs free energy of saturated water and of saturated steam at 100°C and verify that the two are equal.

---

14. The vapor pressures of liquid gallium are as follows:

t, °C	1029	1154	1350
P, mm	0.01	0.1	1

Calculate ΔH°, ΔG°, and ΔS° for the vaporization of gallium at 1154°C. [*Ans.* $\Delta H^\circ = 55$ kcal; $\Delta G^\circ = 26.6$ kcal; $\Delta S^\circ = 21$ cal deg^{-1}]

15. At 25°C, the heat of combustion of diamond is 94.484 kcal per mole and that of graphite is 94.030. The molar entropies are 0.5829 and 1.3609 cal per deg mole, respectively. Find the ΔG for the transition graphite $\rightarrow$ diamond at 25°C and 1 atm. The densities are 3.513 g per cc for diamond and 2.260 for graphite. Estimate the pressure at which the two forms would be in equilibrium at 25°C and 1000°C. You may assume the densities to be independent of pressure. [*Ans.* 685.9 cal mole^{-1}; 14 700 atm (the assumption of constant densities has made this figure much too low an approximation)]

16. Bridgman found the following melting points t (°C) and volume changes on melting ΔV (cc per g) for Na:

P, kg/cm^2	1	2000	4000	6000
t	97.6	114.2	129.8	142.5
ΔV	0.0279	0.0236	0.0207	0.0187

Estimate the heat of fusion of sodium at 3000 atm. [*Ans.* 26.6 cal g^{-1}]

17. Sketch graphs of G, S, V, and C_P against T at constant P, and P at constant T, for typical first- and second-order phase transitions.

18. The heat capacity of liquid zinc from 419.5° to 907°C can be represented by

$$C_P(\text{Zn, l}) = 7.09 + 1.15 \times 10^{-3}T$$

Zinc forms a monatomic gas with $C_P(\text{Zn, g}) = \frac{5}{2}R$. The normal boiling point of zinc is 907°C. Calculate the vapor pressure of zinc at 500°C, assuming it to be an ideal gas. What would be the result of calculation if you neglected the variation of the heat of vaporization with T?

19. The vapor pressure of water is given by

$$\log_{10} P = A - \frac{2121}{T}$$

The heat of vaporization of water at 100°C is 538 cal g^{-1}. [The value of A depends on units chosen for P.]

(a) What is the volume occupied by 1 gram of water vapor at 1 atm and 100°C?
(b) One introduced 10 g of water into an evacuated vessel of fixed volume equal to 10 l. At a temperature of 50°C, what will be the mass of the liquid water?
(c) The temperature is then raised gradually. At what temperature will all the water be vaporized? Consider the latent heat of vaporization to be constant.

5 SOLUTIONS AND PHASE EQUILIBRIA

A solution is any phase containing more than one component. This phase may be gaseous, liquid, or solid. Gases are in general miscible in all proportions, so that all mixtures of gases, at equilibrium, are solutions. Liquids often dissolve a wide variety of gases, solids, or other liquids, and the composition of these liquid solutions can be varied over a wide or narrow range depending on the solubility relationships in the particular system. Solid solutions are formed when a gas, a liquid, or another solid dissolves in a solid. They are often characterized by very limited concentration ranges, although pairs of solids are known, for example copper and nickel, that are mutually soluble in all proportions.

1. MEASURES OF COMPOSITION

The mole fraction is the most convenient way to describe the composition of a solution in theoretical discussions. Suppose a solution contains n_A moles of component A, n_B moles of component B, n_C moles of component C, etc. Then the mole fraction X_A of component A is

$$X_A = \frac{n_A}{n_A + n_B + n_C + \ldots} \tag{5.1}$$

If there are only two components,

$$X_A = \frac{n_A}{n_A + n_B}$$

The *molality* m_B of a component B in a solution is defined as the number of moles of component B per 1000 g of some other component chosen as the solvent. One advantage of *molality* is that it is easy to prepare a solution of given molality by accurate weighing procedures. The relation between molality m_B and mole fraction X_B for a solution of two components, in which the solvent A has molecular weight M_A, is

$$X_B = \frac{m_B}{(1000/M_A) + m_B}$$

or

$$X_B = \frac{m_B M_A}{1000 + m_B M_A} \tag{5.2}$$

Notice that in dilute solution, as $m_B M_A$ becomes much less than 1000, the mole fraction becomes proportional to the molality, $X_B \approx m_B M_A/1000$.

The *concentration* of a component B in a solution is the amount of the component, expressed in some suitable units, in a unit volume of the solution. For some purposes, a convenient concentration is simply the number of particles (atoms, ions, or molecules) per cc. In other cases, the molar concentration or *molarity* c is used: the number of moles of a component in one liter of solution. For a solution of two components, in which M_A, M_B are the molecular weights of solvent and solute, respectively, and ρ is the density of the solution,

$$X_B = \frac{c_B}{(1000\rho - c_B M_B)/M_A + c_B}$$

or

$$X_B = \frac{c_B M_A}{1000\rho + c_B(M_A - M_B)} \tag{5.3}$$

In dilute solutions, ρ approaches ρ_A the density of pure solvent, and $c_B(M_A - M_B)$ becomes much less than 1000 ρ_A, so that

$$X_B \approx \frac{c_B M_A}{1000\rho_A}$$

The mole fraction then becomes proportional to molarity. In *dilute aqueous solutions* $\rho \approx \rho_A \approx 1$, so that molarity becomes approximately equal to molality.

Since the density of a solution varies with the temperature, we see from Eqs. (5.3) and (5.2) that the molarity c_B must also vary with temperature, whereas the molality m_B and mole fraction X_B are independent of temperature.

The methods of describing the composition of solutions are summarized in Table 5.1.

TABLE 5.1 THE COMPOSITION OF SOLUTIONS

Name	*Symbol*	*Definition*
Molarity	c	Moles solute in 1 liter solution
Molality	m	Moles solute in 1 kg solvent
Volume molality	m'	Moles solute in 1 liter solvent
[Weight] per cent	%	Grams solute in 100 g solution
Mole fraction	X_A	Moles component A divided by total moles of all components

2. PARTIAL MOLAR QUANTITIES: PARTIAL MOLAR VOLUME

The equilibrium properties of solutions are described in terms of the thermodynamic state functions, such as P, T, V, E, S, G, H. One of the most important problems in the theory of solutions is how these properties depend on the concentrations of the various components.

Consider a solution containing n_A moles of A and n_B moles of B. Let the volume of the solution be V, and assume that this volume is so large that the addition of one extra mole of A or of B does not change the concentration of the solution to an appreciable extent. Now add one mole of A to this large amount of solution and measure the resulting increase in the volume of the solution *at constant temperature and pressure.* This increase in volume per mole of A is called the *partial molar volume* of A in the solution at the specified pressure, temperature and composition. It is denoted by the symbol $\overline{V}_A$.* It is the change of volume V, with moles of A, n_A, at constant temperature, pressure, and moles of B, and is therefore written as

$$\overline{V}_A = \left(\frac{\partial V}{\partial n_A}\right)_{T,P,n_B} \tag{5.4}$$

One reason for introducing such a function is that the volume of a solution is not, in general, simply the sum of the volumes of the individual components. For example, if 100 ml of alcohol are mixed at 25°C with 100 ml of water, the volume of the solution is not 200 ml, but about 190 ml. The volume change on mixing depends on the relative amounts of each component in the solution.

If dn_A moles of A and dn_B are added to a solution, the increase in volume at constant temperature and pressure is given by the complete differential,

$$dV = \left(\frac{\partial V}{\partial n_A}\right)_{n_B} dn_A + \left(\frac{\partial V}{\partial n_B}\right)_{n_A} dn_B$$

or

$$dV = \overline{V}_A\, dn_A + \overline{V}_B\, dn_B \tag{5.5}$$

This expression can be integrated, which corresponds physically to increasing the volume of the solution without changing its composition, $\overline{V}_A$ and $\overline{V}_B$ hence being constant.† The result is

$$V = \overline{V}_A\, n_A + \overline{V}_B\, n_B \tag{5.6}$$

This equation tells us that the volume of the solution equals the number of moles of A times the partial molar volume of A, plus the number of moles of B times the partial molar volume of B.

On differentiation, Eq. (5.6) yields

$$dV = \overline{V}_A\, dn_A + n_A\, d\overline{V}_A + \overline{V}_B\, dn_B + n_B\, d\overline{V}_B$$

* We have used the same symbol for the molar volume of pure A and the partial molar volume of A in solution. In fact the partial molar volume becomes the molar volume in the case of a pure component. It is only rarely that any confusion can arise between these two quantities. If necessary we shall denote the molar volume of pure A as $\overline{V}_A^\circ$.

† Mathematically, the integration is equivalent to the application of Euler's theorem to the homogeneous differential expression. See D. V. Widder, *Advanced Calculus* (New York: Prentice-Hall, 1947), p. 15.

By comparison with Eq. (5.5), we find

$$n_A\, d\overline{V}_A + n_B\, d\overline{V}_B = 0$$

or

$$d\overline{V}_A = -\frac{n_B}{n_A}\, d\overline{V}_B \tag{5.7}$$

Equation (5.7) is one example of the *Gibbs-Duhem equation.* This particular application is in terms of the partial molar volumes, but any other partial molar quantity can be substituted for the volume. We can define these partial molar quantities for any extensive state function. For example:

$$\overline{S}_A = \left(\frac{\partial S}{\partial n_A}\right)_{T,P,n_B} \qquad \overline{H}_A = \left(\frac{\partial H}{\partial n_A}\right)_{T,P,n_B} \qquad \overline{G}_A = \left(\frac{\partial G}{\partial n_A}\right)_{T,P,n_B}$$

The partial molar quantities are themselves intensity factors, since they are capacity factors per mole. The partial molar free energy is the chemical potential μ.

All the thermodynamic relations derived in earlier chapters can be applied to the partial molar quantities. For example:

$$\left(\frac{\partial \overline{G}_A}{\partial P}\right)_T = \left(\frac{\partial \mu_A}{\partial P}\right)_T = \overline{V}_A; \qquad \left(\frac{\partial \mu_A}{\partial T}\right)_P = -\overline{S}_A; \qquad \left(\frac{\partial \overline{H}_A}{\partial T}\right)_P = \overline{C}_{PA} \tag{5.8}$$

The general thermodynamic theory of solutions is expressed in terms of these partial molar functions and their derivatives just as the theory for pure substances is based on the ordinary thermodynamic functions.

3. THE DETERMINATION OF PARTIAL MOLAR QUANTITIES

The evaluation of the partial quantities will now be described, using the partial molar volume as an example. The methods for $\overline{H}_A$, $\overline{S}_A$, $\overline{G}_A$, and so on, are exactly similar.

The partial molar volume $\overline{V}_A$, defined by Eq. (5.4) is equal to the slope of the curve obtained when the volume of the solution is plotted against the molality m_A of A. This follows since m_A is the number of moles of A in a *constant* quantity, namely 1000 grams, of component B.

The determination of partial molar volumes by this slope method is rather inaccurate; the *method of intercepts* is therefore usually preferred. To employ this method, a quantity is defined, called the *molar volume of the solution* $\overline{V}$, which is the volume of the solution divided by the total number of moles of the various constituents. For a two-component solution,

$$\overline{V} = \frac{V}{n_A + n_B}$$

Then,

$$V = \overline{V}(n_A + n_B)$$

and
$$\overline{V}_A = \left(\frac{\partial V}{\partial n_A}\right)_{n_B} = \overline{V} + (n_A + n_B)\left(\frac{\partial \overline{V}}{\partial n_A}\right)_{n_B} \tag{5.9}$$

Now the derivative with respect to mole number of A, n_A, is transformed into a derivative with respect to mole fraction of B, X_B.

$$\left(\frac{\partial \overline{V}}{\partial n_A}\right)_{n_B} = \frac{d\overline{V}}{dX_B}\left(\frac{\partial X_B}{\partial n_A}\right)_{n_B}$$

since

$$X_B = \frac{n_B}{n_A + n_B}, \quad \left(\frac{\partial X_B}{\partial n_A}\right)_{n_B} = -\frac{n_B}{(n_A + n_B)^2}$$

Thus Eq. (5.9) becomes

$$\overline{V}_A = \overline{V} - \frac{n_B}{n_A + n_B}\frac{d\overline{V}}{dX_B}$$

$$\overline{V} = X_B\frac{d\overline{V}}{dX_B} + \overline{V}_A \tag{5.10*}$$

The application of this equation is illustrated in Fig. 5.1, where $\overline{V}$ for a solution is plotted against the mole fraction. The slope S_1S_2 is drawn tangent to the curve at point P, corresponding to a definite mole fraction X'_B. The intercept O_1S_1 at $X_B = 0$ is $\overline{V}_A$, the partial molar volume of A at the particular composition X'_B. It can readily be shown that the intercept on the other axis, O_2S_2, is the partial molar volume of B, $\overline{V}_B$.

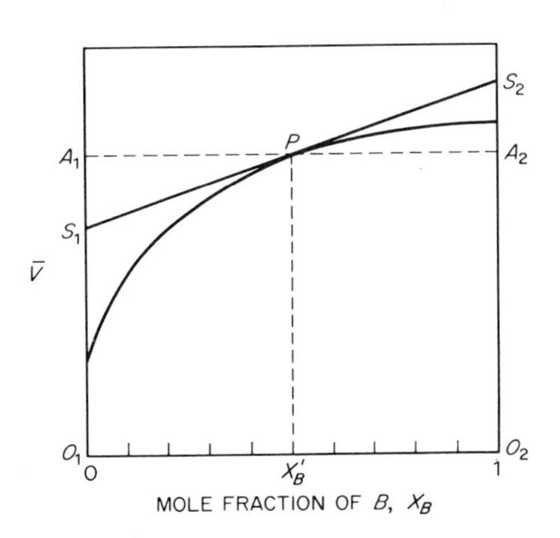

FIG. 5.1 Determination of partial molar volumes — intercept method.

This convenient method of intercepts is usually used to determine partial molar quantities. It is not restricted to volumes, but can be applied to any extensive state function, S, H, E, G, and so on, given the necessary data. It can also be applied to heats of solution, and the partial molar heats of solution so obtained are the same as the differential heats described in Chapter 2.

If the variation with concentration of a partial molar quantity is known for one component in a binary solution, the Gibbs-Duhem equation (5.7) permits the calculation of the variation for the other component. This calculation can be accomplished by graphical integration of Eq. (5.7). For example:

$$\int d\overline{V}_A = -\int \frac{n_B}{n_A}\,d\overline{V}_B = -\int \frac{X_B}{X_A}\,d\overline{V}_B$$

* Recall the standard slope-intercept form of the straight line: $y = mx + b$.

where X is the mole fraction. If X_B/X_A is plotted against $\overline{V}_B$, the area under the curve gives the change in $\overline{V}_A$ between the upper and lower limits of integration. The $\overline{V}_A$ of pure A is simply the molar volume of pure A, $\overline{V}_A^\circ$, and this can be used as the starting point for the evaluation of $\overline{V}_A$ at any other concentration.

Figure 5.2 shows the partial molar volumes of both components in solutions of water and ethanol.

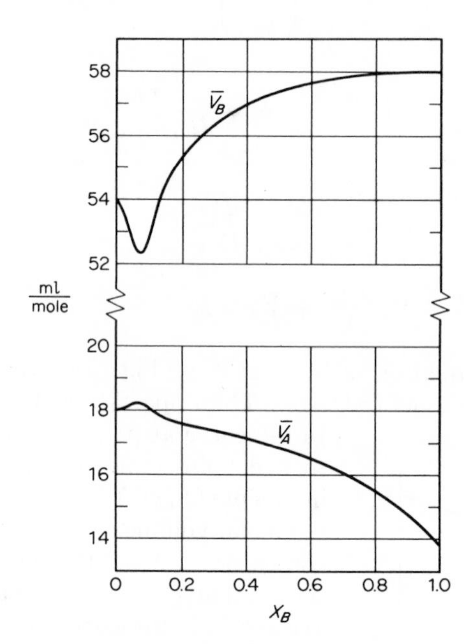

FIG. 5.2 Partial molar volumes in solutions of water and ethanol at 20°C $\overline{V}_A$ (water), $\overline{V}_B$ (ethanol), X_B mole fraction ethanol.

4. THE IDEAL SOLUTION – RAOULT'S LAW

The concept of the ideal gas has played a most important role in discussions of the thermodynamics of gases and vapors. Many cases of practical interest are treated adequately by means of the ideal gas approximations, and even systems deviating largely from ideality are conveniently referred to the norm of behavior set by the ideal case. It would be most helpful to find some similar concept to act as a guide in the theory of solutions, and fortunately this is indeed possible. Because they are very much more condensed than gases, liquid or solid solutions cannot be expected to behave ideally in the sense of obeying an equation of state such as the ideal gas law. Ideality in a gas implied a complete *absence* of cohesive forces; the internal pressure, $(\partial E/\partial V)_T = 0$. Ideality in a solution is defined by complete *uniformity* of cohesive forces. If there are two components A and B, the forces between A and A, B and B, and A and B are all the same.

An important property in the theory of solutions is the vapor pressure of a component above the solution. This partial vapor pressure is a good measure of the tendency of the given species to escape from the solution into the vapor phase. The tendency of a component to escape from solution is a direct reflection of the physical state of affairs within the solution, so that by studying the escaping tendencies, or partial vapor pressures, as functions of temperature, pressure, and concentration, we obtain a description of the properties of the solution. We may think of an analogy in which a nation represents a solution and its citizens the molecules. If life in the nation is a good one, the tendency to emigrate will be low. This presupposes, of course, the absence of artificial barriers.

The partial vapor pressure of a component A in solution is related to the chemical potential μ_A. Consider a solution in equilibrium with its vapor. From Eq. (4.11), at equilibrium,

$$\mu_A^{\text{soln}} = \mu_A^{\text{vapor}}$$

$$\mu_B^{\text{soln}} = \mu_B^{\text{vapor}}$$

From Eq. (5.8), the μ_A^{vapor} can be related to the partial vapor pressure by

$$d\mu_A^{\text{vapor}} = \overline{V}_A \, dP_A = RT \, d \ln P_A$$

If μ_A° is the value of μ_A when $P = 1$ atm, we find on integration,

$$\mu_A^{\text{vapor}} = \mu_A^\circ + RT \ln P_A$$

Hence the chemical potential of A in the solution is related to the partial vapor pressure of A above the solution by

$$\mu_A^{\text{soln}} = \mu_A^\circ + RT \ln P_A \tag{5.11}$$

This equation is rigorously true only when the vapor behaves as an ideal gas, but the correction for nonideality of the gas is usually small; it is discussed in Section 6.18.

A solution is said to be ideal if the escaping tendency of each component is proportional to the mole fraction of that component in the solution. It is helpful to look at this concept from a molecular point of view. Consider an ideal solution of A and B. The definition of ideality implies that a molecule of A in the solution will have the same tendency to escape into the vapor whether it is surrounded entirely by other A molecules, entirely by B molecules, or partly by A and partly by B molecules. This means that the intermolecular forces between A and A, A and B, and B and B, are all essentially the same. It is immaterial to the behavior of a molecule what sort of neighbors it has. The escaping tendency of component A from such an ideal solution, as measured by its partial vapor pressure, is accordingly the same as that from pure liquid A, except that it is proportionately reduced on account of the lowered fraction of A molecules in the solution.

This law of behavior for the ideal solution was first given by François Marie Raoult in 1886, being based on experimental vapor-pressure data. It can be expressed as

$$P_A = X_A P_A^\circ \tag{5.12}$$

Here P_A is the partial vapor pressure of A above a solution in which its mole fraction is X_A, and P_A° is the vapor pressure of pure liquid A at the same temperature.

If the component B added to pure A lowers the vapor pressure, Eq. (5.12) can be written in terms of a *relative vapor pressure lowering*,

$$\frac{P_A^\circ - P_A}{P_A^\circ} = (1 - X_A) = X_B \qquad (5.13)$$

This form of the equation is especially useful for solutions of a relatively involatile solute in a volatile solvent.

The vapor pressures of the system ethylene bromide — propylene bromide are plotted in Fig. 5.3. The experimental results almost coincide with the theoretical curves predicted by Eq. (5.12). In this instance the agreement with Raoult's Law is excellent.

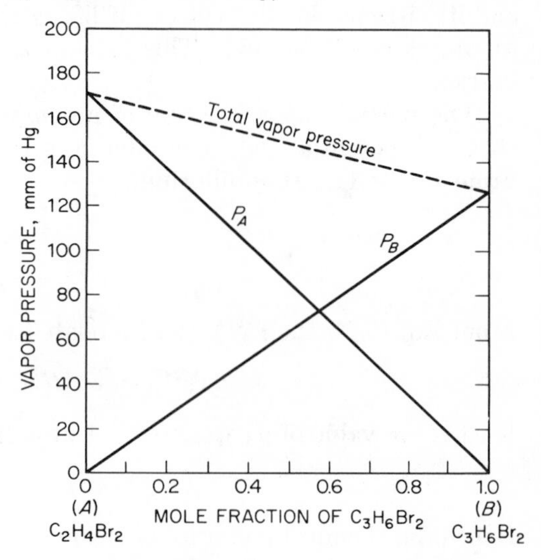

FIG. 5.3 Pressures of vapors above solutions of ethylene bromide and propylene bromide at 85°C. The solutions follow Raoult's Law.

We seldom find solutions that follow Raoult's Law closely over an extended range of concentrations. This is because ideality in solutions implies a complete similarity of interaction between the components, which can rarely be achieved. Solutions of isotopes, however, provide good examples of ideal solutions, even in the solid state.

5. THERMODYNAMICS OF IDEAL SOLUTIONS

When we put Raoult's Law, Eq. (5.12), into Eq. (5.11), we obtain

$$\mu_A = \mu_A^\circ + RT \ln P_A^\circ + RT \ln X_A \qquad (5.14)$$

At any constant T and P, the first two terms are constants, independent of composition, and we can combine them as $\mu_A^{\circ\prime}\ (T, P)$. Hence, for any component in an ideal solution,

$$\mu_A = \mu_A^{\circ\prime} + RT \ln X_A \qquad (5.15)$$

From Eq. (5.14) we can calculate the partial molar volume of A in the solution, since

$$\overline{V}_A = (\partial\mu_A/\partial P)_T \qquad (5.8)$$

The first and third terms on the right in Eq. (5.14) are independent of pressure. Thus, from Eq. (4.23),

$$\overline{V}_A = RT\left(\frac{\partial \ln P_A^\circ}{\partial P}\right)_T = \overline{V}_A^\circ \tag{5.16}$$

The partial molar volume of a component in an ideal solution equals the molar volume of the pure component. There is therefore no change in volume ($\Delta V = 0$) when components are mixed to form an ideal solution.

In a similar way, from $\partial(\mu_A/T)/\partial T = -\overline{H}_A/T^2$ and Eq. (5.14), we can show that

$$\overline{H}_A^{\text{vap}} - \overline{H}_A = \overline{H}_A^{\text{vap}} - \overline{H}_A^\circ \tag{5.17}$$

Thus there is no heat of solution ($\Delta H = 0$) when components are mixed to form an ideal solution.

6. THE ENTROPY OF MIXING

Consider two gases at a pressure P. If these gases are brought together at constant temperature and pressure, they will become mixed spontaneously by interdiffusion. The spontaneous process will be associated with an increase in entropy. This entropy of mixing is of interest in a number of applications, and it can be calculated as follows.

In the final mixture of gases the partial pressure of gas (1) is $P_1 = X_1P$, of gas (2), $P_2 = X_2P$, where X_1 and X_2 are the mole fractions. The ΔS of mixing is equal to the ΔS required to expand each gas from its initial pressure P to its partial pressure in the gas mixture. On the basis of one mole of ideal gas mixture,

$$\Delta S = X_1R\ln\frac{P}{P_1} + X_2R\ln\frac{P}{P_2}$$

$$= X_1R\ln\frac{1}{X_1} + X_2R\ln\frac{1}{X_2}$$

$$\Delta S = -R(X_1\ln X_1 + X_2\ln X_2)$$

This result can be extended to any number of gases in a mixture, yielding

$$\Delta S = -R\sum_i X_i \ln X_i \tag{5.18}$$

The equation is valid also for ideal liquid or solid solutions.*

---

* PROOF: From Eqs. (5.8) and (5.14),

$$\overline{S}_A = -\left(\frac{\partial \mu_A}{\partial T}\right)_P = \overline{S}_A^\circ - R\ln X_A$$

For mixing n_A moles of A and n_B moles of B,

$$\Delta S = n_A(\overline{S}_A - \overline{S}_A^\circ) + n_B(\overline{S}_B - \overline{S}_B^\circ)$$

$$\Delta S = -n_AR\ln X_A - n_BR\ln X_B$$

Per mole:

$$\Delta S/(n_A + n_B) = -R(X_A\ln X_A + X_B\ln X_B)$$

Let us calculate the entropy of mixing the elements in air, taking the composition to be 79 per cent N_2, 20 per cent O_2, and 1 per cent argon.

$$\Delta S = -R(0.79 \ln 0.79 + 0.20 \ln 0.20 + 0.01 \ln 0.01)$$

$$\Delta S = 1.10 \text{ cal deg}^{-1} \text{ per mole of mixture}$$

7. HENRY'S LAW

Consider a solution of component B, which may be called the solute, in A, the solvent. If the solution is sufficiently diluted, a condition ultimately is attained in which each molecule of B is effectively completely surrounded by component A. The solute B is then in a uniform environment irrespective of the fact that A and B may form solutions that are far from ideal at higher concentrations.

In such a very dilute solution, the escaping tendency of B from its uniform environment is proportional to its mole fraction, but the proportionality constant k no longer is P_B°. We may write

$$P_B = kX_B \tag{5.19}$$

This equation was established and extensively tested by William Henry in 1803 in a series of measurements of the dependence on pressure of the solubility of gases in liquids. Some results of this type are collected in Table 5.2. The k's are almost constant, so that Henry's Law is nearly but not exactly obeyed.

TABLE 5.2 THE SOLUBILITY OF GASES IN WATER ILLUSTRATING HENRY'S LAW, $P_B = kX_B$

Partial Pressure (atm)	Henry's Law Constant ($k \times 10^{-4}$)		
	N_2 at 19.4°	O_2 at 23°	H_2 at 23°
1.18	8.24	4.58	...
2.63	8.32	4.59	7.76
3.95	8.41	4.60	7.77
5.26	8.49	4.68	7.81
6.58	8.59	4.73	7.89
7.90	8.74	4.80	8.00
9.20	8.86	4.88	8.16

As an example, let us calculate the volume of oxygen (at STP) dissolved in 1 liter of water in equilibrium with air at 23°. From Eq. (5.19) the mole fraction of O_2 is $X_B = P_B/k$. Since $P_B = 0.20$, and from the table $k = 4.58 \times 10^4$, $X_B = 4.36 \times 10^{-6}$. In 1 liter of H_2O there are $1000/18 = 55.6$ moles. Thus $X_B = n_B/(n_B + 55.6)$, or $n_B = 2.43 \times 10^{-4}$. This number of moles of oxygen equals 5.45 cc at STP.

Henry's Law is not restricted to gas-liquid systems, but is followed by a wide variety of fairly dilute solutions and by *all* solutions in the limit of extreme dilution.*

* The form of the law for dissociated solutes, such as electrolytes, is discussed in Sect. 9.15.

8. TWO-COMPONENT SYSTEMS

For systems of two components the phase rule, $f = c - p + 2$, becomes $f = 4 - p$. The following cases are possible:

$p = 1,$	$f = 3$	trivariant system
$p = 2,$	$f = 2$	bivariant system
$p = 3,$	$f = 1$	univariant system
$p = 4,$	$f = 0$	invariant system

The maximum number of degrees of freedom is three. A complete graphical representation of a two-component system therefore requires a three-dimensional diagram, with coordinates corresponding to pressure, temperature and composition. Since a three-dimensional representation is usually inconvenient, we hold one variable constant while we plot the behavior of the other two. In this way we obtain plane graphs showing pressure vs. composition at constant temperature, or pressure vs. temperature at constant composition.

9. PRESSURE-COMPOSITION DIAGRAMS

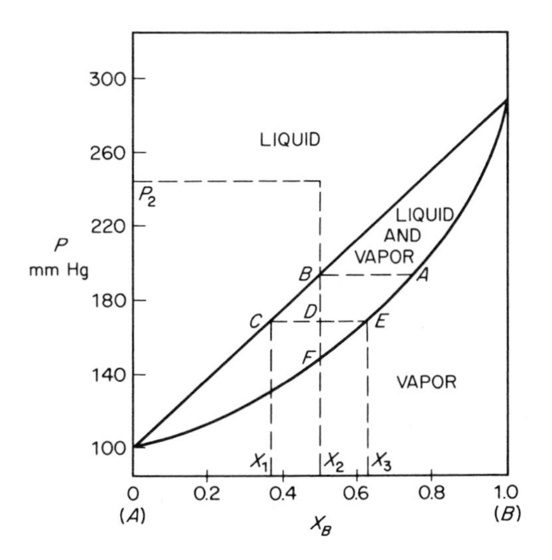

FIG. 5.4 Pressure-composition (mole fraction) diagram at 60°C for the system 2-methyl propanol-1 (A) — propanol-2 (B) which form practically ideal solutions.

The example of a (P-X) diagram in Fig. 5.4 shows the system 2 methyl-propanol-1—propanol-2, which obeys Raoult's Law quite closely over the entire range of compositions. The straight upper line represents the dependence of the total vapor pressure above the solution on the mole fraction in the liquid. The curved lower line represents the dependence of the pressure on the composition of the vapor.

Consider a liquid of composition X_2 at a pressure P_2. This point lies in a one-phase region, in which there would be three degrees of freedom. One of these is used by the requirement of constant temperature for the diagram. Thus for any arbitrary composition X_2, the liquid solution at constant T can exist over a range of different pressures.

As the pressure is decreased along the dashed line of constant composition, nothing happens until the *liquidus curve* is reached at B. At this point liquid begins to vaporize. The vapor that is formed is richer than the liquid in the more volatile component, propanol-2. The composition of the first vapor to appear is given by the point A on the vapor curve.

As the pressure is further reduced below B, a two-phase region on the diagram is entered. This represents the region of stable coexistence of liquid and vapor. The dashed line passing horizontally through a typical point D in the two-phase region is called a *tie line*; it connects the liquid and vapor compositions that are in equilibrium.

The overall composition of the system at point D in the two-phase region is X_2. This is made up of liquid having a composition X_1, and vapor having a composition X_3. We can calculate the relative amounts of liquid and vapor required to yield the overall composition. Let n_l and n_v be the sum of the numbers of moles of both components A and B in liquid and in vapor, respectively. From a material balance applied to component B,

$$X_2(n_l + n_v) = X_1 n_l + X_3 n_v$$

or

$$\frac{n_l}{n_v} = \frac{X_3 - X_2}{X_2 - X_1} = \frac{DE}{DC} \tag{5.20}$$

This expression is called the *lever rule*. It applies to any two compositions of two phases in equilibrium connected by a tie line in a phase diagram of a two component system. If the diagram is plotted in mass fractions instead of mole fractions, the ratio of the line segments gives the ratio of the masses of the two phases.

As the pressure is still further decreased along BF, more and more liquid is vaporized until finally, at F, no liquid remains. Further decrease in pressure then proceeds in the one-phase, all-vapor region.

In the two-phase region, the system is bivariant. One of the degrees of freedom is used by the requirement of constant temperature, and only one remains. When the pressure is fixed in this region, therefore, the compositions of *both* the liquid and the vapor phases are also definitely fixed. They are given, as we have seen, by the end points of the tie line.

10. TEMPERATURE-COMPOSITION DIAGRAMS

The temperature-composition diagram of the liquid-vapor equilibrium is the boiling-point diagram of the solutions at the constant pressure chosen. If the pressure is one atmosphere, the boiling points are the *normal* ones. The diagram for the 2-methylpropanol-1—propanol-2 system is shown in Fig. 5.5.

The boiling-point diagram for an ideal solution can be calculated if the vapor pressures of the pure components are known as functions of temperature. The two end points of the boiling-point diagram shown in Fig. 5.5 are the temperatures at which the pure components have vapor pressures of 760 mm, viz., 82.3°C and 108.5°C. The composition of the solution that boils anywhere between these two temperatures, say at 100°C, is found as follows:

If X_A is the mole fraction of C_4H_9OH, from Raoult's Law,

$$760 = P_A^\circ X_A + P_B^\circ(1 - X_A)$$

At 100°, the vapor pressure of C_3H_7OH is 1440 mm, of C_4H_9OH, 570 mm. Thus, $760 = 570X_A + 1440\ (1 - X_A)$, or $X_A = 0.781$, $X_B = 0.219$. This gives one intermediate point on the liquidus curve; the others are calculated in the same way.

The composition of the vapor is given by Dalton's Law:

$$X_A^{\text{vap}} = \frac{P_A}{760} = \frac{X_A^{\text{liq}} P_A^\circ}{760} = 0.781 \times \frac{570}{760} = 0.585$$

$$X_B^{\text{vap}} = \frac{P_B}{760} = \frac{X_B^{\text{liq}} P_B^\circ}{760} = 0.219 \times \frac{1440}{760} = 0.415$$

The vapor-composition curve is therefore readily constructed from the liquidus curve.

11. FRACTIONAL DISTILLATION

The application of the boiling-point diagram to a simplified representation of distillation is shown in Fig. 5.5. The solution of composition X begins to boil at temperature t_1. The first vapor that is formed has a composition Y, richer in the more volatile component. If this is condensed and reboiled, vapor of composition Z is obtained. This process is repeated until the distillate is composed of pure component B. In practical cases, the successive fractions will each cover a range of compositions, but the vertical lines in Fig. 5.5 may be considered to represent average compositions within these ranges.

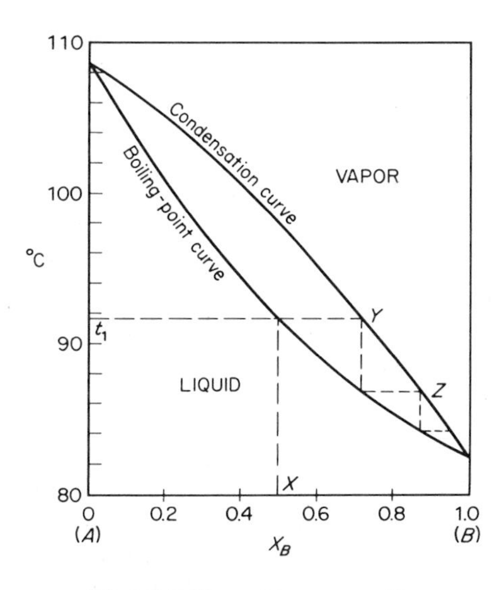

FIG. 5.5 Boiling point vs. composition diagram for the system 2-methyl propanol-1 (A) — propanol-2 (B), which form practically ideal solutions.

A fractionating column is a device that carries out automatically the successive condensations and vaporizations required for fractional distillation. An especially clear example is the "bubble-cap" type of column in Fig. 5.6. As the vapor ascends from the boiler, it bubbles through a film of liquid on the first plate. This liquid is somewhat cooler than that in the boiler, so that a partial condensation takes place. The vapor that leaves the first plate is therefore richer than the vapor from the boiler in the more volatile component. A similar enrichment takes place on each successive plate. Each attainment of equilibrium between liquid and vapor corresponds to one of the steps in Fig. 5.5.

The efficiency of a distilling column is measured by the number of such equilibrium stages that it achieves. Each stage is called a *theoretical plate*. In a well designed bubble-cap column, each unit acts very nearly as one theoretical plate. We also describe the performance of various types of packed columns in terms of theoretical plates. The separation of liquids whose boiling points lie close together requires a column with a considerable number of plates. The number actually required depends on the *cut* that is taken from the head of the column, i.e., the ratio of distillate taken off to that returned to the column.*

Let us suppose, for example, that we start with a solution with mole fraction $X_B = 0.500$ of butanol (A) in propanol (B), and distill it in a column with three theoretical plates. The first distillate that is taken will have a composition, as read from Fig. 5.5, of $X_B = 0.952$ propanol.

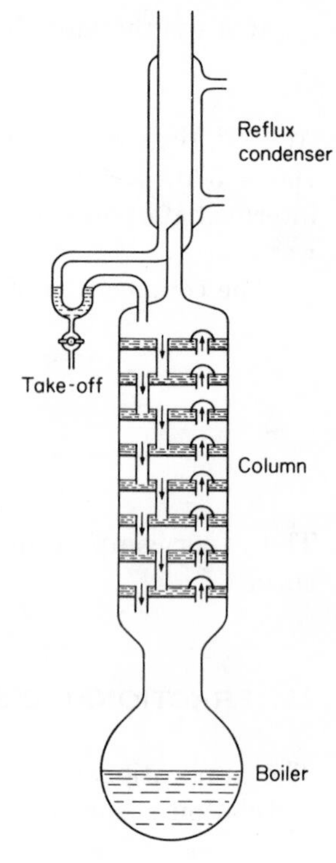

FIG. 5.6 A bubble-cap fractionating column.

12. BOILING-POINT ELEVATION

If a small amount of a nonvolatile solute is dissolved in a volatile solvent, the solution being sufficiently dilute to behave ideally, the lowering of the vapor pressure can be calculated from Eq. (5.13). As a consequence of the lowered vapor pressure, the boiling point of the solution is higher than that of the pure solvent. This fact is evident from the vapor-pressure curves in Fig. 5.7.

The condition for equilibrium of a component A, the volatile solvent, between the liquid and vapor phases is simply $\mu_A^v = \mu_A^l$. From Eq. (5.15),

$$\mu_A^l = \mu_A^{\circ l} + RT \ln X_A$$

where $\mu_A^{\circ l}$ is the chemical potential of pure liquid A, i.e., μ_A^l when $X_A = 1$. At the boiling point the pressure is 1 atm, so that $\mu_A^v = \mu_A^{\circ v}$, the chemical potential of pure A vapor at 1 atm. Therefore ($\mu_A^v = \mu_A^l$) becomes $\mu_A^{\circ v} = \mu_A^{\circ l} + RT \ln X_A$. For the pure component A, the chemical potentials μ° are identical with the molar free energies $\overline{G}^\circ$. Hence,

$$\overline{G}_A^{\circ v} - \overline{G}_A^{\circ l} = RT \ln X_A$$

* For details of methods for determining the number of theoretical plates in a column, see C. S. Robinson and E. R. Gilliland, *Fractional Distillation* (New York: McGraw-Hill, 1950.)

From Eq. (3.36), $\partial(G/T)/\partial T = -H/T^2$, so that differentiating the above yields

$$\overline{H}_A^{\circ v} - \overline{H}_A^{\circ l} = -RT^2 \frac{d \ln X_A}{dT}$$

Since $\overline{H}_A^{\circ v} - \overline{H}_A^{\circ l}$ is the molar heat of vaporization λ_v,

$$-d \ln X_A = \frac{\lambda_v}{RT^2} dT$$

Taking λ as constant over the temperature range, we integrate this equation between the limits set by the pure solvent ($X_A = 1$, $T = T_0$) and the solution (X_A, T).

$$-\int_1^{X_A} d \ln X_A = \frac{\lambda_v}{R} \int_{T_0}^{T} \frac{dT}{T^2}$$

$$-\ln X_A = \frac{\lambda_v}{R}\left(\frac{1}{T_0} - \frac{1}{T}\right) = \frac{\lambda_v}{R}\left(\frac{T - T_0}{TT_0}\right)$$

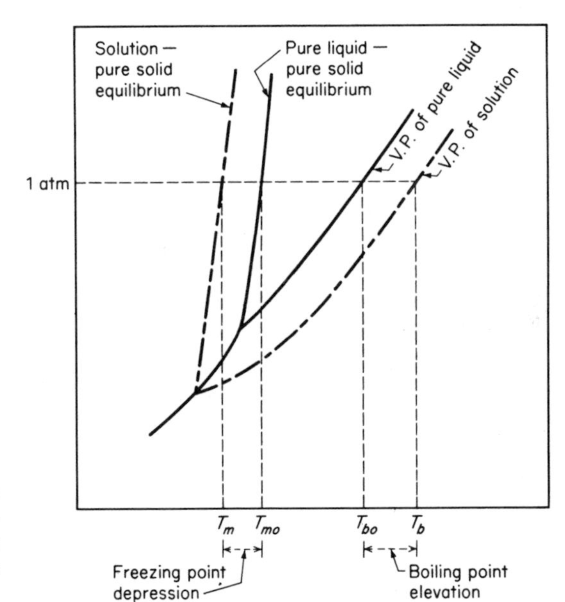

FIG. 5.7 Diagram showing the elevation of the boiling point and depression of the freezing point caused by addition of a nonvolatile solute to a pure liquid.

When the boiling-point elevation is not large, TT_0 can be replaced by T_0^2. If X_B is the mole fraction of solute, the term on the left can be written $-\ln(1 - X_B)$, and then expanded in a power series. Writing ΔT_B for the boiling-point elevation, $T - T_0$, we obtain

$$\frac{\lambda_v \Delta T_B}{RT_0^2} = X_B + \tfrac{1}{2}X_B^2 + \tfrac{1}{3}X_B^3 + \ldots$$

When the solution is dilute, X_B is a small fraction whose higher powers may be neglected. Then,

$$\Delta T_B = \frac{RT_0^2}{\lambda_v} X_B \tag{5.21}$$

In the dilute solutions for which Eq. (5.21) is valid, it is also a good approximation to replace X_B by $(w_B M_A)/(w_A M_B)$; w_B, M_B, and w_A, M_A being the masses and molecular weights of solute and solvent. Then

$$\Delta T_B = \frac{RT_0^2}{\lambda_v} \cdot \frac{w_B M_A}{w_A M_B} = \frac{RT_0^2}{l_v} \cdot \frac{w_B}{w_A M_B}$$

where l_v is the latent heat of vaporization *per gram*. Finally $w_B/w_A M_B$ is set equal to $m/1000$, m being the molality, moles of solute per 1000 grams of solvent. Thus,

$$\Delta T_B = \frac{RT_0^2}{l_v} \cdot \frac{m}{1000} = K_B m \tag{5.22}$$

and K_B is called the *molal boiling-point elevation constant.*

For example, for water $T_0 = 373.2$, $l_v = 538$ cal per g. Hence

$$K_B = \frac{(1.987)(373.2)^2}{(538)(1000)} = 0.514$$

For benzene, $K_B = 2.67$; for acetone, 1.67, etc.

The expression (5.22) is used frequently for *molecular-weight determination* from the boiling-point elevation. From K_B and the measured T_B, we calculate m, and then the molecular weight from $M_B = 1000\ w_B/m w_A$. For many combinations of solute and solvent, perfectly *normal* molecular weights are obtained. In certain instances, however, there is apparently an association or dissociation of the solute molecules in the solution. For example, the molecular weight of benzoic acid in acetone solution is found to be equal to the formula weight of 122.1, but in one per cent solution in benzene, benzoic acid has an apparent molecular weight of 242. Thus to a considerable extent the acid is dimerized into double molecules. The extent of association is greater in more concentrated solutions. From molecular-weight determinations at different concentrations, it is possible to calculate the equilibrium constant of the reaction,

$$(C_6H_5COOH)_2 \rightleftharpoons 2\ C_6H_5COOH$$

13. SOLID AND LIQUID PHASES IN EQUILIBRIUM

The properties of solutions related to the vapor pressure are called *colligative* from the Latin, *colligatus*, collected together. They are properties which depend on the collection of particles present, that is, on the number of particles, rather than on the kind. A colligative property amenable to the same sort of treatment as the boiling-point elevation is the depression of the freezing point. Fig. 5.7

shows that this also has its origin in the lowering of the vapor pressure in solutions. The freezing point of pure solvent, T_{m0} is lowered to T_m in the solution.

It should be understood that *freezing-point depression curve* and *solubility curve* are merely two different names for the same thing — that is, a temperature vs. composition curve for a solid-liquid equilibrium at some constant pressure, usually chosen as one atmosphere. Such a diagram is shown in Fig. 5.8 for the system benzene-naphthalene. The curve CE may be considered to illustrate either (1) the depression of the freezing point of naphthalene by the addition of benzene, or (2) the solubility of solid naphthalene in the solution. Both interpretations are fundamentally equivalent: in one case, we consider T as a function of X; in the other, X as a function of T. The lowest point E on the solid-liquid diagram is called the *eutectic point* (εὐτηκτός, easily melted).

In this diagram, the solid phases that separate are shown as pure naphthalene (A) on one side and pure benzene (B) on the other. This is not exactly correct, since there is usually at least a slight solid solution of B in A and of A in B. Nevertheless, the absence of any solid solution is in many cases a good enough approximation.

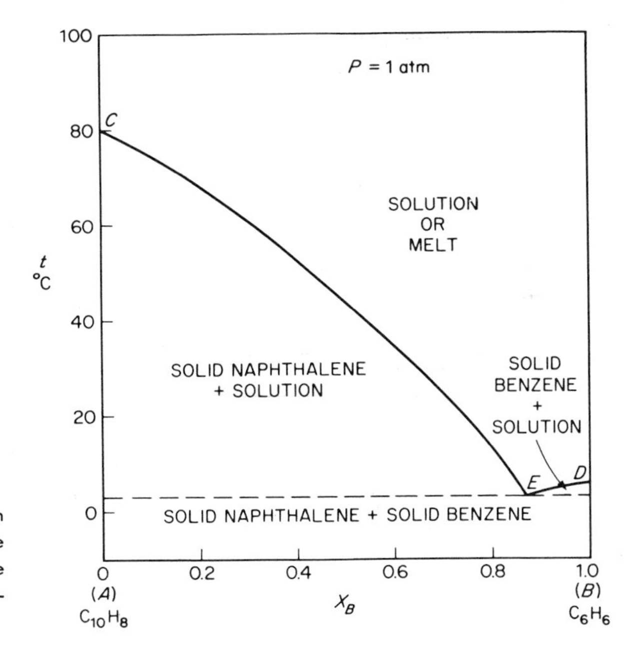

FIG. 5.8 Temperature-composition diagram for the system naphthalene (A) and benzene (B). The solids are mutually insoluble and the liquid solution is practically ideal.

The equation for the freezing-point depression, or the solubility equation for ideal solutions, is derived by essentially the same method used for the boiling-point elevation. In order for a pure solid A to be in equilibrium with a solution containing A, it is necessary that the chemical potentials of A be the same in the two phases, $\mu_A^s = \mu_A^l$. From Eq. (5.15) the chemical potential of component A in an ideal solution is $\mu_A^l = \mu_A^{\circ l} + RT \ln X_A$, where $\mu_A^{\circ l}$ is the chemical potential of pure liquid A. Thus the equilibrium condition can be written $\mu_A^s = \mu_A^{\circ l} + RT \ln X_A$. Now μ_A^s and $\mu_A^{\circ l}$ are simply the molar free energies of pure solid and pure liquid. Hence,

$$\frac{\overline{G}_A^{\circ s} - \overline{G}_A^{\circ l}}{RT} = \ln X_A \tag{5.23}$$

Since we have $\partial(G/T)/\partial T = -H/T^2$ from Eq. (3.36), differentiation of Eq. (5.23) with respect to T yields (with λ_f the latent heat of fusion):

$$\frac{\overline{H}_A^{\circ l} - \overline{H}_A^{\circ s}}{RT^2} = \frac{\lambda_f}{RT^2} = \frac{d \ln X_A}{dT} \tag{5.24}$$

Integrating this expression from T_0, the freezing point of pure A, mole fraction unity, to T, the temperature at which pure solid A is in equilibrium with solution of mole fraction X_A, we obtain*

$$\frac{\lambda_f}{R}\left(\frac{1}{T_0} - \frac{1}{T}\right) = \ln X_A \tag{5.25}$$

This is the equation for the temperature variation of the solubility X_A of a pure solid in an ideal solution.

As an example, let us calculate the solubility of naphthalene in an ideal solution at 25°C. Naphthalene melts at 80°C, and its heat of fusion at the melting point is 4610 cal per mole. Thus, from Eq. (5.25),

$$\frac{4610}{1.987}(353.2^{-1} - 298.2^{-1}) = 2.303 \log X_A$$

$$X_A = 0.298$$

This is the mole fraction of naphthalene in any ideal solution, whatever the solvent may be. Actually, the solution will approach ideality only if the solvent is rather similar in chemical and physical properties to the solute. Typical experimental values for the solubility X_A of naphthalene in various solvents at 25°C are as follows: chlorobenzene, 0.317; benzene, 0.296; toluene, 0.286; acetone, 0.224; hexane, 0.125.

The simplification of Eq. (5.25) for dilute solutions follows as in the case of the boiling-point elevation. The final expression for the depression of the freezing point $\Delta T_F = T_0 - T$ is

$$\Delta T_F = K_F m$$

with

$$K_F = \frac{RT_0^2}{l_F \, 1000} \tag{5.26}$$

K_F is called the *molal freezing point depression constant*. For water, $K_F = 1.855$; benzene, 5.12; camphor, 40.0, and so on. Because of its exceptionally large K_F, camphor is used in a micro-method for molecular-weight determination by freezing-point depression.

* It is a good approximation to take λ_f independent of T over moderate ranges of temperature.

14. OSMOTIC PRESSURE

The classical trio of colligative properties, of which boiling-point elevation and freezing-point depression are the first two members, is completed by the phenomenon of osmotic pressure.

In 1748, J. A. Nollet described an experiment in which a solution of "spirits of wine" was placed in a cylinder, the mouth of which was closed with an animal bladder and immersed in pure water. The bladder was observed to swell greatly and sometimes even to burst. The animal membrane is *semipermeable*; water can pass through it, but alcohol cannot. The increased pressure in the tube, caused by diffusion of water into the solution, was called the *osmotic pressure* (from ωσμός — *impulse*).

The first detailed quantitative study of osmotic pressure is found in a series of researches by W. Pfeffer, published in 1887. Ten years earlier, Moritz Traube had observed that colloidal films of cupric ferrocyanide acted as semipermeable membranes. Pfeffer deposited this colloidal precipitate within the pores of earthenware pots, by soaking them first in copper sulfate and then in potassium ferrocyanide solution. Some typical results of measurements made with such artificial membranes are summarized in Table 5.3.

TABLE 5.3 OSMOTIC PRESSURES OF SOLUTIONS OF SUCROSE IN WATER AT 20°

Molality (m)	Molar Concentration (c)	Observed Osmotic Pressure (atm)	Calculated Osmotic Pressure		
			Eq. (5.27)	Eq. (5.31)	Eq. (5.29)
0.1	0.098	2.59	2.36	2.40	2.44
0.2	0.192	5.06	4.63	4.81	5.46
0.3	0.282	7.61	6.80	7.21	7.82
0.4	0.370	10.14	8.90	9.62	10.22
0.5	0.453	12.75	10.9	12.0	12.62
0.6	0.533	15.39	12.8	14.4	15.00
0.7	0.610	18.13	14.7	16.8	17.40
0.8	0.685	20.91	16.5	19.2	19.77
0.9	0.757	23.72	18.2	21.6	22.15
1.0	0.825	26.64	19.8	24.0	24.48

In 1885, J. H. van't Hoff pointed out that in dilute solutions the osmotic pressure Π obeyed the relationship $\Pi V = nRT$, or

$$\Pi = cRT \tag{5.27}$$

where $c = n/V$ is the concentration of solute in moles per liter. The validity of the equation can be judged by comparison of the calculated and experimental values of Π in Table 5.3.

An osmotic pressure can arise when two solutions of different concentrations (or a pure solvent and a solution) are separated by a semipermeable membrane. A simple illustration can be found in the case of a gaseous solution of hydrogen and nitrogen. Thin palladium foil is permeable to hydrogen, but practically impermeable to nitrogen. If pure nitrogen is put on one side of a palladium barrier and a solution of nitrogen and hydrogen on the other side, the requirements for osmosis are satisfied. Hydrogen flows through the palladium from the hydrogen-rich to the hydrogen-poor side of the membrane. This flow continues until the chemical potential of the H_2, μ_{H_2}, is the same on both sides of the barrier.

In this example, the nature of the semipermeable membrane is rather clear. Hydrogen molecules are catalytically dissociated into atoms at the palladium surface, and these atoms, perhaps in the form of protons and electrons, diffuse through the barrier. A solution mechanism of some kind probably is responsible for many cases of semipermeability. For example, protein membranes, like those employed by Nollet, can dissolve water but not alcohol.

In other cases, the membrane may act as a sieve, or as a bundle of capillaries. The cross sections of these capillaries may be very small, so that they can be permeated by small molecules like water, but not by large molecules like carbohydrates or proteins.

Irrespective of the mechanism by which the semipermeable membrane operates, the final result is the same. Osmotic flow continues until the chemical potential of the diffusing component is the same on both sides of the barrier. If the flow takes place into a closed volume, the pressure inside necessarily increases. The final equilibrium osmotic pressure can be calculated by thermodynamic methods.

15. MEASUREMENTS OF OSMOTIC PRESSURE

We are principally indebted to two groups of workers for precise measurements of osmotic pressure: H. N. Morse, J. C. W. Frazer, and their colleagues at Johns Hopkins, and R. T. Rawdon (Berkeley) and E. G. J. Hartley at Oxford.*

The method used by the Hopkins group is shown in Fig. 5.9 (a). The porous cell impregnated with copper ferrocyanide is filled with water and immersed in a vessel containing the aqueous solution. The pressure is measured by means of an attached manometer. The system is allowed to stand until there is no further increase in pressure. Then the osmotic pressure is just balanced by the hydrostatic pressure in the column of solution. The pressures studied extended up to several hundred atmospheres, and a number of ingenious methods of measurement were developed. These included the calculation of the pressure from the change in the refractive index of water on compression, and the application of piezoelectric gauges.

The English workers used the apparatus shown schematically in Fig. 5.9 (b). Instead of waiting for equilibrium to be established and then reading the pressure,

* An excellent detailed discussion of this work is to be found in J. C. W. Frazer's article, "The Laws of Dilute Solutions" in *A Treatise on Physical Chemistry*, 2nd ed., edited by H. S. Taylor (New York: Van Nostrand, 1931), pp. 353–414.

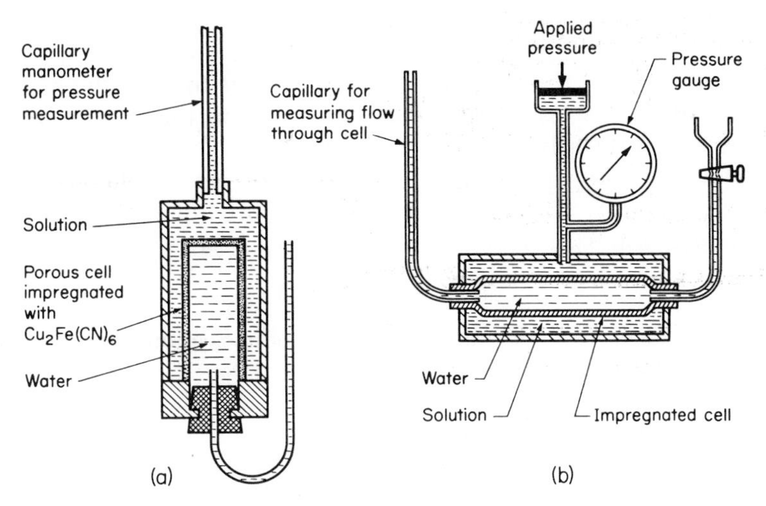

FIG. 5.9 Osmotic pressure measurements: (a) method of Frazer; (b) method of Berkeley and Hartley.

they applied an external pressure to the solution just sufficient to balance the osmotic pressure. They could detect this balance precisely by observing the level of liquid in the capillary tube, which would fall rapidly if there was any flow of solvent into the solution.

16. OSMOTIC PRESSURE AND VAPOR PRESSURE

Consider a pure solvent A, which is separated from a solution of B in A by a membrane permeable to A alone. At equilibrium an osmotic pressure Π has developed. The condition for equilibrium is that the chemical potential of A is the same on both sides of the membrane, $\mu_A^\alpha = \mu_A^\beta$. Thus at equilibrium the μ_A in the solution must equal that of the pure A. There are two factors tending to cause the value of μ_A in the solution to depart from that in pure A. These factors must therefore have exactly equal and opposite effects on μ_A. The first is the change in μ_A produced by dilution of A in the solution. This change causes a lowering of μ_A equal to $\Delta\mu = RT \ln P_A/P_A^\circ$ (Eq. 5.11). Exactly counteracting this is the increase in μ_A in the solution due to the imposed pressure Π. From Eq. (5.8) $d\mu = \overline{V}\, dP$, so that $\Delta\mu = \int_0^\Pi \overline{V}_A\, dP$.

At equilibrium, therefore, in order that μ_A in solution should equal μ_A° in the pure liquid,

$$\int_0^\Pi \overline{V}_A\, dP = -RT \ln (P_A/P_A^\circ)$$

If it is assumed that the partial molar volume $\overline{V}_A$ is independent of pressure, i.e., the solution is practically incompressible,

$$\overline{V}_A \Pi = RT \ln (P_A^\circ/P_A) \tag{5.28}$$

The significance of this equation can be stated as follows: the osmotic pressure is the external pressure that must be applied to the solution to raise the vapor pressure of the solvent A to that of pure A.

In most cases the partial molar volume of solvent in solution, $\overline{V}_A$, can be well approximated by the molar volume of the pure liquid $\overline{V}_A^\circ$. In the special case of an ideal solution, Eq. (5.28) then becomes

$$\Pi \overline{V}_A^\circ = -RT \ln X_A \tag{5.29}$$

By replacing X_A by $(1 - X_B)$ and expanding as in Section 5-12, we obtain the dilute-solution formula,

$$\Pi \overline{V}_A^\circ = RTX_B \tag{5.30}$$

Since the solution is dilute,

$$\Pi = \frac{RT}{V_A^\circ} \cdot \frac{n_B}{n_A} \simeq RTm' \tag{5.31}$$

This is the equation used by Frazer and Morse as a better approximation than the van't Hoff Equation (5.27). As the solution becomes very dilute, m' the volume molality approaches c the molar concentration, and we find as the end product of the series of approximations

$$\Pi = RT\, c \tag{5.27}$$

The adequacy with which Eqs. (5.27), and (5.29), and (5.31) represent the experimental data can be judged from the comparisons in Table 5.3.*

17. DEVIATIONS FROM RAOULT'S LAW

Only a few of the many liquid solutions that have been investigated follow Raoult's Law over the complete range of concentrations. For this reason the greatest practical application of the ideal equations is made in the treatment of dilute solutions. As a solution becomes more dilute, the behavior of the solute B approaches more closely to that given by Henry's Law. Henry's Law is thus a limiting law that is followed by all solutes in the limit of extreme dilutions, as $X_B \to 0$. The behavior of the solvent, as the solution becomes more dilute, approaches more closely to that given by Raoult's Law. In the limit of extreme dilution, as $X_A \to 1$, all solvents obey Raoult's Law as a limiting law.

One of the most instructive ways of discussing the properties of nonideal solutions is in terms of their deviations from ideality. The first extensive measurements of vapor pressure, permitting such comparisons, were made by Jan von Zawidski around 1900. Two general types of deviation were distinguished, *positive* and *negative*.

A system exhibiting a *positive deviation* from Raoult's Law is water-dioxane, whose vapor pressure vs. composition diagram is shown in Fig. 5.10(a). An

* The osmotic pressures of solutions of high polymers and proteins provide some of the best data on their thermodynamic properties. A typical investigation is that of Shick, Doty, and Zimm, *J. Am. Chem. Soc.*, *72*, 530 (1950).

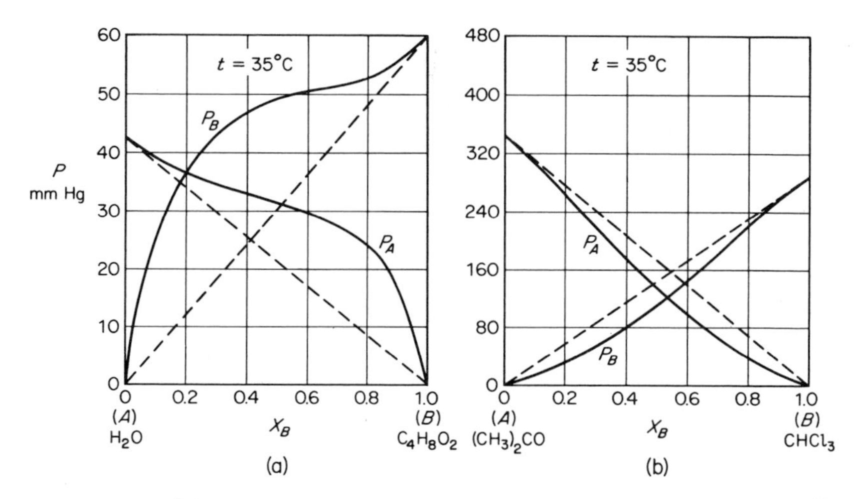

FIG. 5.10 (a) Positive deviation from Raoult's Law. Partial vapor pressures in water—dioxane system at 35°C. (b) Negative deviation from Raoult's Law. Partial vapor pressures in the acetone—chloroform system at 35°C. (The Raoult's Law values are shown as dashed straight lines.)

ideal solution would follow the dashed lines. The positive deviation is characterized by vapor pressures higher than those calculated for ideal solution. The escaping tendencies of the components in the solution are accordingly higher than the escaping tendencies in the individual pure liquids. The effect has been ascribed to cohesive forces between unlike components smaller than those within the pure liquids, resulting in a trend away from complete miscibility. To put it naively, the components are happier by themselves than when they are mixed together; they are unsociable. A scientific translation is obtained by equating a happy component to one in a state of low free energy. We should expect this incipient immiscibility to be reflected in an increase in volume on mixing and also in an absorption of heat on mixing.

The other general type of departure from Raoult's Law is the *negative deviation*, illustrated by the system chloroform-acetone in Fig. 5.10(b). In this case, the escaping tendency of a component from solution is less than it would be from the pure liquid. This fact may be the result of attractive forces between the unlike molecules in solution greater than those between the like molecules in the pure liquids. In some cases, actual association or compound formation may occur in the solution. As a result, in cases of negative deviation, we should expect a contraction in volume and an evolution of heat on mixing.

In some cases of deviation from ideality, the simple picture of varying cohesive forces may not be adequate. For example, positive deviations are often observed in aqueous solutions. Pure water is itself strongly associated and addition of a second component may partially depolymerize the water, causing an increased partial vapor pressure.

A sufficiently great positive deviation from ideality may lead to a maximum in the PX diagram, and a sufficiently great negative deviation, to a minimum.

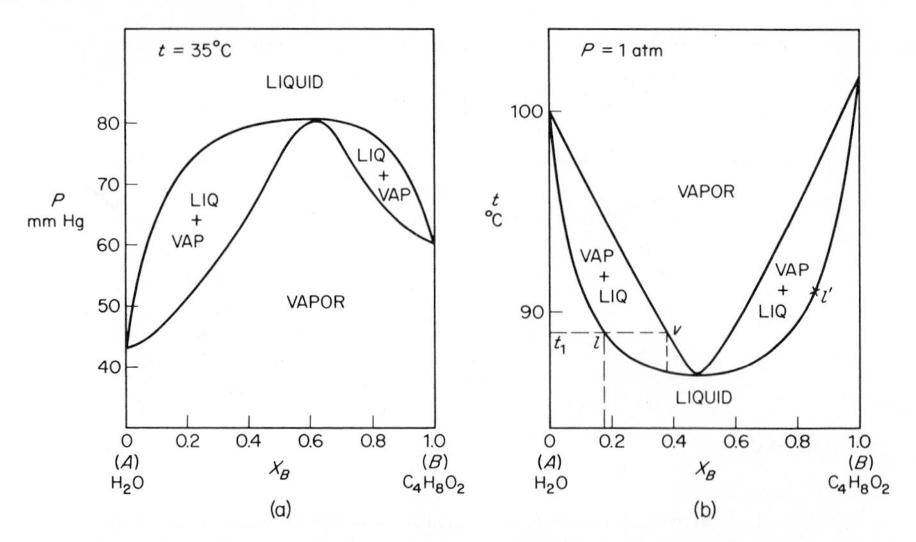

FIG. 5.11 The dioxane—water system illustrates positive deviation from Raoult's Law. (a) *PX* diagram at 35°C. (b) *TX* diagram at 1 atm (normal boiling-point diagram).

An illustration of such behavior is shown in Fig. 5.11(a). It is now no longer meaningful to say that the vapor is richer than the liquid in the "more volatile component." The following more general statement (Konovalov's Rule) is employed: the vapor is richer than the liquid with which it is in equilibrium in that component by addition of which to the system the vapor pressure is raised. At a maximum or minimum in the vapor-pressure curve, the vapor and the liquid must have the same composition.

18. BOILING-POINT DIAGRAMS

The *PX* diagram in Fig. 5.11(a), has its counterpart in the boiling-point diagram in Fig. 5.11(b). A maximum in the *PX* curve corresponds to a minimum in the *TX* curve.

A solution with the composition corresponding to a maximum or minimum point on the boiling-point diagram is called an *azeotropic solution* (ζηιν, to boil; α-τρόπος, unchanging), since there is no change in composition on boiling. Such solutions cannot be separated by distillation at constant pressure. In fact, it was thought at one time that they were real chemical compounds, but changing the pressure changes the composition of the azeotropic solution.

The distillation of a system with a maximum or minimum boiling point can be discussed by reference to Fig. 5.11(b). If the temperature of a solution having the composition l is raised, it begins to boil at the temperature t_1. The first vapor that distills has the composition v, richer than the original liquid in component B. The residual solution therefore becomes richer in A; and if the vapor is continuously removed the boiling point of the residue rises, as its composition moves along the liquidus curve from l toward pure A. If a fractional distillation is carried out, a final separation into pure A and the azeotropic solution is achieved. Similarly a solution of original composition l' can be separated into pure B and azeotrope.

19. PARTIAL MISCIBILITY

If the positive deviation from Raoult's Law becomes sufficiently large, the components may no longer form a continuous series of solutions. As successive portions of one component are added to the other, a limiting solubility is finally reached, beyond which two distinct liquid phases are formed. Usually, but not always, increasing temperature tends to promote solubility, as the thermal kinetic energy overcomes the reluctance of the components to mix freely. In other words, the $T\,\Delta S$ term in $\Delta G = \Delta H - T\,\Delta S$ becomes more important. A solution that displays a large positive deviation from ideality at elevated temperatures therefore frequently splits into two phases when it is cooled.

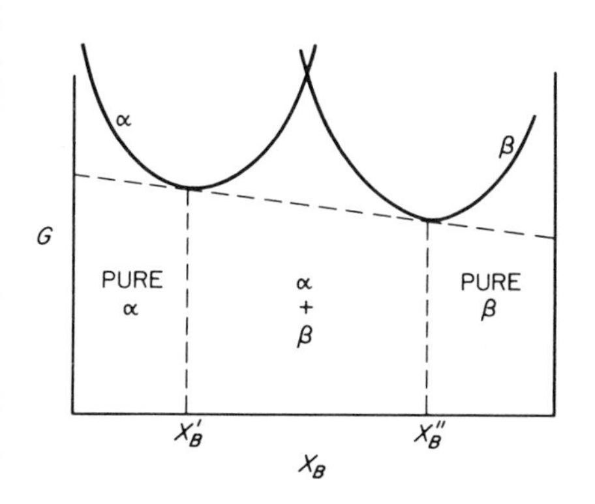

FIG. 5.12 Partial miscibility determined by free energy.

The interpretation of the *solubility gap* can be given in terms of the free energy of the system. At some constant temperature, let us plot the molar free energy of the system, defined as $\overline{G} = G/(n_A + n_B)$, against the mole fraction of B, X_B, for both the α and β phases. For example, these phases may be two immiscible liquid solutions. The diagram obtained, Fig. 5.12, is an exact analog of Fig. 5.1, which was used to determine partial molar volumes. In this case, the intercept of the common tangent to the two $\overline{G}$ vs. X curves gives the value of the partial molar free energies, or chemical potentials, of the two components. At this composition, therefore, $\mu_A^\alpha = \mu_A^\beta$, and $\mu_B^\alpha = \mu_B^\beta$, i.e., the condition for equilibrium of components A and B between the two phases is fulfilled. The corresponding mole fractions represent the phase-boundary compositions; at any composition between X'_B and X''_B, the system will split into two distinct phases, since in this way it can reach its minimum free energy. For $X_B < X'_B$, however, pure phase α gives the lowest free energy, and for $X_B > X''_B$, pure phase β.

A PX diagram for a partially miscible liquid system, such as aniline and water, is shown in Fig. 5.13(a). The point x lies in the two-phase region and corresponds to a system of two liquid solutions, one a dilute solution of aniline in water having the composition y, and the other a dilute solution of water in aniline having the composition z. These are called *conjugate solutions*. The relative amounts of the two phases are given by the ratios of the distances along the tie line, xy/xz. In the two-phase region, the phase rule shows that the

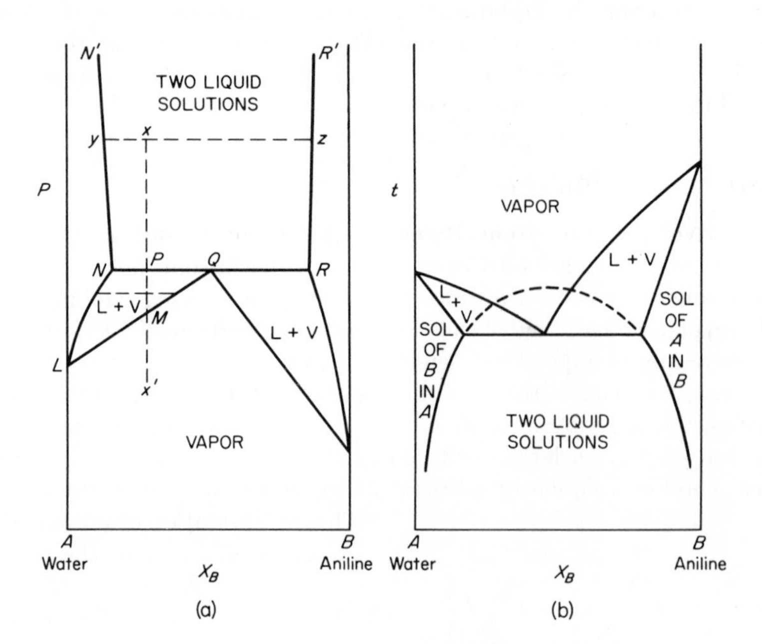

FIG. 5.13 Schematic diagrams for aniline—water system, showing limited solubility of liquids. (a) *PX* diagram at constant *T*. (b) *TX* diagram at constant *P*.

system is bivariant since $p = 2$ and $c = 2, f = c - p + 2 = 2$. Because of the requirement of constant temperature imposed on the PX diagram, only one degree of freedom remains. Once the pressure is fixed, the compositions of both phases are fixed, which is indeed what the diagram indicates. The overall composition x is of course not fixed, since this depends on the relative amounts of the two conjugate solutions, about which the phase rule has nothing to say.

Let us follow the sequence of events as the pressure is gradually reduced along the line of constant composition, or *isopleth*, xx'. At the point P, vapor having a composition corresponding to point Q begins to appear. There are now three phases coexisting in equilibrium, so that the system is invariant. If the volume available to the vapor is increased, the amount of the vapor phase will increase, at constant pressure, until all the aniline-rich solution, of composition R, has vaporized. When this process is complete, there will remain a vapor of composition Q and a solution of composition N, so that the system becomes univariant again as the pressure falls below that at P.

Since the vapor that is formed is richer in aniline, the composition of the residual solution becomes richer in water. The liquid composition moves along the line NL, and the vapor composition moves along QL until all the liquid has been transformed into vapor, at the point M. After this, further decrease in pressure proceeds at constant vapor composition along MX'.

We should note that the two conjugate solutions N and R have the same total vapor pressure and the same vapor composition. It follows that the partial vapor pressure of component A above a saturated solution of A in B is the same as the vapor pressure of A above a saturated solution of B in A. For example, if benzene and water are mixed at 25°C, two immiscible layers are formed, one containing 0.09 per cent C_6H_6 and 99.91 per cent H_2O, the other 99.81 per cent C_6H_6 and 0.19 per cent H_2O. The partial pressure of benzene above either of these solutions is the same, namely, 85 mm.

In Fig. 5.13(a), the lines NN' and RR' are almost vertical, since the solubility limits depend only slightly on pressure. Change in temperature, on the other hand, may greatly affect the mutual solubility of two liquids. In Fig. 5.13(b), the TX diagram for the water—aniline system is drawn for the constant pressure of one atmosphere (normal boiling-point diagram). Increasing the temperature tends to decrease the difference between the concentrations of the two conjugate solutions, or as we say, to *close the solubility gap.*

20. CONDENSED LIQUID SYSTEMS

In Fig. 5.13, the variation of solubility with temperature is shown for only one pressure. At a high enough temperature boiling occurs, and it is therefore not possible to trace the ultimate course of the solubility curves. One might expect that the solubility gap would close completely if the system was studied at a higher pressure so that a higher temperature could be reached before the onset of boiling. This expectation is represented by the dashed line in the figure.

A number of *condensed systems* have been studied, which illustrate complete liquid-liquid solubility curves. An example is the phenol — water system of Fig. 5.14 (a). At the temperature and composition indicated by the point x, two phases coexist, the conjugate solutions represented by y and z. The relative amounts of the two phases are proportional, as usual, to the segments of the tie line. As the temperature is increased along the isopleth XX', the amount of the phenol-rich phase decreases and the amount of water-rich phase increases. Finally, at Y the phenol-rich phase disappears completely, and at temperatures above Y there is only one solution.

This gradual disappearance of one solution is characteristic of systems having all compositions except one. The exception is the composition corresponding to the maximum in the TC curve. This composition is called the *critical composition* and the temperature at the maximum is the *critical solution temperature* or *upper consolute temperature.* As a two-phase system having the critical composition is gradually heated (line CC' in Fig. 5.14(a)) there is no gradual disappearance of one phase. Even in the immediate neighborhood of the maximum d, the ratio of the segments of the tie line remains practically constant. The compositions of the two conjugate solutions gradually approach each other until, at the point d, the boundary line between the two phases suddenly disappears and a single phase remains.

As the critical temperature is slowly approached from above, a curious phenomenon is observed. Just before the single homogeneous phase passes over into two distinct phases, the solution is suffused by a pearly opalescence. This *critical opalescence* is believed to be caused by the scattering of light from small regions of slightly differing density, which are formed in the liquid in the incipient

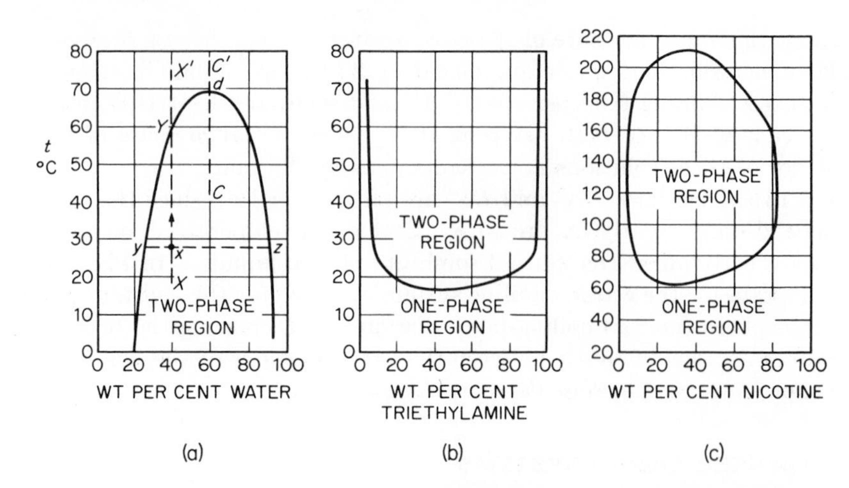

FIG. 5.14 Partial miscibility of two liquids. (a) phenol—water system. (b) triethylamine—water system. (c) nicotine—water system.

separation of the two phases. X-ray studies have revealed that such regions may persist even several degrees above the critical point.*

Strangely enough, some systems exhibit a lower consolute temperature. At high temperatures, two partially miscible solutions are present, which become completely intersoluble when sufficiently cooled. An example is the triethylamine—water system in Fig. 5.14(b), with a lower consolute temperature of 18.5°, at 1 atm pressure. Note the great increase in solubility as the temperature approaches this point. This strange behavior suggests that large negative deviations from Raoult's Law (e.g., compound formation) become sufficient at the lower temperatures to counteract the positive deviations responsible for the immiscibility.

Finally, systems have been found with both upper and lower consolute temperatures. These are more common at elevated pressures, and we might expect all systems with a lower consolute temperature to display an upper one at sufficiently high temperature and pressure. An example at atmospheric pressure is the nicotine—water system of Fig. 5.14(c).

21. GAS-SOLID EQUILIBRIA

A gas-solid system of two components in which there is practically no formation of solid solutions is exemplified by ($CaCO_3 \rightleftarrows CaO + CO_2$). Since $c = 2$, $f = 4 - p$. If the two solid phases are present together with the gaseous phase CO_2, the system is univariant, $f = 4 - 3 = 1$. At a given temperature, the pressure of CO_2 has a fixed value. For example, if CO_2 is admitted to a sample of CaO at 700°C, there is no reaction until a pressure of 25 mm is reached; then the CaO takes up CO_2 at constant pressure until it is completely converted into $CaCO_3$, whereupon further addition of CO_2 again results in an increase in pressure.

* G. Brady, *J. Chem. Physics*, *32*, 45 (1960).

The pressure-temperature diagram for such a system is therefore similar to the vapor-pressure curve of a pure liquid or solid. The CO_2 pressure has been loosely called the *dissociation pressure of $CaCO_3$*. Since the pressure has a definite value only when the vapor phase is in equilibrium with *both solid phases*, it is more correct to speak of the *dissociation pressure in the system $CaCO_3$–CaO–CO_2*.

It is also important to specify both the solid phases in systems formed by various salts, their hydrates, and water vapor. The case of copper sulfate, water is shown in Fig. 5.15, on a three-dimensional PTc diagram, and in different sections. As long as only the two phases are present, a salt hydrate can exist in equilibrium with water vapor at any temperature if the pressure of water vapor is (1) above the dissociation pressure to lower hydrate or anhydrous salt and (2) below the dissociation pressure of the next higher hydrate or the vapor

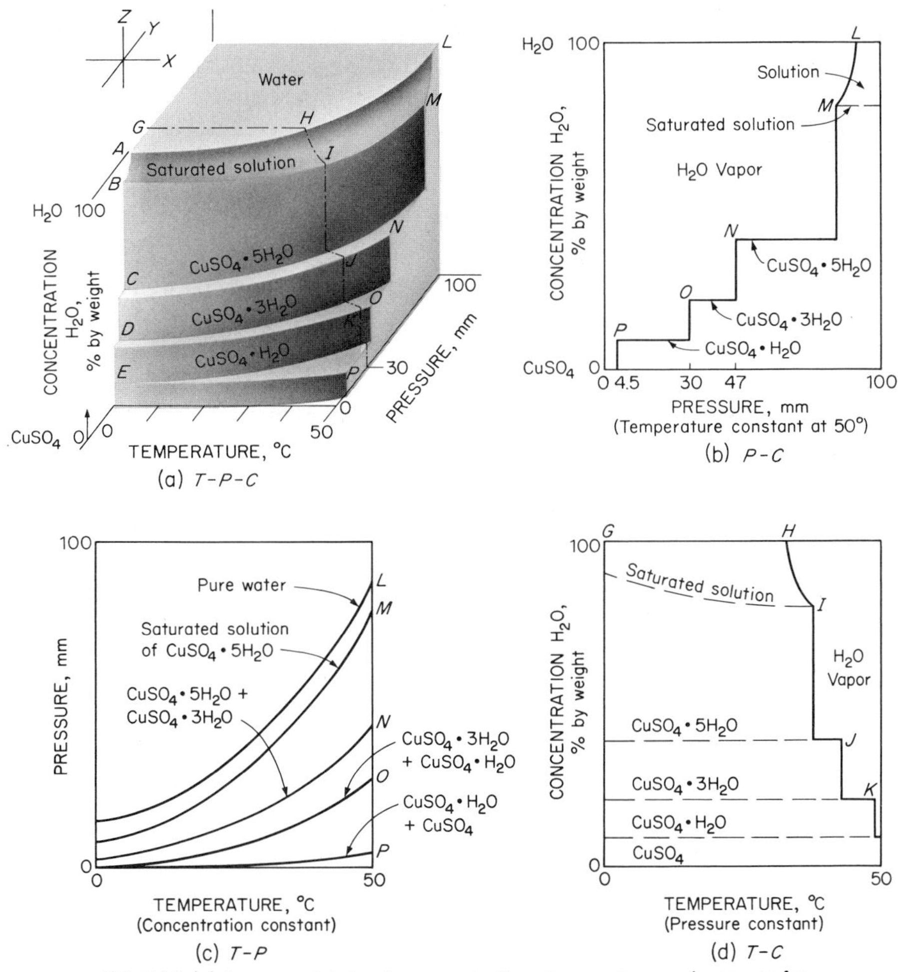

FIG. 5.15 (a) Space model showing concentrations, temperature, and pressure for the system cupric sulfate—water. (b) Section at constant *T*. (c) Sections at various constant c. (d) Section at constant *P*. (After F. Daniels and R. A. Alberty, *Physical Chemistry*, 2nd ed. John Wiley, New York, 1961).

pressure of the saturated solution. Statements in the older literature that a given hydrate "loses water at 110°C" are devoid of precise meaning.

When the pressure of water vapor falls below the dissociation pressure for the system, *efflorescence* occurs, as the hydrate loses water and its surface becomes covered with a layer of lower hydrate or anhydrous salt. When the vapor pressure exceeds that of the saturated aqueous solution, *deliquescence* occurs, and the surface of hydrate becomes covered with a layer of saturated solution.

Let us consider the $CuSO_4$—H_2O system at a constant temperature of 50° and see what happens as we increase the pressure. This increase corresponds to the section along PONML in the space diagram, and is shown in Fig. 5.15(b). Below 4.5 mm pressure the system consists of anhydrous $CuSO_4$ and water vapor. Since $c = 2$ and $p = 2$, $f = c - p + 2 = 2$. One degree of freedom is used by the requirement of constant temperature, and the pressure is free to vary as long as no second solid phase is formed. When the water-vapor pressure reaches 4.5 mm, the monohydrate $CuSO_4 \cdot H_2O$ appears and the variance drops to $f = 2 - 3 + 2 = 1$. Thus at the constant temperature of 50°, the pressure remains constant at 4.5 mm until all the anhydrous salt has been converted to monohydrate. This conversion is completed at the point P. At 50° the monohydrate can exist in contact with water vapor at any pressure between 4.5 and 33 mm. Reference to Fig. 5.15(c) will show how this *field* of existence depends on the temperature. The dissociation pressure of the system $CuSO_4 \cdot 3H_2O \rightleftarrows CuSO_4 \cdot H_2O + 2H_2O$ is 33 mm at 50°C. The conversion of monohydrate to trihydrate is completed at point 0, and the field of stability of the trihydrate extends from 33 to 42 mm. At 42 mm $CuSO_4 \cdot 5H_2O$ begins to form, a change completed at point N. The range of stability of $CuSO_4 \cdot 5H_2O$ extends from 42 to 90 mm. At 90 mm we reach the equilibrium pressure at 50° of the saturated solution of $CuSO_4$ in water.

22. SOLID-LIQUID EQUILIBRIA: SIMPLE EUTECTIC DIAGRAMS

Two-component solid-liquid equilibria in which the liquids are intersoluble in all proportions and in which there is no appreciable solid-solid solubility give the simple diagram of Fig. 5.16. Examples of systems of this type are collected in Table 5.4.

TABLE 5.4 SYSTEMS WITH SIMPLE EUTECTIC DIAGRAMS SUCH AS FIG. 5.16

Component A	M. pt. A (°C)	Component B	M. pt. B (°C)	Eutectic	
				°C	Mole per cent B
$CHBr_3$	7.5	C_6H_6	5.5	−26	50
$CHCl_3$	−63	$C_6H_5NH_2$	−6	−71	24
Picric acid	122	TNT	80	60	64
Sb	630	Pb	326	246	81
Cd	321	Bi	271	144	55
KCl	790	AgCl	451	306	69
Si	1412	Al	657	578	89
Be	1282	Si	1412	1090	32

Consider the behavior of a solution of composition X on cooling along the isopleth XX'. When point P is reached, pure solid A begins to separate from the solution. As a result, the residual solution becomes richer in the other component B, its composition falling along the line PE. At any point Q in the two-phase region, the relative amounts of pure A and residual solution are given as usual by the ratio of the tie-line segments. When point R is reached, the residual solution has the eutectic composition E. Further cooling now results in the simultaneous precipitation of a mixture of A and B in relative amounts corresponding to E.

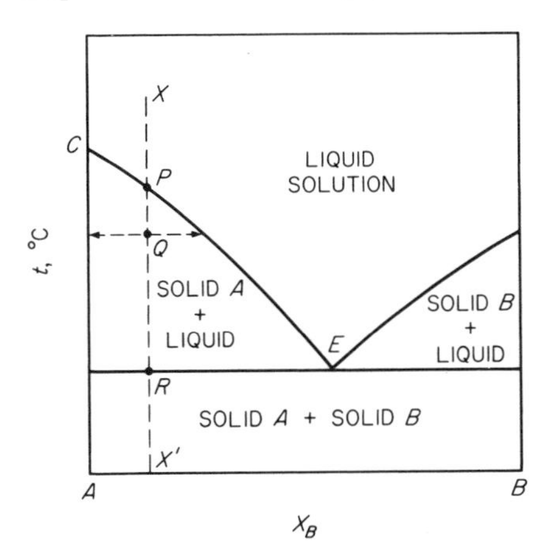

FIG. 5.16 Simple eutectic diagram for two components, A and B, completely intersoluble as liquids but with negligible solid-solid solubility.

The eutectic point is an invariant point on a constant-pressure diagram; since three phases are in equilibrium, $f = c - p + 2 = 2 - p + 2 = 4 - 3 = 1$, and the single degree of freedom is used by the choice of the constant-pressure condition.

Microscopic examination of alloys often reveals a structure indicating that they have been formed from a melt by a cooling process similar to that considered along the isopleth XX' of Fig. 5.16. Crystallites of pure metal are found dispersed in a matrix of finely divided eutectic mixture. An example is given in Fig. 5.17.

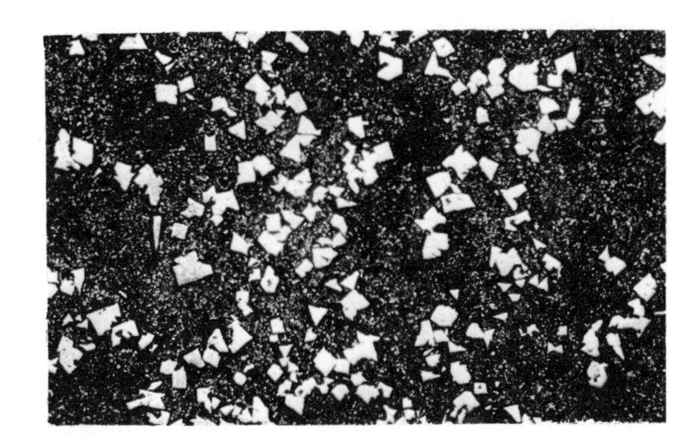

FIG. 5.17 Photomicrograph at 50× of 80 per cent Pb—20 per cent Sb, showing crystals of Sb in a eutectic matrix. (Arthur Phillips, Yale University.)

23. COOLING CURVES

The method of cooling curves is one of the most useful for the experimental study of solid-liquid systems. A two-component system is heated until a homogeneous melt is obtained. A thermocouple, or other convenient device for temperature measurement, is immersed in the liquid, which is kept in a fairly well insulated container. As the system slowly cools, the temperature is recorded at regular time intervals. Examples of such curves for the system shown in Fig. 5.16 are drawn in Fig. 5.18.

The curve *a* for pure *A* exhibits a gradual decline until the melting point of *A* is reached. It then remains perfectly flat as long as solid and liquid *A* are both present, and resumes its decline only after all the liquid has solidified. The curve for cooling along the isopleth XX' is shown in *b*. The decline as the homogeneous melt is cooled becomes suddenly less steep when the temperature is reached corresponding to point *P*, where the first solid begins to separate from the solution. This change of slope is a consequence of the liberation of latent heat of fusion during the solidification of *A*. The more gradual decline continues until the eutectic temperature is reached. Then the cooling curve becomes absolutely flat. This is because the eutectic point in a two-component system, like the melting point of one component, is an invariant point at constant overall pressure. If the initially chosen composition of the system happened to be the same as that of the eutectic, the cooling curve would be that drawn in *c*.

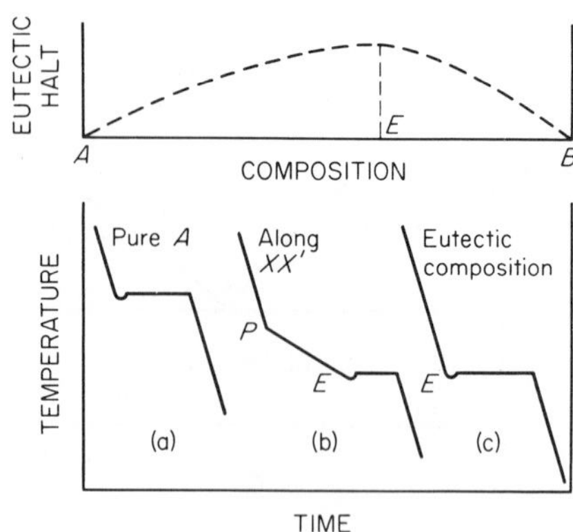

FIG. 5.18 Cooling curves for various compositions on the simple eutectic diagram of Fig. 5.16.

The duration of the constant-temperature period at the eutectic temperature is called the *eutectic halt*. This halt is a maximum for a melt having the eutectic composition. Each cooling-curve determination yields one point on the *TX* diagram (point of initial break in slope) in addition to a value for the eutectic temperature. In this way the entire diagram can be constructed.

24. FORMATION OF COMPOUNDS

If aniline and phenol are melted together in equimolar proportions, a definite compound crystallizes on cooling, $C_6H_5OH \cdot C_6H_5NH_2$. Pure phenol melts at 40°C, pure aniline at −6.1°C, and the compound melts at 31°C. The complete *TX* diagram for this system, in Fig. 5.19, is typical of many instances in which stable compounds occur as solid phases. The most convenient way of looking at such a diagram is to imagine it to be made up of two diagrams of the simple eutectic type placed side by side. In this case, one such diagram would be the phenol—compound diagram, and the other the aniline—compound diagram. The phases corresponding with the various regions of the diagram are labeled.

A maximum such as the point *C* is said to indicate the formation of a compound with a *congruent melting point*, since if a solid having the composition

$C_6H_5OH \cdot C_6H_5NH_2$ is heated to 31°C, it melts to a liquid of identical composition. Compounds with congruent melting points are readily detected by the cooling-curve method. A liquid having the composition of the compound exhibits no eutectic halt, behaving in every respect like a single pure component.

25. SOLID COMPOUNDS WITH INCONGRUENT MELTING POINTS

In some systems, solid compounds are formed that do not melt to a liquid having the same composition, but instead decompose before such a melting point is reached. An example is the silica—alumina system (Fig. 5.20), which includes a compound, $3Al_2O_3 \cdot SiO_2$, called *mullite*.

If a melt containing 40 per cent Al_2O_3 is prepared and cooled slowly, solid mullite begins to separate at about 1780°C. If some of this solid compound is removed and reheated along the line XX', it decomposes at 1800°C into solid corundum and a liquid solution (melt) having the composition P. Thus: $3Al_2O_3 \cdot SiO_2 \rightarrow Al_2O_3$ + solution. Such a change is called *incongruent melting*, since the composition of the liquid differs from that of the solid.

The point P is called the *incongruent melting point* or the *peritectic point* (τηκτος, melting; περι, around). The suitability of this name becomes evident if

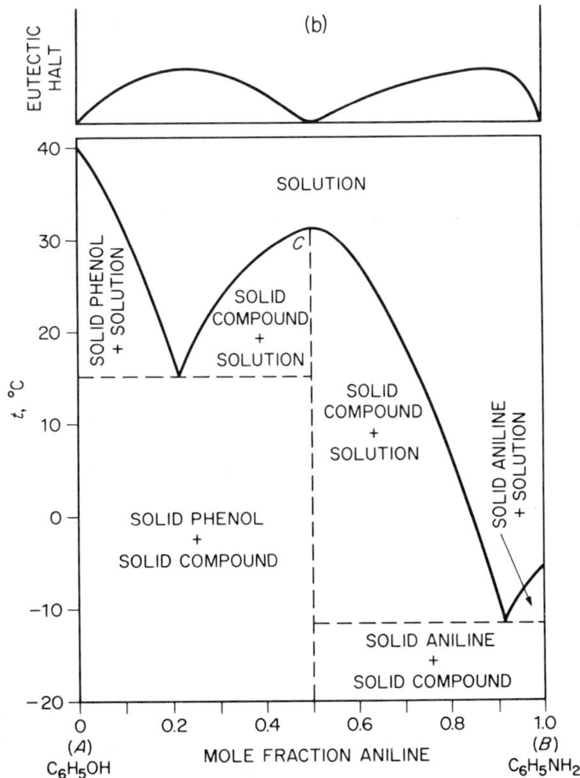

FIG. 5.19 The system phenol-aniline, illustrating the formation of an intermolecular compound.

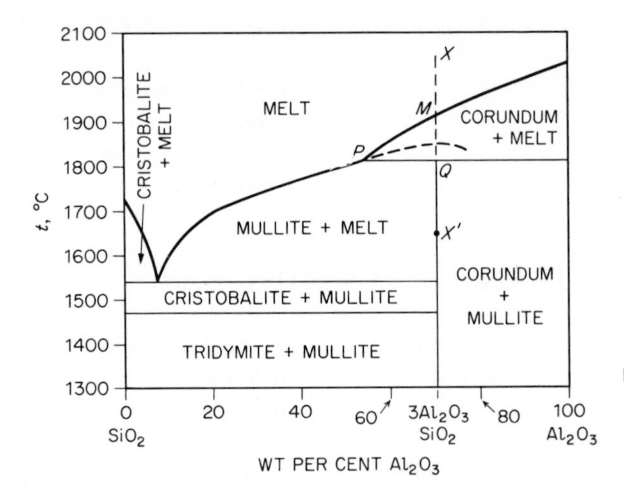

FIG. 5.20 System displaying peritectic.

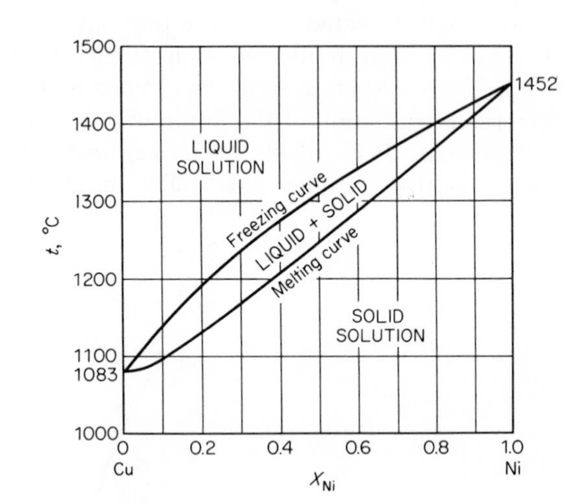

FIG. 5.21 The copper — nickel system — a continuous series of solid solutions.

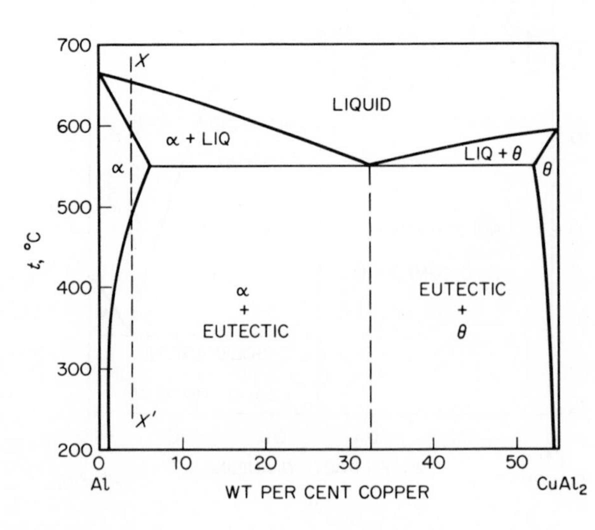

FIG. 5.22 A section of the aluminum — copper system. Alloys containing up to 6 per cent copper exhibit age-hardening.

one follows the course of events as a solution with composition $3Al_2O_3 \cdot SiO_2$ is gradually cooled along XX'. When the point M is reached, solid corundum (Al_2O_3) begins to separate from the melt, whose composition therefore becomes richer in SiO_2, falling along the line MP. When the temperature falls below that of the peritectic at P, the following change occurs: liquid + corundum → mullite. The solid Al_2O_3 that has separated reacts with the surrounding melt to form the compound mullite. If a specimen taken at a point such as Q is examined, the solid material is found to consist of two phases, a core of corundum surrounded by a coating of mullite. It was from this characteristic appearance that the term *peritectic* originated.

26. SOLID SOLUTIONS

In the theory of phase equilibria, solid solutions are no different from other kinds of solution: they are simply solid phases containing more than one component. The phase rule makes no distinction between the kind of phase (gas, liquid, or solid) that occurs, being concerned only with how many phases are present. Therefore, most of the diagrams discussed in the preceding chapter as typical of liquid-vapor and liquid-liquid systems are found to have their counterparts among the solid-liquid and solid-solid systems.

Two general classes of solid solution can be distinguished on structural grounds. A *substitutional* solid solution is one in which solute atoms, or groups of atoms, are substituted for solvent atoms or groups in the crystal structure. For example, nickel has a face-centered cubic structure; if some of the nickel atoms are replaced at random by copper atoms, a solid solution is obtained. This substitution of one group for another is possible only when the substituents do not differ greatly in size. An *interstitial* solid solution is one in which the solute atoms or groups occupy interstices in the crystal structure of the solvent. For example, a number of carbon atoms may occupy holes in the nickel structure. This situation can occur to an appreciable extent only when the solute atoms are small compared with the solvent atoms.

An example of a system with a continuous series of solid solutions is copper—nickel, Fig. 5.21. Important industrial alloys, such as Constantan (60Cu,40Ni) and Monel (60Cu, 35Ni, 5Fe) are solid solutions of this kind.

27. LIMITED SOLID-SOLID SOLUBILITY

For intermetallic systems the simple eutectic diagram of Fig. 5.16 is usually an oversimplification. In many cases, however, the solubility gap extends across *almost* the entire diagram. Usually, too, the gap increases considerably with decreasing temperature. An interesting case is shown in the aluminum—copper diagram of Fig. 5.22. Only the portion of the system extending from pure Al to the intermetallic compound $CuAl_2$ is covered. The solid solution of copper in

FIG. 5.23 Direct transmission electron micrograph of Al-Cu (N. Takahashi and K. Ashinuma, University of Yamanashi).

aluminum is called the α phase, and the solid solution of aluminum in the compound $CuAl_2$ is called the θ phase.

The phenomenon of *age hardening* of alloys is interpreted in terms of the effect of temperature on the solubility gap in solid solutions. If a melt containing about 4% Cu and 96% Al is cooled along XX', it first solidifies to a solid solution α. This solid solution is soft and ductile. If it is quenched rapidly to room temperature, it becomes metastable. Changes in the solid state are usually sluggish, so that the metastable solution can persist for some time. It changes slowly, however, to the stable form, which is a *mixture* of two phases — solid solution α and solid solution θ. This two-phase alloy is much less plastic than the homogeneous solid solution α. The exact mechanism of the hardening is still not completely elucidated, but it is always associated with the change from single-phase to two-phase alloy.

Figure 5.23 shows a remarkable lamellar structure in an alloy of 33% Cu and 67% Al examined under the electron microscope. The dark ribbons are the θ phase, the lighter ones, the α phase.

28. THE IRON-CARBON DIAGRAM

No discussion of phase diagrams should omit the iron-carbon system, which is the theoretical basis for ferrous metallurgy. The part of the diagram of greatest interest extends from pure iron to the compound iron carbide, or *cementite*, Fe_3C. This section is reproduced in Fig. 5.24.

Pure iron exists in two different modifications. The stable crystalline form up to 910°C, called α *iron*, has a body-centered cubic structure. At 910° transition occurs to a face-centered cubic structure, γ *iron*; but at 1401° γ iron transforms back to a body-centered cubic structure, now called δ *iron*. This is an interesting, but not unique, example of an allotrope that is stable, at constant pressure, both below and above a certain temperature range. The solid solutions of carbon in the iron structures are called *ferrite*.

Apart from the small section of the diagram concerned with δ ferrite, the upper portion of the diagram is a typical example of limited solid-solid solubility.

The curve qq' shows how the transformation temperature of α to γ ferrite is lowered by interstitial solution of carbon in the iron. The region labeled α ferrite represents the range of solid solutions of C in α iron. The region γ represents solid solutions of C in γ iron, which are given a special name, *austenite*. The decrease in the transition temperature $\alpha \rightarrow \gamma$ is terminated at q' where the curve intersects the solid solubility curve rq' of carbon in γ iron. A point such as q', which has the properties of a eutectic but occurs in a completely solid region, is often called a *eutectoid*.

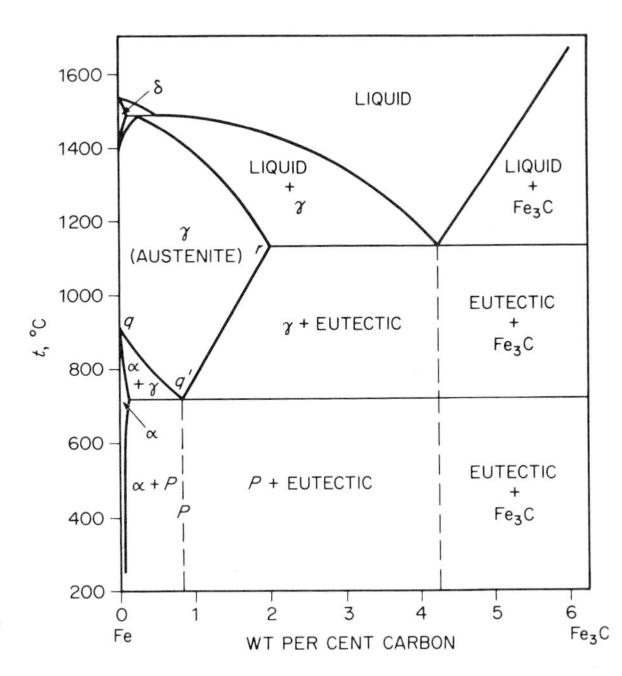

FIG. 5.24 A section of the iron-carbon system.

The two phases formed by the eutectoid decomposition of austenite are α ferrite and cementite. These phases form a lamellar structure of alternate bands which is called *pearlite*. If the composition is close to the eutectoid, the steel is composed entirely of pearlite. If the composition is richer in carbon, or *hypereutectoid*, it may contain other grains of cementite in addition to those occurring in the pearlite. If a *hypoeutectoid* steel is cooled slowly, it may contain additional grains of ferrite. Fig. 5.25 shows the formation and appearance of pearlite. The first stage in the formation seems to be the nucleation of a crystallite of cementite. As this grows, it removes carbon from the surrounding austenite. Nucleation of ferrite then occurs at the surface of the cementite since low carbon favors the transformation of γ to α.

The diagram Fig. 5.24 explains the distinction between the steels and the cast irons. Any composition below 2 per cent carbon can be heated until a homogeneous solid solution (austenite) is obtained. In this condition the alloy is readily hot rolled or submitted to other forming operations. On cooling, segregation of two phases occurs. Cementite is a hard, brittle material, and its occurrence in the pearlitic steels is responsible for their high strength. The way in which the cooling is carried out determines the rate of segregation of the two phases and their grain sizes, and provides a great many possibilities for obtaining different mechanical properties by annealing and tempering.

Compositions above 2 per cent in carbon belong to the general class of cast irons. They cannot be brought into a homogeneous solid solution by heating, and therefore cannot conveniently be mechanically worked. They are formed by casting from the molten state, and used where hardness and corrosion resistance are desirable and where the brittleness due to high cementite content is not deleterious.

29. THREE-COMPONENT SYSTEMS

In three-component or *ternary* systems, the phase rule requires that the degrees of freedom be $f = 5 - p$. The following cases may then arise: $p = 1, f = 4$; $p = 2, f = 3$; $p = 3, f = 2$; $p = 4, f = 1$; $p = 5, f = 0$.

The four degrees of freedom for the single-phase system would be, for example, temperature, pressure, and two concentration variables. The complete representation of a three-component system would therefore require a four-dimensional diagram, which presents some difficulties for a draftsman.

If systems at constant pressure are considered, $f = 4 - p$, and for $p = 1$, three variables are required, temperature and two concentrations. It is therefore possible to represent ternary systems at constant pressure by means of solid figures. Usually the concentrations are plotted on an equilateral triangle, and a vertical axis is used to plot the temperature. A convenient triangular system of coordinates employs the network suggested by Roozeboom, which is shown in Fig. 5.26. The corners of the triangle represent the pure components A, B, and C. The percentage of A is plotted along the sides AB and AC. Thus on any line drawn parallel to BC the percentage of A is constant. Components B

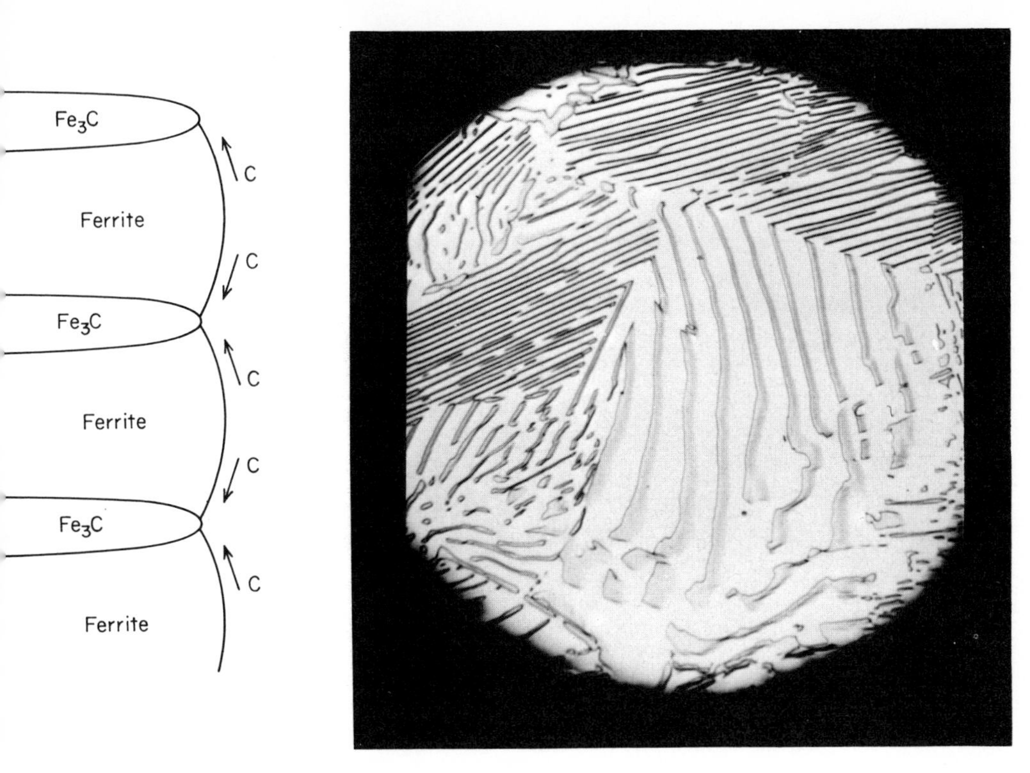

FIG. 5.25 Formation and appearance of peorlite. The photo micrograph is at 1250X. (U. S. Steel Corporation Research Center.)

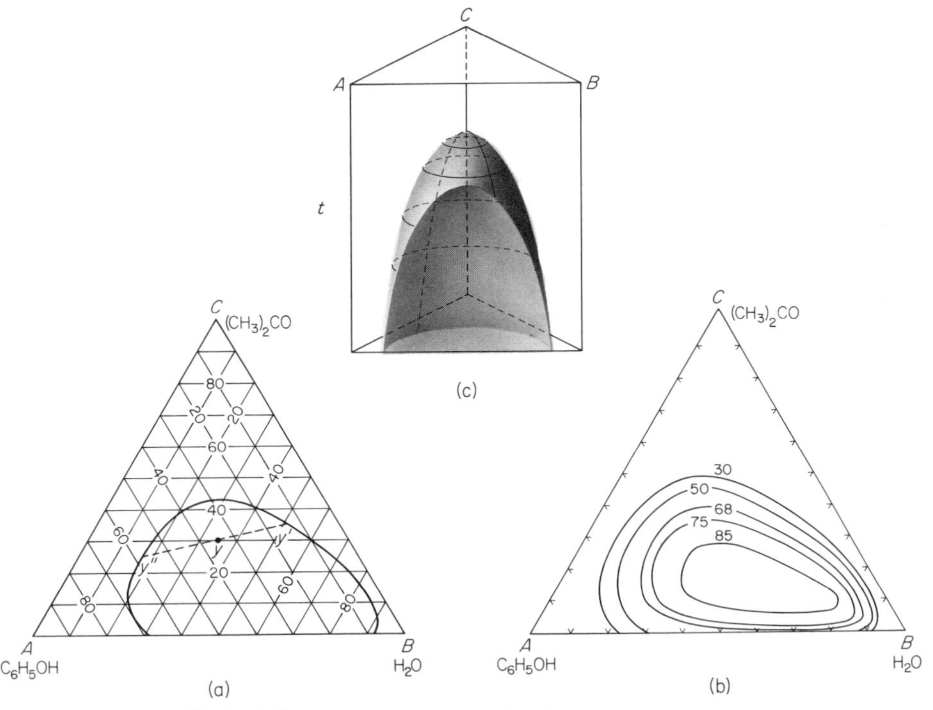

FIG. 5.26 Three component system: phenol — water — acetone.

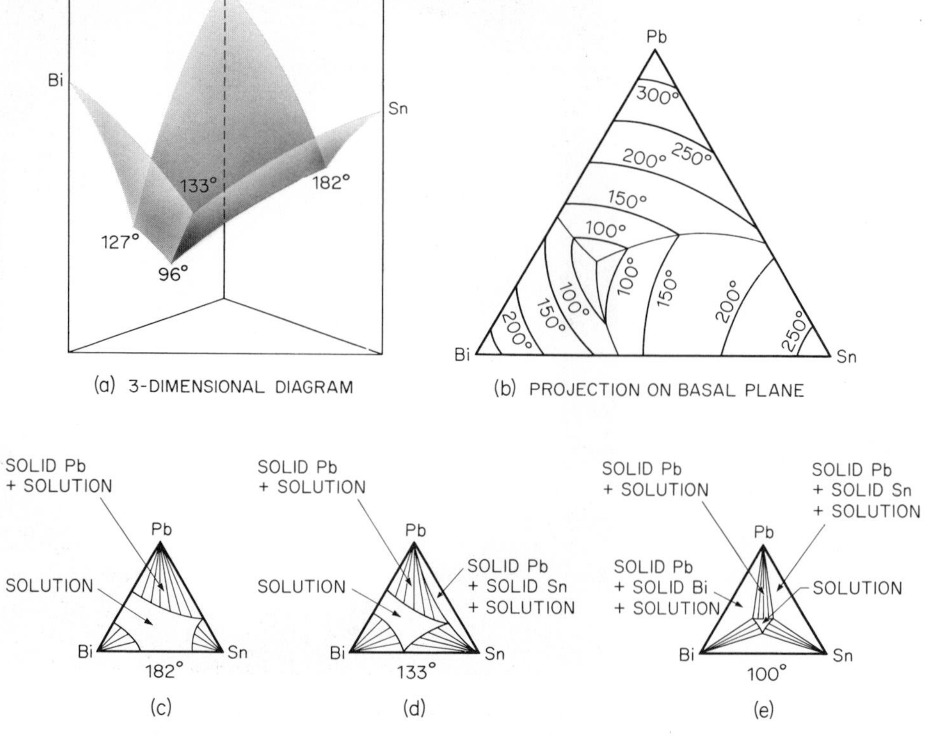

FIG. 5.27 The system Pb—Bi—Sn: Three-dimensional diagram and isothermal sections.

and C are plotted similarly. For example, the point y on the diagram represents 30 per cent C, 35 per cent B, 35 per cent A. Along any line drawn from one vertex of the triangle to the opposite side, the relative amount of two components remains constant. Thus along the line Cy the ratio of A to B remains at 1:1 while C decreases from 100% to 0%.

An example of the use of the triangular diagram may be taken from the study of liquid-liquid solutions. On p. 143 the system phenol-water and its upper consolute temperature were described. The ternary system phenol-water-acetone at 50°C is shown in Fig. 5.26 (a). We can see that it is always possible to add enough acetone to a two-phase phenol-water system to obtain a single homogeneous solution. Points such as y, within the two-phase area, correspond to two conjugate solutions, having the compositions y' and y'' at the ends of the tie line. These tie lines are determined experimentally by analysis of the conjugate solutions.

Figure 5.26 (b) shows a set of isotherms at different temperatures. If we plot the temperature as a vertical axis, we can use these to construct the three-dimensional diagram shown in Fig. 5.26 (c).

30. SYSTEM WITH TERNARY EUTECTIC

In Fig. 5.27 is a representation of the lead—tin—bismuth system. These three metals do not form solid solutions to any considerable extent, and therefore are shown on a simple eutectic type of diagram. Each face of the prism depicts a binary *TX* diagram. For example, pure tin melts at 232°C and pure bismuth at 271°C, their eutectic being at 133°C and 42 per cent Sn. The Sn—Bi eutectic temperature is lowered by the addition of lead to a minimum at 96°C and a composition of 32 per cent Pb, 16 per cent Sn, 52 per cent Bi. This is the ternary eutectic point.

Without using a solid model, we can best illustrate the behavior of this system by a series of *isothermal sections*, as shown in Fig. 5.27. Above 327°C, the melting point of pure lead, there is a single liquid solution. At about 315°C the system consists of solid Pb and solution. The section at 182°C (c) indicates the binary eutectic of Sn and Pb. Below this temperature, solid Pb and solid Sn both separate from the solution. At 133°C the binary eutectic between Sn and Bi is reached (d). Finally, in (e) at 100°C there is shown a section slightly above the ternary eutectic.

31. SOLUTIONS OF TWO SALTS WITH A COMMON ION

These solutions comprise an important class of 3-component systems. The degrees of freedom are *P*, *T* and two independent concentration variables. The effects of pressure can usually be ignored. Then at any constant temperature we may represent the concentrations by a triangular diagram.*

* Various rectangular diagrams are also sometimes used. See A. Findlay, A. N. Campbell and N. O. Smith, *The Phase Rule and its Applications* (New York: Dover, 1951), Chapter 17.

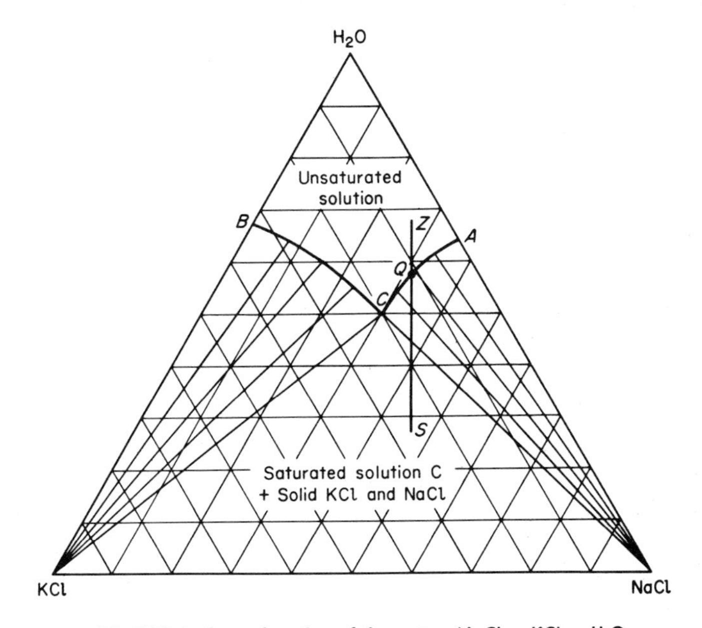

FIG 5.28 Isothermal section of the system NaCl — KCl — H_2O.

In the simplest case the two salts do not form any double salt or hydrate at the temperature in question. An example is the system NaCl–KCl–H_2O shown in Fig. 5.28.

The point A represents the solubility of NaCl, B that of KCl. The curve AC shows how the solubility of NaCl changes as KCl is dissolved in the aqueous phase. Curve BC shows how the solubility of KCl changes as NaCl is added to the aqueous phase. At the intersection C, the solution is saturated with both NaCl and KCl. Since $p = 3$, $f = 3 - 3 + 2 = 2$, and at constant T and P, the concentrations of all phases are invariant. In fact, any point within the triangle NCK corresponds to invariant compositions, viz. solution of composition C, pure solid NaCl and pure solid KCl. Any point within NAC corresponds to pure NaCl and solution, any point within KBC, to pure KCl and solution. Within $HACB$ the solution is unsaturated in both salts.

Let us suppose we have a solution of composition Z and gradually remove water by evaporation. The system moves along the line ZS, with the ratio of NaCl to KCl remaining constant. At Q, the solution becomes saturated in NaCl, and as more water is evaporated, NaCl crystallizes out. The composition of the residual solution moves along QC. When the composition of the system crosses CN, the residual solution is at C, and is then saturated in both NaCl and KCl. As further water is removed from the solution, both NaCl and KCl are deposited, but the composition of the solution remains invariant at C until all the water is removed.

The subject of ternary diagrams is an extended and important one, and only a few of the introductory aspects have been mentioned. For further details special treatises are available and should be consulted.*

PROBLEMS

1. Solutions are prepared at 25°C containing 1000 g of water and n moles of NaCl. The volume in ml is found to vary with n as $V = 1001.38 + 16.6253\, n + 1.7738\, n^{3/2} + 0.1194\, n^2$. Draw a graph showing the partial molar volumes of H_2O and NaCl in the solution as a function of the molality from 0 to 2 molal.

2. When 2 g of nonvolatile hydrocarbon containing 94.4 per cent C is dissolved in 100 g benzene, the vapor pressure of benzene at 20°C is lowered from 74.66 mm to 74.01 mm. Calculate the molecular formula of the hydrocarbon. [*Ans.* $C_{14}H_{10}$]

3. Pure water is saturated with a 2:1 mixture of hydrogen and oxygen at a total pressure of 5 atm. The water is then boiled to remove all the gases. Calculate the per cent composition of the gases driven off (after drying). Use data from Table 5.2. [*Ans.* 54% H_2; 46% O_2]

* J. S. Marsh, *Principles of Phase Diagrams* (New York: McGraw-Hill, 1935); G. Masing, *Introduction to the Theory of Three-Component Systems* (New York: Reinhold, 1944). Also Findlay, Campbell and Smith, *op. cit.*

4. Water and nitrobenzene can be considered to be immiscible liquids. Their vapor pressures are: H_2O, 92.5 mm at 50°C and 760 mm at 100°C; $C_6H_5NO_2$, 22.4 mm at 100°C and 148 mm at 150°C. Estimate the boiling point of a mixture of water and nitrobenzene at 1 atm pressure. In a steam distillation at 1 atm, how many grams of steam would be condensed to obtain one gram of nitrobenzene in the distillate? [*Ans.* 98.6°C; 5.75 g steam. By different interpolation, 99.2°C, 5 g]

5. A compound insoluble in water is steam distilled at 97°C, the distillate containing 68 wt per cent H_2O. The vapor pressure of water is 682 mm at 97°C. What is the molecular weight of the compound? [*Ans.* 74]

6. Calculate the weight of (a) methanol and (b) ethylene glycol, which, when dissolved in 4 l of water, would just prevent the formation of ice at −10°C. [*Ans.* 690 g; 1340 g]

7. The osmotic pressure at 25°C of a solution of ρ-lactoglobulin containing 1.346 g protein per 100 cc solution was found to be 9.91 cm of water. Estimate the molecular weight of the protein. [*Ans.* 34 200]

8. The equilibrium pressures for the system $CaSO_4 \cdot 2\,H_2O \rightleftharpoons CaSO_4 + 2\,H_2O$, and the vapor pressures of pure water, at various temperatures are

t, °C	50	55	60	65
$CaSO_4$ system, mm	80	109	149	204
H_2O, mm	92	118	149	188

The solubility of $CaSO_4$ in water is so low that the vapor pressure of the saturated solution can be taken to equal that of pure water. (a) State what happens on heating the dihydrate in a previously evacuated sealed tube from 50° to 65°C. (b) What solid phase separates when a solution of $CaSO_4$ is evaporated at 65° and at 55°C? (c) What solid phase separates on evaporating at 55° if, when the solution becomes saturated, enough $CaCl_2$ is added to reduce its v.p. by 10 per cent? [*Ans.* (a) Water vapor pressure rises from 80 to 204 mm; (b) 65°, $CaSO_4$; 55°, $CaSO_4 \cdot 2\,H_2O$; (c) $CaSO_4$]

9. When cells of the skeletal vacuole of a frog were placed in a series of NaCl solutions of different concentrations, it was observed microscopically that they remained unchanged in 0.7% of NaCl solution, shrank in more concentrated solutions, and swelled in more dilute solutions. This particular salt solution freezes at −0.406°C. What is the osmotic pressure of the cell protoplasm at 25°C? [*Ans.* 5.33 atm]

10. The vapor pressure of a solution containing 11.94 g of a substance in 100 g H_2O is 740.9 mm at 100°C. What is the molecular weight of the substance? [*Ans.* 83.43]

11. 13.79 g of diphenyl at 70.5°C were added to 511 g of water at 15.078°C. The temperature of the mixture became constant at 16.41°C. The specific heat of water is 1 cal g^{-1} and that of diphenyl is 0.386 (mean over range 15° to 75°C). Diphenyl melts at 70°C. Calculate the lowering of the freezing point produced by the addition of 0.3345 g of CCl_4 to 10.779 g of diphenyl. [*Ans.* 1.660°C]

12. A certain mass of a substance in 100 g benzene lowers the f. pt. by 1.280°C. The same mass of solute in 100 g water lowers the f. pt. by 1.395°C. If the substance has a normal molecular weight in C_6H_6 and is completely dissociated in water, into how many ions does it dissociate in water? [*Ans.* 3]

13. From Trouton's Rule, show that for a dilute solution of a nonvolatile solute, $X_A T_b^{-21/R}$ is approximately constant. (The Trouton constant $\simeq 21$, X_A is mole fraction of solvent and T_b is the boiling point.)

14. The osmotic pressure of a solution containing 32.6 g l^{-1} of a solute was 2.43 atm at 0°C. What would be the osmotic pressure at 20°C of a solution containing 90.1 g l^{-1} of the same solute? [*Ans.* 7.21 atm]

15. Liquids A and B form an ideal solution. A certain solution of A and B contains 25 mole per cent of A, whereas the vapor in equilibrium with the solution at 25°C contains 50 mole per cent of A. The heat of vaporization of A is 5 kcal $mole^{-1}$, whereas that of B is 7 kcal $mole^{-1}$. Calculate: (a) the ratio of the vapor pressure of pure A to that of pure B at 25°C; (b) the value for the same ratio at 100°C.

16. The vapor pressure of a certain liquid, which obeys Trouton's Rule, increases by 15 mm Hg per degree at temperatures around its boiling point. Calculate the heat of vaporization and the boiling point of this liquid.

17. Liquids A and B form an ideal solution. At 50°C, the total vapor pressure of a solution consisting of 1 mole of A and 2 moles of B is 250 mm Hg. On addition of one more mole of A to the solution, the vapor pressure increases to 300 mm Hg. Calculate P_A° and P_B°.

18. Two 10 liter bulbs are connected by a stopcock. One bulb contains 100 g of water and the other bulb contains a gas at 2 atm pressure. Both bulbs are at 25°C. The solubility of the gas in water at 25°C and at 1 atm pressure is 2 moles per 1000 g of water. The vapor pressure of pure water may be taken as 24 mm Hg at 25°C. Calculate the total pressure in the system if the stopcock is opened and equilibrium is established at 25°C. Assume the gas neither dissociates nor associates in solution.

19. A new antibiotic has been isolated by a lengthy series of extractions, biological tests, and so forth. A few milligrams are available, and by the ultra-centrifuge method, it has been found that the molecular weight is 10 000. It is desired to check this by another method. Calculate the freezing-point depression, boiling-point elevation, change in vapor pressure,

and osmotic pressure in cm H_2O for such a substance dissolved in water. Assume the temperature is 25°C for the osmotic pressure measurements. In each case, assume 1 gram of the substance is dissolved in 100 grams of pure water. Which method could be most easily carried out on the basis of your calculations?

20. At 20°C, the vapor pressure of benzene is 100 mm and that of octane is 20 mm. If one mole of octane is dissolved in four moles of benzene, and the resulting solution is ideal, calculate the total vapor pressure of the solution and the composition of the vapor.

21. At 1 atm pressure of CO_2, 1.7 gm of CO_2 will dissolve in 1000 gm of water at 20°C, whereas only 1 gm will dissolve under 1 atm pressure at 40°C. (a) If a bottle is unsafe with a pressure of over two atmospheres of gas in it, what is the maximum pressure of CO_2 at 20°C that is safe for a bottled beverage that might be exposed to 40°C? (b) What is the mole fraction of CO_2 in the resulting solution? Assume the solution obeys Henry's law.

22. Write down the number of components and the number of phases and evaluate the number of degrees of freedom (over and above those already set down) in the following examples:
   (a) A 10 molar aqueous solution of sulfuric acid (dissociating partly into hydrogen, bisulfate, and sulfate ions) at 1 atm.
   (b) Pure, partly frozen sulfuric acid at 1 atm and 0°C (the normal melting point is 10.36°C).
   (c) A dilute solution of water in sulfuric acid, in equilibrium with solid sulfuric acid.
   (d) Ammonium chloride vapor, partly dissociated into ammonia and hydrogen chloride.
   (e) System (*d*), with some extra ammonia gas admitted.
   (f) Solid carbon in equilibrium with gaseous CO, CO_2 ,and O_2, at 100°C.
   (g) Liquid water in the presence of air (79% nitrogen and 21% oxygen) at 1 atm. (Compare problem 30).

   [*Ans.* (a) 2, 1, 1; (b) 1, 2, −1; (c) 2, 2, 2; (d) 1, 1, 2; (e) 2, 1, 3; (f) 2, 2, 1; (g) 3, 2, 1]

23. 4.450 g 100 per cent sulfuric acid was added to 82.20 g water, and the density of the solution was found to be 1.029 g cm^{-3} at 25°C and 1 atm pressure. Calculate: (a) the weight per cent; (b) the mole fraction; (c) the mole per cent; (d) the molality; (e) the molarity; (f) the normality of sulfuric acid in the solution under these conditions. [*Ans.* (a) 5.14 wt. %; (b) 0.00985; (c) 0.985 mole %; (d) 0.552 molal; (e) 0.539 molar (f) 1.078 N]

24. Formic acid boils at 101°C. When combined with water, it forms a constant boiling point mixture containing 77.5 per cent formic acid and boiling at 107°C. Sketch the temperature-composition curves for this system. De-

scribe the results of prolonged fractional distillation of two aqueous solutions of formic acid, the first containing 50 per cent formic acid and the second containing 85 per cent.

25. Konovalov's rule states: "The vapor in equilibrium with a binary liquid mixture is richer in that component whose addition to the liquid mixture (at constant temperature) increases the total vapor pressure." Discuss whether this rule applies to boiling-point versus composition diagrams exhibiting a maximum or a minimum. Does the rule apply to the azeotropic mixtures?

26. A mixture of chlorobenzene and bromobenzene behaves ideally. If the vapor pressures of the pure components at 137°C are respectively 863 mm and 453 mm, calculate both algebraically and graphically: (a) The composition (in mole fractions) of the liquid mixture which has a normal boiling point of 137°C (i.e., which boils at 137°C when the pressure is 1 atm); (b) The composition of the vapor which is in equilibrium with this liquid at its boiling point; (c) The composition of the vapor, and the total pressure, over a solution at 137°C containing an equal number of moles of chlorobenzene and bromobenzene. [*Ans.* mole fraction of C_6H_5Cl = (a) 0.749; (b) 0.850; (c) 0.656, 658 mm]

27 A liquid A that is immiscible with water was steam distilled, giving a distillate 200 ml of which contained 57.2 ml of A. The observed boiling point for the distillation was 98.2°C and the barometric pressure was 758 mm. The vapor pressure of water at 98.2°C is 712 mm. The relative density of the liquid was found to be 1.83. From these data, calculate the molecular weight of the liquid. [*Ans.* 204]

28. Two metals A and B form a simple eutectic system. Three samples are presented to you consisting of: (a) one of the pure components; (b) an alloy with the eutectic composition; (c) an alloy of another composition. What physical measurements would you use to identify the samples?

29. Magnesium (melting point 651°C) and zinc (melting point 419°) form two eutectic mixtures, one at 368°C and 3.2 per cent by weight Mg, and the other at 347°C and 49 per cent by weight Mg. The melting-point curve for the system has a maximum at 590°C for a mixture containing 15.7 per cent by weight Mg.
    (a) Draw a phase diagram (temperature-composition in mole fractions) for this condensed system, labelling each region to show what phases are in equilibrium under the conditions it represents.
    (b) Explain, by use of the diagram and by appeal to the Phase Rule, what will happen when liquid mixtures containing (1) 80 per cent by weight Mg, (2) 30 per cent by weight Mg are cooled slowly from 700°C to 300°C.
    (c) Sketch the type of cooling curve expected in case (1) above and also for the cooling of a liquid containing 49 per cent by weight Mg. (Atomic weights are Mg = 24.3, Zn = 65.4.)

30. The solubility in water of nitrogen at one atm pressure and 0°C is 23.5 ml liter^{-1}, and of oxygen 48.9 ml liter^{-1}. Calculate: (a) the solubility of N_2 and O_2 in water at 0°C exposed to air consisting of 79% nitrogen and 21% oxygen; (b) the difference in freezing points between air-saturated water and air-free water. The cryoscopic constant for water is 1.86 deg mole^{-1} kg. [*Ans.* (a) N_2, 0.000828 mole liter^{-1}; O_2, 0.000458 mole liter^{-1}; (b) 0.0024°C]

31. The vapor pressure of pure water at 25°C is 23.756 mm. When 6 g of a nonvolatile substance was dissolved in 100 g of water, the vapor pressure was found to be 23.332 mm. What was the molecular weight of the solute? [*Ans.* 59.6]

32. The vapor pressures at 20°C were determined for the following systems: sulfur; pure carbon disulfide; and a solution of 2 g of sulfur in 100 g of carbon disulfide. The values were found to be 3×10^{-4}, 854, and 848.9 mm of mercury, respectively. What is the molecular complexity of the sulfur in the solution? The atomic weights of C and S are, respectively, 12.01 and 32.06. [*Ans.* 7.91, or approx. S_8]

33. An antifreeze mixture for a car radiator contains 10% by weight of ethylene glycol, $HOCH_2CH_2OH$. Given that the cryoscopic constant for water is 1.86 deg mole^{-1} kg, calculate the temperature at which ice begins to separate out of the mixture. Why is your answer approximate? [*Ans.* −3.3°C]

34. A mixture of benzene, C_6H_6 (vapor pressure 268 mm) and ethylene chloride, $C_2H_4Cl_2$ (vapor pressure 236 mm) behaves ideally at 50°C. What is the total vapor pressure of a liquid mixture consisting of equal weights of the two components? What is the molar composition of the vapor?

35. When a mixture of chlorobenzene (C_6H_5Cl) and water (immiscible) is heated, it boils at 91°C at one atm. The vapor pressures at 91°C of the constituents are 220 mm and 540 mm respectively. Assuming that the vapors behave as ideal gases, calculate the molar composition of the distillate. Calculate also its weight composition.

36. A liquid *A* that is immiscible with water was steam distilled, giving a distillate 100 ml of which contained 57.2 ml of *A*. The observed boiling point for the distillation was 98.2°C. The barometric pressure was 758 mm. The vapor pressure of water at 98.2°C is 712 mm. The relative density of the liquid was found to be 1.83. From these data, calculate the molecular weight of the liquid.

37. Draw phase diagrams (temperature-composition) for the following condensed systems, labeling each region to show phases in equilibrium within them: (a) Magnesium (m.p. 651°C) and lead (327°C) form $PbMg_2$, which melts at 530°C; (b) Magnesium and nickel (1452°C) form a compound $MgNi_2$ that melts at 1145°C and a compound Mg_2Ni that decomposes at

770°C into a liquid containing 50% (by weight) of Ni and the other compound. The eutectics are at 23% Ni and 510°C and at 89% Ni and 1080°.

38. The following data were obtained for the boiling points at 1 atm of solutions of CCl_4 in C_2Cl_4:

Mole fraction CCl_4 in liq.	0	0.1	0.2	0.4	0.6	0.8	1
Mole fraction CCl_4 in vap.	0	0.469	0.67	0.861	0.918	0.958	1
Boiling point °C	120.8	108.5	100.8	89.3	83.5	79.9	76.9

If half of a solution 30 mole per cent in CCl_4 is distilled, what is the composition of the distillate? If a solution 50 mole per cent in CCl_4 is distilled until the residue is 20 mole per cent CCl_4, what is the approximate composition of the distillate? Specify whether the distillate is being removed or not. [*Ans.* 57 mole % CCl_4; 79 mole % CCl_4]

---

39. The solubility of picric acid in benzene is:

t, °C	5	10	15	20	25	35
g/100 g C_6H_6	3.70	5.37	7.29	9.56	12.66	21.38

The melting points of benzene and picric acid are 5.5°C and 121.8°C. Calculate the heat of fusion of picric acid. [*Ans.* 8.5 ± 1.0 kcal]

40. For the ideal solutions of 2-methyl-propanol-1 and propanol-2 (p. 129), draw a curve showing how the mole fraction of $C_2H_4Br_2$ in the vapor varies with that in the liquid. Use this curve to estimate the number of theoretical plates required in a column in order to yield a distillate with mole fraction of $C_2H_4Br_2 = 0.9$ from a solution of mole fraction 0.1. Assume total reflux. [*Ans.* 13 plates]

41. The melting points and heats of fusion of *o, p, m* dinitrobenzenes are: 116.9°C; 173.5°C; 89.8°C; and 3905; 3345; 4280 cal per mole [Johnston, *J. Phys. Chem.*, *29*, 882, 1041 (1925)]. Assuming the ideal solubility law, calculate the ternary eutectic temperature and composition for mixtures of *o, m, p* compounds. [*Ans.* 46°C; ortho, $X = 0.33$; meta, 0.23; para, 0.44]

42. The following boiling points are obtained for solutions of oxygen and nitrogen at 1 atm:

b. pt. °K	77.3	78	79	80	82	84	86	88	90.1
Mole % O_2 in liq.	0	8.1	21.6	33.4	52.2	66.2	77.8	88.5	100
Mole % O_2 in vap.	0	2.2	6.8	12	23.6	36.9	52.2	69.6	100

Draw the TX diagram. If 90 per cent of a mixture containing 20 per cent O_2 and 80 per cent N_2 is distilled, what will be the composition of the residual liquid and its b. pt.? Plot an activity a vs. mole fraction X diagram from the data. [*Ans.* 74.7% O_2, b. pt. 85.5°K]

43. For a two-component system (A, B) show that

$$\log \gamma_A = \int_0^{X_B} \frac{\log \gamma_B}{(1 - X_B)^2} dX_B - \frac{X_B}{1 - X_B} \log \gamma_B$$

44. Pedder and Barratt [*J. Chem. Soc.* *537* (1933)] measured the vapor pressures of potassium amalgams at 387.5°C, at which temperature the vapor pressure of K is 3.25 mm, of Hg 1280 mm.

Mole % K in liq.	41.1	46.8	50	56.1	63	72
P of Hg, mm	31.87	17.3	13	9.11	6.53	3.7
P of K, mm	0.348	0.68	1.07	1.69	2.26	2.95

Calculate the activity coefficients of K and Hg in the amalgams and plot them vs. the composition in the range studied. [*Ans.*:

x of K	0.411	0.468	0.5	0.561	0.63	0.72
γ of K	0.261	0.447	0.658	0.927	1.1	1.26
γ of Hg	0.0423	0.0254	0.0203	0.0162	0.0138	0.0103]

6 THERMODYNAMICS AND CHEMICAL EQUILIBRIUM

The problem of chemical affinity may be summarized in the question, "What are the factors that determine the position of equilibrium in chemical reactions?"

The earliest reflections on this subject were those of the ancient alchemists, who endowed their chemicals with almost human natures, and answered simply that reactions occurred when the reactants loved each other. Robert Boyle, in *The Sceptical Chymyst* (1661), commented upon these theories without enthusiasm:

> *I look upon amity and enmity as affections of intelligent beings, and I have not yet found it explained by any, how those appetites can be placed in bodies inanimate and devoid of knowledge or of so much as sense.*

Newton's interest in gravitation led him to consider also the problem of chemical attraction, which he thought might spring from the same causes. In 1701, he surveyed some of the existing experimental knowledge as follows:

> *When oil of vitriol is mix'd with a little water . . . in the form of spirit of vitriol, and this spirit being poured upon iron, copper, or salt of tartar, unites with the body and lets go the water, doth not this show that the acid spirit is attracted by the water, and more attracted by the fix'd body? And is it not also from a natural attraction that the spirits of soot and seasalt unite and compose the particles of sal-ammoniac . . . and that the particles of mercury uniting with the acid particles of spirit of salt compose mercury sublimate, and with particles of sulphur, compose cinnaber . . . and that in subliming cinnaber from salt of tartar, or from quick lime, the sulphur by a stronger attraction of the salt or lime lets go the mercury, and stays with the fix'd body?*

Such considerations achieved a more systematic form in the early *Tables of Affinity,* such as that of Etienne Geoffroy in 1718, which recorded the order in which acids would expel weaker acids from combination with bases.

Claude Louis Berthollet, in 1801, pointed out in his famous book, *Essai de Statique Chimique,* that these tables were wrong in principle, since the quantity of reagent present plays a most important role, and a reaction can be reversed by adding a sufficient excess of one of the products. While serving as scientific adviser to Napoleon with the expedition to Egypt in 1799, he noted the deposition of sodium carbonate along the shores of the salt lakes there. The reaction $Na_2CO_3 + CaCl_2 \rightarrow CaCO_3 + 2NaCl$ as carried out in the laboratory was known to proceed to completion as the $CaCO_3$ precipitated. Berthollet recognized that the large excess of sodium chloride present in the evaporating brines could cause the reaction to be reversed, converting the limestone into sodium carbonate. But, unfortunately, he went too far, and finally maintained that the actual *composition* of chemical compounds could be changed by varying the proportions of the reaction mixture. In the ensuing controversy with Louis Proust the Law of Definite Proportions was well established, but Berthollet's ideas on chemical equilibrium, the good with the bad, were discredited, and consequently neglected for some fifty years.*

1. DYNAMIC EQUILIBRIUM

It is curious that the correct form of what we now call the *Law of Chemical Equilibrium* was obtained as the result of a series of studies of chemical reaction rates, and not of equilibria. In 1850, Ludwig Wilhelmy investigated the hydrolysis of sugar with acids and found that the rate was proportional to the concentration of sugar remaining undecomposed. In 1862, Marcellin Berthelot and Péan de St. Gilles reported similar results in their famous paper† on the hydrolysis of esters, data from which are shown in Table 6.1. The effect on the products of varying the concentrations of the reactants is readily apparent.

TABLE 6.1 DATA OF BERTHELOT AND ST. GILLES ON THE REACTION
$C_2H_5OH + CH_3COOH \rightleftharpoons CH_3COOC_2H_5 + H_2O$
(*One mole* of acetic acid is mixed with varying amounts of alcohol, and the amount of ester present at equilibrium is found)

Moles of Alcohol	*Moles of Ester Produced*	*Equilibrium Constant* $K = \frac{[EtAc][H_2O]}{[EtOH][HAc]}$
0.05	0.049	2.62
0.18	0.171	3.92
0.50	0.414	3.40
1.00	0.667	4.00
2.00	0.858	4.52
8.00	0.966	3.75

In 1863, the Norwegian chemists, C. M. Guldberg and P. Waage expressed these relations in a very general form and applied the results to the problem of chemical equilibrium. They recognized that chemical equilibrium is a dynamic

* We now recognize many examples of definite departures from stoichiometric composition in various inorganic compounds such as metallic oxides and sulfides, which are appropriately called *berthollide compounds*.

† *Ann. chim. phys.* (3), *65*, 385 (1862).

and not a static condition. It is characterized not by the cessation of all reaction but by the fact that the rates of the forward and reverse reactions have become the same.

Consider the general reaction, $A + B \rightleftarrows C + D$. According to the *Law of Mass Action*, the rate of the forward reaction is proportional to the concentrations of A and B. If these are written as $[A]$ and $[B]$, $v_{\text{forward}} = k_f[A][B]$. Similarly, $v_{\text{backward}} = k_b[C][D]$. At equilibrium, therefore, $v_{\text{forward}} = v_{\text{backward}}$, so that

$$k_f[A][B] = k_b[C][D]$$

Thus,

$$\frac{[C][D]}{[A][B]} = \frac{k_f}{k_b} = K$$

More generally, if the reaction is $aA + bB \rightleftarrows cC + dD$, at equilibrium,

$$\frac{[C]^c[D]^d}{[A]^a[B]^b} = K \tag{6.1}$$

Equation (6.1) is a statement of Guldberg and Waage's *Law of Chemical Equilibrium*. The constant K is called the *equilibrium constant* of the reaction. It provides a quantitative expression for the dependence of chemical affinity on the concentrations of reactants and products. By convention, the concentration terms for the reaction products are always placed in the numerator of the expression for the equilibrium constant.

Actually, this work of Guldberg and Waage does not constitute a general proof of the equilibrium law, since it is based on a special type of rate equation, which is certainly not always obeyed, as we shall see when we take up the study of chemical kinetics. Their work was important because they recognized that chemical affinity is influenced by two factors, a *concentration effect*, and what might be called a *specific affinity*, which depends on the chemical nature of the reacting species, their temperature, and pressure. We shall later derive the equilibrium law from thermodynamic principles.

2. FREE ENERGY AND CHEMICAL AFFINITY

The free-energy function described in Chapter 3 provides the true measure of chemical affinity under conditions of constant temperature and pressure. The free-energy change in a chemical reaction can be defined as $\Delta G = G(\text{products}) - G(\text{reactants})$. When the free-energy change is zero, there is no net work obtainable by any change or reaction at constant temperature and pressure. The system is in a state of equilibrium. When the free-energy change is positive for a proposed reaction, net work must be put into the system to effect the reaction, otherwise it cannot take place. When the free-energy change is negative, the reaction can proceed spontaneously with the accomplishment of net work. The larger the amount of this work that can be accomplished, the farther removed is the reaction from equilibrium. For this reason, $-\Delta G$ has often been called the *driving force* of the reaction. From the statement of the equilibrium law, it is evident that this driving force depends on the concentrations of the reactants and products. It also depends on their specific chemical constitution, and on the temperature and pressure, which determine the molar free energies of reactants and products.

If we consider a reaction at constant temperature, e.g., one conducted in a thermostat, $-\Delta G = -\Delta H + T\,\Delta S$. The driving force is made up of two parts, the $-\Delta H$ term and a $T\,\Delta S$ term. The $-\Delta H$ term is the reaction heat at constant pressure, and the $T\,\Delta S$ term is the heat change when the process is carried out reversibly. The difference is the amount of reaction heat that can be converted into net work, i.e., total heat minus unavailable heat.

If a reaction at constant volume and temperature is considered, the decrease in the work function, $-\Delta A = -\Delta E + T\,\Delta S$, would be used as the proper measure of the affinity of the reactants, or the driving force of the reaction. The condition of constant volume is met less frequently in laboratory practice.

We now can see why the principle of Berthelot and Thomsen (p. 63) is wrong. They considered only one of the two factors that make up the driving force of a chemical reaction, namely, the heat of reaction. They neglected the $T\,\Delta S$ term. The reason for the apparent validity of their principle was that for many reactions the ΔH term far outweighs the $T\,\Delta S$ term. This is especially so at low temperatures; at higher temperatures the $T\,\Delta S$ term naturally increases.

The fact that the driving force for a reaction is large (ΔG is a large negative quantity) does not mean that the reaction will necessarily occur under any given conditions. An example is a bulb of hydrogen and oxygen on the laboratory shelf. For the reaction, $H_2 + \frac{1}{2}O_2 \rightarrow H_2O(g)$, $\Delta G_{298} = -54\ 640$ cal. Despite the large negative ΔG, the reaction mixture can be kept for years without any detectable formation of water vapor. If, after ten years on the shelf, a pinch of platinum-sponge catalyst is added, the reaction takes place with explosive violence. The necessary affinity certainly existed, but the *rate* of attainment of equilibrium depended on entirely different factors.

Another example is the resistance to oxidation of reactive metals like aluminum and magnesium. $2Mg + O_2$ (1 atm) $\rightarrow 2MgO(c)$; $\Delta G_{298} = -136\ 370$ cal. In this case, after the metal is exposed to air it becomes covered with a very thin layer of oxide and further reaction occurs at an immeasurably slow rate since the reactants must diffuse through the oxide film. Thus the equilibrium condition is never attained. The incendiary bomb and the thermite reaction, on the other hand, remind us that the large $-\Delta G$ for this reaction is a valid measure of the great affinity of the reactants.

3. CONDITION FOR CHEMICAL EQUILIBRIUM

We shall now give a more exact mathematical derivation of the condition for equilibrium. Consider a chemical reaction,

$$\nu_1 A_1 + \nu_2 A_2 + \ldots \longrightarrow \nu_n A_n + \nu_{n+1} A_{n+1} + \ldots \tag{6.2}$$

This can be written briefly as

$$\sum \nu_i A_i = 0 \tag{6.3}$$

if we recall the convention that stoichiometric mole numbers ν_i are positive for products and negative for reactants.

We can denote the extent to which a reaction proceeds by its *degree of advancement* ξ. A change from ξ to $\xi + d\xi$ means that $\nu_1\, d\xi$ moles of A_1, $\nu_2\, d\xi$ moles of A_2, etc. have reacted to form $\nu_n\, d\xi$ moles of A_n, $\nu_{n+1}\, d\xi$ moles of A_{n+1}, etc. Thus ξ is a convenient dimensionless measure of extent of reaction. The number of moles reacted of any component i is

$$dn_i = \nu_i\, d\xi \tag{6.4}$$

Let us consider a system containing the reactants and products of Eq. (6.2) in equilibrium at constant T and P. In order to derive the equilibrium condition, we follow the procedure previously used in discussing phase equilibria (p. 99). We suppose that there could be a reaction of extent $d\xi$. The change in the free energy of the system would be given from Eq. (4.5) as

$$dG = \sum \mu_i\, dn_i$$

From Eq. (6.4), therefore,

$$dG = \sum \nu_i \mu_i\, d\xi$$

Hence,

$$dG/d\xi = \sum \nu_i \mu_i$$

At equilibrium, however, G must be a minimum with respect to any displacement of the reaction. Thus,

$$(dG/d\xi)_{\text{equil}} = 0$$

We thus derive the equilibrium condition,

$$\left(\sum \nu_i \mu_i\right)_{\text{equil}} = 0 = \Delta G_{\text{equil}} \tag{6.5}$$

The Belgian thermodynamicist de Donder introduced the function $-\left(\dfrac{dG}{d\xi}\right)_{P,T}$ in 1922 and called it the *Affinity*.

4. STANDARD FREE ENERGIES

In Chapter 2 we introduced the definition of standard states in order to simplify calculations with energies and enthalpies. Similar conventions are helpful for use with free energy, and various choices of the standard state have been made.

A standard state frequently used is *the state of the substance under one atmosphere pressure.* This is a useful definition for gas reactions; for reactions in solution, other choices of standard state may be more convenient and will be introduced as needed. A superscript circle will be used to indicate a standard state. The absolute temperature will be written as a subscript.

The most stable form of an *element* in the standard state (1 atm pressure) and at a temperature of 25°C will by convention be assigned a free energy of zero.

The *standard free energy of formation of a compound* is the free energy of the reaction by which it is formed from its elements, when all the reactants and products are in the standard states. For example,

$$H_2 \text{ (1 atm)} + \tfrac{1}{2}O_2 \text{ (1 atm)} \longrightarrow H_2O \text{ (g; 1 atm)} \qquad \Delta G^\circ_{298} = -54\,638 \text{ cal}$$

$$S \text{ (rhombic crystal)} + 3F_2 \text{ (1 atm)} \longrightarrow SF_6 \text{ (g; 1 atm)}, \qquad \Delta G^\circ_{298} = -235\,000 \text{ cal}$$

In this way it is possible to make tabulations of standard free energies such as that given by Latimer,* examples from which are collected in Table 6.2. The methods used to determine these values will be described later.

TABLE 6.2 STANDARD FREE ENERGIES OF FORMATION AT 25°C

Compound	State	ΔG°_{298} (kcal mole^{-1})	Compound	State	ΔG°_{298} (kcal mole^{-1})
AgCl	c	−26.224	H_2O	g	−54.635
AgBr	c	−22.930	H_2O	l	−56.690
AgI	c	−15.85	H_2O_2	g	−24.73
$CaCO_3$	c	−269.78	H_2O_2	l	−28.23
$CaSO_4$	c	−315.56	D_2O	g	−56.067
CH_4	g	−12.140	D_2O	l	−58.206
C_2H_2	g	50.0	HDO	g	−55.828
C_2H_4	g	16.282	HDO	l	−57.925
C_2H_6	g	−7.860	H_2S	g	−7.892
C_6H_6	g	30.989	H_2SO_4	aq	−177.34
C_6H_6	l	29.756	NaCl	c	−91.785
CO	g	−32.8079	NH_3	g	−3.976
CO_2	g	−94.2598	N_2O	g	24.76
CuO	c	−30.40	NO	g	20.719
Cu_2O	c	−34.98	NO_2	g	12.390
$CuBr_2$	c	−30.3	N_2O_4	g	23.44
Fe_2O_3	c	−177.1	SO_2	g	−71.79
FeS_2	c	−39.84	SO_3	g	−88.52

Free-energy equations can be added and subtracted just as thermochemical equations are, so that the free energy of any reaction can be calculated from the sum of the free energies of the products minus the sum of the free energies of the reactants.

$$\Delta G^\circ = G^\circ \text{ (products)} - G^\circ \text{ (reactants)}$$

If we adopt the convention that the stoichiometric number ν_i of moles of a product i is positive and the number ν_i of moles of a reactant is negative in the summation, this equation can be written concisely as

$$\Delta G^\circ = \sum \nu_i \overline{G}_i^\circ \tag{6.6}$$

* W. M. Latimer, *The Oxidation States of the Elements*, 2nd ed. (New York: Prentice-Hall, 1952). Since ΔG° often varies rapidly with the temperature, it is not a suitable function for tables of thermodynamic data, from which interpolation is usually necessary. Thus $-(G_T^\circ - H_{298}^\circ)/T$ or $-(G_T^\circ - H_0^\circ)/T$ are usually tabulated. In these functions the free energy is expressed with reference to the enthalpy at either 298°K or 0°K. See K. S. Pitzer and L. Brewer, *Thermodynamics* (Lewis and Randall), (New York: McGraw-Hill, 1961), pp. 166, 669.

For example:

$$Cu_2O(c) + NO(g) \longrightarrow 2CuO(c) + \tfrac{1}{2}N_2(g)$$

From Table 6.2,

$$\Delta G^\circ_{298} = 2(-30.40) + \tfrac{1}{2}\,(0) - 20.72 - (-34.98) = -46.54 \text{ kcal}$$

5. FREE ENERGY AND EQUILIBRIUM IN IDEAL GAS REACTIONS

Many important applications of equilibrium theory are in the field of homogeneous gas reactions, that is, reactions taking place entirely between gaseous products and reactants. To a good approximation in many such cases, the gases may be considered to obey the ideal gas laws.

The variation at constant temperature of the free energy per mole of an ideal gas is given from Eq. (3.30) as

$$d\overline{G} = \overline{V}\,dP = RT\,d\ln P$$

When we integrate from $\overline{G}^\circ$ and P°, the free energy and pressure in the chosen standard state, to $\overline{G}$ and P, the values in any other state,

$$\overline{G} - \overline{G}^\circ = RT\ln(P/P^\circ) \tag{6.7}$$

Since $P^\circ = 1$ atm, this becomes

$$\overline{G} - \overline{G}^\circ = RT\ln P \tag{6.8}$$

Equation (6.8) gives the free energy of one mole of an ideal gas at pressure P and temperature T, minus its free energy in a standard state at $P = 1$ atm and temperature T.

If an ideal mixture of ideal gases is considered, Dalton's Law of Partial Pressures must be obeyed, and the total pressure is the sum of the pressures that the gases would exert if each one occupied the entire volume by itself. These pressures are called the *partial pressures* of the gases in the mixture, $P_1, P_2, \ldots P_n$. Thus if n_i is the number of moles of gas i in the mixture,

$$P_iV = n_iRT \tag{6.9}$$

For each individual gas i in the ideal mixture Eq. (6.8) can be written

$$\overline{G}_i - \overline{G}_i^\circ = RT\ln P_i \tag{6.10}$$

For n_i moles,

$$n_i(\overline{G}_i - \overline{G}_i^\circ) = RTn_i\ln P_i$$

For a chemical reaction, therefore, from Eq. (6.6),

$$\Delta G - \Delta G^\circ = RT\sum \nu_i \ln P_i \tag{6.11}$$

If we now consider the pressures P_i to be the equilibrium pressures in the gas mixture, ΔG must be equal to zero for the reaction at equilibrium [Eq. (6.5)]. Thus we obtain the important relation,

$$-\Delta G^\circ = RT \sum \nu_i \ln P_i^{\text{eq}} \tag{6.12}$$

or

$$\sum \nu_i \ln P_i^{\text{eq}} = -\Delta G^\circ/RT$$

Since ΔG° is a function of the temperature alone, the left side of this expression is equal to a constant at constant temperature. For a typical reaction $aA + bB \rightleftharpoons cC + dD$, the summation can be written out as

$$\sum \nu_i \ln P_i^{\text{eq}} = \ln \frac{(P_C^{\text{eq}})^c (P_D^{\text{eq}})^d}{(P_A^{\text{eq}})^a (P_B^{\text{eq}})^b}$$

This expression is simply the logarithm of the equilibrium constant in terms of partial pressures, which we denote as K_P. Eq. (6.12) therefore becomes

$$-\Delta G^\circ = RT \ln K_P \tag{6.13}$$

The analysis in this section has now established two important results. We have given a rigorous thermodynamic proof that for a reaction between ideal gases, there exists an equilibrium constant K_P, defined by

$$K_P = \frac{P_C^c P_D^d}{P_A^a P_B^b} \tag{6.14}$$

This constitutes a thermodynamic proof of the Law of Chemical Equilibrium. Secondly, an explicit expression has been derived, Eq. (6.13), which *relates the equilibrium constant to the standard free-energy change* in the chemical reaction. We are now able, from thermodynamic data, to calculate the equilibrium constant, and thus the concentration of products from any given concentration of reactants. This was one of the fundamental problems that chemical thermodynamics aimed to answer.*

It may be noted from Eq. (6.13) that K_P is a function of temperature, $K_P(T)$, and ΔG° is itself a function of T. K_P, however, is independent of the total pressure, and independent of variations in the individual partial pressures. These partial pressures are varied by changing the proportions of reactants and products in the initial reaction mixture. After the mixture comes to equilibrium, the partial pressures must conform to Eq. (6.14). It should not be forgotten, however, that our equilibrium theory has so far been restricted to ideal gas mixtures.

6. EQUILIBRIUM CONSTANT IN CONCENTRATIONS

Sometimes the equilibrium constant is expressed in terms of concentrations c_i.

* The dimensions of K_P sometimes cause difficulty. From Eq. (6.13), it is evident that K_P is dimensionless, but Eq. (6.14) might seem to imply that it has the dimensions of $P^{\Delta\nu}$. The apparent paradox is resolved when we consider that Eq. (6.8) was obtained from Eq. (6.7) by setting $P^\circ = 1$ atm. Thus the "pressures" that appear in Eq. (6.14) are really ratios of pressures to a standard pressure of 1 atm, and hence dimensionless. It is therefore necessary always to use the atmosphere as the pressure unit in K_P expressions, because we have chosen $P^\circ = 1$ atm as our standard state.

For an ideal gas $P_i = n_iRT/V = c_iRT$. Substituting in Eq. (6.14) we find

$$K_P = \frac{c_C^c c_D^d}{c_A^a c_B^b} (RT)^{c+d-a-b}$$

$$K_P = K_c(RT)^{\Delta\nu} \tag{6.15}$$

Here K_c is the equilibrium constant in terms of concentrations (e.g., moles per liter) and $\Delta\nu$ is the number of moles of products less that of reactants in the stoichiometric equation for the reaction.

Another way of expressing the composition of the equilibrium mixture is in terms of mole fractions. The total pressure in an ideal gas mixture is given by

$$PV = (\sum n_i) RT$$

where $\sum n_i$ is the sum of all the mole numbers. Therefore, from Eqs. (6.9) and (5.1),

$$P_i = X_iP \qquad \text{and} \qquad X_i = P_i/P$$

Therefore the equilibrium constant in terms of the mole fractions is

$$K_X = \frac{X_C^c X_D^d}{X_A^a X_B^b} = K_P P^{-\Delta\nu} \tag{6.16}$$

Since K_P for ideal gases is independent of pressure, it is evident that K_X is a function of pressure except when $\Delta\nu = 0$. It is thus a "constant" only with respect to variations of the X's at constant T and P.

7. THE MEASUREMENT OF HOMOGENEOUS GAS EQUILIBRIA

The experimental methods for measuring gaseous equilibria can be classified as either static or dynamic.

In the static method, known amounts of the reactants are introduced into suitable reaction vessels, which are closed and kept in a thermostat until equilibrium has been attained. The contents of the vessels are then analyzed in order to determine the equilibrium concentrations. If the reaction proceeds very slowly at temperatures below those chosen for the experiment, it is sometimes possible to "freeze the equilibrium" by chilling the reaction vessel rapidly. The vessel may then be opened and the contents analyzed chemically. This was the procedure used by Max Bodenstein* in his classic investigation of the hydrogen–iodine equilibrium: $H_2 + I_2 \rightleftarrows 2HI$. The reaction products were treated with an excess of standard alkali; iodide and iodine were determined by titration, and the hydrogen gas was collected and its volume measured. For the formation of hydrogen iodide, $\Delta\nu = 0$; there is no change in the number of moles during the reaction. Therefore, $K_P = K_c = K_X$.

* *Z. Physik. Chem. 22*, 1 (1897); *29*, 295 (1899).

If the initial numbers of moles of H_2 and I_2 are a and b, respectively, they will be reduced to $a - x$ and $b - x$ with the formation of $2x$ moles of HI. The total number of moles at equilibrium is therefore $a + b + c$, where c is the initial number of moles of HI.

Accordingly the equilibrium constant can be written,

$$K_P = K_X = \frac{(c + 2x)^2}{(a - x)(b - x)}$$

The $(a + b + c)$ terms required to convert *numbers of moles* into *mole fractions* have canceled between numerator and denominator. In a run at 448°C, Bodenstein mixed 22.13 cc at STP of H_2 with 16.18 of I_2, and found 25.72 cc of HI at equilibrium. Hence

$$K = \frac{(25.72)^2}{(22.13 - 12.86)(16.18 - 12.86)} = 21.5$$

In the dynamic method for studying equilibria, the reactant gases are passed through a thermostated hot tube at a rate slow enough to allow complete attainment of equilibrium. This condition can be tested by making runs at successively lower flow rates, until there is no longer any change in the observed extent of reaction. The effluent gases are rapidly chilled and then analyzed. Sometimes a catalyst is included in the hot zone to speed the attainment of equilibrium. This is a safer method if a suitable catalyst is available, since it minimizes the possibility of any back reaction occurring after the gases leave the reaction chamber. A catalyst changes the rate of the reaction, not the position of final equilibrium.

These flow methods were extensively used by W. Nernst and F. Haber (around 1900) in their pioneer work on technically important gas reactions. An example is the *water-gas equilibrium*, which was studied both with and without an iron catalyst.* The reaction is

$$H_2 + CO_2 \longrightarrow H_2O + CO \qquad \text{and} \qquad K_P = \frac{P_{H_2O}P_{CO}}{P_{H_2}P_{CO_2}}$$

If we consider an original mixture containing a moles of H_2, b moles of CO_2, c moles of H_2O, and d moles of CO, the analysis of the data is as follows:

Constituent	*Original Moles*	At Equilibrium *Moles*	At Equilibrium *Mole Fraction*	At Equilibrium *Partial Pressure*
H_2	a	$a - x$	$(a - x)/(a + b + c + d)$	$[(a - x)/n]P$
CO_2	b	$b - x$	$(b - x)/(a + b + c + d)$	$[(b - x)/n]P$
H_2O	c	$c + x$	$(c + x)/(a + b + c + d)$	$[(c + x)/n]P$
CO	d	$d + x$	$(d + x)/(a + b + c + d)$	$[(d + x)/n]P$

Total Moles at Equilibrium $a + b + c + d = n$

Substituting the partial pressures, we obtain

* *Z. anorg. Chem.*, *38*, 5 (1904).

$$K_P = \frac{(c + x)(d + x)}{(a - x)(b - x)}$$

The values for the equilibrium composition, obtained by analysis of the product gases, have been used to calculate the constants in Table 6.3.

TABLE 6.3 THE WATER GAS EQUILIBRIUM, $H_2 + CO_2 = H_2O + CO$, [at 986°C and 1 atm]

Initial Composition (mole per cent)		Equilibrium Composition (mole per cent)			
CO_2	H_2	CO_2	H_2	$CO = H_2O$	K_P
10.1	89.9	0.69	80.52	9.40	1.59
30.1	69.9	7.15	46.93	22.96	1.57
49.1	51.9	21.44	22.85	27.86	1.58
60.9	39.1	34.43	12.68	26.43	1.61
70.3	29.7	47.51	6.86	22.82	1.60

It is often possible to calculate the equilibrium constant for a reaction from the known values of the constants of other reactions. This is a principle of great practical utility. For example, from the dissociation of water vapor and the water-gas equilibrium one can calculate the equilibrium constant for the dissociation of carbon dioxide.

$$H_2O \longrightarrow H_2 + \tfrac{1}{2}O_2 \qquad K_P = P_{H_2}P_{O_2}^{1/2}/P_{H_2O}$$

$$CO_2 + H_2 \longrightarrow H_2O + CO \qquad K'_P = P_{H_2O}P_{CO}/P_{CO_2}P_{H_2}$$

$$CO_2 \longrightarrow CO + \tfrac{1}{2}O_2 \qquad K''_P = P_{CO}P_{O_2}^{1/2}/P_{CO_2}$$

It is apparent that $K''_P = K'_P K_P$.

8. THE PRINCIPLE OF LE CHATELIER

The effects of variables such as pressure, temperature and concentration on the position of chemical equilibrium have been succinctly summarized by Henry Le Chatelier (1888).

> *Any change in one of the variables that determines the state of a system in equilibrium causes a shift in the position of equilibrium in a direction that tends to counteract the change in the variable under consideration.*

This is a principle of broad and general utility, and it can be applied not only to chemical equilibria but to equilibrium states in any physical system. It is possible that it can be applied also with good success in the psychological, economic and sociological fields.

The principle indicates, for example, that if heat is evolved in a chemical reaction, increasing the temperature tends to reverse the reaction; if the volume decreases in a reaction, increasing the pressure shifts the equilibrium position farther toward the product side. Quantitative expressions for the effect of variables such as temperature and pressure on the position of equilibrium will now be obtained by thermodynamic methods.

9. PRESSURE DEPENDENCE OF EQUILIBRIUM CONSTANT

The equilibrium constants K_P and K_c are independent of the pressure for ideal gases; the constant K_X is pressure-dependent. Since $K_X = K_P P^{-\Delta\nu}$, $\ln K_X = \ln K_P - \Delta\nu \ln P$. Then,

$$\frac{d \ln K_X}{dP} = \frac{-\Delta\nu}{P} = -\frac{\Delta V}{RT} \tag{6.17}$$

When a reaction occurs without any change in the total number of moles of gas in the system, $\Delta\nu = 0$. An example is the previously considered water-gas reaction. In such instances, the constant K_P is the same as K_X or K_c, and for ideal gases the position of equilibrium does not depend on the total pressure. When $\Delta\nu$ is not equal to zero, the pressure dependence of K_X is given by Eq. (6.17). When there is a decrease in the mole numbers ($\Delta\nu < 0$) and thus a decrease in the volume, K_X increases with increasing pressure. If there is an increase in ν and V ($\Delta\nu > 0$), K_X decreases with increasing pressure.

An important class of reactions for which $\Delta\nu \neq 0$ is that of molecular dissociations. An extensively studied example is the dissociation of nitrogen tetroxide into the dioxide, $N_2O_4 \rightarrow 2NO_2$. In this case,

$$K_P = P^2_{NO_2}/P_{N_2O_4}$$

If one mole of N_2O_4 is dissociated at equilibrium to a fractional extent a, $2a$ moles of NO_2 are produced. The total number of moles at equilibrium is then $(1 - a) + 2a = 1 + a$. It follows that

$$K_X = \frac{[2a/(1 + a)]^2}{(1 - a)/(1 + a)} = \frac{4a^2}{1 - a^2}$$

Since for this reaction $\Delta\nu = +1$,

$$K_P = K_X P = \frac{4a^2}{1 - a^2} P$$

When a is small compared to unity, this expression predicts that the degree of dissociation a varies inversely as the square root of the pressure.

Experimentally it is found that N_2O_4 is appreciably dissociated even at room temperatures. As a result, the observed pressure for a mole of N_2O_4 is greater than that predicted by the ideal gas law, since each mole yields $1 + a$ moles of gas after dissociation. Thus $P(\text{ideal}) = RT/\overline{V}$, whereas $P(\text{observed}) = (1 + a)RT/\overline{V}$. Hence

$$a = (\overline{V}/RT)(P_{\text{obs}} - P_{\text{ideal}})$$

This behavior provides a simple means for measuring a. For example, in an experiment at 318°K and 1 atm pressure, a is found to be 0.38. Therefore $K_X = 4(0.38)^2/(1 - 0.38^2) = 0.67$. At 10 atm pressure, $K_X = 0.067$ and a is 0.128.

Dissociations of the elementary gases are important in high temperature processes and in research on the upper atmosphere. The constants for a few of these equilibria are collected in Table 6.4.

TABLE 6.4 EQUILIBRIUM CONSTANTS OF DISSOCIATION REACTIONS

Temp. (°K)	K_P				
	$O_2 \rightleftharpoons 2\,O$	$H_2 \rightleftharpoons 2\,H$	$N_2 \rightleftharpoons 2\,N$	$Cl_2 \rightleftharpoons 2\,Cl$	$Br_2 \rightleftharpoons 2\,Br$
600	1.4×10^{-37}	3.6×10^{-33}	1.3×10^{-56}	4.8×10^{-16}	6.18×10^{-12}
800	9.2×10^{-27}	1.2×10^{-23}	5.1×10^{-41}	1.04×10^{-10}	1.02×10^{-7}
1000	3.3×10^{-20}	7.0×10^{-18}	1.3×10^{-31}	2.45×10^{-7}	3.58×10^{-5}
1200	8.0×10^{-16}	5.05×10^{-14}	2.4×10^{-25}	2.48×10^{-5}	1.81×10^{-3}
1400	1.1×10^{-12}	2.96×10^{-11}	7.5×10^{-21}	8.80×10^{-4}	3.03×10^{-2}
1600	2.5×10^{-10}	3.59×10^{-9}	1.8×10^{-17}	1.29×10^{-2}	2.55×10^{-1}
1800	1.7×10^{-8}	1.52×10^{-7}	7.6×10^{-15}	0.106	
2000	5.2×10^{-7}	3.10×10^{-6}	9.8×10^{-13}	0.570	

10. EFFECT OF AN INERT GAS ON EQUILIBRIUM

In reactions in which there is no change in the total number of moles, $\Delta\nu = 0$, and thus the addition of an inert gas does not affect the extent of reaction at equilibrium. If, however, $\Delta\nu \neq 0$, the inert gas does affect the extent of reaction at equilibrium, since it must be included in calculating the mole fractions and the total pressure P.

Let us consider as an example the technically important gas reaction, $SO_2 + \frac{1}{2}O_2 \rightarrow SO_3$. In this case $\Delta\nu = -\frac{1}{2}$, and $K_P = K_X P^{-1/2}$. Let the initial reactant mixture contain a moles of SO_2, b moles of O_2, and c moles of inert gas, for example N_2. If y moles of SO_3 are formed at equilibrium, the equilibrium mole fractions are

$$X_{SO_2} = \frac{a - y}{n}; \qquad X_{O_2} = \frac{b - (y/2)}{n}; \qquad X_{SO_3} = \frac{y}{n}$$

Here n is the total number of moles at equilibrium: $n = a + b + c - y/2$. The equilibrium constant,

$$K_X = K_P P^{1/2} = \frac{y/n}{[(a-y)/n]([b-(y/2)]/n)^{1/2}} = \frac{yn^{1/2}}{[a-y][b-(y/2)]^{1/2}}$$

It follows that

$$\frac{y}{a-y} = K_P\left[\frac{b-(y/2)P}{n}\right]^{1/2}$$

$$\frac{n_{SO_3}}{n_{SO_2}} = \left[\frac{n_{O_2}}{n}P\right]^{1/2} K_P$$

where n_{SO_3}, n_{SO_2}, n_{O_2}, n are the equilibrium mole numbers.

Let us now consider three cases. (1) If the pressure is increased by compressing the system without addition of gas from outside, n is constant, and as P increases, n_{SO_3}/n_{SO_2} also increases. (2) If an inert gas is added at constant volume, both n and P increase in the same ratio, so that the equilibrium conversion of SO_2 to SO_3, n_{SO_3}/n_{SO_2} remains unchanged. (3) If an inert gas is added at constant pressure, n is increased while P remains constant, and this dilution of the mixture with the inert gas decreases the extent of conversion n_{SO_3}/n_{SO_2}.

The reaction is exothermic, and therefore increasing the temperature decreases the formation of products. The practical problem is to run the reaction at a temperature high enough to secure a sufficiently rapid velocity, without reaching so high a temperature that the equilibrium lies too far to the left. In practice, a temperature around 500°C is chosen, with a platinum or vanadium-pentoxide catalyst to accelerate the reaction. The equilibrium constant from 700° to 1200°K is represented quite well by the equation $\ln K_P = (22\,600/RT) - (21.36/R)$. At 800°K, therefore, $K_P = 33.4$.

Let us consider two different gas mixtures, the first containing 20% SO_2 and 80% O_2 at 1 atm pressure, and a second containing in addition a considerable admixture of nitrogen, e.g., 2% SO_2, 8% O_2, 90% N_2, at 1 atm pressure. Letting y = moles SO_3 at equilibrium, we obtain:

I	II
$K_X = K_P P^{1/2} = 33.4$	$K_X = K_P P^{1/2} = 33.4$
$= \dfrac{\dfrac{y}{1-(y/2)}}{\dfrac{0.2-y}{1-(y/2)}\left[\dfrac{0.8-(y/2)}{1-(y/2)}\right]^{1/2}}$	$= \dfrac{\dfrac{y}{1-(y/2)}}{\dfrac{0.02-y}{1-(y/2)}\left[\dfrac{0.08-(y/2)}{1-(y/2)}\right]^{1/2}}$
$y^3 - 2.000y^2 + 0.681y - 0.0641 = 0$	$y^3 - 0.1985y^2 + 6.81 \times 10^{-3}y - 64.06 \times 10^{-6} = 0$
$y = 0.190$	$y = 0.0180$
95% conversion of SO_2 to SO_3	90% conversion of SO_2 to SO_3

The cubic equations arising in problems like this are probably best solved by successive approximations. Beginning with a reasonable value guessed for the percentage conversion, we can usually obtain a sufficiently accurate solution after three or four trials.

11. TEMPERATURE DEPENDENCE OF THE EQUILIBRIUM CONSTANT

An expression for the variation of K_P with temperature is derived by combining Eqs. (6.13) and (3.36). Since

$$-\Delta G^\circ = RT \ln K_P \tag{6.13}$$

and

$$\left[\frac{\partial}{\partial T}\left(\frac{\Delta G^\circ}{T}\right)\right]_P = \frac{-\Delta H^\circ}{T^2} \tag{3.36}$$

therefore,

$$\left(\frac{\partial \ln K_P}{\partial T}\right)_P = \frac{d \ln K_P}{dT} = \frac{\Delta H^\circ}{RT^2} \tag{6.18}$$

If the reaction is endothermic (ΔH° positive) the equilibrium constant increases with temperature; if the reaction is exothermic (ΔH° negative) the equilibrium constant decreases as the temperature is raised. Eq. (6.18) can also be written

$$\frac{d \ln K_P}{d(1/T)} = \frac{-\Delta H^\circ}{R} \tag{6.19}$$

Thus if $\ln K_P$ is plotted against $1/T$, the slope of the curve at any point is equal to $-\Delta H^\circ/R$. As an example of this treatment, the data* for the variation with temperature of the $2\,HI \rightleftharpoons H_2 + I_2$ equilibrium are plotted in Fig. 6.1. The curve is a straight line, indicating the ΔH° is constant for the reaction over the experimental temperature range. The value calculated from the slope is $\Delta H^\circ = 2945$ cal.

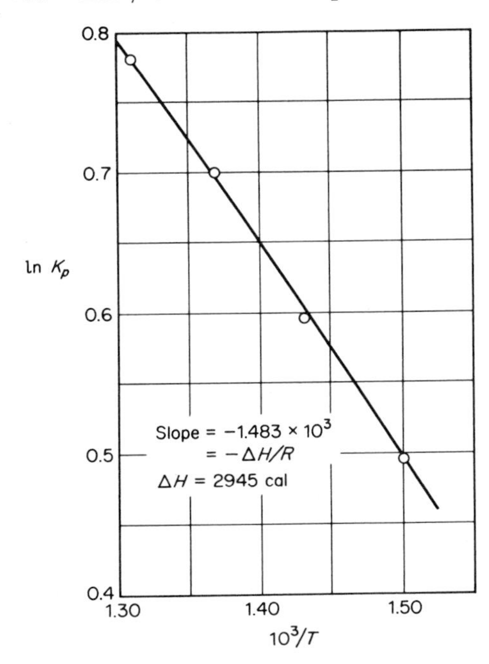

FIG. 6.1 Variation with temperature of $K_P = P_{H_2}P_{I_2}/P_{HI}^2$

It is also possible to measure the equilibrium constant at one temperature and with a value of ΔH° obtained from thermochemical data to calculate the constant at other temperatures. Equation (6.18) can be integrated to give

$$\ln \frac{K_P(T_2)}{K_P(T_1)} = \int_{T_1}^{T_2} \frac{\Delta H^\circ}{RT^2}\, dT$$

Since, over a short temperature range ΔH° may often be nearly constant, we obtain

$$\ln \frac{K_P(T_2)}{K_P(T_1)} = \frac{-\Delta H^\circ}{R}\left(\frac{1}{T_2} - \frac{1}{T_1}\right) \tag{6.20}$$

If the heat capacities of the reactants and products are known as functions of temperature, an explicit expression for the temperature dependence of ΔH° can

* A. H. Taylor and R. H. Crist, *J. Am. Chem. Soc.*, *63*, 1377 (1941).

be derived from Eq. (2.38). This expression for $\Delta H°$ as a function of temperature can then be substituted into Eq. (6.18), whereupon integration yields an explicit equation for K_P as a function of temperature. This has the form

$$\ln K_P = -\Delta H_0^\circ/RT + A \ln T + BT + CT^2 \ldots + I \tag{6.21}$$

The value of the integration constant I can be determined if the value of K_P is known at any one temperature, either experimentally or by calculation from $\Delta G°$. It will be recalled that one value of $\Delta H°$ is needed to determine ΔH_0°, the integration constant of the Kirchhoff equation.

To summarize, from a knowledge of the heat capacities of the reactants and products, and of one value each for $\Delta H°$ and K_P, it is possible to calculate the equilibrium constant at any temperature.

As an example, consider the calculation of the constant for the water-gas reaction as a function of the temperature.

$$CO + H_2O(g) \longrightarrow H_2 + CO_2; \qquad K_P = \frac{P_{H_2}P_{CO_2}}{P_{CO}P_{H_2O}}$$

From Table 6.2, the standard free-energy change at 25°C is

$$\Delta G_{298}^\circ = -94\,260 - (-54\,640 - 32\,810) = -6810$$

Thus,

$$\ln K_{P298} = \frac{6810}{298R} = 11.48, \qquad \text{or} \qquad K_{P298} = 9.55 \times 10^4$$

From the enthalpies of formation on page 52,

$$\Delta H_{298}^\circ = -94\,050 - (-\,57\,800 - 26\,420) = -9830$$

The heat capacity table on page 63 yields for this reaction

$$\Delta C_P = C_P(CO_2) + C_P(H_2) - C_P(CO) - C_P(H_2O)$$
$$= -0.515 + 6.23 \times 10^{-3}T - 29.9 \times 10^{-7}T^2$$

From Eq. (2.38),

$$\Delta H° = \Delta H_0^\circ - 0.515T + 3.12 \times 10^{-3}T^2 - 10.0 \times 10^{-7}T^3$$

Substituting $\Delta H° = -9830$, $T = 298°K$, and solving for ΔH_0°, we get $\Delta H_0^\circ = -9921$. Then the temperature dependence of the equilibrium constant, Eq. (6.21) becomes

$$\ln K_P = \frac{9221}{RT} - \frac{0.515}{R}\ln T + \frac{3.12 \times 10^{-3}}{R}T - \frac{10.0 \times 10^{-7}}{2R}T^2 + I$$

By inserting the value of $\ln K_P$ at 298°K, the integration constant can be evaluated as $I = -3.97$. The final expression for K_P as a function of temperature is, therefore,

$$\ln K_P = -3.97 + \frac{4990}{T} - 0.259 \ln T + 1.56 \times 10^{-3}T - 2.53 \times 10^{-7}T^2$$

For example, at 800°K, $\ln K_P = 1.63$, $K_P = 5.10$.

12. EQUILIBRIUM CONSTANTS FROM THERMAL DATA

We have now seen how a knowledge of the heat of reaction and of the temperature variation of the heat capacities of reactants and products allows us to calculate the equilibrium constant at any temperature, provided there is a single experimental measurement of either K_P or ΔG° at some one temperature. If we had an independent method for finding the integration constant I in Eq. (6.21), we could calculate K_P without any recourse to experimental measurements of the equilibrium or of the free-energy change. This calculation would be equivalent to the evaluation of the entropy change ΔS° from thermal data alone, i.e., from heats of reaction and heat capacities. If we know ΔS° and ΔH°, K_P can be found from $\Delta G^\circ = \Delta H^\circ - T\,\Delta S^\circ$.

From Eq. (3.41), the entropy of a substance at temperature T is given by

$$S = \int_0^T (C_P/T)\,dT + S_0$$

where S_0 is the entropy at 0°K.* If any changes of state occur between the temperature limits, the corresponding entropy changes must be added. For a gas at temperature T the general expression for the entropy therefore becomes

$$S = \int_0^{T_f} \frac{C_P\text{ (crystal)}}{T}\,dT + \frac{\Delta H_{\text{fus}}}{T_f} + \int_{T_f}^{T_b} \frac{C_P\text{ (liquid)}}{T}\,dT + \frac{\Delta H_{\text{vap}}}{T_b} + \int_{T_b}^{T} \frac{C_P\text{ (gas)}}{T}\,dT + S_0 \tag{6.22}$$

All these terms can be measured except the constant S_0. The evaluation of this constant becomes possible by virtue of the third fundamental law of thermodynamics.

13. THE APPROACH TO ABSOLUTE ZERO

The science of the production and use of low temperatures is called *cryogenics.* Some remarkable properties of matter become evident only at temperatures within a few degrees of absolute zero, e.g., superconductivity of metals and the transition to superfluid helium. The limiting value of the entropy of a substance as T approaches 0°K is the constant S_0 in Eq. (6.22). We shall first consider the methods used to attain very low temperatures, and then see how the entropy behaves in this region.

A gas will be cooled in a Joule-Thomson expansion provided the coefficient $\mu_{\text{J.T.}} > 0$. The Joule-Thomson effect was discussed in Chapter 3. In 1860, William Siemens devised a countercurrent heat exchanger, which greatly enhanced the utility of the Joule-Thomson method. It was applied in the Linde

* Be careful not to confuse S°, the entropy in the standard state of 1 atm pressure, and S_0, the entropy at 0°K.

process for the production of liquid air. Chilled compressed gas is cooled further by passage through a throttling valve. The expanded gas passes back over the inlet tube, cooling the unexpanded gas. When the cooling is sufficient to cause condensation, the liquid air can be drawn off at the bottom of the apparatus. Liquid nitrogen boils at 77°K, liquid oxygen at 90°K, and they are easily separated by fractional distillation.

In order to liquefy hydrogen, it is necessary to chill it below its Joule-Thomson inversion temperature at 193°K; the Linde process can then be used to bring it below its critical temperature at 33°K. The production of liquid hydrogen was first achieved in this way by James Dewar in 1898.

The boiling point of hydrogen is 20°K. In 1908, Kammerlingh-Onnes, founder of the famous cryogenic laboratory at Leiden, used liquid hydrogen to cool helium below its inversion point at 100°K, and then liquefied it by an adaptation of the Joule-Thomson principle. Temperatures as low as 0.84°K have been obtained with liquid helium boiling under reduced pressures. This temperature is about the limit of such a method, since gigantic pumps become necessary to carry off the gaseous helium.

In 1926, William Giauque and Peter Debye independently proposed a new refrigeration technique, called *adiabatic demagnetization.** Giauque brought the method to experimental realization in 1933. Certain salts, notably of the rare earths, have high paramagnetic susceptibilities.† The cations act as little magnets which line up in the direction of an applied external magnetic field. The salt is then *magnetized.* When the field is removed, the alinement of the little magnets disappears, and the salt is *demagnetized.*

An apparatus used for adiabatic demagnetization is shown in Fig. 6.2. The salt, gadolinium sulfate, for example, is placed within the inner chamber of a double Dewar vessel. It is magnetized while being cooled with liquid helium, which is introduced around the inner chamber. The liquid helium is then pumped away, leaving the chilled magnetized salt thermally isolated from its environment by the adiabatic barrier of the evacuated space. The magnetic field is then reduced to zero; this process effects the *adiabatic demagnetization* of the salt; since there is no heat transfer, $q = 0$.

This demagnetization is not strictly reversible, but no serious error is caused if we consider it to be so. For an adiabatic reversible demagnetization, $\Delta S = 0$. Figure 6.3 therefore represents the experiment of Giauque on a TS diagram. Two curves are shown for the salt, one in the demagnetized state in the absence of a field ($H = 0$) and one in the magnetized state in the presence of a field ($H = H_i$). In a particular experiment H_i was 8000 oersteds and the initial isothermal magnetization was done at 1.5°K.

At any constant temperature, the magnetized salt is in a state of lower entropy than the demagnetized salt. At constant T the transition

$$\text{demagnetized salt} \longrightarrow \text{magnetized salt}$$

* *J. Am. Chem. Soc.*, *49*, 1870 (1927).

† Cf. Sect. 14.8.

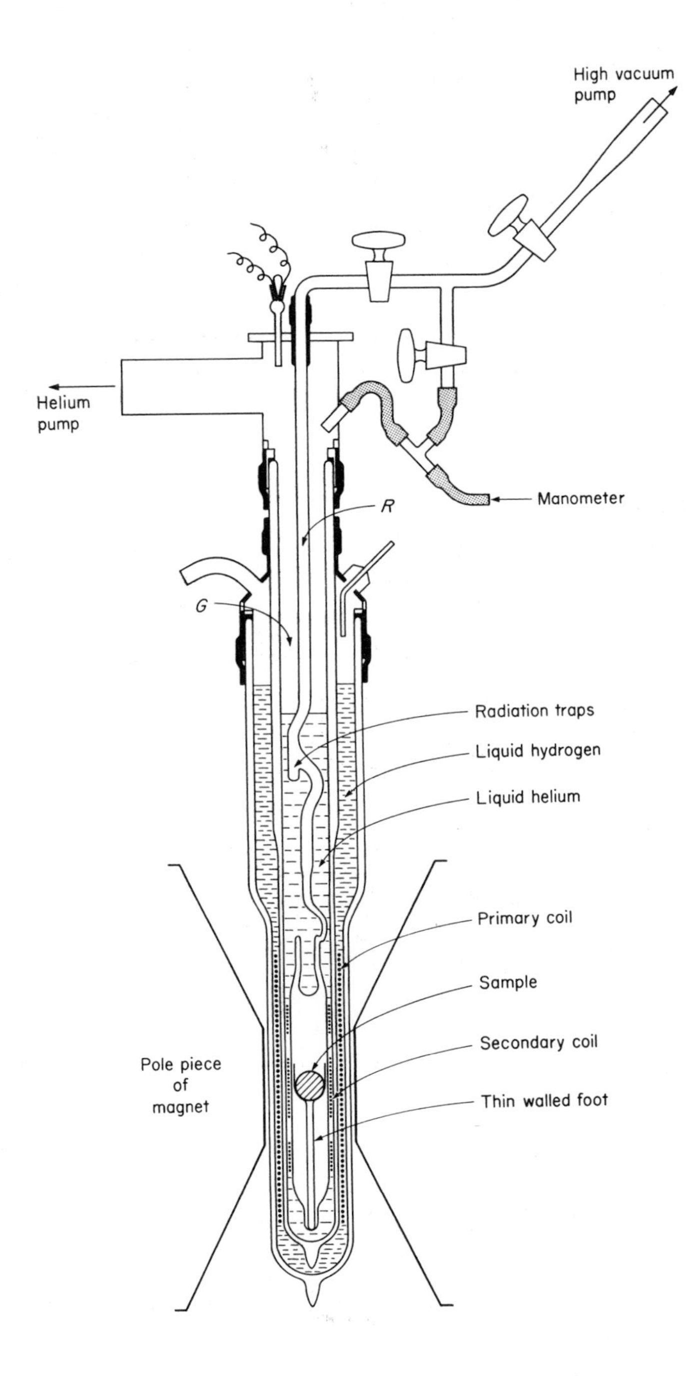

FIG. 6.2a Typical demagnetization cryostat, as used at Leiden. (D. de Klerk and M. J. Steenland, Kammerlingh-Onnes Laboratorium, Leiden.)

FIG. 6.2b Demagnetization apparatus mounted in the great electromagnet of C.N.R.S. Laboratory, Bellevue, France. The diameter of the coils is about 200 cm. (N. Kurti, University of Oxford).

goes from a state of higher entropy and energy to a state of lower entropy and energy. (It is analogous in this respect to the transition, liquid → solid.) The transition is shown as 1 → 2 on the TS diagram. When the field is reduced to zero, there is an isentropic ($\Delta S = 0$) change in the system back to the $H = 0$ curve. This change is shown as 2 → 3 on the TS diagram. It is evident that the temperature must fall. In the experiment cited, the temperature fell from 1.5 to 0.25°K.

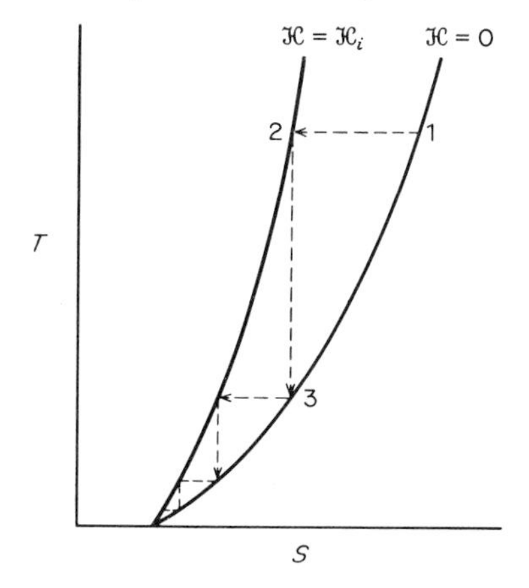

FIG. 6.3 Cooling by adiabatic demagnetization represented on a T-S diagram.

In 1950, workers at Leiden reached 0.0014°K by adiabatic demagnetization of a paramagnetic salt. Still lower temperatures have been reached by applying the same principle to nuclear magnetic moments,* about 2×10^{-5}°K being the current record.† The measurement of such low temperatures presents special problems. A vapor-pressure thermometer using helium is satisfactory down to 1°K. Below this, the magnetic properties themselves can provide a temperature scale. For example, the Curie-Weiss Law for the paramagnetic susceptibility can be used:

$$\chi = \text{constant}/T$$

14. THE THIRD LAW OF THERMODYNAMICS

The approach to within 2×10^{-5} degrees of absolute zero does not mean that there remains only a small step, which soon will be taken. On the contrary, the detailed analysis of these experiments near 0°K definitely indicates that the absolute zero is absolutely unattainable.

The situation we face is shown in Fig. 6.3. In the successive stages of isothermal magnetization and adiabatic demagnetization, the fractional cooling obtained in each stage steadily decreases. Thus, even if perfect reversibility could be achieved, we would attain absolute zero only as the limit of an infinite series of steps. All possible cooling processes are subject to this same limitation. As we did for the First and Second Laws, we therefore postulate the Third Law of Thermodynamics as an inductive generalization.

It is impossible by any procedure no matter how idealized to reduce the temperature of any system to the absolute zero in a finite number of operations.††

---

* Cf. Sect. 14.13.

† D. de Klerk, M. J. Steenland, and C. J. Gorter, *Physica 16*, 571 (1950).

†† R. H. Fowler and E. A. Guggenheim, *Statistical Thermodynamics* (London: Cambridge Univ. Press, 1940), p. 224.

If we again refer to Fig. 6.3, we can see that the unattainability of absolute zero is connected with the fact that in the limit as $T \to 0$, the entropies of the magnetized and demagnetized states approach each other. For the isothermal magnetization, therefore, the limit $\Delta S_0 \to 0$ as $T \to 0$. There is nothing special about the magnetic case; any cooling procedure can be reduced to a TS diagram of this sort. Thus, for any isothermal reversible process $a \to b$, the Third Law requires that in the limit as $T \to 0$, $S_0^a \to S_0^b$, or

$$S_0^a - S_0^b = \Delta S_0 = 0 \qquad (6.23)$$

This statement of the Third Law is similar to the famous *heat theorem* proposed by Walther Nernst in 1906.

Actually the first satisfactory statement of the principle was given in 1923 in the first edition of the book *Thermodynamics and the Free Energy of Chemical Substances* by G. N. Lewis and M. Randall. Their statement was as follows:

> *If the entropy of each element in some crystalline state be taken as zero at the absolute zero of temperature, every substance has a finite positive entropy; but at the absolute zero of temperature the entropy may become zero, and does so become in the case of perfect crystalline substances.*

15. AN ILLUSTRATION OF THE THIRD LAW

Only changes or differences in entropy have any physical meaning in thermodynamics. When we speak of the entropy of a substance at a certain temperature, we mean the difference between its entropy at that temperature and its entropy at some other temperature, usually 0°K. Since the chemical elements are unchanged in any physicochemical process, we can assign any arbitrary values to their entropies at 0°K without affecting in any way the values of ΔS for any chemical change. It is most convenient, therefore, to take the value of S_0 for all the *chemical elements* as equal to zero. This is a convention first proposed by Max Planck in 1912, and incorporated in the statement of Lewis and Randall.

It then follows, from Eq. (6.23), that the entropies of all pure *chemical compounds* in their stable states at 0°K are also zero, because for their formation from the elements, $\Delta S_0 = 0$. This formulation is equivalent to setting the constant S_0 in Eq. (6.22) equal to zero.

As an example of the Third Law, consider the element sulfur. Let us set $S_0 = 0$ for rhombic sulfur and determine experimentally the S_0 for monoclinic sulfur to see how the Third Law is followed. The transition temperature for S (rhombic) $\to$ S (monoclinic) is 368.5°K and the latent heat of transition is 96.0 calories per mole. From Eq. (6.22):

$$S_{368.5}^{\mathrm{rh}} = S_0^{\mathrm{rh}} + \int_0^{368.5} (C_P/T)\, dT$$

$$S_{368.5}^{\mathrm{mono}} = S_0^{\mathrm{mono}} + \int_0^{368.5} (C_P/T)\, dT$$

In order to evaluate S_0^{mono} it is necessary to have heat capacities for supercooled monoclinic sulfur from 0 to 368.5°K. This measurement causes no difficulties, since the rate of change of monoclinic to rhombic is extremely small at low temperatures. Excellent heat capacities are therefore available for both monoclinic* and rhombic* sulfurs. The integrations of the C_P/T vs. T curves yield:

$$S_{368.5}^{rh} = S_0^{rh} + 8.81(\pm 0.05) \text{ cal deg}^{-1} \text{ mole}^{-1}$$

$$S_{368.5}^{mono} = S_0^{mono} + 9.04\ (\pm 0.10) \text{ cal deg}^{-1} \text{ mole}^{-1}$$

Thus $$S_{368.5}^{rh} - S_{368.5}^{mono} = S_0^{rh} - S_0^{mono} - 0.23 \pm 0.15$$

But $$S_{368.5}^{rh} - S_{368.5}^{mono} = \frac{-96.0}{368.5} = -0.261 \pm 0.002$$

Hence, $$S_0^{rh} - S_0^{mono} = -\ 0.03 \pm 0.15$$

which is zero within experimental error. Thus if we set $S_0^{rh} = 0$, we have $S_0^{mono} = 0$ also.

Many checks of this kind have been made both for elements and crystalline compounds. We must not forget, however, that $S_0 = 0$ is restricted to *perfect crystalline substances.* Thus glasses, solid solutions, and crystals retaining a structural disorder even near absolute zero, are excluded from the rule $S_0 = 0$. The discussion of such exceptions follows so naturally from the statistical interpretation of entropy that we shall not pursue it further until this subject is introduced in Chapters 7 and 16.

16. THIRD-LAW ENTROPIES

It is now possible to use heat-capacity data extrapolated to 0°K to determine so-called *third-law entropies,* which can be used in equilibrium calculations. As an example, the determination of the standard entropy, S_{298}°, for hydrogen chloride gas is shown in Table 6.5. The value $S_{298}^{\circ} = 44.4$ cal deg^{-1} mole^{-1} is for

TABLE 6.5 Evaluation of Entropy of Hydrogen Chloride from Heat-Capacity Measurements

Contribution	*cal deg^{-1} mole^{-1}*
1. Extrapolation from 0–16°K (Debye Theory, Sec. 16.27)	0.30
2. $\int C_P\, d \ln T$ for Solid I from 16°–98.36°	7.06
3. Transition, Solid I → Solid II, 2843/98.36	2.89
4. $\int C_P\, d \ln T$ for Solid II from 98.36°–158.91°	5.05
5. Fusion, 476.0/158.91	3.00
6. $\int C_P\, d \ln T$ for Liquid from 158.91°–188.07°	2.36
7. Vaporization, 3860/188.07	20.52
8. $\int C_P\, d \ln T$ for Gas from 188.07°–298.15°K	3.22
	$S^{\circ}_{298.15} = 44.40 \pm 0.10$

* E. D. Eastman and W. C. McGavock, *J. Am. Chem. Soc. 59*, 145 (1937). E. D. West, *ibid.*, *81*, 29 (1959).

HCl at 25°C and 1 atm pressure. A small correction due to nonideality of the gas raises the figure to 44.6. A number of third-law entropies are collected in Table 6.6.

TABLE 6.6 THIRD-LAW ENTROPIES
(Substances in the Standard State at 25°C)

Substance	S°_{298} (cal deg^{-1} mole^{-1})	*Substance*	S°_{298} (cal deg^{-1} mole^{-1})
		Gases	
H_2	31.211	CO_2	51.08
D_2	34.602	H_2O	45.106
HD	34.34	NH_3	46.01
N_2	45.77	SO_2	59.40
O_2	49.01	CH_4	44.50
Cl_2	53.29	C_2H_2	47.997
HCl	44.64	C_2H_4	52.45
CO	47.20	C_2H_6	54.85
		Liquids	
Mercury	18.17	Benzene	41.3
Bromine	36.4	Toluene	52.5
Water	16.73	Bromobenzene	49.7
Methanol	30.3	*n*-Hexane	70.7
Ethanol	38.4	Cyclohexane	48.9
		Solids	
C (diamond)	.583	I_2	27.76
C (graphite)	1.361	NaCl	17.30
S (rhombic)	7.62	LiF	8.87
S (monoclinic)	7.78	LiH	5.9
Ag	10.21	$CuSO_4.5H_2O$	73.0
Cu	7.97	$CuSO_4$	27.1
Fe	6.49	AgCl	23.00
Na	12.2	AgBr	25.60

The standard entropy change ΔS° in a chemical reaction can be calculated immediately, if the standard entropies of products and reactants are known.

$$\Delta S^\circ = \sum \nu_i S_i^\circ$$

One of the most satisfactory experimental checks of the Third Law is provided by the comparison of ΔS° values obtained in this way from low-temperature heat capacity measurements, with ΔS° values derived either from measured equilibrium constants and reaction heats or from the temperature coefficients of cell emf's (Sect. 10.7). Examples of such comparisons are shown in Table 6.7. The Third Law is now considered to be on a firm experimental basis. Its full meaning will become clearer when its statistical interpretation is considered in a later chapter.

The great utility of Third-Law measurements in the calculation of chemical equilibria has led to an intensive development of low-temperature heat-capacity techniques, using liquid hydrogen and helium as refrigerants. The experimental procedure consists essentially in a careful measurement of the temperature rise caused in an insulated sample by a carefully measured energy input.

TABLE 6.7 · CHECKS OF THE THIRD LAW OF THERMODYNAMICS

Reaction	Temp. (°K)	Third Law $\Delta S°$ (cal deg^{-1} mole^{-1})	Experimental $\Delta S°$	Method
Ag (c) + $\frac{1}{2}Br_2$ (l) → AgBr (c)	265.9	-3.01 ± 0.40	-3.02 ± 0.10	emf
Ag (c) + $\frac{1}{2}Cl_2$ (g) → AgCl (c)	298.16	-13.85 ± 0.25	-13.73 ± 0.10	emf
Zn (c) + $\frac{1}{2}O_2$ (g) → ZnO (c)	298.16	-24.07 ± 0.25	-24.24 ± 0.05	K and ΔH
C + $\frac{1}{2}O_2$ (g) → CO (g)	298.16	-21.09 ± 0.20	-21.38 ± 0.05	K and ΔH
$CaCO_3$ (c) → CaO (c) + CO_2 (g)	298.16	38.40 ± 0.20	38.03 ± 0.20	K and ΔH

We have now seen how thermodynamics has been able to answer the old question of chemical affinity by providing a quantitative method for calculating (from thermal data alone) the position of equilibrium in chemical reactions.

17. EQUILIBRIA IN NONIDEAL SYSTEMS – FUGACITY AND ACTIVITY

We have discussed the thermodynamic theory of chemical equilibrium with special reference to reacting mixtures of ideal gases. We need to consider next how the theory can be extended to apply to nonideal gases, solutions in condensed phases, and heterogeneous systems.

The development of the theory for ideal gases started with the equation

$$dG = V\,dP - S\,dT \tag{6.24}$$

We introduced $\overline{V} = RT/P$ and obtained at constant temperature,

$$d\overline{G} = RT\,d\ln P \tag{6.25}$$

Upon integration, we found for the free energy per mole,

$$\overline{G} = \overline{G}° + RT\ln P \tag{6.26}$$

For the general case of a component A in a nonideal solution, instead of Eq. (6.24), we have

$$d\mu_A = \overline{V}_A\,dP - \overline{S}_A\,dT \tag{6.27}$$

Or, at constant temperature,

$$d\mu_A = \overline{V}_A\,dP \tag{6.28}$$

Equation (6.26) led to results in such convenient form for equilibrium calculations, that we should like to keep as close to it as possible. With this end in view, G. N. Lewis introduced a new function, called the *fugacity* f. He defined it by an equation analogous to (6.25),

$$d\mu_A = d\overline{G}_A = RT\,d\ln f_A = \overline{V}_A\,dP \tag{6.29}$$

Integrating between the given state and some freely chosen standard state, we obtain

$$\mu_A = \mu_A^\circ + RT\ln f_A/f_A^\circ \tag{6.30}$$

The fugacity is the true measure of the escaping tendency of a component in solution. We can think of it as a sort of idealized partial pressure or partial vapor pressure. It becomes equal to the partial pressure only when the vapor behaves as an ideal gas.

The ratio of the fugacity f_A to the fugacity in a standard state, f_A°, is called the *activity* a_A. This new function was also introduced by Lewis.

$$a_A = f_A/f_A^\circ \tag{6.31}$$

In terms of the activity, Eq. (6.30) becomes

$$\mu_A = \mu_A^\circ + RT \ln a_A \tag{6.32}$$

It is important to note that the activity is the *ratio* of a fugacity to a fugacity in some standard state. It is thus a dimensionless quantity. Whenever we talk about *activity*, we must know what standard state has been chosen. Various examples will be given later.

The treatment of equilibrium in Section 5 can be carried through in terms of chemical potentials and activities. This leads to an expression K_a for the equilibrium constant, which is always valid, not just for ideal gases, but also for nonideal gases and solutions.

$$K_a = \frac{a_C^c\, a_D^d}{a_A^a\, a_B^b} \tag{6.33}$$

$$\Delta\mu^\circ = -RT \ln K_a \tag{6.34}$$

To translate the equilibrium calculations back into measurable terms, we must have some way of computing the actual concentrations in the reaction mixture from the calculated activities.

18. NONIDEAL GASES – FUGACITY AND STANDARD STATE

We define the standard state of a real gas A as that state in which the gas has unit fugacity, $f_A^\circ = 1$, and in which, furthermore, the gas behaves as if it were ideal. Note that for a gas, therefore, the activity equals the fugacity

$$\text{(for a gas)} \quad a_A = f_A \tag{6.35}$$

This definition of the standard state may seem curious, since it is not a real state of the gas, but a "hypothetical state." We want to make the gas behave ideally in its standard state, so that we can compare properties of different gases in ideal standard states with one another and with theoretical calculations.

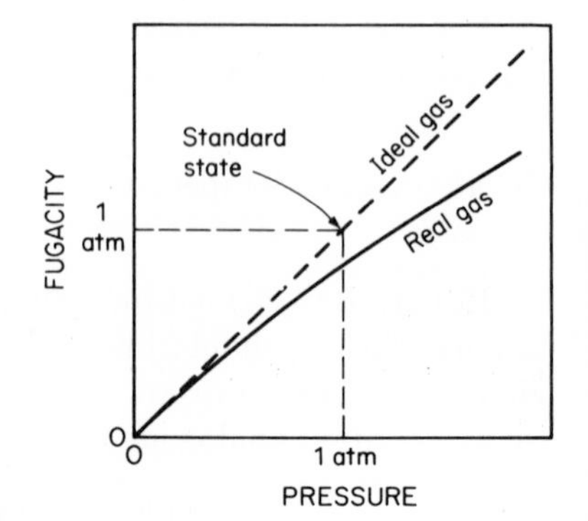

FIG. 6.4 Definition of standard state of unit fugacity.

The definition of the standard state of unit fugacity should be clear from Fig. 6.4. At a sufficiently low pressure every gas behaves ideally and its fugacity then becomes equal to its pressure. To get the property of a gas in its standard state, we must move along the experimental curve (as a function of pressure) until it joins the ideal curve, and then move back along the ideal curve until we reach the point of unit fugacity. There is no problem in calculating the change in a property along the ideal curve, since we have simple equations for the properties of an ideal gas.

The fugacity of a pure gas or of a gas in a mixture can be evaluated if sufficiently detailed PVT data are available. In the case of a pure gas,

$$d\overline{G} = d\mu = \overline{V}\, dP \tag{6.36}$$

If the gas is ideal, $\overline{V} = RT/P$. For a nonideal gas, we write

$$\alpha = \overline{V}\text{ (ideal)} - \overline{V}\text{ (real)} = (RT/P) - \overline{V}$$

whence $\overline{V} = (RT/P) - \alpha$. Substituting this expression into Eq. (6.29), we find that

$$RT\, d \ln f = d\overline{G} = d\mu = RT\, d \ln P - \alpha\, dP$$

The equation is integrated from $P' = 0$ to P.

$$RT \int_{f,P=0}^{f} d \ln f' = RT \int_{P=0}^{P} d \ln P' - \int_0^P \alpha\, dP'$$

As its pressure approaches zero, a gas approaches ideality, and for an ideal gas the fugacity equals the pressure, $f = P$ [cf. Eqs. (6.7) and (6.30)]. The lower limits of the first two integrals must therefore be equal, so that we obtain

$$RT \ln f = RT \ln P - \int_0^P \alpha\, dP' \tag{6.37}$$

This equation enables us to evaluate the fugacity at any pressure and temperature, provided PVT data for the gas are available. If the deviation from ideality of the gas volume is plotted against P, the integral in Eq. (6.37) can be evaluated graphically. Alternatively, an equation of state can be used to calculate an expression for α as a function of P, making it possible to evaluate the integral by analytic methods.

In Chapter 1, it was pointed out that the deviations of gases from ideality are approximately determined by their closeness to the critical point. This behavior is confirmed by the fact that at the same reduced pressures all gases have approximately the same ratio of fugacity to pressure.

The ratio of fugacity to pressure is called the *activity coefficient*,

$$\gamma = f/P \tag{6.38}$$

Figure 6.5 shows a family of curves* relating the activity coefficient of a gas to its reduced pressure P_R at various values of the reduced temperature T_R. To the approximation that the law of corresponding states is valid, all gases have the

* R. H. Newton, *Ind. Eng. Chem.* *27*, 302 (1935). Graphs for other ranges of P_R and T_R are included in this paper.

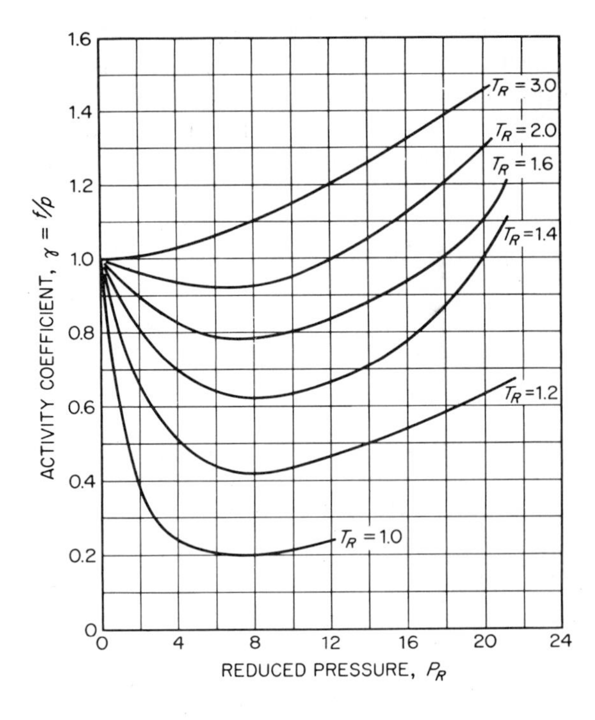

FIG. 6.5 Variation of activity coefficient of a gas with reduced pressure at various reduced temperatures-

same value of γ when they are in corresponding states, i.e., at equal P_R and T_R. This is a useful principle, for it allows us to estimate the fugacity of a gas solely from a knowledge of its critical constants.

19. USE OF FUGACITY IN EQUILIBRIUM CALCULATIONS

From Eqs. (6.33, 6.35, and 6.38) we find for the equilibrium constant of a reaction between nonideal gases,

$$K_f = \frac{f_C^c f_D^d}{f_A^a f_B^b} = \frac{\gamma_C^c \gamma_D^d}{\gamma_A^a \gamma_B^b} \cdot \frac{P_C^c P_D^d}{P_A^a P_B^b} \tag{6.39}$$

or

$$K_f = K_\gamma K_P$$

Of course, K_γ is not an equilibrium constant but simply the ratio of activity coefficients needed to convert the partial pressures in K_P into the fugacities in K_f.

As an example of the use of fugacities in equilibrium problems, let us consider the synthesis of ammonia, $\frac{1}{2}N_2 + \frac{3}{2}H_2 \rightarrow NH_3$. The industrially important reaction is carried out under high pressures, at which the ideal-gas approximation would fail badly. The reaction has been carefully investigated up to 1000 atm by Larson and Dodge.* The per cent of NH_3 in equilibrium with a three-to-one H_2—N_2 mixture at 450°C and various total pressures is shown in Table 6.8. In the third column of the table are the values of $K_P = P_{NH_3}/P_{N_2}^{1/2}P_{H_2}^{3/2}$ calcu-

* *J. Am. Chem. Soc.* *45*, 2918 (1923); *46*, 367 (1924).

lated from these data. Since K_P for ideal gases should be independent of the pressure, these results show the large departure from ideality at the higher pressures.

Let us calculate the equilibrium constant K_f using Newton's graphs to obtain the activity coefficients. We thereby adopt the approximation that the activity coefficient of a gas in a mixture is determined only by the temperature and by the *total pressure.* This approximation ignores specific interactions between the components in the mixture of gases.

Consider the calculation of the activity coefficients at 450°C (723°K) and 600 atm.

	P_c	T_c	P_R	T_R	γ
N_2	33.5	126	17.9	5.74	1.35
H_2	12.8	33.3	46.8	21.7	1.19
NH_3	111.5	405.6	5.38	1.78	0.85

The activity coefficients γ are read from the graphs, at the proper values of reduced pressure P_R and reduced temperature T_R. (Only the NH_3 values are found in Fig. 6.5; the complete graphs must be consulted for the other gases.)

TABLE 6.8 EQUILIBRIUM IN THE AMMONIA SYNTHESIS AT 450°C WITH 3 : 1 RATIO OF H_2 TO N_2

Total Pressure (atm)	Per cent NH_3 at Equilibrium	K_P	K_γ	K_f
10	2.04	0.00659	0.995	0.00655
30	5.80	0.00676	0.975	0.00659
50	9.17	0.00690	0.945	0.00650
100	16.36	0.00725	0.880	0.00636
300	35.5	0.00884	0.688	0.00608
600	53.6	0.01294	0.497	0.00642
1000	69.4	0.02328	0.434	0.01010

In this case $K_\gamma = \gamma_{NH_3}/\gamma_{N_2}^{1/2}\gamma_{H_2}^{2/3}$. The values of K_γ and K_f are shown in Table 6.8. There is a marked improvement in the constancy of K_f as compared with K_P. Only at 1000 atm does the approximate treatment of the fugacities appear to fail. To carry out an exact thermodynamic treatment, it would be necessary to calculate the fugacity of each gas in the particular mixture under study. Extensive PVT data on the mixture would be needed for such a calculation.

Often, knowing $\Delta G°$ for the reaction, we wish to calculate the equilibrium concentrations in a reaction mixture. The procedure is to obtain K_f from $-\Delta G° = RT \ln K_f$, to estimate K_γ from the graphs, and then to calculate the partial pressures from $K_P = K_f/K_\gamma$.

20. STANDARD STATES FOR COMPONENTS IN SOLUTION

The expression obtained in Eq. (6.33) for the equilibrium constant K_a in terms of activities represents a perfectly general solution to the problem of chemical equilibrium in solutions. Before we can apply it to practical cases, we must choose and define the standard states for components in a solution.

There are two different standard states in common use. With increasing dilution, the solvent in a solution always approaches the ideal behavior specified by Raoult's Law, and the solute always approaches the behavior specified by Henry's Law. One standard state (I) is therefore based on Raoult's Law as a limiting law, and the other standard state (II) is based on Henry's Law. We may choose whichever definition seems most convenient for any component in a particular solution.

CASE I. *Standard state for a component considered as a solvent.* In this case the standard state of a component A in a solution is taken to be the pure liquid or pure solid at one atmosphere pressure and at the temperature in question.

Thus the activity

$$a_A = \frac{f_A}{f_A^\circ} \approx \frac{P_A}{P_A^\circ} \tag{6.40}$$

where P_A° is the vapor pressure of pure A under one atmosphere total pressure. (Cf. Sec. 4.9) It is almost always sufficiently accurate to take the activity equal to the ratio of the partial pressure P_A of A above the solution to the vapor pressure of pure A (at 1 atm pressure). It is always possible, however, to convert these vapor pressures to fugacities, should the vapors depart appreciably from ideal-gas behavior.

With this choice of standard state, Raoult's Law becomes

$$a_A = \frac{P_A}{P_A^\circ} = X_A \tag{6.41}$$

Thus, for the ideal solution, or for any solution in the limit as $X_A \to 1$, we have $X_A = a_A$.

By analogy with Eq. (6.38), we define an activity coefficient ${}^x\gamma_A$ by

$$a_A = {}^x\gamma_A X_A \tag{6.42}$$

Thus, as $X_A \to 1$, ${}^x\gamma_A \to 1$.

CASE II. *Standard state for a component considered as a solute.* In this case we choose the standard state so that in the limit of extreme dilution, as $X_B \to 0$, $a_B \to X_B$. As long as Henry's Law is obeyed, as shown in Fig. 6.6,

$$f_B = k_H X_B \tag{6.43}$$

The standard state is obtained by extrapolating the Henry's Law line to $X_B = 1$. Thus we see that the fugacity in the standard state, f_B° is simply equal to k_H, the constant of Henry's Law.

$$f_B^\circ = k_H \tag{6.44}$$

As in the case of the nonideal gas, the standard state is a *hypothetical* state. We can think of it in physical terms as a state in which the pure solute $B(X_B = 1)$ has the properties it would have in an infinitely dilute solution in the solvent A.

When we consider solutions of electrolytes, we shall define a standard state in terms of molalities, also based on Henry's Law [Sec. 9.15].

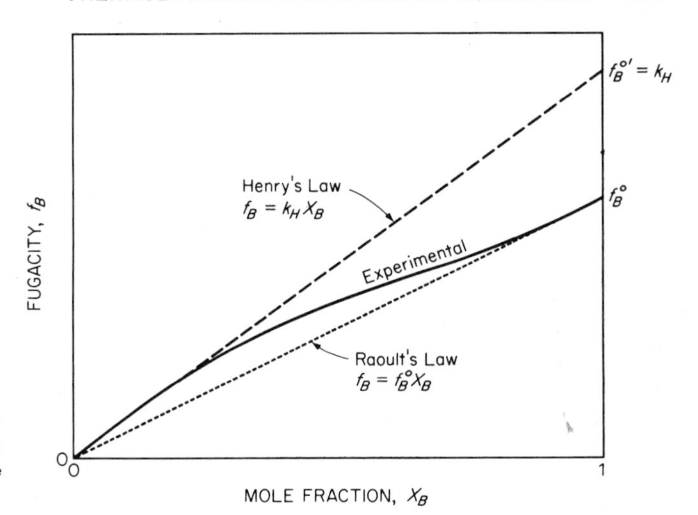

FIG. 6.6 Definition of standard state for a solute B, based on Henry's Law in dilute solution.

21. AN EXAMPLE OF THE DETERMINATION OF ACTIVITIES

Let us consider how the activities of water A and of sucrose B are determined from data on the vapor pressures of the solution.

The sucrose is practically nonvolatile, so that the total vapor pressure above the solution in this case equals the partial vapor pressure of the water, P_A. If we neglect the small correction for nonideality of the water vapor, we can readily tabulate the activities a_A of the water from

$$a_A = P_A/P_A^\circ$$

The results are shown in Table 6.9 for the particular temperature of 50°C. For example, at 50°C, P_A° the vapor pressure of pure water is 92.51 mm. The vapor pressure of a sucrose solution in which the mole fraction of water is $X_A = .9665$ is $P_A = 88.97$ mm. Hence, $a_A = 88.97/92.51 = .9617$. The activity coefficient $\gamma_A = .9617/.9665 = 0.9949$ at this concentration. Note that the standard state for the solvent, water, is chosen as the pure liquid at 1 atm pressure. As $X_A \rightarrow 1$, $a_A \rightarrow X_A$, and $\gamma_A \rightarrow 1$.

The activity of the sucrose obviously cannot be determined from its partial vapor pressure, since this is immeasuraby low. If we had a volatile solute, alcohol for instance, we would doubtless take pure alcohol to be its standard state, and compute its activity from Eq. (6.40). In the case of sucrose, on the other hand, we clearly should choose the second definition of standard state, that which is based on Henry's Law for the solute.

There is no need, however, to try to measure directly the activity of the sucrose, since it can be calculated easily from the Gibbs-Duhem Equation (5.7),

$$n_A \, d\mu_A + n_B \, d\mu_B = 0$$

From Eq. (6.32), this becomes

$$n_A \, d \ln a_A + n_B \, d \ln a_B = 0$$

Dividing by $n_A + n_B$, we obtain

$$X_A\, d \ln a_A + X_B\, d \ln a_B = 0$$

Hence,

$$\int d \ln a_B = -\int (X_A/X_B)\, d \ln a_A = -\int (X_A/(1 - X_A)\, d \ln a_A \quad (6.45)$$

We wish to calculate a_B from the measurements giving a_A as a function of X_A. There seems to be a little difficulty in using the above integration, since $X_B \to 0$, $X_A \to 1$, and the integrals approach $-\infty$. This difficulty is easily avoided by starting the integration, not at $X_A = 1$, but at a value of X_A at which the solvent begins to follow Raoult's Law, i.e., at which $X_A = a_A$. At this value $X_B = a_B$, where a_B is defined on the basis of Henry's Law. Therefore, the integrals in Eq. (6.45) have lower limits corresponding to extremely dilute solutions. The results of such a calculation of the activities of the sucrose in aqueous solution are shown in Table 6.9.

TABLE 6.9 Activities of Water and Sucrose in Their Solutions at 50°C Obtained from Vapor Pressure Lowering and the Gibbs-Duhem Equation

Mole Fraction of Water X_A	Activity of Water a_A	Mole Fraction of Sucrose X_B	Activity of Sucrose a_B
0.9940	0.9939	0.0060	0.0060
0.9864	0.9934	0.0136	0.0136
0.9826	0.9799	0.0174	0.0197
0.9762	0.9697	0.0238	0.0302
0.9665	0.9617	0.0335	0.0481
0.9559	0.9477	0.0441	0.0716
0.9439	0.9299	0.0561	0.1037
0.9323	0.9043	0.0677	0.1390
0.9098	0.8758	0.0902	0.2190
0.8911	0.8140	0.1089	0.3045

22. EQUILIBRIUM CONSTANTS IN SOLUTION

The relation,

$$\Delta G^\circ = -RT \ln K_a$$

is universally valid, but in fact it simply summarizes the mathematical analysis of the equilibrium problem. We might paraphrase the content of this equation as follows:

(1) Define a standard state for each of the reactants and products in a chemical equilibrium $aA + bB \rightleftarrows cC + dD$.

(2) Compute ΔG° for the reaction where all components are in this standard state.

(3) Then there will always be a function $K_a(T, P)$ which will be related to the activities of the components in the equilibrium mixture, as

$$K_a = \frac{a_C^c a_D^d}{a_A^a a_B^b}$$

In order to obtain any information on the actual composition of this equilibrium mixture, or in order to calculate K_a and hence $\Delta G°$ from the equilibrium composition, we must be able to relate the activities to some composition variables. The most logical choice is to define an activity coefficient (${}^x\gamma$) such that

$$a = \gamma X$$

where X is the mole fraction. Hence,

$$K_a = \left(\frac{\gamma_C^c \gamma_D^d}{\gamma_A^a \gamma_B^b}\right)\left(\frac{X_C^c X_D^d}{X_A^a X_B^b}\right) = K_\gamma K_X$$

Note that K_γ is not an equilibrium constant, but simply the indicated product of activity coefficients. In general, K_X will not be an equilibrium constant either, since it will not be constant at constant T and P as we vary the composition of the equilibrium mixture. In some cases, however, it may happen that K_γ does not change much as we vary the composition. In particular, in dilute solutions, in which the solutes approximately follow Henry's Law and the solvent approximately follows Raoult's Law, we can choose the standard states (as shown in the previous section) so that the γ's all approach unity. In this case,

$$K_a \longrightarrow K_X$$

and

$$\Delta G° \longrightarrow -RT \ln K_X$$

To the extent that these approximations are satisfactory, we shall be able to use an equilibrium constant K_X in terms of the mole fractions in the solution. Let us not disdain such an approximate equilibrium constant, because often the experimental data do not justify a more elaborate thermodynamic treatment of the equilibrium anyway. We must, however, keep clearly in mind the choice of standard states for the $\Delta G°$. For all the reactants the standard states would be those of $X = 1$. In the case of the solvent, this would be the pure liquid. In the case of the solutes, these would be the hypothetical states in which $X = 1$ but the environment would be that in an extremely dilute solution.

An example of the calculation of K_X was shown in Sec. 6.1 for the esterification equilibrium. Actually there are not many careful studies of equilibrium in solution which do not involve electrolytes, and hence effects due to ionization. (Such systems are discussed in Chapter 9.) One example often cited is the early work (1895) of Cundall on the dissociation $N_2O_4 \rightleftarrows 2NO_2$ in chloroform solution. Some of his data are shown in Table 6.10, together with the calculated K_X.

TABLE 6.10 Dissociation of N_2O_4 in Chloroform Solution at 8.2°C

$X(N_2O_4)$	$X(NO_2)$	K_X	$c(N_2O_4)$	$c(NO_2)$	K_c
1.03×10^{-2}	0.93×10^{-6}	8.37×10^{-11}	0.129	1.17×10^{-3}	1.07×10^{-5}
1.81	1.28	9.05	0.227	1.61	1.14
2.48	1.47	8.70	0.324	1.85	1.05
3.20	1.70	9.04	0.405	2.13	1.13
6.10	2.26	8.35	0.778	2.84	1.04
	Mean	8.70×10^{-11}		Mean	1.09×10^{-5}

We have also included the computed values of an equilibrium constant in terms of concentrations,

$$K_c = c_{NO_2}^2/c_{N_2O_4}$$

where c is the concentration in moles per liter. We must not fail to note carefully that the use of K_c implies a derivation from $\Delta G^\circ = -RT \ln K_a$ based on a new and distinctive choice of standard states. We then must have a new set of activity coefficients γ', so that

$$a = \gamma' c$$

and as $c \to 0$, $\gamma' \to 1$, and $K_a \to K_c$. The corresponding standard state is the hypothetical state of the solute at a concentration of one mole per liter ($c = 1$), but with an environment the same as that in an extremely dilute solution.

For the choice of standard states consistent with K_X, we find for the $N_2O_4 \rightleftarrows 2NO_2$ reaction,

$$\Delta G^\circ = -RT \ln K_X = 12\,900 \text{ cal deg}^{-1}$$

For the choice of standard states consistent with K_c, we find

$$\Delta G^{\circ\prime} = -RT \ln K_c = 6390 \text{ cal deg}^{-1}$$

Caveat lector: It is folly to use ΔG° values for reactions in solution unless you are sure you understand the exact standard state upon which they are based.

23. THE EFFECT OF PRESSURE ON ACTIVITY

We saw in Section 6.17 how the activity (fugacity) of a gaseous component is related to its pressure. In contrast with the strong dependence of activity on pressure for a gas, the activity of a component in a liquid or solid phase depends only weakly on pressure. At moderate pressures, we may even neglect entirely the effect of pressure on activities in condensed phases, without serious error. At high pressures, however, the total effect of pressure can become appreciable. In any case, we should know how to include the effect of pressure on condensed phases in our thermodynamic theory of equilibrium.

At any constant temperature we can calculate the dependence of the fugacity of a component A on the total pressure from Eq. (6.36),

$$d\mu_A = RT\, d \ln f_A = \overline{V}_A\, dP$$

The ratio Γ of the fugacity at any pressure P_2 to the fugacity at one atmosphere is therefore given by

$$\ln \Gamma = \ln \frac{f_A^{(P_2)}}{f_A^{(1\text{ atm})}} = \frac{1}{RT} \int_1^{P_2} \overline{V}_A\, dP \tag{6.46}$$

where we have written

$$\Gamma = f_A^{(P_2)}/f_A^{(1\text{ atm})}$$

Hence,

$$\frac{f_A^{(P_2)}}{f_A^\circ} = \Gamma \frac{f_A^{(1\text{ atm})}}{f_A^\circ}$$

Or, since f_A° is the fugacity of A in its standard state,

$$a(\text{at } P_2) = \Gamma a \text{ (at 1 atm)} \tag{6.47}$$

If we use the standard state based on mole fractions, Eq. (6.47) becomes

$$a = \Gamma \gamma X \tag{6.48}$$

For a pure liquid or solid, the activity *at 1 atm* equals unity if the standard state is defined as a pure liquid or solid at 1 atm.

As an example of the use of Eq. (6.46), let us use the data of Bridgman* to calculate the activity of pure liquid water at 50°C and 10^4 atm. In this case $\overline{V}_A = \overline{V}$ and the integration in Eq. (6.46) can be carried out graphically by plotting the molar volume of water against the pressure and taking the area under the curve. The calculation is shown in Fig. 6.7. The integration yields $\Gamma = 439$, so that the activity of pure liquid water at 50°C and 10^4 atm is $a = 439$. At 100 atm, the activity would be about 1.40. Thus at moderate pressures, we often neglect the effect of pressure on the activity of condensed phases.

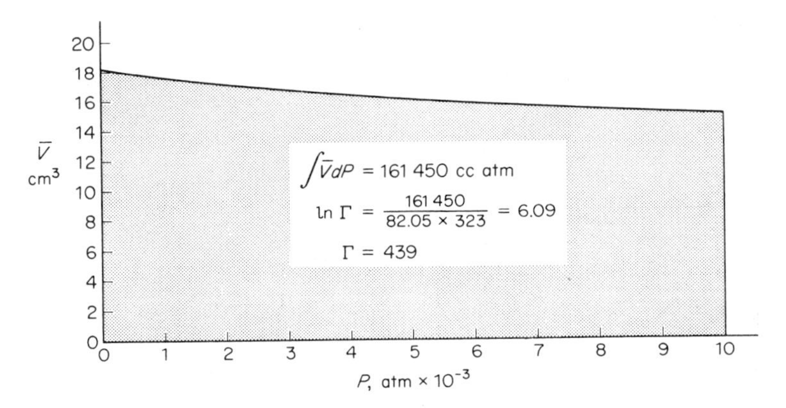

FIG. 6.7 Calculation of the activity of water at 50°C and 10^4 atm.

24. CHEMICAL EQUILIBRIA INVOLVING CONDENSED PHASES

The simplest examples of such equilibria include pure liquid or solid reactants. Let us consider a typical case:

$$NiO(s) + CO \longrightarrow Ni(s) + CO_2$$

The general expression for the equilibrium constant is

$$K_a = \frac{a_{Ni}\, a_{CO_2}}{a_{NiO}\, a_{CO}}$$

* P. W. Bridgman, *The Physics of High Pressure* (London: Bell, 1949), p. 130.

This expression may be rewritten as

$$K_a = \frac{f_{CO_2}}{f_{CO}} \cdot \frac{\Gamma_{Ni}}{\Gamma_{NiO}}$$

At moderate pressures, Γ_{Ni} and $\Gamma_{NiO} = 1$ (i.e., the activities of the pure solids = 1). If we consider that the gases behave ideally, K_a becomes simply

$$K_p = P_{CO_2}/P_{CO}$$

The general rule is that the activities of pure solid and liquid substances are simply set equal to unity in the equilibrium constant, so that no terms are included for such reactants. For the reaction cited at 1500°K, $\Delta G° = -19.38$ kcal, so that

$$K_P = P_{CO_2}/P_{CO} = 6.68 \times 10^2$$

Any ratio of P_{CO_2} to P_{CO} less than 6.68×10^2 will reduce NiO to Ni. Any ratio greater than this will oxidize Ni to NiO.

PROBLEMS

1. From the standard free energies in Table 6.2 calculate $\Delta G°$ and K_P at 25°C for the following reactions:

$$\text{(a)}\ N_2O + 4H_2 \longrightarrow 2NH_3 + H_2O(g)$$

$$\text{(b)}\ H_2O_2(g) \longrightarrow H_2O(g) + \tfrac{1}{2}O_2$$

$$\text{(c)}\ CO + H_2O(l) \longrightarrow CO_2 + H_2$$

[*Ans.* (a) -87.35 kcal, 1.26×10^{64}; (b) -29.91 kcal, 8.5×10^{21}; (c) -4.762 kcal, 3.11×10^3]

2. At 900°K, the reaction $C_2H_6 \rightarrow C_2H_4 + H_2$ has $\Delta H° = 24.42$, $\Delta G° = 5.35$ kcal. Calculate the per cent H_2 present at equilibrium if pure C_2H_6 is passed over a dehydrogenation catalyst at this temperature and 1 atm pressure. Estimate the per cent H_2 at equilibrium at 1000°K. [*Ans.* 20.8%; 28.9%]

3. If an initial mixture of 10 per cent C_2H_4, 10 per cent C_2H_6, and 80 per cent N_2 is passed over the catalyst at 900°K and 1 atm, what is the per cent composition of effluent gas at equilibrium? What if the same mixture is used at 100 atm? (Cf. data in Problem 2.) [*Ans.* At 1 atm: C_2H_6 — 6.9%, C_2H_4 — 12.5%, H_2 — 2.8%, N_2 — 77.8%; at 100 atm: C_2H_6 — 9.95%, C_2H_4 — 10.05%, H_2 — 0.05%, N_2 — 79.95%]

4. For the reaction $N_2O_4 \rightarrow 2NO_2$, calculate: K_P; K_X; K_c at 25°C and 1 atm from the free energies of formation of the compounds (Table 6.2). [*Ans.* 0.157 atm; 0.157 atm; 6.40×10^{-3} ml^{-1}]

5. PCl_5 vapor decomposes on heating according to $PCl_5 \rightarrow PCl_3 + Cl_2$. The density of a sample of partially dissociated PCl_5 at 1 atm and 230°C was found to be 4.80 g per liter. Calculate the degree of dissociation α and $\Delta G°$ for the dissociation at 230°C. [*Ans.* 0.051; 5940 cal]

6. Using the Third-Law entropies in Table 6.6 and the standard heats of formation, calculate the equilibrium constants at 25°C of the following reactions

$$H_2 + Cl_2 \longrightarrow 2HCl$$

$$CH_4 + 2O_2 \longrightarrow CO_2 + 2H_2O(g)$$

$$2Ag(s) + Cl_2 \longrightarrow 2AgCl(s)$$

[*Ans.* 2.8×10^{33}; 2.4×10^{140}; 2.8×10^{38}]

7. AgCl forms two compounds with NH_3, $AgCl \cdot 3\,NH_3$ and $AgCl \cdot \frac{3}{2}\,NH_3$, with decomposition pressures at 24°C of 110 and 940 torr (mm). Suppose we place 10^{-2} moles of AgCl and 5×10^{-2} moles of NH_3 into a five liter vessel at 24°C. Describe the state of the resulting system.

8. The Deacon reaction is the oxidation of HCl by O_2,

$$HCl + \tfrac{1}{4}O_2 \rightleftarrows \tfrac{1}{2}Cl_2 + \tfrac{1}{2}H_2O$$

At a pressure of 735 torr, and with an initial mixture containing 8.5 per cent HCl and 91.5 per cent O_2, the degree of decomposition of the HCl is 0.83. What is the equilibrium partial pressure of oxygen? [*Ans.* 658 torr]

9. Sulfonyl chloride dissociates as $SO_2Cl_2 \rightleftarrows SO_2 + Cl_2$. At 157°C, 1.95 g of the compound yield exactly 1 liter of gas at 1 atm pressure. What are the dissociation constants, K_P, K_c, and K_X, at this temperature?

10. The following data are available for the reaction $NiO(c) + CO(g) \rightleftarrows Ni(c) + CO_2(g)$,

T°K	936	1027	1125
K_P	4.54×10^3	2.55×10^3	1.58×10^3

Calculate $\Delta H°$, $\Delta G°$ and $\Delta S°$ for the reaction at 1000°K. Would an atmosphere of 20 per cent CO_2, 5 per cent CO, and 75 per cent N_2 oxidize nickel at 1000°K?

11. Deoxygenated nitrogen is often prepared in the laboratory by passing the tank nitrogen over hot copper. The reaction is $2Cu(s) + \frac{1}{2}O_2(g) \rightleftarrows Cu_2O(s)$, for which $\Delta G° = -39\,850 + 15.06T$. What would be the residual concentration of oxygen in the nitrogen if equilibrium was achieved at 600°C?

12. For the reaction, $Ca(l) + ThO_2(s) \rightarrow CaO(s) + Th(s)$, the $\Delta G°$ is -3.4 kcal at 1000°C, -2.5 at -1100°C, and -2 at 1200°C. Calculate the maximum temperature at which Ca(l) will reduce ThO_2.

13. For the reaction

$$FeCl_3(g) \rightleftharpoons FeCl_2(g) + \tfrac{1}{2}Cl_2(g)$$

$K_P = 7.4 \times 10^{-13}$ at 1200°C; and 1.2×10^{-11} at 1500°C. Calculate ΔH° and ΔS° for the reaction at 1500°K. What is the per cent Cl_2 in the gas at 1500°K and 1 atm?

14. For the reaction

$$3Si(c) + 2N_2(g) \rightleftharpoons Si_3N_4(s)$$

$\Delta G^\circ = -177\,000 - 5.76T \log T + 96.3T$. For

$$Si(c) \rightleftharpoons Si(l)$$

$\Delta G^\circ = 12\,000 - 7.18T$. Calculate the equilibrium pressure of nitrogen when silicon is heated with $Si_3N_4(s)$ at 1300°C; at 1000°C.

15. 0.1 mole of H_2 and 0.2 mole of CO_2 are introduced into an evacuated flask at 450°C. The reaction

$$H_2 + CO_2 \longrightarrow H_2O + CO \quad (1)$$

occurs and at equilibrium the pressure is 0.5 atm. Analysis of the mixture shows that it contains 10 mole per cent water. A mixture of excess CoO and Co (both solids) is then introduced so that the additional equilibria are established

$$CoO + H_2 \longrightarrow Co + H_2O \quad (2)$$

$$CoO + CO \longrightarrow Co + CO_2 \quad (3)$$

Analysis of the new equilibrium mixture shows it to contain 30 mole per cent water. Calculate K_1, K_2, and K_3. If K_1 increases by one per cent per degree for temperature around 450°C, calculate ΔH_1°.

16. For the reaction

$$C(graphite) + 2H_2(g) \longrightarrow CH_4(g)$$

the change in enthalpy is $-21\,045$ cal mole^{-1} at 600°C. The third-law entropies at 600°C and 1 atm are (in cal deg^{-1} mole^{-1} units): 4.8 for C(graphite); 38.9 for H_2; 56.6 for CH_4. (a) Calculate the equilibrium constant for the reaction at 600°C. (b) What experimental information would you need, besides that given above, in order to be able to evaluate K_P at any temperature? Make a suitable approximation that is adequate over a short temperature range and use it to estimate the equilibrium constant at 750°C. (c) Is it better to use high or low temperatures to get the maximum yield of CH_4? High or low pressures?

17. A mixture of 6.22 mole of hydrogen and 5.71 mole of iodine vapor was maintained at 357°C until equilibrium was attained. It was then found

that the amount of free iodine had decreased to 0.91 mole. (a) Calculate the equilibrium constant K_c at 357° for the equilibrium $H_2(g) + I_2(g) \rightarrow 2\,HI(g)$. (b) What would be the composition of the system when 5 mole of hydrogen iodide is kept at 357°C until equilibrium is attained? (c) At 25°C, the equilibrium constant for this reaction is 808 and the vapor pressure of $I_2(s)$ is 0.308 mm Hg. What would be the partial pressure of hydrogen in equilibrium with crystalline iodine and hydrogen iodide at one atmosphere? [*Ans.* (a) $K_c = 71.3$; (b) 9.56 per cent mole H_2, I_2, 80.88 per cent mole HI; (c) 432.5 mm Hg]

18. At 500°C, the equilibrium constant for the formation of ammonia by the reaction $N_2 + 3H_2 \rightarrow 2NH_3$ is $K_P = 1.50 \times 10^{-5}$. (a) What is K_c in terms of concentrations in mole liter^{-1}? (Assume the gases obey the gas laws.) (b) What fraction of a stoichiometric mixture of nitrogen and hydrogen (i.e., in the molar ratio 1:3) could be converted to ammonia with the total pressure kept at 1 atmosphere; at 500 atmospheres? [*Ans.* (a) $K_c = 6.05 \times 10^{-2}$ mole^{-2} liter^2; (b) 0.25 per cent; 46.6 per cent]

19. The degree of dissociation of steam into hydrogen and oxygen at 1000°C and 1 atm is 2.4×10^{-5}. Calculate the equilibrium constant K_P for the reaction

$$2H_2O \longrightarrow 2H_2 + O_2$$

at this temperature and pressure. [*Ans.* 6.9×10^{-15}]

20. At high temperature and pressure, a quite good equation of state for gases is $P(V - b) = RT$. Calculate the fugacity of N_2 at 1000 atm and 1000°C according to this equation, if $b = 39.1$ cc per mole. [*Ans.* 1450 atmospheres.

---

21. The equilibrium $LaCl_3(s) + H_2O(g) \rightarrow LaOCl(s) + 2HCl(g)$. [*J. Am. Chem. Soc.* *74*, 2349 (1952)] was found to have $K_P = 0.63$ at 804°K; and 0.125 at 733°K. Estimate ΔH for the reaction. If the equilibrium HCl vapor pressure at 900°K is 2 mm, estimate the equilibrium H_2O vapor pressure. [*Ans.* $\Delta H_{768} = 26.7$ kcal; 1.4×10^{-3} mm]

22. The following results were obtained for the degree of dissociation of $CO_2 (CO_2 \rightarrow CO + \frac{1}{2}O_2)$ at 1 atm:

°K	1000	1400	2000
α	2×10^{-7}	1.27×10^{-4}	1.55×10^{-2}

What is $\Delta S°$ for the reaction at 1400°K? [*Ans.* 16 cal deg^{-1}]

23. The free energy of formation of H_2S is given by $\Delta G° = -19\,200 + 0.94\,T \ln T - 0.00165\,T^2 - 0.00000037\,T^3 + 1.65\,T$. $H_2 + \frac{1}{2}S_2(g) \rightarrow H_2S(g)$. If H_2S at 1 atm is passed through a tube heated to 1200°K, what is per cent H_2 in the gas at equilibrium? [*Ans.* 3.95 per cent]

24. Jones and Giauque obtained the following values for C_P of nitromethane.*

°K	15	20	30	40	50	60	70	80	90	100
C_P	0.89	2.07	4.59	6.90	8.53	9.76	10.70	11.47	12.10	12.62
°K	120	140	160	180	200	220	240	260	280	300
C_P	13.56	14.45	15.31	16.19	17.08	17.98	18.88	25.01	25.17	25.35

The melting point is 244.7°K, heat of fusion 2319 cal per mole. The vapor pressure of the liquid at 298.1°K is 3.666 cm. The heat of vaporization at 298.1°K is 9147 cal per mole. Calculate the Third-Law entropy of CH_3NO_2 gas at 298.1°K and 1 atm pressure (assuming ideal gas behavior). [*Ans.* 65.70 cal deg^{-1}]

25. For the reaction $CO + 2H_2 \rightarrow CH_3OH(g)$, $\Delta G° = -3220$ cal at 700°K. Calculate the per cent CH_3OH at equilibrium with a 2:1 mixture of $H_2 + CO$ at a pressure of 600 atm, using: (a) ideal gas law; (b) Newton's fugacity charts. [*Ans.* 98.8 per cent; 99.2 per cent]

26. Show that

$$\mu_i = \left(\frac{\partial G}{\partial n_i}\right)_{T,P,n_j} = \left(\frac{\partial A}{\partial n_i}\right)_{T,V,n_j} = \left(\frac{\partial H}{\partial n_i}\right)_{S,P,n_j} = \left(\frac{\partial E}{\partial n_i}\right)_{S,V,n_j}$$

27. Amagat measured the molar volume of CO_2 at 60°C.

Pressure, atm	13.01	35.42	53.65	74.68	85.35
Volume, cc	2000	666.7	400	250	200

Calculate the activity coefficient $\gamma = f/P$ for CO_2 at 60°C and pressures of 10, 20, 40, and 80 atm. [*Ans.* 0.964; 0.93; 0.862; 0.733]

28. When *n*-pentane is passed over an isomerization catalyst at 600°K, the following reactions occur

$$\text{(A)} \quad CH_3CH_2CH_2CH_2CH_3 \longrightarrow CH_3CH(CH_3)CH_2CH_3 \quad \text{(B)}$$
$$\longrightarrow C(CH_3)_4 \quad \text{(C)}$$

The free energies of formation at 600°K are: (A) 33.79; (B) 32.66; (C) 35.08 kcal per mole. Calculate the composition of the mixture when complete equilibrium is attained. [*Ans.* 25.5 per cent (A), 65.9 per cent (B), 8.6 per cent (C)]

29. For the reaction $3\ CuCl(g) \rightarrow Cu_3Cl_3(g)$, Brewer and Lofgren [*J. Am. Chem. Soc. 72*, 3038 (1950)] found $\Delta G° = -126\ 400 - 12.51\ T \log T + 104.7\ T$. What are the $\Delta H°$ and $\Delta S°$ of the reaction at 2000°K? What is the equilibrium mole fraction of trimer in the gas at 1 atm and 2000°K? [*Ans.* $\Delta H° = -68.7$ kcal; $\Delta S° = -34.6$ cal deg^{-1}; $X = 0.315$]

---

* *J. Am. Chem. Soc. 69*, 983 (1947).

30. The solubility of excess oxygen in Cu_2O is given by

$$\log_{10} y = \tfrac{1}{4} \log_{10} P(\mathrm{mm}) - \frac{4300}{T} - 0.06$$

where y is the number of gram atoms of oxygen in excess per mole of Cu_2O. The oxygen dissolves with the formation of a vacant copper site V_{Cu}^{+} in accord with

$$\tfrac{1}{4}O_2 \longrightarrow \tfrac{1}{2}O^{2-} + V_{\mathrm{Cu}}^{+}$$

Calculate the $\Delta S°$ for this reaction at 1000°C.

7 THE KINETIC THEORY

The Intellect: "Apparently there is color, apparently sweetness, apparently bitterness, actually there are only atoms and the void."
The Senses: "Poor Intellect, do you hope to defeat us, while from us you borrow your very evidence. Your victory is in fact your defeat."

DEMOCRITUS (c.420 B.C.)

Thermodynamics is a science that takes things more or less as it finds them. It deals with pressures, volumes, temperatures and energies, and the relations between them, without seeking to elucidate further the nature of these entities. For thermodynamics, matter is a continuous substance, and energy behaves in many ways like an incompressible, weightless fluid. The analysis of nature provided by thermodynamics is effective in a limited field. Almost from the beginning of human thought, however, man has tried to achieve an insight into the structure of things, and to find an indestructible reality beneath the ever changing appearances of natural phenomena. The best example of this endeavor has been the development of the atomic theory.

1. ATOMS

The word *atom* is derived from the Greek ατομος, meaning *indivisible;* the atoms were believed to be the ultimate and eternal particles of which all material things were made. Our knowledge of Greek atomism comes mainly from the long poem of the Roman, Lucretius, *De Rerum Natura* — "Concerning the Nature of Things," written in the first century before Christ. Lucretius expounded the theories of Epicurus and of Democritus:

The same letters, variously selected and combined
Signify heaven, earth, sea, rivers, sun,
Most having some letters in common.
But the different subjects are distinguished
By the arrangement of letters to form the words.
So likewise in the things themselves,
When the intervals, passages, connections, weights,
Impulses, collisions, movement, order,
And position of the atoms interchange,
So also must the things formed from them change.

The properties of substances were determined by the forms of their atoms. Atoms of iron were hard and strong with spines that locked them together into a solid; atoms of water were smooth and slippery like poppy seeds; atoms of salt were sharp and pointed and pricked the tongue; whirling atoms of air pervaded all matter.

Later philosophers were inclined to discredit the atomic theory. They found it hard to explain the many qualities of materials, color, form, taste and odor, in terms of naked, colorless, tasteless, odorless atoms. Many followed the lead of Heraclitus and Aristotle, considering matter to be formed from the four "elements," earth, air, fire and water, in varying proportions. Among the alchemists there came into favor the *tria prima* of Paracelsus (1493–1541), who wrote:

> *Know, then, that all the seven metals are born from a threefold matter, namely, Mercury, Sulphur, and Salt, but with distinct and peculiar colorings.*

Atoms were almost forgotten till the seventeenth century, as the alchemists sought the philosopher's stone by which the "principles" could be blended to make gold.

2. THE RENAISSANCE OF THE ATOM

The writings of Descartes (1596–1650) helped to restore the idea of a corpuscular structure of matter. Gassendi (1592–1655) introduced many of the concepts of the present atomic theory; his atoms were rigid, moved at random in a void, and collided with one another. These ideas were extended by Hooke, who first proposed (1678) that the *elasticity* of a gas was the result of collisions of its atoms with the retaining walls.

In his *Essay on Human Understanding* (1690), John Locke took up the old problem of how the atoms could account for all the qualities perceived by the senses in material things. The qualities were divided into two classes. The *primary qualities* were those of shape, size, motion, and situation. These were the properties inherent in the corpuscles or atoms that make up matter. *Secondary qualities*, such as color, odor, and taste, existed only in the mind of the observer. They arose when certain arrangements of the atoms of matter interacted with other arrangements of atoms in the sense organs of the observer. Thus a *hot object* might produce a change in the size, motion, or situation of the corpuscles of the skin, which then produced in the mind the sensations of warmth or of pain.

The consequences of Locke's empiricism have been admirably summarized by J. C. Gregory.*

> *The doctrine of qualities was a curiously dichotomized version of perception. A snowflake, as perceived, was half in the mind and half out of it, for its shape was seen but its whiteness was only in the mind .... This had quick consequences for phil-*

---

* *A Short History of Atomism* (London: A. & C. Black, Ltd., 1931).

osophy. . . . The division between science and philosophy began about the time of Locke, as the one turned, with its experimental appliances, to the study of the corpuscular mechanism and the other explored the mind and its ideas. The severance had begun between science and philosophy and, although it only gradually progressed into the nineteenth century cleft between them, when the seventeenth century closed, physical science was taking the physical world for her domain, and philosophy was taking the mental world for hers.

In the early part of the eighteenth century, the idea of the atom became widely accepted. Newton wrote in 1718:

It seems probable to me that God in the beginning formed matter in solid, massy, hard, impenetrable, movable particles, of such sizes and figures, and with such other properties, and in such proportion, as most conduced to the end for which He formed them.

Newton suggested, incorrectly, that the pressure of a gas was due to repulsive forces between its constituent atoms. In 1738, Daniel Bernoulli correctly derived Boyle's Law by considering the collisions of atoms with the container wall.

3. ATOMS AND MOLECULES

Boyle had discarded the alchemical notion of elements and defined them as substances that had not been decomposed in the laboratory. Until the work of Antoine Lavoisier from 1772 to 1783, however, chemical thought was dominated by the phlogiston theory of Georg Stahl, which was actually a survival of alchemical conceptions. With Lavoisier's work, the elements took on their modern meaning and chemistry became a quantitative science. The Law of Definite Proportions and the Law of Multiple Proportions had become fairly well established by 1808, when John Dalton published his *New System of Chemical Philosophy.*

Dalton proposed that the atoms of each element had a characteristic atomic weight, and that these atoms were the combining units in chemical reactions. This hypothesis provided a clear explanation for the Laws of Definite and Multiple Proportions. Dalton had no unequivocal way of assigning atomic weights, and he made the unfounded assumption that in the most common compound between two elements, one atom of each was combined. According to this system, water would be HO, and ammonia NH. If the atomic weight of hydrogen was set equal to unity, the analytical data would then give $O = 8$, $N = 4.5$, in Dalton's system.

At about this time, Gay-Lussac was studying the chemical combinations of gases, and he found that the ratios of the volumes of the reacting gases were small whole numbers. This discovery provided a more logical method for assigning atomic weights. Gay-Lussac, Berzelius, and others felt that the volume occupied by the atoms of a gas must be very small compared to the total gas volume, so that equal volumes of gas should contain equal numbers of atoms. The weights of such equal volumes would therefore be proportional to the atomic weights. This idea was received coldly by Dalton and many of his contemporaries, who pointed to reactions such as that which they wrote as $N + O \rightarrow NO$. Experimentally the nitric oxide was found to occupy the same volume as the nitrogen and oxygen from which it was formed, although it evidently contained only half as many "atoms."*

Not till 1860 was the solution to this problem understood by most chemists, although half a century earlier it had been given by Amadeo Avogadro. In 1811, he published in the *Journal de physique* an article that clearly drew the distinction between the molecule and the atom. The "atoms" of hydrogen, oxygen, and nitrogen are in reality *molecules* containing two atoms each. Equal volumes of gases should contain the same number of molecules (Avogadro's Principle).

Since a molecular weight in grams (mole) of any substance contains the same number of molecules, according to Avogadro's Principle the molar volumes of all gases should be the same. The extent to which real gases conform to this rule may be seen from the molar volumes in Table 7.1 calculated from the mea-

TABLE 7.1 Molar Volumes of Gases in cc at 0°C and 1 Atm Pressure

Gas	Volume	Gas	Volume
Hydrogen	22 432	Argon	22 390
Helium	22 396	Chlorine	22 063
Methane	22 377	Carbon dioxide	22 263
Nitrogen	22 403	Ethane	22 172
Oxygen	22 392	Ethylene	22 246
Ammonia	22 094	Acetylene	22 085

sured gas densities. For an ideal gas at 0°C and 1 atm, the molar volume would be 22 414 cc. The number of molecules in one mole is now called *Avogadro's Number L.*

The work of Avogadro was ignored until it was forcefully presented by Cannizzaro at the Karlsruhe Conference in 1860. The reason for this neglect was probably the deeply rooted feeling that chemical combination occurred by virtue of an affinity between unlike elements. After the electrical discoveries of Galvani and Volta, this affinity was generally ascribed to the attractions between unlike charges. The idea that two identical atoms of hydrogen might combine into the compound molecule H_2 was abhorrent to the chemical philosophy of the early nineteenth century.

4. THE KINETIC THEORY OF HEAT

Even the most primitive peoples knew the connection between heat and motion through frictional phenomena. As the kinetic theory became accepted during the seventeenth century, heat became identified with the mechanical motion of the atoms or corpuscles. Francis Bacon (1561–1626) wrote:

* The elementary corpuscles of compounds were then called "atoms" of the compound.

When I say of motion that it is the genus of which heat is a species I would be understood to mean, not that heat generates motion or that motion generates heat (though both are true in certain cases) but that heat itself, its essence and quiddity, is motion and nothing else. . . . Heat is a motion of expansion, not uniformly of the whole body together, but in the smaller parts of it . . . the body acquires a motion alternative, perpetually quivering, striving, and struggling, and initiated by repercussion, whence springs the fury of fire and heat.

Although such ideas were widely discussed during the intervening years, the caloric theory, considering heat as a weightless fluid, was the working hypothesis of most natural philosophers until the quantitative work of Rumford and Joule brought about the general adoption of the mechanical theory. This was rapidly developed by Boltzmann, Maxwell, Clausius, and others, from 1860 to 1890.

According to the tenets of the kinetic theory, both temperature and pressure are thus manifestations of molecular motion. Temperature is a measure of the average translational kinetic energy of the molecules, and pressure arises from the average force resulting from repeated impacts of molecules with the containing walls.

5. THE PRESSURE OF A GAS

The simplest kinetic-theory model of a gas assumes that the volume occupied by the molecules may be neglected compared to the total volume. It is further assumed that the molecules behave like rigid spheres, with no forces of attraction or repulsion between them except during actual collisions.

In order to calculate the pressure in terms of molecular quantities, let us consider a volume of gas contained in a cubical box of side a. The velocity c of any molecule may be resolved into components u, v, and w, parallel to the three mutually perpendicular axes X, Y, and Z, so that its magnitude is given by

$$c^2 = u^2 + v^2 + w^2 \tag{7.1}$$

Collisions between a molecule and the walls are assumed to be perfectly elastic; the angle of incidence equals the angle of reflection, and the velocity changes in direction but not in magnitude. At each collision with a wall that is perpendicular to X, the velocity component u changes sign from $+u$ to $-u$, or vice versa; the momentum component of the molecule accordingly changes from $\pm mu$ to $\mp mu$, where m is the mass of the molecule. The magnitude of the change in momentum is therefore $2\,m|u|$, where $|u|$ denotes the absolute value of u.

The number of collisions in unit time with the two walls perpendicular to X is equal to $|u|/a$, and thus the change in the X component of momentum in unit time is $2mu\cdot(u/a) = 2mu^2/a$.

If there are N molecules in the box, the change in momentum in unit time becomes $2(Nm\overline{u^2}/a)$, where $\overline{u^2}$ is the average value of the square of velocity component* u. This rate of change of momentum is simply the force exerted

* Not to be confused with the square of the average value of the velocity component, which would be written $\bar{u}^2$. In this derivation we are averaging u^2, not u.

by the molecules colliding against the two container walls normal to X, whose area is $2a^2$. Since pressure is defined as the force normal to unit area,

$$P = \frac{2Nm\overline{u^2}}{2a^2 \cdot a} = \frac{Nm\overline{u^2}}{V}$$

Now there is nothing to distinguish the magnitude of one particular component from another in Eq. (7.1) so that on the average $\overline{u^2} = \overline{v^2} = \overline{w^2}$. Thus $3\overline{u^2} = \overline{c^2}$ and the expression for the pressure becomes

$$P = \frac{Nm\overline{c^2}}{3V} \tag{7.2}$$

The quantity $\overline{c^2}$ is called the *mean square speed* of the molecules, and may be given the special symbol C^2. Then $C = (\overline{c^2})^{1/2}$ is called the *root mean square speed.* The total translational kinetic energy E_k of the molecules is $\frac{1}{2}NmC^2$. Therefore, from Eq. (7.2),

$$PV = \tfrac{1}{3}NmC^2 = \tfrac{2}{3}E_k \tag{7.3}$$

Since the total kinetic energy is a constant, unchanged by the elastic collisions, Eq. (7.3) is equivalent to Boyle's Law.

6. GAS MIXTURES AND PARTIAL PRESSURES

If we use the perfect gas model of Section 5 to calculate the pressure of a gas mixture, we obtain a sum of terms like Eq. (7.3), one for each gas,

$$P_1 = \frac{2}{3}\frac{E_{k_1}}{V}$$

$$P_2 = \frac{2}{3}\frac{E_{k_2}}{V} \quad \text{etc.}$$

The P_1 is the pressure which gas (1) would exert if it occupied the total volume all by itself. It is called the *partial pressure of gas (1)*.

According to our model, the gas molecules can interact only by elastic collisions, so that the kinetic energy of the mixture must equal the sum of the individual kinetic energies.

$$E_k = E_{k_1} + E_{k_2} \ldots + E_{k_c}$$

From Eq. (7.3) the total pressure of the mixture is

$$P = \frac{2}{3}\frac{E_k}{V}$$

Therefore,

$$P = P_1 + P_2 \ldots + P_c \tag{7.4}$$

This is *Dalton's Law of Partial Pressures* which is valid for ideal gas mixtures.

The extent of the deviation for nonideal gases may be considerable, as is shown in the rather typical example of a mixture of 50.06% argon and 49.94% ethylene:

Actual pressure, atm	30.00	70.00	110.00
Calculated from Dalton's Law	29.15	64.55	101.85

7. KINETIC ENERGY AND TEMPERATURE

The concept of temperature was first introduced in connection with the study of thermal equilibrium. When two bodies are placed in contact, energy flows from one to the other until a state of equilibrium is reached. The two bodies are then at the same temperature. We have found that the temperature can be measured conveniently by means of an ideal-gas thermometer, this empirical scale being identical with the thermodynamic scale derived from the Second Law.

A distinction was drawn in thermodynamics between mechanical work and heat. According to the kinetic theory, the transformation of mechanical work into heat is simply a degradation of large-scale motion into motion on the molecular scale. An increase in the temperature of a body is equivalent to an increase in the average translational kinetic energy of its constituent molecules. We may express this mathematically by saying that the temperature is a function of E_k alone, $T = f(E_k)$. We know that this function must have the special form $T = \frac{2}{3}(E_k/nR)$, or

$$E_k = \tfrac{3}{2}nRT \tag{7.5}$$

so that Eq. (7.3) may be consistent with the ideal-gas relation, $PV = nRT$.

Temperature is thus not only a function of, but in fact proportional to the average translational kinetic energy of the molecules. The kinetic-theory interpretation of absolute zero is thus the complete cessation of all molecular motion — the zero point of kinetic energy.*

If the total energy of a gas is equal to this translational kinetic energy,

$$E = E_k = \tfrac{3}{2}nRT$$

The heat capacity per mole is

$$\overline{C}_V = \left(\frac{\partial \overline{E}}{\partial T}\right)_V = \tfrac{3}{2}R \tag{7.6}$$

If the heat capacity exceeds this value, we can conclude that the gas is taking up some form of energy other than translational kinetic energy.

The average translational kinetic energy may be resolved into components in the three *degrees of freedom* corresponding to velocities parallel to the three rectangular coordinates. Thus, for one mole of gas, where L is the Avogadro Number,

$$E_k = \tfrac{1}{2}LmC^2 = \tfrac{1}{2}Lm\overline{u^2} + \tfrac{1}{2}Lm\overline{v^2} + \tfrac{1}{2}Lm\overline{w^2}$$

---

* It will be seen later that this picture has been somewhat changed by quantum theory, which requires a small residual energy even at the absolute zero.

For each translational degree of freedom, therefore, from Eq. (7.5),

$$E_k = \tfrac{1}{2}Lm(\overline{u^2}) = \tfrac{1}{2}RT \tag{7.7}$$

This is a special case of a more general theorem known as the *Principle of Equipartition of Energy.*

8. MOLECULAR SPEEDS

Equation (7.3) may be written

$$C^2 = \frac{3P}{\rho} \tag{7.8}$$

where $\rho = Nm/V$ is the density of the gas. From Eqs. (7.3) and (7.5) we obtain for the *root mean square speed* C, if M is the molecular weight,

$$C^2 = \frac{3RT}{Lm} = \frac{3RT}{M}$$

$$C = \left(\frac{3RT}{M}\right)^{1/2} \tag{7.9}$$

The *average speed* $\bar{c}$, as we shall see later, differs only slightly from the root mean square speed:

$$\bar{c} = \left(\frac{8RT}{\pi M}\right)^{1/2} \tag{7.10}$$

From Eqs. (7.8), (7.9), or (7.10), we can readily calculate average or root mean square speeds of the molecules of a gas at any temperature. Some results are shown in Table 7.2. The average molecular speed of hydrogen at 25°C is 1768 m per sec or 6365 km per hr, about the speed of a rifle bullet. The average speed of a mercury vapor atom would be only about 638 km per hr.

TABLE 7.2 AVERAGE SPEEDS OF GAS MOLECULES AT 0°C

Gas	*Meters/sec*	*Gas*	*Meters/sec*
Ammonia	582.7	Hydrogen	1692.0
Argon	380.8	Deuterium	1196.0
Benzene	272.2	Mercury	170.0
Carbon dioxide	362.5	Methane	600.6
Carbon monoxide	454.5	Nitrogen	454.2
Chlorine	285.6	Oxygen	425.1
Helium	1204.0	Water	566.5

In accordance with the principle of equipartition of energy, we note that at any constant temperature the lighter molecules have the higher average speeds. This principle extends even to the phenomenon of Brownian motion, where the dancing particles are some thousand times heavier than the molecules colliding with them, but nevertheless have the same average kinetic energy.

9. MOLECULAR EFFUSION

A direct experimental illustration of the different average speeds of molecules of different gases can be obtained from the phenomenon called *molecular effusion*. Consider the arrangement shown in Fig. 7.1 (a). Molecules from a vessel of gas under pressure escape through a tiny orifice, so small that the distribution of the velocities of the gas molecules remaining in the vessel is not affected in any way; that is, no appreciable mass flow occurs in the direction of the orifice. The number of molecules escaping in unit time is then equal to the number that, in their random motion, happen to hit the orifice, and this number is proportional to the average molecular speed.

Figure 7.1 (b) shows an enlarged view of the orifice, which has an area ds. If all the molecules were moving perpendicular to the opening with their mean velocity in one dimension $\bar{u}$, in one second all those molecules would hit the opening that were contained in an element of volume of base ds and height $\bar{u}$, or volume $\bar{u}\,ds$, for a molecule at a distance $\bar{u}$ will just reach the orifice at the end of one second. If there are N molecules per cc, the number striking would be $N\bar{u}\,ds$. To a first approximation only half of all the molecules are moving toward the opening, and the number striking the orifice would therefore be $\frac{1}{2}N\bar{u}\,ds$, or per unit area $\frac{1}{2}N\bar{u}$. We can show that $\bar{u} = \frac{1}{2}\bar{c}$. This gives the result: number of molecules striking unit area per second = number of molecules effusing through unit area per second = $\frac{1}{4}N\bar{c}$. It is instructive to consider how this result is obtained, since the averaging method is typical of many kinetic-theory calculations.

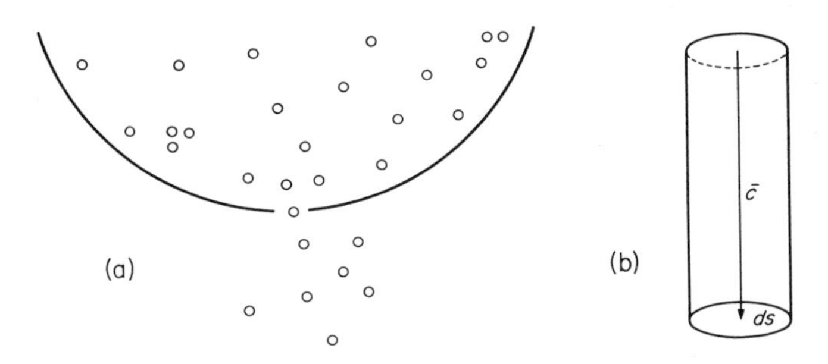

FIG. 7.1 Effusion of gases.

If the direction of the molecules is no longer normal to the wall, instead of the situation of Fig. 7.1, we have that of Fig. 7.2 (a). For any given direction the number of molecules hitting ds in unit time will be those contained in a cylinder of base ds and slant height $\bar{c}$. The volume of this cylinder is $\bar{c}\cos\theta\,ds$, and the number of molecules in it is $N\bar{c}\cos\theta\,ds$.

The next step is to discover how many molecules out of the total have velocities in the specified direction. The velocities of the molecules will be referred to

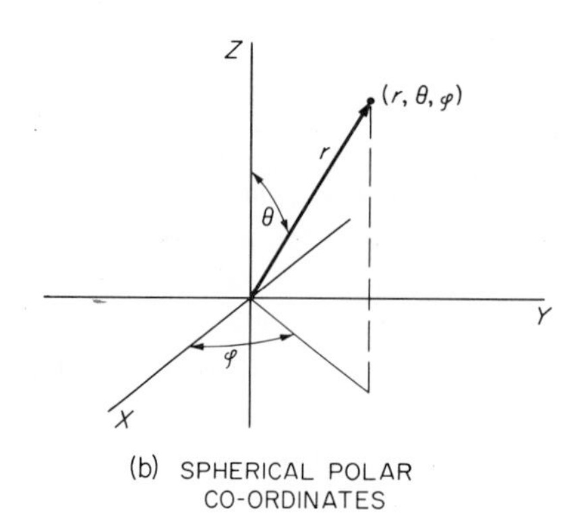

(b) SPHERICAL POLAR CO-ORDINATES

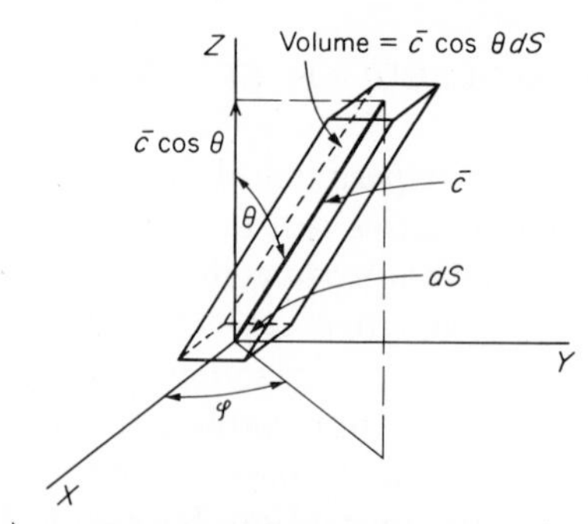

(a) ELEMENT OF VOLUME FROM WHICH MOLECULES HIT SURFACE IN UNIT TIME

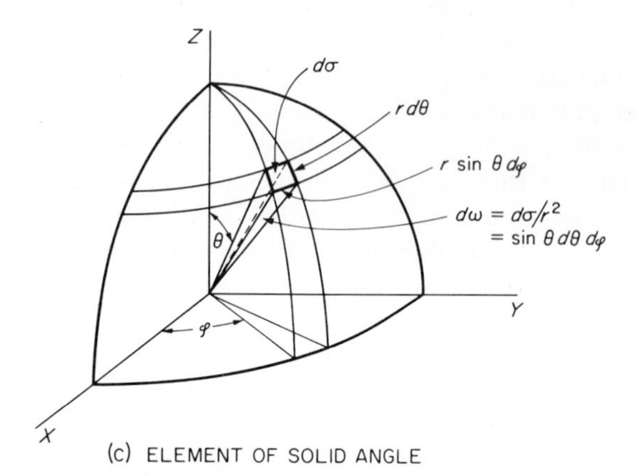

(c) ELEMENT OF SOLID ANGLE

FIG. 7.2 Calculation of gaseous effusion.

a system of polar coordinates (Fig. 7.2 (b)) with its origin at the wall of the vessel. We call such a representation a plot of the molecular velocities in *velocity space*. The distance from the origin $\bar{c}$ defines the magnitude of the velocity, and the angles θ and ϕ represent its direction. Any particular direction from the origin is specified by the differential solid angle $d\omega$. The fraction of the total number of molecules having their velocities within this particular spread of directions is $d\omega/4\pi$ since 4π is the total solid angle subtended by the surface of a sphere. In polar coordinates this solid angle is given* by $\sin\theta\, d\theta\, d\phi$.

The number of molecules hitting the surface ds in unit time from the given direction (θ, ϕ) becomes $(1/4\pi)\, N\bar{c}\cos\theta\sin\theta\, d\theta\, d\phi\, ds$. Or, for unit surface, it is $(1/4\pi)\, N\bar{c}\cos\theta\sin\theta\, d\theta\, d\phi$. In order to find the total number striking from all directions, dN'/dt, this expression must be integrated:

$$\frac{dN'}{dt} = \int_0^{\pi/2}\int_0^{2\pi} \frac{1}{4\pi} N\bar{c}\cos\theta\sin\theta\, d\phi\, d\theta$$

* G. P. Harnwell, *Principles of Electricity and Electromagnetism* (New York: McGraw-Hill, 1949), p. 649.

The limits of integration of ϕ are from 0 to 2π, corresponding to all the directions around the circle at any given θ. Then θ is integrated from 0 to $\pi/2$. The final result for the number of molecules striking unit area in unit time is then

$$\frac{dN'}{dt} = \tfrac{1}{4}N\bar{c} \tag{7.11}$$

The steps of the derivation may be reviewed by referring to Fig. 7.2.

If ρ is the gas density, the mass of gas that effuses in unit time is

$$\frac{dm}{dt} = \tfrac{1}{4}\rho\bar{c} \tag{7.12}$$

From Eq. (7.10)

$$\frac{dm}{dt} = \rho\left(\frac{RT}{2\pi M}\right)^{1/2} \tag{7.13}$$

It follows that at constant temperature the rate of effusion varies inversely as the square root of the molecular weight. Thomas Graham (1848) was the first to obtain experimental evidence for this law. Some of his data are shown in Table 7.3.

TABLE 7.3 THE EFFUSION OF GASES*

Gas	Relative Velocity of Effusion	
	Observed	Calculated from Eq. (7.12)
Air	(1)	(1)
Nitrogen	1.0160	1.0146
Oxygen	0.9503	0.9510
Hydrogen	3.6070	3.7994
Carbon dioxide	0.8354	0.8087

* *Source:* Graham, "On the Motion of Gases," *Phil. Trans. Roy. Soc.* (London), *136*, 573 (1846).

It appears from Graham's work, and also from that of later experimenters, that Eq. (7.13) is not perfectly obeyed. It fails when one goes to higher pressures and larger orifices. Under these conditions the molecules can collide many times with one another in passing through the orifice, and a hydrodynamic flow toward the orifice is set up throughout the container, leading to the formation of a jet of escaping gas.*

Equation (7.13) suggests that effusive flow may provide a good method for separating gases of different molecular weights. Permeable barriers with fine pores are used in the separation of isotopes. Because the lengths of the pores are considerably greater than their diameters, the flow of gas through such barriers does not follow the simple equation of orifice effusion. The dependence on molecular weight is the same, since each molecule passes through the barrier independently of any others.

* For a discussion of jet flow, see H. W. Liepmann and A. E. Puckett, *Introduction to Aerodynamics of a Compressible Fluid* (New York: Wiley, 1947), pp. 32 et seq.

10. IMPERFECT GASES—THE VAN DER WAALS EQUATION

The calculated properties of the *perfect gas* of the kinetic theory are the same as the experimental properties of the *ideal gas* of thermodynamics. Extension of the model of the perfect gas may therefore provide an explanation for observed deviations from ideal-gas behavior.

The first improvement of the model is to abandon the assumption that the volume of the molecules themselves can be neglected in comparison with the total gas volume. The effect of the finite volume of the molecules is to decrease the available void space in which the molecules are free to move. Instead of the V in the perfect gas equation, we must write $V - nb$, where b is called the *excluded volume* per mole. This is not just equal to the volume occupied by the molecules, but actually to four times that volume. This can be seen in a qualitative way by considering the two molecules of Fig. 7.3 (a), regarded as impenetrable spheres each with a *diameter* d. The centers of these two molecules cannot approach each other more closely than the distance d; the excluded volume for the pair is therefore a sphere of *radius* d. This volume is $8(\frac{4}{3})\pi r^3$ per pair, or $4(\frac{4}{3})\pi r^3$ per molecule, which is four times the volume of the molecule. Consideration of the finite molecular volumes leads therefore to a gas equation of the form,

$$P(V - nb) = nRT$$

A second correction to the perfect-gas formula comes from the forces of cohesion between the molecules. We recall that the thermodynamic definition of the ideal gas includes the requirement that $(\partial E/\partial V)_T = 0$. If this condition is not fulfilled, the energy of the gas will depend on its volume, owing to the forces of cohesion between the molecules. The way in which these forces enter the gas equation may be seen by considering Fig. 7.3 (b). The molecules completely surrounded by other gas molecules are in a uniform field of force, whereas the molecules near to or colliding with the container walls experience a net attraction toward the body of the gas. This tends to decrease the pressure compared to that which would be exerted by molecules in the absence of such attractive forces.

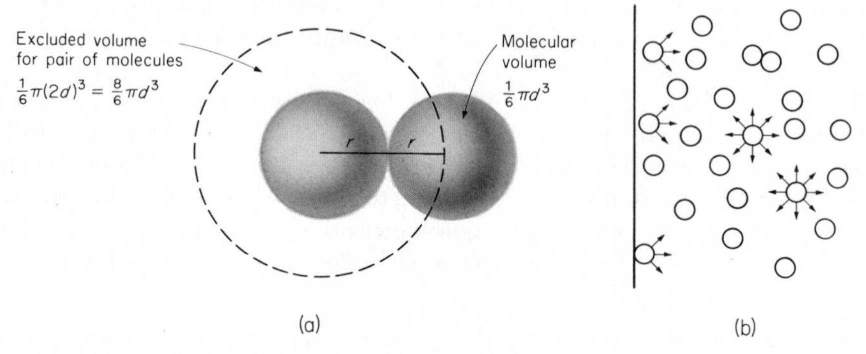

FIG. 7.3 Corrections to perfect-gas law. (a) Excluded volume. (b) Intermolecular forces.

The total pull is proportional to the number of molecules (ν) in the surface layer and to the number of molecules (ν) in the adjacent inner layer of the gas. Note that these numbers ν are assumed to be the same. The inward pull is therefore proportional to ν^2. At any given temperature, ν is inversely proportional to V/n, the volume per mole of the gas. Therefore the correction to the pressure due to these cohesive forces is proportional to $(V/n)^{-2}$, or may be set equal to $a(V/n)^{-2}$, where a is the constant of proportionality. We must therefore add n^2a/V^2 to the experimental pressure P to compensate for the attractive forces.

By this line of reasoning, van der Waals in 1873 obtained his famous equation of state,

$$\left(P + \frac{n^2a}{V^2}\right)(V - nb) = nRT \tag{7.14}$$

This equation provides a good representation of the behavior of gases at moderate densities, but deviations become large at higher densities. The values of the constants a and b are obtained from the experimental PVT data at moderate densities, or more usually from the critical constants of the gas. Some of these values were collected in Table 1.1.

11. COLLISIONS BETWEEN MOLECULES

Now that the oversimplification that the molecules of a gas occupy no volume themselves has been abandoned, it is possible to consider further the phenomena that depend on collisions between the molecules. Let us suppose that the molecules are rigid spheres with a diameter d and that they do not attract one another. The approach of a molecule A toward another molecule B is shown in Fig. 7.4. A *collision* occurs whenever the distance between their centers becomes as small as d. Let us imagine the center of A to be surrounded by a sphere of *radius* d. A collision occurs whenever the *center* of another molecule comes within this sphere. If A is traveling with the average speed $\bar{c}$, its "sphere of influence" sweeps out in unit time a volume $\pi d^2\bar{c}$. Since this volume contains N molecules per cc, there are $\pi N d^2\bar{c}$ collisions experienced by A per second. The quantity πd^2 is called the *collision cross section* for the rigid-sphere model.

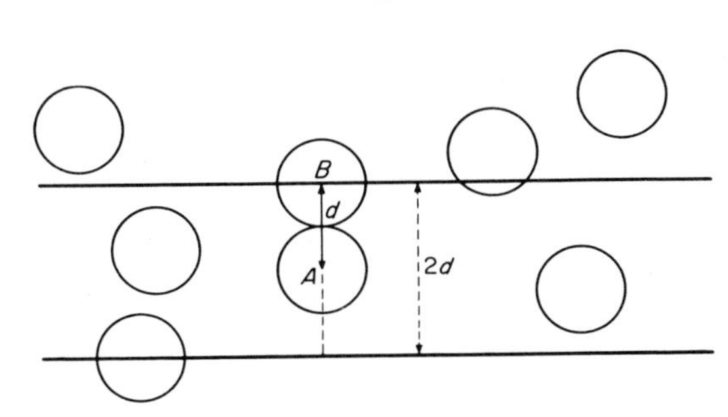

FIG. 7.4 Molecular collisions.

A more exact calculation takes into consideration that only the speed of a molecule relative to other moving molecules determines the number of collisions Z_1 that it experiences. This fact leads to the expression,

$$Z_1 = 2^{1/2}\pi N d^2\bar{c} \tag{7.15}$$

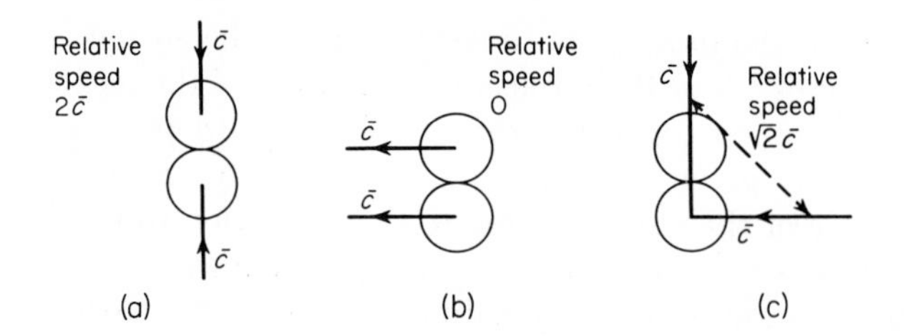

FIG. 7.5 Relative speeds. (a) Head-on collision. (b) Grazing collision. (c) Right-angle collision.

The origin of the $2^{1/2}$ factor may be seen by considering, in Fig. 7.5, the relative velocities of two molecules just before or just after a collision. The limiting cases are the head-on collision and the grazing collision. The average case appears to be the 90° collision, after which the magnitude of the relative velocity is $2^{1/2}\bar{c}$.

If we now examine the similar motions of all the molecules, the total number of collisions per second of all the N molecules contained in one cc of gas is found, from Eq. (7.15), to be

$$Z_{11} = \tfrac{1}{2}(2)^{1/2}\pi N^2 d^2 \bar{c} \tag{7.16}$$

The factor $\frac{1}{2}$ is introduced so that each collision is not counted twice (once as A hits B, and once as B hits A).

12. MEAN FREE PATH

An important quantity in kinetic theory is the average distance a molecule travels between collisions. This is called the *mean free path.* The average number of collisions experienced by one molecule in unit time (one second) is Z_1 in Eq. (7.15). In this time the molecule has traveled a distance $\bar{c}$. The mean free path λ is therefore $\bar{c}/Z_1$, or

$$\lambda = \frac{1}{2^{1/2}\pi N d^2} \tag{7.17}$$

In order to calculate the mean free path, we must know the molecular diameter d. This might be obtained, for example, from the van der Waals $b = \frac{2}{3}\pi L d^3$ if the value of the Avogadro Number L were known. So far, our development of kinetic theory has provided no method for obtaining this number. The theory of gas viscosity as developed by James Clerk Maxwell presented a key to this problem, affording one of the most striking demonstrations of the power of the kinetic theory.

13. THE VISCOSITY OF A GAS

The concept of viscosity is first met in problems of fluid flow, treated by hydrodynamics and aerodynamics, as a measure of the frictional resistance that a fluid in motion offers to an applied shearing force. The nature of this resistance may be seen from Fig. 7.6 (a). If a fluid is flowing past a stationary plane surface, the layer of fluid adjacent to the plane boundary is stagnant; successive layers have increasingly higher velocities. The frictional force f, resisting the relative motion of any two adjacent layers, is proportional to S, the area of the interface between them, and to dv/dr, the velocity gradient between them. This is Newton's Law of Viscous Flow,

$$f = \eta S \frac{dv}{dr} \tag{7.18}$$

The proportionality constant η is called the *coefficient of viscosity*. It is evident that the dimensions of η are $m\, l^{-1}t^{-1}$. In the cgs system, the unit is g cm^{-1} sec^{-1}, called the *poise*.

The kind of flow governed by this relationship is called *laminar* or *streamline* flow. It is evidently quite different in character from the effusive (or diffusive) flow previously discussed, since it is a massive flow of fluid, in which there is superimposed on all the random molecular velocities a component of velocity in the direction of flow.

An especially important case of viscous flow is the flow through pipes or tubes when the diameter of the tube is large compared to the mean free path in the fluid. The study of flow through tubes has been the basis for many of the experimental determinations of the viscosity coefficient. The theory of the process was first worked out by J. L. Poiseuille, in 1844.

Consider an incompressible fluid flowing through a tube of circular cross section with radius R and length l. The fluid at the walls of the tube is assumed

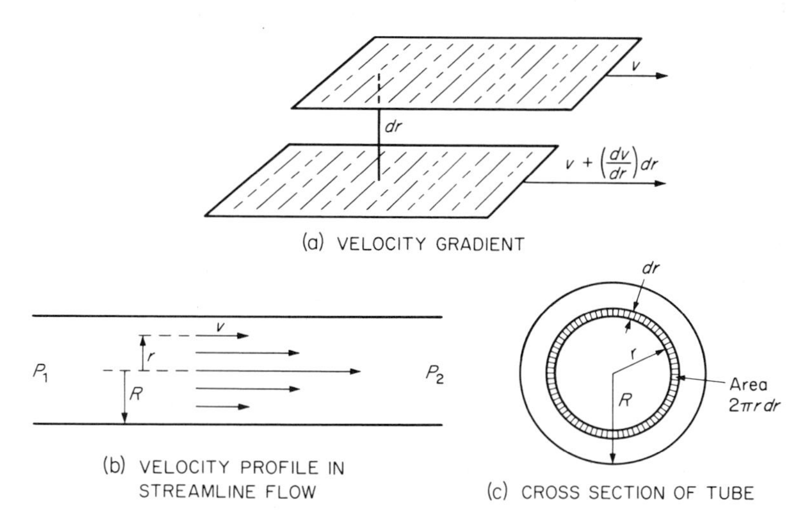

FIG. 7.6 Viscosity of fluids.

to be stagnant, and the rate of flow increases to a maximum at the center of the tube [see Fig. 7.6 (b)]. Let v be the linear velocity at any distance r from the axis of the tube. A cylinder of fluid of radius r experiences a viscous drag given by Eq. (7.18) as

$$f_r = -\eta \frac{dv}{dr} \cdot 2\pi r l$$

For steady flow, this force must be exactly balanced by the force driving the fluid in this cylinder through the tube. Since pressure is the force per unit area, the driving force is

$$f_r = \pi r^2 (P_1 - P_2)$$

where P_1 is the fore pressure and P_2 the back pressure.

Thus, for steady flow,

$$-\eta \frac{dv}{dr} \cdot 2\pi r l = \pi r^2 (P_1 - P_2)$$

$$dv = -\frac{r}{2\eta l} (P_1 - P_2)\, dr$$

On integration,

$$v = -\frac{(P_1 - P_2)}{4\eta l} r^2 + \text{constant}$$

According to our hypothesis, $v = 0$ when $r = R$; this boundary condition enables us to determine the integration constant, so that we obtain finally

$$v = \frac{(P_1 - P_2)}{4\eta l} (R^2 - r^2) \tag{7.19}$$

The total volume of fluid flowing through the tube per second is calculated by integrating over each element of cross-sectional area, given by $2\pi r\, dr$ [see Fig. 7.6 (c)]. Thus,

$$\frac{dV}{dt} = \int_0^R 2\pi r v\, dr = \frac{\pi (P_1 - P_2) R^4}{8 l \eta} \tag{7.20}$$

This is Poiseuille's equation. It was derived for an incompressible fluid and therefore may be satisfactorily applied to liquids but not to gases. For gases, the volume is a strong function of the pressure. The average pressure along the tube is $(P_1 + P_2)/2$. If P_0 is the pressure at which the volume is measured, the equation becomes

$$\frac{dV}{dt} = \frac{(P_1 - P_2) R^4}{8 l \eta} \cdot \frac{P_1 + P_2}{2 P_0} = \frac{\pi (P_1^2 - P_2^2) R^4}{16 l \eta P_0} \tag{7.21}$$

By measuring the volume rate of flow through a tube of known dimensions, we can determine the viscosity η of the gas. Some results of such measurements are collected in Table 7.4.

TABLE 7.4 Transport Phenomena in Gases
(At 0°C and 1 atm)

Gas	Mean Free Path λ, Å	Viscosity η, poise ($\times 10^6$)	Thermal Conductivity κ, cal/g sec °C ($\times 10^6$)	Specific Heat, c_v cal/g °K	$\eta c_v/\kappa$
Ammonia	441	97.6	51.3	0.399	0.76
Argon	635	213	38.8	0.0750	0.41
Carbon dioxide	397	138	34.3	0.153	0.62
Carbon monoxide	584	168	56.3	0.177	0.53
Chlorine	287	123	18.3	0.0818	0.55
Ethylene	345	93.3	40.7	0.286	0.66
Helium	1798	190	336	0.743	0.42
Hydrogen	1123	84.2	406	2.40	0.50
Nitrogen	600	167	58.0	0.176	0.51
Oxygen	647	192	58.9	0.155	0.51

14. KINETIC THEORY OF GAS VISCOSITY

The kinetic picture of gas viscosity has been represented by the following analogy: Two railroad trains are moving in the same direction, but at different speeds, on parallel tracks. The passengers on these trains amuse themselves by jumping back and forth from one to the other. When a passenger jumps from the more rapidly moving train to the slower one he transports momentum of amount $m\ \Delta v$, where m is his mass and Δv the excess velocity of his train. He tends to speed up the more slowly moving train when he lands upon it. A passenger who jumps from the slower to the faster train, on the other hand, tends to slow it down. The net result of the jumping game is thus a tendency to equalize the velocities of the two trains. An observer from afar who could not see the jumpers might simply note this result as a frictional drag between the trains.

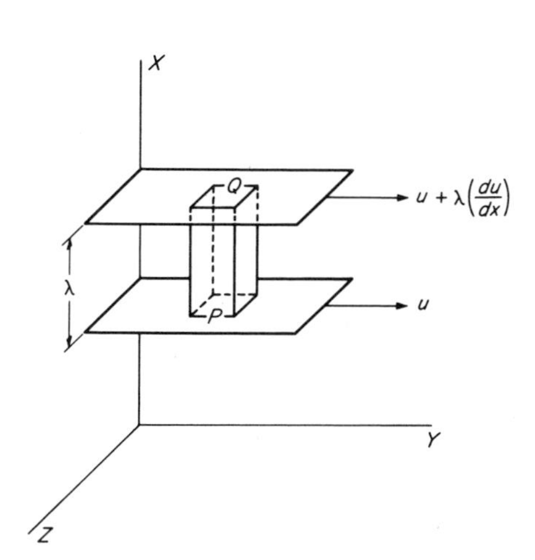

FIG. 7.7 Kinetic theory of gas viscosity.

The mechanism by which one layer of flowing gas exerts a viscous drag on an adjacent layer is exactly similar, the gas molecules taking the role of the playful passengers. Consider in Fig. 7.7 a gas in a state of laminar flow parallel to the Y axis. Its velocity increases from zero at the plane $x = 0$ to larger values of u

with increasing x. If a molecule at P crosses to Q, in one of its free paths between collisions, it will bring to Q, on the average, an amount of momentum which is less than that common to the position Q by virtue of its distance along the X axis. Conversely, if a molecule travels from Q to P it will transport to the lower, more slowly moving layer, an amount of momentum in excess of that belonging to that layer. The net result of the random thermal motions of the molecules is to decrease the average velocities of the molecules in the layer at Q and to increase those in the layer at P. This transport of momentum tends to counteract the velocity gradient set up by the shear forces acting on the gas.

The length of the mean free path λ may be taken as the average distance over which momentum is transferred. If the velocity gradient is du/dx, the difference in velocity between the two ends of the free path is $\lambda\, du/dx$. A molecule of mass m, passing from the upper to the lower layer, thus transports momentum equal to $m\lambda\, du/dx$. From Eq. (7.11), the number crossing unit area *up and down* per second per square cm is $\frac{1}{2}N\bar{c}$. The momentum transport per second is then $\frac{1}{2}N\bar{c}\cdot m\lambda(du/dx)$.

This momentum change with time is equivalent to the frictional force of Eq. (7.18) which was $f = \eta(du/dx)$ per unit area. Hence,

$$\eta \frac{du}{dx} = \tfrac{1}{2}Nm\bar{c}\lambda \frac{du}{dx}$$

$$\eta = \tfrac{1}{2}Nm\bar{c}\lambda = \tfrac{1}{2}\rho\bar{c}\lambda \tag{7.22}$$

The measurement of the viscosity thus allows us to calculate the value of the mean free path λ. Some values obtained in this way are included in Table 7.4, in Ångstrom units (1Å $= 10^{-8}$ cm).

By eliminating λ between Eqs. (7.17) and (7.22), one obtains

$$\eta = \frac{m\bar{c}}{2(2)^{1/2}\pi d^2} \tag{7.23}$$

This equation indicates that the viscosity of a gas is independent of its density. This seemingly improbable result was predicted by Maxwell, and its subsequent experimental verification was one of the triumphs of the kinetic theory. The physical reason for the result is clear from the preceding derivation: at lower densities, fewer molecules jump from layer to layer in the flowing gas, but, because of the longer free paths, each jump carries proportionately greater momentum. For imperfect gases, the equation fails and the viscosity increases with density.

The second important conclusion from Eq. (7.23) is that the viscosity of a gas increases with increasing temperature, linearly with $\bar{c} \propto T^{1/2}$. This conclusion has been well confirmed by experimental results, although the viscosity increases somewhat more rapidly than predicted by the $T^{1/2}$ law. This is because the molecules are not actually hard spheres, but must be regarded as somewhat soft, or surrounded by fields of force. This is true even for the atom-molecules of the inert gases. The higher the temperature, the faster the molecules are moving, and hence the deeper one molecule can penetrate into the field of force of another, before it is repelled or bounced away. This correction has been embodied in a formula due to Sutherland (1893),

$$d^2 = d_\infty \left(1 + \frac{A}{T}\right) \tag{7.24}$$

Here d_∞ and A are constants, d_∞ being interpreted as the value of d as T approaches infinity.

More recent work has sought to express the temperature coefficient of the viscosity in terms of the laws of force between the molecules. Thus here, just as in the discussion of the equation of state, the qualitative picture of rigid molecules must be modified to consider the fields of force between molecules.

15. THERMAL CONDUCTIVITY AND DIFFUSION

Gas viscosity depends on the transport of momentum across a momentum (velocity) gradient. It is a typical *transport phenomenon.* An exactly similar theoretical treatment is applicable to thermal conductivity and to diffusion. The thermal conductivity of a gas is a consequence of the transport of kinetic energy across a temperature (i.e., kinetic energy) gradient. Diffusion in a gas is the transport of mass across a concentration gradient.

The thermal conductivity coefficient κ is defined as the heat flow per unit time $\dot{q}$, per unit temperature gradient across unit cross-sectional area, i.e., by

$$\dot{q} = \kappa \cdot S \cdot \frac{dT}{dx}$$

By comparison with Eq. (7.22),

$$\kappa \frac{dT}{dx} = \tfrac{1}{2} N \bar{c} \lambda \frac{d\epsilon}{dx}$$

where $d\epsilon/dx$ is the gradient of ϵ, the average kinetic energy per molecule. Now

$$\frac{d\epsilon}{dx} = \frac{dT}{dx} \cdot \frac{d\epsilon}{dT} \quad \text{and} \quad \frac{d\epsilon}{dT} = mc_v$$

where m is the molecular mass and c_v is the specific heat (heat capacity per gram). It follows that

$$\kappa = \tfrac{1}{2} N m c_v \bar{c} \lambda = \tfrac{1}{2} \rho c_v \bar{c} \lambda = \eta c_v \tag{7.25}$$

Some thermal conductivity coefficients are included in Table 7.4. It should be emphasized that, even for an ideal gas, the simple theory is approximate, since it assumes that all the molecules are moving with the same speed $\bar{c}$ and that energy is exchanged completely at each collision.

The treatment of diffusion is again similar. Generally one deals with the diffusion in a mixture of two different gases. The diffusion coefficient D is the number of molecules per second crossing unit area under unit concentration gradient. It is found to be*

$$D = \tfrac{1}{3}\lambda_1\bar{c}_1X_2 + \tfrac{1}{3}\lambda_2\bar{c}_2X_1$$

where X_1 and X_2 are the mole fractions of the two gases in the mixture. If the two kinds of molecules are essentially the same, for example radioactive chlorine in normal chlorine, the *self-diffusion coefficient* is obtained as

$$D = \tfrac{1}{3}\lambda\bar{c} \tag{7.26}$$

The results of the mean-free-path treatments of the transport processes may be summarized as follows:

Process	Transport of	Simple Theoretical Expression†	cgs Units of Coefficient
Viscosity	Momentum, mv	$\eta = \frac{1}{2}\rho\bar{c}\lambda$	g cm^{-1} sec^{-1}
Thermal Conductivity	Kinetic energy, $\frac{1}{2}mv^2$	$\kappa = \frac{1}{2}\rho\bar{c}\lambda c_v$	erg cm^{-1} sec^{-1} degree^{-1}
Diffusion	Mass, m	$D = \frac{1}{3}\lambda\bar{c}$	cm^2 sec^{-1}

16. AVOGADRO'S NUMBER AND MOLECULAR DIMENSIONS

From Eq. (7.10) we can write Eq. (7.23) as

$$\eta = \frac{M\bar{c}}{2(2)^{1/2}L\pi d^2} = \frac{(RTM)^{1/2}}{\pi^{3/2}Ld^2}$$

Now the van der Waals b is given by

$$b = 4Lv_M = 4L\cdot\pi\frac{d^3}{6} = \tfrac{2}{3}\pi Ld^3 \tag{7.27}$$

Multiplying these two equations, and solving for d, we have

$$d = \tfrac{3}{2}(\pi/RTM)^{1/2}\,\eta b \tag{7.28}$$

Let us substitute the appropriate values for the hydrogen molecule H_2, all in cgs units: $M = 2.016$, $\eta = 0.93 \times 10^{-4}$, $b = 26.6$, $T = 298°K$, $R = 8.314 \times 10^7$. Solving for d, we find $d = 1.5 \times 10^{-8}$ cm.

This value may be substituted back into Eq. (7.27) to obtain a value for Avogadro's Number L equal to about 10^{24}.

* For example, see E. H. Kennard, *Kinetic Theory of Gases* (New York: McGraw-Hill, 1938), p. 188.

† The exact kinetic theory of gases for *rigid sphere molecules* yields the coefficients $(\frac{1}{3})(\frac{15}{32})$; $(\frac{1}{3})(\frac{75}{64})$; $(\frac{1}{3})(\frac{9}{16})$ for η, κ, D respectively.

Because of the known approximations involved in the van der Waals formula, this value of L is only approximate. It is nevertheless of the correct order of magnitude, and it is interesting that the value can be obtained purely from kinetic-theory calculations. Later methods, which will be discussed in a subsequent chapter, give the value $L = 6.022 \times 10^{23}$.

We may use this figure to obtain more accurate values for molecular diameters from viscosity or thermal conductivity measurements. Some of these values are shown in Table 7.5, together with values obtained from the van der Waals b, and by the following somewhat different method.

TABLE 7.5 Molecular Diameters
(Ångstrom Units)

Molecule	From Gas Viscosity	From van der Waals' b	From Molecular Refraction*	From Closest Packing
Ar	2.86	2.86	2.96	3.83
CO	3.80	3.16	—	4.30
CO_2	4.60	3.24	2.86	—
Cl_2	3.70	3.30	3.30	4.65
He	2.00	2.48	1.48	—
H_2	2.18	2.76	1.86	—
Kr	3.18	3.14	3.34	4.02
Hg	3.60	2.38	—	—
Ne	2.34	2.66	—	3.20
N_2	3.16	3.14	2.40	4.00
O_2	2.96	2.90	2.34	3.75
H_2O	2.72	2.88	2.26	—

* The theory of this method is discussed in Section 11–18.

In the solid state the molecules are closely packed together. Let us assume that the molecules are spherical. The closest possible packing of spheres leaves a void space of 26 per cent of the total volume. The volume occupied by a mole of molecules is M/ρ, where M is the molecular weight and ρ the density of the solid. For spherical molecules, therefore, $(\pi/6)Ld^3 = 0.74(M/\rho)$. Values of d obtained from this equation are good approximations for the monatomic gases (He, Ne, Ar, Kr) and for spherical molecules like CH_4, CCl_4. The equation is only roughly applicable to diatomic molecules like N_2 or O_2.

The diversity of values often obtained for molecular diameters calculated by different methods indicates that a rigid-sphere model is not adequate even for simple molecules.

The tinyness of a molecule and the enormousness of the Avogadro Number L are strikingly shown by two popular illustrations given by James Jeans. If the molecules in a glass of water were turned into grains of sand, there would be enough sand produced to cover the United States to a depth of about 30 meters. A man breathes out about 400 cc at each breath, or about 10^{22} molecules. The earth's atmosphere contains about 10^{44} molecules. Thus, one molecule is the same fraction of a breath of air as the breath is of the entire atmosphere. If the last breath of Socrates has become scattered throughout the entire atmosphere, the chances are that we inhale one molecule from it in each breath we take.

17. THE BAROMETRIC FORMULA

So far in this chapter we have dealt with average properties of large collections of molecules, average velocities, mean free paths, viscosities, and so on. In what follows, we shall consider the contributions of the individual molecules to these averages.

The density of the earth's atmosphere decreases with increasing altitude. If one makes the simplifying assumption that a column of gas extending upward into the atmosphere is at constant temperature, a formula can be derived for this variation of gas pressure in the gravitational field. The situation is pictured in Fig. 7.8.

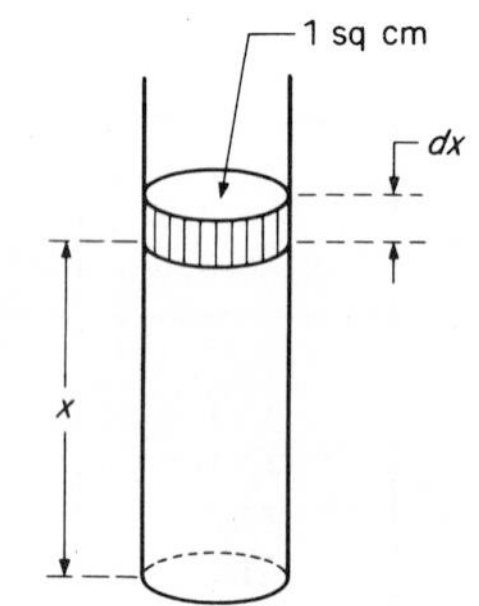

FIG. 7.8 Barometric formula.

The weight of a thin layer of gas of thickness dx and one cm² cross section is its mass times the acceleration due to gravity, or $\rho g\, dx$, where ρ is the gas density. The difference in pressure between the upper and lower boundaries of the layer is $(-dP/dx)\, dx$, equal to the weight of the layer of unit cross section. Thus

$$-dP = \rho g\, dx$$

For an ideal gas,

$$\rho = \frac{PM}{RT}$$

Therefore,

$$-\frac{dP}{P} = \frac{Mg}{RT}\, dx$$

Integrating between the limits $P = P_0$ at $x = 0$, and P at x, we get

$$\ln \frac{P}{P_0} = -\frac{Mgx}{RT}$$

$$P = P_0 e^{-Mgx/RT} \tag{7.29}$$

Now, Mgx is simply the gravitational potential energy at the point x, which may be written as E_p per mole. Then,

$$P = P_0 e^{-E_p/RT} \tag{7.30}$$

If, instead of the molar energy, we consider that of the individual molecule, ϵ_p, Eq. (7.30) becomes

$$P = P_0 e^{-\epsilon_p/kT} \tag{7.31}$$

The constant k is called the *Boltzmann constant.* It is the gas constant per molecule.

$$k = \frac{R}{L} = \frac{8.314 \times 10^7 \text{ erg/°C mole}}{6.022 \times 10^{23}\text{/mole}} = 1.381 \times 10^{-16} \text{ erg/°C}$$

18. THE BOLTZMANN DISTRIBUTION LAW

Equation (7.31) is one special case of a general law derived by Ludwig Boltzmann in 1886. This law states that if N_0 is the number of particles in any given state, the number N_i in a state whose potential energy is ϵ_i above that of the given state is

$$N_i = N_0 e^{-\epsilon_i/kT} \tag{7.32}$$

If each state of the system has a characteristic and distinct energy level ϵ_i, Eq. (7.32) gives the number of particles having the energy ϵ_i. In some cases, however, several distinct states may have the same energy. If g_i states have the same energy ϵ_i, the number of particles in the energy level ϵ_i becomes

$$N_i = g_i N_0 e^{-\epsilon_i/kT} \tag{7.33}$$

The number g_i is called the *degeneracy* of the level ϵ_i.

We can also express the Boltzmann relation as the fraction out of the total number of molecules in a system which possesses a given energy ϵ_i. The total number of molecules,

$$N = \sum N_i = N_0 \sum g_i e^{-\epsilon_i/kT}$$

Hence the required fraction is

$$\frac{N_i}{N} = \frac{g_i e^{-\epsilon_i/kT}}{\sum g_i e^{-\epsilon_i/kT}} = \frac{g_i}{f} e^{-\epsilon_i/kT} \tag{7.34}$$

where we have written f for the sum over states, $\sum g_i e^{-\epsilon_i/kT}$, called the *partition function*. An example of a Boltzmann distribution is shown in Table 7.6 for a set of energy levels with $g = 1$ equally spaced a distance kT apart. Note that the partition function $f = 1.582$ in this case.

TABLE 7.6 An Example of a Boltzmann Distribution

Number of Level	$x_i = \epsilon_i/kT$	e^{-x_i}	N_i for $N = 1000$
0	0	1.000	633
1	1	0.368	233
2	2	0.135	85
3	3	0.050	32
4	4	0.018	11
5	5	0.007	4
6	6	0.002	1
7	7	0.001	1
8	8	0.0003	0
9	9	0.0001	0
10	10	0.0000	0
		Σe^{-x_i} 1.582	

19. THE DISTRIBUTION OF MOLECULAR VELOCITIES

In their constant motion, the molecules of a gas collide many times with one another, and these collisions provide the mechanism through which the velocities of individual molecules are continually changing. As a result, there exists a distribution of velocities among the molecules; most have velocities with magnitudes quite close to the average, and relatively few have velocities far above or far below the average.

The distribution of velocities among molecules in a gas was calculated by the Scotch theoretical physicist, James Clerk Maxwell, long before it was measured experimentally. From 1860 to 1865 Maxwell was professor of Natural Philosophy at Kings College, London. During these years he published his derivation of the distribution law, and also the great paper which laid the foundations of electromagnetic theory.

We shall not derive the distribution law in the way devised by Maxwell, but begin instead with a related problem in the theory of probability, the *random walk*.

20. ONE DIMENSIONAL RANDOM WALK

In its most picturesque statement, we consider an inebriated sailor who leaves a waterfront bistro still able to walk but unable to navigate. He is just as likely, the story goes, to take a step east as a step west. Each step has a probability $\frac{1}{2}$ of being in either direction. The problem is: after he has taken N steps, what is the probability that he is a distance x from his starting point, if the length of each step is l?

After N steps, the sailor could be at positions denoted by $-N$, $-N+1$, ... -1, 0, 1, $N-1$, N. Let $p(m, N)$ be the probability that he is at point m after N steps.

The probability of any definite sequence of N steps is $(\frac{1}{2})^N$, since each step in the sequence has a probability of $\frac{1}{2}$. Therefore,

$$p(m, N) = (\tfrac{1}{2})^N \times (\text{the number of distinct sequences that reach } m \text{ after } N \text{ steps})$$

To get to m, some set of $(N+m)/2$ steps must be positive, and the other $(N-m)/2$ must be negative. Therefore, the number of distinct sequences that reach m is

$$\frac{N!}{[\frac{1}{2}(N+m)]![\frac{1}{2}(N-m)]!}$$

Therefore,

$$p(m, N) = \frac{N!}{[\frac{1}{2}(N+m)]![\frac{1}{2}(N-m)]!}\left(\frac{1}{2}\right)^N \tag{7.35}$$

This expression is evaluated by means of the Stirling formula,*

$$\log N! = (N + \tfrac{1}{2}) \log N - N + \tfrac{1}{2} \log 2\pi \tag{7.36}$$

This is an excellent approximation for large N. When N is large, $m \ll N$.
When we apply Eq. (7.36) to Eq. (7.35), we obtain

$$\log p(m, N) = (N + \tfrac{1}{2}) \log N - \tfrac{1}{2}(N + m + 1) \log \left[\frac{N}{2}\left(1 + \frac{m}{N}\right)\right]$$

$$- \frac{1}{2}(N - m + 1) \log \left[\frac{N}{2}\left(1 - \frac{m}{N}\right)\right] - \frac{1}{2} \log 2\pi - N \log 2 \tag{7.37}$$

Since $m \ll N$, we can expand

$$\log\left(1 \pm \frac{m}{N}\right) = \pm \frac{m}{N} - \frac{m^2}{2N^2} \pm \cdots$$

Then Eq. (7.37) becomes

$$\log p(m, N) = (N + \tfrac{1}{2}) \log N - \tfrac{1}{2} \log 2\pi - N \log 2$$

$$-\tfrac{1}{2}(N + m + 1)\left(\log N - \log 2 + \frac{m}{N} - \frac{m^2}{2N^2}\right)$$

$$-\tfrac{1}{2}(N - m + 1)\left(\log N - \log 2 - \frac{m}{N} - \frac{m^2}{2N^2}\right)$$

Hence, $$\log p(m, N) \simeq - \tfrac{1}{2} \log N + \log 2 - \tfrac{1}{2} \log 2\pi - \frac{m^2}{2N}$$

or, $$p(m, N) \simeq \left(\frac{2}{\pi N}\right)^{1/2} \exp\left(-\frac{m^2}{2N}\right) \tag{7.38}$$

We now introduce the length of each step l, so that the distance $x = ml$. We consider a section of path Δx which contains many steps, and ask what is the probability $p(x, N)$ that the sailor (or any particle) is in the interval between x and $x + \Delta x$ after N steps. We have

$$p(x, N)\, \Delta x = p(m, N)\, \frac{\Delta x}{2l}$$

We write $\Delta x = 2l\, \Delta m$, since m can take only even or odd values depending on whether N is even or odd, and hence $\Delta x/l$ must be even.

Equation (7.38) therefore yields

$$p(x, N)\Delta x = \left(\frac{1}{2\pi l^2 N}\right)^{1/2} \exp\,(-x^2/2Nl^2)\Delta x \tag{7.39}$$

This is in fact the famous Gaussian error curve, which gives the normal dis-

* A proof is given by W. Feller, *An Introduction to Probability Theory and its Applications.* (New York: John Wiley, 1957), p. 50.

tribution of any set of measurements having only random errors. It is usually written in this case as

$$p(x) = \frac{1}{(2\pi)^{1/2}\sigma} e^{-x^2/2\sigma^2} \tag{7.40}$$

where σ is called the *standard deviation from the mean.* It is the root mean square deviation, σ^2 being the average of the squares of the deviations from the mean. The curve is plotted in Fig. 7.9 for two different values of the parameter σ.

For example, if you made a large number of measurements of the molarity of a standard solution of a reagent by titrating successive 20 ml samples, the results should be distributed on a curve like Fig. 7.9, provided the titrations were all equally trustworthy, and only random errors of measurement occurred.

In the random walk, the mean displacement is zero, and σ^2 is simply the mean square displacement $\overline{\Delta x^2}$.

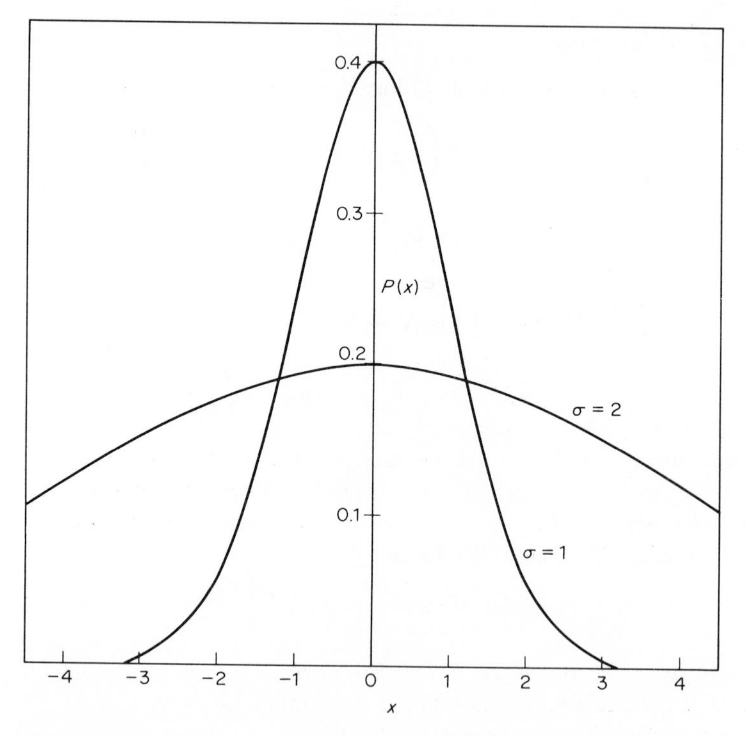

FIG. 7.9 Gaussian error curves. The curve for $\sigma = 1$ is called the normal density function $\phi(x) = (2\pi)^{-1/2} \exp(-x^2/2)$.

21. ONE-DIMENSIONAL VELOCITY DISTRIBUTION

To apply the random walk to the problem of molecular velocities, we replace the wandering sailor by a gas molecule, and we replace the displacement x by a velocity component u along the x axis. Instead of a sailor taking N steps at random under his own residual will power, we must visualize a gas molecule receiving increments of velocity from random collisions with other molecules. From Eq. (7.40) the probability that the molecule attains a velocity u is simply

$$p(u) = (2\pi\sigma^2)^{-1/2} \exp(-u^2/2\sigma^2)$$

In this case, we already know the value of $\overline{u^2}$, the mean square velocity in one dimension. From Eq. (7.7) it is

$$\overline{u^2} = kT/m$$

Since the velocity can be either positive or negative, its mean value $\bar{u}$ is zero, and hence $\sigma^2 = \overline{u^2}$. The probability that a molecule has a velocity component between u and $u + du$ is therefore

$$p(u)\,du = (m/2\pi kT)^{1/2} \exp(-mu^2/2kT)\,du \tag{7.41}$$

For example, the probability that the velocity component of an N_2 molecule lies between 999.5 and 1000.5 m sec^{-1} at 300°K is

$$\begin{aligned} p(u) &= \left(\frac{m}{2\pi kT}\right)^{1/2} \exp\left(\frac{-mu^2}{2kT}\right) \\ &= \left(\frac{28}{2\pi \times 8{\cdot}317 \times 10^7 \times 300}\right)^{1/2} \exp\left(\frac{-28 \times 10^{10}}{2 \times 8{\cdot}317 \times 10^7 \times 300}\right) \\ &= 4.84 \times 10^{-6} \end{aligned}$$

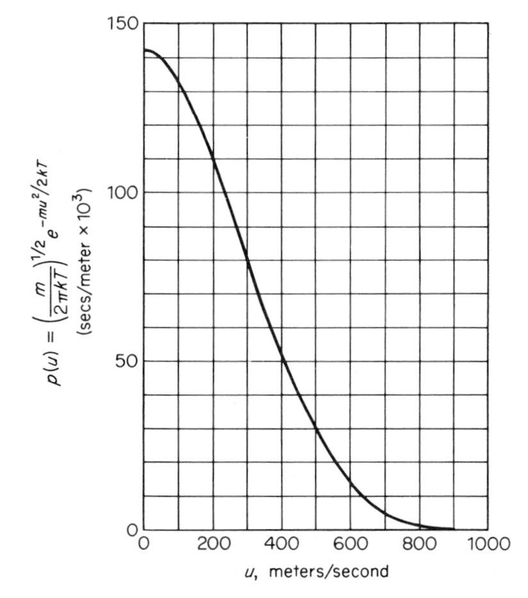

FIG. 7.10 One-dimensional velocity distribution (nitrogen at 0°C).

In a large collection of N_0 molecules, the fraction dN/N_0 with a velocity between u and $u + du$ is simply $p(u)\,du$ in Eq. (7.41).

The one-dimensional velocity distribution is plotted for nitrogen at 0°C in Fig. 7.10. We note that the fraction of the molecules with a velocity component in a given range declines at first slowly and then rapidly as the velocity is increased. From the curve and from a consideration of Eq. (7.41), it is evident that as long as $\frac{1}{2}mu^2 < kT$ the fraction of molecules having a velocity u falls off slowly with increasing u. When $\frac{1}{2}mu^2 = 10kT$, the fraction has decreased to e^{-10}, or 5×10^{-5} times its value at $\frac{1}{2}mu^2 = kT$. Thus only a small fraction of any lot of molecules can have kinetic energies much greater than kT per degree of freedom.

22. VELOCITY DISTRIBUTION IN TWO DIMENSIONS

If, instead of a one-dimensional gas (one degree of freedom of translation), a two-dimensional gas is considered, we can prove* that the probability that a molecule has a given u in no way depends on the value of its y component v. The fraction of the molecules having simultaneously velocity components between u and $u + du$, and v and $v + dv$, is then simply the product of the two individual probabilities.

$$\frac{dN}{N_0} = \frac{m}{2\pi kT} \exp\left(\frac{-m(u^2 + v^2)}{2kT}\right) du\, dv \tag{7.41}$$

This sort of distribution may be graphically represented as in Fig. 7.11, where a coordinate system with u and v axes has been drawn. Any point in the (u, v) plane represents a simultaneous value of u and v; the plane is a two-dimensional velocity space. The dots have been drawn so as to represent schematically the density of points in this space, i.e., the relative frequency of occurrence of sets of simultaneous values of u and v.

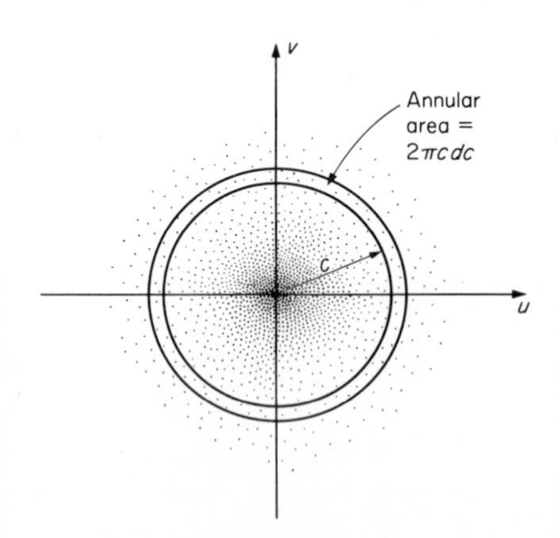

FIG. 7.11 Distribution of points in two-dimensional velocity space.

The graph bears a striking resemblance to a target that has been peppered with shots by a marksman aiming at the bull's-eye. In the molecular case, each individual molecular-velocity component, u or v, aims at the value zero. The resulting distribution represents the statistical summary of the results. The more skilful the marksman, the more closely will his results cluster around the center of the target. For the molecules, the skill of the marksman has its analogue in the coldness of the gas. The lower the temperature, the better the chance that a molecular-velocity component will come close to zero.

If, instead of the individual components u and v, the resultant speed c is considered, where $c^2 = u^2 + v^2$, it is evident that its most probable value is not zero. This is because the number of ways in which c can be made up from u and v increases in direct proportion with c, whereas at first the probability of any value of u or v declines rather slowly with increasing velocity.

From Fig. 7.11, it appears that we can obtain the distribution of c, regardless

* For a discussion of this theorem see, for example, J. Jeans, *Introduction to the Kinetic Theory of Gases* (Cambridge Univ. Press, 1940), p. 105.

of direction, by integrating over the annular area between c and $c + dc$, which is $2\pi c\, dc$. The required fraction is then

$$\frac{dN}{N_0} = \frac{m}{kT} \exp(-mc^2/2kT)\, c\, dc \tag{7.43}$$

23. DISTRIBUTION LAW IN THREE DIMENSIONS

We can now obtain the three-dimensional distribution law by a simple extension of this treatment. The fraction of molecules having simultaneously a velocity component between u and $u + du$, v and $v + dv$, and w and $w + dw$, is

$$\frac{dN}{N_0} = \left(\frac{m}{2\pi kT}\right)^{3/2} \exp\left(\frac{-m(u^2 + v^2 + w^2)}{2kT}\right) du\, dv\, dw \tag{7.44}$$

We wish an expression for the number with a speed between c and $c + dc$, regardless of direction, where $c^2 = u^2 + v^2 + w^2$. These are the molecules whose velocity points lie within a spherical shell of thickness dc at a distance c from the origin. The volume of this shell is $4\pi c^2 dc$, and therefore the desired distribution function is

$$\frac{dN}{N_0} = 4\pi \left(\frac{m}{2\pi kT}\right)^{3/2} \exp(-mc^2/2kT)\, c^2\, dc \tag{7.45}$$

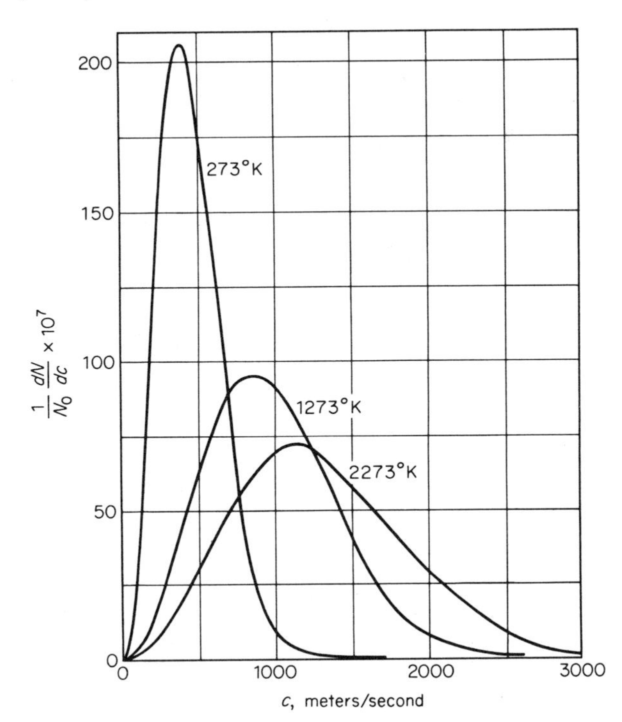

FIG. 7.12 Distribution of molecular speeds (nitrogen).

This is the usual expression of the distribution equation as derived by Maxwell in 1860.

The equation is plotted in Fig. 7.12 at several different temperatures. The curve becomes broader and less peaked at the higher temperatures, as the average speed increases and the distribution about the average becomes wider.

24. THE AVERAGE SPEED

We obtain the average value $\bar{r}$ of any property r of the molecules by multiplying each value r_i of r by the number of molecules N_i having this value, adding these products, and then dividing by the total number of molecules. Thus,

$$\bar{r} = \frac{\sum N_i r_i}{\sum N_i} = \frac{1}{N_0} \sum N_i r_i \tag{7.46}$$

where $\sum N_i = N_0$ is the fixed total number of molecules.

In case N is known as a continuously varying function of r, $N(r)$, instead of the summations of Eq. (7.46) we have the integrations,

$$\bar{r} = \frac{\int_0^\infty r\, dN(r)}{\int_0^\infty dN(r)} = \frac{1}{N_0} \int_0^\infty r\, dN(r) \tag{7.47}$$

This formula may be illustrated by the calculation of the average molecular speed $\bar{c}$. Using Eqs. (7.45) and (7.47), we have

$$\bar{c} = \frac{1}{N_0} \int_0^\infty c\, dN = 4\pi \left(\frac{m}{2\pi kT}\right)^{3/2} \int_0^\infty e^{-mc^2/2kT} c^3\, dc$$

The evaluation of this integral can be obtained* from

$$\int_0^\infty e^{-ax^2} x^3\, dx = \frac{1}{2a^2}$$

Making the appropriate substitutions, we find

$$\bar{c} = \left(\frac{8kT}{\pi m}\right)^{1/2} \tag{7.48}$$

* Letting $x^2 = z$,

$$\int_0^\infty e^{-ax^2} x\, dx = \frac{1}{2} \int_0^\infty e^{-az}\, dz = \frac{1}{2}\left(\frac{e^{-az}}{-a}\right)_0^\infty = \frac{1}{2a}$$

Then,

$$\int_0^\infty e^{-ax^2} x^3\, dx = -\frac{d}{da} \int_0^\infty e^{-ax^2} x\, dx = \frac{1}{2a^2}$$

Similarly, the average kinetic energy is

$$\tfrac{1}{2}\overline{mc^2} = \frac{m}{2N_0}\int_0^\infty c^2 dn$$

This yields

$$\tfrac{1}{2}(\overline{mc^2}) = \tfrac{3}{2}kT \tag{7.49}$$

25. THE EQUIPARTITION OF ENERGY

Equation (7.49) gives the average translational kinetic energy of a molecule in a gas. Note that the average energy is independent of the mass of the molecule. Per mole of gas,

$$E_k(\text{translational}) = \tfrac{3}{2}LkT = \tfrac{3}{2}RT \tag{7.50}$$

For a monatomic gas, like helium, argon, or mercury vapor, this translational kinetic energy is the total kinetic energy of the gas. For diatomic gases, like N_2 or Cl_2, and polyatomic gases, like CH_4 or N_2O, there is also energy associated with rotational and vibrational motions.

A useful model for a molecule is obtained by supposing that the masses of the constituent atoms are concentrated at points. As we shall see in Chapter 11, almost all the atomic mass is in fact concentrated in a tiny nucleus, the radius of which is about 10^{-13} cm. Since the overall dimensions of molecules are of the order of 10^{-8} cm, a model based on point masses is physically most reasonable. Consider a molecule composed of N atoms. In order to represent the instantaneous locations in space of N mass points, we require $3N$ coordinates. The number of coordinates required to locate all the mass points (atoms) in a molecule is called the number of its *degrees of freedom.* Thus a molecule of N atoms has $3N$ degrees of freedom.

The atoms comprising each molecule move through space as a connected entity, and we can represent the translational motion of the molecule as a whole by the motion of the *center of mass* of its constituent atoms. Three coordinates (degrees of freedom) are required to represent the instantaneous position of the center of mass. The remaining $(3N - 3)$ coordinates represent the so-called *internal degrees of freedom.*

The internal degrees of freedom may be further subdivided into *rotations* and *vibrations.* Since the molecule has moments of inertia I about suitably chosen axes, it can be set into rotation about these axes. If its angular velocity about an axis is ω, the rotational kinetic energy is $\tfrac{1}{2}I\omega^2$. The vibratory motion, in which the atoms in a molecule oscillate about their equilibrium positions, is associated with both kinetic and potential energies, being in this respect exactly like the vibration of an ordinary spring. The vibrational kinetic energy is also represented by a quadratic expression, $\tfrac{1}{2}\mu v^2$. The vibrational potential energy can in some cases be represented also by a quadratic expression, but in the coordinates q rather than in the velocities, for example, $\tfrac{1}{2}\kappa q^2$. Each vibrational degree of freedom would then contribute two quadratic terms to the total energy of the molecule.

By an extension of the derivation leading to Eq. (7.49), it can be shown that each of these quadratic terms that comprise the total energy of the molecule has an average value of $\frac{1}{2}kT$. This conclusion, a direct consequence of the Maxwell-Boltzmann distribution law, is the most general expression of the Principle of the Equipartition of Energy.

26. ROTATION AND VIBRATION OF DIATOMIC MOLECULES

We may visualize the rotation of a diatomic molecule by reference to the rigid rotor model in Fig. 7.13, which might represent a molecule such as H_2, N_2, HCl, or CO. The masses of the atoms, m_1 and m_2, are concentrated at points, distant r_1 and r_2, respectively, from the center of mass. The molecule, therefore, has moments of inertia about the X and Z axes, but not about the Y axis on which the mass points lie. The equilibrium distance between the mass points is fixed at r, so that such a molecule is called a *rigid rotor*.

The energy of rotation of a rigid body is given by

$$E_{\text{rot}} = \tfrac{1}{2}I\omega^2 \tag{7.51}$$

where ω is the angular velocity of rotation, and I is the moment of inertia. For the dumbbell model,

$$I = m_1r_1^2 + m_2r_2^2$$

The distances r_1 and r_2 from the center of mass are

$$r_1 = \frac{m_2}{m_1 + m_2}r, \qquad r_2 = \frac{m_1}{m_1 + m_2}r$$

Thus,

$$I = \frac{m_1m_2}{m_1 + m_2}r^2 = \mu r^2 \tag{7.52}$$

The quantity,

$$\mu = \frac{m_1m_2}{m_1 + m_2} \tag{7.53}$$

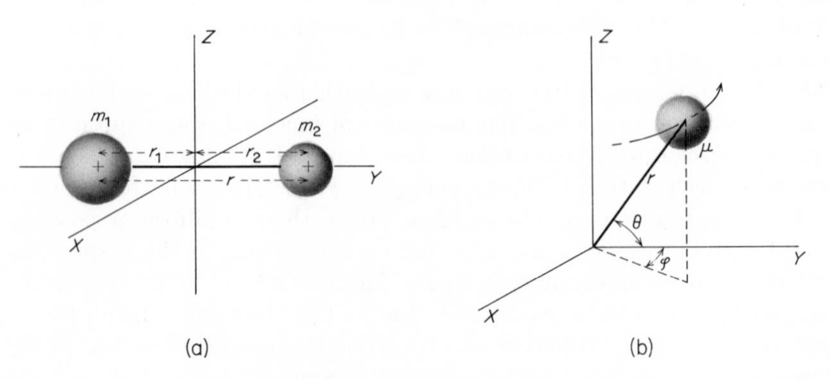

FIG. 7.13 Model of diatomic molecule as a rigid rotor.

is called the *reduced mass* of the molecule. The rotational motion is equivalent to that of a mass μ at a distance r from the intersection of the axes.

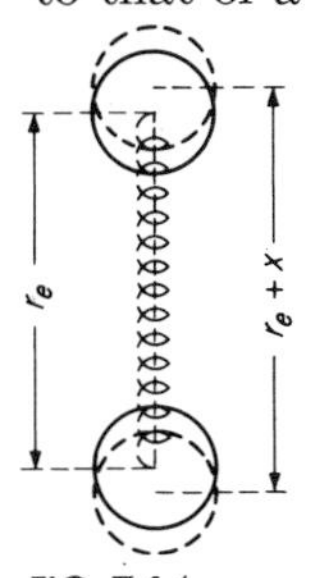

FIG. 7.14 Model of diatomic vibrator.

Only two coordinates are required to describe such a rotation completely; for example, two angles θ and ϕ suffice to fix the orientation of the rotor in space. There are thus two degrees of freedom for the rotation of a diatomic rotor. According to the principle of the equipartition of energy, the average molar rotational energy should therefore be $\overline{E}_{\text{rot}} = 2L(\frac{1}{2}kT) = RT$.

The simplest model for a vibrating diatomic molecule (Fig. 7.14) is the harmonic oscillator. From mechanics we know that simple harmonic motion occurs when a particle is acted on by a restoring force directly proportional to its distance from the equilibrium position $x = r - r_e$. Thus

$$f = -\kappa x = m\frac{d^2x}{dt^2} \tag{7.54}$$

The same equation applies to the vibrating diatomic molecule when we set $m = \mu$, the reduced mass. The constant κ is called the *force constant*. The motion of a particle under the influence of such a restoring force may be represented by a potential energy function $U(x)$.

$$f = -\left(\frac{\partial U}{\partial x}\right) = -\kappa x$$

$$U(x) = \tfrac{1}{2}\kappa x^2$$

This is the equation of a parabola and the potential-energy curve is drawn in Fig. 7.15. The motion of the system, as has been pointed out in previous cases, is analogous to that of a ball moving on such a surface. Starting from rest at any position x, it has only potential energy, $U = \frac{1}{2}\kappa x^2$. As it rolls down the surface, it gains kinetic energy up to a maximum at position $x = 0$, where $r = r_e$ equilibrium interatomic distance. The kinetic energy is then reconverted to potential energy as the ball rolls up the other side of the incline. The total energy at any time is always a constant,

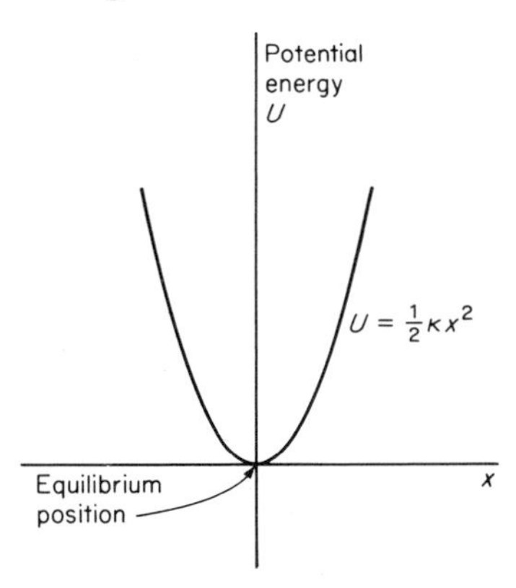

FIG. 7.15 Potential-energy curve of harmonic oscillator.

$$E_{\text{vib}} = \tfrac{1}{2}\mu\left(\frac{dx}{dt}\right)^2 + \tfrac{1}{2}\kappa x^2$$

It is apparent, therefore, that vibrating molecules when heated can take up energy as both potential and kinetic energy of vibration. The equipartition principle states that the average energy for each vibrational degree of freedom is therefore kT, $\frac{1}{2}kT$ for the kinetic energy plus $\frac{1}{2}kT$ for the potential energy.

For a diatomic molecule the total average energy per mole therefore becomes

$$\overline{E} = \overline{E}_{\text{trans}} + \overline{E}_{\text{rot}} + \overline{E}_{\text{vib}} = \tfrac{3}{2}RT + RT + RT = \tfrac{7}{2}RT$$

27. MOTIONS OF POLYATOMIC MOLECULES

The motions of polyatomic molecules can also be represented by the simple mechanical models of the rigid rotator and the harmonic oscillator. If the molecule contains N atoms, there are $(3N - 3)$ internal degrees of freedom. In the case of the diatomic molecule, $3N - 3 = 3$. Two of the three internal coordinates are required to represent the rotation, leaving one vibrational coordinate.

In the case of a triatomic molecule, $3N - 3 = 6$. In order to divide these six internal degrees of freedom into rotations and vibrations, we must first consider whether the molecule is linear or bent. If it is linear, all the atomic mass points lie on one axis, and there is therefore no moment of inertia about this axis. A linear molecule behaves like a diatomic molecule in regard to rotation, and there are only two rotational degrees of freedom. For a linear triatomic molecule, there are thus $3N - 3 - 2 = 4$ vibrational degrees of freedom. The average energy of the molecules according to the Equipartition Principle would therefore be

$$\begin{aligned}\overline{E} &= \overline{E}_{\text{trans}} + \overline{E}_{\text{rot}} + \overline{E}_{\text{vib}} \\ &= 3(\tfrac{1}{2}RT) + 2(\tfrac{1}{2}RT) + 4(RT) = 6\tfrac{1}{2}\,RT \text{ per mole}\end{aligned}$$

A nonlinear (bent) triatomic molecule has three principal moments of inertia, and therefore three rotational degrees of freedom. Any nonlinear polyatomic molecule has $3N - 6$ vibrational degrees of freedom. For the triatomic case, there are therefore three vibrational degrees of freedom. The average energy according to the Equipartition Principle would be

$$\begin{aligned}\overline{E} &= 3(\tfrac{1}{2}RT) + 3(\tfrac{1}{2}RT) + 3(RT) \\ &= 6\,RT \text{ per mole}\end{aligned}$$

Examples of linear triatomic molecules are HCN, CO_2, and CS_2. Bent triatomic molecules include H_2O and SO_2.

The vibratory motion of a collection of mass points bound together by linear restoring forces (i.e., a polyatomic molecule in which the individual atomic displacements obey Eq. (7.54)) may be quite complicated. It is always possible, however, to represent the complex vibratory motion by means of a number of simple motions, the so-called *normal modes of vibration*. In a normal mode of vibration, each atom in the molecule is oscillating with the same frequency. Examples of the normal modes for linear and bent triatomic molecules are shown in Fig. 7.16. The bent molecule has three distinct normal modes, each with a characteristic frequency. The frequencies of course have different numerical

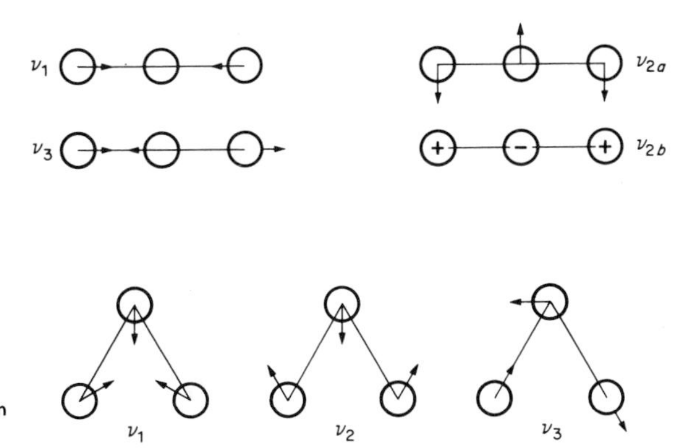

FIG. 7.16 Normal modes of vibration of triatomic molecules.

values in different compounds. In the case of the linear molecule, there are four normal modes; two correspond to stretching of the molecule (ν_1, ν_3) and two correspond to bending (ν_{2a}, ν_{2b}). The two bending vibrations differ only in that one is in the plane of the paper and one (denoted by + and −) normal to the plane. These vibrations have the same frequency, and are called *degenerate vibrations*.

When we described the translational motions of molecules and their consequences for the kinetic theory of gases, it was desirable at first to employ a very simplified model. The same procedure has been followed in this discussion of the internal molecular motions. Thus diatomic molecules do not really behave as rigid rotors, since, at rapid rotation speeds, centrifugal force tends to separate the atoms by stretching the bond between them. Likewise, a more detailed theory shows that the vibrations of the atoms are not strictly harmonic.

28. THE EQUIPARTITION PRINCIPLE AND HEAT CAPACITIES

According to the equipartition principle, a gas on warming should take up energy in all its degrees of freedom, $\frac{1}{2}RT$ per mole for each translational or rotational coordinate, and RT per mole for each vibration. The heat capacity at constant volume, $C_V = (\partial E/\partial T)_V$, could then be readily calculated from the average energy.

From Eq. (7.50) the translational contribution to $\overline{C}_V$ is $(\frac{3}{2})R$. Since $R = 1.987$ cal °C^{-1}, the molar heat capacity is 2.98 cal °C^{-1}. When this figure is compared with the experimental values in Table 7.7, it is found to be confirmed for the monatomic gases, He, Ne, Ar, Hg, which have no internal degrees of freedom. The observed heat capacities of the diatomic and polyatomic gases are always higher, and increase with temperature, so that it may be surmised that rotational and vibrational contributions are occurring.

For a diatomic gas, the equipartition principle predicts an average energy of $(\frac{7}{2})RT$, or $\overline{C}_V = (\frac{7}{2})R = 6.93$. This value seems to be approached at high

TABLE 7.7 MOLAR HEAT CAPACITY OF GASES, CAL DEG^{-1}

Gas	Temperature (°C)				
	−100	0	100	400	600
He, Ne, Ar, Hg	2.98	2.98	2.98	2.98	2.98
H_2	4.18	4.92	4.97	4.99	5.00
N_2	4.95	4.95	4.96	5.30	5.42
O_2	4.98	5.00	5.15	5.85	6.19
Cl_2	—	5.85	5.88	6.24	6.40
H_2O	—	—	6.37	6.82	7.60
CO_2	—	6.75	7.68	9.86	10.90

temperatures for H_2, N_2, O_2, and Cl_2, but at lower temperatures the experimental $\overline{C}_V$ values fall much below the theoretical ones. For polyatomic gases, the discrepancy with the simple theory is even more marked. The equipartition principle cannot explain why the observed C_V is less than predicted, why C_V increases with temperature, nor why the C_V values differ for the different diatomic gases. The theory is thus satisfactory for translational motion, but most unsatisfactory when applied to rotation and vibration.

Since the equipartition principle is a direct consequence of the kinetic theory, and in particular of the Maxwell-Boltzmann distribution law, it is evident that an entirely new basic theory will be required to cope with the heat-capacity problem. Such a development is found in the quantum theory introduced in Chapter 12.

29. BROWNIAN MOTION

In 1827, shortly after the invention of the achromatic lens, the botanist Robert Brown* studied pollen grains under his microscope and watched a curious behavior.

> *While examining the form of these particles immersed in water, I observed many of them very evidently in motion; their motion consisting not only of a change of place in the fluid, manifested by alterations of their relative positions, but also not infrequently of a change in form of the particle itself; a contraction or curvature taking place repeatedly about the middle of one side, accompanied by a corresponding swelling or convexity on the opposite side of the particle. In a few instances the particle was seen to turn on its longer axis. These motions were such as to satisfy me, after frequently repeated observations, that they arose neither from currents in the fluid, nor from its gradual evaporation, but belonged to the particle itself.*

In 1888, G. Gouy proposed that the particles were propelled by collisions with the rapidly moving molecules of the suspension liquid. Jean Perrin recog-

* Brown, *Phil. Mag.* 4, 161 (1828); 6, 161 (1829); 8, 41 (1830).

nized that the microscopic particles provide a visible illustration of many aspects of the kinetic theory. The dancing granules should be governed by the same laws as the molecules in a gas.

Perrin discovered a striking confirmation of this hypothesis in his work on the distribution of colloidal particles in a gravitational field, the sedimentation equilibrium. By careful fractional centrifuging, he was able to prepare suspensions of gamboge* particles that were spherical in shape and very uniform in size. It was possible to measure the radius of the particles either microscopically or by weighing a counted number. If these granules behave in a gravitational field like gas molecules, their equilibrium distribution throughout a suspension should obey the Boltzmann equation

$$N = N_0 e^{-mgh/kT} \tag{7.56}$$

Instead of m we may write $\frac{4}{3}\pi r^3(\rho - \rho_l)$ where r is the radius of the particle, and ρ and ρ_l are the densities of the gamboge and of the suspending liquid. Then Eq. (7.56) becomes

$$\ln \frac{N_0}{N} = \frac{\frac{4}{3}\pi r^3 gh(\rho - \rho_l)}{RT/L} \tag{7.57}$$

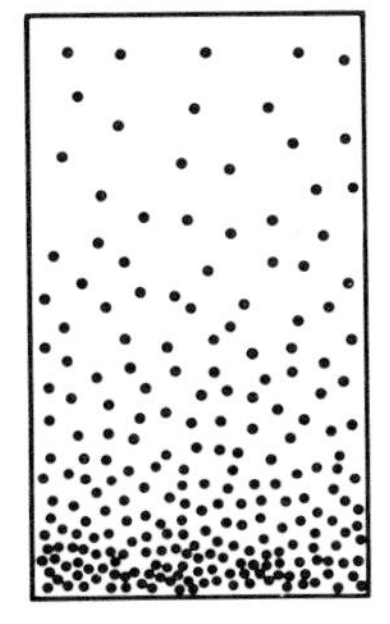

FIG. 7.17 Sedimentation equilibrium.

By determining the difference in the numbers of particles at heights separated by h, we can calculate a value for Avogadro's Number L.

A drawing of the results of Perrin's microscopic examination of the equilibrium distribution with granules of gamboge 0.6μ in diameter† is shown in Fig. 7.17. The relative change in density observed in 10μ of this suspension is equivalent to that occurring in 6 km of air, a magnification of six hundred million.

The calculation from Eq. (7.57) resulted in a value of $L = 6.5 \times 10^{23}$. The good agreement of this value with other determinations is evidence that the visible microscopic particles are behaving as giant molecules in accordance with the kinetic theory.

30. THERMODYNAMICS AND BROWNIAN MOTION

A striking feature of the Brownian motion of microscopic particles is that it never stops, but goes on continuously without any diminution of its activity. This perpetual motion is not in contradiction with the First Law, for the source of the energy that moves the particles is the kinetic energy of the molecules of the suspending liquid. We may assume that in any region where the colloid

* Gamboge is a gummy material from the desiccation of the latex secreted by *garcinia morella* (Indo-China). It is used as a bright yellow water color.

† 1 micron (μ) = 10^{-3} mm = 10^{-6} m.

particles gain kinetic energy, there is a corresponding loss in kinetic energy by the molecules of the fluid, which undergoes a localized cooling.

The study of Brownian motion thus reveals an important limitation of the scope of the Second Law, which also allows us to appreciate its true nature. The increase in potential energy in small regions of a colloidal suspension is equivalent to a spontaneous decrease in the entropy of the region. On the average, of course, over long periods of time the entropy of the entire system does not change. In any microscopic region, however, the entropy fluctuates, sometimes increasing and sometimes decreasing.

On the macroscopic scale such fluctuations are never observed, and the Second Law is completely valid. No one observing a book lying on a desk would expect to see it spontaneously fly up to the ceiling as it experienced a sudden chill. Yet it is not *impossible* to imagine a situation in which all the molecules in the book move spontaneously in a given direction. Such a situation is only extremely *improbable*, since there are so many molecules in any macroscopic portion of matter.

31. ENTROPY AND PROBABILITY

The law of the increase of entropy is thus a probability law. When the number of molecules in a system becomes sufficiently small, the probability of observing a spontaneous decrease in entropy becomes appreciable.

To illustrate the relation between entropy and probability, let us consider (Fig. 7.18) two different gases, A and B, in separate containers. When the partition is removed the gases diffuse into each other, the process continuing until they are perfectly mixed. If they were originally mixed, we should never expect them to become spontaneously unmixed by diffusion, since this condition would require the simultaneous adjustment of some 10^{24} different velocity components per mole of gas.

The mixed condition is the condition of greater randomness, of greater disorder; it is the condition of greater entropy since it arises spontaneously from the unmixed condition. (The entropy of mixing was given in Eq. (5.18).) Hence entropy is a measure of the degree of disorder or of randomness in a system. The system of greatest randomness is also the system of highest statistical probability, because many arrangements of molecules can comprise a disordered

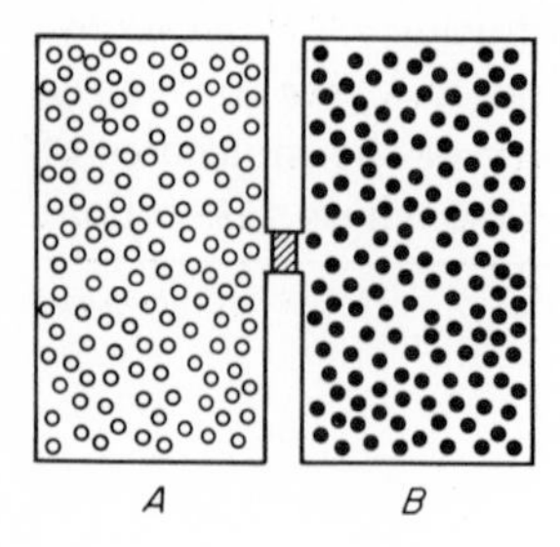

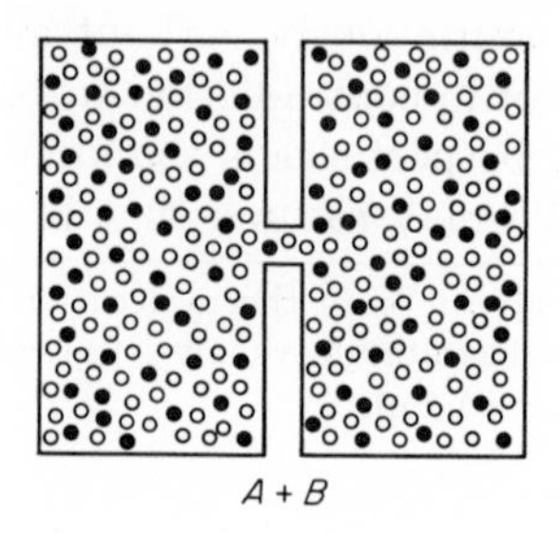

FIG. 7.18 Increase in randomness and entropy on mixing.

system, but only a few can give an ordered system. When we recall how seldom thirteen spades are dealt in a bridge hand,* we can realize how much more probable is the mixed condition in a system contraining 10^{24} molecules.

Mathematically, the probabilities of independent individual events are multiplied together to obtain the probability of the combined event. The probability of drawing a spade from a pack of cards is $\frac{1}{4}$, the probability of drawing two spades in a row is $(\frac{1}{4})(\frac{12}{51})$; the probability of drawing the ace of spades is $(\frac{1}{4})(\frac{1}{13}) = (\frac{1}{52})$. Thus $p_{12} = p_1p_2$. Entropy, on the other hand, is an additive function, $S_{12} = S_1 + S_2$. This difference enables us to state that the relation between entropy S and probability p must be a logarithmic one. Thus,

$$S = a \ln p + b \tag{7.58}$$

The value of the constant a may be derived by analyzing, from the viewpoint of probability, a simple change for which the ΔS is known from thermodynamics. Consider the expansion of one mole of an ideal gas, originally at pressure P_1 in a container of volume V_1, into an evacuated container of volume V_2. The final pressure is P_2 and the final volume, $V_1 + V_2$. For this change,

$$\Delta S = S_2 - S_1 = R \ln \left(\frac{V_1 + V_2}{V_1}\right) = k \ln \left(\frac{V_1}{V_1 + V_2}\right)^{-L} \tag{7.59}$$

When the containers are connected, the probability of finding one given molecule in the first container is simply the ratio of the volume V_1 to the total volume $V_1 + V_2$ or $V_1/(V_1 + V_2)$. Since probabilities are multiplicative, the chance of finding all L molecules in the first container, i.e., the probability p_1 of the original state of the system, is

$$p_1 = \left(\frac{V_1}{V_1 + V_2}\right)^L$$

Since in the final state all the molecules must be in one or the other of the containers, the probability $p_2 = 1^L = 1$.

Therefore, from Eq. (7.58),

$$\Delta S = S_2 - S_1 = a \ln \frac{p_2}{p_1} = a \ln \left[\frac{1}{V_1/(V_1 + V_2)}\right]^L = a \ln \left[\left(\frac{V_1}{V_1 + V_2}\right)\right]^{-L}$$

Comparison with Eq. (7.59) shows that a is equal to k, the Boltzmann constant. Thus

$$S = k \ln p + b$$

$$\Delta S = S_2 - S_1 = k \ln \frac{p_2}{p_1} \tag{7.60}$$

This relation was first given by Boltzmann in 1896.

We cannot actually calculate S from Eq. (7.60) until we have more detailed information about the energy states of atoms and molecules. This development is considered in Chapter 15.

---

* Once in 635 013 559 600 deals, if the decks are well shuffled and the dealers virtuous.

The relative probability of observing a decrease in entropy of ΔS below the equilibrium value may be obtained by inverting Eq. (7.60):

$$\frac{p}{p_{\text{eq}}} = e^{-\Delta S/k}$$

For one mole of helium, S/k at 273°K = 4×10^{25}. The chance of observing an entropy decrease one-millionth of this amount is about $e^{-10^{19}}$. It is evident, therefore, that anyone who sees a book flying spontaneously into the air is dealing with a poltergeist and not an entropy fluctuation (probably!). Only when the system is very small is there an appreciable chance of observing a large *relative* decrease in entropy.

Let us consider again the driving force of a chemical reaction or other change, $-\Delta G = -\Delta H + T\,\Delta S$. It is made up of two terms, the heat of the reaction and the increase in randomness times the temperature. The higher the temperature, the greater is the driving force due to the increase in disorder. This may be physically clearer in the converse statement: The lower the temperature, the more likely it is that ordered states can persist. The drive toward equilibrium is a drive toward minimum potential energy and toward maximum randomness. In general, both cannot be achieved in the same system under any given set of conditions. The free-energy minimum represents (at constant T and P) the most satisfactory compromise that can be attained.

PROBLEMS

1. At what speeds would molecules of hydrogen and oxygen have to leave the surface of (a) the earth, (b) the moon, in order to escape into space? At what temperatures would the average speeds of these molecules equal these "speeds of escape"? The mass of the moon can be taken as $\frac{1}{80}$ that of the earth. [*Ans.* Escape speed from moon, cm/sec: H_2 2.38×10^5, O_2 2.38×10^5; escape speed from earth, cm/sec: H_2 1.12×10^6, O_2 1.12×10^6; moon T°K: H_2 535, O_2 8500; earth T°K: H_2 11 900, O_2 18 900]

2. Calculate the number of (a) ergs per molecule, (b) kcal per mole corresponding to one electron volt per molecule. The electron volt is the energy acquired by an electron in falling through a potential difference of one volt. What is the mean kinetic energy of a molecule at 25°C in ev? What is k in ev per °C? [*Ans.* (a) 1.6×10^{-12}; (b) 23.05; (c) 0.0385 ev; (d) 8.63×10^{-5}]

3. The density of solid nitrogen at 0°C and 3000 atm is 0.835 g per cc. Calculate the average distance apart of the centers of the molecules. How does this compare with the molecular diameter calculated from van der Waals' b = 39.1 cc per mole? [*Ans.* 3.81 Å, 3.16 Å from b]

4. In the method of Knudsen [*Ann. Physik 29*, 179 (1909)], the vapor pressure is determined by the rate at which the substance, under its equilibrium pressure, diffuses through an orifice. In one experiment, beryllium powder was placed inside a molybdenum bucket having an effusion hole 0.318 cm in diameter. At 1537°K, it was found that 0.00888 g of Be effused in 15.2 min. Calculate the vapor pressure of Be at 1537°K. [*Ans.* 3.56×10^{-6} atm]

5. Two concentric cylinders are 10 cm long, and 2.00 and 2.20 cm in diameter. The space between them is filled with nitrogen at 10^{-2} mm pressure. Estimate the heat flow by conduction between the two cylinders when one is at 20° and the other at 0°C. [*Ans.* At 0°C, tabulated thermal conductivity gives 0.02 cal sec^{-1}, but λ at pressure cited is comparable to distance between walls, so that heat conduction is lower.]

6. What is the mean free path of argon at 25°C and a pressure of 1 atm? Of 10^{-5} atm? [*Ans.* with $d = 2.86$ Å, $\lambda = 1115$ Å at 1 atm, 1.115 cm at 10^{-5} atm]

7. Perrin studied the distribution of uniform spherical (0.212 μ radius) grains of gamboge ($\rho = 1.206$) suspended in water at 15°C by taking counts on four equidistant horizontal planes across a cell 100 μ deep. The relative concentrations of grains at the four levels were

level:	5 μ	35 μ	65 μ	95 μ
concentration:	100	47	22.6	12

Estimate Avogadro's Number from these data. [*Ans.* 6.5×10^{23}]

8. The number of collisions per second between unlike molecules A and B, in one cc of gas is

$$Z_{12} = \pi n_A n_B \left(\frac{d_A + d_B}{2}\right) \sqrt{\frac{8kT}{\pi\mu}}$$

where the reduced mass, $\mu = (m_A m_B)/(m_A + m_B)$. In an equimolar mixture of H_2 and I_2 at 500°K and 1 atm calculate the number of collisions per sec per cc between H_2 and H_2, H_2 and I_2, I_2 and I_2. For H_2 take $d = 2.18$ Å, for I_2, $d = 3.76$ Å.

9. The force constant of O_2 is 11.8×10^5 dynes per cm and $r_0 = 1.21$ Å. Estimate the potential energy per mole at $r = 0.8\ r_0$. [*Ans.* 2.08×10^5 joules]

10. Calculate the moments of inertia of the following molecules: (a) NaCl, $r_0 = 2.51$ Å; (b) H_2O, $r_{OH} = 0.957$ Å, $\angle$HOH $= 105° 3'$. [*Ans.* (a) 146×10^{-40} g cm^2; (b) 1.02, 1.92, 2.95×10^{-40}]

11. In a carefully designed high vacuum system it is possible to reach a pressure as low as 10^{-10} mm. Calculate the mean free path of helium at this pressure and 25°C. [*Ans.* 1.11×10^8 cm]

12. The permeability constant at 20°C of Pyrex glass to helium is given as 6.4×10^{-12} cc sec^{-1} per cm^2 area per mm thickness per cm of Hg pressure difference. The helium content of the atmosphere at sea level is about 5×10^{-4} mole per cent. Suppose a 100 cc round Pyrex flask with walls 2 mm thick was evacuated to 10^{-10} mm and sealed. What would be the pressure at the end of one year due to inward diffusion of helium? [*Ans.* 6.5×10^{-4} mm]

13. Calculate (1) the average speed (2) the rms speed of molecules of hydrogen, oxygen, and mercury at 0°C, 1000°C.

14. In an ultrahigh vacuum system, suppose the oxygen pressure has been reduced to 10^{-10} torr. A clean surface of sodium is formed, 1 cm^2 in area. If the density of Na is 0.97 g cm^{-3} and the density of Na_2O is 2.80, estimate how long it would take for the surface to be covered with a layer 1 molecule thick of Na_2O (at 20°C), if every oxygen molecule striking the surface was converted to oxide.

---

15. What is the chance that an oxygen molecule in air at STP travels (a) 10^{-6} cm, (b) 1 cm without experiencing a collision?

16. What is the fraction of molecules that has an energy greater than kT in one degree of translational freedom, in two degrees of freedom, in three degrees of freedom?

17. The van der Waals constant b of N_2O is 0.0442 l mole^{-1}. Estimate a molecular diameter from this value, and hence calculate the viscosity of N_2O at 25°C. [Experimental value 145 micropoise.]

18. In the one-dimensional random walk problem, how many steps must the sailor take in order to have an even chance ($p = 0.5$) of covering a distance 10 l, 100 l?

19. Calculate the pressure in mm of Hg of a barometer in an airplane which is at an altitude of 10 000 m. Assume the pressure is 760 mm at sea level and the mean temperature is −30°C. Use the average molecular weight of air (80 per cent nitrogen and 20 per cent oxygen) and a mean diameter of 3 Å. Calculate the total number of collisions per second and the mean free path at this altitude. Express the mean free path in meters.

20. At 25°C what fraction of the molecules in hydrogen gas have a kinetic energy within $kT \pm 10$ per cent? What fraction at 500°C? What fraction of molecules in mercury vapor? [*Ans.* 0.0729, same fraction in all cases]

21. Derive an expression for the fraction of molecules in a gas that have an energy greater than a given value E in two degrees of freedom. [*Ans.* $e^{-E/RT}$]

22. Show that the *most probable speed* of a molecule in a gas equals $\sqrt{2kT/m}$. For the most probable speed the distribution function is a maximum.

23. Derive the expression $(\frac{1}{2}\,\overline{mc^2}) = \frac{3}{2}kT$ from the Maxwell distribution law.

24. In a cc of oxygen at 1 atm and 300°K, how many molecules have translational kinetic energies greater than 2 electron volts? At 1000°K? [*Ans.* none; 4×10^8]

25. A pinhole 0.2 micron in diameter is punctured in a liter vessel containing chlorine gas at 300°K and 1 mm pressure. If the gas effuses into a vacuum, how long will it take for the pressure to fall to 0.5 mm? [*Ans.* 82 hours]

26. In Fig. 7.18, assume that there are 10 white balls and 10 black balls distributed at random between the two containers of equal volume. What is the ΔS between the random configuration and one in which there are 8 white balls and 2 black balls in the left-hand container, and 2 whites and 8 blacks in the right? Calculate the answer by Eq. (7.60) and also by Eq. (5.18). What is the explanation of the different answers? [*Ans.* Eq. (7.60): 3.44 k; Eq. (5.18): 4.43 k. Equation (5.18) is only valid for numbers so large that equilibrium configuration and most probable configuration are indistinguishable.]

27. A tube 10 cm long is mounted on a vertical axis midway between its ends and spun at 50 000 rpm at 20°C. The tube is filled with hydrogen and nitrogen at 1 atm. Calculate the ratio of the concentrations at the ends and center of the tube for each gas at equilibrium.

8 CHEMICAL KINETICS

Now forasmuch as the Elements, unless they be altered, cannot constitute mixt bodies; nor can they be altered unless they act and suffer one from another; nor can they act and suffer unless they touch one another, we must first speak a little concerning contact or mutual touching, Action, passion and Reaction.

DANIEL SENNERT (1660)

The basic questions in physical chemistry are two: "Where are chemical reactions going?" and "How fast are they getting there?" The first is the problem of equilibrium, or chemical statics; the second is the problem of the rate of attainment of equilibrium, or chemical kinetics.

Chemical kinetics is usually subdivided into the study of homogeneous reactions, those occurring entirely within one phase, and of heterogeneous reactions, those occurring at an interface between phases. Some reactions consisting of a number of steps may begin at a surface, continue in a homogeneous phase, and sometimes terminate on a surface.

1. THE RATE OF CHEMICAL CHANGE

Qualitative observations of the velocity of chemical reactions were recorded by early writers on metallurgy, brewing, and alchemy, but the first significant quantitative investigation was by L. Wilhelmy, in 1850. He studied the inversion of cane sugar (sucrose) in aqueous solutions of acids, following the change with a polarimeter:

$$H_2O + \underset{\text{Sucrose}}{C_{12}H_{22}O_{11}} \rightarrow \underset{\text{Glucose}}{C_6H_{12}O_6} + \underset{\text{Fructose}}{C_6H_{12}O_6}$$

The rate of decrease in the concentration of sugar c with time t was proportional to the concentration of sugar remaining unconverted. This reaction velocity was written as

$$-dc/dt = k_1 c$$

The constant k_1 is called the *rate constant* or the *specific rate* of the reaction.* Its value was found to be proportional to the acid concentration. Since the acid does not appear in the stoichiometric equation for the reaction, it is acting as a catalyst, increasing the reaction rate without being consumed itself.

Wilhelmy integrated the differential equation for the rate, obtaining

$$\ln c = -k_1 t + \text{constant}$$

At $t = 0$, the concentration has its initial value c_0, so that the constant is $\ln c_0$. Therefore, $\ln c = -k_1 t + \ln c_0$, or

$$c = c_0 \, e^{-k_1 t}$$

The experimental concentrations of sucrose closely followed this exponential decrease with time. On the basis of this work, Wilhelmy deserves to be called the founder of chemical kinetics.

The important paper of Guldberg and Waage, which appeared in 1863 (Sec. 6.1), emphasized the dynamic nature of chemical equilibrium. Van't Hoff later set the equilibrium constant equal to the ratio of rate constants, $K = k_f/k_b$.

In 1865–1867, A. V. Harcourt and W. Esson† studied the reaction between potassium permanganate and oxalic acid. They showed how to calculate rate constants for a reaction in which the velocity is proportional to the product of the concentrations of two reactants. They also discussed the theory of consecutive reactions.

2. EXPERIMENTAL METHODS IN KINETICS

An experimental determination of reaction velocity usually requires a good thermostat to maintain the system at constant temperature and a good clock to measure the passage of time. These two requisites are not hard to obtain. It is the pursuit of the third variable, the concentration of reactants or products, that is the source of most difficulties.

A reaction cannot be turned on and off like a stopcock, although a reaction occurring at an elevated temperature can often be virtually stopped by chilling the system. If one takes a sample of the reaction mixture at 2:00 P.M., one

* The words *rate*, *speed*, *velocity* are all synonymous in chemical kinetics, though not so in physical mechanics. Chemical kinetics is sometimes divided into two branches: (1) the formulation and study of reaction rates in terms of concentrations of reactants and rate constants, (2) the explanation of the values of the rate constants in terms of the structures and interactions of the reactants.

† A. V. Harcourt and W. Esson, *Proc. Roy. Soc. 14*, 470 (1865). *Phil. Trans. 156*, 193 (1866); *157*, 117 (1867).

would like to know the composition at 2:00 P.M., but few analytical methods are that rapid. It may be 2:05 before the result is obtained, and thus, especially in rapid reactions, it is difficult to determine the concentration c at a definite time t by any sampling technique.

The best method of analysis is therefore one that is practically continuous, and does not require the removal of successive samples from the reaction mixture. Physical properties can be used in this way in appropriate cases. Wilhelmy's use of optical rotation is a case in point. Other physical methods have included:

(1) Absorption spectra and colorimetric analysis;

(2) The measurement of dielectric constant*;

(3) The measurement of refractive index†;

(4) Dilatomeric methods, based on the change in volume due to reaction.

One of the most frequently used techniques, applicable to many gas reactions, is to follow the change in pressure. This can be read almost instantaneously, or it can be recorded automatically. The method would be ideal if gas reactions often ran smoothly according to a single stoichiometric equation. Unfortunately, many gas reactions are beset by complications and side reactions so that following the pressure change without concurrent analysis of the reaction products often leads to deceptive results. For example, the decomposition of ethane according to $C_2H_6 \rightarrow C_2H_4 + H_2$ changes the pressure, but actually some methane, CH_4, is included among the products.

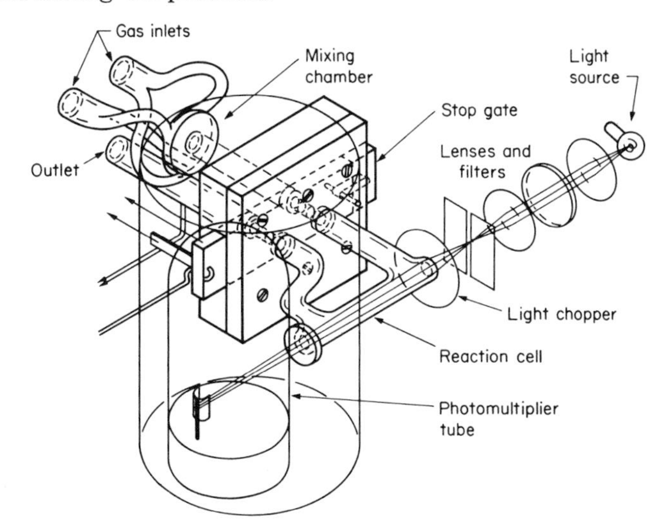

FIG. 8.1 Apparatus of Johnston and Yost for study of a rapid gas reaction: isometric projection of mixing chamber, stop gate, and 2mm diameter reaction cell, with schematic drawing of the light source, filters and lenses.

There is unlimited scope for experimental ingenuity in the measurement of extremely rapid reactions. An early example is the work of Johnston and Yost†† on $2NO_2 + O_3 \rightarrow N_2O_5 + O_2$ under conditions in which reaction is complete within 0.1 sec. Their apparatus is shown in Fig. 8.1. A stream of $O_2 + NO_2$

* T. G. Majury and H. W. Melville, *Proc. Roy. Soc. A 205*, 496 (1951).

† N. Grassie and H. W. Melville, *ibid., A 207*, 285 (1951).

†† H. S. Johnston and D. M. Yost, *J. Chem. Phys. 17*, 386 (1949).

was mixed with a stream of $O_3 + O_2$ in a chamber with tangential jets. After mixing, which was complete within 0.01 sec, a magnetically operated steel gate trapped a portion of the gas mixture. The disappearance of the NO_2, which is brown, was followed by the change of intensity of a beam of transmitted light. The beam was chopped with a rotating sector wheel 300 times per second, and the pulses were allowed to fall on a photomultiplier tube, the output of which was connected to an oscillograph. The pulsations on the oscillograph screen were photographed, the height of each peak giving the NO_2 concentration at intervals of $\frac{1}{300}$ sec.

3. ORDER OF A REACTION

The experimental data of chemical kinetics are records of concentrations of reactants and products at various times, the temperature usually being held constant throughout any one run. On the other hand, the theoretical expressions for reaction rates as functions of the concentrations of reactants, and sometimes of proucts, are differential equations of the general form, $dc_1/dt = f(c_1, c_2 \ldots c_n)$. Here c_1 is the particular product or reactant whose concentration is being followed. Before comparing theory with experiment, it is necessary either to integrate the theoretical rate law, or to differentiate the experimental concentration vs. time curve.

The rate laws are of practical importance since they provide concise expressions for the course of the reaction and can be applied in calculating reaction times, yields, and optimum economic conditions. Also, the laws often afford an insight into the *mechanism** by which the reaction proceeds. On the molecular scale the course of a reaction may be complex, and sometimes the form of the empirical rate law will suggest the particular path via which the reaction takes place.

In many instances the rate, which will be written as the decrease in concentration of reactant A, $-dc_A/dt$, is found to depend on the product of concentration terms. For example,

$$\frac{-dc_A}{dt} = k' c_A^a c_B^b \ldots c_N^n$$

The *order* of the reaction is defined as the sum of the exponents of the concentration terms in this rate law.

For example, the decomposition of nitrogen pentoxide, $2N_2O_5 \rightarrow 4NO_2 + O_2$, is found to follow the law, $-d[N_2O_5]/dt = k_1[N_2O_5]$. This is therefore a *first-order reaction.*

The decomposition of nitrogen dioxide, $2NO_2 \rightarrow 2NO + O_2$, follows the law, $-d[NO_2]/dt = k_2[NO_2]^2$. This is a *second-order reaction.* The reaction rate in benzene solution of triethylamine and ethyl bromide, $(C_2H_5)_3N + C_2H_5Br \rightarrow$

* The word *chemism* seems preferable but it has not been popular in English. In the German, *Chemismus* is often used.

$(C_2H_5)_4NBr$, follows the equation, $-d[C_2H_5Br]/dt = k_2[C_2H_5Br][(C_2H_5)_3N]$. This is also a second-order reaction. It is said to be *first-order with respect to* C_2H_5Br, *first-order with respect to* $(C_2H_5)_3N$, and *second-order overall.*

The decomposition of acetaldehyde, $CH_3CHO \rightarrow CH_4 + CO$, in the gas phase at 450°C fits the rate expression, $-d[CH_3CHO]/dt = k'[CH_3CHO]^{3/2}$. This is a reaction of the *three-halves order.*

It is to be noted that the order of a reaction need not be a whole number, but may be zero or fractional. It is determined solely by the best fit of a rate equation with the empirical data. Secondly, it is important to realize that there is no necessary connection between the form of the stoichiometric equation for the reaction and the kinetic order. Thus the decompositions of N_2O_5 and of NO_2 have equations of identical form, yet one is a first-order and the other a second-order reaction.

4. MOLECULARITY OF A REACTION

Many chemical reactions are not kinetically simple; they proceed through a number of steps or stages between initial reactants and final products. Each of the individual steps is called an *elementary reaction.* Complex reactions are made up of a sequence of elementary reactions, each of which proceeds in a single step.

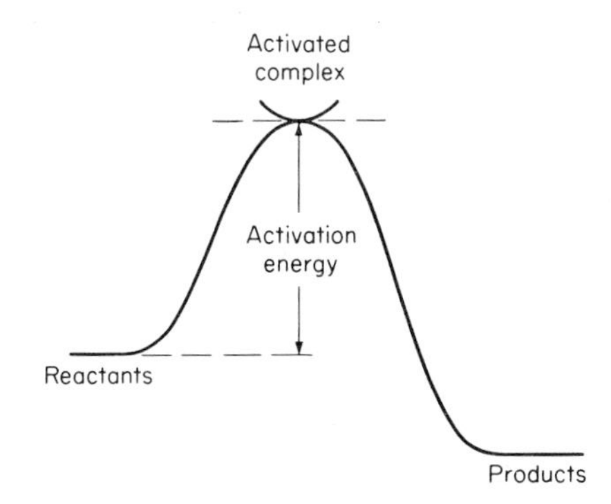

FIG. 8.2 Energy barrier surmounted by a system in chemical reaction.

In the earlier literature, the terms "unimolecular," "bimolecular," and "trimolecular" were used to denote reactions of the first, second, and third orders. We now reserve the concept of the *molecularity* of a reaction to indicate the molecular mechanism by which it proceeds. Thus careful studies indicate that the decomposition of hydrogen iodide, $2HI \rightarrow H_2 + I_2$, takes place when two HI molecules come together with sufficient kinetic energy to rearrange the chemical bonds from two H—I bonds to an H—H bond and an I—I bond. The elementary process involves two molecules, and this is therefore called a *bimolecular reaction.*

It will be shown later that before the usual chemical reaction can take place the molecule or molecules involved must be raised to a state of higher potential energy. They are then said to be activated or to form an *activated complex.* This process is shown in schematic form in Fig. 8.2. Reactants and products are both at stable potential-energy minima; the activated complex is the state at the top of the potential-energy barrier.

In terms of the activated complex, it is possible to give a more exact definition of the molecularity of a reaction. It is equal to the number of molecules of reactants that are used to form the activated complex. In the case of the hydrogen-iodide decomposition, the complex is formed from two HI molecules, and the reaction is *bimolecular*. Clearly the molecularity of a reaction must be a whole number, and in fact it is found to be one, two, or rarely, three.

The experimental rate measurements show that the rate of decomposition of hydrogen iodide is $-d[HI]/dt = k_2[HI]^2$. This is therefore a second-order reaction. All bimolecular reactions are second-order, but the converse is not true; there are second-order reactions that are not bimolecular.

A good example of a *unimolecular* reaction is a radioactive decay, e.g., $Ra \rightarrow Rn + \alpha$. Only one atom is involved in each disintegration, and the reaction is unimolecular. It also follows a first-order law, $-dN_{Ra}/dt = k_1 N_{Ra}$, where N_{Ra} is the number of radium atoms present at any time.

The concept of molecularity should be applied only to individual elementary reactions. If a reaction proceeds through several stages, we do not talk about its molecularity, since one step may involve two molecules, another three, and so on.

At the risk of repetition: *reaction order* applies to the experimental rate equation; *molecularity* applies to the theoretical mechanism.

5. REACTION MECHANISMS

Two meanings for the term "reaction mechanism" are in common use. In one sense, "reaction mechanism" means the particular sequence of elementary reactions that leads to the overall chemical change whose kinetics is under study. In the second sense, "reaction mechanism" means the detailed analysis of how the chemical bonds (or the nuclei and electrons) in the reactants rearrange to form the activated complex. For the present we shall understand the mechanism of a reaction to be established when we have found a sequence of elementary reactions that explain the observed kinetic behavior. We admit that each of these elementary reactions itself has a definite "mechanism," but theory is not yet able to elucidate this finer detail.

Consider, for example, the gas reaction,

$$2O_3 \longrightarrow 3O_2$$

We cannot predict the kinetic law this reaction follows simply by looking at its stoichiometric equation. If it were a bimolecular elementary reaction, it would follow the rate law

$$\frac{-d[O_3]}{dt} = k_2[O_3]^2$$

(Such a rate law is a necessary but not a sufficient condition for the reaction to be bimolecular.) As a matter of fact, experiment shows that the rate law is

$$\frac{-d[O_3]}{dt} = \frac{k_a[O_3]^2}{[O_2]}$$

With this information, we can suggest a reasonable mechanism:

$$O_3 \underset{k_{-1}}{\overset{k_1}{\rightleftharpoons}} O_2 + O$$

$$O + O_3 \underset{k_2}{\longrightarrow} 2O_2$$

The reversible dissociation is assumed to be rapid, leading to an equilibrium concentration of oxygen atoms,

$$[O] = \frac{K[O_3]}{[O_2]}$$

where $K = k_1/k_{-1}$.
Then the slower second step gives the net rate of decomposition of O_3,

$$\frac{-d[O_3]}{dt} = k_2[O][O_3] = \frac{k_2K[O_3]^2}{[O_2]}$$

Thus the suggested mechanism leads to the observed rate law. This agreement does not prove that the mechanism is correct. It is a necessary but not a sufficient condition for its correctness.

A skeptic might say that a sufficient condition can never be found in an experimental subject like chemical kinetics, but we shall be content with a reasonably sufficient condition based on the weight of the evidence. (A kinetic problem, like a crime, calls for a proof beyond "reasonable doubt" and not a mathematical proof.) Once a mechanism has been found that gives the observed kinetics, it can be tested in various ways. We might, for example, measure independently the individual reaction rates and equilibrium constants involved, to see whether the predicted relation is a fact confirmed. In the ozone decomposition, for instance,

$$k_a = k_2K$$

We could measure or calculate K and measure k_2 by introducing oxygen atoms of known concentration into ozone.

Evidently the proof of a mechanism is not an easy job. Thus there are many reactions whose kinetics are well known; there are some for which reasonable mechanisms have been proposed; but there are only a few for which the mechanisms have been proved.

6. THE REACTION-RATE CONSTANT

The experimental data in a kinetic experiment are values of concentrations at various times. Unless otherwise specified, the concentration unit is moles per liter, and the time is measured in seconds. It is purely a matter of convenience whether the reaction is followed by the decrease in one of the reactants or by the increase in one of the products. These quantities are related by the stoichiometric equation for the reaction.

Consider the decomposition of nitrogen pentoxide, $2N_2O_5 \rightarrow 4NO_2 + O_2$. Velocity can be expressed in three ways: the rate of disappearance of N_2O_5, $-d[N_2O_5]/dt$; the rate of formation of NO_2, $+d[NO_2]/dt$; the rate of formation of O_2, $+d[O_2]/dt$. Actually, the NO_2 dimerizes to N_2O_4, but the equilibrium for this association is established very rapidly and can easily be taken into account, since the equilibrium constant is well known. It is found that the N_2O_5 decomposition follows a first-order law over a range of pressures (10^{-2} to 10 atm) and temperatures (0 to 200°C). This law can be written in three ways:

$$\frac{-d[N_2O_5]}{dt} = k_1[N_2O_5], \qquad \frac{+d[NO_2]}{dt} = k_1'[N_2O_5], \qquad \frac{+d[O_2]}{dt} = k_1''[N_2O_5]$$

From the stoichiometry it is evident that $k_1 = \frac{1}{2}k_1' = 2k_1''$. The lesson to be learned is that it is always desirable to state clearly what rate law is being used to express the experimental results. Then the rate constant will have an unambiguous meaning. The choice is arbitrary but it should be explicit.

The units of the rate constant depend on the order of the reaction. For first order, $-dc/dt = k_1c$, the units of k_1 are mole liter^{-1} sec^{-1} × liter mole^{-1} = sec^{-1}. For second order, $-dc/dt = k_2c^2$, the units of k_2 are mole liter^{-1} sec^{-1} × (liter mole^{-1})^2 = liter mole^{-1} sec^{-1}. In general, for a reaction of the nth order, the dimensions of the constant k_n are (time)$^{-1}$ (concentration)$^{1-n}$.

7. FIRST-ORDER RATE EQUATIONS

The differential rate equation is almost always integrated before it is applied to the experimental data, although occasionally slopes of concentration vs. time curves are taken to determine dc/dt directly.

Consider a first-order reaction, $A \rightarrow B + C$. Let the initial concentration of A be a moles per liter. If after a time t, x moles per liter of A have decomposed, the remaining concentration of A is $a - x$, and x moles per liter of B or C have been formed. The rate of formation of B or C is thus dx/dt, and for a first-order reaction this is proportional to the instantaneous concentration of A, so that

$$\frac{dx}{dt} = k_1(a - x) \tag{8.1}$$

Separating the variables and integrating, we obtain

$$-\ln(a - x) = k_1t + \text{constant}$$

The usual initial condition is that $x = 0$ at $t = 0$, whence the constant $= -\ln a$, and the integrated equation becomes

$$\ln \frac{a}{a - x} = k_1t \tag{8.2}$$

or,

$$x = a(1 - e^{-k_1t})$$

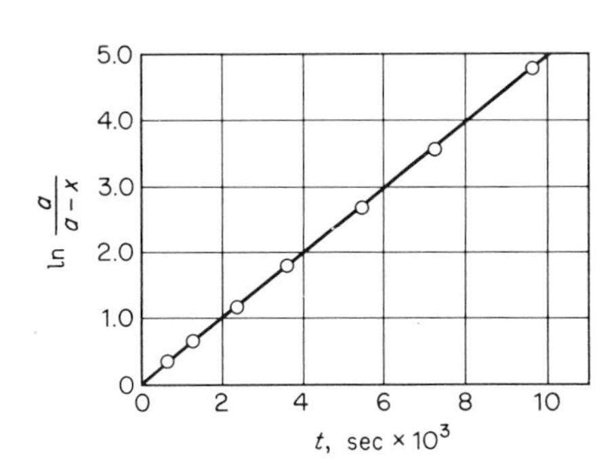

FIG. 8.3 A first-order reaction. The thermal decomposition of nitrogen pentoxide, plotted according to Eq. (8.2).

If $\ln[a/(a-x)]$ is plotted against t, a straight line passing through the origin is obtained, the slope of which is the first-order rate constant k_1.

If Eq. (8.1) is integrated between limits x_1 to x_2 and t_1 to t_2, the result is

$$\ln \frac{a - x_1}{a - x_2} = k_1(t_2 - t_1)$$

This interval formula can be used to calculate the rate constant from any pair of concentration measurements.

Applications of these equations to the first-order decomposition of gaseous N_2O_5 are shown in Table 8.1 and Fig. 8.3.*

TABLE 8.1 DECOMPOSITION OF NITROGEN PENTOXIDE
(Temperature, 45°C)

Time, t (Seconds)	$P_{N_2O_5}$ (mm)	k_1 (sec^{-1})	Time, t (Seconds)	$P_{N_2O_5}$ (mm)	k_1 (sec^{-1})
0	348.4	—	4200	44	0.000478
600	247	—	4800	33	0.000475
1200	185	0.000481	5400	24	0.000501
1800	140	0.000462	6000	18	0.000451
2400	105	0.000478	7200	10	0.000515
3000	78	0.000493	8400	5	0.000590
3600	58	0.000484	9600	3	0.000467
			∞	0	—

Another test of a first-order reaction is found in its half life τ, the time required to reduce the concentration of A to half its initial value. In Eq. (8.2) when $x = a/2$, $t = \tau$, and

$$\tau = (\ln 2)/k_1 \tag{8.3}$$

Thus the half life is independent of the initial concentration of reactant. In a first-order reaction, it would take just as long to reduce the reactant concentration from 0.1 mole per liter to 0.05 as it would to reduce it from 10 to 5.

8. SECOND-ORDER RATE EQUATIONS

Consider a reaction written as $A + B \rightarrow C + D$. Let the initial concentrations at $t = 0$ be a mole l^{-1} of A and b mole l^{-1} of B. After a time t, x mole l^{-1} of A,

* F. Daniels, *Chemical Kinetics* (Ithaca: Cornell Univ. Press, 1938), p. 9.

and of B, will have reacted, forming x mole l^{-1} of C and of D. If a second-order rate law is followed,

$$\frac{dx}{dt} = k_2(a - x)(b - x) \tag{8.4}$$

Separating the variables, we have

$$\frac{dx}{(a - x)(b - x)} = k_2\, dt$$

The expression on the left is integrated by breaking it into partial fractions. The integration yields

$$\frac{\ln (a - x) - \ln (b - x)}{a - b} = k_2 t + \text{constant}$$

When $t = 0$, $x = 0$, and constant $= \ln (a/b)/(a - b)$. Therefore the integrated second-order rate law is

$$\frac{1}{a - b} \ln \frac{b(a - x)}{a(b - x)} = k_2 t \tag{8.5}$$

A reaction found to be second order is that between ethylene bromide and potassium iodide in 99% methanol,

$$C_2H_4Br_2 + 3KI \longrightarrow C_2H_4 + 2KBr + KI_3$$

Sealed bulbs containing the reaction mixture were kept in a thermostat. At intevalrs of two or three minutes a bulb was withdrawn, and its contents were analyzed for I_2 (KI_3) by means of the thiosulfate titration. The second-order rate law is $d[I_2]/dt = dx/dt = k_2[C_2H_4Br_2][KI] = k_2(a - x)(b - 3x)$, and the integrated equation is*

$$\frac{1}{3a - b} \ln \frac{b(a - x)}{a(b - 3x)} = k_2 t$$

Figure 8.4 is a plot of the left side of this equation against time. The excellent linearity confirms the second-order law. The slope of the line is the rate constant, $k_2 = 0.299$ liter mole^{-1} min^{-1}.

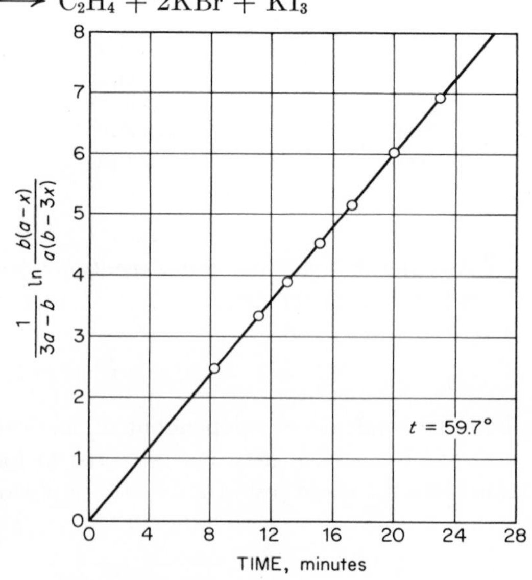

FIG. 8.4 The second-order reaction, $C_2H_4Br_2 + 3\,KI \rightarrow C_2H_4 + 2\,KBr + KI_3$ [From R. T. Dillon, *J. Am. Chem. Soc.*, *54*, 952 (1932)].

* Note that we can express all concentrations in equivalents per unit volume and always use Eq. (8.5).

A special case of the general second-order Eq. (8.4) arises when the initial concentrations of both reactants are the same, $a = b$. This condition can be purposely arranged in any case, but it will be necessarily true whenever only one reactant is involved in a second-order reaction. An example is the decomposition of gaseous hydrogen iodide, $2HI \rightarrow H_2 + I_2$, which follows the rate law, $-d[HI]/dt = k_2[HI]^2$.

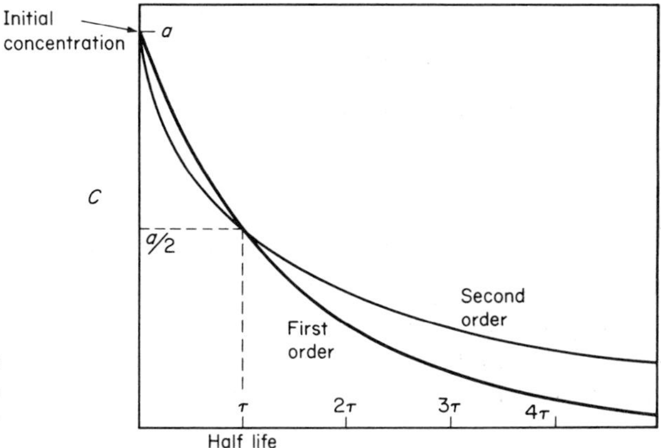

FIG. 8.5 Concentration vs. time curves for first and second order reactions with same initial concentrations a and same half lives τ.

In these cases the integrated Eq. (8.5) cannot be applied, since when $a = b$ it reduces to $k_2t = 0/0$, which is indeterminate. It is best to return to the differential equation, which becomes $dx/dt = k_2(a - x)^2$. Integration yields

$$1/(a - x) = k_2t + \text{constant}$$

When $t = 0$, $x = 0$, so that constant $= a^{-1}$. The integrated rate law is therefore

$$\frac{x}{a(a - x)} = k_2t \tag{8.6}$$

The half life of a second-order decomposition is found from Eq. (8.6) by setting $x = a/2$ when $t = \tau$, so that

$$\tau = 1/k_2a \tag{8.7}$$

The half life varies inversely as the initial concentration. For instance, the partial pressure of decomposing HI would take twice as long to fall from 100 to 50 mm as it would to fall from 200 to 100 mm.

Figure 8.5 shows the concentration vs. time curve of a first-order and a second-order reaction which have the same half life. The second-order reaction is of the type $2A \rightarrow$ products.

9. THIRD-ORDER RATE EQUATION

In the gas phase, third-order reactions are quite rare, and all that have been studied fall into the class,

$$\begin{matrix} 2A & + & B & \longrightarrow & \text{products} \\ a-2x & & b-x & & x \end{matrix}$$

The differential rate equation is accordingly $dx/dt = k_3(a - 2x)^2(b - x)$. This equation can be integrated by breaking it into partial fractions. The result, after we apply the initial condition, $x = 0$ at $t = 0$, is

$$\frac{1}{(2b-a)^2}\left[\frac{(2b-a)2x}{a(a-2x)} + \ln\frac{b(a-2x)}{a(b-x)}\right] = k_3 t$$

Examples of gas reactions of the third order, following this rate law, are

$$2NO + O_2 \longrightarrow 2NO_2$$

$$2NO + Br_2 \longrightarrow 2NOBr$$

$$2NO + Cl_2 \longrightarrow 2NOCl$$

In every case, $-d[NO]/dt = k_3[NO]^2[X_2]$.

The recombination of atoms in the gas phase usually requires the presence of a third body M to take up the excess energy of the exothermic reaction. Thus these reactions are often third order,

$$Cl + Cl + M \longrightarrow Cl_2 + M, \text{ etc.}$$

10. OPPOSING REACTIONS

If a reaction is to proceed for some time at a measurable rate, the initial conditions must evidently be fairly remote from the final equilibrium. In many instances the position of equilibrium is so far on the product side, at the temperature and pressure chosen for the experiment, that for all practical purposes one can say that the reaction goes "to completion." This is the case in the N_2O_5 decomposition and the oxidation of iodide ion that have been described. There are other cases in which a considerable concentration of reactants remains when equilibrium is reached. A well known example is the hydrolysis of ethyl acetate in aqueous solution,

$$CH_3COOC_2H_5 + H_2O \rightleftharpoons CH_3COOH + C_2H_5OH$$

In such instances, as the product concentrations are gradually increased, the velocity of the reverse reaction becomes appreciable. The measured rate of change is thereby decreased, and in order to deduce a rate equation to fit the empirical data, the opposing reaction must be taken into consideration.

Consider opposing first-order reactions, $A \rightleftharpoons B$. Let the first-order rate constant in the forward direction be k_1, in the reverse, k_{-1}. Initially at $t = 0$ the concentration of A is a and of B is b. If after a time t, x moles per liter of A have been transformed into B, the concentration of A is $a - x$, and that of B is $b + x$. The differential rate equation is therefore

$$\frac{dx}{dt} = k_1(a - x) - k_{-1}(b + x)$$

or
$$\frac{dx}{dt} = (k_1 + k_{-1})(m - x)$$

where $m = (k_1a - k_{-1}b)/(k_1 + k_{-1})$. Integration yields

$$\ln \frac{m}{m - x} = (k_1 + k_{-1})t \tag{8.8}$$

By Guldberg and Waage's principle, the equilibrium constant $K = k_1/k_{-1}$. Thus equilibrium measurements can be combined with rate data to separate the forward and reverse constants in Eq. (8.8).

Such reversible first-order reactions are found in some of the intramolecular rearrangements and isomerizations studied by G. B. Kistiakowsky and his co-workers.* The cis-trans isomerization of styryl cyanide vapor was followed by the change in the refractive index of the solution obtained on condensation.

$$\begin{array}{ccc} C_6H_5\text{—}CH & & C_6H_5\text{—}CH \\ \| & \rightleftharpoons & \| \\ NC\text{—}CH & & CH\text{—}CN \end{array}$$

Equilibrium at 300°C is at about 80 per cent trans-isomer.

The case of opposing bimolecular reactions was first treated by Max Bodenstein in his classic study of the combination of hydrogen and iodine.† Between 250 and 500°C the reaction $H_2 + I_2 \rightarrow 2\ HI$ can be conveniently studied, but at higher temperatures the equilibrium lies too far on the reactant side. Even in the cited temperature range the reverse reaction must be considered in order to obtain satisfactory rate constants. The concentrations at time t will be denoted as follows:

$$\begin{array}{ccccc} H_2 & + & I_2 & \underset{k_{-2}}{\overset{k_2}{\rightleftharpoons}} & 2\ HI \\ a - (x/2) & & b - (x/2) & & x \end{array}$$

The net rate of formation of HI is

$$\frac{d[\mathrm{HI}]}{dt} = \frac{dx}{dt} = k_2\left(a - \frac{x}{2}\right)\left(b - \frac{x}{2}\right) - k_{-2}x^2 \tag{8.9}$$

When the equilibrium constant $K = k_2/k_{-2}$ is introduced into Eq. (8.9) and the equation integrated, the result is

$$k_2 = \frac{2}{mt}\left[\ln\left(\frac{\dfrac{a + b - m}{1 - 4K} - x}{\dfrac{a + b + m}{1 - 4K} - x}\right) + \ln\left(\frac{a + b - m}{a + b + m}\right)\right]$$

with
$$m = \sqrt{(a + b)^2 - 4ab(1 - 4K)}$$

* Kistiakowsky et al., *J. Am. Chem. Soc.* *54*, 2208 (1932); *56*, 638 (1934); *57*, 269 (1935); *58*, 2428 (1936).

† Bodenstein, *Z. physik. Chem.* *13*, 56 (1894); *22*, 1 (1897); *29*, 295 (1898).

Good constants obtained from this rather formidable expression are shown in Table 8.2 for a number of temperatures, together with values of K and k_{-2} from separate experiments.

TABLE 8.2 RATE CONSTANTS FOR THE REACTION $H_2 + I_2 \rightleftharpoons 2HI$

T(°K)	liter mole^{-1} sec^{-1}		$K = k_2/k_{-2}$
	k_2	k_{-2}	
556	4.45×10^{-5}	7.04×10^{-7}	63.2
575	1.32×10^{-4}	2.50×10^{-6}	52.8
629	2.52×10^{-3}	6.04×10^{-5}	41.7
666	1.41×10^{-2}	4.38×10^{-4}	32.2
700	6.43×10^{-2}	2.32×10^{-3}	27.7
781	1.34	7.90×10^{-2}	17.0

11. CONSECUTIVE REACTIONS

It often happens that the product of one reaction becomes itself the reactant of a following reaction. There may be a series of consecutive steps. Only in the simplest cases has it been possible to obtain solutions to the differential equations of these reaction systems. They are especially important in polymerization and depolymerization processes.

A simple consecutive-reaction scheme that can be treated exactly is one involving only irreversible first-order steps. The general case of n steps has been solved,* but only the example of two steps will be discussed. This can be written

$$\begin{array}{ccccc} A & \xrightarrow[k_1]{} & B & \xrightarrow[k_1']{} & C \\ x & & y & & z \end{array}$$

The simultaneous differential equations are

$$-\frac{dx}{dt} = k_1 x, \qquad -\frac{dy}{dt} = -k_1 x + k_1' y, \qquad \frac{dz}{dt} = k_1' y$$

The first equation can be integrated directly, giving $-\ln x = k_1 t + \text{const.}$ When $t = 0$, let $x = a$, the initial concentration of A. Then const. $= -\ln a$, and $x = ae^{-k_1 t}$. The concentration of A declines exponentially with the time, as in any first-order reaction.

Substitution of the value found for x into the second equation gives

$$\frac{dy}{dt} = -k_1' y + k_1 a e^{-k_1 t}$$

* H. Dostal, *Monatshefte* (Vienna) *70*, 324 (1937). For second-order steps, see P. J. Flory, *J. Am. Chem. Soc. 62*, 1057, 1561, 2255 (1940).

This is a linear differential equation of the first order, whose solution* is

$$y = e^{-k_1't}\left[\frac{k_1ae^{(k_1'-k_1)t}}{k_1'-k_1} + \text{const.}\right]$$

When $t = 0$, $y = 0$, so that const. $= -k_1a/(k_1' - k_1)$.

We now have expressions for x and y. In the reaction scheme followed there is no change in the total number of molecules, since every time an A disappears a B appears, and every time a B disappears a C appears. Thus $x + y + z = a$, and z is calculated to be

$$z = a\left(1 - \frac{k_1'e^{-k_1t}}{k_1'-k_1} + \frac{k_1e^{-k_1't}}{k_1'-k_1}\right) \tag{8.10}$$

In Fig. 8.6, the concentrations x, y, z are plotted as functions of the time, for the case $k_1 = 2k_1'$. The intermediate concentration y rises to a maximum and then falls asymptotically to zero, while the final product rises gradually to the value of a.

Such a reaction sequence was found in the thermal decomposition (pyrolysis) of acetone.†

$$(CH_3)_2CO \longrightarrow CH_2{=}CO + CH_4$$
$$CH_2{=}CO \longrightarrow \tfrac{1}{2}C_2H_4 + CO$$

The concentration of the intermediate, ketene, rises to a maximum and then declines during the course of the reaction. Actually, however, the decomposition is more complex than the simple equations would imply.

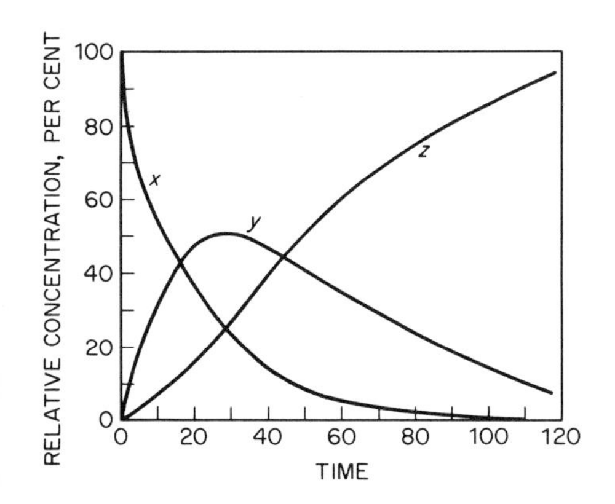

FIG. 8.6 Concentration changes in consecutive first-order reactions.

In dealing with consecutive reactions, the important *bottleneck principle* can sometimes be applied. If one of the steps proceeds much more slowly than any of the others, the overall reaction velocity will be determined by the speed of this slow step. For instance, in the example above, if $k_1 \ll k_1'$, Eq. (8.10) reduces to

$$z = a(1 - e^{-k_1t})$$

which is identical with Eq. (8.2) and includes only the constant of the slow step.

12. PARALLEL REACTIONS

Sometimes a given substance can react or decompose in more than one way.

---

* Granville, *op. cit.* (*Calculus*), p. 380.

† C. A. Winkler and C. N. Hinshelwood, *Proc. Roy. Soc. A 149*, 340 (1935).

Then the alternative parallel reactions must be included in analyzing the kinetic data. Consider a schematic reaction,

$$A \begin{cases} \xrightarrow{k_1} B \\ \xrightarrow{k_1'} C \end{cases}$$

In the case of such parallel processes, the most rapid rate determines the predominant path of the overall reaction. If $k_1 \gg k_1'$, the decomposition of A will yield mostly B. For example, alcohols can be either dehydrated to olefins or dehydrogenated to aldehydes,

$$C_2H_5OH \begin{cases} \xrightarrow{k_1} C_2H_4 + H_2O \\ \xrightarrow{k_1'} CH_3CHO + H_2 \end{cases}$$

By suitable choice of catalyst and temperature one rate can be made much faster than the other. The product obtained depends upon the relative rates and not upon the equilibrium constants for the two reactions.

13. RELAXATION METHODS

Suppose we subject a reversible reaction system at equilibrium to a disturbance that displaces it slightly from the equilibrium condition. For example, we might suddenly raise the temperature a few degrees, or change the pressure by means of a sudden compression. Provided the displacement from equilibrium is small enough, the rate of restoration of equilibrium will always follow a first-order kinetic law, irrespective of the kinetics of the forward and reverse reactions.

For example, consider the ionization of a weak acid,

$$HA + H_2O \underset{k_{-1}}{\overset{k_1}{\rightleftharpoons}} H_3O^+ + A^-$$

Let a be the concentration of $HA + A^-$, and x be the concentration of H_3O^+ (equal to that of A^-). If x_e is the equilibrium value of x, the displacement from equilibrium is $\Delta x = x - x_e$. At any instant,

$$dx/dt = k_1(a - x) - k_{-1}x^2$$

At equilibrium, $dx/dt = 0$, and

$$k_1(a - x_e) = k_{-1}x_e^2$$

Therefore,

$$d(\Delta x)/dt = k_1(a - x_e - \Delta x) - k_{-1}(x_e + \Delta x)^2$$

When the departure from equilibrium Δx is very small, the term in $(\Delta x)^2$ is negligible, and we obtain

$$d(\Delta x)/dt = -(k_1 + 2k_{-1}x_e)\,\Delta x = -\Delta x/\tau \tag{8.11}$$

The quantity $\tau = (k_1 + 2k_{-1}x_e)^{-1}$, the reciprocal of the rate constant for the restoration of equilibrium, is called the *relaxation time*. If Δx_0 is the initial displacement from equilibrium, we find from Eq. (8.11), as for any first order process,

$$\frac{\Delta x}{\Delta x_0} = \exp(-t/\tau)$$

When $t = \tau$, the displacement will have declined to $1/e$ of its initial value.

We now have shown that for sufficiently small displacements of a system from equilibrium, the rate of restoration of the system to equilibrium is proportional to the displacement.

If a method is available for following rapid changes in a property of the reaction system, the relaxation method can be used to measure extremely rapid reaction rates. For example, in one study by Eigen,* a condenser was discharged through a conductance cell which was in a Wheatstone bridge circuit (Sec. 9.4). After the abrupt rise in temperature, the weak acid in the cell must dissociate further to restore the equilibrium with its ions. The resultant change in conductivity was followed on an oscilloscope. From such experiments, the following rate constants were derived:

$$\begin{array}{lll}
H^+ + SO_4^{-2} \longrightarrow HSO_4^- & & k_2 = 10^{11}\ \text{l mole}^{-1}\ \text{sec}^{-1} \\
NH_4^+ + OH^- \longrightarrow NH_3 \cdot H_2O & & k_2 = 4 \times 10^{10}\ \text{l mole}^{-1}\ \text{sec}^{-1} \\
H^+ + OH^- \longrightarrow H_2O & & k_2 = 1.5 \times 10^{11}\ \text{l mole}^{-1}\ \text{sec}^{-1} \\
NH_3 \cdot H_2O \longrightarrow NH_4^+ + OH^- & & k_1 = 2 \times 10^{5}\ \text{sec}^{-1} \\
H_2O \cdot H_2O \longrightarrow H_3O^+ + OH^- & & k_1 = 2 \times 10^{-5}\ \text{sec}^{-1}
\end{array}$$

14. DETERMINATION OF THE REACTION ORDER

In simple reactions of the first or second order, it is not hard to establish the order and evaluate the rate constants. The experimental data are simply inserted into the different integrated rate equations until a constant k is found. The graphical methods leading to linear plots are useful. In more complicated reactions, it is often desirable to adopt other methods for at least a preliminary survey of the kinetics.

The *initial reaction rate* often provides helpful information, for in a sufficiently slow reaction, the rate dx/dt can be found with some precision before there has been any extensive chemical change. It is then possible to assume that all the reactant concentrations are still effectively constant at their initial values. If $A + B + C \rightarrow$ products, and the initial concentrations are a, b, c, the rate can be written quite generally as

$$\frac{dx}{dt} = k(a - x)^{n_1}(b - x)^{n_2}(c - x)^{n_3}$$

* M. Eigen, *Disc. Faraday Soc. 17*, 194 (1954).

If x is very small, the initial rate will be

$$\frac{dx}{dt} = k\, a^{n_1}\, b^{n_2}\, c^{n_3}$$

While we keep b and c constant, the initial concentration of a can be varied, and the resultant change of the initial rate measured. In this way the value of n_1 is estimated. Similarly, by keeping a and c constant while we vary b, a value of n_2 is found; and with a and b constant, variation of c yields n_3.

The initial-rate method is especially useful in those reactions that cannot be trusted to progress to any appreciable extent without becoming involved in labyrinthine complications. If the order of reaction found by using initial rates differs from that found by using the integrated rate equation, it is probable that the products are interacting with the initial reactants.

A frequently useful way of finding the reaction order is the *isolation method*, devised by W. Ostwald. If all the reactants save one, say A, are present initially in high concentrations, their concentrations during the reaction will be relatively much less changed than that of A. In fact, they may be taken to be effectively constant, and the rate equation will have the approximate form:

$$\frac{dx}{dt} = k(a - x)^{n_1}\, b^{n_2}\, c^{n_3} \ldots = k'(a - x)^{n_1}$$

By comparing the data with integrated forms of this equation for various choices of n_1, it is possible to determine the order of the reaction with respect to component A. The orders with respect to B, C, etc., are found in like manner.

The isolation method is often practiced of necessity in reactions in solution if the solvent is one reactant. For example, in the hydrolysis of ethyl acetate,

$$CH_3COOC_2H_5 + H_2O \rightleftharpoons CH_3COOH + C_2H_5OH$$

the ester concentration is much lower than that of the solvent, water. The reaction follows a rate law that is first order with respect to the ester, the water concentration being effectively constant:

$$\frac{-d[CH_3COOC_2H_5]}{dt} = k_2[CH_3COOC_2H_5][H_2O] = k_1[CH_3COOC_2H_5]$$

Another way of holding constant the concentration of a reactant is to use a saturated solution with an excess of pure solute phase always present.

15. REACTIONS IN FLOW SYSTEMS

The rate equations that have been discussed all apply to *static systems*, in which the reaction mixture is enclosed in a vessel at constant volume and temperature. We must now consider *flow systems*, in which reactants enter continuously at the inlet of a reaction vessel, while the product mixture is withdrawn at the outlet.

We shall describe two examples of flow systems: (a) a reactor in which there is no stirring; (b) a reactor in which complete mixing is effected at all times by vigorous stirring.

Figure 8.7 shows a tubular reactor through which the reaction mixture passes at a volume rate of flow u (e.g., in liters per sec). Let us consider an element of volume dV sliced out of this tube, and focus attention on one particular component k, which enters this volume element at a concentration c_k, and leaves at $c_k + dc_k$. If there is no longitudinal mixing, the net change with time of the number of moles of k within dV, (dn_k/dt) will be the sum of two terms, one due to chemical reaction within dV, and the other equal to the excess of k entering dV over that leaving. Thus,

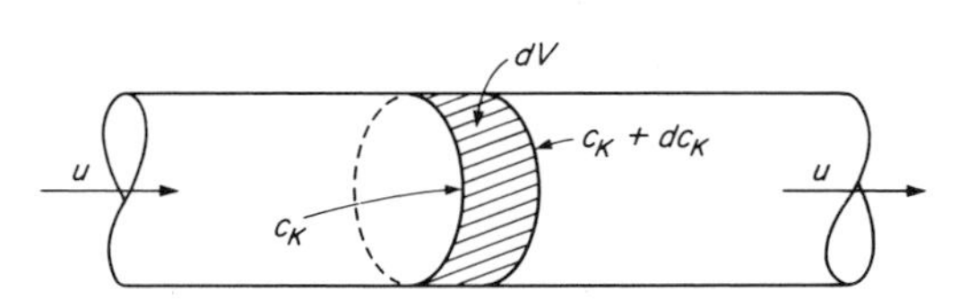

FIG. 8.7 Element of volume in a flow reactor.

$$\frac{dn_k}{dt} = r_k\, dV - u\, dc_k \tag{8.12}$$

The chemical reaction rate per unit volume is denoted by r_k. The explicit form of r_k is determined by the rate law for the reaction: for a reaction first order with respect to k, $r_k = -k_1c_k$; for second order, $r_k = -k_2c_k^2$, etc.

After reaction in the flow system has continued for some time, a *steady state* is attained, in which the number of moles of each component in any volume element no longer changes with time, the net flow into the element exactly balancing the reaction within it. Then $dn_k/dt = 0$, and Eq. (8.12) becomes

$$r_k\, dV - u\, dc_k = 0 \tag{8.13}$$

After r_k is introduced as a function of c_k, the equation can be integrated. For example, with $r_k = -k_1c_k$,

$$-k_1\frac{dV}{u} = \frac{dc_k}{c_k}$$

The integration is carried out between the inlet and the outlet of the reactor.

$$\frac{-k_1}{u}\int_0^{V_0} dV = \int_{c_{k1}}^{c_{k2}} \frac{dc_k}{c_k}$$

$$-k_1\frac{V_0}{u} = \ln\frac{c_{k_2}}{c_{k_1}} \tag{8.14}$$

The total volume of the reactor is V_0, and c_{k_2} and c_{k_1} are the concentrations of k at the outlet and inlet, respectively.

It may be noted that Eq. (8.14) reduces to the integrated rate law for a first-order reaction in a static system if the time t is substituted for V_0/u. The quantity V_0/u is called the *contact time* for the reaction; it is the average time that a molecule would take to pass through the reactor. Thus Eq. (8.14) allows us to evaluate the rate constant k_1 from a knowledge of the contact time and of the concentrations of reactant fed to the tube and recovered at the end of the tube. For other reaction orders also, the correct flow-reactor equation is obtained by substituting V_0/u for t in the equation for the static system. Many reactions that are too swift for convenient study in a static system can be followed readily in a flow system, in which the contact time is reduced by use of a high flow rate and a small volume.*

The derivation of Eq. (8.13) tacitly assumed that there was no volume change ΔV as a result of the reaction. Any ΔV would affect the flow rate at constant pressure. In liquid-flow systems, the effects of ΔV are generally negligible, but for gaseous systems the form of the rate equations is considerably modified. A convenient collection of integrated rate laws including such cases is given by Hougen and Watson.†

An example of a *stirred flow reactor*†† is shown in Fig. 8.8. The reactants enter the vessel at A, and stirring at 3000 rpm effects mixing within about a second. The product mixture is removed at B at a rate exactly balancing the feed. After a steady state is attained, the composition of the mixture in the reactor remains unchanged as long as the composition and rate of supply of reactants is unchanged. Eq. (8.13) still applies, but in this case $dV = V_0$, the total reactor volume, and $dc_k = c_{k_2} - c_{k_1}$ where c_{k_1} and c_{k_2} are the initial and final concentrations of reactant k. Thus

$$r_k = \frac{u}{V_0}(c_{k_2} - c_{k_1}) = \frac{dc_k}{dt}$$

With this method, there is no need to integrate the rate equation. One point on the rate curve is obtained from each steady-state measurement, and a number of runs with different feed rates and initial concentrations is required to determine the order of the reaction.

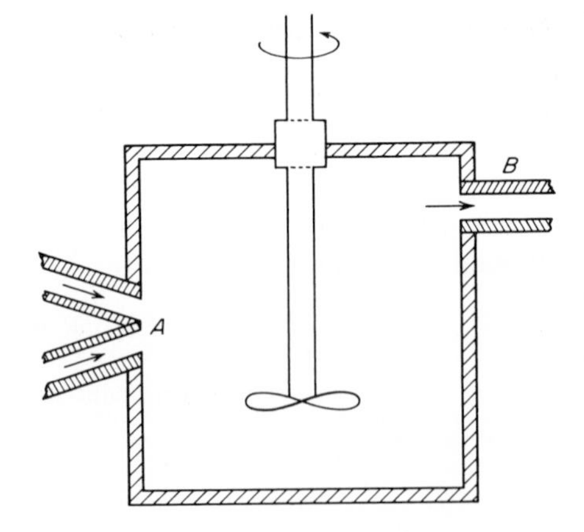

FIG. 8.8 A stirred flow reactor.

An important application of the stirred flow reactor is the study of transient intermediates, the concentration of which in a static system might quickly reach a maximum value and then fall to zero (as was shown in Fig. 8.6). For example, in the reaction between Fe^{+3} and $Na_2S_2O_3$, a violet color appears, which fades

* Experimental methods are described in *Techniques of Organic Chemistry* (New York: Interscience, 1953), pp. 669–738.

† O. A. Hougen and K. M. Watson, *Chemical Process Principles* (Part 3) (New York: Wiley, 1947), p. 834.

†† K. G. Denbigh, *Trans. Faraday Soc.* *40*, 352 (1944); *Disc. Faraday Soc.* *2*, 263 (1947).

within one or two minutes. In a stirred flow reactor, the conditions can be adjusted so that the color is maintained, and the intermediate responsible, which appears to be $FeS_2O_3^+$, can be studied by absorption spectrometry.

The living cell is in some ways analogous to a continuous flow reaction vessel, in which reactants and products are transferred by diffusion across the cell membrane.

16. EFFECT OF TEMPERATURE ON REACTION RATE

So far we have been concerned with the problem of finding how the chemical kinetics depends on the concentrations of the various components of the reaction system. This first step is necessary in reducing the raw material of the experimental data to a refined form suitable for theoretical interpretation. The next question is how the constants of the rate equations depend on variables such as temperature and total pressure. The temperature effect has been tremendously useful in providing an insight into the theory of all rate processes.

In 1889, Arrhenius pointed out that since the van't Hoff equation for the temperature coefficient of the equilibrium constant was $d \ln K_c/dT = \Delta E/RT^2$, whereas the mass-action law related the equilibrium constant to a ratio of rate constants, $K_c = k_f/k_b$, a reasonable equation for the variation of rate constant with temperature might be

$$\frac{d \ln k}{dT} = \frac{E_a}{RT^2} \tag{8.15}$$

The quantity E_a is called the *activation energy* of the reaction.

If E_a is not itself temperature dependent, Eq. (8.15) yields on integration

$$\ln k = -\frac{E_a}{RT} + \ln A \tag{8.16}$$

where $\ln A$ is the constant of integration. Hence

$$k = A \exp(-E_a/RT) \tag{8.17}$$

A is called the *frequency factor* or *pre-exponential factor*. This is the famous Arrhenius equation for the rate constant.

From Eq. (8.16) it follows that a plot of the logarithm of the rate constant against the reciprocal of the absolute temperature should be a straight line. The validity of the equation is excellently confirmed in this way for a large number of experimental velocity constants. An example from the data of Bodenstein on the $H_2 + I_2 \rightarrow 2HI$ reaction is shown in Fig. 8.9. We shall see later that the Arrhenius equation is only an approximate representation of the temperature dependence of k, but the approximation is usually a very good one.

According to Arrhenius, Eq. (8.17) indicated that molecules must acquire a certain critical energy E_a before they can react, the Boltzmann factor $e^{-E_a/RT}$

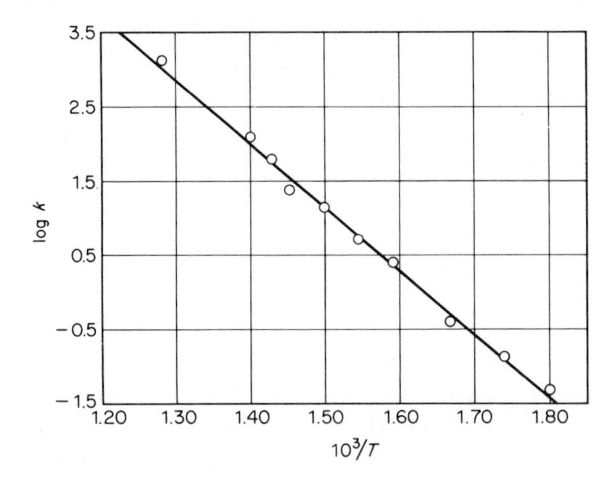

FIG. 8.9 Temperature dependence of rate constant for formation of hydrogen iodide, illustrating applicability of the Arrhenius equation.

being the fraction of molecules that manages to obtain the necessary energy. This interpretation is still held to be essentially correct.

By referring back to Fig. 8.2, we can obtain a picture of the activation energy as the potential-energy hill that must be climbed to reach the activated state. It is evident also that the heat of reaction q_v is the difference between the activation energies of forward and backward reactions,

$$\Delta E = q_v = E_f - E_b \tag{8.18}$$

17. COLLISION THEORY OF GAS REACTIONS

Reaction velocities have been studied in gaseous, liquid and solid solutions, and at the interfaces between phases. Homogeneous reactions in liquid solutions have undoubtedly been investigated most extensively, because they are of great practical importance and usually require only relatively simple experimental techniques. From a theoretical point of view, however, they suffer from the disadvantage that our understanding of liquids and solutions is inadequate, especially on the molecular scale that is important in chemical changes.

Homogeneous gas reactions, therefore, though harder to follow experimentally, should be more amenable to theoretical elucidation. The statistical theory of gases is well developed and provides an insight into the factors governing the reaction rates.

The first theory of gas reactions postulated that in order for molecules to interact, they must approach each other so closely that they can be said to be in collision. Sometimes a rearrangement of chemical bonds occurs during a collision, forming new molecules from the old ones. The speed of the reaction is equal to the number of collisions per second times the fraction of the collisions that are effective in producing chemical change.

The formula for the number of collisions per second between like molecules in one cc of gas is obtained from Eq. (7.16).

$$Z_{11} = \tfrac{1}{2}\sqrt{2}\pi N^2 d^2 \sqrt{\frac{8kT}{\pi m}} = 2N^2 d^2 \sqrt{\frac{\pi kT}{m}} \tag{8.19}$$

Here N is the number of molecules per cc, d is the molecular diameter, and $\sqrt{8kT/\pi m}$ is the average speed of a molecule of mass m. In the case of unlike molecules whose concentrations are N_1 and N_2, the collision frequency becomes

$$Z_{12} = \pi N_1 N_2 d_{12}^2 \sqrt{\frac{8kT}{\pi\mu}} \tag{8.20}$$

Now $d_{12} = (d_1 + d_2)/2$ is the mean molecular diameter and the reduced mass $\mu = m_1m_2/(m_1 + m_2)$. Note that the factor $\frac{1}{2}$ is not included in the expression for unlike molecules since a collision of the type $B \rightarrow A$ is now distinguishable from $A \rightarrow B$.

Let us calculate Z_{11} for hydrogen-iodide molecules at 700°K and 1 atm pressure. From gas viscosity, $d = 4 \times 10^{-8}$ cm. The mass $m = 127.9/6.02 \times 10^{23} = 2.12 \times 10^{-22}$ g; $N = PVL/RT = 1 \times 1 \times 6.02 \times 10^{23}/82.05 \times 700 = 1.05 \times 10^{19}$. Substituting in Eq. (8.19), we find $Z_{11} = 1.33 \times 10^{28}$. At a given temperature and pressure the Z_{11} for different molecules hardly ever varies by a factor of more than 50, and for molecules of low molecular weight the variations are much less. (The variable factor is $d^2/m^{1/2}$ and d may run from 2 to 20 Å.)

Now it is obvious that not every collision can lead to reaction; the collision frequency is so extremely high that if such were the case all chemical reactions would be completed in a fraction of a second. We therefore make the hypothesis that only those collisions lead to reaction in which the sum of the energies of the colliding molecules exceeds a certain critical value E.* The problem is therefore to calculate the chance that a pair of molecules has an energy greater than E.

The first question that arises is what energy is to be taken into consideration. A complex molecule can acquire energy in various degrees of freedom: translational kinetic energy, rotational kinetic energy, vibrational kinetic and potential energy. Can all of this energy be utilized in effecting the rearrangement of bonds that is called a "chemical reaction"?

The simplest form of the collision theory says that only two degrees of freedom are utilized. These degrees of freedom can best be visualized as the components of the translation of each molecule along the line of centers at the time of collision. In other words, only the velocity components in the direction of a head-on collision are effective. The chance that two molecules have a relative head-on velocity c, such that $\frac{1}{2}mc^2 = E$, has already been calculated, under a slightly different guise, in Chapter 7. Since the choice of direction is entirely arbitrary, it is simply the distribution law in two dimensions, Eq. (7.43):

* This hypothesis, that if energy is less than E there is never reaction, but if greater than E there is always reaction, is not very reasonable. A reaction probability that is some function of the energy would be more logical and is indeed used in more detailed theories.

$$\frac{dN}{N_0} = \left(\frac{m}{kT}\right) \exp\,(-mc^2/2kT)\; c\, dc$$

We wish to transform this expression into the distribution function for the kinetic energy per mole, $E = \frac{1}{2}Lmc^2$. Since $dE = Lmc\,dc$, and $R = Lk$, the result is

$$\frac{dN}{N_0} = \frac{1}{RT}\, e^{-E/RT}\, dE$$

This is the chance of a molecule's having an energy between E and $E + dE$ in two degrees of freedom. The chance of its having an energy greater than E is obtained by integrating from E to ∞:

$$\frac{\Delta N}{N_0} = \int_E^\infty \frac{1}{RT}\, e^{-E'/RT}\, dE' = -e^{-E'/RT}\Big|_E^\infty = e^{-E/RT}$$

The simple collision theory for a bimolecular reaction therefore gives for the number of molecules reacting per second:

$$\frac{dN}{dt} = \text{number of collisions per sec} \times \text{chance of collision having energy } E \text{ or greater}$$

$$= Z_{12}\, e^{-E/RT}$$

The velocity is usually expressed in moles per liter reacting per second, $dc/dt = k_2c_1c_2$. Since $c = 10^3N/L$, $dc/dt = (10^3/L)dN/dt$. The reaction rate is, accordingly,

$$\frac{dc}{dt} = \frac{10^3}{L}\frac{dN}{dt} = k_2c_1c_2 = k_2\,\frac{10^6}{L^2}\,N_1N_2$$

Thus,

$$k_2 = \frac{L}{10^3N_1N_2}\cdot\frac{dN}{dt} \qquad \text{with} \qquad \frac{dN}{dt} = Z_{12}\, e^{-E/RT}$$

Substituting the kinetic-theory expression for Z_{12} from Eq. (8.20), we have

$$k_2 = Ae^{-E/RT} = \frac{\pi L d_{12}^2}{10^3}\sqrt{\frac{8kT}{\pi\mu}}\; e^{-E/RT} = A'T^{1/2}\, e^{-E/RT} \qquad (8.21)$$

18. TESTS OF THE COLLISION THEORY

This theoretical expression can be compared with experiment in several ways. It contains three quantities that are not known *a priori*, the rate constant k_2, the collision diameter d_{12}, and the activation energy E. The following comparisons are possible: (1) With a value of E from the Arrhenius equation for the temperature coefficient, and a value of d_{12} from kinetic theory (e.g., viscosity), k_2 can be calculated and compared with experiment. (2) With the experimental k_2 at one temperature and the kinetic-theory d_{12}, a calculated value of E can be compared with the value from the temperature coefficient. (3) With the experimental E and k_2, a d_{12} can be calculated and compared with kinetic-theory or electron-diffraction diameters.

Let us apply method (1) to the HI decomposition. Using the previously cited values for the constants and for d_{12}, we obtain

$$k_2 = \frac{L}{10^3 N^2} Z_{11}\, e^{-E/RT} = \frac{(6.02 \times 10^{23})(1.33 \times 10^{28})}{10^3(1.05 \times 10^{19})^2}\, e^{-E/RT}$$

$$= 7.26 \times 10^{10}\, e^{-E/RT}$$

The experimental E is 43 700 cal. Thus at 700°K the calculated rate constant is 1.63×10^{-3} liter mole^{-1} sec^{-1}. The experimental value obtained by Bodenstein was 2.32×10^{-3}. The success of the collision theory in this case is quite remarkable.

Unfortunately, there are few simple second-order gas reactions that can be similarly tested. Table 8.3 contains some of the available data. The frequency factors A' are usually around 10^{11} in units of liter mole^{-1} sec^{-1}, so that observed differences in the reaction velocities are caused mainly by activation-energy differences. The experimental A' values sometimes deviate considerably from those calculated from the collision theory.

The collision theory gives a physical picture of how bimolecular gas reactions occur which is roughly correct, but factors other than an activation energy and a rigid-sphere collision frequency may influence the rate of reaction. It is necessary to rewrite the theoretical equation (8.21) as $k_2 = pAe^{-E/RT}$, where p is called the *steric factor*. Originally p was supposed to measure the geometrical requirements that must be met if two colliding molecules are to interact. It is likely that many other factors can affect p, and it has become simply a measure of the discrepancy between simple collision theory and the experimental results, as can be seen from Table 8.3.

TABLE 8.3 RATE CONSTANTS OF SECOND-ORDER GAS REACTIONS COMPARED WITH CALCULATIONS BY COLLISION THEORY

Reaction	Pre-exponential Factor log ($A/T^{1/2}$, liter mole^{-1} sec^{-1})	Activation Energy kcal mole^{-1}	Steric Factor p
$H_2 + I_2 \rightarrow 2HI$	9.78	40.7	0.33
$2HI \rightarrow H_2 + I_2$	10.00	45.9	0.10
$NO + O_3 \rightarrow NO_2 + O_2$	7.80	2.3	0.008
$CO + Cl_2 \rightarrow COCl + Cl$	8.5	51.3	0.04
$H + D_2 \rightarrow HD + H$	9.00	6.5	0.044
$Br + H_2 \rightarrow HBr + H$	9.31	17.6	0.12
$I + H_2 \rightarrow HI + H$	9.75	33.4	0.35
$NO_2 + NO_2 \rightarrow N_2O_4$	7.78	0	0.010
C_2H_4 + butadiene → cyclohexene	5.80	26.7	4.0×10^{-5}
isobutene + HCl → t-C_4H_9Cl	4.6	24.1	3.0×10^{-6}

The collision-theory expression for the rate constant contains, in addition to the strongly temperature dependent $e^{-E/RT}$ term, a mild temperature dependence in the frequency factor. Equation (8.21) can be written

$$\ln k_2 = \ln A' + \tfrac{1}{2} \ln T - \frac{E}{RT}$$

Hence, $d \ln k_2/dT = (E + \frac{1}{2}RT)/RT^2$. Thus the Arrhenius energy of activation is $E_a = E + \frac{1}{2}RT$. It is worthwhile to make this correction in performing calculations with the theory, but it hardly affects the linear plot of $\ln k$ vs. $1/T$.

There is no reason to assume that the activation energy should be strictly independent of temperature and in careful work a slight temperature dependence has often been noted. The dependence of the heat of reaction, ΔE or ΔH, on temperature is given by Kirchhoff's Equation (Sec. 2.19) and E_a may behave similarly.

19. FIRST-ORDER REACTIONS AND COLLISION THEORY

The collision theory was developed about the time of World War I by M. Trautz, W. C. McC. Lewis, and others, and as we have seen, it gives a fairly satisfactory account of bimolecular reactions. At the same time a number of gas reactions were being studied that were kinetically of the first order and apparently simple unimolecular decompositions. These reactions presented a paradox: the necessary activation energy must evidently come from the kinetic energy transferred during collisions, yet the reaction velocity did not depend on the collision frequency.

In 1922, F. A. Lindemann (Cherwell) showed how a collisional mechanism for activation could lead to first-order kinetics.* Consider a molecule A which decomposes according to $A \rightarrow B + C$, with a first-order rate law, $-d[A]/dt = k_1'[A]$. In a vessel full of $[A]$, the intermolecular collisions are continually producing molecules with higher than average energy, and indeed sometimes molecules with an energy above some critical value necessary for the *activation* that precedes decomposition. Let us suppose that there is a certain time lag between activation and decomposition; the activated molecule does not immediately fall to pieces, but moves around for a while in its activated state. Sometimes it may meet an energy-poor molecule, and in the ensuing collision it may be robbed of enough energy to be *deactivated*.

The situation can be represented as follows:

$$A + A \underset{k_{-2}}{\overset{k_2}{\rightleftharpoons}} A + A^{\star} \qquad A^{\star} \xrightarrow{k_1} B + C$$

Activated molecules are denoted by $A^{\star}$. The bimolecular rate constant for activation is k_2, for deactivation k_{-2}. The decomposition of an activated molecule is a true unimolecular reaction with rate constant k_1.

The process called *activation* consists essentially in the transfer of translational kinetic energy into energy stored in internal degrees of freedom, especially vibra-

* *Trans. Faraday Soc. 17*, 598 (1922). An essentially correct interpretation had previously been given by I. Langmuir, *J. Am. Chem. Soc. 42*, 2190 (1920).

tional degrees of freedom. The mere fact that a molecule is moving rapidly, i.e., has a high translational kinetic energy, does not make it unstable. In order to cause reaction, the energy must get into the chemical bonds, where high-amplitude vibrations will lead to ruptures, decompositions and rearrangements. The transfer of energy from translation to vibration can occur only in collisions with other molecules or with the wall. The situation is like that of two rapidly moving automobiles; their kinetic energies will not wreck them unless they happen to collide and the kinetic energy of the whole is transformed into internal energy of the parts.

The point of the Lindemann theory is that there is a lag between the activation of the internal degrees of freedom and the subsequent decomposition. The reason is that a polyatomic molecule can take up collisional energy into a number of its $3N - 6$ vibrational degrees of freedom, and then some time may elapse before this energy flows into the one bond that breaks.

The Lindemann scheme cannot be treated exactly since the differential equations to which it leads are not soluble in closed form. They are

$$\frac{d[A^\star]}{dt} = k_2[A]^2 - k_{-2}[A^\star][A] - k_1[A^\star]$$

$$\frac{-d[A]}{dt} = k_2[A]^2 - k_{-2}[A^\star][A]$$

$$\frac{d[B]}{dt} = k_1[A^\star]$$

An approximation is therefore made that is frequently used in chemical kinetics when the mathematical going becomes too rough. This is the *steady state approximation.* We assume that after the reaction has been under way for a short time, the rate of formation of activated molecules equals their rate of disappearance, so that the net rate of change in $[A^\star]$ is zero, $d[A^\star]/dt = 0$. In justification of this assumption it can be said that there are not many activated molecules present in any event. The value of $[A^\star]$ is necessarily small, so that the value of its rate of change will be small, and can usually be set equal to zero without serious error.

With $d[A^\star]/dt = 0$, the first equation above gives for the steady-state concentration of $A^\star$,

$$[A^\star] = \frac{k_2[A]^2}{k_{-2}[A] + k_1}$$

The reaction velocity is the rate at which $A^\star$ decomposes into B and C, or

$$\frac{d[B]}{dt} = k_1[A^\star] = \frac{k_1k_2[A]^2}{k_{-2}[A] + k_1} \tag{8.22}$$

Two special cases now arise.

If the rate of decomposition of $A^\star$ is much greater than its rate of deactivation, $k_1 \gg k_{-2}[A]$ and the net rate reduces to

$$\frac{d[B]}{dt} = k_2[A]^2$$

This expression is the ordinary second-order law.

On the other hand, if the rate of deactivation of $A^\star$ is much greater than its rate of decomposition, $k_{-2}[A] \gg k_1$, and the overall rate becomes

$$\frac{d[B]}{dt} = \frac{k_1 k_2}{k_{-2}}[A] = k_1'[A]$$

It is evident that we can obtain first-order kinetics while preserving a collisional mechanism for activation. This will be the result whenever the activated molecule has so long a lifetime that it is usually deactivated by collision before it has a chance to break into fragments.

Fortunately, there is a fairly critical experimental test of the Lindemann theory. As the pressure in the reacting system is decreased, the rate of deactivation, $k_{-2}[A^\star][A]$, must likewise decrease, and at low enough pressures the condition for first-order kinetics must always fail when $k_{-2}[A]$ is no longer much greater than k_1. The observed first-order rate constant should therefore fall off at low pressures to reach eventually a second-order constant.

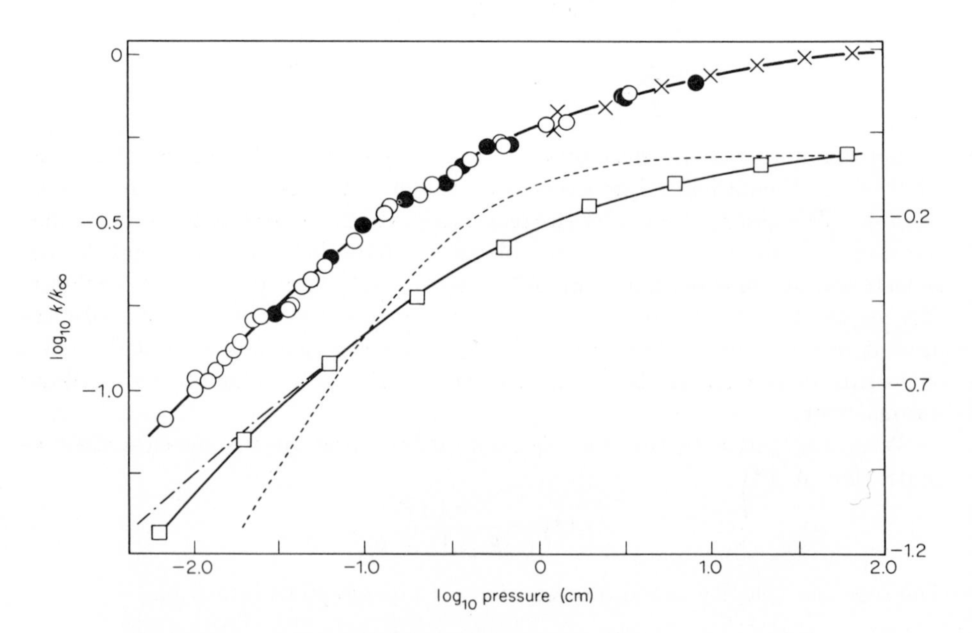

FIG. 8.10 The dependence of the rate of isomerization of cyclopropane on pressure. Upper curve: ○, runs to about 30% conversion; ●, runs to about 70% conversion; x, results of Chambers & Kistiakowsky. Lower curves: —, experimental results displaced by 0.3 log units; – – – –, calculated Lewis-Smith curve; —·—·—·, calculated Kassel curve; □, points calculated by Slater.

In Fig. 8.10 are plotted the rate constants obtained by Trotman-Dickenson and his coworkers* for the first-order thermal isomerization of cyclopropane at various pressures.

$$\begin{array}{c} CH_2 \\ / \quad \backslash \\ CH_2\text{—}CH_2 \end{array} \longrightarrow CH_3\text{—}CH\text{=}CH_2$$

In most of the first-order reactions that have been investigated, the rate constant decreases at low pressures (usually 10 to 100 mm). If the falling rate constant is merely the result of a lowered probability of deactivation, it should be possible to restore the initial rate by adding a sufficient pressure of a completely inert gas. This inert-gas effect has been noted in a number of cases.

TABLE 8.4. Relative Efficiencies of Added Gases in Maintaining the Rate of Isomerization of Cyclopropane

Molecule	Efficiency (pressure/pressure)	Collision Diameter (Å)	Efficiency (collision/collision)
Cyclopropane	1.000	5.0	1.000
Helium	0.060 ± 0.011	2.2	0.048
Argon	0.053 ± 0.007	3.6	0.070
Hydrogen	0.24 ± 0.03	2.7	0.12
Nitrogen	0.060 ± 0.003	3.8	0.070
Carbon Monoxide	0.072 ± 0.009	3.8	0.084
Methane	0.27 ± 0.03	4.1	0.24
Water	0.79 ± 0.11	4.0	0.74
Propylene	~ 1.0	5.0	~ 1.0
Benzotrifluoride	1.09 ± 0.13	8.5	0.75
Toluene	1.59 ± 0.13	8.0	1.10
Mesitylene	1.43 ± 0.26	9.0	0.89

TABLE 8.5. Unimolecular Gas Phase Decompositions†

Reactant	Products	log A (sec^{-1})	E_a (kcal mole^{-1})
$CH_3.CH_2Cl$	$C_2H_4 + HCl$	14.6	60.8
$CCl_3.CH_3$	$CCl_2\text{=}CH_2 + HCl$	12.5	47.9
t-Butyl Bromide	Isobutene + HBr	14.0	42.2
t-Butyl Alcohol	Isobutene + H_2O	11.5	54.5
$ClCOOC_2H_5$	$C_2H_5Cl + CO_2$	10.7	29.4
$ClCOOCCl_3$	$COCl_2$	13.15	41.5
Cyclobutane	C_2H_4	15.6	62.5
Perfluorocyclobutane	C_2F_4	15.95	74.1
N_2O_4	NO_2	16	13.0

* H. O. Pritchard, R. G. Sowden and A. F. Trotman-Dickenson, *Proc. Roy. Soc. A.* *217*, 563 (1953).

† From Sidney W. Benson, *The Foundations of Chemical Kinetics*, (New York: McGraw-Hill, 1960).

Table 8.4 summarizes the relative efficiencies of various gases in restoring the rate content of the cyclopropane isomerization to its high pressure value.

The Lindemann theory of unimolecular reactions is plausible and provides the best explanation for many experiments. In Table 8.5 we give some reactions now believed to be true unimolecular processes. Many reactions once thought to be simple unimolecular decompositions have been shown to proceed via complex chain mechanisms, which often yield deceptively simple rate laws. This aspect of gas kinetics will be considered a little later in the chapter.

20. ACTIVATION IN MANY DEGREES OF FREEDOM

When the first-order rate constant begins to fall at lower pressures, the rate of formation of activated molecules is no longer much greater than their rate of decomposition, and in fact the overall rate is beginning to be determined by the rate of supply of activated molecules. According to simple collision theory, therefore, the rate at this point should be about $Z_{11}e^{-E/RT}$. When this prediction was compared with experiment in a typical case, like the cyclopropane isomerization, it was found that the reaction was going about 5×10^5 times faster than was permissible by simple collision theory.

A solution to this contradiction was given by G. N. Lewis and D. F. Smith.† The $e^{-E/RT}$ term used to calculate the fraction of activated molecules is based on the condition that the critical energy is acquired in two translational degrees of freedom only. If energy in various internal degrees of freedom also can be transferred in collisions, the probability that a molecule gets the necessary E is much enhanced. Instead of a simple $e^{-E/RT}$ term, the chance is now*

$$P_E = \frac{e^{-E/RT}(E/RT)^{(s/2)-1}}{[(s/2) - 1]!} = f_s e^{-E/RT} \tag{8.23}$$

Here s is the number of "square terms" in which the energy can be acquired: translational or rotational energy has one square term per degree of freedom, $\frac{1}{2}mv^2$ or $\frac{1}{2}I\omega^2$; vibrational energy has one for kinetic energy, $\frac{1}{2}mv^2$, and one for potential energy, $\frac{1}{2}\kappa x^2$.

The rate of activation may now be increased by a large factor f_s. For the cyclopropane case, with $E = 28\,300$ cal, $T = 764°K$, the factor $f_s = 5 \times 10^5$ when $s = 14$. The observed rate of activation can therefore be explained by calling on 14 square terms or about 7 vibrational degrees of freedom. Since the molecule contains 9 atoms, there are altogether $3N - 6 = 21$ vibrations. The theory of Lewis and Smith would include a third of these in the activation process.

It has so far proved possible in every case to find a value of s that explains

* This is a good approximate formula when $E \gg RT$. A derivation is given by E. A. Moelwyn-Hughes, *Physical Chemistry*, 2nd ed. (New York: Pergamon Press, 1961), p. 1156.

† *J. Am. Chem. Soc.* *47*, 1508 (1925).

the observed activation rate.* Since it may not be easy to transfer energy from translation to vibration and from one vibration to another, the Lewis-Smith theory would seem to necessitate rather sticky collisions. Moreover, a clear-cut decision on the validity of the theory is prevented by the possible occurrence of chain reactions in many first-order decompositions.

21. THEORY OF UNIMOLECULAR REACTIONS

The essential theoretical problem in unimolecular reactions is to interpret the kinetic constants in terms of the molecular structures and vibration frequencies of the reacting molecules. Once a molecule has obtained more than a certain critical amount of internal energy, it is said to be activated. The first part of the problem is to calculate the rate at which a molecule can accumulate this energy. The next question is how long will it take, on the average, for this energy to flow into the bond which is to be broken in the decomposition process. Kassel† and others, in 1932, modified the simple Equation (8.22) to take into consideration the fact that the lifetime of an activated molecule must depend upon the amount of internal energy it has acquired in excess of the minimum critical amount required for dissociation. This theory assumes that energy can flow freely between the various normal modes of vibration in an activated molecule. On the other hand, the theory of N. B. Slater†† assumes that each normal mode acquires its supply of energy only during the collision process. The activated molecule then decomposes when the normal mode vibrations come into a suitable phase relationship such that the amplitude of vibration of the bond to be broken exceeds a certain critical value. For the limiting high-pressure rate (first-order rate constant), Slater finds the expression

$$k_1 = \nu e^{-E_0/RT} \tag{8.24}$$

* R. A. Ogg, *J. Chem. Phys.* *21*, 2079 (1953), has proposed an interesting chain mechanism for the N_2O_5 case, which previously appeared exceptional.

$$N_2O_5 \underset{2}{\overset{1}{\rightleftharpoons}} NO_2 + NO_3$$

$$NO_2 + NO_3 \xrightarrow{3} NO + O_2 + NO_2$$

$$NO + NO_3 \xrightarrow{4} 2NO_2$$

The stationary state treatment applied to $[NO_3]$ and $[NO]$ gives

$$\frac{-d[N_2O_5]}{dt} = k_0[N_2O_5] = \frac{2k_3k_1}{k_2 + k_3}[N_2O_5]$$

so that the first-order rate constant k_0 is composite.

† L. S. Kassel, *J. Chem. Phys.* *21*, 1093 (1953). This paper contains references to the earlier work.

†† N. B. Slater, *Proc. Roy. Soc. A* *218*, 224 (1953); *Phil. Trans. A* *246*, 57 (1953).

where ν is a weighted average of the frequencies of the normal modes of vibration of the molecule. Molecular vibration frequencies ν are of the order of 10^{13} sec^{-1}, and the frequency factors of most unimolecular reactions cluster closely about this figure.*

Another difficult part of the theory is to calculate the pressure dependence of the rate in the region where the collisional activations are insufficient to maintain a first-order kinetics. Kassel, Slater and others have provided different approaches to this problem, but its correct solution is one of the great unsolved questions of chemical kinetics.

22. CHAIN REACTIONS: FORMATION OF HYDROGEN BROMIDE

After Bodenstein had completed his study of the hydrogen-iodine reaction, he turned to hydrogen-bromine, $H_2 + Br_2 \rightarrow 2HBr$, probably expecting to find another example of biomolecular kinetics. The results† were surprisingly different, for the reaction velocity was found to fit the rather complicated expression,

$$\frac{d[\mathrm{HBr}]}{dt} = \frac{k[\mathrm{H_2}][\mathrm{Br_2}]^{1/2}}{m + [\mathrm{HBr}]/[\mathrm{Br_2}]}$$

where m and k are constants. Thus the velocity is inhibited by the product, HBr. In the initial stages of the combination, $[HBr]/[Br_2]$ is a small fraction so that $d[\mathrm{HBr}]/dt = k'[\mathrm{H_2}][\mathrm{Br_2}]^{1/2}$, with an over-all order of 3/2.

There was no interpretation of this curious rate law for thirteen years. Then the problem was solved independently and almost simultaneously by Christiansen, Herzfeld, and Polanyi. They proposed a chain of reactions with the following steps:

Chain initiation	(1)	$Br_2 \xrightarrow{k_1} 2Br$
Chain propagation	(2)	$Br + H_2 \xrightarrow{k_2} HBr + H$
	(3)	$H + Br_2 \xrightarrow{k_3} HBr + Br$
Chain inhibition	(4)	$H + HBr \xrightarrow{k_4} H_2 + Br$
Chain breaking	(5)	$2Br \xrightarrow{k_5} Br_2$

The reaction is initiated by bromine atoms from the thermal dissociation $Br_2 \rightarrow 2Br$. The chain propagating steps (2) and (3) form two molecules of HBr and regenerate the bromine atom, ready for another cycle. Thus very few

* N. B. Slater, *Theory of Unimolecular Reactions* (Ithaca: Cornell Univ. Press, 1959), but A. Kuppermann has shown (1962) that the models of Slater and of Kassel are both invalid when treated by classical mechanics for small molecules.

†M. Bodenstein and S. C. Lind, *Z. physik. Chem. 57*, 168 (1906).

bromine atoms are needed to cause an extensive reaction. Step (4) is introduced to account for the observed inhibition by HBr; since this inhibition is proportional to the ratio $[HBr]/[Br_2]$ it is evident that HBr and Br_2 compete, so that the atom being removed must be H rather than Br.

In order to derive the kinetic law from the chain mechanism, the stationary-state treatment is applied to the reactive atoms, which must be present in low concentrations.

$$\frac{d[Br]}{dt} = 0 = 2k_1[Br_2] - k_2[Br][H_2] + k_3[H][Br_2] + k_4[H][HBr] - 2k_5[Br]^2$$

$$\frac{d[H]}{dt} = 0 = k_2[Br][H_2] - k_3[H][Br_2] - k_4[H][HBr]$$

These two simultaneous equations are solved for the steady-state concentrations of the atoms, giving

$$[Br] = \left[\frac{k_1}{k_5}[Br_2]\right]^{1/2} \qquad [H] = k_2 \frac{(k_1/k_5)^{1/2}[H_2][Br_2]^{1/2}}{k_3[Br_2] + k_4[HBr]}$$

The rate of formation of the product, HBr, is

$$\frac{d[HBr]}{dt} = k_2[Br][H_2] + k_3[H][Br_2] - k_4[H][HBr]$$

Introducing the values for [H] and [Br] and rearranging, we find

$$\frac{d[HBr]}{dt} = 2\frac{k_3k_2k_4^{-1}k_1^{1/2}k_5^{-1/2}[H_2][Br_2]^{1/2}}{k_3k_4^{-1} + [HBr][Br_2]^{-1}}$$

This agrees exactly with the empirical expression, but now the constants k and m are interpreted as composites of constants for step reactions in the chain. Note that $k_1/k_5 = K$ is the equilibrium constant for the dissociation $Br_2 \rightleftharpoons 2Br$.

The $H_2 + Cl_2 \rightarrow 2HCl$ reaction is more difficult to study. It is exceedingly sensitive to light, which starts a chain reaction by photodissociation of chlorine, $Cl_2 + h\nu \rightarrow 2Cl$. The subsequent reaction steps are similar to those with Br_2. The thermal reaction proceeds similarly but it is complicated by wall effects and traces of moisture and oxygen.

Why is the reaction of iodine with hydrogen so different from that of bromine or chlorine? In the iodine case the most rapid mechanism is a homogeneous bimolecular combination, whereas with bromine the chain mechanism provides a more rapid path. Whenever parallel processes are possible, the most rapid one predominates. Approximate activation energies for the different steps in the $H_2 + X_2 \rightarrow 2HX$ reactions are shown in Table 8.6. The most significant differences are in the $X + H_2 \rightarrow HX + H$ reaction. In the case of X = Br, this has an E = 18 kcal, and for X = I, E = 33 kcal. The higher activation energy greatly decreases the chain-propagation reaction with iodine atoms.

TABLE 8.6 THE HYDROGEN-HALOGEN REACTIONS
ACTIVATION ENERGIES OF ELEMENTARY STEPS

	I	Br	Cl	F
$H_2 + X_2 \rightarrow 2HX$ . . .	41	41	50	>25
$X_2 \rightarrow 2X$	34	45	60	37
$X + H_2 \rightarrow HX + H$ . . .	33	18	5	8
$H + X_2 \rightarrow HX + X$ . . .	0	1	2	4
$H + HX \rightarrow H_2 + X$ . . .	1	1	4	36

23. FREE-RADICAL CHAINS

During the 1920's, a number of decompositions of organic molecules were investigated that seemed to be straightforward unimolecular reactions displaying a marked Lindemann effect at low pressures. It now appears that many of these reactions may actually have complicated chain mechanisms. The clue to their character was found in the transient existence of organic *free radicals.*

In 1900, Moses Gomberg discovered that hexaphenylethane dissociates in solution into two triphenylmethyl radicals,

$$(C_6H_5)_3C—C(C_6H_5)_3 \longrightarrow 2\,(C_6H_5)_3C$$

Such compounds with trivalent carbon atoms were at first believed to be chemical anomalies capable of occurring only in complex molecules.

One of the first suggestions that simple radicals might act as chain carriers in chemical reactions was made in 1925 by Hugh S. Taylor.* If a mixture of hydrogen and mercury vapor is irradiated with ultraviolet light of $\lambda = 2537$ Å, the mercury atoms are raised to a higher electronic state. They then react with hydrogen molecules, producing hydrogen atoms:

$$Hg(^1S_0) + h\nu(2537\ \text{Å}) \longrightarrow Hg(^3P_1)$$
$$Hg(^3P_1) + H_2 \longrightarrow HgH + H$$

If ethylene is added to the reaction mixture, there is a rapid reaction to form ethane, butane, and some higher polymeric hydrocarbons. Taylor suggested that the hydrogen atom combined with ethylene, forming a free ethyl radical, C_2H_5, which then started a chain reaction.

$$H + C_2H_4 \longrightarrow C_2H_5$$
$$C_2H_5 + H_2 \longrightarrow C_2H_6 + H, \text{ etc.}$$

In 1929, F. Paneth and W. Hofeditz obtained good evidence that aliphatic free radicals occur in the decomposition of molecules of the metallic alkyls such as mercury dimethyl and lead tetraethyl. The experiment of Paneth† is repre-

* *Trans. Faraday Soc. 21*, 560 (1925).
† *Berichte 62* 1335 (1929).

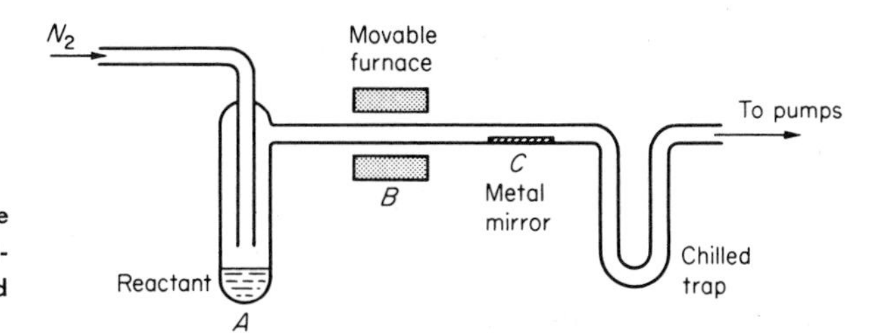

FIG 8.11. Paneth experiment. The lifetime of the radical can be calculated from position of mirror and rate of its removal.

sented in Fig. 8.11. A current of pure nitrogen at 2 mm pressure was saturated with lead tetramethyl vapor by passing over the liquid in A. The vapors were next passed through a tube heated at B to about 450°C. A lead mirror was deposited on the tube at the heated section, owing to the decomposition of the $Pb(CH_3)_4$. The vapors from the decomposition, after flowing down the tube a distance of 10 to 30 cm, passed over a previously deposited mirror of lead at 100°C. It was observed that this mirror was gradually removed. It appears therefore that the metal alkyl first breaks into free methyl radicals, $Pb(CH_3)_4 \rightarrow Pb + 4CH_3$. These are carried along in the stream of nitrogen for a considerable distance before they recombine to stable hydrocarbons. They remove metallic mirrors by reacting with the metal to form volatile alkyls. Thus if the mirror is zinc, $Zn(CH_3)_2$ can be recovered; if antimony, $Sb(CH_3)_3$ is recovered as the mirror is removed.

From 1932 to 1934, F. O. Rice and his collaborators* showed that the thermal decomposition by the Paneth technique of many organic compounds such as $(CH_3)_2CO$, C_2H_6 and other hydrocarbons, gave products that would remove metal mirrors. They therefore concluded that free radicals were formed in the primary steps of the decomposition of all these molecules.

In 1935 an important theoretical advance was made by Rice and Herzfeld.† They showed how free-radical chain mechanisms could be devised that would lead to a simple overall kinetics. The products from the decompositions were in good agreement with the proposed radical mechanisms. A typical example is the following possible mechanism for the decomposition of acetaldehyde, $CH_3CHO \rightarrow CH_4 + CO$.

$$(1)\quad CH_3CHO \xrightarrow{k_1} CH_3 + CHO$$
$$(2)\quad CH_3CHO + CH_3 \xrightarrow{k_2} CH_4 + CO + CH_3$$
$$(3)\quad 2CH_3 \xrightarrow{k_3} C_2H_6$$

One primary split into methyl radicals can result in the decomposition of many CH_3CHO molecules, since the chain carrier, CH_3, is regenerated in step (2). The steady-state treatment of the CH_3 concentration yields

* F. O. Rice, *J. Am. Chem. Soc. 53*, 1959 (1931); F. O. Rice, W. R. Johnston, and B. L. Evering, *ibid.*,*54*, 3529 (1932); F. O. Rice and A. L. Glasebrook, *ibid.*, *56*, 2381 (1934).

† *J. Am. Chem. Soc. 56*, 284 (1934).

$$\frac{d[CH_3]}{dt} = 0 = k_1[CH_3CHO] - k_3[CH_3]^2$$

so that

$$[CH_3] = \left(\frac{k_1}{k_3}\right)^{1/2} [CH_3CHO]^{1/2}$$

The reaction rate based on methane formation is then

$$\frac{d[CH_4]}{dt} = k_2[CH_3][CH_3CHO] = k_2\left(\frac{k_1}{k_3}\right)^{1/2} [CH_3CHO]^{3/2}$$

The free-radical scheme predicts an order of $\frac{3}{2}$. Actually the experimental data do not permit a clear decision between a $\frac{3}{2}$-order reaction and a first-order reaction falling off gradually to second order in accordance with the Lindemann theory.

According to the chain mechanism the empirical rate constant is actually composite: $k_{3/2} = k_2(k_1/k_3)^{1/2}$. The empirical activation energy is therefore related to the activation energies of the elementary reactions by $E_a = E_2 + \frac{1}{2}(E_1 - E_3)$. The activation energy of the primary split E_1 can be calculated from the heat of reaction, since $\Delta E = E_1 - E_1'$, where E_1' is the E for the reverse reaction. For a radical recombination E_1' is almost zero, so that $\Delta E = E_1$. Thus E_1 can be set equal to the strength of the C—C bond, about 84 kcal. The energy E_2 is about 8 kcal and E_3 is close to 0. Therefore, the predicted $E_a = 8 + \frac{1}{2}(84 - 0) = 50$ kcal. The experimental E_a is 46 kcal.

A primary split into free radicals usually requires a high activation energy whereas E for an elementary decomposition into the final products may be considerably lower. Yet a rapid reaction is possible in spite of the high initial E because of the long chain of steps of low activation energy following the formation of the radicals. Sometimes the scales may be delicately balanced between the two mechanisms, and in certain temperature ranges the radical mechanism and the intramolecular-decomposition mechanism simultaneously occur to appreciable extents. Free-radical chains play an important role in the pyrolyses of hydrocarbons, aldehydes, ethers, ketones, metal alkyls, and many other organic compounds.

The observed first-order rate constants often decline with pressure, but the free-radical theory also has an explanation for this behavior. At low pressures it is easier for radicals to diffuse to the walls of the reaction vessel where they are destroyed by adsorption and recombination. Thus the radical chains are shorter at lower pressures and the rate constant declines.

Sometimes a good test for the radical mechanism can be made by studying a mixture of isotopically substituted species. Suppose, for example, we heat a mixture of CH_3CHO and CD_3CDO. If the *intramolecular* mechanism is followed,

$$CH_3CHO \longrightarrow CH_4 + CO$$

$$CD_3CDO \longrightarrow CD_4 + CO$$

We should obtain a mixture of CH_4 and CD_4 in the products. If the chain mechanism is followed, we should obtain also CH_3D and CD_3H from the steps,

$$CH_3 + CD_3CDO \longrightarrow CH_3D + CO + CD_3$$

$$CD_3 + CH_3CHO \longrightarrow CD_3H + CO + CH_3$$

Actually all the isotopically mixed methanes are found, so that the radical mechanism is indicated.

24. BRANCHING CHAINS—EXPLOSIVE REACTIONS

The most spectacular chemical reactions are explosions, which proceed so swiftly that they are completed within a fraction of a second. Special techniques are required to study their kinetics.* The theory of chain reactions gives a good interpretation of many of their peculiar features.

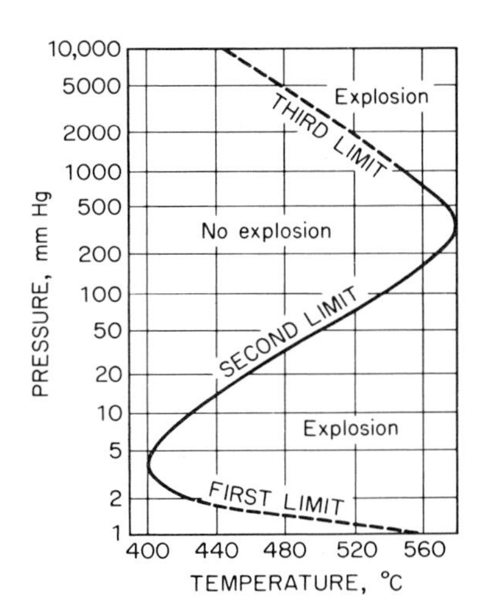

FIG. 8.12 Explosion limits of a stoichiometric hydrogen-oxygen mixture in a spherical KCl-coated vessel of 7.4 cm diameter. [After B. Lewis and G. v. Elbe, *Combustion, Flames and Explosions of Gases* (New York: Academic Press, 1953) p. 29.]

The formation of H_2O from H_2 and O_2 when the mixture is heated or reaction is otherwise initiated has been the subject of hundreds of papers, and is still a problem for active research. This reaction displays the upper and lower pressure limits characteristic of many explosions, as shown in Fig. 8.12. If the pressure of a 2:1 mixture of H_2 and O_2 is kept below the lower line on the diagram, the thermal reaction proceeds slowly. At a temperature of 500°, this lower pressure limit is shown at 1.5 mm, but its value depends on the size of the reaction vessel. If the pressure is raised above this value, the mixture explodes. As the pressure is raised still further, there is a rather unexpected phenomenon. Above a pressure of 50 mm at 500°C there is no longer an explosion, but once again a comparatively slow reaction. This upper explosion limit is strongly temperature-dependent, but it does not vary with size of vessel.

There are two general reasons for an explosive reaction. If an exothermic reaction is carried out in a confined space, the heat evolved often cannot be dissipated. The temperature therefore increases, so that the rate of reaction increases and there is a corresponding rise in the rate of heat production. The reaction velocity increases practically without bound and the result is called a *thermal explosion*.

* See, for example, *Third Symposium on Combustion, Flame, and Explosion Phenomena* (Baltimore: Williams and Wilkins, 1949).

In other systems the thermal effects are less decisive, and the explosion is due to a different cause, namely, the occurrence of *branched chains* in the reaction mechanism. In the chain reactions discussed so far, each propagating sequence leads to the formation of a molecule of product and the regeneration of the chain carrier. If more than one carrier is produced from the original one, we have a branched chain.

Let us see how the possibility of branching can influence the kinetics of the following schematic chain reaction, in which R represents the reactive chain carrier:

$$A \xrightarrow{k_1} R$$
$$R + A \xrightarrow{k_2} P + \alpha R$$
$$R \xrightarrow{k_3} \text{destruction}$$

In this scheme P is the final product and α is the number of chain carriers formed from one initial R in the chain propagating step. The destruction of chain carriers can occur in two ways. They may diffuse to the walls of the reaction vessel where they become adsorbed and combine in a surface reaction, or they may be destroyed in the gas phase.

If the above scheme is to yield a steady reaction rate, $d[R]/dt$ must be zero.

$$\frac{d[R]}{dt} = 0 = k_1[A]^n - k_2[R][A] + \alpha k_2[R][A] - k_3[R]$$

or

$$[R] = \frac{k_1[A]^n}{k_2[A](1 - \alpha) + k_3}$$

The probability of destruction, proportional to k_3, can be written as the sum of two terms, one k_g for the gas phase reaction, the other k_w for the wall reaction. Then,

$$[R] = \frac{k_1[A]^n}{k_2[A](1 - \alpha) + k_g + k_w} \tag{8.25}$$

In all the cases previously treated α has been unity, so that $(1 - \alpha) = 0$, leaving a radical concentration proportional to the rate of formation over the rate of destruction.

If α is greater than unity, chain branching occurs. In particular, a critical situation arises when α becomes so large that $k_2[A](\alpha - 1) = k_g + k_w$, for then the denominator becomes zero and the carrier concentration goes to infinity. The reaction rate is proportional to the concentration of the carrier, so that it also increases without bound at this critical condition. The steady-state treatment fails completely, and the reaction goes so rapidly that there is an explosion.

It is now clear why there can be both upper and lower explosion limits. The destruction rate at the wall k_w depends on diffusion of carriers to the wall and this is more rapid at low pressures. Thus when the pressure falls to a point at which chain carriers are being destroyed at the wall as rapidly as they are being produced, an explosive reaction is no longer possible. This lower pressure limit therefore depends on the size and material of the reaction vessel: in a larger vessel fewer radicals reach the wall.

The upper explosion limit is reached when destructive collisions in the gas phase outweigh the chain branching. This upper limit usually increases sharply with temperature, because the chain initiating and propagating steps have an appreciable activation energy, whereas the chain breaking steps, being recombinations of atoms or radicals, need little activation energy. In fact, the presence of a third body is often required to carry off the excess energy generated in the highly exothermic recombination reactions. The velocity above the upper pressure limit often becomes so great that the reaction passes over into a thermal explosion.

For the hydrogen-oxygen reaction a chain scheme somewhat like the following appears to be reasonable:

$$H_2 + O_2 \longrightarrow HO_2 + H \quad (1)$$
$$H_2 + HO_2 \longrightarrow OH + H_2O \quad (2)$$
$$OH + H_2 \longrightarrow H_2O + H \quad (3)$$
$$O_2 + H \longrightarrow OH + O \quad (4)$$
$$H_2 + O \longrightarrow OH + H \quad (5)$$
$$HO_2 + \text{wall} \longrightarrow \text{removal} \quad (6)$$
$$H + \text{wall} \longrightarrow \text{removal} \quad (7)$$
$$OH + \text{wall} \longrightarrow \text{removal} \quad (8)$$

The hydroxyl radical, OH, has been spectroscopically detected in the reaction mixture. Chain branching occurs in steps (4) and (5) since OH, O and H are all active chain propagators.

25. TRIMOLECULAR REACTIONS

The necessity of a third body to carry off the excess energy in atom recombinations is well established. Studies have shown that such reactions as $M + H + H \rightarrow H_2 + M$ and $M + Cl + Cl \rightarrow Cl_2 + M$ are of the third order. The factors that determine the relative efficiencies in promoting recombination of different third bodies M are of great interest in connection with the problem of energy transfer between molecules. In a study of the recombination of iodine and bromine atoms produced by thermal decomposition of the molecules, Rabinowitsch* measured the rate constants for the reaction, $X + X + M \rightarrow X_2 + M$: $-d[X]/dt = k_3[X]^2[M]$. The values of k_3 in units of (molecules/cc)$^{-2}$ sec^{-1} $\times 10^{32}$ were:

M =	He	A	H_2	N_2	O_2	CH_4	CO_2	C_6H_6
X = Br	0.76	1.3	2.2	2.5	3.2	3.6	5.4	—
X = I	1.8	3.8	4.0	6.6	10.5	12	18	100

* *Trans. Faraday Soc.* *33*, 283 (1937).

It is difficult to calculate the number of *triple collisions* that occur in a gas, but a fairly good estimate should be that the ratio of binary collisions Z_{12} to triple collisions Z_{121} is equal to the ratio of the mean free path to the molecular diameter, λ/d. As d is of the order of 10^{-8} cm, and λ at 1 atm pressure is about 10^{-5} cm for most gases, the ratio is about 1000. Rabinowitsch found that this ratio, Z_{12}/Z_{121}, closely paralleled the rate constants of the halogen atom-recombination reactions. In this case at least, the efficiency of the third body seems to depend mainly on the number of triple collisions it undergoes.

Besides three-body recombinations, the only known gas reactions that may be trimolecular are the third-order reactions of nitric oxide mentioned on page 264. Trautz showed that these may actually consist of two bimolecular reactions; for example,

$$(1) \qquad 2\,NO \longrightarrow N_2O_2$$

$$(2) \qquad N_2O_2 + O_2 \xrightarrow{k_2} 2\,NO_2$$

If equilibrium is set up in (1), $K = [N_2O_2]/[NO]^2$. Then, from (2),

$$\frac{d[NO_2]}{dt} = k_2[N_2O_2][O_2] = k_2K[NO]^2[O_2]$$

The observed third-order constant is $k_3 = k_2K$.

26. THE PATH OF REACTION AND THE ACTIVATED COMPLEX

When we consider the rate of a reaction in terms of simple hard-sphere collision theory, we are using a model that is clearly a pretty rude approximation. A red billiard ball hits a green billiard ball, they disappear instantaneously, two yellow balls career away. To accept this picture is to give up any hope of following the intricate gradual changes that take place in an actual reaction process.

For example, consider again the reaction,

$$H_2 + I_2 \longrightarrow 2\,HI$$

The H_2 and I_2 molecules do not interact as two hard spheres. If we could follow the motions of the two H nuclei and the two I nuclei, we should see a gradual rearrangement as the reaction progresses. As H_2 approaches I_2, the H atoms begin to form tenuous bonds with the I atoms, while the molecules are still quite far apart. At the same time, the H—H and I—I bonds are somewhat weakened and begin to stretch. The closer H_2 approaches I_2, the greater are these effects. In most cases the molecules do not have enough kinetic energy to overcome their mutual repulsion and to approach each other closely enough to complete the process of reaction. Sometimes, however, their kinetic energy is great enough, and they achieve a critical configuration from which they can proceed to the formation of the product, 2 HI. The critical configuration may be drawn as a square complex (Fig. 8.13), in which the H—H and I—I bonds are considerably lengthened and weakened and definite H—I bonds have begun to form. This intermediate configuration, which is formed when the molecules have enough energy to react ($E > E_a$, the activation energy), is called the *activated complex* or *transition state*. If we consider the process of reaction to require the surmounting of a hill of potential energy, we can identify the activated complex as the configuration of the system at the maximum of the potential-energy barrier.

In principle, we may be able eventually to calculate the exact path of a reaction by the methods of quantum mechanics (Chapter 13).

The reaction between hydrogen atoms and hydrogen molecules can be followed by using deuterium. Then,

$$D + H - H \longrightarrow D\cdot\cdot H\cdot\cdot H \longrightarrow DH + H$$

The activation energy is 8.5 kcal.

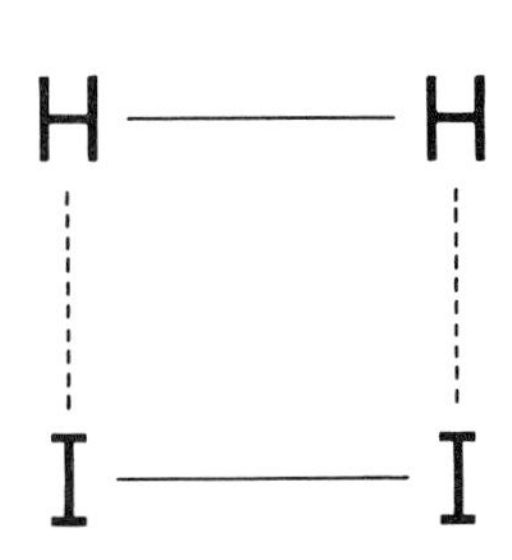

FIG. 8.13 Probable activated complex for the reaction $H_2 + I_2 \rightleftharpoons 2HI$.

Quantum mechanics treats the reaction as the problem of calculating the potential energy of a system of three hydrogen atoms for all possible distances of separation between the nuclei.* It would seem at first that at least six coordinates have to be used: atom (1) could be taken as fixed, and then we could use $x_2y_2z_2$ for atom (2) and $x_3y_3z_3$ for atom (3). Fortunately, preliminary calculations showed that such great detail is not necessary; it is sufficient to calculate the potential energy of the system as one atom, say D, approaches along the line of centers of the molecule H—H. This path will be the most favorable for a reaction to follow, for in this way the approaching atom is repelled by only one of the two other atoms. Only two coordinates are therefore needed: r_2, the distance between the two hydrogen nuclei H_A and H_B, and r_1, the distance of D from H_A.

The reaction then consists in moving the atom D along a straight line through H—H until it reaches an intermediate configuration D—H—H. As the D atom nears the H—H; the H atom on the opposite side gradually stretches away, and finally, if reaction occurs, it departs along the line of centers, leaving as final product D—H + H.

To plot the potential energy E as a function of r_1 and r_2, a three-dimensional diagram is needed, but this plot can be represented by contour lines on a planar map. A schematic diagram for the system D + H − H is shown in Fig. 8.14. It will repay careful study until the three-dimensional form of the potential energy landscape can be clearly visualized from the map.

Consider a cut taken through the map at $r_2 = 4.0$ Å, i.e., at a H—H separation sufficiently large to leave the D—H molecule practically undistorted. The cross section, shown in (b), Fig. 8.14, is then simply the potential energy curve for the HD molecule (described in Sec. 13.3).

If one travels along the valley floor, following the dashed line on the map, the

* H. Eyring and M. Polanyi, *Z. physik. Chem. B12*, 279 (1931).

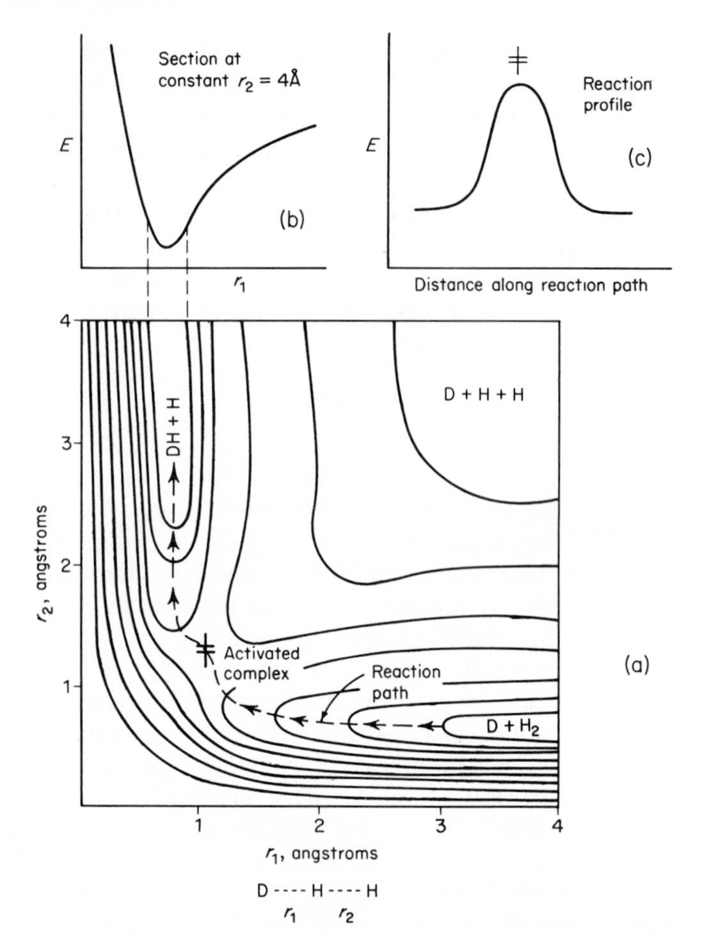

FIG. 8.14 (a) Schematic potential energy surface for reaction $D + H_2 \longrightarrow DH + H$ showing energy contours as function of r_1 and r_2. (b) Section at constant r_2. (c) Potential-energy profile along reaction path.

view to right and left looks like the cross section in (b), Fig. 8.14. The elevation, however, gradually rises as one traverses the mountain pass, reaching a height of 14 kcal at the saddle point. This is the configuration of the activated complex which occurs at $r_1 = r_2 = 0.95$ Å. This distance is considerably greater than the normal internuclear separation in H_2, which is 0.74 Å. When the system reaches this configuration, it can either decompose into DH + H by moving down into the other valley, or return along its original path into $D + H_2$.

If the potential energy is drawn as a function of distance along the reaction path (dashed line), Fig. 8.14 (c) is obtained.

The potential-energy surface gives a picture of a chemical reaction from beginning to end. In any reaction there is always a certain configuration at the top of the barrier, the activated complex, which must be reached by the reactants before transformation to products can occur. Only in very simple examples can the potential-energy surface be calculated and then only by means of drastic approximations. The important feature of the new theory, however, is the clear physical picture it gives. The concept of a collision of hard spheres is replaced by that of a smooth and continuous transition from reactants to products.

In Section 8.5, we used the term *mechanism of reaction* for the sequence of elementary reactions that make up a given complex reaction. Now we shall say that each elementary reaction has its own *mechanism*, by which we mean the description of how the bonds of the reactants rearrange to form the particular activated complex for the reaction. One of the most important objectives of a chemical kinetic study is to formulate a reasonable structure for the activated complex of the reaction.

In practice, we rely on chemical reasoning based on the accumulated data on the rates and equilibria of chemical reactions. As an example, let us consider the important general reaction types found in the hydrolysis of organic halides.

The reaction between hydroxide ion and α-chloroethylacetate is second order, first order with respect to each of the two reactants. A mechanism consistent with this order would proceed as follows:

$$HO^- + Cl—CH_2—CO_2C_2H_5 \longrightarrow HO \text{----} \underset{\underset{CO_2C_2H_5}{|}}{\overset{H\quad H}{\overset{\diagdown\diagup}{C}}} \text{----} Cl \longrightarrow HOCH_2CO_2C_2H_5 + Cl^-$$

The O nucleus of the HO^- ion approaches the C nucleus from the side opposite the C—Cl bond. This interaction is called a *nucleophilic substitution* (S_N). Since two molecules of reactant combine to form the activated complex, the reaction is bimolecular. In the notation of Ingold,* the mechanism is denoted as S_{N2}.

The hydrolysis of tertiary butyl chloride is a first-order reaction. A mechanism consistent with this kinetics is a slow step of ionization, which is rate determining, followed by a fast rapid combination of the carbonium ion with a hydroxyl ion.

$$\text{(I)}\quad (CH_3)_3C—Cl \xrightarrow{\text{slow}} \underset{\text{Activated Complex I}}{(CH_3)_3C^+\cdots\cdots Cl^-} \longrightarrow (CH_3)_3C^+ + Cl^-$$

$$\text{(II)}\quad (CH_3)_3C^+ + OH^- \xrightarrow{\text{fast}} \underset{\text{Activated Complex II}}{(CH_3)_3C^+\cdots\cdots OH^-} \longrightarrow (CH_3)_3C—OH$$

---

* C. K. Ingold, *Structure and Mechanism in Organic Chemistry* (Ithaca: Cornell Univ. Press, 1953).

The overall kinetics of the hydrolysis is determined entirely by the slow step, so that when we measure the rate, we are in fact measuring the rate of reaction (I). Since only one molecule of reactant is involved in formation of the activated complex, this reaction is *unimolecular*. In the notation of Ingold, it has an S_{N1} mechanism.

27. THE TRANSITION-STATE THEORY

The rate of any chemical reaction can be formulated in terms of its activated complex.* The rate of reaction is the number of activated complexes passing per second over the top of the potential-energy barrier. This rate is equal to the concentration of activated complexes times the average velocity with which a complex moves across to the product side.

The calculation of the concentration of activated complexes is greatly simplified if we assume that they are in equilibrium with the reactants. This equilibrium can then be treated by means of thermodynamics or statistical mechanics. The activated complex is not a state of stable equilibrium since it lies at a maximum and not a minimum of potential energy. Yet more detailed calculations have shown that there is probably little error in treating the equilibrium by ordinary thermodynamic or statistical methods, except in the case of extremely rapid reactions.†

For example, consider a simple bimolecular reaction:

$$A + B \longrightarrow [AB]^{\ddagger} \longrightarrow \text{products}$$

If the activated complex $[AB]^{\ddagger}$ is in equilibrium with reactants, the equilibrium constant for the formation of complexes is $K^{\ddagger} = [AB^{\ddagger}]/[A][B]$. The concentration of complexes is $[AB]^{\ddagger} = K^{\ddagger}[A][B]$.

According to the transition-state theory, the rate of reaction is $-d[A]/dt = [AB]^{\ddagger} \times$ (rate of passage over barrier). The rate of passage over the barrier is equal to the frequency with which the complex flies apart into the products. The complex flies apart when one of its vibrations becomes a translation, and what was formerly one of the bonds holding the complex together becomes simply

* The quantitative formulation of absolute reaction rates in terms of activated complexes was first extensively used in the work of H. Eyring [*J. Chem. Phys. 3*, 107 (1935); *Chem. Rev. 17*, 65 (1935)]. This theory has been applied to a wide variety of "rate processes" besides chemical reactions, such as the flow of liquids, diffusion, dielectric loss, internal friction in high polymers. Other noteworthy contributions to the basic theory were made by M. G. Evans and M. Polanyi [*Trans. Faraday Soc. 31*, 875 (1935)], H. Pelzer and E. Wigner [*Z. physik. Chem. B 15*, 445 (1932)].

† R. D. Present, *J. Chem. Phys. 31*, 747 (1959). Even when the activation energy is as low as $5RT$, the reaction rate is only about 8 per cent less than that predicted by equilibrium theory. It is possible, however, to derive a transition-state expression for the rate constant of a bimolecular reaction without recourse to the untenable hypothesis of equilibrium [John Ross and Peter Mazur, *J. Chem. Phys. 35*, 19 (1961)]. This derivation also leads to a much deeper understanding of the parameters which enter the theory.

the line of centers between separating fragments. The frequency ν is equal to ϵ/h where ϵ is the average energy of the vibration that leads to decomposition. Since this is by hypothesis a thoroughly excited vibration at the temperature T, it has its classical energy $\epsilon = kT$, and the corresponding frequency becomes $\nu = kT/h$.

The reaction rate is therefore

$$-\frac{d[A]}{dt} = k_2[A][B] = \mathrm{K}^\ddagger[A][B]\frac{kT}{h}$$

The rate constant is

$$k_2 = \frac{kT}{h}\mathrm{K}^\ddagger \tag{8.26}$$

This is the general expression given by the transition-state theory for the rate constant of any elementary reaction. To be precise, this expression for k_2 should be multiplied by a factor κ, the *transmission coefficient*, which is the probability that the complex will dissociate into products instead of back into reactants. For most reactions κ is between 0.5 and 1.0.

The activated complex is similar to a normal stable molecule in every respect save one. The sole difference is that one of its vibrational degrees of freedom is missing, having been transformed into the translation along the reaction coordinate that leads to disruption of the complex. Instead of $3N - 6$ vibrations, therefore, a nonlinear complex has $3N - 7$. A linear complex has $3N - 6$ instead of the $3N - 5$ for a linear normal molecule.

We can formulate k_2 in thermodynamic terms by introducing the standard free-energy change,

$$\Delta G^{\circ\ddagger} = -RT \ln K_c^\ddagger$$

Note that this is the difference between the free energy of the activated complex and that of the reactants, when all are in their standard states. In this case the standard state has been taken to be the state of *unit concentration*, because rate constants are usually expressed in terms of concentrations. Since $\Delta G^{\circ\ddagger} = \Delta H^{\circ\ddagger} - T\Delta S^{\circ\ddagger}$, Eq. (8.26) becomes

$$k_2 = \frac{kT}{h}e^{-\Delta G^{\circ\ddagger}/RT} = \frac{kT}{h}e^{\Delta S^{\circ\ddagger}/R}\,e^{-\Delta H^{\circ\ddagger}/RT} \tag{8.27}$$

The quantities $\Delta G^{\circ\ddagger}$, $\Delta H^{\circ\ddagger}$, and $\Delta S^{\circ\ddagger}$ are called the *free energy of activation*, the *enthalpy* or *heat of activation*, and the *entropy of activation*.

Now $\Delta H^{\circ\ddagger}$ is almost equivalent to the experimental energy of activation E_a in the Arrhenius equation. Actually $\Delta H^{\circ\ddagger} = \Delta E^{\circ\ddagger} + \Delta(PV^{\circ\ddagger})$. In *liquid and solid systems* the ΔPV term is negligible at ordinary pressures, so that from Eq. (8.27),

$$\frac{d \ln k_2}{dT} = \frac{E_a}{RT^2} = \frac{\Delta H^{\circ\ddagger} + RT}{RT^2}, \quad \text{and} \quad E_a = \Delta H^{\circ\ddagger} + RT$$

In *ideal gases,*

$$\Delta H^{\circ\ddagger} = \Delta E^{\circ\ddagger} + \Delta(PV^{\circ\ddagger}) = \Delta E^{\circ\ddagger} + \Delta n^{\ddagger}RT.$$

In this case, therefore,

$$\frac{d \ln k_2}{dt} = \frac{E_a}{RT^2} = \frac{\Delta H^{\circ\ddagger} - (\Delta n^{\ddagger} - 1)RT}{RT^2}$$

and

$$E_a = \Delta H^{\circ\ddagger} - (\Delta n^{\ddagger} - 1)RT \tag{8.28}$$

The term $\Delta n^{\ddagger}$ is the number of moles of complex, always equal to one, minus the number of moles of reactants. In a unimolecular reaction, therefore, $\Delta n^{\ddagger} = 0$; in a bimolecular reaction, $\Delta n^{\ddagger} = -1$, etc. The entropy of activation can therefore readily be calculated from the experimental k_2 and E_a.

28. THE ENTROPY OF ACTIVATION

We can calculate the experimental entropy of activation for a reaction if we know the rate constant at a given temperature and the experimental activation energy. As an example, consider the dimerization of butylene:

$$2\ C_4H_8 \longrightarrow C_8H_{16} \quad \text{(3-vinylcyclohexene)}$$

From 440 to 660°K, the experimental rate constant is given by

$$k_2 = 9.2 \times 10^9 \exp(-23\,690/RT) \text{ cc mole}^{-1} \text{ sec}^{-1}$$

From Eq. (8.28),

$$E_a = \Delta H^{\circ\ddagger} + RT$$

At 600°K, $\Delta H^{\circ\ddagger} = 23\,690 - 1190 = 22\,500$ cal

From Eq. (8.27),

$$k_2 = e(kT/h) \exp(\Delta S^{\ddagger}/R) \exp(-E_a/RT)$$

At 600°K, $9.2 \times 10^9 = (2.713)(1.25 \times 10^{13}) \exp(\Delta S^{\ddagger}/R)$

$$\Delta S^{\circ\ddagger} = -16.3 \text{ cal deg}^{-1}$$

We should note that the standard state is at a unit concentration of one mole per cc.

A decrease in entropy corresponds to a more ordered or less random molecular configuration. We often find quite large negative entropies of activation for dimerization and association reactions. We can conclude that the two reactant molecules are already bound together in the transition state, with a considerable loss of freedom. It is often possible to calculate the value of $\Delta S^{\circ\ddagger}$ from reasonable models of the transition state. Putting it another way, the experimental $\Delta S^{\circ\ddagger}$ provides one of the best indications of the nature of the transition state.

The introduction of this concept of *activation entropy* is a definite improvement over the less precise concept of the *steric factor*, which was used in collision theory. The idea of an entropy of activation was developed by Rodebush,

La Mer, and others, before the advent of the activated-complex theory, which gave it a precise formulation.

A positive activation entropy $\Delta S^{\ddagger}$ means that the entropy of the complex is greater than the entropy of the reactants. A loosely bound complex has a higher entropy than a tightly bound one. More often there is a decrease in entropy in passing to the activated state.

In bimolecular reactions the complex is formed by association of two individual molecules, and there is a loss of translational and rotational freedom, so that $\Delta S^{\ddagger}$ is negative. In fact, sometimes $\Delta S^{\ddagger}$ is not notably different from ΔS for the complete reaction. This situation is often found in reactions of the type $A + B \rightarrow AB$, and indicates that the activated complex $[AB]^{\ddagger}$ is similar in structure to the product molecule AB. Formerly such reactions were considered to be "abnormal" since they had to be assigned very low steric factors. It is now clear that the low steric factor is the result of the increase in order, and consequent decrease in entropy, when the complex is formed.

29. REACTIONS IN SOLUTION

We cannot make a complete theoretical analysis of the rates of reactions in liquid solutions, although many special aspects of such reactions are quite well understood. It might seem that collision theory should hardly be applicable at all, since there is no unequivocal way of calculating collision frequencies. It turns out, however, that even the gas-kinetic expressions sometimes give reasonable values for the frequency factors.

First-order reactions, such as the decomposition of N_2O_5, Cl_2O, or CH_2I_2, and the isomerization of pinene, proceed at about the same rate in gas phase and in solution. It appears, therefore, that the rate is the same whether a molecule becomes activated by collision with solvent molecules or by gas-phase collisions with others of its own kind. It is more remarkable that many second-order, presumably bimolecular, reactions have rates close to those predicted from the gas-kinetic collision theory. Some examples are shown in the last column of Table 8.7. The explanation of such an agreement seems to be the following.

TABLE 8.7. EXAMPLES OF REACTIONS IN SOLUTION

Reaction	Solvent	E_a kcal mole^{-1}	A (eq. 8.21) liter mole^{-1} sec^{-1}	A_{calc}/A_{obs}
$C_2H_5ONa + CH_3I$	C_2H_5OH	19.5	2.42×10^{11}	0.8
$C_2H_5ONa + C_6H_5CH_2I$	C_2H_5OH	19.9	0.15×10^{11}	14.5
$NH_4CNO \rightarrow (NH_2)_2CO$	H_2O	23.2	42.7×10^{11}	0.1
$CH_2ClCOOH + OH^-$	H_2O	25.9	4.55×10^{11}	0.6
$C_2H_5Br + OH^-$	C_2H_5OH	21.4	4.30×10^{11}	0.9
$(C_2H_5)_3N + C_2H_5Br$	C_6H_6	11.2	2.68×10^{2}	1.9×10^{9}
$CS(NH_2)_2 + CH_3I$	$(CH_3)_2CO$	13.6	3.04×10^{6}	1.2×10^{5}
$C_{12}H_{22}O_{11} + H_2O \rightarrow 2C_6H_{12}O_6$ (sucrose)	$H_2O(H^+)$	25.8	1.5×10^{15}	1.9×10^{-4}

Any given reactant solute molecule will have to diffuse for some distance through the solution before it meets another reactant molecule. Thus the number of such encounters will be lower than in the gas phase. Having once met, however, the two reactant molecules will remain close to each other for a considerable time, being surrounded by a *cage* of solvent molecules. Thus repeated collisions may occur between the same pair of reactant molecules. The net result is that the effective collision number is not much different from that in the gas phase.

There are other cases in which the calculated constant deviates by factors ranging from 10^9 to 10^{-9}. A high frequency factor corresponds to a large positive $\Delta S^\ddagger$, and a low frequency factor to a negative $\Delta S^\ddagger$. The remarks on the significance of $\Delta S^\ddagger$ in gas reactions apply equally well here. We expect association reactions to have low frequency factors owing to the decrease in entropy when the activated complex is formed. An example is the Menschutkin reaction, combination of an alkyl halide with a tertiary amine:

$$(C_2H_5)_3N + C_2H_5Br \longrightarrow (C_2H_5)_4NBr$$

Such reactions have values of $\Delta S^\ddagger$ from -35 to -50 cal deg^{-1} mole^{-1}, usually nearly equal to the ΔS for the complete reaction.

A striking example of another kind is found in the rates of denaturation of proteins. Every time we boil an egg, we carry out, among other reactions, the denaturation of egg albumin from a soluble globular protein to an insoluble fibrous protein. A remarkable property of the denaturation reaction is its unusually high temperature coefficient. Atop Pikes Peak, where water boils at 91°C, it would take 12 hours to hardboil an egg (without a pressure cooker). Since about 10 minutes are required at 100°C the corresponding energy of activation is 130 kcal. This is a surprisingly high figure when it is remembered that the usual reaction proceeding at a measurable rate at 100°C has an activation energy of about 15 kcal. From an activation-energy standpoint one might think that it should be impossible to hardboil an egg at all. The reason why the reaction does proceed quite rapidly is that it has the extraordinarily high positive entropy of activation of $+315.7$ cal deg^{-1}.

The native protein is a highly organized structure; it is the very antithesis of randomness or disorder. The denaturated protein, by contrast, is disordered and random. In such a change there is a great entropy increase, and apparently the activated complex partakes of a good deal of the disorderliness of the final product. Bound water molecules or ions may be set free on denaturation, also contributing to the increase in entropy. Hence the high $\Delta S^\ddagger$ and the possibility of the hardboiled egg.

The kinetics of reactions between ions will be discussed in the next chapter after we have considered some properties of solutions of electrolytes.

30. CATALYSIS

The word *catalysis* (*Katalyse*) was coined by Berzelius in 1835: "Catalysts are substances which by their mere presence evoke chemical reactions that would not otherwise take place." The Chinese *Tsoo Mei* is more picturesque; it also means *the marriage broker*, and so implies a theory of catalytic action. The idea of catalysis extends far back into chemical history. The quest of the alchemist for the philosopher's stone seems like the search of the modern chemist for the magical catalyst that will convert crude petroleum into high octane fuel. In a fourteenth-century Arabian manuscript, Al Alfani described the "Xerion, aliksir, noble stone, magisterium, that heals the sick, and turns base metals into gold, *without in itself undergoing the least change.*"

Noteworthy was the idea that a mere trace of catalyst suffices to produce great changes, without itself being changed. Its action has been likened to that of a coin inserted in a slot machine that yields valuable products and also returns the coin. In a chemical reaction the catalyst enters at one stage and leaves at another. The essence of catalysis is not the entering but the falling out.

Wilhelm Ostwald was the first to emphasize that the catalyst influences the rate of a chemical reaction but has no effect on the position of equilibrium. His famous definition was: "A catalyst is a substance that changes the velocity of a chemical reaction without itself appearing in the end products." Ostwald showed that a catalyst cannot change the equilibrium position by a simple argument based on the First Law of Thermodynamics. Consider a gas reaction that proceeds with a change in volume. The gas is confined in a cylinder fitted with a piston; the catalyst is in a small receptacle within the cylinder, and can be alternately exposed and covered. If the equilibrium position were altered by exposing the catalyst, the pressure would change, the piston would move up and down, and a perpetual-motion machine would be available.

Since a catalyst can change the rate but not the equilibrium, it follows that a catalyst must accelerate the forward and reverse reactions in the same proportion, since $K = k_f/k_b$. Thus catalysts that accelerate the hydrolysis of esters must also accelerate the esterification of alcohols; dehydrogenation catalysts like nickel and platinum are also good hydrogenation catalysts; enzymes like pepsin and papain that catalyze the splitting of peptides must also catalyze their synthesis from the amino acids.

A distinction is generally made between homogeneous catalysis, the entire reaction occurring in a single phase, and heterogeneous catalysis at phase interfaces. The latter is also called *contact* or *surface catalysis.*

31. HOMOGENEOUS CATALYSIS

An example of homogeneous catalysis in the gas phase is the effect of iodine vapor on the decomposition of aldehydes and ethers. The addition of a few per cent of iodine often increases the rate of pyrolysis several hundredfold. The reaction velocity follows the equation,

$$\frac{-d\,[\text{ether}]}{dt} = k_2[\mathrm{I_2}][\text{ether}]$$

Dependence of the rate on catalyst concentration is characteristic of homogeneous catalysis. The catalyst acts by providing a mechanism for the decomposition that has a considerably lower activation energy than the uncatalyzed mechanism.* In this instance the uncatalyzed pyrolysis has an $E_a = 53$ kcal, whereas with added iodine the E_a drops to 34 kcal. The most likely mechanism is $I_2 \rightarrow 2I$, followed by an attack of I atoms on the ether to yield radicals.

Most examples of homogeneous catalysis have been studied in liquid solutions. In fact, catalysis in solution is the rule rather than the exception, and it can even be maintained that most reactions in liquid solutions would not proceed at an appreciable rate if catalysts were rigorously excluded. Examples of catalysis by acids and bases are discussed in Sec. 9.31.

The reaction, $2I^- + S_2O_8^= \rightarrow I_2 + 2SO_4^=$, is markedly catalyzed by ferrous or ferric ions. Copper ions have a lesser effect. When Fe^{++} and Cu^{++} ions are both added, their effects are not simply additive; the rate is still more enhanced. This phenomenon is called *promoter action* and is often observed in catalysis. For example, N/2 500 000 Cu^{++} has itself no detectable effect on the velocity, but added to a reaction mixture that already contains N/32 000 Fe^{++}, it increases the rate by 15 per cent. A possible explanation is that the promoter selectively catalyzes the decomposition of an intermediate formed with the first catalyst.

32. HETEROGENEOUS REACTIONS

There are many reactions whose velocities are immeasurably slow in homogeneous gaseous or liquid solutions, but which go quite swiftly if a suitable solid surface is available. The earliest instance of this *contact action* or *contact catalysis* was the dehydrogenation of alcohols by metals studied by van Marum in 1796. In 1817, Davy and Döbereiner investigated the glowing of certain metals in a mixture of air and combustible gases; and in 1825, Faraday worked on the catalytic combination of hydrogen and oxygen. These studies laid the experimental foundations of heterogeneous kinetics.

An interesting example was found† in the bromination of ethylene: $C_2H_4 + Br_2 \rightarrow C_2H_4Br_2$. This reaction goes readily in a glass vessel at 200°C; it was at first thought to be an ordinary homogeneous combination, but the rate seemed to be higher in smaller reaction vessels. When the vessel was packed with lengths of glass tubing or with glass beads, the rate was considerably enhanced. This method is frequently used for detecting wall reactions. An increased rate in a packed vessel indicates that a considerable share of the observed reaction is heterogeneous, on the packing and wall, rather than homogeneous, in the gas phase only. A further test was made by coating the inside of the reaction bulb with paraffin wax. This coating inhibited the reaction almost completely.

* Cf. G. M. Schwab, H. S. Taylor, and R. Spence, *Catalysis* (New York: Van Nostrand, 1937), p. 68.

† R. G. W. Norrish, *J. Chem. Soc.*, 3006 (1923).

The decomposition of formic acid illustrates the specificity often displayed by surface reactions. If the acid vapor is passed through a heated glass tube, the reaction is about one-half dehydration and one-half dehydrogenation.

$$(1) \qquad HCOOH \longrightarrow H_2O + CO$$

$$(2) \qquad HCOOH \longrightarrow H_2 + CO_2$$

If the tube is packed with Al_2O_3, only reaction (1) occurs; but if it is packed with ZnO, (2) is the exclusive result. Thus different surfaces can accelerate different parallel paths, and so in effect determine the nature of the products.

It seems evident that the catalytic action of a surface depends on its adsorption of the reactants. A surface reaction can usually be broken into the following elementary steps:

(1) Diffusion of reactants to surface
(2) Adsorption of reactants at surface
(3) Chemical reaction on the surface
(4) Desorption of products from surface
(5) Diffusion of products away from the surface

These are consecutive steps and if any one is much slower than all the others, it will become rate-determining. Steps (1) and (5) are usually rapid. Only with extremely active catalysts might they determine the overall rate. Diffusion has a $T^{1/2}$ and chemical reaction has an $e^{-E/RT}$ temperature dependence. Therefore, if a catalytic reaction rate increases only slightly with temperature, it may be diffusion controlled. Steps (2) and (4) are generally more rapid than step (3), but reactions are known in which they may be the slow stages. Usually, however, the reaction at the surface, step (3), is rate determining. In some cases, instead of reaction entirely on the surface, a molecule from the fluid phase may react with an adsorbed species.

33. THE LANGMUIR ADSORPTION ISOTHERM

The first quantitative discussion of the adsorption of gases on solids was given by Irving Langmuir in 1916. He based his model for adsorption on the following assumptions:

1. The solid surface contains a fixed number of adsorption sites. At equilibrium at any temperature and gas pressure, a fraction θ of the sites is occupied by adsorbed molecules, and a fraction $1 - \theta$ is not occupied.
2. Each site can hold one adsorbed molecule.
3. The heat of adsorption is the same for all the sites and does not depend on the fraction covered θ.
4. There is no interaction between molecules on different sites. The chance that a molecule condenses at an unoccupied site or leaves an occupied site does not depend on whether or not neighboring sites are occupied.

The equation which relates the amount of gas adsorbed on a surface to the pressure of the gas at constant temperature is called the *adsorption isotherm.*

We can derive the Langmuir adsorption isotherm from a kinetic discussion of the condensation and evaporation of gas molecules at the surface. If θ is the fraction of the surface area covered by adsorbed molecules at any time, the rate of evaporation of molecules from the surface is proportional to θ or equal to $k_d\theta$, where k_d is a constant at constant T. The rate of condensation of molecules on the surface is proportional to the fraction of surface that is bare, $1 - \theta$, and to the rate at which molecules strike the surface, which, at a given temperature, varies directly with the gas pressure. The rate of condensation is therefore set equal to $k_aP(1 - \theta)$. At equilibrium the rate of condensation equals the rate of evaporation,

$$k_d\theta = k_aP(1 - \theta)$$

Solving for θ, we obtain

$$\theta = \frac{k_aP}{k_d + k_aP} = \frac{bP}{1 + bP} \tag{8.29}$$

where b is the ratio of rate constants, k_a/k_d, sometimes called the *adsorption coefficient.*

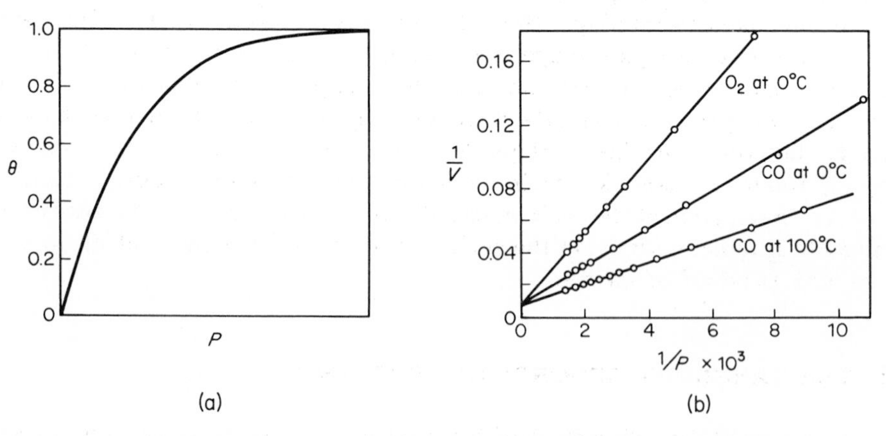

FIG. 8.15 (a) Langmuir isotherm. (b) Adsorption of gases on silica plotted in accord with Eq. (8.30). The volume adsorbed (proportional to θ)is in cm^3 at STP per gram and the pressure is in mm of Hg. E. C. Markham and A. F. Benton, *J. Am. Chem. Soc.*, 53, 497 (1931).

The Langmuir isotherm of Eq. (8.29) is plotted in Fig. 8.15 (a). Sometimes it is more convenient to use a plot which gives a straight line. Equation (8.29) can be rewritten as

$$\frac{1}{\theta} = 1 + \frac{1}{bP} \tag{8.30}$$

In Fig. 8.15(b), we have plotted some data for the adsorption of gases on silica in this form. The good straight lines indicate that the results conform to the Langmuir isotherm.

Two limiting cases of the Langmuir isotherm are often of special interest. Where $bP \ll 1$, i.e., when the pressure is very low or the adsorption coefficient is very small,

$$\theta = bP \qquad (8.31)$$

Such a linear dependence of θ on P is always found in the low-pressure region of the adsorption curve. When $bP \gg 1$, i.e., at high pressures, or with particularly strong adsorption at lower pressures, the isotherm reduces to

$$1 - \theta = \frac{1}{bP} \qquad (8.32)$$

This expression holds in the flat upper region of the isotherm: the fraction of bare surface becomes inversely proportional to the pressure.

34. GAS REACTIONS AT SOLID SURFACES

The Langmuir isotherm is based on the gradual coverage of a surface with adsorbed molecules, saturation occurring when the adsorbed layer is uniformly one molecule thick. The isotherm is especially applicable to cases of *chemisorption,* in which the adsorbed molecules are held to the surface by bonds comparable with those in chemical compounds. This is also the kind of adsorption that can greatly accelerate reaction rates, the chemisorbed layer playing the role of an intermediate compound in catalyzing the reaction.

The Langmuir isotherm can be roughly divided into three sections: (a) the range of small adsorption or nearly bare surface, where the fractional surface coverage $\theta = bP$; (b) an intermediate region in which approximately $\theta = bP^{1/n}$; (c) the region of almost complete coverage, where effectively $\theta = 1$ over a considerable pressure range. The particular adsorbate gas and adsorbent solid will determine the region of the isotherm useful in a given system. If a gas is strongly adsorbed, the surface may be almost covered even at low pressures; but if a gas is weakly adsorbed, the linear section $\theta = bP$ may extend to quite high pressures.

In a heterogeneous gas reaction, it can usually be assumed that only the adsorbed gas undergoes reaction.* If a single reactant is being decomposed at an active surface, three simple special cases can arise. The reaction rate will be proportional to θ, the fraction of surface covered.

(1) Single reactant, weakly adsorbed, $\theta = bP$. Rate: $-dP/dt = k\theta = kbP = k'P$. The reaction is first order. Examples of this kind include the decomposition of arsine and phosphine on glass, $AsH_3 \rightarrow As + \frac{3}{2}H_2$; hydrogen iodide on platinum, $2HI \rightarrow H_2 + I_2$.

(2) Single reactant, moderately adsorbed, $\theta = bP^{1/n}$. Rate: $-dP/dt = k\theta = kbP^{1/n} = k'P^{1/n}$. An example is the decomposition of arsine on a surface of metallic arsenic, following the equation $-dP/dt = kP^{0.6}$.

* I. Langmuir, *Trans. Faraday Soc. 17*, 621 (1921). Such mechanisms are called *Langmuir mechanisms*. Reaction of a gas molecule with an adsorbed species is called a *Rideal mechanism* [D. D. Eley and E. K. Rideal, *Proc. Roy. Soc.* (London) *A 178*, 429 (1941)].

(3) Single reactant, strongly adsorbed, $\theta = 1$. Rate: $-dP/dt = k_0 = k_0P^0$. In such a case the reaction velocity is independent of the pressure. This is called a *zero-order reaction*, a variety of concentration dependence having no parallel in purely homogeneous reactions. The integrated rate equation is $-P = k_0t +$ constant or,

$$P_0 - P = k_0t \tag{8.33}$$

where P_0 is the initial pressure. When $P = \frac{1}{2}P_0$, $t = \tau$ the half life, so that $\tau = \frac{1}{2}(P_0/k_0)$. Examples of zero-order reactions include the decomposition of hydrogen iodide on gold and of ammonia on tungsten. Note that HI on Pt is first order, but HI on Au is zero order.

Many of these reactions on metal surfaces can be conveniently studied by means of wire filaments sealed into bulbs that can be filled with reactant. The wire can be heated by passage of an electric current and its temperature calculated from the electric resistance. A manometer is attached to the bulb to measure pressure changes.

35. INHIBITION BY PRODUCTS

So far only adsorption of the reactants has been considered. In other reactions the products are also adsorbed by the solid catalyst, and the competition between reactant and product molecules for the available surface is revealed in the rate equations.

If two adsorbates, A and B, are rivals for the same surface, the kinetic treatment of Langmuir can be applied to the condensation and evaporation of each of them. Corresponding with Eq. (8.29), the following result is obtained for θ_A and θ_B, the fractions of area covered by A and B at partial pressures P_A and P_B, with adsorption coefficients b_A and b_B.

$$\theta_A = \frac{b_AP_A}{1 + b_AP_A + b_BP_B} \qquad \theta_B = \frac{b_BP_B}{1 + b_AP_A + b_BP_B} \tag{8.34}$$

The kinetic equations that arise owing to adsorption of two gases can usually be interpreted by these Langmuir isotherms. The following are important special cases:

(1) Reactant A is weakly adsorbed and a product B is strongly adsorbed. Then $b_AP_A \ll b_BP_B \gg 1$. The reaction velocity is still proportional to θ_A, the surface covered with reactant, which in this case, from Eq. (8.34), is $\theta_A = b_AP_A/b_BP_B$. Thus, $-dP_A/dt = k'\theta_A = kP_A/P_B$. An example of this behavior is found in the decomposition of ammonia on a platinum filament, $2\ NH_3 \rightarrow N_2 + 3\ H_2$, the rate law being $-dP_{NH_3}/dt = kP_{NH_3}/P_{H_2}$. The product, H_2, is strongly adsorbed and inhibits the reaction.

(2) Both reactant and product are strongly adsorbed. Then $b_AP_A \gg 1 \ll b_BP_B$, and $\theta = b_AP_A/(b_AP_A + b_BP_B)$. In the dehydration of ethanol on a copper catalyst,

$$C_2H_5OH \longrightarrow C_2H_4 + H_2O$$

$$\frac{-dP_{C2H5OH}}{dt} = \frac{kP_{C_2H_5OH}}{bP_{C_2H_5OH} + b'P_{H_2O}}$$

Traces of water are strongly adsorbed and severely inhibit the reaction.

36. EFFECT OF TEMPERATURE ON SURFACE REACTIONS

In all the surface reactions so far discussed it would appear that the slowest step is the actual chemical change occurring in the adsorbed molecules. Neither the rate of adsorption nor the rate of desorption seems to be directly rate determining, since a satisfactory explanation of the kinetics is given by the Langmuir isotherm, which assumes that the adsorption-desorption equilibrium is established. The observed rate is then determined by the amount of surface covered by reacting molecules and by the specific velocity of the surface reaction. The influence of temperature on the rate therefore must include two factors, the effect on the surface area covered, and the effect on the surface reaction itself.

The plot of log k vs. $1/T$ is usually linear for a heterogeneous reaction, just as it is in the homogeneous case. From the slope of the straight line an activation energy E_a can be calculated by using the Arrhenius equation. This E_a is called the *apparent activation energy*, since it is usually a composite quantity, including not only the true activation energy of the surface reaction E_t, but also heats of adsorption of reactants and products. The relation between E_a and E_t depends on the particular kinetics followed.

A zero-order reaction is a particularly simple case, since here $\theta = 1$ and as long as the reaction remains zero-order, the fraction of surface covered is independent of temperature, and E_a always equals E_t. The decomposition of HI on gold is a zero-order reaction with $E_a = E_t = 25$ kcal. The homogeneous gas phase decomposition has an $E_a = 44$ kcal. The lowering of the activation energy by 19 kcal is a measure of the marked catalytic effect of the metal surface. An even greater lowering is observed in the zero-order decomposition of ammonia on tungsten with $E_a = 39$ kcal. The homogeneous reaction has an activation energy of over 90 kcal.

If the reactant is weakly adsorbed there are two superimposed temperature effects on the velocity, since the fraction of surface covered is usually strongly temperature-dependent. The relation between true and apparent activation energies becomes $E_a = E_t - \lambda$, where λ is the heat of adsorption. The true activation energy of the surface reaction is lowered by an amount equal to the heat of adsorption.*

If $-dP/dt = kP_A/P_B$ (reactant A weakly adsorbed, product or second reactant B strongly adsorbed) the relation is $E_a = E_t - \lambda_A + \lambda_B$. For example, Hinshelwood found $E_a = 140$ kcal for the decomposition of ammonia on platinum.

* The reader can easily outline the derivations. See Schwab, Taylor, and Spence, *op. cit.*, p. 236.

Then $E_a = E_t - \lambda_{NH_3} + \lambda_{H_2}$. The heat of adsorption of hydrogen is about 110 kcal. Since the ammonia is weakly adsorbed, λ_{NH_3} is probably only about 5 kcal. Thus $140 = E_t - 5 + 110$, or $E_t = 35$ kcal. On tungsten, the ammonia decomposition is zero order, and $E_a = E_t = 39$ kcal.

37. ACTIVATED ADSORPTION

Often the potential-energy barrier that must be surmounted before adsorption can occur is small or negligible, and the adsorption rate is governed by the rate of supply of gas to the bare surface. Sometimes, however, a considerable activation energy, E_{ad}, may be required for adsorption, and its rate, $Ae^{-E_{ad}/RT}$, may become slow enough to determine the overall speed of a surface reaction. Adsorption that requires an appreciable activation energy has been called *activated adsorption.*

The chemisorption of gases on metals usually does not require any appreciable activation energy. The work of J. K. Roberts* showed that the adsorption of hydrogen on carefully cleaned metal filaments proceeds rapidly even at about 25°K, to form a tightly held monolayer of adsorbed hydrogen atoms. The heat of adsorption is close to that expected for the formation of covalent metal-hydride bonds. These results were confirmed and extended to other metal-gas systems in the work of O. Beeck with evaporated metal films.†

One important exception to this type of behavior has been found in the adsorption of nitrogen on an iron catalyst at about 400°C.†† This adsorption is a slow activated adsorption and it seems to be the rate-determining step in the synthesis of ammonia on these catalysts. If S is the catalyst surface, the reaction can be represented as follows:

$$N_2 \longrightarrow \left.\begin{matrix} N \\ N \end{matrix}\right\} S$$

$$\ldots\ldots \longrightarrow NH\}\,S \longrightarrow NH_2\}\,S \longrightarrow NH_3\}\,S \longrightarrow NH_3$$

Surface reaction Desorption

$$H_2 \longrightarrow \left.\begin{matrix} H \\ H \end{matrix}\right\} S$$

Activated adsorption

The adsorption and activation of the hydrogen was ruled out as the slow step because the exchange reaction $H_2 + D_2 \rightleftharpoons 2\,HD$ occurs on the catalyst even at liquid-air temperatures, presumably via the dissociation of H_2 and D_2 into adsorbed atoms. Then it was found that the hydrogens in NH_3 are readily exchanged with deuterium from D_2 on the catalyst at room temperature. This indicates that processes involving N—H bonds are not likely to be rate-determining. The only possible slow step seems to be the activated adsorption of

* J. K. Roberts, *Some Problems in Adsorption* (London: Cambridge Univ. Press, 1939).

† O. Beeck, *Discussions Faraday Soc. 8*, 118 (1950).

†† P. H. Emmett and S. Brunauer, *J. Am. Chem. Soc. 62*, 1732 (1940).

N_2 itself, and this probably governs the speed of the synthetic ammonia reaction. It should be noted that this mechanism is distinctly different from the rate-determining reaction on the surface, which is the basis of the Langmuir treatment.

38. POISONING OF CATALYSTS

A catalyst can be poisoned by small amounts of foreign substances. Faraday emphasized that platinum used in catalyzing the combination of H_2 and O_2 must be clean and free of grease, and that carbon monoxide must be absent. The highly effective catalytic action of platinum on the oxidation of SO_2 to SO_3 was known early in the nineteenth century, but the process could not be applied practically because the catalyst soon lost all its activity. Not until the reactant gases were obtained in a highly purified state, free of sulfur and arsenic compounds, was it possible to run the reaction for extended periods of time.

It is not just a coincidence that catalyst poisons such as CO, H_2S, arsenicals, and the like are also strong physiological poisons. The reason they poison animals is that they inhibit vital biochemical reactions by poisoning the enzymes that catalyze them.

Poison and reactants compete for the available catalyst surface. If the poison wins, the catalyst cannot act. Thus poisons for metallic catalysts are compounds that are strongly adsorbed by the metals. An important question now arises: does the extent of inhibition of the catalyst correspond quantitatively with the fraction of its surface that is seized by the poison? In some cases it does, but cases are also known in which a small amount of poison produces more inhibition than can be explained by a surface-area effect alone.

39. THE NATURE OF THE CATALYTIC SURFACE

Even the smoothest solid surface is rough on a 10 Å scale. Examination of the cleavage faces of crystals by the most refined optical techniques* reveals that they have terrace-like surfaces. Experiments on photoelectric or thermionic emission from metals indicate that the surfaces are a patchwork of areas with different work functions. F. C. Frank† has elucidated a mechanism by which crystals often grow from vapor or solution: new atoms or molecules are not deposited on the planar surfaces, but at jogs in the surface associated with *dislocations* in the crystal structure, the resultant surface structure is a miniature replica of the spiral growth pattern of the Babylonian ziggurat. (Sec. 16.22.) It has been suggested that crystal edges and corners, grain boundaries, and other physical irregularities of the surface may provide *active centers*†† of unusually high

---

* S. Tolansky, *Multiple Beam Interferometry* (London: Methuen, 1948).

† F. C. Frank, *Advances in Physics, 1* (1952).

†† H. S. Taylor, *Proc. Roy. Soc. A 108*, 105 (1925).

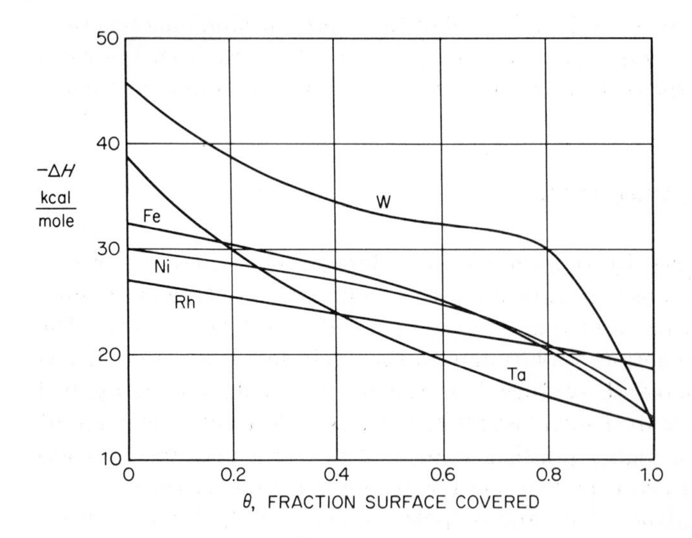

FIG. 8.16 Heat of adsorption of hydrogen on clean metal surfaces. [O. Beeck, *Disc. Faraday Soc.*, 8, 118 (1950)].

catalytic activity. Adsorption may well be stronger on such special sites, but it must be remembered that strong adsorption is not necessarily conducive to high catalytic activity, and may in fact inhibit the catalysis.

The heat of adsorption often declines markedly with increasing surface coverage. Typical results are shown in Fig. 8.16. This effect obviously indicates a nonuniform surface. The lack of uniformity, however, may either pre-exist in the different adsorption sites, or be caused by the repulsive forces between adsorbed atoms or molecules. Especially if the surface to adsorbate bond is partially ionic, as much recent evidence suggests, the repulsions may become large, markedly lowering the heat of adsorption at higher coverages.

An especially successful explanation of the catalytic mechanism has been made in the case of the cracking of hydrocarbons. The catalysts are silica-alumina mixtures formed by calcining the hydrous oxides. The distribution of the products suggests that the cracking process proceeds through the intermediate formation of carbonium ions.* Let us first consider a simple example of a carbonium-ion mechanism, that proposed for the Friedel-Crafts reaction with an $AlCl_3$ catalyst:

$$(1) \qquad CH_3Cl + AlCl_3 \longrightarrow CH_3^+(AlCl_4)^-$$

$$(2) \qquad CH_3^+ + C_6H_6 \longrightarrow C_6H_5CH_3 + H^+$$

$$(3) \qquad H^+ + (AlCl_4)^- \longrightarrow HCl + AlCl_3$$

The $AlCl_3$ acts as a *Lewis acid*, an acceptor of a pair of electrons. The reaction is thus an example of a generalized acid catalysis in nonaqueous solution (cf. Sec. 9.31).

The solid silica-alumina cracking catalysts† also have acidic properties: they

* B. S. Greensfelder, H. H. Voge, and G. M. Good, *Ind. Eng. Chem. 41*, 2573 (1949).

† T. H. Milliken, G. A. Mills, and A. G. Oblad, *Disc. Faraday Soc. 8*, 279 (1950).

react with carbonate solutions to evolve carbon dioxide; they catalyze the inversion of sucrose; they react with and are poisoned by volatile bases such as ammonia and quinoline. The acidic, active centers appear to be sites in which an Al^{+3} ion is surrounded by $O^{=}$ ions tetrahedrally coordinated to Si^{+4} ions. Such a site may act as a strong Lewis acid (Sec. 9.26) as follows:

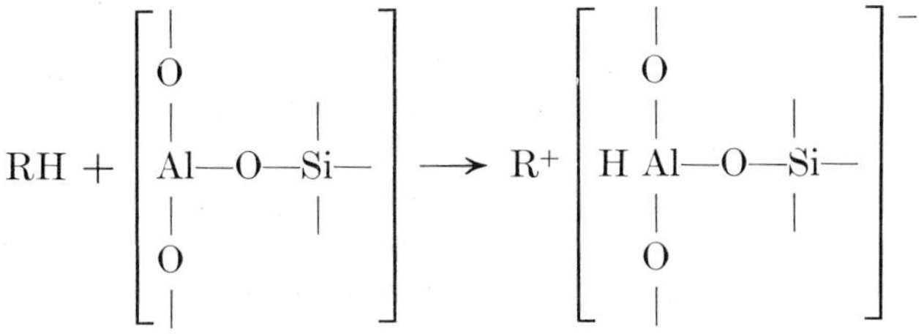

$$\text{RH} + \left[\begin{array}{ccc} | & & \\ \text{O} & & \\ | & & | \\ \text{Al}- & \text{O} & -\text{Si}- \\ | & & | \\ \text{O} & & \\ | & & \end{array}\right] \longrightarrow \text{R}^{+} \left[\begin{array}{cccc} & | & & \\ & \text{O} & & \\ & | & & | \\ \text{H} & \text{Al}- & \text{O} & -\text{Si}- \\ & | & & | \\ & \text{O} & & \\ & | & & \end{array}\right]^{-}$$

The subsequent cracking reaction is a cleavage of the carbonium ion R^{+} at a position one carbon atom away from the C^{+}.

From the examples given, it is evident that no single theory can account for all the phenomena of contact catalysis. The field has been of great interest to physical chemists because it combines the problems of chemical kinetics with those of the fundamental theory of the solid state. It also has many exciting industrial applications.

40. ENZYME REACTIONS

The catalysts devised by man have accomplished noteworthy results as accelerators of chemical reaction rates. Yet their successes appear insignificant compared with the catalytic activity of the enzymes elaborated by living cells to promote physiological processes.

Consider one example among many, the formation of proteins. This is a synthesis the most skillful organic chemist has been unable to achieve in the laboratory, yet it is carried out rapidly and continuously by living cells. The isotopic tracer experiments of R. Schoenheimer* have shown that protein molecules in the liver tissue of the rat have an average lifetime of only ten days. In addition to this continuous self-replacement, the liver synthesizes glycogen or animal starch from glucose; it manufactures urea which is excreted as the end product of nitrogen metabolism; and it also undertakes to detoxicate any number of unwanted substances, rendering them harmless to the animal organism. This extensive metabolic activity of the liver is approached, but nowhere equaled, by the chemical activity of other kinds of cells.

H. Büchner was the first to establish, in 1897, that the intact cell is not necessary for many of these catalytic actions, since cell-free filtrates could be prepared containing the *enzymes* in solution. Enzymes are specific, colloidal catalysts. Since all known enzymes are proteins, they are necessarily colloids,

* R. Schoenheimer, *The Dynamic State of Body Constituents* (Cambridge, Mass.: Harvard Univ. Press, 1946).

falling in the range of particle diameter from 100 to 1000Å. Enzyme catalysis is therefore midway between homogeneous and heterogeneous catalysis, and is sometimes called *microheterogeneous.* A theoretical discussion can be based either on intermediate compound formation between enzyme and substrate molecules in solution, or on adsorption of substrate at the surface of the enzyme.

Enzymes are extremely specific in their catalytic actions. *Urease* will catalyze the hydrolysis of urea, $(NH_2)_2CO$, in dilutions as high as one part of enzyme in ten million of solution, yet it has no detectable effect on the hydrolysis rate of substituted ureas, e.g., methyl urea, $(NH_2)(CH_3NH)CO$. *Pepsin* will catalyze the hydrolysis of the peptide glycyl-L-glutamyl-L-tyrosine, but it is completely ineffective if one of the amino acids has the opposite optical configuration of the D-form, or if the peptide is slightly different, e.g., L-glutamyl-L-tyrosine.

Little is yet known about the detailed mechanism of enzyme action. Almost all enzymes fall into one of two large classes, the hydrolytic enzymes and the oxidation-reduction enzymes. The enzymes of the first class appear to be complex acid-base catalysts, accelerating ionic reactions, principally the transfer of hydrogen ions. The protein enzymes contain both NH_3^+ and COO^- groups, and therefore act as both acids and bases, and should be very effective in this type of catalysis provided geometrical conditions are satisfied. The oxidation-reduction enzymes catalyze electron transfers, perhaps through intermediate radical formation.

41. KINETICS OF ENZYME REACTIONS

A reactant in an enzyme catalyzed reaction is called a *substrate.* Mechanisms for enzyme kinetics begin with a first step which is the combination of enzyme with substrate to form a complex. This formulation was first clearly given by V. Henri in 1903. He assumed that the complex was in equilibrium with free enzyme and substrate. Michaelis and Menten used the same formulation in 1913. In 1925, Briggs and Haldane showed that a steady-state treatment could be applied to enzyme kinetics.

For the simplest mechanism, which involves only one substrate and no competitive reactions, the reaction scheme is as follows:

$$E + S \underset{k_{-1}}{\overset{k_1}{\rightleftharpoons}} ES \overset{k_2}{\longrightarrow} E + P$$

The reverse reaction between enzyme and product P $(E + P \rightarrow ES)$ has been left out, as is permissible in the early stages of the reaction of substrate S.

The rate equations are:

$$\text{(A)} \qquad -\frac{d[S]}{dt} = \frac{d[P]}{dt} = k_1[E][S] - k_{-1}[ES] = k_2[ES]$$

$$\text{(B)} \qquad \frac{d[ES]}{dt} = k_1[E][S] - k_{-1}[ES] - k_2[ES]$$

After a transient initial stage, the concentration of complex reaches a steady state, with $d[ES]/dt = 0$. This condition applied to Eq. (B) gives

$$[ES] = \frac{k_1[E][S]}{k_{-1} + k_2} \tag{C}$$

Suppose we start with an initial concentration of enzyme $[E]_0$ which is much less than the initial concentration of substrate $[S]_0$. Then the conservative equations are

$$[E]_0 = [E] + [ES] \tag{D}$$

$$[S]_0 = [S] + [P] \tag{F}$$

Substituting (D) into (C), we obtain

$$[ES] = \frac{k_1[E]_0[S]}{k_{-1} + k_2 + k_1[S]}$$

Then, from (A), the rate of formation of product is

$$\frac{-d[S]}{dt} = \frac{d[P]}{dt} = \frac{k_1k_2[E]_0[S]}{k_{-1} + k_2 + k_1[S]}$$

The combination of constants,

$$K_s = \frac{k_{-1} + k_2}{k_1}$$

is called the *Michaelis constant*. Thus

$$\frac{-d[S]}{dt} = \frac{k_2[E]_0[S]}{K_s + [S]} \tag{8.35}$$

It is often best to study enzyme kinetics by measuring the initial velocity of reaction. In this case the substrate concentration has not changed appreciably from its initial value $[S]_0$ and Eq. (8.35) becomes

$$\text{Initial rate} = v_0 = \frac{V_s}{1 + K_s/[S]_0} \tag{8.36}$$

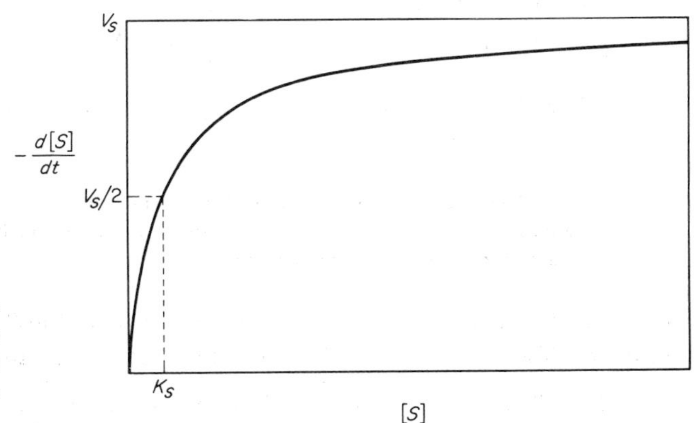

FIG. 8.17 Plot of the Michaelis-Menten equation (8.36). Note that when the rate is half the maximum, the substrate concentration $[S] = K_s$.

or

$$\frac{1}{v_0} = \frac{1}{V_s} + \frac{K_s}{V_s[S]_0} \tag{8.37}$$

If we plot the reaction rate $-d[S]/dt$ against the initial substrate concentration $[S]_0$ we obtain a curve like that shown in Fig. 8.17. The maximum rate is that found when $[S]_0 \gg K_s$.

$$\left(-\frac{d[S]}{dt}\right)_{\max} = V_s = k_2[E]_0$$

If we vary the initial substrate concentration for a constant enzyme concentration, we can plot $1/v_0$ against $1/[S]_0$. The intercept of the plot gives $1/V_s$ and the slope gives K_s/V_s. Thus we can obtain the Michaelis constant and the rate constant k_2 from such data.

We should note that only in the special case that $k_{-1} \gg k_2$ does the Michaelis constant equal the dissociation constant of the enzyme-substrate complex. Then $K_s = k_{-1}/k_1$ and the complex is in equilibrium with free enzyme and substrate, as originally suggested by Henri.

In some cases the concentration of complex has been measured directly. An example is the transfer of oxygen from H_2O_2 to an acceptor A, catalyzed by the enzyme *peroxidase* (P). The measurements of Britton Chance* on this system, with malachite green as the acceptor, are shown in Fig. 8.18. The mechanism is:

$$P + H_2O_2 \underset{k_{-1}}{\overset{k_1}{\rightleftharpoons}} P\text{—}H_2O_2$$
$$A + P\text{—}H_2O_2 \xrightarrow[k_2]{} P + H_2O + AO$$

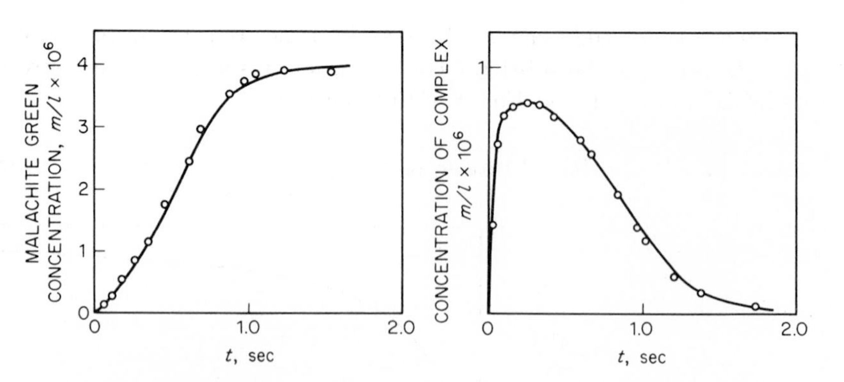

FIG. 8.18 The oxidation of leucomalachite green to malachite green by H_2O_2 catylized by peroxidase. The circles are experimental results and the curves are calculated from the rate constants.

In a typical run the enzyme concentration was 10^{-6} m/l and the initial concentration of H_2O_2 was 4×10^{-6} m/l. The rate constants were $k_1 = 0.9 \times 10^7$

* *J. Biol. Chem. 151*, 553 (1943). [Notice that the total reaction time was 2 sec. If possible, consult the original paper to learn how Chance accomplished these measurements.]

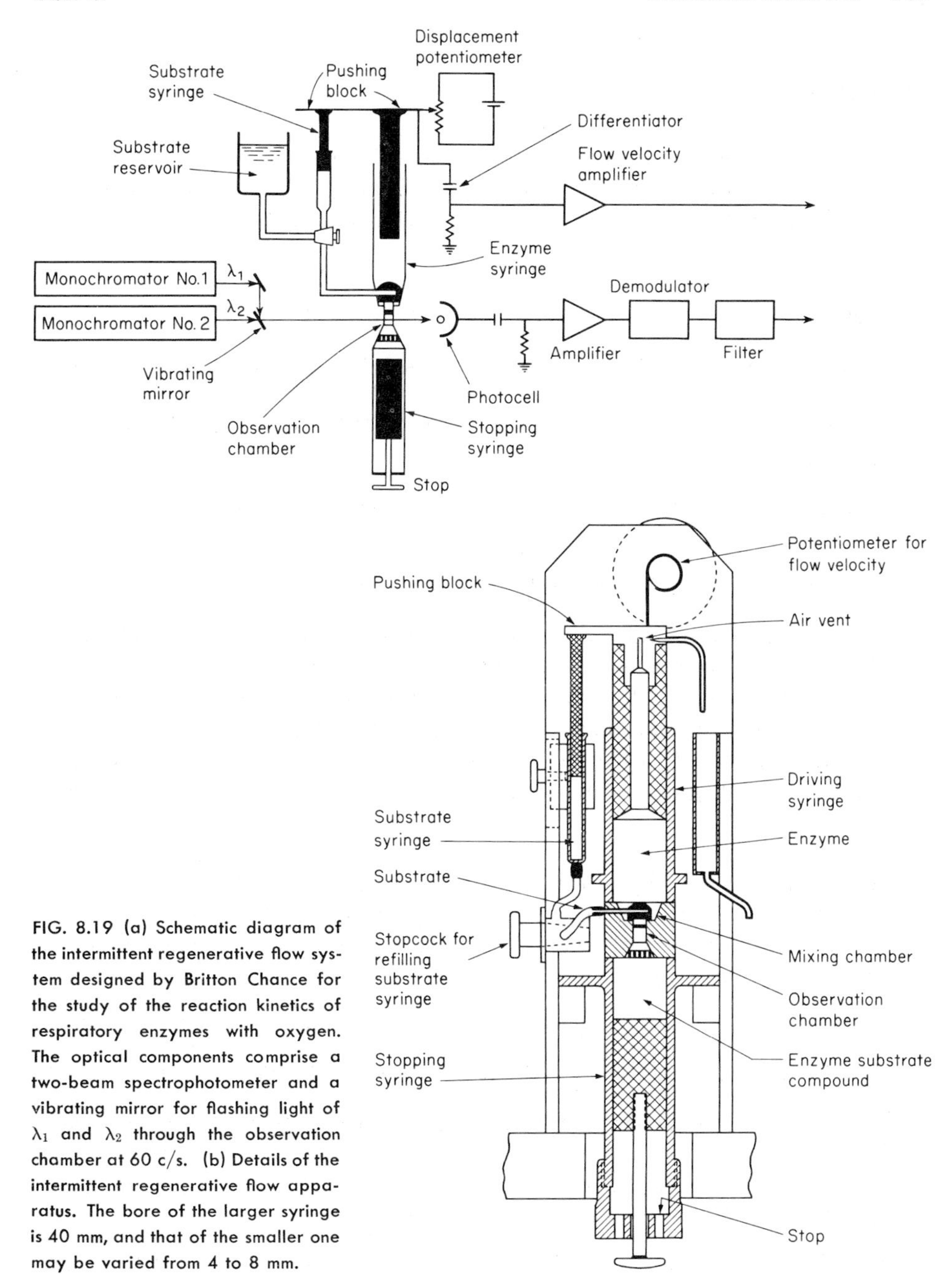

FIG. 8.19 (a) Schematic diagram of the intermittent regenerative flow system designed by Britton Chance for the study of the reaction kinetics of respiratory enzymes with oxygen. The optical components comprise a two-beam spectrophotometer and a vibrating mirror for flashing light of λ_1 and λ_2 through the observation chamber at 60 c/s. (b) Details of the intermittent regenerative flow apparatus. The bore of the larger syringe is 40 mm, and that of the smaller one may be varied from 4 to 8 mm.

liter/mole sec, $k_{-1} \sim 0$; and $k_2 = 4.5 \text{ sec}^{-1}$. In this case, the complex is not in equilibrium with E and S, since $k_2 \gg k_{-1}$, but the steady-state treatment works well. Such enzyme systems are usually studied in some form of rapid-flow reactor. The ingenious apparatus used by Chance is shown in Fig. 8.19.

PROBLEMS

1. The conversion of acetochloroacetanilide (A) into *p*-chloroacetanilide (B) was followed by adding KI solution and titrating the iodine liberated with standardized thiosulfate solution. The KI reacts with A only.

Time, hr:	0	1	2	3	4	6	8
ml 0.1 N $S_2O_3^=$:	49.3	35.6	25.75	18.5	14.0	7.3	4.6

Calculate the first-order rate constant in sec^{-1}. [*Ans.* 8.5×10^{-5} sec^{-1}]

2. The inversion of sucrose, $C_{12}H_{22}O_{11} + H_2O \rightarrow C_6H_{12}O_6 + C_6H_{12}O_6$, proceeded as follows at 25°C:

Time, min:	0	30	60	90	130	180
Sucrose inverted, moles per liter:	0	0.1001	0.1946	0.2770	0.3726	0.4676

The initial concentration of sucrose was 1.0023 moles per liter. Calculate the first-order rate constant and the half life of the reaction. Why does this reaction follow a first-order law despite the fact that water enters into the stoichiometric equation? How long would it take to invert 95 per cent of a kilo of sugar? [*Ans.* 5.7×10^{-5} sec^{-1}; 1.18×10^4 sec; the water is present in such great excess that its concentration is practically constant; 855 min]

3. The hydrolysis of ethylnitrobenzoate by hydroxyl ions ($NO_2C_6H_4COOC_2H_5 + OH^- \rightarrow NO_2C_6H_4COOH + C_2H_5OH$) proceeds as follows at 15°C [*J. Chem. Soc. 1357* (1936)] when the initial concentrations of both reactants are 0.05 mole per liter.

Time, sec:	120	180	240	330	530	600
% hydrolyzed:	32.95	41.75	48.8	58.05	69.0	70.35

Calculate the second-order rate constant. [*Ans.* 8.0×10^{-2} $mole^{-1}$ sec^{-1}]

4. The reaction $2NO + 2H_2 \rightarrow N_2 + 2H_2O$ was studied with equimolar quantities of NO and H_2 at various initial pressures:

Initial pressure, mm:	354	340.5	375	288	251	243	202
Half life, τ min:	81	102	95	140	180	176	224

Calculate the overall order of reaction. [*Ans.* $n = 2.54$ (probably $\frac{5}{2}$ order within experimental error)]

5. The reaction $SO_2Cl_2 \rightarrow SO_2 + Cl_2$ is a first-order gas reaction with $k_1 = 2.2 \times 10^{-5}\ sec^{-1}$ at 320°C. What per cent of SO_2Cl_2 is decomposed on heating at 320°C for 90 min? [*Ans.* 11.20%]

6. In what proportion of bimolecular collisions does the energy of the "head-on" collision exceed 60 kcal at 300°K, at 600°K, at 1000°K? [*Ans.* 1.59×10^{-44}; 1.17×10^{-22}; 7.25×10^{-14}]

7. A certain reaction is 20 per cent complete in 15 min at 40°C and in 3 min at 60°C. Estimate its activation energy. [*Ans.* 16.4 kcal]

8. The thermal decomposition reaction of a hydrocarbon in the gas phase at 500°C and an initial pressure of 1 atm had a half life of 2 sec. When the initial pressure was reduced to 10^{-1} atm the half life increased to 20 sec. What is the rate constant of the reaction?

9. Consider the exchange reaction

$$AX + BX^{\star} \rightleftharpoons AX^{\star} + BX$$

where $X^{\star}$ is a radioactive isotope present in trace amounts. Show that the rate of exchange will be first order regardless of the order of the individual forward or reverse reactions. [See A. A. Frost and R. G. Pearson, *Kinetics and Mechanism* (New York: Wiley, 1961) p. 192.]

10. If all reactants have initial concentrations a and the reaction has an order of n, show that the half life is given by

$$\tau = (2^{n-1} - 1)/a^{n-1}k(n - 1)$$

where k is the rate constant.

11. The compound $CH_3—O—N{=}O$ has an internal rotation about the O—N bond as follows:

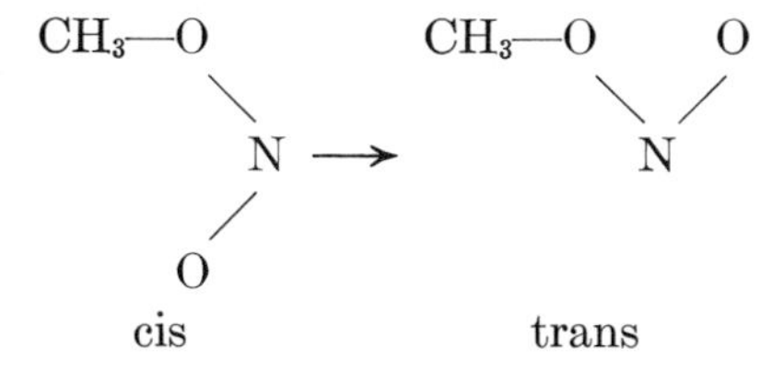

The half life of the first order disappearance of the cis form can be measured by NMR techniques. It is 10^{-6} s at 25°C. What is the rate constant k_1? Assuming $\Delta S^{\ddagger} = 0$ for this reaction, calculate the height of the barrier to rotation.

12. The decomposition of nitramide, $NH_2NO_2 \rightarrow N_2O + H_2O$ is catalyzed by bases. Devise a mechanism to explain this catalytic effect. How could you test this mechanism?

13. In a certain photochemical reaction the mechanism is

$$A + h\nu \longrightarrow A^\star \qquad k_1$$

$$A^\star + M \longrightarrow A + M \qquad k_2$$

$$A^\star \longrightarrow B \qquad k_3$$

where $h\nu$ represents light adsorbed, M represents any molecule present, including added inert gases, and $A^\star$ is an activated form of A. Obtain an expression for the rate of production of B. Show the limiting form at high and low pressure. Compare the results with the Lindemann mechanism for gaseous unimolecular reactions.

14. Consider liquid mercury in equilibrium with its vapor at the normal boiling point of 357°C. Suppose every molecule that strikes the surface is condensed to liquid. The heat of vaporization of mercury at 357°C is 4170 cal mole^{-1}. Derive a formula for the rate of evaporation of liquid mercury. Use the formula to calculate the maximum rate of evaporation of mercury at (a) 357° (b) 100°C.

15. The decomposition of phosphine at 950°K is followed by noting the change in total pressure as a function of time. The reaction is

$$4PH_3 \longrightarrow P_4(g) + 6H_2$$

The following measurements were made on a system containing only PH_3 initially.

time, min.	0	40	80
P total (mm Hg)	100	150	166.7

Show what the order of the reaction is and calculate the rate constant.

16. The thermal decomposition of acetaldehyde vapor ($CH_3CHO \rightarrow CH_4 + CO$) is an irreversible process whose rate at 518°C is given by the following two sets of data for pressure changes at constant temperature and volume.

Initial pressure of pure acetaldehyde	Total pressure of the system after 100 sec.
400 mm Hg	500 mm Hg
200 mm Hg	229 mm Hg

(a) Find the order of the decomposition with respect to acetaldehyde. (b) Calculate the rate constant at 518°C. (c) The energy of activation is 45.5 kcal. At what temperature will the rate constant be twice what it is at 518°C?

17. The reaction $2NO + H_2 \rightarrow N_2O + H_2O$ goes to completion and is known to follow the rate laws:

$$dP_{N_2O}/dt = k\, P_{NO}^2\, P_{H_2}$$

Given the following table of data:

P°_{NO}	$P^{\circ}_{H_2}$	Half-time	
600	10	19.2	820°C
600	20	—	820°C
10	600	835	820°C
20	600	—	820°C
600	10	10	840°C

(Initial pressures P° are in mm Hg, and the half-time is the time in seconds for half completion of the reaction, that is for the species not in excess to fall to half of its initial pressure. The runs are at constant temperature and volume.)

(a) Insert the missing half-times. (b) Calculate k at 820°C, in (mm Hg)$^{-2}$ sec^{-1}. (c) Calculate the activation energy. (d) Suggest a mechanism giving the above rate law, which involves only bimolecular steps or reaction sequences. (e) Calculate the half time at 820°C if $P^{\circ}_{NO} = 20$ and $P^{\circ}_{H_2} = 10$ (Note: the rate law reduces to a special case in this instance.)

18. Given the following reaction:

$$2NO_2 \longrightarrow 2NO + O_2 \text{ (no back reaction)}$$

(a) derive an integrated relation between the total pressure in a reaction vessel originally containing pure NO_2 and the time. (b) It is found that when a 2 liter vessel is filled with NO_2 at a pressure of 600 mm of Hg and a temperature of 600°C, the reaction is half over after 3 min. Calculate the rate constant.

19. For the Reaction $A \rightarrow$ products, the rate $(-dA/dt)$ of the reaction was found to be 1×10^{-3} moles l^{-1} min^{-1} initially and 0.25×10^{-3} moles l^{-1} min^{-1} after 1 hour. (a) Assuming the reaction to be first order in A, calculate (i) the specific rate constant k in the rate expression $dA/dt = -kA$; (ii) the half-life, $t_{1/2}$; (iii) the initial concentration. (b) Show that the above data would fit a second-order rate expression, i.e., $dA/dt = -k'[A]^2$, if k' is taken to be 10^3(mole l^{-1})$^{-1}$ hr^{-1}.

20. Given the reaction,

$$A(g) \underset{k_2}{\overset{k_1}{\rightleftharpoons}} B(g) + C(g)$$

where k_1 and k_2 have the values 0.20 sec^{-1} and 4×10^{-4} sec^{-1} atm^{-1} at 25°C, and each value is doubled on going to 35°C, calculate: (a) the equilibrium constant at 25°C; (b) the activation energy for the forward and for the reverse reaction; (c) ΔH° for the overall reaction; (d) the time for P (total) to reach 1.5 atm, if one starts with A only at 1 atm (25°C).

21. The forward rate of the reaction

$$2NO + O_2 \longrightarrow 2NO_2$$

obeys the equation: Rate $= k[NO]^2[O_2]$. The specific rate constant k is found to decrease with increasing temperature. Give a reasonable explanation for this unusual behavior.

22. Chemists often assume that lowering the temperature at which a reaction is carried out will increase the proportion of the main reaction product and decrease the proportion of by-products. Show that this assumption is justified if the reaction which forms the main product has the same entropy of activation as the reactions which lead to by-products.

23. Show that for a first order reaction the time required for 99.9 per cent of the reaction to take place is ten times that required for one-half the reaction.

24. The following results were obtained for decomposition of N_2O_5 in CCl_4 at 40°C. The rate was followed by measuring the cc of oxygen liberated V.

t (sec)	600	1200	1800	2400	3000	∞
V (cc)	6.30	11.40	15.53	18.90	21.70	34.75

Calculate the first order rate constant graphically.

---

25. The racemization of an optically active halide in solution is first order with respect to the reactant in each direction and the rate constants are equal. $R_1R_2R_3CX$ (dextro) $\rightleftharpoons R_1R_2R_3CX$ (laevo). If the initial reactant is pure dextro and the rate constant is 1.90×10^{-6} sec^{-1}, find (a) the time to 10 per cent reaction, (b) the per cent reaction after 24 hours. [*Ans.* (a) 980 min till 10% of D changed to L; (b) 13.8%]

26. The reaction $C_2H_6 \rightarrow C_2H_4 + H_2$ follows approximately a 3/2-order law in its initial stages. At 910°K the rate constant is 1.13 sec^{-1} lit$^{1/2}$ mole$^{-1/2}$. Calculate the initial rate, $-d(C_2H_6)/dt$, for an ethane pressure of (a) 100 mm, (b) 300 mm. [*Ans.* $8.37 \times 10^{-5}, 4.35 \times 10^{-4}$ mole l^{-1}s^{-1}]

27. Find the reaction order and rate constant for $C_6H_5N_2Cl \rightarrow C_6H_5Cl + N_2$ at 50°C if the initial diazobenzenechloride concentration is 10 g per liter and:

t, min:	6	9	12	14	18	22	24	26	30	∞
N_2 evolved, cc:	19.3	26.0	32.6	36.0	41.3	45.0	46.5	48.4	50.4	58.3

[*Ans.* First order, $k = 1.09 \times 10^{-3}$ sec^{-1}]

28. Find the rate law of the reaction $3HNO_2 \rightarrow H_2O + 2NO + H^+ + NO_3^-$ if the first two of the following steps rapidly attain equilibrium and the third step is slow:

$$(1)\ 2HNO_2 \longrightarrow NO + NO_2 + H_2O$$

$$(2)\ 2NO_2 \longrightarrow N_2O_4$$

$$(3)\ N_2O_4 + H_2O \longrightarrow HNO_2 + H^+ + NO_3^-$$

29. Explain the following facts from the standpoint of the adsorption properties of the reactant and product molecules:

(a) The decomposition of NH_3 on W is zero order.
(b) The decomposition of N_2O on Au is first order.
(c) The recombination of H atoms on Au is second order.
(d) The decomposition rate of NH_3 on Pt is proportional to P_{NH_3}/P_{H_2}.
(e) The decomposition rate of NH_3 on Mo is strongly retarded by N_2 but does not approach zero as the surface becomes saturated with N_2.
(f) The rate of $2SO_2 + O_2 \rightarrow 2SO_3$ on Pt is $k_1(SO_2)/(SO_3)^{1/2}$ when O_2 is in excess.

[*Ans.* (a) NH_3 strongly adsorbed on W, surface completely covered. (b) N_2O weakly adsorbed on Au, linear region of Langmuir isotherm. (c) H atoms weakly adsorbed and rate proportional to collisions of two H atoms on the surface or of a gaseous H atom with a surface H atom. (d) Product H_2 strongly, and reactant NH_3 weakly adsorbed. (e) Product N_2 is strongly adsorbed but adsorption coefficient decreases with surface coverage so that N_2 and NH_3 can compete for available surface when it is nearly covered with N_2. Another explanation, probably more likely, is that the Fe—N surface is itself a fair catalyst for decomposition of NH_3. (f) The surface is covered to great extent by adsorbed oxygens so that reaction is zero order with respect to O_2. The SO_2 and SO_3 compete for remaining surface, with the SO_3 being adsorbed more strongly than SO_2 but less than O_2.]

30. The following mechanism has been proposed for the thermal decomposition of acetone:

(1) $CH_3COCH_3 - k_1 \longrightarrow CH_3 + CH_3CO$ $\quad E = 84$ kcal

(2) $CH_3CO - k_2 \longrightarrow CH_3 + CO$ $\quad E = 10$ kcal

(3) $CH_3 + CH_3COCH_3 - k_3 \longrightarrow CH_4 + CH_2COCH_3$ $\quad E = 15$ kcal

(4) $CH_2COCH_3 - k_4 \longrightarrow CH_3 + CH_2CO$ $\quad E = 48$ kcal

(5) $CH_3 + CH_2COCH_3 - k_5 \longrightarrow C_2H_5COCH_3$ $\quad E = 5$ kcal

Express the overall rate in terms of the individual rate constants, taking reaction (1) to be first order. Calculate (a) the overall energy of activation; (b) the chain length given by the ratio of the chain propagating reaction to the chain stopping reaction. What is the order of the overall reaction if reaction (1) becomes second order? [*Ans.* $E = \frac{1}{2}(E_1 + E_3 + E_4 - E_5) =$ 71 kcal, reaction being first order; at 1000°K, chain length $= (k_3k_4/k_1k_5)^{1/2} \approx 690$; 3/2 order.]

31. In the polymerization reactions, $A + A \rightarrow A_2$; $A_2 + A \rightarrow A_3$; $A_3 + A \rightarrow A_4, \ldots$, etc., if all the rate constants are identical, the integrated rate equation has the form

$$y = akt\left[\frac{4 + kt}{(2 + kt)^2}\right]$$

Here y is the amount of polymer ($A_2 + A_3 + A_4 + \ldots A_n$), a is the initial amount of reactant A, k is the rate constant, and t is the time. Find the equation for dy/dt, the polymerization rate. What will be the apparent order of reaction during a single run? What will be the order based on the initial rates if the concentration a is varied? [*Ans.* $dy/dt = 8ak/(2 + kt)^3$; zero order; first order]

32. For the decomposition of N_2O_5,

Temperature, °C:	25	35	45	55	65
$10^5 k_1$, sec^{-1}:	1.72	6.65	24.95	75	240

Calculate A and E for the reaction, in the equation $k_1 = Ae^{-E/RT}$. Calculate $\Delta G^\ddagger$, $\Delta H^\ddagger$, and $\Delta S^\ddagger$ for the reaction at 50°C. [*Ans.* $E = 24.4$ kcal; $A = 1.51 \times 10^{13}$ sec^{-1}; $\Delta G^\ddagger = 24.3$ kcal; $\Delta H^\ddagger = 23.7$ kcal; $\Delta S^\ddagger = -1.9$ cal deg^{-1}]

33. The rate constant of $2N_2O \rightarrow 2N_2 + O_2$ is $4.2 \times 10^9 \exp(-53\,000/RT)$ sec^{-1}. A stream of N_2O is passed through a tube 20 mm in diameter and 20 cm long at a rate of 1 liter (STP) per min. At what temperature should the tube be heated in order to have 1.0 per cent O_2 in the exit gas? [*Ans.* 931°K]

34. A sample of nickel foil weighing 5.328 g and having a surface area of 258 cm^2 per g was exposed to pure oxygen at 500°C and 10 cm pressure.

Time, hr:	2	3	4	5	6	7	8	9	10
O_2 uptake, cc at 10 mm, 20°C:	52.4	70.2	85.1	97.9	106.6	118.0	127.7	137.0	146.3

The reaction is $Ni + \frac{1}{2}O_2 \rightarrow NiO$. Fit the data to the parabolic rate law $dy/dt = a/y$ where y is the film thickness, t is the time and a is the rate constant. Calculate a. (*Note*: Integrate the rate equation assuming that at $t = 0$, $y = y_0$, and cast the integrated equation into a linear form. Then plot the results.)

35. The reaction

$$N + C_2H_4 \longrightarrow HCN + CH_3$$

was studied in a stirred flow reactor by introducing atomic N at a flow rate of 10^{-6} mole s^{-1} in a stream of N_2 at 3.6×10^{-5} mole s^{-1}. The C_2H_4 flow rate was 6×10^{-6} mole s^{-1}. The rate constant of the reaction at 40°C was 1.6×10^{-13} sec^{-1} (molecules/cc)$^{-1}$. What is the concentration of CH_3 radicals within the reactor? [E. Milton and H. Dunford, *J. Chem. Phys.* *34*, 51 (1961)]

9 ELECTROCHEMISTRY: CONDUCTANCE AND IONIC REACTIONS

There is nothing in the Universe but alkali and acid, from which Nature composes all things.

Otto Tachenius (1671)

All chemical interactions are electrical at the atomic level so that in a sense all chemistry is electrochemistry. In a more restricted sense, electrochemistry has come to mean the study of solutions of electrolytes and of the phenomena occurring at electrodes immersed in these solutions. The electrochemistry of solutions may claim our special interest because physical chemistry first emerged as a distinct science in this field. Its first journal, *Zeitschrift für physikalische Chemie*, was founded in 1887 by Wilhelm Ostwald, and the early volumes are devoted mainly to the researches in electrochemistry of Ostwald, van't Hoff, Kohlrausch, Arrhenius, and others of their school.

1. ELECTRICITY

William Gilbert, Queen Elizabeth's physician, coined the work *electric* in 1600 from the Greek, ἤλεκτρον, *amber*. He applied it to bodies that when rubbed with fur attracted small bits of paper or pith. Gilbert was unwilling to admit the possibility of "action at a distance," and in his treatise *De Magnete* he advanced an ingenious theory for the electrical attraction.

> *An effluvium is exhaled by the amber and is sent forth by friction. Pearls, carnelian, agate, jasper, chalcedony, coral, metals, and the like, when rubbed are inactive; but is there nought emitted from them also by heat and friction? There is indeed, but what is emitted from the dense bodies is thick and vaporous* [*and thus not mobile enough to cause attractions*]. *A breath, then . . . reaches the body that is to be attracted and as soon as it is reached it is united to the attracting electric. For as no*

action can be performed by matter save by contact, these electric bodies do not appear to touch, but of necessity something is given out from the one to the other to come into close contact therewith, and to be a cause of incitation to it.

Further investigation revealed that materials such as glass, after being rubbed with silk, exerted forces opposed to those from amber. Two varieties of electric fluid were thus distinguished, the vitreous and the resinous. Frictional machines were devised for generating high electrostatic potentials, and used to charge condensers in the form of Leiden jars.

Benjamin Franklin (1747) simplified matters by proposing a one-fluid theory, according to which bodies rubbed together acquire a surplus or deficit of electric fluid, depending on their relative attractions for it. The resultant difference in charge causes the observed forces. Franklin established the convention that the vitreous type of electricity is positive (fluid in excess), and the resinous type is negative (fluid in defect).

In 1791, Luigi Galvani accidentally brought the bare nerve of a partially dissected frog's leg into contact with a discharging electrical machine. The sharp convulsion of the leg muscles led to the discovery of galvanic electricity,* for it was soon found that the electric machine was unnecessary and that the twitching could be produced simply by bringing the nerve ending and the end of the leg into contact through a metal strip. The action was enhanced when two dissimilar metals completed the circuit. Galvani, a physician, named the new phenomenon "animal electricity" and believed it to be characteristic of living tissues only.

Alessandro Volta, a physicist, Professor of Natural Philosophy at Pavia, soon discovered that the electricity could have an inanimate origin. From a stack of dissimilar metals in contact with moist paper, he was able to charge an electroscope. In 1800, he constructed his famous *pile*, consisting of many consecutive plates of silver, zinc, and cloth soaked in salt solution. From the terminals of the pile he drew the shocks and sparks previously observed only with electrostatic devices.

The news of Volta's pile aroused an enthusiasm and amazement like those caused by the uranium pile in 1945. In May of 1800, Nicholson and Carlyle decomposed water into hydrogen and oxygen by means of the electric current, the oxygen appearing at one pole of the pile and the hydrogen at the other. Solutions of various salts were soon decomposed, and in 1806–1807, Humphry Davy used a pile to isolate sodium and potassium from their hydroxides. The theory that the atoms in a compound were held together by the attraction between unlike charges immediately gained a wide acceptance.

2. FARADAY'S LAWS AND ELECTROCHEMICAL EQUIVALENTS

In 1813 Michael Faraday, then 22 years old and a bookbinder's apprentice, went to the Royal Institution as Davy's laboratory assistant. In the following years,

* Vans Gravesande and Adanson independently discovered the intense discharges of electric fish in 1750.

he carried out the series of researches that were the foundations of electrochemistry and electromagnetism.

Faraday studied intensively the decomposition of solutions of salts, acids, and bases by the electric current. With the assistance of William Whewell, he devised the nomenclature universally used in these studies: *electrode, electrolysis, electrolyte, ion, anion, cation.* The electrode *toward* which the cations move in a cell is called the *cathode.* The electrode *toward* which the anions move is called the *anode.*

Faraday proceeded to study quantitatively the relation between the amount of electrolysis, or chemical action produced by the current, and the quantity of electricity. The unit of electric quantity is now the coulomb or ampere second. The results were summarized as follows:*

> *The chemical power of a current of electricity is in direct proportion to the absolute quantity of electricity which passes.... The substances into which these [electrolytes] divide, under the influence of the electric current, form an exceedingly important general class. They are combining bodies, are directly associated with the fundamental parts of the doctrine of chemical affinity; and have each a definite proportion, in which they are always evolved during electrolytic action. I have proposed to call ... the numbers representing the proportions in which they are evolved* electrochemical equivalents. *Thus hydrogen, oxygen, chlorine, iodine, lead, tin, are* ions; *the three former are* anions, *and two metals are* cations, *and 1, 8, 36, 125, 104, 58 are their electrochemical equivalents nearly.*
>
> *Electrochemical equivalents coincide, and are the same, with ordinary chemical equivalents. I think I cannot deceive myself in considering the doctrine of definite electrochemical action as of the utmost importance. It touches by its facts more directly and closely than any former fact, or set of facts, have done, upon the beautiful idea that ordinary chemical affinity is a mere consequence of the electrical attractions of different kinds of matter.*

We now recognize that ions in solution may bear more than one elementary charge, and that the electrochemical equivalent weight is the atomic weight M divided by the number of charges on the ion $|z|$. The constant amount of electricity always associated with one equivalent of electrochemical reaction is called the faraday F. It is equal to 96 479 coulombs.

Thus Faraday's Laws of electrolysis can be summarized in the equation

$$\frac{m}{M} = \frac{I\,t}{|z|\,F} = \frac{Q}{|z|\,F} \tag{9.1}$$

Here m is the mass of an element of atomic weight M liberated at an electrode, by the passage of current I through a solution for a time t.

The fact that a definite quantity of electric charge, or a small integral multiple thereof, is always associated with each charged atom in solution strongly suggested that electricity itself is atomic in nature. Hence, in 1874, G. Johnstone Stoney addressed the British Association as follows:

> *Nature presents us with a single definite quantity of electricity which is independent of the particular bodies acted on. To make this clear, I shall express Faraday's Law*

* *Phil. Trans. Roy. Soc.* *124*, 77 (1834).

in the following terms. . . . For each chemical bond which is ruptured within an electrolyte a certain quantity of electricity traverses the electrolyte which is the same in all cases.

In 1891, Stoney proposed that this natural unit of electricity should be given a special name, the *electron*. Hence one mole of electrons would be one faraday of electrical charge.

$$F = Le \tag{9.2}$$

3. COULOMETERS

A careful measurement of the amount of chemical reaction caused by the passage of a certain amount of electrical charge through an electrolytic cell gives a precise measure of the amount of electric charge that passed. Such a device for measuring charge passed is called a *coulometer*.

An example is the *silver coulometer* which uses platinum electrodes in aqueous silver nitrate. The gain in weight of the cathode is measured after a current is passed through a solution of $AgNO_3$. The reaction at the cathode can be written

$$Ag^+ + e \longrightarrow Ag$$

One atomic weight of silver, 107.87 g, deposits on the cathode for each faraday passed through the coulometer. Thus one coulomb is equivalent to

$$107.87/96\,479 = 1.1181 \times 10^{-3} \text{ g of silver}$$

4. CONDUCTIVITY MEASUREMENTS

From the beginning, one of the fundamental theoretical problems in electrochemistry was how the solutions of electrolytes conducted an electric current.

Metallic conductors were known to obey Ohm's Law,

$$I = \frac{E}{R} \tag{9.3}$$

where I is the current (amperes), E is the electromotive force, emf (volts), and the proportionality constant R is called the *resistance* (ohms). The resistance depends on the dimensions of the conductor:

$$R = \frac{\rho l}{A} \tag{9.4}$$

Here l is the length and A the cross-sectional area, and the specific resistance ρ (ohm cm) is called the *resistivity*. The reciprocal of the resistance is called the *conductance* (ohm^{-1}) and the reciprocal of the resistivity, the *specific conductance* or *conductivity* κ ($ohm^{-1}\ cm^{-1}$).

The earliest studies of the conductivity of solutions were made with rather large direct currents. The resulting electrochemical action was so great that erratic results were obtained, and it appeared that Ohm's Law was not obeyed; i.e., the conductivity seemed to depend on the emf. This result was largely due to *polarization* at the electrodes of the conductivity cell, i.e., a departure from equilibrium conditions in the surrounding electrolyte.

These difficulties were overcome by the use of an alternating-current bridge, such as that shown in Fig. 9.1. With a-c frequencies in the audio range (1000 – 4000 cycles per sec) the direction of the current changes so rapidly that polarization effects are eliminated. One difficulty with the a-c bridge is that the cell acts as a capacitance in parallel with a resistance, so that even when the resistance arms are balanced there is a residual unbalance due to the capacitances. This effect can be partially overcome by inserting a variable capacitance in the other arm of the bridge, but for very precise work further refinements are necessary.*

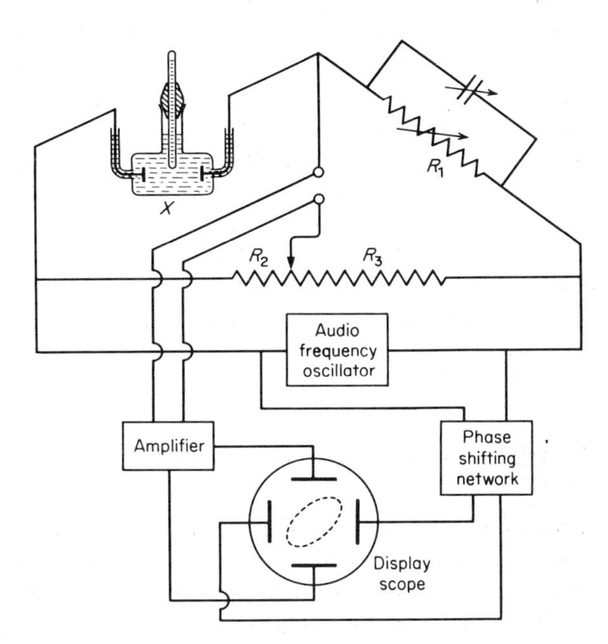

FIG. 9.1 AC Wheatstone bridge for measurement of conductance of electrolytes.

Earphones formerly were used to indicate the balance point of the bridge, but the preferred indicator is now the cathode-ray oscilloscope.† The voltage from the bridge midpoint is filtered, amplified, and fed to the vertical plates of the oscilloscope. A small portion of the bridge input signal is fed to the horizontal plates through a suitable phase-shifting network. When the two signals are properly phased, the balance of capacitance is indicated by the closing of the loop on the oscilloscope screen, and the balance of resistance is indicated by the tilt of the loop from horizontal.

A typical conductivity cell is also shown in Fig. 9.1. Instead of measuring

* T. Shedlovsky, *J. Am. Chem. Soc. 54*, 1411 (1932); W. F. Luder, *ibid.*, *62*, 89 (1940).
† For example, E. Edelson and R. M. Fuoss, *J. Chem. Ed. 27*, 610 (1950).

their dimensions, we now usually calibrate these cells before use with a solution of known conductivity, such as one-molar potassium chloride. The cell must be well thermostated since the conductivity increases with the temperature.

As soon as reliable conductivity data were available, it became apparent that solutions of electrolytes followed Ohm's Law. The resistance was independent of the emf, and the smallest applied voltage sufficed to produce a current of electricity. Any conductivity theory would have to explain this fact: the electrolyte is always ready to conduct electricity and this capability is not something produced by the applied emf.

On this score, the ingenious theory proposed in 1805 by C. J. von Grotthuss must be judged inadequate. He supposed the molecules of electrolyte to be polar, with positive and negative ends. An applied field lined them up in a chain. Then the field caused the molecules at the end of the chain to dissociate, the free ions thus formed being discharged at the electrodes. Thereupon, there was an exchange of partners along the chain. Before further conduction could occur, each molecule had to rotate under the influence of the field to reform the original oriented chain. Despite its shortcomings, the Grotthuss theory was valuable in emphasizing the necessity of having free ions in the solution to explain the observed conductivity. We shall see later that a mechanism similar to that of Grotthuss actually occurs in some cases.

In 1857, Clausius proposed that especially energetic collisions between undissociated molecules in electrolytes maintained at equilibrium a small number of charged particles. These particles were believed to be responsible for the observed conductivity.

5. EQUIVALENT CONDUCTIVITIES

From 1869 to 1880, Friedrich Kohlrausch and his coworkers published a long series of careful conductivity investigations. The measurements were made over a range of temperatures, pressures, and concentrations.

Typical of this painstaking work was the extensive purification of the water used as a solvent. After 42 successive distillations *in vacuo,* they obtained a *conductivity water* with $\kappa = 0.043 \times 10^{-6}$ ohm^{-1} cm^{-1} at 18°C. Ordinary distilled water in equilibrium with the carbon dioxide of the air has a conductivity of about 0.7×10^{-6}.

To reduce his results to a common concentration basis, Kohlrausch defined a function called the *equivalent conductivity,*

$$\Lambda = \frac{1000\,\kappa}{c_{\text{eq}}} = \frac{\kappa}{c^{\star}} \tag{9.5}$$

The concentration $c^{\star}$ is in units of equivalents per cm^3. To calculate $c^{\star}$ we must know the formula of the solute in solution. For example, a one molar solution of $Fe_2(SO_4)_3$ would contain $\frac{6}{1000}$ equivalents/cm^3. The equivalent conductivity would be the conductance between a pair of plates 1 cm apart between which there is a layer of solution of sufficient volume to contain one equivalent of dissolved electrolyte.

Some values for Λ are plotted in Fig. 9.2. We can distinguish two classes of electrolytes on the basis of their conductivities. Strong electrolytes, such as

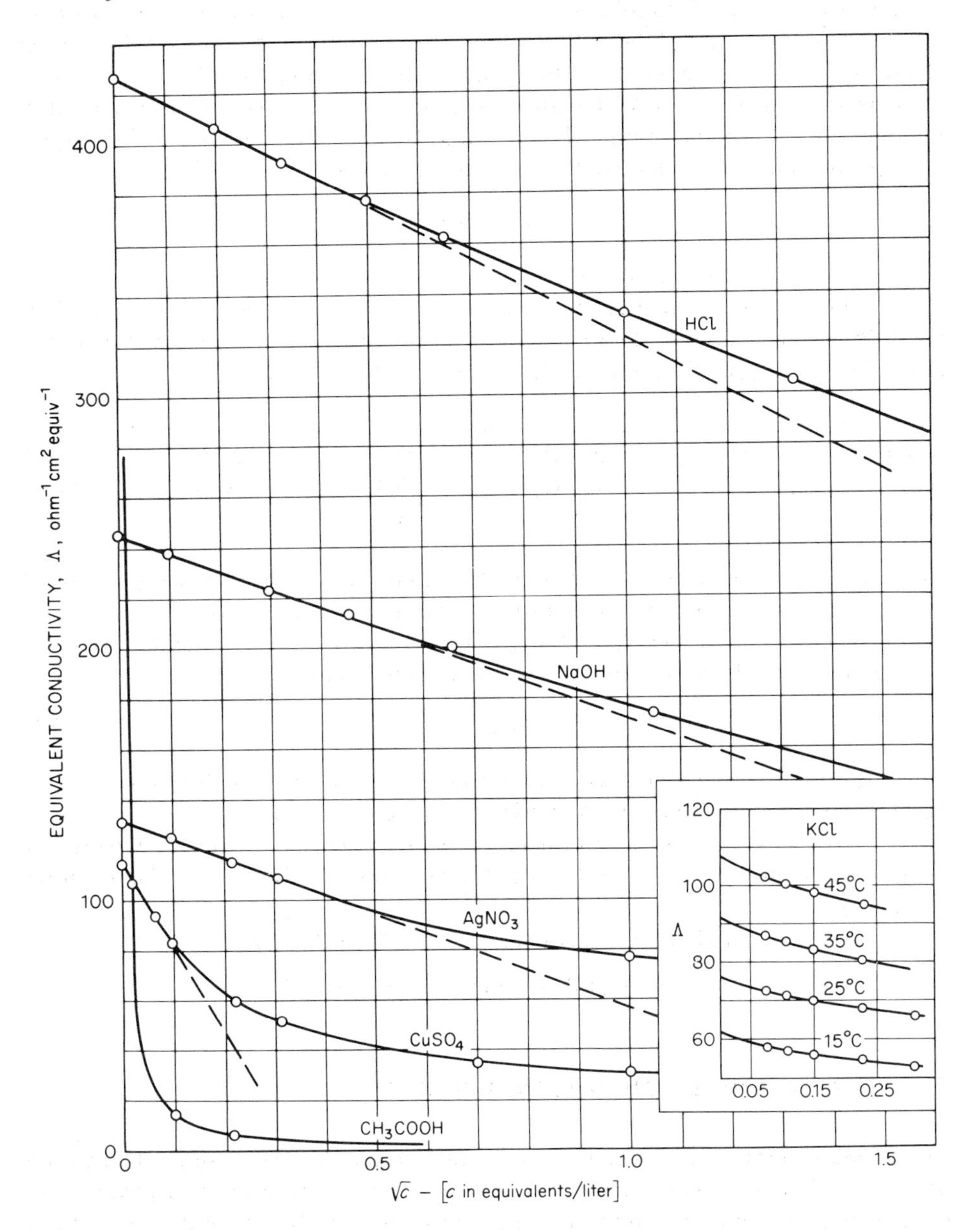

FIG. 9.2 Equivalent conductivities of electrolytes in aqueous solution vs. square roots of concentrations. Insert shows variation with temperature of Λ for KCl.

most salts and acids like hydrochloric, nitric, and sulfuric, have high equivalent conductivities which increase only moderately with increasing dilution. Weak electrolytes, such as acetic and other organic acids and aqueous ammonia, have much lower equivalent conductivities at high concentrations, but the values increase greatly with increasing dilution.

The value of Λ extrapolated to zero concentration is called the *equivalent conductivity at infinite dilution*, Λ_0. The extrapolation is made readily for strong electrolytes but is impossible to make accurately for weak electrolytes because of their steep increase in Λ at high dilutions, where the experimental measurements become very uncertain. It was found that the data for strong electrolytes were fairly well represented by the empirical equation

$$\Lambda = \Lambda_0 - k_c c^{1/2} \tag{9.6}$$

where k_c is an experimental constant.

Kohlrausch observed certain interesting relations between the values of Λ_0 for different electrolytes; the difference in Λ_0 for pairs of salts having a common ion was always approximately constant. For example (at 25°C):

	Λ_0		Λ_0		Λ_0
NaCl	128.1	$NaNO_3$	123.0	NaOH	246.5
KCl	149.8	KNO_3	145.5	KOH	271.0
	21.7		22.5		24.5

Thus no matter what the anion may be, there is an approximately constant difference between the conductivities of potassium and sodium salts. This behavior can be readily explained if Λ_0 is the sum of two independent terms, one characteristic of the anion and one of the cation. Thus

$$\Lambda_0 = \lambda_0^+ + \lambda_0^- \tag{9.7}$$

where λ_0^+ and λ_0^- are the *equivalent ionic conductivities* at infinite dilution. This is Kohlrausch's *law of the independent migration of ions*.

This rule makes it possible to calculate the Λ_0 for weak electrolytes like organic acids from values for their salts, which are strong electrolytes. For example (at 25°C):

$$\Lambda_0(\text{HAc}) = \Lambda_0(\text{NaAc}) + \Lambda_0(\text{HCl}) - \Lambda_0(\text{NaCl})$$
$$= 91.0 + 425.0 - 128.1 = 387.9$$

6. THE ARRHENIUS IONIZATION THEORY

From 1882 to 1886, Julius Thomsen published data on the heats of neutralization of acids and bases. He found that the heat of neutralization of a strong acid by a strong base in dilute solution was always very nearly constant, being about 13 800 calories per equivalent at 25°C. The neutralization heats of weak acids and bases were lower, and indeed the "strength" of an acid appeared to be proportional to its heat of neutralization by a strong base such as NaOH.

These results and the available conductivity data led Svante Arrhenius in 1887 to propose a new theory for the behavior of electrolyte solutions. He suggested that an equilibrium exists in the solution between undissociated solute molecules and ions which arise from these by *electrolytic dissociation.* Strong acids and bases being almost completely dissociated, their interaction was in every case simply $H^+ + OH^- \rightarrow H_2O$, thus explaining the constant heat of neutralization.

While Arrhenius was working on this theory, the osmotic-pressure studies of van't Hoff appeared, which provided a striking confirmation of the new ideas. We recall (Sec. 5.14) that van't Hoff found that the osmotic pressures of dilute solutions of nonelectrolytes often followed the equation $\Pi = cRT$. The osmotic pressures of electrolytes were always higher than predicted from this equation, often by a factor of two, three, or more, so that a modified equation was written as

$$\Pi = icRT \tag{9.8}$$

The van't Hoff *i factor* for strong electrolytes was close to the number of ions that would be formed if a solute molecule dissociated according to the Arrhenius theory. Thus for NaCl, KCl, and other uniunivalent electrolytes, $i = 2$; for $BaCl_2$, K_2SO_4, and other unibivalent species, $i = 3$; for $LaCl_3$, $i = 4$.

On April 13, 1887, Arrhenius wrote to van't Hoff as follows:

> *It is true that Clausius had assumed that only a minute quantity of dissolved electrolyte is dissociated, and that all other physicists and chemists had followed him, but the only reason for this assumption, so far as I can understand, is a strong feeling of aversion to a dissociation at so low a temperature, without any actual facts against it being brought forward. . . . At extreme dilution all salt molecules are completely dissociated. The degree of dissociation can be simply found on this assumption by taking the ratio of the equivalent conductivity of the solution in question to the equivalent conductivity at the most extreme dilution.*

Thus Arrhenius would write the degree of dissociation α as

$$\alpha = \frac{\Lambda}{\Lambda_0} \tag{9.9}$$

The van't Hoff i factor can also be related to α. If one molecule of solute capable of dissociating into ν ions per molecule is dissolved, the total number of particles present will be $i = 1 - \alpha + \nu\alpha$. Therefore

$$\alpha = \frac{i - 1}{\nu - 1} \tag{9.10}$$

Values of α for weak electrolytes calculated from Eqs. (9.9) and (9.10) were in good agreement.

Applying the mass-action principle to ionization, Ostwald obtained a *dilution law,* governing the variation of equivalent conductivity Λ with concentration.

For a binary electrolyte AB with degree of dissociation α, whose concentration is c moles per liter:

$$AB \rightleftarrows A^+ + B^-$$

$$c(1-\alpha) \qquad \alpha c \qquad \alpha c$$

$$K = \frac{\alpha^2 c}{(1-\alpha)}$$

From Eq. (9.9), therefore,

$$K = \frac{\Lambda^2 c}{\Lambda_0(\Lambda_0 - \Lambda)} \tag{9.11}$$

This equation was closely obeyed by weak electrolytes in dilute solutions. An example is shown in Table 9.1. In this case, the "law" is obeyed at concentrations below about 0.1 molar, but discrepancies begin to appear at higher concentrations.

TABLE 9.1 TEST OF OSTWALD'S DILUTION LAW
Acetic Acid at 25°C, $\Lambda_0 = 387.9$*

c (moles/liter)	Λ	Per Cent Dissociation $100\alpha = 100(\Lambda/\Lambda_0)$	Eq. (9.11) $K \times 10^5$
1.011	1.443	0.372	1.405
0.2529	3.221	0.838	1.759
0.06323	6.561	1.694	1.841
0.03162	9.260	2.389	1.846
0.01581	13.03	3.360	1.846
0.003952	25.60	6.605	1.843
0.001976	35.67	9.20	1.841
0.000988	49.50	12.77	1.844
0.000494	68.22	17.60	1.853

* D. A. MacInnes and T. Shedlovsky, *J. Am. Chem. Soc.* *54*, 1429 (1932).

The accumulated evidence gradually won acceptance for the Arrhenius theory, although chemists at the time still found it hard to believe that a stable molecule when placed in water spontaneously dissociated into ions. This criticism was in fact justified and it soon became evident that the solvent must play more than a purely passive role in the formation of an ionic solution.

We now know that the crystalline salts are themselves formed of ions in regular array, so that there is no question of "ionic dissociation" when they dissolve. The process of solution simply allows the ions to separate from one another. The separation is particularly easy in aqueous solutions owing to the high dielectric constant of water, $\epsilon = 78.5$ at 25°C. If we compare, for water and a vacuum, the energy necessary to separate two ions, say Na^+ and Cl^-, from a distance of 2 Å to infinity, we find:*

* This assumes that ϵ in the neighborhood of an ion is the same as ϵ for bulk water, which is an approximation. In the calculation we take charge in coulombs and hence $f = e_1e_2/4\pi\epsilon_0 r^2$ where ϵ_0 is permittivity of free space. A good description of electrical and magnetic units is given by the Bleaneys: *Electricity and Magnetism* (Oxford: Clarendon Press, 1957), pp. 643–658.

Vacuum

$$\Delta E = \int_{2A}^{\infty} f\,dr = \int_{2A}^{\infty} \frac{e_1 e_2}{4\pi\epsilon_0 r^2}\,dr$$

$$= \frac{(1.60 \times 10^{-19})^2}{4\pi(8.854 \times 10^{-12})(2 \times 10^{-10})}$$

$$= 1.15 \times 10^{-18} \text{ joule}$$

$$= 7.19 \text{ ev}$$

Water

$$\Delta E = \int_{2A}^{\infty} \frac{e_1 e_2}{4\pi\epsilon_0 \epsilon r^2}\,dr = \frac{\Delta E \text{ (Vacuum)}}{\epsilon}$$

$$= \frac{1.15 \times 10^{-18}}{78.5}$$

$$= 1.47 \times 10^{-20} \text{ joule}$$

$$= .0915 \text{ ev}$$

Counteracting the energy necessary to separate the ions is the energy of hydration of the ions, which arises from the strong ion-dipole attractions. Thus in many cases the solution of ionic salts is an exothermic reaction. The equilibrium position is of course determined by the change in free energy. The increased randomness of the ions in solution, compared with the ionic crystal, leads to an increase in entropy, but this is sometimes outweighed by an entropy decrease due to the ordering effect of the ions on the water molecules.

In the case of acids such as HCl, the solution process probably occurs as follows: $HCl + H_2O \rightarrow OH_3^+ + Cl^-$. In both HCl and H_2O the bonds are predominantly covalent in character. The ionization that occurs in solution is promoted by the high energy of hydration of the proton to form the hydronium ion, OH_3^+.

Whatever the detailed mechanisms may be, it has been clear since the work of Arrhenius that the solute in electrolytic solutions is ionized, and the transport of the ions in an electric field is responsible for the conductivity of the solutions.

7. TRANSPORT NUMBERS AND MOBILITIES

The fraction of the current carried by a given ionic species in solution is called the *transport number* or *transference number* of that ion.

From Kohlrausch's Law, Eq. (9.7), the transference numbers t_0^+ and t_0^- of cation and anion at infinite dilution may be written

$$t_0^+ = \frac{\lambda_0^+}{\Lambda_0}, \qquad t_0^- = \frac{\lambda_0^-}{\Lambda_0} \tag{9.12}$$

The *mobility* u of an ion is defined as its velocity in an electric field of unit strength. The usual units are cm sec^{-1} per volt cm^{-1} (cm^2 sec^{-1} volt^{-1}).

The general expression for a conductivity is

$$\kappa = Nu|ze| \tag{9.13}$$

where n is the number of charge carriers in unit volume, $|ze|$ is the absolute value of their charge. If there are several different carriers, we add their contributions to give $\kappa = \sum N_i\,|z_i e|\,u_i$.

The conductivity calculated for one faraday of charge in one cc is the equivalent ionic conductivity λ. Hence, when $N|z|e = F$ in Eq. (9.13), $\kappa = \lambda$. Thus

$$\lambda = Fu = t\Lambda \tag{9.14}$$

This relation applies to each ion in a solution. If we know the transference number t of an ion we can therefore calculate its mobility from the equivalent conductivity Λ of the solution.

8. MEASUREMENT OF TRANSPORT NUMBERS—HITTORF METHOD

The method of Hittorf is based on concentration changes in the neighborhood of the electrodes caused by the passage of current through the electrolyte. The principle of the method may be illustrated by reference to Fig. 9.3. Imagine a cell divided into three compartments as shown. The situation of the ions before the passage of any current is represented schematically as (a), each + or − sign indicating one equivalent of the corresponding ion.

Now let us assume that the mobility of the positive ion is three times that of the negative ion, $u_+ = 3u_-$. Let 4 faradays of electric charge be passed through the cell. At the anode, therefore, four equivalents of negative ions are discharged, and at the cathode, four equivalents of positive ions. Four faradays must pass across any boundary plane drawn through the electrolyte parallel to the electrodes. Since the positive ions travel three times faster than the negative ions, 3 faradays are carried across the plane from left to right by the positive ions while one faraday is being carried from right to left by the negative ions. This transfer is depicted in panel (b) of the picture. The final situation is shown in (c). The change in number of equivalents around the anode, $\Delta n_a = 6 - 3 = 3$; around the cathode, $\Delta n_c = 6 - 5 = 1$. The ratio of these concentration changes is necessarily identical with the ratio of the ionic mobilities: $\Delta n_a/\Delta n_c = u_+/u_- = 3$.

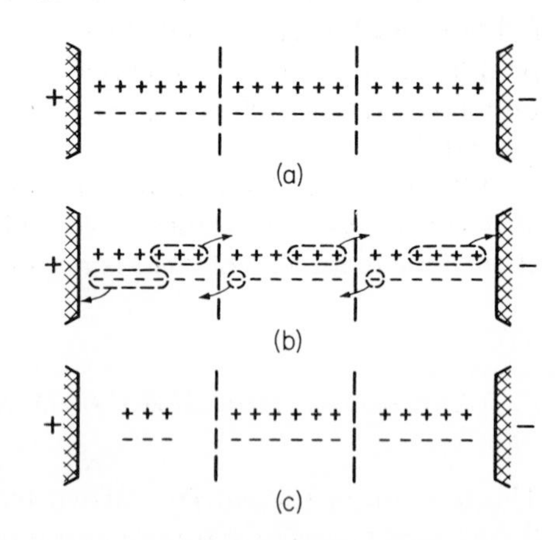

FIG. 9.3 Transport numbers (Hittorf method).

Suppose the amount of electricity passed through the cell was measured by a coulometer in series, and found to be Q coulombs. Provided the electrodes are inert, Q/F equivalents of cations have therefore been discharged at the cathode, and Q/F equivalents of anions at the anode. The net *loss* of solute from the cathode compartment is

$$\Delta n_c = \frac{Q}{F} - t_+ \frac{Q}{F} = \frac{Q}{F}(1 - t_+) = \frac{Qt_-}{F}$$

Thus
$$t_- = \frac{\Delta n_c}{Q/F}, \qquad t_+ = \frac{\Delta n_a}{Q/F} \tag{9.15}$$

where Δn_a is the net loss of solute from the anode compartment. Since $t_+ + t_- = 1$, both transport numbers can be determined from measurements on either compartment, but it is useful to have both analyses as a check.

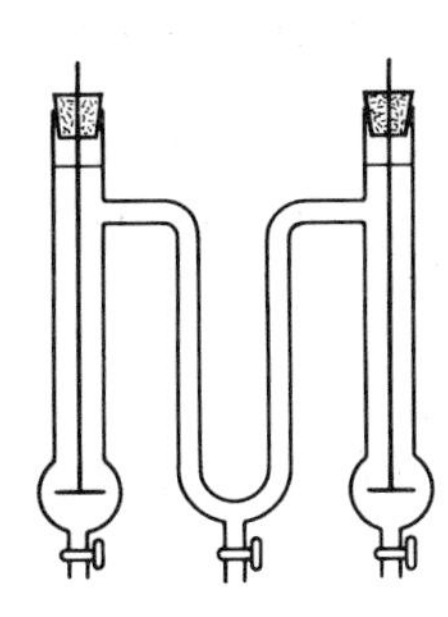

FIG. 9.4 Hittorf transport apparatus.

In the experiment just described, the electrodes were inert. In other cases, ions may pass into the solution from the electrodes. Consider, for example, a silver anode in a silver nitrate solution. When electricity passes through the cell, there is a net increase in the amount of electrolyte in the anode compartment, equal to the number of equivalents of silver entering the solution at the anode minus the number of equivalents of silver crossing the boundary of the anode compartment.

An experimental apparatus for carrying out these determinations is shown in Fig. 9.4. The apparatus is filled with a standardized electrolyte solution and a current, kept low to minimize thermal effects, is passed through the solution for some time. The total amount of electricity is measured with a coulometer.

The changes in concentration occur in the neighborhoods of the electrodes and extend back into the body of the solution. The exact place where we divide the solutions after the run does not matter, provided we make the division far enough back to include all the region around an electrode in which any detectable change in concentration has occurred. The solutions are drawn separately from the three sections of the cell and analyzed. Analysis gives the mass of solute and the mass of solvent in the solutions from the electrode compartments. Since the mass of solute originally associated with this mass of solvent is known, Δn_a and Δn_c can be found by difference. Ideally there should be no change in concentration in the middle compartment, but small changes caused by diffusion may detract from the accuracy of the determination.

As an example of the Hittorf method, consider the following problem. A 4.00 molal solution of $FeCl_3$ was electrolyzed between platinum electrodes. After electrolysis the cathode portion was 3.15 molal in $FeCl_3$ and 1.00 molal in $FeCl_2$. What was the transference number of Fe^{+3}? The reaction at the cathode was $Fe^{+3} + e \rightarrow Fe^{+2}$; therefore one faraday of charge passed through the cell per 1000 g of water in the cathode portion. The Fe^{+3} that passed into the cathode region must have amounted to 0.15 moles per this 1000 g of water $(3.15 + 1.00 - 4.00)$. But 0.15 moles of Fe^{+3} corresponds to 0.45 faradays of charge, and hence $t_+ = 0.45$. The concentrations are all reported here in molalities. In the actual experiment a weighed amount of cathode solution was analyzed to find these reported molalities.

9. TRANSPORT NUMBERS—MOVING BOUNDARY METHOD

This method is based on the early work of Oliver Lodge (1886) who used an indicator to follow the migration of ions in a conducting gel. For example, a solution of barium chloride was placed around platinum electrodes serving as anode and cathode. The two sides of the cell were then connected by means of a tube filled with gelatin acidified with acetic acid to make it conducting and containing a small amount of dissolved silver sulfate as indicator. As the current passed, the Ba^{++} and Cl^- ions migrated into the gel from opposite ends, forming precipitates of $BaSO_4$ and AgCl, respectively. From the rate of progression of the white precipitate boundaries, the relative velocities of the ions could be estimated.

The more recent applications of this method discard the gel and indicator and use an apparatus such as that in Fig. 9.5, to follow the moving boundary between two liquid solutions. For example, the electrolyte to be studied, CA, is introduced into the apparatus in a layer above a solution of a salt with a common anion, $C'A$, and a cation whose mobility is considerably less than that of the ion C^+. As an example, a layer of KCl solution could be introduced above a layer of $CdCl_2$ solution. The mobility of Cd^{++} is considerably lower than that of K^+. When a current is passed through the cell, A^- ions move downwards toward the anode, while C^+ and C'^+ ions move upwards toward the cathode. A sharp boundary is preserved between the two solutions since the more slowly moving C'^+ ions never overtake the C^+ ions; nor do the following ions, C'^+, fall far behind, because if they began to lag, the solution behind the boundary would become more dilute, and its higher resistance and therefore steeper potential drop would increase the ionic velocity. Even with colorless solutions, the sharp boundary is visible owing to the different refractive indices of the two solutions.

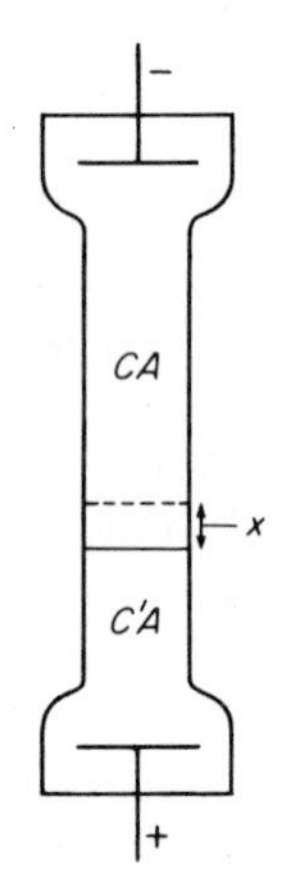

FIG. 9.5 Moving-boundary cell.

Suppose the boundary moves a distance x for the passage of Q coulombs. The number of equivalents transported is then Q/F, of which t_+Q/F are carried by the positive ion. Recalling that $c^\star$ is the concentration in equivalents per cc, the volume of solution swept out by the boundary during the passage of Q coulombs is $t_+Q/Fc^\star$. If a is the cross-sectional area of the tube, $xa = t_+Q/Fc^\star$, or

$$t_+ = \frac{Fxac^\star}{Q} \tag{9.16}$$

10. RESULTS OF TRANSFERENCE EXPERIMENTS

Some measured transport numbers are summarized in Table 9.2. With these values it is possible to calculate from Eq. (9.14) the equivalent ionic conductivities λ_0, some of which are given in Table 9.3. By the use of Kohlrausch's rule, they may be combined to yield values for the equivalent conductivities Λ_0 of a wide variety of electrolytes. For example, for $BaCl_2$, Λ_0 would be $63.64 + 76.34 = 139.98$.

TABLE 9.2 TRANSPORT NUMBERS OF CATIONS IN WATER SOLUTIONS AT 25°C*

Solution Normality	$AgNO_3$	$BaCl_2$	LiCl	NaCl	KCl	KNO_3	$LaCl_3$	HCl
0.01	0.4648	0.440	0.3289	0.3918	0.4902	0.5084	0.4625	0.8251
0.05	0.4664	0.4317	0.3211	0.3876	0.4899	0.5093	0.4482	0.8292
0.10	0.4682	0.4253	0.3168	0.3854	0.4898	0.5103	0.4375	0.8314
0.50	—	0.3986	0.300	—	0.4888	—	0.3958	—
1.0	—	0.3792	0.287	—	0.4882	—	—	—

* L. G. Longsworth, *J. Am. Chem. Soc.*, *57*, 1185 (1935); *60*, 3070 (1938).

TABLE 9.3 EQUIVALENT IONIC CONDUCTIVITIES AT INFINITE DILUTION, λ_0, AT 25°C*

Cation	λ_0	Anion	λ_0
H^+	349.82	OH^-	198.0
Li^+	38.69	Cl^-	76.34
Na^+	50.11	Br^-	78.4
K^+	73.52	I^-	76.8
NH_4^+	73.4	NO_3^-	71.44
Ag^+	61.92	CH_3COO^-	40.9
$\frac{1}{2}$ Ca^{++}	59.50	ClO_4^-	68.0
$\frac{1}{2}$ Ba^{++}	63.64	$\frac{1}{2}$ $SO_4^=$	79.8
$\frac{1}{2}$ Sr^{++}	59.46		
$\frac{1}{2}$ Mg^{++}	53.06		
$\frac{1}{3}$ La^{+++}	69.6		

* D. MacInnes, *Principles of Electrochemistry* (New York: Reinhold, 1939).

It has been mentioned that ions in solution are undoubtedly hydrated, so that the observed transport numbers are actually not those of "bare ions" but of solvated ions. From the equivalent ionic conductivities it is possible to calculate the mobilities of the ions by use of Eq. (9.14). Some results are given in Table 9.4. The effect of hydration is shown in the set of values for Li^+, Na^+, K^+. Although Li^+ is undoubtedly the smallest ion, it has the lowest mobility, i.e., the resistance to its motion through the solution is highest. This resistance must be partly due to a tightly held sheath of water molecules, bound by the intense electric field of the small ion.

TABLE 9.4 MOBILITIES OF IONS IN WATER SOLUTIONS AT 25°C
($cm^2\ sec^{-1}\ volt^{-1}$)

Cations	Mobility	Anions	Mobility
H^+	36.30×10^{-4}	OH^-	20.50×10^{-4}
K^+	7.62×10^{-4}	$SO_4^=$	8.27×10^{-4}
Ba^{++}	6.59×10^{-4}	Cl^-	7.91×10^{-4}
Na^+	5.19×10^{-4}	NO_3^-	7.40×10^{-4}
Li^+	4.01×10^{-4}	HCO_3^-	4.61×10^{-4}

The passage of an ion through a liquid under the influence of an applied electric field E might be treated approximately as a hydrodynamic problem similar to the fall of a spherical body through a viscous medium under the influence of a gravitational field (cf. the oil drop experiment, Sec. 11.6, and the Höppler viscometer, Sec. 17.13). Then, for steady flow, the viscous resistance, given by the Stokes formula, would be balanced by the electric force: $6\pi\eta r v = zeE$. Or, since $v = Eu$, $u\eta = ze/6\pi r$. From this follows the relation, $\eta\Lambda_0 =$ constant, known as *Walden's rule*. It has a rather wide range of experimental validity when tested by measuring the Λ_0 of electrolytes in solutions of different viscosities. Its derivation from Stokes's Law is probably a specious one, for it seems unreasonable to apply the hydrodynamic equation, meant for a continuous fluid, to the motion of ions whose radii are about the same as those of the solvent molecules. Walden's rule may therefore simply imply that ionic conductance and viscous flow proceed by similar mechanisms. In water, for example, both have a temperature coefficient corresponding to an $e^{-\Delta E/RT}$ term with ΔE around 3500 calories per mole.

11. MOBILITIES OF HYDROGEN AND HYDROXYL IONS

Table 9.4 reveals that, with two exceptions, the ionic mobilities in aqueous solutions do not differ as to order of magnitude, being all around 6×10^{-4} cm^2 sec^{-1} volt^{-1}. The exceptions are the hydrogen and hydroxyl ions with the abnormally high mobilities of 36.3×10^{-4} and 20.5×10^{-4}.

The high mobility of the hydrogen ion is observed only in hydroxylic solvents such as water and the alcohols, in which it is strongly solvated, for example, in water to the hydronium ion, OH_3^+. It is believed to be an example of a Grotthuss type of conductivity, superimposed on the normal transport process. Thus the OH_3^+ ion is able to transfer a proton to a neighboring water molecule,

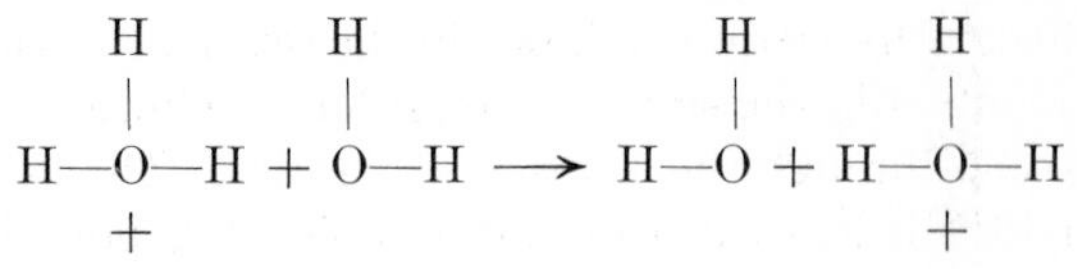

$$\begin{array}{ccccccccccccccccccc}
 & & \mathrm{H} & & & & \mathrm{H} & & & & & & \mathrm{H} & & & & \mathrm{H} & & \\
 & & | & & & & | & & & & & & | & & & & | & & \\
\mathrm{H} & — & \mathrm{O} & — & \mathrm{H} & + & \mathrm{O} & — & \mathrm{H} & \longrightarrow & \mathrm{H} & — & \mathrm{O} & + & \mathrm{H} & — & \mathrm{O} & — & \mathrm{H} \\
 & & + & & & & & & & & & & & & & & + & &
\end{array}$$

This process may be followed by the rotation of the donor molecule so that it is again in a position to accept a proton.

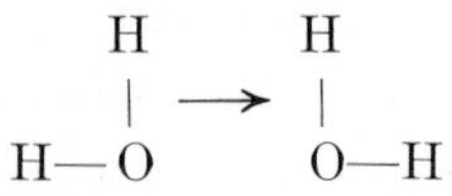

$$\begin{array}{ccccc}
 & \mathrm{H} & & \mathrm{H} & \\
 & | & \longrightarrow & | & \\
\mathrm{H}— & \mathrm{O} & & \mathrm{O} & —\mathrm{H}
\end{array}$$

The high mobility of the hydroxyl ion in water is also believed to be caused by a proton transfer, between hydroxyl ions and water molecules,

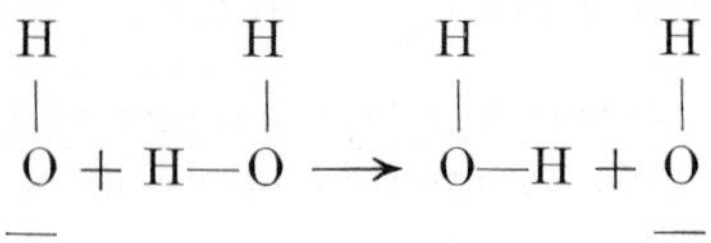

$$\begin{array}{ccccccccccc}
\mathrm{H} & & & & \mathrm{H} & & \mathrm{H} & & & & \mathrm{H} \\
| & & & & | & & | & & & & | \\
\mathrm{O} & + & \mathrm{H} & — & \mathrm{O} & \longrightarrow & \mathrm{O} & — & \mathrm{H} & + & \mathrm{O} \\
- & & & & & & & & & & -
\end{array}$$

Protons play an important part in electrical phenomena in living systems and the exact mechanisms by which they move are being actively investigated. Eigen* has suggested that the predominant form of the proton in water is the ion $H_9O_4^+$, consisting of a hydronium ion OH_3^+ that holds three water molecules by hydrogen bonds (Sec. 13.19),

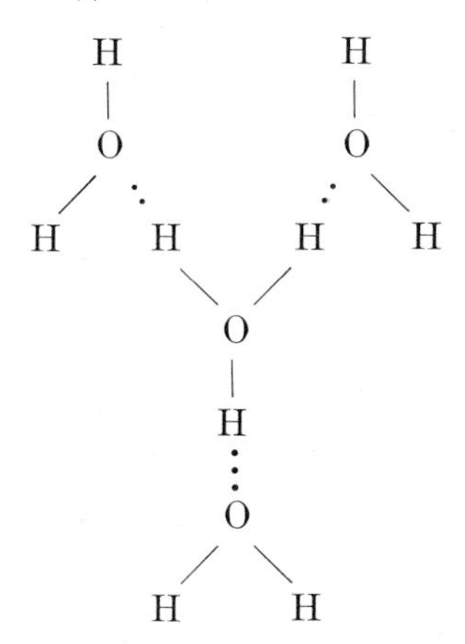

Other water molecules might be more loosely attached to this complex, but the structure shown has exceptional stability. When a proton passes along the hydrogen bond, a new hydronium ion is formed, which at first is not coordinated with its three water molecules. There will therefore be a certain lag in time before this coordination sheath is established about the newly formed OH_3^+. Eigen believes that the reformation of the complex $H_9O_4^+$ is the slow step that determines the overall mobility of protons in water. It is a sort of "structural diffusion" of the water bound to the OH_3^+. The mobility of the proton in ice appears to be about fifty times higher than that in water at 0°C. In the structure of ice, a proton can simply jump (or tunnel) from one site to the next in the rigid structure, and there is no migration of water associated with its motion. Hence the higher mobility in ice reflects the true rate of the proton transfer along the hydrogen bond. It is so fast as to suggest a quantum-mechanical tunneling of the H^+ from one site to the next (Sec. 12.19).

12. DIFFUSION AND IONIC MOBILITY

The speed v of an ion of charge Q in an electric field E is related to its mobility u by $v = Eu$. The driving force in such ionic migration is the negative gradient of the *electric potential* U: $E = -\partial U/\partial x$. Even in the absence of an external electric field, however, ions can migrate if there is a difference in *chemical potential* μ between different parts of the system. The migration of a substance under the action of a difference in chemical potential is called *diffusion*. Just as the electric

* M. Eigen, *Proc. Roy. Soc. A 247*, 505 (1958).

force (per unit charge) on each particle equals the negative gradient of electric potential, so the diffusive force equals the negative gradient of chemical potential. In one dimension, therefore, the force on a particle of the ith kind is

$$f_i = -\frac{1}{L}\left(\frac{\partial \mu_i}{\partial x}\right)_T$$

Since μ_i refers to one mole of particles, it has been divided by Avogadro's Number L. The velocity under the action of unit force is u/Q, so that $v_i = (-u_i/LQ_i)(\partial\mu_i/\partial x)$. The net flow of material through unit cross section in unit time is therefore

$$S_{ix} = -\frac{u_i}{Q_i}\frac{c_i}{L}\cdot\left(\frac{\partial \mu_i}{\partial x}\right)_T$$

where c_i is the molar concentration in unit volume. For a sufficiently dilute solute, $\mu_i = RT \ln c_i + \mu_i^\circ$, and $\partial\mu_i/\partial x = (RT/c_i)(\partial c_i/\partial x)$. Hence,

$$S_{ix} = -kT\frac{u_i}{Q_i}\left(\frac{\partial c_i}{\partial x}\right)_T$$

In 1855 Fick stated in his empirical *First Law of Diffusion* that the flow S_{ix} is proportional to the gradient of concentration:

$$S_{ix} = -D_i\frac{\partial c_i}{\partial x} \tag{9.17}$$

The proportionality factor D_i is called the *diffusion coefficient*. Thus,

$$D_i = \frac{kT}{Q_i}u_i \tag{9.18}$$

Or, from Eq. (9.14),

$$D_i = \frac{RT}{F^2}\frac{\lambda_i}{|z_i|}$$

This equation was derived by Nernst* in 1888. It indicates that diffusion experiments can yield much the same kind of information about ionic mobilities as that obtained from conductivity data. Equation (9.18) obviously applies to the diffusion of a single ionic species only. An experimental example would be the diffusion of a small amount of HCl dissolved in a solution of KCl. The Cl^- concentrations would be constant throughout the system, and the experiment would measure diffusion of the H^+ ions alone. In other cases, such as diffusion of salts from concentrated to dilute solution, it is necessary to use a suitable average value of the diffusion coefficients of the ions to represent the overall D. For instance, Nernst showed that for electrolytes of type CA, the proper average is

$$D = \frac{2D_C C_A}{D_C + D_A}$$

* *Z. physik. Chem.* *2*, 613 (1888).

13. A SOLUTION OF THE DIFFUSION EQUATION

Equation (9.17) gives only the steady-state condition for diffusion, but the way in which the concentration may change with time in any region of the solution can be found as follows: Consider a region of unit cross-section and of length dx, extending from x to $x + dx$. The increase in concentration within this region in unit time is the excess of material diffusing into the region over that diffusing out, divided by the volume dx:

$$\frac{\partial c}{\partial t} = \frac{1}{dx}\left[-D\left(\frac{\partial c}{\partial x}\right)_x + D\left(\frac{\partial c}{\partial x}\right)_{x+dx}\right]$$

But,

$$\left(\frac{\partial c}{\partial x}\right)_{x+dx} = \left(\frac{\partial c}{\partial x}\right)_x + \frac{\partial}{\partial x}\left(\frac{\partial c}{\partial x}\right) dx$$

Therefore,

$$\frac{\partial c}{\partial t} = D\left(\frac{\partial^2 c}{\partial x^2}\right) \tag{9.19}$$

This equation is Fick's *Second Law of Diffusion*. It has the same form as the equation for heat conduction, $\partial T/\partial t = K(\partial^2 T/\partial x^2)$, where K is the thermal conductivity divided by the heat capacity per unit volume. Thus all the solutions of heat conduction problems, which have been obtained for a great variety of boundary conditions, can be directly applied to problems of diffusion.

We shall consider one solution only, which illustrates the phenomena of interest. Suppose an extremely thin, effectively planar layer of the diffusing substance is introduced at the interface $x = 0$ in the diffusion medium. Thus at $t = 0$, $x = 0$, $c = c_0$; but at $t = 0$, for all $x \neq 0$, $c = 0$.

The diffusing ion in this problem is simply another analog of the drunken sailor of Sec. 7.20. In the one dimensional random walk problem, suppose the sailor, particle, or ion suffers n displacements in unit time. Thus $N = nt$, and Eq. (7.38) becomes

$$\frac{c}{c_0} = p(x, t) = \frac{1}{2(\pi D t)^{1/2}} \exp\left(-x^2/4Dt\right) \tag{9.20}$$

where

$$D = \tfrac{1}{2} n l^2 \tag{9.21}$$

The same result could be obtained by a conventional solution of the differential equation.*

An example of a concentration vs. displacement curve that was found for diffusion of KCl in water is shown in Fig. 9.6. The original sharply defined source of diffusing material broadens with time; the resulting curves are Gaussian distributions. The diffusion data can be evaluated from Eq. (9.20) by plotting,

* J. Crank, *The Mathematics of Diffusion* (New York: Oxford Univ. Press, 1956).

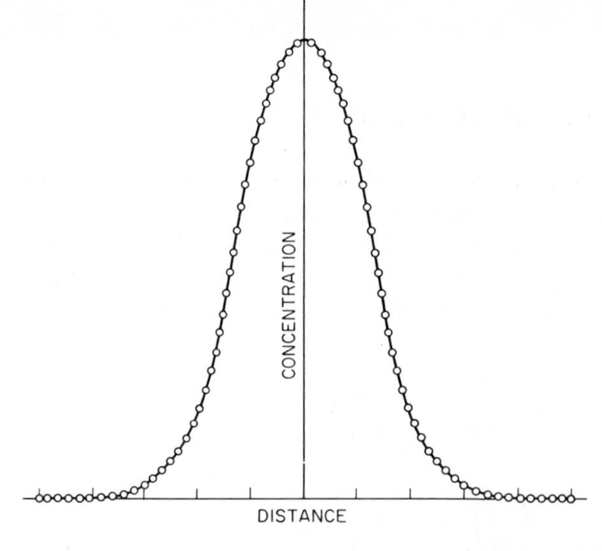

FIG. 9.6 Diffusion of 0.1N KCl in water at 20°C. [O. Lamm, *Nova Acta Regiae Soc. Sci. Uppsaliensis* (4), 10, 6 (1937)]. The experimental points are shown with the theoretical curve of Eq. (9.20).

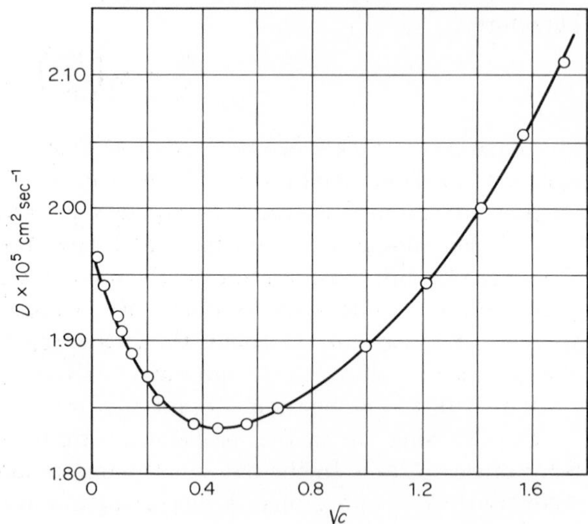

FIG. 9.7 Diffusion coefficient of KCl in water at 25°C [H. S. Harned].

for a given time, ln c vs. x^2; the slope of the straight line equals $(4Dt)^{-1}$. Fig. 9.7 shows precise diffusion coefficients for KCl in water measured by H. S. Harned.

The probability $p(x)\,dx$ that a given particle has diffused from $x = 0$ to a region between x and $x + dx$ is simply proportional to the concentration in this region. The average distance traversed by the diffusing particles is given by the mean square displacement:*

$$\overline{\Delta x^2} = \int_{-\infty}^{+\infty} x^2 p(x)\,dx = \int_{-\infty}^{+\infty} x^2 (4\pi Dt)^{-1/2}\, e^{-x^2/4Dt}\,dx$$

* One averages the square of the distance since diffusion in both the positive and the negative x directions can occur.

Hence, $$\overline{\Delta x^2} = 2Dt \qquad (9.22)$$

This result could also be obtained directly by comparing Eq. (7.39) and (9.20). The displacements of a large number of individual particles after a time t are squared and averaged to give $\overline{\Delta x^2}$. Equation (9.22) also is often used to give a rapid estimate of the mean distance of diffusion in various solid and liquid systems.*

14. DEFECTS OF THE ARRHENIUS THEORY

After the controversy over ionic dissociation, it began to be realized that the Arrhenius theory was unsatisfactory on a number of points, none of which was among those urged against it by its fierce original opponents.

The behavior of strong electrolytes presented many anomalies. The Ostwald dilution law was not closely followed by moderately strong electrolytes like dichloroacetic acid, although it agreed well with the data for weak acids like acetic. Also values for the degree of dissociation α of strong electrolytes obtained from conductance ratios were not in agreement with those from van't Hoff i factors, and the "dissociation constants" calculated by the mass-action law were far from constant.

Another discrepancy was in the heats of neutralization of strong acids and bases. Although one of the first supports for the ionization theory was the constancy of these ΔH values for different acid–base pairs, more critical examination indicated that the ΔH values were actually too concordant to satisfy the theory. According to Arrhenius, there should have been small differences in the extents of ionization of acids such as HCl, H_2SO_4, HNO_3, at any given concentration, and these differences should have been reflected in corresponding differences in the ΔH values, but such distinctions were not in fact observed.

Another flaw was the variation of transport numbers with concentration c. At low concentrations, these numbers were found to follow an equation of the form $t = t_0 - Ac^{1/2}$, where t_0 is the value at infinite dilution and A is a constant. The Arrhenius theory predicted that the numbers of both positive and negative current carriers should increase equally with increasing dilution. It provided no explanation of why their relative mobilities should vary.

A further argument against the partial dissociation of strong electrolytes was provided by the ionic structure of crystalline salts.

The absorption spectra of dilute solutions of strong electrolytes revealed no evidence for undissociated molecules.

As early as 1902, a possible explanation of many of the deficiencies of the simple dissociation theory was suggested by van Laar, who called attention to

* Experimental methods for measuring diffusion coefficients in solutions are discussed in detail by A. L. Geddes and R. B. Pontius, "Determination of Diffusivity," in *Technique of Organic Chemistry* (3rd ed.), Vol. 1, Part 2, pp. 895–1006. Ed. by A. Weissberger (New York: Interscience, 1960).

the strong electrostatic forces that must be present in an ionic solution and their influence on the behavior of the dissolved ions. In 1912, S. R. Milner gave a detailed discussion of this problem, but his excellent results were not widely understood.

In 1923, P. Debye and E. Hückel attacked the problem and devised a theory which is the basis for the modern treatment of strong electrolytes. It starts with the assumption that in strong electrolytes the solute is completely dissociated into ions. The observed deviations from ideal behavior, e.g., apparent degrees of dissociation of less than 100 per cent, are ascribed entirely to the electrical interactions of the ions in solution. These deviations are therefore greater with more highly charged ions and in more concentrated solutions.

The electrical-interaction theory can be applied to equilibrium problems, and also to the important transport problems in the theory of electrical conductivity. Before describing these applications we shall discuss the nomenclature and conventions employed for the thermodynamic properties of electrolytic solutions.

15. ACTIVITIES AND STANDARD STATES

As shown in Sec. 6.20, the standard state for a component considered as a solute B is based on Henry's Law. In the limit as $X_B \to 0$, $a_B \to X_B$, and the activity coefficient $\gamma_B \to 1$. The departure of γ_B from unity is a measure of the departure of the behavior of the solute from that prescribed by Henry's Law. Henry's Law implies the absence of interaction between molecules of solute (component B sees only solvent A surrounding it). Therefore the deviations of the activity coefficients from unity measure the effects of interactions between solute species in solution.

We need to make two changes in the definition of standard state given in Sec. 6.20 before we use it for solutions of electrolytes. The composition of electrolytic solutions is almost always expressed in molalities instead of in mole fractions. Also we need to consider the effect of dissociation of the electrolyte, by which a molecule of added solute yields two or more molecules or ions in the solution. Thus for NaCl in water, the limiting form of Henry's Law would be*

$$f_B = k_H m_B^2 \tag{9.23}$$

where f_B and m_B are the fugacity and molality of the NaCl. For an electrolyte yielding ν particles on dissociation

$$f_B = k_H a_B^{\nu}$$

The usual standard state for an electrolyte in solution is illustrated in Fig. 9.8, for the case of NaCl. It is a hypothetical state in which the solute would exist at

* Consider a molecule that dissociates in solution as $B \to 2A$. Then the equilibrium constant $K_a = a_A{}^2/a_B$. In very dilute solution, dissociation is practically complete, and $a_A \to m_A$. Hence $a_B = K_a^{-1} m_A{}^2$. But when dissociation is complete, m_A is twice the molality of B initially added, $2m_B{}^0$, so that $a_B = K_a^{-1}(2m_B{}^0)^2$.

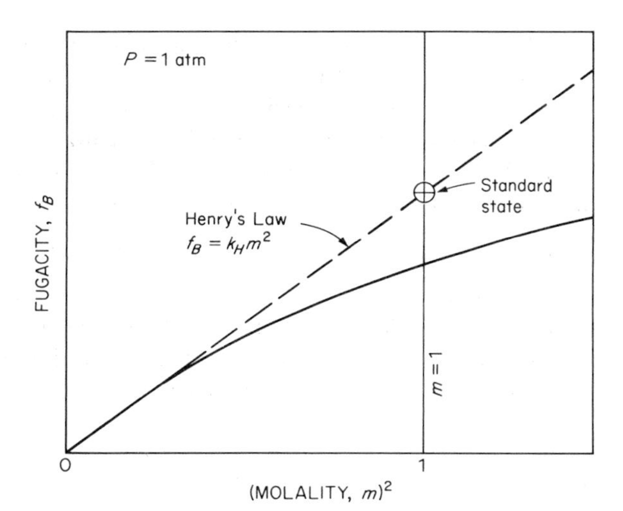

FIG. 9.8 Definition of standard state for a 1:1 electrolyte like NaCl in solution, based on Henry's Law in dilute solutions.

unit molality and one atmosphere pressure but would still have the environment typical of an extremely dilute solution that followed Henry's Law [Eq. (9.23)].

The activity of B is therefore

$$a_B = f_B/f_B^s \qquad \text{where} \qquad f_B^s = k_H$$

and

$$a_B = \gamma_B m_B$$

We have not used a special symbol to distinguish these activities and standard states from those based on the choice of mole fraction as the variable of composition. It is clear that they are not the same, but no confusion can arise because we shall use only molalities throughout this chapter.

16. ION ACTIVITIES

In dealing with electrolytic solutions it would apparently be most convenient to use the activities of the different ionic species present in the solution. There are serious difficulties in the way of such a procedure. The requirement of overall electrical neutrality in the solution prevents any increase in the charge due to positive ions without an equal increase in the charge due to negative ions. For example, we can change the concentration of a solution of sodium chloride by adding equal numbers of sodium ions and chloride ions. If we could possibly add sodium ions alone or chloride ions alone, the solution would acquire a net electric charge. The properties of ions in such a charged solution would differ considerably from their properties in the normal uncharged solution. There is in fact no conceivable way of *measuring* the individual ion activities, for there is no way of separating effects due to positive ions from those due to the accompanying negative ions in an uncharged solution.

It is nevertheless convenient to define an expression for the activity of an electrolyte in terms of the ions into which it dissociates. Consider, for example, a solute like NaCl, dissociated in solution according to $NaCl \rightarrow Na^+ + Cl^-$. The activity a of the NaCl is readily measurable from osmotic pressure, freezing point depression, or in other ways. We denote the activity of the cation as a_+ and that of the anion as a_-, and write *as definitions*,

$$a = a_+ a_- = a_\pm^2 \tag{9.24}$$

If we recall that an activity is always a ratio of a fugacity to the fugacity in a standard state which we are free to choose, we may regard* Eq. (9.24) as defining the standard states for the conventional individual ionic activities a_+ and a_-. The quantity $a_\pm$, the *geometric mean* of a_+ and a_-, is called the *mean activity* of the ions.

For more complex types of electrolyte, these definitions can be generalized. Consider an electrolyte that dissociates as

$$C_{\nu+}A_{\nu-} \longrightarrow \nu_+ C^+ + \nu_- A^-$$

The total number of ions is $\nu = \nu_+ + \nu_-$. We then write

$$a = a_+^{\nu_+} a_-^{\nu_-} = a_\pm^{\nu} \tag{9.25}$$

For example,

$$La_2(SO_4)_3 \longrightarrow 2\ La^{+3} + 3\ SO_4^{-2}$$

$$a = a_{La}^2 a_{SO_4}^3 = a_\pm^5$$

We can also define individual ionic activity coefficients γ_+ and γ_- by

$$a_+ = \gamma_+ m_+ \quad \text{and} \quad a_- = \gamma_- m_- \tag{9.26}$$

In practice, only the geometric means of the coefficients ($\gamma_\pm$) will be measurable, where

$$\gamma_\pm^{\nu} = \gamma_+^{\nu_+} \gamma_-^{\nu_-} \tag{9.27}$$

Equation (9.25) can then be written

$$a = m_+^{\nu_+} m_-^{\nu_-} \gamma_+^{\nu_+} \gamma_-^{\nu_-}$$

or

$$a_\pm = a^{1/\nu} = (m_+^{\nu_+} m_-^{\nu_-} \gamma_+^{\nu_+} \gamma_-^{\nu_-})^{1/\nu} \tag{9.28}$$

Substituting Eq. (9.27) into Eq. (9.28), we obtain

$$\gamma_\pm = \frac{a_\pm}{(m_+^{\nu_+} m_-^{\nu_-})^{1/\nu}} \tag{9.29}$$

This equation applies in any solution, whether the ions are added together as a single salt, or added separately as a mixture of salts.

---

* Another way of looking at Eq. (9.24) is that it amounts to setting $\Delta G^\circ = 0$ for the reaction $NaCl \rightarrow Na^+ + Cl^-$, since then $K = a_+ a_-/a = e^{-\Delta G^\circ/RT} = 1$. In other words, we choose the standard states of Na^+ and Cl^- so that $\Delta G^\circ = 0$.

For a solution of a single salt, of molality m,

$$m_+ = \nu_+ m \qquad \text{and} \qquad m_- = \nu_- m$$

In this case Eq. (9.29) becomes

$$\gamma_\pm = \frac{a_\pm}{m(\nu_+^{\nu_+}\nu_-^{\nu_-})^{1/\nu}} = \frac{a_\pm}{m_\pm} \tag{9.30}$$

In the case of $La_2(SO_4)_3$, for example, $\nu_+ = 2$ and $\nu_- = 3$, so that

$$\gamma_\pm = \frac{a_\pm}{m(2^2 3^3)^{1/5}} = \frac{a_\pm}{108^{1/5} m} \tag{9.31}$$

The activity coefficient as defined in Eq. (9.30) becomes unity at infinite dilution.

The activities can be determined by several different methods. Among the most important are measurements of the colligative properties of solutions, like freezing-point depression and osmotic pressure, measurements of the solubilities of sparingly soluble salts, and methods based on the emf of electrochemical cells. We shall describe the first method now, postponing consideration of the emf method until cell reactions have been considered in more detail.

17. ACTIVITY COEFFICIENTS FROM FREEZING POINTS

For a two-component solution with solute (1) and solvent (0), the Gibbs-Duhem equation may be written

$$n_1\, d\mu_1 + n_0\, d\mu_0 = 0$$

Combination with Eq. (6.32) yields

$$n_1\, d \ln a_1 + n_0\, d \ln a_0 = 0$$

Equation (5.24) applies to an ideal solution. For a dilute, nonideal solution, we have instead

$$\frac{d \ln a_0}{dT} = \frac{\lambda}{RT^2}$$

The freezing point depression $\Delta T = T_0 - T$, and since $T^2 \approx T_0^2$,

$$-d \ln a_0 = \frac{\lambda}{RT_0^2}\, d(\Delta T)$$

Therefore,

$$d \ln a_1 = -\left(\frac{n_0}{n_1}\right) d \ln a_0 = \left(\frac{n_0}{n_1}\right)\left(\frac{\lambda}{RT_0^2}\right) d(\Delta T)$$

If M_0 is the molecular weight of solvent, we have in 1000 g of solvent:

$$n_0 = \frac{1000}{M_0}, \quad \frac{n_0}{n_1} = \frac{1000}{n_1 M_0}$$

Thus,
$$d \ln a_1 = \left(\frac{1000}{n_1 M_0}\right) \frac{\lambda}{RT_0^2} d(\Delta T) = \frac{1}{m_1 K} d(\Delta T)$$

Here K is the molal freezing point depression constant (p. 134), and the number of moles of (1) in 1000 g solvent is $n_1 = m_1$.

From Eq. (9.30),
$$a_1 = a_{\pm}^{\nu} = \gamma_{\pm}^{\nu} m^{\nu} (\nu_+^{\nu_+} \nu_-^{\nu_-})$$

so that,
$$d \ln a_{\pm} = d \ln \gamma_{\pm} m = d \ln \gamma_{\pm} + d \ln m = \frac{d(\Delta T)}{\nu m K} \tag{9.32}$$

Let $j = 1 - (\Delta T/\nu m K)$, whereupon,
$$dj = \frac{-d(\Delta T)}{\nu m K} + \left(\frac{\Delta T}{\nu K m^2}\right) dm$$

or,
$$\frac{d(\Delta T)}{\nu m K} = -dj + (1 - j) \frac{dm}{m}$$

By comparing this with Eq. (9.32), we have
$$d \ln \gamma_{\pm} = -dj - j\, d \ln m \tag{9.33}$$

As m approaches 0, the solution approaches ideality, and $\gamma_{\pm} \to 1$ while $j \to 0$. (Since for an ideal solution $\Delta T/\nu m K = 1$.) Therefore, on integration of Eq. (9.33), we obtain
$$\int_1^{\gamma_{\pm}} d \ln \gamma'_{\pm} = \int_0^m - j\, d \ln m' - \int_0^j dj'$$
$$\ln \gamma_{\pm} = -j - \int_0^m \left(\frac{j}{m'}\right) dm' \tag{9.34}$$

The integration in this expression can be carried out graphically from a series of measurements of the freezing point depression in solutions of low known concentrations. We plot j/m vs. m, extrapolate to zero concentration, and measure the area under the curve.

A similar treatment is applicable to osmotic-pressure data.

18. THE IONIC STRENGTH

Many properties of ionic solutions depend on the electrostatic interaction between the ionic charges. The electrostatic force between a pair of doubly charged ions would be four times the force between two ions carrying unit charge. A most useful function of ionic concentration was devised to include such effects of ionic charge. This function is called the *ionic strength* and is defined by
$$I = \tfrac{1}{2} \sum m_i z_i^2 \tag{9.35}$$

The summation is taken over all the different ions in a solution, multiplying the molality of each by the square of its charge.

For example, a 1.00 molal solution of NaCl would have an ionic strength $I = \frac{1}{2}(1.00) + \frac{1}{2}(1.00) = 1.00$. A 1.00 molal solution of $La_2(SO_4)_3$ would have

$$I = \tfrac{1}{2}[2(3)^2 + 3(2^2)] = 15.0$$

In dilute solutions, the activity coefficients of electrolytes, the solubilities of sparingly soluble salts, rates of ionic reactions, and other related properties become functions of the ionic strength.

If the molar concentration c is used instead of the molality m,

$$c = \frac{m\rho}{1 + (mM/1000)}$$

where ρ is the density of the solution and M is the molecular weight of the solute.

In dilute solution, this relation approaches

$$c = \rho_0 m$$

where ρ_0 is the density of the solvent.

Therefore,

$$I = \tfrac{1}{2}\sum m_i z_i^2 \approx \frac{1}{\rho_0}\,\tfrac{1}{2}\sum c_i z_i^2 \tag{9.36}$$

19. ACTIVITY COEFFICIENTS FROM SOLUBILITIES

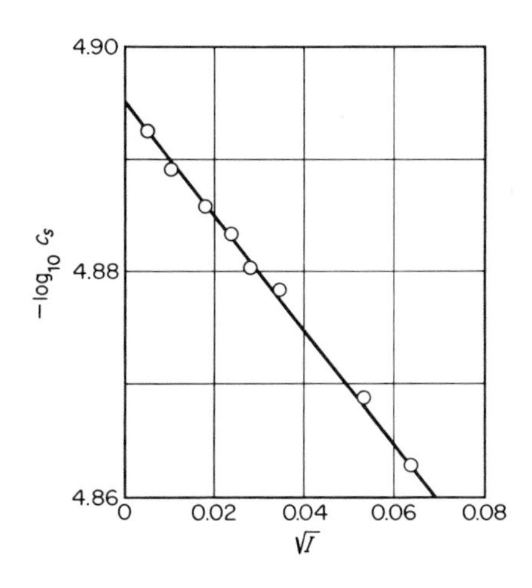

FIG. 9.9 Solubility of AgCl in aqueous KNO_3 at 25°C as a function of square root of the ionic strength.

This method, applicable to sparingly soluble salts, may be illustrated by the typical example of silver chloride, AgCl. For the solution of AgCl in water we may write: $AgCl \rightarrow Ag^+ + Cl^-$. The equilibrium constant becomes $K' = a_+a_-/a_s$ but since a_s is invariable for a pure solid phase, we usually write the so-called *solubility product constant* as

$$K_{sp} = a_{Ag}a_{Cl} = a_+a_- = \gamma_+\gamma_-c_+c_- \tag{9.37}$$

where c is the molar concentration. The solubility of AgCl is simply $c_s = c_+ = c_-$. The solubility product constant may therefore be written $K_{sp} = \gamma_\pm^2 c_s^2$, whence

$$\gamma_\pm = \frac{K_{sp}^{1/2}}{c_s} \tag{9.38}$$

Note that this is the activity coefficient in terms of molar concentrations. If we can find the constant K_{sp}, we can at once obtain activity coefficients from the measured solubilities c_s.

At infinite dilution, or zero concentration, the activity coefficient $\gamma_\pm$ approaches 1, and thus as the concentration approaches 0, c_s approaches $K_{sp}^{1/2}$. The procedure adopted is therefore to measure the solubility, of AgCl for example, in a series of solutions containing decreasing concentrations of an added electrolyte, such as KNO_3. If the logarithm of the solubility is plotted against the square root of ionic strength $I^{1/2}$, a good straight line is obtained. It is therefore possible to make an accurate extrapolation to $I = 0$ to obtain K_{sp}. In calculating I we must include the ions from both the dissolved AgCl and the added KNO_3.

Results from such experiments are plotted in Fig. 9.9. The extrapolated value of $\log c_s = -4.8952$. Thus $\log K_{sp}^{1/2} = -4.8952$ and $K_{sp} = 1.621 \times 10^{-10}$.

20. RESULTS OF ACTIVITY-COEFFICIENT MEASUREMENTS

Activity coefficients obtained by various methods* are summarized in Table 9.5 and plotted in Fig. 9.10. It will be noted that quite typically the coefficients decline markedly with increasing concentration in dilute solution, but then pass through minima and rise again in more concentrated solutions. The interpretation of this behavior constitutes one of the principal problems in the theory of strong electrolytes.

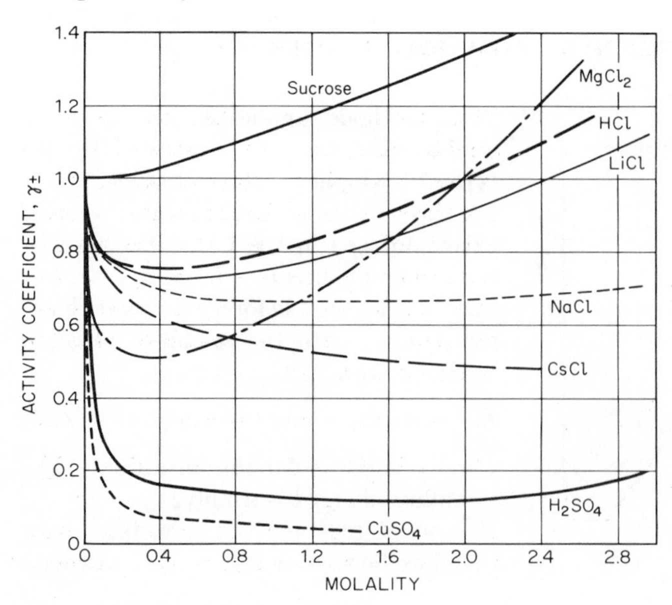

FIG. 9.10 Mean molal activity coefficients of electrolytes.

* An extensive tabulation was given by W. M. Latimer, *Oxidation Potentials* (New York: Prentice-Hall, 2nd ed., 1952).

TABLE 9.5 Mean Molal Activity Coefficients of Electrolytes

m	0.001	0.002	0.005	0.01	0.02	0.05	0.1	0.2	0.5	1.0	2.0	4.0
HCl	0.966	0.952	0.928	0.904	0.875	0.830	0.796	0.767	0.758	0.809	1.01	1.76
HNO_3	0.965	0.951	0.927	0.902	0.871	0.823	0.785	0.748	0.715	0.720	0.783	0.982
H_2SO_4	0.830	0.757	0.639	0.544	0.453	0.340	0.265	0.209	0.154	0.130	0.124	0.171
NaOH	—	—	—	—	—	0.82	—	0.73	0.69	0.68	0.70	0.89
$AgNO_3$	—	—	0.92	0.90	0.86	0.79	0.72	0.64	0.51	0.40	0.28	—
$CaCl_2$	0.89	0.85	0.785	0.725	0.66	0.57	0.515	0.48	0.52	0.71	—	—
$CuSO_4$	0.74	—	0.53	0.41	0.31	0.21	0.16	0.11	0.068	0.047	—	—
KCl	0.965	0.952	0.927	0.901	—	0.815	0.769	0.719	0.651	0.606	0.576	0.579
KBr	0.965	0.952	0.927	0.903	0.872	0.822	0.777	0.728	0.665	0.625	0.602	0.622
KI	0.965	0.951	0.927	0.905	0.88	0.84	0.80	0.76	0.71	0.68	0.69	0.75
LiCl	0.963	0.948	0.921	0.89	0.86	0.82	0.78	0.75	0.73	0.76	0.91	1.46
NaCl	0.966	0.953	0.929	0.904	0.875	0.823	0.780	0.730	0.68	0.66	0.67	0.78

For comparison, the activity coefficient of a typical nonelectrolyte, sucrose, is also shown in Fig. 9.10.

The effect of interionic forces is to decrease the chemical potential (free energy) of the solute and hence to decrease γ ($\mu = \mu^\circ + RT \ln \gamma m$). The effect of the ions on the solvent molecules is to hold the solvent more tightly in solution, thereby decreasing its vapor pressure or fugacity. This effect decreases the γ of the solvent, and conversely, as can be seen from the Gibbs–Duhem relation [Eq. (5.7)] it increases the γ of the solute. We can see therefore, in a general way, why the log γ vs. molality curves pass through minima. Actually, however, the effects in more concentrated solution are too complicated for any simple model.

21. THE DEBYE-HÜCKEL THEORY

The theory of Debye and Hückel is based on the assumption that strong electrolytes are completely dissociated into ions. Observed deviations from ideal behavior are then ascribed to electrical interactions between the ions. To obtain theoretically the equilibrium properties of the solutions, it is necessary to calculate the extra free energy arising from these electrostatic interactions.

If the ions were distributed completely at random, the chances of finding a positive or a negative ion in the neighborhood of a given ion would be identical. In such a random distribution there would be no electrostatic energy, since, on the average, attractive configurations would be exactly balanced by repulsive configurations. It is evident that this cannot be the physical situation, since in the immediate neighborhood of a positive ion, a negative ion is more likely to be found than another positive ion. Indeed, were it not for the fact that the ions are continually being batted about by molecular collisions, an ionic solution might acquire a well ordered structure similar to that of an ionic crystal. The thermal motions effectively prevent any complete ordering, but the final situation is a dynamic compromise between the electrostatic interactions tending to produce ordered configurations and the kinetic collisions tending to destroy them.

The electrolyte is assumed to be completely dissociated and all deviations from ideal behavior are ascribed to the electrical interactions. Our problem is to calculate the average electric potential U of a given ion in the solution due to all the other ions. Knowing U we can calculate the work that must be expended to charge the ions reversibly to this potential, and this work will be the free energy due to electrostatic interactions. The extra electric free energy is simply related to the ionic activity coefficient, since both are a measure of the deviation from ideality.

22. THE POISSON-BOLTZMANN EQUATION

The starting point in the calculation of the potential U is an expression for the average distribution of the ions, which we shall obtain in the next section. Let us call the average density of electric charge in any region of the solution σ, e.g., in units of esu per cc. Those conversant with electrical theory will recall that the potential U is related to σ by Poisson's differential equation. In the case of a spherically symmetric distribution of charges about a central ion, the potential U is a function only of r, the distance from the central ion. In this case Poisson's equation is*

$$\frac{1}{r^2}\frac{d}{dr}\left(r^2\frac{dU}{dr}\right) = \frac{4\pi\sigma}{\epsilon} \tag{9.39}$$

where ϵ is the dielectric constant.

On the average a given ion will be surrounded by a spherically symmetrical distribution of oppositely charged ions, forming the so-called *ionic atmosphere.* We wish to calculate the average electrostatic potential due to a central ion and its surrounding atmosphere. The solutions of Eq. (9.39) give the potential in any region as a function of the charge density σ. The next step is therefore to calculate σ for the array of ions.

The Boltzmann theorem (Sec. 7.18) informs us that if N_i is the average number of ions of kind i in unit volume in the solution, the number N'_i in any particular region of the solution whose potential energy is ϵ_p above the average is

$$N'_i = N_i e^{-\epsilon_p/kT}$$

If an ion of charge Q_i is brought to a region of potential U, its potential energy is Q_iU. For such ions the Boltzmann equation is therefore

$$N'_i = N_i e^{-Q_iU/kT} \tag{9.40}$$

The charge density in a region whose potential is U is simply the summation of this expression over the different kinds of ion that may be present in the solution, each multiplied by its appropriate charge Q_i.

$$\sigma = \sum N'_iQ_i = \sum N_iQ_i e^{-Q_iU/kT} \tag{9.41}$$

* A derivation is given in any book on "Electricity and Magnetism."

The Debye-Hückel treatment now considers a solution so dilute that ions will rarely be close together. This condition implies that the interionic potential energy is small, and indeed much less than the average thermal energy, so that $Q_iU \ll kT$. Then the exponential factor in Eq. (9.40) may be expanded as follows:

$$e^{-Q_iU/kT} = 1 - \frac{Q_iU}{kT} + \frac{1}{2!}\left(\frac{Q_iU}{kT}\right)^2 - \cdots$$

Terms higher than the second being negligible, Eq. (9.41) becomes

$$\sigma = \sum N_iQ_i - \frac{U}{kT}\sum N_iQ_i^2$$

The first term vanishes by virtue of the requirement of overall electrical neutrality, and with $Q_i = z_ie$,

$$\sigma = -\frac{e^2U}{kT}\sum N_iz_i^2 \tag{9.42}$$

It should be noted that $\sum N_iz_i^2$ is closely related to the *ionic strength*, which was defined as $I = \frac{1}{2}\sum m_iz_i^2$.

By substituting Eq. (9.42) into Eq. (9.39), there is obtained the Poisson-Boltzmann equation,

$$\frac{1}{r^2}\cdot\frac{d}{dr}\left(r^2\frac{dU}{dr}\right) = \frac{4\pi e^2U}{\epsilon kT}\sum N_iz_i^2$$

or,

$$\frac{d}{dr}\left(r^2\frac{dU}{dr}\right) = b^2r^2U \tag{9.43}$$

where,

$$b^2 = \frac{4\pi e^2}{\epsilon kT}\sum N_iz_i^2 \tag{9.44}$$

The quantity $1/b$ has the dimensions of a length, and is called the *Debye length.* It may be thought of as an approximate measure of the *thickness of the ionic atmosphere*, i.e., the distance over which the electrostatic field of an ion extends with appreciable strength. For example, in a one-molar aqueous solution of uniunivalent electrolyte at 25°C, $1/b = 3.1$ Å.

The Poisson-Boltzmann Equation (9.43) can be readily solved by making the substitution $u = rU$, whence $d^2u/dr^2 = b^2u$, so that

$$u = Ae^{-br} + Be^{br} \tag{9.45}$$

or

$$U = \frac{A}{r}e^{-br} + \frac{B}{r}e^{br}$$

A and B are constants of integration, to be determined from the boundary conditions. In the first place, U must vanish as r goes to infinity, so that

$$0 = \frac{Ae^{-\infty}}{\infty} + \frac{Be^{\infty}}{\infty}$$

This can be true only if $B = 0$, since the limit of e^r/r as r goes to infinity is not zero. We then have left,

$$U = \frac{A}{r} e^{-br} \equiv \frac{A}{r} \exp(-br)$$

The constant A can be determined by the fact that when $b = 0$, the concentration is zero, and therefore the potential is simply that of a single ion in the absence of any other charges, namely $U = ze/\epsilon r$. Thus $ze/\epsilon r = A/r$ and $A = ze/\epsilon$. Therefore the final solution becomes

$$U = \frac{ze}{\epsilon r} \exp(-br) \tag{9.46}$$

Once again, for the case of the very dilute solution (since b is a function of the concentration) the exponential may be expanded, giving

$$U = \frac{ze}{\epsilon r} \exp(-br) \approx \frac{ze}{\epsilon r}(1 - br)$$

$$U \approx \frac{ze}{\epsilon r} - \frac{zeb}{\epsilon} \tag{9.47}$$

Here it is evident that the first term $ze/\epsilon r$ is simply the potential at a distance r due to an ion of charge ze in a medium of dielectric constant ϵ. The term zeb/ϵ is then the potential due to the other ions, those forming the ionic atmosphere of the given ion. It is this extra potential that is related to the extra free energy of the ionic solution.

23. THE DEBYE-HÜCKEL LIMITING LAW

Let us imagine a given ion to be introduced into the solution in an uncharged state (this process requires negligible electrical energy). Then let us increase the charge Q gradually to its final value ze. The electrical energy required is

$$\Delta G = \int_0^{ze} U\, dQ = \int_0^{ze} \frac{-bQ}{\epsilon}\, dQ = -\frac{b}{2\epsilon} z^2e^2 \tag{9.48}$$

On the assumption that deviations of the dilute ionic solution from ideality are caused entirely by the electrical interactions, it can now be shown that this extra electric free energy per ion is simply $kT \ln \gamma_i$, where γ_i is the conventional ion activity coefficient. Let us write for the chemical potential of an ionic species i,

$$\mu_i = RT \ln a_i + \mu_i^\circ$$

$$\mu_i = \mu_i\,(\text{ideal}) + \mu_i\,(\text{electric})$$

Since

$$\mu_i\,(\text{ideal}) = RT \ln m_i + \mu_i^\circ$$

and

$$a_i = \gamma_i m_i$$

$$\mu_i \text{ (electric)} = RT \ln \gamma_i$$

This is the extra electric free energy per mole. The extra free energy per ion is therefore equal to $kT \ln \gamma_i$, but this is equal to the expression in Eq. (9.48). Therefore

$$\ln \gamma_i = -\frac{z_i^2 e^2 b}{2\epsilon kT} \tag{9.49}$$

We may substitute for b from Eq. (9.44),

$$b = \left(\frac{4\pi e^2}{\epsilon kT} \sum N_i z_i^2\right)^{1/2}$$

Since N_i (ions per cc) and c_i (moles per liter) are related by $N_i = c_i L/1000$,

$$b = \left(\frac{4\pi L^2 e^2}{1000\epsilon RT} \sum c_i z_i^2\right)^{1/2}$$

In the dilute solutions being considered, $c_i = m_i \rho_0$, where ρ_0 is the solvent density, so that the ionic strength, Eq. (9.35), may be introduced:

$$b = \left(\frac{8\pi L^2 e^2 \rho_0}{1000\epsilon RT}\right)^{1/2} I^{1/2} = BI^{1/2} \tag{9.50}$$

Since the individual ion activity coefficients cannot be measured, the mean activity coefficient is calculated in order to obtain an expression that can be compared with experimental data. From Eq. (9.27),

$$(\nu_+ + \nu_-) \ln \gamma_\pm = \nu_+ \ln \gamma_+ + \nu_- \ln \gamma_-$$

Therefore from Eq. (9.49),

$$\ln \gamma_\pm = -\left(\frac{\nu_+ z_+^2 + \nu_- z_-^2}{\nu_+ + \nu_-}\right) \frac{e^2 b}{2\epsilon kT}$$

Since $|\nu_+ z_+| = |\nu_- z_-|$,

$$\ln \gamma_\pm = -|z_+ z_-| \left(\frac{e^2 b}{2\epsilon kT}\right) \tag{9.51}$$

The valence factor can be evaluated as follows for the different electrolyte types:

Type	*Example*	*Ionic Charges*	*Valence factor* $\lvert z_+ z_- \rvert$
uniunivalent	NaCl	$z_+ = 1,\ z_- = -1$	1
unibivalent	$MgCl_2$	$z_+ = 2,\ z_- = -1$	2
unitrivalent	$LaCl_3$	$z_+ = 3,\ z_- = -1$	3
bibivalent	$MgSO_4$	$z_+ = 2,\ z_- = -2$	4
bitrivalent	$Fe_2(SO_4)_3$	$z_+ = 3,\ z_- = -2$	6

Let us now transform Eq. (9.51) into base-10 logarithms and introduce the values of the universal constants. If e is taken as 4.80×10^{-10} esu, R must be 8.31×10^7 erg per °C mole. The result is the Debye-Hückel *limiting law* for the activity coefficient,

$$\log \gamma_\pm = -1.825 \times 10^6 |z_+z_-| \left(\frac{I\rho_0}{\epsilon^3 T^3} \right)^{1/2} = -A|z_+z_-|I^{1/2} \tag{9.52}$$

For water at 25°C, $\epsilon = 78.54$, $\rho_0 = 0.997$, and the equation becomes

$$\log \gamma_\pm = -0.509|z_+z_-|I^{1/2} \tag{9.53}$$

In the derivation of the limiting law it was consistently assumed that the analysis applied only to dilute solutions. It is not to be expected therefore that the equation should hold for concentrated solutions, nor does it. As solutions become more and more dilute, however, the equation should represent the experimental data more and more closely. This expectation has been fulfilled by numerous measurements, so that the Debye-Hückel theory for very dilute solutions may be considered to be well substantiated.

For example, in Fig. 9.11 some experimental activity coefficients are plotted against the square roots of the ionic strengths. These data were obtained by applying the solubility method to sparingly soluble complex salts in the presence of added salts such as NaCl, $BaCl_2$, KNO_3. The straight lines indicate the theoretical curves predicted by the limiting law, and it is evident that these limiting slopes are followed at low ionic strengths.

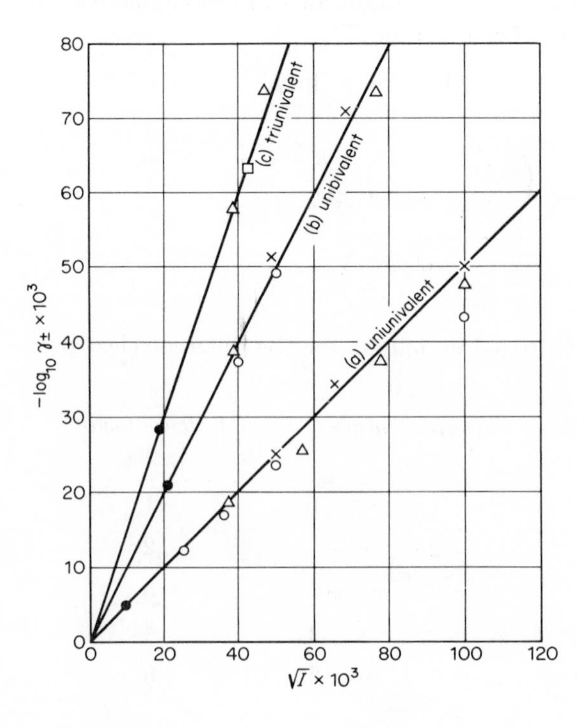

FIG. 9.11 Activity coefficients of sparingly soluble salts in salt solutions [after Bronsted and LaMer, *J. Am. Chem. Soc. 46*, 555 (1924)].

Another successful experimental test has been the measurement of activity coefficients for the same electrolyte in solvents with various dielectric constants.*

24. THEORY OF MORE CONCENTRATED SOLUTIONS

It would of course be desirable to have a theory that could be applied to solutions more concentrated than those for which the D-H treatment is valid, solutions usually so dilute that they have been uncharitably called slightly contaminated distilled water. Like the general theory of liquids, this is one of the major unsolved problems in physical chemistry, for when the assumption of extreme dilution is abandoned, the mathematics become complex.

A real difficulty in all these problems is to obtain any kind of clear cut answer to the question "what do we mean by degree of dissociation in an electrolyte?" There is no such difficulty in a gas such as $N_2O_4 \rightleftarrows 2\,NO_2$. When an N_2O_4 molecule dissociates into two NO_2 molecules, the NO_2 on the average will exist for a considerable time (order of seconds) before recombining with another NO_2 to reform N_2O_4. During this time the NO_2 travels freely through the gas for a mile or so in a zigzag path with collisions. Most of the time it is either definitely dissociated or definitely associated. All measurements made on the gas (density, absorption spectra, heat capacity, etc.) give the same value for the degree of dissociation.

In the case of a molecule such as HNO_3 in water, the situation is different in two important respects. The dissociation of the molecule to give H^+ (hydrated) and NO_3^- requires the separation of the oppositely charged ions. The electrostatic attraction between these two ions decreases relatively slowly as they separate, so that some kind of association still exists between them even when they are several molecular diameters apart. Also, the rates of dissociation and reformation of molecules or complexes from ions in solution are extraordinarily high. Thus the mean lifetime of a complex or of a dissociated ion may be only of the order 10^{-10} sec instead of one second as in a gas. In this short time few ions can become really free, and the most likely step after they separate is an almost immediate re-association. Therefore, one method that gives a value for the degree of dissociation of HNO_3 in solution may yield a result quite different from an independent measurement by a second method. For example, in more concentrated solutions the Raman spectra reveal bands for both HNO_3 and NO_3^-. We could calculate a degree of dissociation from the intensities of these bands,† but we would get a different value from a measurement of osmotic pressure or conductance. X-ray studies of concentrated ionic solutions can give direct information about ionic association.†† Fig. 9.12 shows some results obtained from a

* H. S. Harned et al., *J. Am. Chem. Soc. 61*, 49 (1939).

† The dissociation constant for HNO_3 at 25°C, $K_a = [a(H^+)a(NO_3^-)]/a(HNO_3)$ is calculated as $K_a = 21.4$ from the spectral data. See O. Redlich, *Chem. Rev. 39*, 333 (1946).

†† G. W. Brady, *J. Chem. Phys. 33*, 1079 (1960).

concentrated solution of erbium chloride. There is a firmly held octahedral arrangement of H_2O molecules about the Er^{+3} ion, and definite Er^{+3}—$(Cl^-)_2$ ion pairs.

The *ionic association theory* for more concentrated solutions has been developed independently by N. Bjerrum and by R. M. Fuoss and C. Kraus. They consider that definite though transient *ion pairs* are brought together by electrostatic attraction. The formation of pairs will be greater the lower the dielectric constant of the solvent and the smaller the ionic radii, both of these factors tending to increase the electrostatic attractions.

The degree of association may become appreciable even in a solvent of high dielectric constant ϵ, such as water. Bjerrum has calculated that in one-molar aqueous solution uniunivalent ions having a diameter of 2.82 Å are 13.8 per cent associated; of 1.76 Å, 28.6 per cent associated. For solvents of lower ϵ the association would be still greater. Such association into ion pairs would lower the value of the ionic activity coefficients.

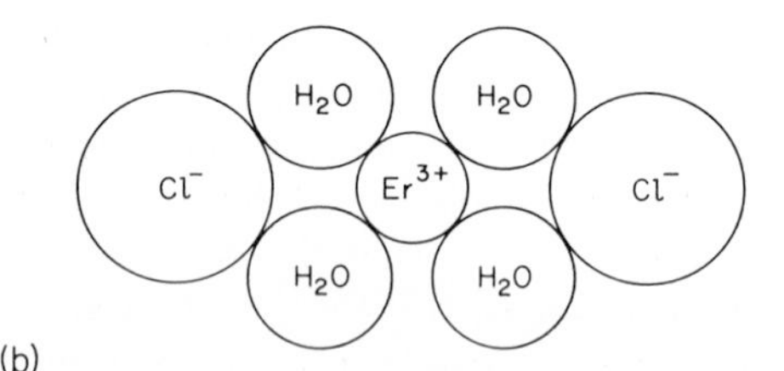

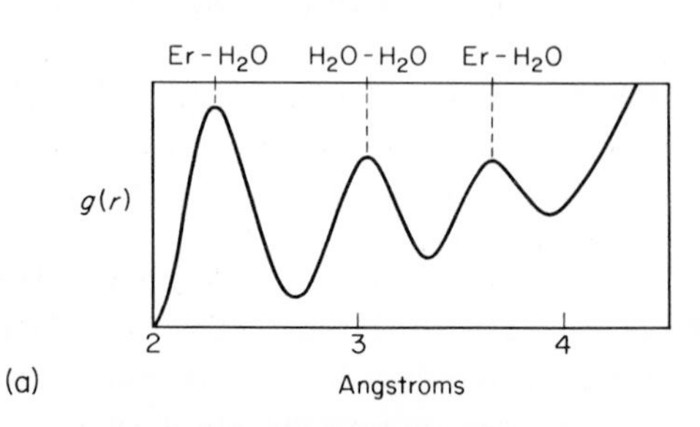

FIG. 9.12 (a) X-ray radial distribution curves (cf. Sec. 17.3). Results of X-ray diffraction of concentrated $ErCl_3$ solutions. (b) Planar model of solution around Er^{3+} ion. There are also H_2O molecules above and below Er^{3+} to give octahedral complex.

There are two other factors, not considered in the D-H treatment, that tend to become important in concentrated solutions. One is the effect of repulsive forces between ions at close distances of approach, called the *ionic size effect*. It is analogous to the b factor in the van der Waals equation, and cuts down the electrostatic interactions by preventing very close approaches between charges. In the derivation of the limiting law, Eq. (9.52), it was assumed that the ions were point charges. Debye and Hückel made an improved theory which took into account the finite sizes of the ions. The resulting expression for the mean activity coefficient is

$$\log \gamma_{\pm} = \frac{-A|z_+z_-|I^{1/2}}{1 + BdI^{1/2}} \tag{9.54}$$

where B and A have the same significance as in Eqs. (9.50) and (9.52), and d is the *average effective diameter* of the ions. The product Bd is usually close to unity.

Probably of greater importance is the effect of the ions on the solvent molecules. It is known from transference experiments that ions in solution are solvated, especially in polar solvents like water. This is confirmed by the well known *salting-out effect*, by which added electrolytes decrease the solubility of nonelectrolytes. Some of the solvent molecules appear to be held so tightly by the ions that they are not able to participate in the solution of neutral solutes. For example, the solubility (25°C) of diethyl ether in pure water is 0.91 mole per liter, but in 15 per cent sodium-chloride solution it is reduced to 0.13 mole per liter.

25. THEORY OF CONDUCTIVITY

The interionic attraction theory was also applied by Debye and Hückel to the electric conductivity of solutions. An improved theory was given by Lars Onsager (1926–1928). The calculation of the conductivity is a difficult problem, and we shall content ourselves with a qualitative discussion.*

Under the influence of an electric field an ion moves through a solution not in a straight line, but in a series of zigzag steps similar to those of Brownian motion. The persistent effect of the potential difference ensures an average drift of the ions in the field direction.

Opposing the electric force on the ion is first of all the frictional drag of the solvent. Although the solvent is not a continuous medium, Stokes's Law is frequently used to estimate this effect (cf. p. 338 and Walden's rule). Since the molecules of solvent and the ions are about the same size, it is more likely that the ion moves by jumping from one "hole" to another in the liquid.

In addition to this *viscous effect*, two important electrical effects must be considered. As shown in (a), Fig. 9.13, an ion in any static position is surrounded by an ionic atmosphere of opposite charge. If the ion jumps to a new position, it will tend to drag with it this oppositely charged aura. The ionic atmosphere, however, has a certain inertia, and cannot instantaneously readjust itself to the new position of its central ion. Thus around a moving ion the atmosphere becomes asymmetric, as in (b), Fig. 9.13. Behind the ion there is a net accumulation of opposite charge, which exerts an electrostatic drag, decreasing the ionic velocity in the field direction. This retardation is called the *asymmetry effect*. It will obviously be greater at higher ionic concentrations.

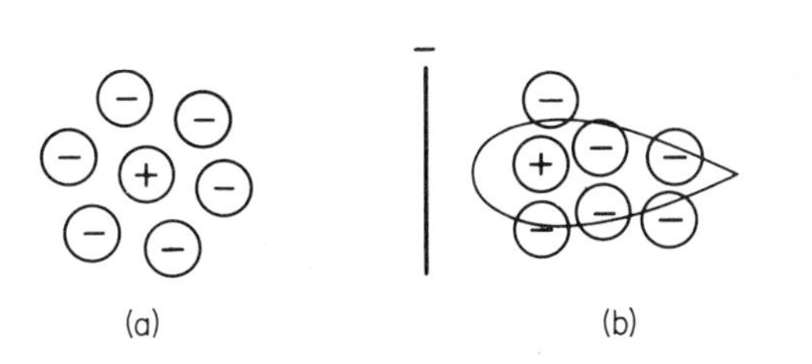

FIG. 9.13 (a) Ionic atmosphere of ion at rest; (b) asymmetric cloud around moving ion.

A second electrical action that lowers the mobility of the ions is called the *electrophoretic effect*. The ions comprising the atmosphere around a given central ion are themselves moving, on the average in the opposite direction, under the influence of the applied field. Since they are solvated, they tend to carry along

* See H. S. Harned and B. B. Owen, *The Physical Chemistry of Electrolytic Solutions* (New York: Reinhold, 1958).

with them their associated solvent molecules, so that there is a net flow of solvent in a direction opposite to the motion of any given (solvated) central ion, which is thus forced to "swim upstream" against this current.

The steady state of motion of an ion can be found by equating the electric driving force to the sum of the frictional, asymmetric, and electrophoretic retardations. Onsager calculated each of the terms in this relationship, and thereby obtained a theoretical equation for the equivalent conductivity of a uni-univalent electrolyte in the limiting case of dilute solutions:

$$\Lambda = \Lambda_0 - \left[\frac{82.48}{(\epsilon T)^{1/2}\eta} + \frac{8.20 \times 10^5}{(\epsilon T)^{3/2}}\Lambda_0\right] c^{1/2} \tag{9.55}$$

Here c is the concentration of *ionized* electrolyte in moles per liter. If dissociation is not complete it must be calculated from the degree of dissociation α. Similar equations were derived for electrolytes of other valence types.*

The Onsager equations provide good agreement with the experimental conductivity data at low concentrations. Their range of validity is greater for uniunivalent electrolytes than for those whose ions bear higher charges, but as limiting laws they hold at extreme dilutions for all valence types. In more concentrated solutions marked deviations from the Onsager equations are found, so that we may even obtain equivalent conductivity vs. concentration curves like that in Fig. 9.14. The minima in such curves are explained by the ionic association theory.† The ion pairs $(+-)$ are electrically neutral and do not

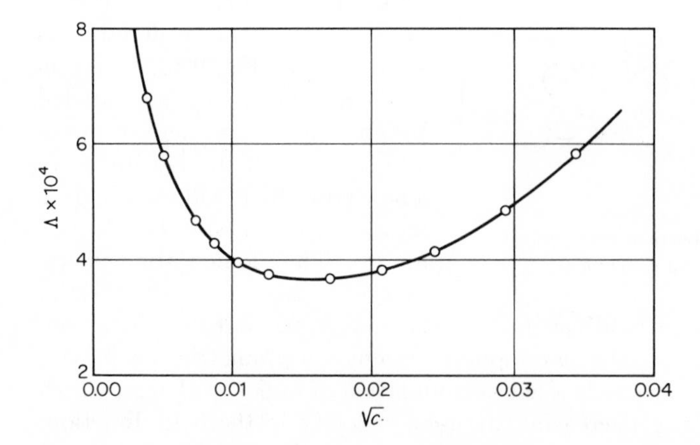

FIG. 9.14 Conductance of tetraisoamyl-ammonium nitrate in dioxane-water. [Fuoss and Kraus, *J. Am. Chem. Soc.* 55, 2387 (1933)].

contribute to the equivalent conductivity, which therefore falls as more pairs are formed. As the solution becomes still more concentrated, triple ions, either $(+ - +)$ or $(- + -)$, begin to be formed from some of the pairs, and since

* See S. Glasstone, *Introduction to Electrochemistry* (New York: Van Nostrand, 1942), p. 89.
† R. Fuoss and C. Kraus, *J. Am. Chem. Soc.* *55*, 21 (1933).

these triplets bear a net charge, they contribute to the conductivity, which therefore increases from its minimum value. The quantitative theory of these effects has not yet been worked out, although progress is being made.*

Further confirmation of the essential correctness of the Debye-Hückel-Onsager picture is obtained from two interesting effects occurring in conductivity measurements. The *Debye-Falkenhagen effect* is observed when conductivities are studied at high a-c frequencies, of the order of 3×10^6 cycles per sec. As the frequency of the electric field is increased, a point is eventually reached at which the ionic atmosphere no longer can follow the rapidly changing field. Then the ions move practically independently of one another as the influence of their atmospheres becomes unimportant. Thus at high enough frequencies an increase in the conductivity of a solution is expected, and has been actually observed. A second support for the ionic atmosphere model is found in the *Wien effect.* At sufficiently high field strengths, of the order of 10^5 volts per cm, the conductivity increases. With these large fields the velocities of the ions become so high that the ionic atmospheres are left behind entirely, and the ions move independently.

26. ACIDS AND BASES

The concepts *acid* and *base* have had a long and interesting share in the history of chemistry. The distinctive behavior of these substances has always presented a challenge to theoretical interpretation.

Arrhenius defined an acid as a compound that dissociated in solution to yield a hydrogen ion, and a base as a compound yielding a hydroxyl ion. Then the process of neutralization was simply $H^+ + OH^- \rightarrow H_2O$. These definitions relied exclusively on the phenomena observed in aqueous solutions, and it was evident that they would have to be broadened in some way.

In 1922–1923, J. N. Bronsted and M. Lowry advanced a new set of criteria. They defined an acid as any compound that can lose a proton, and a base as any compound that can accept a proton. Thus,

$$\underset{\text{acid}}{A} \rightleftarrows \underset{\text{proton}}{H^+} + \underset{\text{base}}{B}$$

The compound B was called the *conjugate base* of the acid A. Some examples would be

$$HAc \rightarrow H^+ + Ac^-$$

$$NH_4^+ \rightarrow H^+ + NH_3$$

Bases and acids might be either neutral molecules or ions.

* J. C. Poirier and J. H. DeLap, *J. Chem. Phys. 35*, 213 (1961).

The free proton probably never occurs in solution, the solvent itself acting as a proton acceptor — in other words, as a base. Therefore, the typical reactions should be written in the symmetrical form:

Acid (I)	+	*Base (II)*	→	*Acid (II)*	+	*Base (I)*
HAc	+	H_2O	→	OH_3^+	+	Ac^-
NH_4^+	+	H_2O	→	OH_3^+	+	NH_3
H_2O	+	CN^-	→	HCN	+	OH^-

Note that, depending on its partner, a compound, such as water in these examples, can act either as an acid or as a base. The similarity between the ammonium ion, NH_4^+, and the hydronium ion, OH_3^+, is apparent.

We find an interesting application of the Bronsted concept in the study of a series of strong acids: $HClO_4$, HNO_3, HBr, HCl, etc. In aqueous solution these acids are all about equally strong. That is to say, the equilibrium, $HX + H_2O \rightleftarrows OH_3^+ + X^-$, lies in every case extremely far to the right, mainly owing to the large hydration energy of the proton. When the acids are dissolved in glacial acetic acid, distinct differences in their strengths become apparent. Then the equilibria are: $HX + CH_3COOH \rightleftarrows CH_3COOH_2^+ + X^-$. The acetic-acid molecule is not anxious to accept a proton, and only when the other acid is a particularly insistent donor does the equilibrium lie sufficiently toward the right to produce a considerable number of ions. In a 0.005 molar solution in glacial acetic acid the equivalent conductivity of $HClO_4$ is more than fifty times that of HNO_3. It is therefore evident that $HClO_4$ is a much stronger acid than HNO_3, once the *leveling effect* of a solvent like water is eliminated.*

The Bronsted picture still does not represent the full generality of acid–base phenomena. Further investigations in nonaqueous solutions, notably by C. A. Kraus and E. C. Franklin, revealed that familiar acid–base properties could be displayed by solutions that contained no protons at all. For example, the following typical neutralization reaction can be followed in chlorobenzene solution with crystal violet as an indicator:

$$\underset{\text{acid}}{BCl_3} + \underset{\text{base}}{(C_2H_5)_3N} \longrightarrow (C_2H_5)_3N : BCl_3$$

The indicator is yellow in the presence of excess acid, and violet in basic solutions.

In 1923, G. N. Lewis advanced a new concept of acids and bases derived from the electronic theory of valence. This generalized theory is indeed so broad that it removes the problem from the confines of the chemistry of ions into the domain of the formation of covalent bonds. Lewis defined an acid as a substance that can accept a pair of electrons from a donor substance, the base. The process called *neutralization* is therefore the formation of a covalent bond in which both electrons of the shared pair are provided by the base. It may be recalled that this is the type of bond that has been called the *dative bond* or the *coordinate link*.

* I. M. Kolthoff and A. Willman, *J. Am. Chem. Soc. 56*, 1007 (1934).

For example:

$$\mathrm{H^+ + :\ddot{\underset{..}{O}}:H^- \rightarrow H:\ddot{\underset{..}{O}}:H}$$

$$\begin{array}{ccc} \mathrm{Cl} & \mathrm{H} & \mathrm{Cl\,H} \\ \mathrm{Cl:\ddot{\underset{..}{B}} + :\ddot{\underset{..}{N}}:H} & \rightarrow & \mathrm{Cl:\ddot{\underset{..}{B}}:\ddot{\underset{..}{N}}:H} \\ \mathrm{Cl} & \mathrm{H} & \mathrm{Cl\,H} \end{array}$$

acid + base → covalent compound

The close relationship between acid–base and oxidation–reduction reactions is now evident. Both acids and oxidizing agents tend to accept electrons. They are said to be *electrophilic* or electron-loving reagents. An acid accepts a share in a pair of electrons held by a base, forming a coordinate covalent bond. An oxidizing agent accepts electrons provided by a reducing agent, but keeps them all to itself instead of sharing them with the donor. Bases and reducing agents are called *electrodotic* or electron-giving reagents.

The same reactant can display either acid–base or oxidation–reduction properties depending upon its reaction partner. Thus the sulfide ion behaves as a base toward water:

$$\mathrm{:\ddot{\underset{..}{S}}:^= + 2\,H:\ddot{\underset{..}{O}}:H \rightarrow H:\ddot{\underset{..}{S}}:H + 2\,:\ddot{\underset{..}{O}}:H^-}$$

On the other hand, it behaves as a reductant toward an oxidizing agent like ferric ion:

$$\mathrm{:\ddot{\underset{..}{S}}:^= + 2\,Fe^{+++} \rightarrow :\underset{..}{S}: + 2\,Fe^{++}}$$

27. DISSOCIATION CONSTANTS OF ACIDS AND BASES

A typical acid HA reacts as follows when dissolved in water: $HA + H_2O \rightarrow OH_3^+ + A^-$. The equilibrium constant may be written:

$$K_a' = \frac{a_{OH_3^+} a_{A^-}}{a_{HA} a_{H_2O}}$$

If the solution is dilute, the activity of the water a_{H_2O} may be taken to be the same as its concentration c, which will effectively be a constant equal to the number of moles of water in one liter. This constant may be divided out of the equilibrium constant K_a' to give the simpler expression:

$$K_a = \frac{a_{OH_3^+} a_{A^-}}{a_{HA}}$$

For a base B, the reaction is $B + H_2O \rightarrow BH^+ + OH^-$. The equilibrium constant becomes

$$K_b = \frac{a_{BH^+} a_{OH^-}}{a_B}$$

These constants, K_a and K_b, are sometimes called the *dissociation constants* for the acid and base, and they provide a measure of their strengths. The constants can be obtained from conductance measurements or by measurements of hydrogen-ion concentrations combined with appropriate activity coefficients. The hydrogen-ion concentration can be measured colorimetrically with *indicators*, but more precise values are obtained by potentiometric methods that will be described later.

Let us write, using the notation H^+ instead of OH_3^+,

$$K_a = \frac{c_{H^+}c_{A^-}}{c_{HA}} \cdot \frac{\gamma_{H^+}\gamma_{A^-}}{\gamma_{HA}}$$

In dilute solution the molecule HA, being uncharged and therefore not subject to electrical interactions, may be assigned an activity coefficient of unity. Then

$$K_a = \left(\frac{c_{H^+}c_{A^-}}{c_{HA}}\right) \gamma_{H^+}\gamma_{A^-}$$

From the Ostwald dilution law,* Eq. (9.11), this would become

$$K_a = \frac{\alpha^2 c}{(1 - \alpha)} (\gamma_{H^+}\gamma_{A^-})$$

with $\alpha = \Lambda/\Lambda_0$. Thus we can evaluate the constant K_a by combining conductivities in dilute solution with suitable activity coefficients obtained either experimentally or from the Debye-Hückel theory.

Some measured constants for acids and bases are summarized in Table 9.6, in the form of pK_a or pK_b values. By analogy with the definition of pH, $pK = -\log K$.

TABLE 9.6 Dissociation of Acids and Bases in Water Solution at 25°C*

Acids	pK_a	Bases	pK_b
Formic	3.752	Ammonia	4.77
Acetic	4.756	Methylamine	3.36
Propionic	4.874	Aniline	9.39
Trimethylacetic	5.05	Methylaniline	9.70
Chloroacetic	2.861	Pyridine	8.80
Benzoic	4.20	Diphenylamine	13.16
p-Nitrobenzoic	3.43	Piperidine	2.88
Phenol	9.50		

Dibasic Acids	pK_{a1}	pK_{a2}
Oxalic	1.30	4.286
Carbonic	6.35	10.25
Hydrogen Sulfide	7.2	11.9
Phthalic	2.89	5.42
Maleic	2.00	6.27

* H. S. Harned and B. B. Owen, *Chem. Rev.*, *25*, 31 (1939); J. F. J. Dippy, *ibid.*, 151.

* More exact methods are based on the Onsager conductivity theory. See Glasstone, *op. cit.*, pp. 163–169.

For an acid and its conjugate base we have the relationship

$$K_a K_b = K_s \tag{9.56}$$

where K_s is the dissociation constant of the solvent. For example, consider acetic acid HAc and its conjugate base Ac^-:

$$HAc + H_2O \longrightarrow OH_3^+ + Ac^-$$

$$Ac^- + H_2O \longrightarrow OH^- + HAc$$

Then,

$$K_a K_b = \frac{a_{OH_3^+} a_{Ac^-}}{a_{HAc}} \cdot \frac{a_{OH^-} a_{HAc}}{a_{Ac^-}} = a_{OH_3^+} a_{OH^-} = K_w$$

K_w is the dissociation constant of the solvent water.

The value of K_w can be calculated from the measurements of Kohlrausch and Heydweiller* on the conductivity of pure water, summarized in Table 9.7 at various temperatures. The degree of dissociation α is calculated from the relation $\alpha = \Lambda/\Lambda_0$, Λ_0 being the sum of the equivalent ionic conductivities of H^+ and OH^- at infinite dilution. From Table 9.3 this sum at 25° is $349.8 + 198.0 = 547.8$. From Eq. (9.5), $\Lambda = \kappa/c^\star$, where $c^\star$ is the number of moles of water in one cc, 0.0553. Thus $\Lambda = 0.062 \times 10^{-6}/0.0553 = 1.05 \times 10^{-6}$. Since the ionic concentrations are very low, the activity coefficients may be taken as unity, so that $K_w = c_{H^+} c_{OH^-} = \alpha^2 c_w^2$, where c_w is the number of moles of liquid water in one liter. The calculated ion products are included in Table 9.7. At 25°, $K_w \approx 10^{-14}$, so that the hydrogen ion concentration $c_{H^+} \approx 10^{-7}$ moles per liter, or the pH ≈ 7.

TABLE 9.7 CONDUCTIVITY AND ION PRODUCT OF WATER

Temperature, °C	0	18	25	34	50
Conductivity, κ ohm^{-1} cm^{-1} $\times 10^6$	0.015	0.043	0.062	0.095	0.187
$10^{14} \cdot K_w = (c_{H^+} c_{OH^-}) \cdot 10^{14}$	0.12	0.61	1.04	2.05	5.66

When an acid and base are mixed, neutralization occurs, but except in the case of strong acids and bases, i.e., those for which dissociation is essentially complete, the compound formed may react with the solvent. This process is called *solvolysis*, or in the special case of water, *hydrolysis*. For a compound BA in water:

$$BA + H_2O \rightleftharpoons HA + BOH$$

The *hydrolysis constant* is

$$K_h' = \frac{a_{HA} a_{BOH}}{a_{BA} a_{H_2O}}, \quad \text{or} \quad K_h = \frac{a_{HA} a_{BOH}}{a_{BA}} \tag{9.57}$$

* *Z. physik. Chem. 14*, 317 (1894).

It can easily be shown that the hydrolysis constants are related to the dissociation constants as follows:

$$\begin{aligned}
&\text{Salt of weak acid and strong base: } K_h = K_w/K_a \\
&\text{Salt of weak base and strong acid: } K_h = K_w/K_b \qquad (9.58) \\
&\text{Salt of weak base and strong acid: } K_h = K_w/K_aK_b
\end{aligned}$$

28. IONIC EQUILIBRIA

The theory of ionic equilibria is essentially the algebraic problem of determining the concentrations of the various ionic and molecular species from the solution of sets of simultaneous equations. A simple example will be given, from which a set of general rules can be formulated.

Example: What is the $[H^+]$ in 0.1 M aqueous acetic acid? We shall use concentrations instead of activities, but if we know the activity coefficients, the treatment in terms of activities is just as straightforward. For simplicity we write X for [X] the concentration of X.

Unknowns		*Equations*	*Basis*
H^+	(1)	$[H^+][OH^-] = K_w$	Equilibria
OH^-	(2)	$[H^+][Ac^-]/[HAc] = K_a$	
Ac^-	(3)	$c = 0.1 = [HAc] + [Ac^-]$	Stoichiometry
HAc	(4)	$[H^+] = [Ac^-] + [OH^-]$	Electroneutrality

The first equation implies that $a_{H_2O} = 1$. Thus we have four equations and four unknowns. In more complex examples, the equations of stoichiometry and electroneutrality may be quite long, while the equations of equilibrium are short. Hence we eliminate the variables from the former by means of the latter. Thus, Eqs. (3) and (4) become

$$(5) \qquad c = \left(\frac{H^+}{K_a} + 1\right) Ac^-$$

$$(6) \qquad H^+ - \frac{K_w}{H^+} = Ac^-$$

We then eliminate Ac^-, obtaining

$$(7) \qquad c = \left(\frac{H^+}{K_a} + 1\right)(H^+ - OH^-)$$

Such an equation is best solved by judicious trial approximations. Since $H^+ > OH^-$, $H^+ = 10^{-3}$ is a reasonable first trial. For $c = 0.1$ mole l^{-1} and $K_a = 1.8 \times 10^{-5}$ mole l^{-1} at 25°C, this gives

$$c = \left(\frac{10^{-3}}{1.8 \times 10^{-5}} + 1\right)(10^{-3} - 10^{-11})$$

Evidently $H^+ \gg OH^-$, and $H^+/K_a \gg 1$. Therefore a very good approximation is obtained from

$$0.1 = (H^+)^2/1.8 \times 10^{-5}$$

or

$$H^+ = (cK_a)^{1/2} = 1.3 \times 10^{-3}$$

The procedure can be formulated in a set of rules:

(1) Write out the equations for the equilibrium constants of the acids in the system, including K_w.

(2) Write out the equations giving known stoichiometric conditions.

(3) Equate the sums of concentrations of negative and positive ions.

(4) Solve the equations, making use of judicious approximations based on chemical knowledge and intuition gained by practice.

A more complex example will now be given, the salt of a weak acid and a weak base. Let us consider ammonium formate, B^+A^-, with $K_a = 1.8 \times 10^{-4}$ and $K_b = 1.8 \times 10^{-5}$ at 25°C. The equations are:

Unknowns		*Equations*
A^-	(1)	$K_w = H^+OH^-$
B^+	(2)	$K_a = H^+A^-/HA$
HA	(3)	$K_b = B^+OH^-/BOH$
BOH	(4)	$c = A^- + HA$
H^+	(5)	$c = BOH + B^+$
OH^-	(6)	$H^+ + B^+ = OH^- + A^-$

From (2) and (4), $A^- = cK_a/(K_a + H^+)$ and from (3) and (5), $B^+ = cK_b/$-$(K_b + OH^-)$. Thus (6) becomes

$$H^+ + \frac{cK_b}{K_b + OH^-} = OH^- + \frac{cK_a}{K_a + H^+}$$

This can be rearranged to

$$H^+\left[1 + \frac{c}{K_a + H^+}\right] = OH^-\left[1 + \frac{c}{K_b + OH^-}\right]$$

After Eq. (1) is applied, this equation can be solved by trial. A convenient form is

$$(7) \qquad H^+ = K_w^{1/2}\left(\frac{\dfrac{1}{c} + \dfrac{1}{K_b + OH^-}}{\dfrac{1}{c} + \dfrac{1}{K_a + H^+}}\right)^{1/2}$$

An approximate solution that is often valid arises when $K_b \gg OH^-$, $K_a \gg H^+$, and $c \gg K_a$ or K_b. In this case

$$(8) \qquad H^+ = \left(\frac{K_wK_a}{K_b}\right)^{1/2}$$

29. KINETICS OF IONIC REACTIONS—SALT EFFECTS

Electrostatic interactions cause the equilibrium properties of ionic solutions to deviate greatly from ideality. The same causes are responsible for a number of unusual features in the kinetics of reactions between ions. The first effective treatment of these reactions was provided by J. N. Bronsted and N. Bjerrum in their *activity-rate theory*. Proposed in 1922, this is essentially an activated-complex theory applied to charged particles.

Consider a reaction between two ions, A^{z_A} and B^{z_B}, z_A and z_B being the ionic charges. It proceeds through an activated complex, $(AB)^{z_A+z_B}$.

$$A^{z_A} + B^{z_B} \longrightarrow (AB)^{z_A+z_B} \longrightarrow \text{products}$$

Example: $$Fe^{3+} + I^- \longrightarrow (Fe{-}I)^{2+} \longrightarrow Fe^{2+} + \tfrac{1}{2}I_2$$

The complex is considered to be in equilibrium with reactants, but since we are dealing with ions, it is necessary to express the equilibrium constant in activities rather than concentrations:

$$K^\ddagger = \frac{a^\ddagger}{a_A a_B} = \frac{c^\ddagger}{c_A c_B} \cdot \frac{\gamma^\ddagger}{\gamma_A \gamma_B}$$

The a's and γ's are the activities and activity coefficients. The concentration of activated complexes is $c^\ddagger = c_A c_B K^\ddagger(\gamma_A \gamma_B)/\gamma^\ddagger$.

The reaction rate is $-(dc_A/dt) = k_2 c_A c_B = (kT/h)c^\ddagger$. The rate constant is

$$k_2 = \frac{kT}{h} K^\ddagger \frac{\gamma_A \gamma_B}{\gamma^\ddagger} = \frac{kT}{h} \cdot \frac{\gamma_A \gamma_B}{\gamma^\ddagger} e^{\Delta S^\ddagger/R} e^{-\Delta H^\ddagger/RT} \tag{9.59}$$

In dilute aqueous solution the activity-coefficient terms can be estimated from the Debye-Hückel theory. From Eq. (9.53), at 25°C in an aqueous solution, $\log_{10} \gamma_i = -0.509 z_i^2 I^{1/2}$. Taking the $\log_{10}$ of Eq. (9.59) and substituting the Debye-Hückel expression, we get

$$\log_{10} k_2 = \log_{10} \frac{kT}{h} K^\ddagger + \log_{10} \frac{\gamma_A \gamma_B}{\gamma^\ddagger}$$

$$= B + [-0.509 z_A^2 - 0.509 z_B^2 + 0.509(z_A + z_B)^2] I^{1/2}$$

$$\log_{10} k_2 = B + 1.018\, z_A z_B\, I^{1/2} \tag{9.60}$$

The constant $\log_{10} (kT/h)K^\ddagger$ has been written as B.

The Bronsted equation (9.60) predicts that the plot of $\log_{10} k_2$ vs. the square root of the ionic strength should be a straight line. For a water solution at 25°C the slope is nearly equal to $z_A z_B$, the product of the ionic charges. Three special cases can occur:

(1) If z_A and z_B have the same sign, $z_A z_B$ is positive, and the rate constant increases with the ionic strength.

(2) If z_A and z_B have different signs, $z_A z_B$ is negative, and the rate constant decreases with the ionic strength.

(3) If one of the reactants is uncharged, $z_A z_B$ is zero and the rate constant is independent of the ionic strength.

These theoretical conclusions have been verified in a number of experimental studies. A few examples are illustrated in Fig. 9.15. This change of k_2 with I is called the *primary kinetic salt effect*. It should be noted that the ionic strength I is calculated from $\sum \frac{1}{2} m_i z_i^2$, and the summation is extended over all the ionic species present in solution, not merely the reactant ions.

Much of the earlier work on ionic reactions is comparatively useless because the salt effect was not understood. It is now often the practice in following the rate of an ionic reaction to add a considerable excess of an inert salt, e.g., NaCl, to the solution, so that the ionic strength is effectively constant throughout the reaction. If pure water is used, the change in ionic strength as the reaction proceeds may lead to erratic velocity constants.

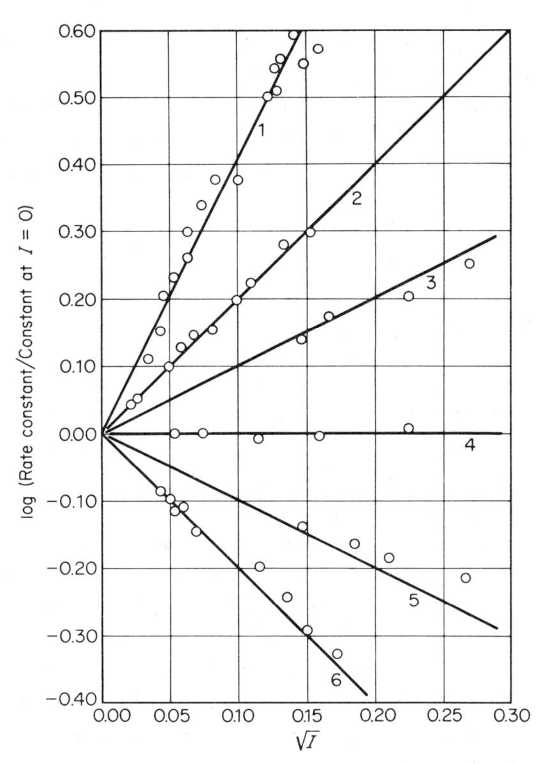

FIG. 9.15 Variations of rates of ionic reactions with the ionic strength. The circles are experimental values; the lines are theoretical, from Eq. (9.60).
(1) $2[Co(NH_3)_5Br]^{++} + Hg^{++} + 2H_2O \rightarrow 2[Co(NH_3)_5H_2O]^{+++} + HgBr_2$
(2) $S_2O_8^{=} + 2I^- \rightarrow I_2 + 2SO_4^{=}$
(3) $[NO_2NCOOC_2H_5] + OH^- \rightarrow N_2O + CO_3^{=} + C_2H_5OH$
(4) Inversion of cane sugar
(5) $H_2O_2 + 2H^+ + 2Br^- \rightarrow 2H_2O + Br_2$
(6) $[Co(NH_3)_5Br]^{++} + OH^{=} \rightarrow [Co(NH_3)_5OH]^{++} + Br^-$

30. IONIC REACTION MECHANISMS

Besides the salt effect discussed by Bronsted, specific interactions between the ions in solution may influence the reaction rates. For reactions between ions of the same charge sign, the salt effect often appears to be governed predominantly by the concentrations and charges of those added ions with a sign opposite to that of the reactant ions.*

The mechanism of ionic reactions is often indirectly determined by electrostatic factors, in particular the strong repulsion between ions of the same sign. The reaction $2Fe^{+3} + Sn^{+2} \rightarrow 2Fe^{+2} + Sn^{+4}$, for example, occurs rapidly, but the mechanism is probably a series of steps involving the transfer of single electrons between species of opposite charge sign:†

$$SnCl_2 + 2Cl^- \rightleftharpoons SnCl_4^=$$

$$SnCl_4^= + Fe^{+3} \longrightarrow Fe^{+2} + SnCl_4^-$$

$$SnCl_4^- + Fe^{+3} \longrightarrow Fe^{+2} + SnCl_4$$

Another instance is the overall reaction,

$$5HBr + HBrO_3 \longrightarrow 3Br_2 + 3H_2O$$

The rate equation is $d[Br_2]/dt = k[H^+]^2[Br^-][BrO_3^-]$. Note that the rate equation bears no relation to the stoichiometric equation. Owing to electrostatic repulsion, it is unlikely that Br^- and BrO_3^- ions react directly, and the following rate controlling step is suggested by the rate equation:

$$HBr + HBrO_3 \longrightarrow HBrO + HBrO_2$$

Rapid secondary reactions yield the final products. Since $[HBr] \propto [H^+][Br^-]$, and $[HBrO_3] \propto [H^+][BrO_3^-]$, the observed kinetics is obtained.

31. ACID–BASE CATALYSIS

Among the most interesting cases of homogeneous catalysis are reactions catalyzed by acids and bases. This acid-base catalysis is of the utmost importance, governing the rates of a great number of organic reactions, and especially many of the processes of physiological chemistry, for it is likely that many enzymes act as acid–base catalysts.

The earliest studies in this field were those by Kirchhoff in 1812 on the conversion of starch to glucose by the action of dilute acids, and by Thénard in 1818 on the decomposition of hydrogen peroxide in alkaline solutions. The classic investigation of Wilhelmy in 1850 dealt with the rate of inversion of cane sugar by acid catalysts. The hydrolysis of esters, catalyzed by both acids and bases, was extensively studied in the latter half of the nineteenth century. The catalytic activity of an acid in these reactions became one of the accepted measures of "acid strength," being very useful to Arrhenius and Ostwald in the early days of the ionization theory.

In Table 9.8 are some of Ostwald's results on sucrose inversion and methylacetate hydrolysis. If we write the acid as HA these reactions are

$$C_{12}H_{22}O_{11} + H_2O + HA \longrightarrow C_6H_{12}O_6 + C_6H_{12}O_6 + HA$$

$$CH_3COOCH_3 + H_2O + HA \longrightarrow CH_3COOH + CH_3OH + HA$$

The reaction rate may be written $dx/dt = k'[CH_3COOCH_3][H_2O][HA]$. Since

* A. R. Olson and T. R. Simonson, *J. Chem. Phys. 17*, 1167 (1949).

† J. Weiss, *J. Chem. Soc.*, 309 (1944).

the water is present in large excess, its concentration is effectively constant. The rate therefore reduces to $dx/dt = k''[HA][CH_3COOCH_3]$. Now k'' is called the *catalytic constant.* The values in Table 9.8 are all relative to 100 for k'' with HCl.

TABLE 9.8 OSTWALD'S DATA ON THE CATALYTIC CONSTANTS OF DIFFERENT ACIDS

Acid	Relative Conductivity	k'' (ester)	k'' (sugar)
HCl	100	100	100
HBr	101	98	111
HNO_3	99.6	92	100
H_2SO_4	65.1	73.9	73.2
CCl_3COOH	62.3	68.2	75.4
$CHCl_2COOH$	25.3	23.0	27.1
HCOOH	1.67	1.31	1.53
CH_3COOH	0.424	0.345	0.400

Ostwald and Arrhenius showed that the catalytic constant of an acid is proportional to its equivalent conductivity. They concluded that the nature of the anion was unimportant, and that the only active catalyst was the hydrogen ion, H^+.

In other reactions it was necessary to consider the effect of the OH^- ion and also the rate of the uncatalyzed reaction. This led to a three-term equation for the observed rate constant, $k = k_0 + k_{H^+}[H^+] + k_{OH^-}[OH^-]$. Since in aqueous solution $K_w = [H^+][OH^-]$,

$$k = k_0 + k_{H^+}[H^+] + \frac{k_{OH^-}K_w}{[H^+]} \qquad (9.61)$$

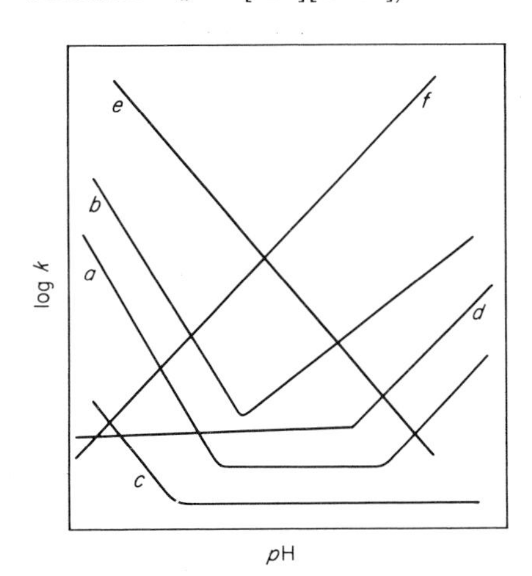

FIG. 9.16 Acid-base catalysis: the influence of pH on rate constants.

Since K_w is about 10^{-14}, in 0.1 N acid $[OH^-]$ is 10^{-13}, and in 0.1 N base $[OH^-]$ is 10^{-1}. There is a 10^{12}-fold change in $[OH^-]$ and $[H^+]$ in passing from dilute acid to dilute base. Therefore the OH^- catalysis will be negligible in dilute acid and the H^+ catalysis negligible in dilute base, except in the unusual event that the catalytic constants for H^+ and OH^- differ by as much as 10^{10}. By measurements in acid and basic solutions it is therefore generally possible to evaluate k_{H^+} and k_{OH^-} separately.

If $k_{H^+} = k_{OH^-}$, a minimum in the over-all rate constant occurs at the neutral point. If either k_{H^+} or k_{OH^-} is very low, there is no rise in k on the corresponding side of the neutral point. These and other varieties of rate constant vs. pH curves, arising from different relative values of k_0, k_{H^+}, and k_{OH^-}, are shown in Fig. 9.16.

Examples of each of the different types have been studied experimentally.* They include the following:

(a) The mutarotation of glucose
(b) Hydrolysis of amides, γ-lactones, esters; halogenation of ketones
(c) Hydrolysis of alkyl orthoacetates
(d) Hydrolysis of β-lactones, decomposition of nitramide, halogenation of nitroparaffins
(e) Inversion of sugars, hydrolysis of diazoacetic ester, acetals
(f) Depolymerization of diacetone alcohol; decomposition of nitrosoacetonamine.

32. GENERAL ACID–BASE CATALYSIS

Advances in our understanding of acid–base catalysis have been closely linked with improvements in the theory of electrolytic solutions. The early notion that the conductance ratio, Λ/Λ_0, of a strong electrolyte measures its degree of dissociation has been superseded by the Debye-Hückel idea of complete ionization. In fact, one of the first evidences for the latter viewpoint was the observation of Bjerrum that the catalytic activity of strong acids is proportional to their total concentration in solution rather than to the H^+ concentration as calculated from the Arrhenius theory.

The influence of added salts in the primary kinetic salt effect has already been noted. In addition to this direct dependence of reaction rate on ionic strength, there is an indirect influence important in catalyzed reactions. In solutions of weak acids and bases, added salts, even if they do not possess a common ion, may change the H^+ or OH^- ion concentration through their effect on the activity coefficients. For an acid $HA \rightarrow H^+ + A^-$,

$$K = \frac{a_{H^+}a_{A^-}}{a_{HA}} = \frac{c_{H^+}c_{A^-}}{c_{HA}} \cdot \frac{\gamma_{H^+}\gamma_{A^-}}{\gamma_{HA}}$$

Any change in the ionic strength of the solution affects the γ terms and hence the concentration of H^+. Consequently, if the reaction is catalyzed by H^+ or OH^- ions, the reaction rate is dependent on the ionic strength. This is called the *secondary kinetic salt effect*. Unlike the primary effect it does not alter the *rate constant* provided this is calculated from the true H^+ or OH^- concentration.

The broader picture of the nature of acids and bases given by the work of Bronsted and Lowry (Sec. 9.26) implies that not only H^+ and OH^- but also the undissociated acids and bases should be effective catalysts. The essential feature of catalysis by an acid is the transfer of a proton from acid to substrate,† and catalysis by a base involves the acceptance of a proton by the base. Thus, in

* See A. Skrabal, *Z. f. Elektrochem.* *33*, 322 (1927); R. P. Bell, *Acid–Base Catalysis* (New York: Oxford Univ. Press, 1941), *The Proton in Chemistry* (Ithaca: Cornell Univ. Press, 1959).

†Substance whose reaction is being catalyzed.

Bronsted-Lowry nomenclature, the substrate acts as a base in acid catalysis, or as an acid in basic catalysis. In the case of hydrogen-ion catalysis in aqueous solution, the acid is really the hydronium ion, OH_3^+.

For example, the hydrolysis of nitramide is susceptible to basic but not to acid catalysis.

$$NH_2NO_2 + OH^- \longrightarrow H_2O + NHNO_2^-$$
$$NHNO_2^- \longrightarrow N_2O + OH^-$$

Not only the OH^- ion but also other bases can act as catalysts, e.g., the acetate ion.

$$NH_2NO_2 + CH_3COO^- \longrightarrow CH_3COOH + NHNO_2^-$$
$$NHNO_2^- \longrightarrow N_2O + OH^-$$
$$OH^- + CH_3COOH \longrightarrow H_2O + CH_3COO^-$$

The reaction rate with different bases B is always $v = k_B(\mathrm{B})(\mathrm{NH_2NO_2})$. Bronsted found that there was a relation between the catalytic constant k_B and the dissociation constant K_b of the base, namely,

$$k_B = CK_b^\beta \tag{9.62}$$

or

$$\log k_B = \log C + \beta \log K_b$$

Here C and β are constants for bases of a given charge type. Thus the stronger the base, the higher the catalytic constant.*

The nitramide hydrolysis displays *general basic catalysis*. Other reactions provide examples of *general acid catalysis*, with a relation like Eq. (9.62) between k_A and K_a. Some reactions also occur with both general acid and general basic catalysis.

Since a solvent like water can act as either an acid or a base, it is often itself a catalyst. What was formerly believed to be the uncatalyzed reaction, represented by k_0 in Eq. (9.61), is in most cases undoubtedly a reaction catalyzed by the solvent acting as acid or base.

PROBLEMS

1. After passage of an electric current for 45 minutes, 7.19 mg of silver are found to be deposited in a silver coulometer. Calculate the average current. [*Ans.* 2.39 ma]

2. A conductivity cell filled with a 0.1 molar solution of potassium chloride at 25°C has a measured resistance of 24.96 ohms. Calculate the cell constant if the conductivity κ for 0.1 molar KCl is 0.011639 ohm^{-1} cm^{-1} and conductivity water with $\kappa = 7.5 \times 10^{-8}$ ohm^{-1} cm^{-1} is used to make up the solutions. Filled with a 0.01 molar solution of acetic acid the cell resistance is 1982

* For polybasic bases, a correction must be made. See R. P. Bell, *op. cit.* (*1*), p. 83.

ohms. Calculate the equivalent conductivity of acetic acid at this concentration. [*Ans.* 0.2902 cm^{-1}; 14.6 $ohm^{-1}\ cm^2\ eq^{-1}$]

3. The following are the conductivities of chloroacetic acid in aqueous solution at 25°C:

c^{-1}(liter/mole)	16	32	64	128	256	512	1024
equiv. cond., Λ	53.1	72.4	96.8	127.7	164	205.8	249.2

If $\Lambda_0^\circ = 362$, are these values in accord with the Ostwald Dilution Law? [*Ans.* yes, $K = (1.53 \pm .04) \times 10^{-3}$]

4. The conductivity of a saturated solution of silver chloride in pure water at 20°C is 1.26×10^{-6} $ohm^{-1}\ cm^{-1}$ higher than that for the water used. Calculate the solubility of AgCl in water. [*Ans.* 9.14×10^{-6} moles $liter^{-1}$]

5. An 0.01 N silver nitrate solution is used with silver electrodes in a determination of the transference number of the Ag^+ ion by the Hittorf method; 32.10 mg of silver are deposited in a silver coulometer in series with the Hittorf cell. At the end of the run the 20.09 g of solution in the anode compartment are found to contain 39.66 mg of Ag; the 27.12 g of solution in the cathode compartment contain 11.14 mg of Ag. Calculate the Ag^+ transference number. [*Ans.* 0.439]

6. In a transport experiment in 0.02 molar NaCl solution at 25°C by the moving boundary method, Longsworth [*J. Am. Chem. Soc.* *54*, 2741 (1932)] found the boundary between NaCl and $CdCl_2$ solutions to move 6.0 cm in 2070 seconds with a current of 0.00160 amp. (Tube cross section 0.12 cm^2.) Calculate t^+. [*Ans.* 0.419]

7. From the molal activity coefficients in Table 9.5, calculate the mean ionic activity in 0.1 molal solution of $AgNO_3$, $CuSO_4$, $CaCl_2$. [*Ans.* 0.072; 0.016; 0.0818]

8. Calculate the ionic strengths of one-molal solutions of KNO_3, K_2SO_4, $K_4Fe(CN)_6$. [*Ans.* 1.0; 3.0; 10.0]

9. Calculate the "thickness of the ionic atmosphere" according to the Debye-Hückel theory in 0.1 and 0.01 molar solutions of a uniunivalent electrolyte in (a) water at 25°C with dielectric constant $\epsilon = 78$; (b) 70 per cent ethanol in water at 25°C with $\epsilon = 38.5$. [*Ans.* (a) 9.21, 29.1 Å; (b) 6.74, 21.3 Å]

10. The solubility of barium sulfate in water at 25°C is 0.957×10^{-5} mole/liter. Using the Debye-Hückel theory, calculate ΔG° for the change: $BaSO_4(s) \rightarrow Ba^{++} + SO_4^{--}$ (aq.). [*Ans.* 13.73 kcal]

11. A 0.1 molar H_3PO_4 solution is titrated with NaOH using methyl orange as an indicator to an endpoint at pH 4.3. The dissociation constants of H_3PO_4 are 7.5×10^{-3}, 6×10^{-8}, and 3.6×10^{-13}. Calculate the fractions of acid converted to $H_2PO_4^-$ and $HPO_4^=$. [*Ans.* 0.951, 0.0114]

12. Calculate the pH of a 0.1 M solution of ammonium lactate at 25°C. Lactic acid, $pK_a = 3.86$; ammonia $pK_b = 4.76$. [*Ans.* 6.55]

13. The pH at which an amphoteric electrolyte yields an equal concentration of positive and negative ions is called the isoelectric point. Show that if the activity coefficients of all the ions are taken as unity, this $pH = \frac{1}{2}(pK_a + pK_b)$.

14. If in a binary solution,

$$a_1 = kx_1(1 + bx_1)$$

obtain an expression for a_2 from the Gibbs-Duhem equation.

15. The conductivity at 25°C was measured for the following solutions.

Solution	Specific Conductance
10^{-3} M Phenanthrolinium chloride (BHCl)	1.360×10^{-4}
10^{-3} M BHCl plus a large excess of Phenanthroline (B)	1.045×10^{-4}
10^{-3} M HCl	4.210×10^{-4}

Phenanthrolinium chloride is a strong electrolyte, i.e., exists as BH^+ and Cl^- ions. Phenanthroline is a nonelectrolyte. Calculate K_a for the acid dissociation: $BH^+ \rightarrow B + H^+$.

16. The specific conductivity of a 0.001 M Na_2SO_4 solution is 2.6×10^{-4}, and rises to 7.0×10^{-4} if the solution is saturated with $CaSO_4$. The equivalent conductivities are 50 and 60 for Na^+ and $\frac{1}{2}$ Ca^{++}. Calculate the K_{sp} for $CaSO_4$.

17. A resistance cell was filled with (1) an aqueous solution of hydrogen sulfide, (2) 20 millimoles of KCl. At 18°C the resistance was (1) 3736 ohms, and (2) 30.08 ohms. 50 ml of the same hydrogen-sulfide solution decolorized 13.75 ml of 101.3 millimoles of I_2 solution (free sulfur is formed in the reaction). The conductivity of the KCl solution was 0.002397 ohm^{-1} cm^{-1}. The equivalent ionic conductances for H^+ and SH^- ions are 318 and 62 cm^2 ohm^{-1} mole^{-1}. Find the K for the first dissociation constant of H_2S.

18. Given the following information:

Salt	Λ
NaCl	126.4
KNO_3	144.9
KCl	149.8

t^+ for Na^+ in NaCl $= 0.39$

calculate Λ for $NaNO_3$, t^+ for Na^+ in $NaNO_3$ solution. (Neglect the change in mobility of these ions with concentration.)

19. A conductivity cell has electrodes 2.00 cm^2 in area 1.00 cm apart. When filled with a solution containing 50.0 g potassium chloride per liter its resistance is 7.25 ohm. Calculate the equivalent conductivity of the solution. [*Ans.* 102.8 ohm^{-1} cm^2 $equiv^{-1}$]

20. The resistance of a conductivity cell filled with 0.0200 *N* KCl at 18°C is 17.60 ohm; filled with 0.1000 N acetic acid the resistance is 91.8 ohm. If the specific conductance of 0.0200 N KCl at 18° is 2.399×10^{-3} ohm^{-1} cm^{-1} and the ionic conductivities at infinite dilution of the hydrogen ion and the acetate ion at 18° are 315 and 35 ohm^{-1} cm^2 $equiv^{-1}$, calculate the degree of dissociation of acetic acid in N/10 solution. [*Ans.* 0.0132]

21. The equivalent conductivity at 18°C of a 0.0100 N aqueous solution of ammonia is 9.6 ohm^{-1} cm^2 $equiv^{-1}$. For NH_4Cl, $\Lambda_o = 129.8$ and the ionic conductivities of OH^- and Cl^- are 174 and 65.6 respectively. Calculate Λ_o for NH_3 and the degree of ionization in 0.01 N solution. [*Ans.* 238.3 ohm^{-1} cm^2 $equiv^{-1}$; 0.0402]

22. The specific conductivity of a saturated solution of silver chloride at 20°C is 1.33×10^{-6} ohm^{-1} cm^{-1}. If the ionic conductivities of Ag^+ and Cl^- at this temperature are 56.9 and 68.4 ohm^{-1} cm^2 $equiv^{-1}$, respectively, calculate the solubility of silver chloride. [*Ans.* 1.06×10^{-5} mole per liter]

23. A current of electricity was passed through a series of cells containing solutions of $AgNO_3$, $CuSO_4$ and H_2SO_4 for 25 min. The weight of silver deposited was 0.5234 g. What was the weight of copper deposited and what was the volume of hydrogen collected over water at 15°C (v.p. = 12.8 mm) and barometric pressure of 750 mm? What was the average current? [*Ans.* 0.1569 g, 60.14 ml, 0.3174 amp]

24. A solution is 0.01 M with respect to manganous ion and 0.1 M with respect to acetic acid. What concentration of acetate ion must be added so that precipitation of manganous sulfide occurs when the solution is saturated with hydrogen sulfide? (Solubility of H_2S is 0.1 mole/liter; K_s(MnS) = 1.4×10^{-15}(g-ion/liter)^2.) [*Ans.* 0.10 M]

25. What is the pH at 25°C of a solution which is twice as alkaline (i.e., which contains twice as many hydroxide ions per liter) as pure water? [*Ans.* 7.30]

26. If the acidity constant of carbonic acid is 3.3×10^{-7} and the pH of blood serum is 7.40, calculate the ratio of the concentration of bicarbonate to carbonic acid in serum. [*Ans.* 8.3]

27. Derive an expression for the acidity constant of a weak acid in terms of the concentration of its solution and its degree of dissociation a. At first, make the approximation that the concentrations of hydrogen ion and of anion of the acid are equal. Secondly, derive a more exact expression without making this approximation. [*Ans.* $K_a' = (a^2c)/(1 - a)$; $K_a'' = K_a'[1 + (1 + 4K_w a^{-2}c^{-2})^{1/2}]/2$

28. The dissociation constant of hydrocyanic acid at 25°C is 7.2×10^{-10}. Calculate the molarity of a solution of hydrocyanic acid which is 0.1 per cent ionized. [*Ans.* 7×10^{-4} M]

29. The *p*H of a saturated solution of benzoic acid (C_6H_5COOH) in water at 20°C is 3.0. If the dissociation constant of benzoic acid at 20° is 6.30×10^{-5} what is the solubility of the acid in water at 20° in grams per liter? [*Ans.* 1.94 g/l]

30. A buffer solution of *p*H 3.9 can be prepared by adding 0.2 M sodium hydroxide to *either* 0.2 M formic acid ($pK_a = 3.7$) *or* 0.2 M acetic acid ($pK_a = 4.8$). What are the relative volumes of ingredients needed in each case? [*Ans.* NaOH: formic acid = 0.62; NaOH: acetic acid = 0.12]

31. Discuss the Lowry-Bronsted concept of acids and bases. Illustrate your answer with particular reference to aqueous solutions of (a) hydrogen chloride, (b) ammonia, (c) sodium carbonate, (d) ammonium nitrate. Given that the ionic product of water is 10^{-14}, K_a for benzoic acid is 6.5×10^{-5}, K_b for ammonia is 2.2×10^{-5}, arrange the Bronsted acids NH_4^+, benzoic acid, H_2O, H_3O^+ in order of decreasing strength.

32. The equivalent conductivities of 0.001 N solutions of potassium chloride, sodium chloride and potassium sulfate are respectively 149.9, 126.5 and 153.3. Calculate an approximate value for the equivalent conductivity of a solution of sodium sulfate of the same concentration. [*Ans.* 129.9 $cm^2\ ohm^{-1}\ equiv^{-1}$]

33. The resistance of a conductivity cell filled with 0.02 N KCl at 18°C is 17.60 ohm. When filled with 0.1 N acetic acid, the resistance is 91.8 ohm. If the specific conductance of 0.02 N KCl at 18°C is $2.399 \times 10^{-3}\ ohm^{-1}\ cm^{-1}$ and the ionic conductances at infinite dilution of the hydrogen ion and the acetate ion at 18°C are 315 and 35 $ohm^{-1}\ cm^2\ equiv^{-1}$, calculate the degree of dissociation of acetic acid in N/10 solution. [*Ans.* 0.01314]

34. If the purest water has a conductivity of $6.2 \times 10^{-8}\ ohm^{-1}\ cm^{-1}$ at 25°C, calculate the κ of a saturated solution of CO_2 in water at 25°C if the CO_2 pressure is maintained at 20 mm and the equilibrium constant for the reaction, $H_2O(l) + CO_2(aq) \rightarrow HCO_3^- + H^+$, is 4.16×10^{-7}. The solubility of CO_2 in water follows Henry's Law with a constant $k' = 0.0290$ mole $lit^{-1}\ atm^{-1}$ [cf. MacInnes and Belek, *J. Am. Chem. Soc. 55*, 2630 (1933)]. [*Ans.* $7.08 \times 10^{-6}\ ohm^{-1}\ cm^{-1}$]

35. Draw a calculated curve showing how the conductivity of the solution varies as 10 ml of 0.1 N NaOH is titrated with 11 ml of 0.1 N HCl. [*Ans.*

ml HCl added:	0	2	5	8	10	11
conductivity $\times 10^6$:	24.8	18.8	12.5	8.4	6.3	8.0

Calculations based on equivalent ionic conductivities at infinite dilution.]

36. From the following freezing-point depressions for aqueous solutions of sodium chloride, calculate the activity coefficient γ_m of NaCl in 0.05 molal solution [G. N. Lewis and M. Randall, *J. Am. Chem. Soc. 43*, 1112 (1921)].

molality, m	0.01	0.02	0.05	0.10	0.20	0.50
f.pt.dep. °C:	0.0361	0.0714	0.1758	0.3470	0.6850	1.677

[*Ans.* $\gamma_\pm = 0.875$]

---

37. The solubility-product constant of AgCl at 25°C is $K_{sp} = (Ag^+)(Cl^-) = 1.20 \times 10^{-10}$. Calculate from the Debye-Hückel theory (limiting law) the solubility of AgCl in water and in a 0.01 M solution of (a) NaCl, (b) $NaNO_3$. [*Ans.* 1.10×10^{-5}, 1.23×10^{-8}, 1.12×10^{-5} mole liter^{-1}]

38. The solubility of $AgIO_3$ in KNO_3 solutions has been measured by Kolthoff and Lingane [*J. Phys. Chem. 42*, 133 (1938)] at 25°C:

KNO_3, m/l	0	0.001301	0.003252	0.006503	0.01410
$AgIO_3$, m/l $\times 10^4$	1.761	1.813	1.863	1.908	1.991

Compare these results with the Debye-Hückel limiting law for solubilities and calculate the activity coefficients of $AgIO_3$ in the solutions. [*Ans.*

$\gamma_\pm$(DH)	.984	.955	.934	.909	.869
$\gamma_\pm$(Exptl.)	.985	.957	.931	.909	.871

39. In water solution, amino acids exist mainly as zwitterions, e.g., glycine as $^+NH_3CH_2COO^-$. For $^+NH_3CH_2COOH \rightarrow {}^+NH_3CH_2COO^- + H^+$, $pK_a = 2.35$; for $^+NH_3CH_2COO^- \rightarrow NH_2CH_2COO^- + H^+$, $pK_b = 9.78$. Calculate the *p*H of a 0.1 M glycine solution. [*Ans.* 6.074]

40. The *p*H of 0.1 M potassium propionate (KC_2H_5COO) is 8.94 at 25°C. Calculate (a) the degree of hydrolysis of the salt, (b) the acidity constant of propionic acid, (c) the concentration of propionic acid necessary in this solution to give the solution a *p*H of 4.50. [*Ans.* (a) 8.7×10^{-5}; (b) 1.3×10^{-5}; (c) 0.24 M]

10 ELECTROCHEMICAL CELLS

If a piece of zinc and a piece of copper be brought in contact with each other, they will form a weak electrical combination, of which the zinc will be positive, and the copper negative; this may be learnt by the use of a delicate condensing electrometer...

HUMPHRY DAVY (1812)

In the last chapter we considered the physical chemistry of solutions of electrolytes. We shall consider now what happens when electrodes are immersed in these solutions and connected via an external metallic conductor. Such an arrangement is a typical *electrochemical cell.* If the cell is used as a source of electrical energy, that is, if it converts the free energy of a physical or chemical change into electrical free energy, it is called a *galvanic cell.* An *electrolytic cell* is one in which a physical or chemical change is caused by electrical energy from some external source.

1. ELECTROMOTIVE FORCE (EMF) OF A CELL

Figure 10.1 shows a typical cell. A zinc electrode dips into a solution of 1.0 m $ZnSO_4$ and a copper electrode dips into a solution of 1.0 m $CuSO_4$. The two solutions are separated by a porous barrier, which allows electrical contact but prevents excessive mixing of the solutions by interdiffusion. This cell is represented by the diagram,

$$\mathrm{Zn} \mid \mathrm{Zn^{+2}}(1.0\ \mathrm{m}) \mid \mathrm{Cu^{+2}}(1.0\ \mathrm{m}) \mid \mathrm{Cu} \qquad \text{(A)}$$

The vertical lines denote phase boundaries.

It is always possible to measure the difference in electrical potential between two pieces of the same kind of metal. We therefore attach to each electrode a length of copper wire and connect these copper leads to a voltmeter or some other device for measuring this difference in potential. In the cell in Fig. 10.1, the copper is the observed + terminal.

The electromotive force (emf) E of the cell is defined as follows:*

The emf is equal in sign and in magnitude to the electrical potential of the metallic conducting lead on the right when that of the similar lead on the left is taken as zero, the cell being open.

Thus, we might write,

$$E = E_{\text{right}} - E_{\text{left}} \tag{10.1}$$

where E_{right} and E_{left} would be the potentials of the right and left leads relative to some common standard. Note that we do not need to know E_{right} or E_{left} separately, since only their difference occurs in the definition. The meaning of "left" and "right" refers to the cell *as written;* it clearly has nothing to do with how the actual cell is arranged on the laboratory bench. If we rewrite the same cell in the reverse direction, the sign of the emf must change. Thus if the cell (A) above has a positive emf, $+|E|$, the cell (B),

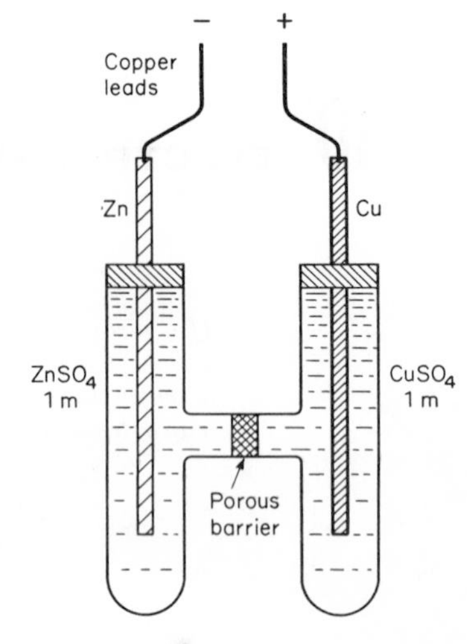

FIG. 10.1 A typical electrochemical cell.

$$\text{Cu} \mid \text{Cu}^{+2}(1.0\ \text{m}) \mid \text{Zn}^{+2}(1.0\ \text{m}) \mid \text{Zn} \tag{B}$$

has a negative emf $-|E|$.

2. MEASUREMENT OF EMF—THE POTENTIOMETER

The definition of emf states that the potential difference is measured while the cell is open, i.e., while no current is being drawn from the external leads. In practice, it is possible to measure E under conditions in which the current drawn from the cell is so small as to be negligible. The method, devised by Poggendorf, uses a circuit known as the *potentiometer*.

A basic potentiometer circuit is shown in Fig. 10.2. The slide wire is calibrated with a scale so that any setting of the contact corresponds to a certain voltage. With the double throw switch in the standard cell position S, we set the slide wire to the voltage reading of

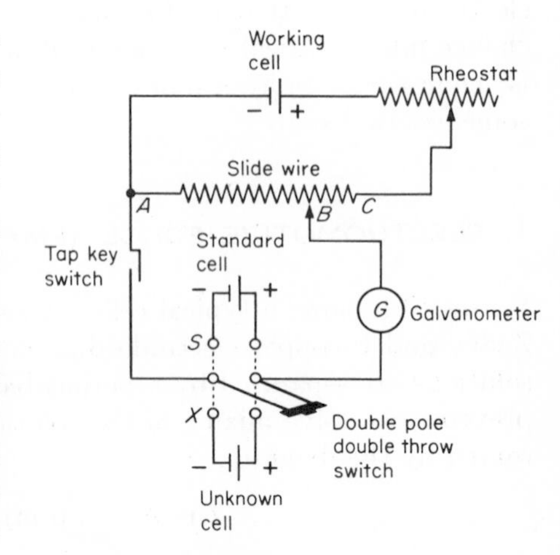

FIG. 10.2 Basic circuit of direct reading potentiometer.

* This is the definition recommended by International Union of Pure and Applied Chemistry (IUPAC) meeting in Stockholm in 1953. The entire text of this *Stockholm Convention* is reprinted in *J. Am. Chem. Soc. 82*, 5517 (1960).

the standard cell, and adjust the rheostat until no current flows through the galvanometer G. At this point the potential difference between A and B, the IR along the section AB of the slide wire, just balances the emf of the standard cell. We then set the switch in the unknown cell position X, and readjust the slide wire contact until no current flows through G. From the new setting we can read directly from the scale of the slide wire the emf of the unknown cell.

The most widely used standard is the Weston cell, shown in Fig. 10.3, which is written:

$$\mathrm{Cd(Hg)} \mid \mathrm{CdSO_4 \cdot \tfrac{8}{3}H_2O} \mid \mathrm{CdSO_4\ (sat.\ sol)} \mid \mathrm{Hg_2SO_4} \mid \mathrm{Hg}$$

The cell reaction is

$$\mathrm{Cd(s) + Hg_2SO_4(s) + \tfrac{8}{3}H_2O(l) \longrightarrow CdSO_4 \cdot \tfrac{8}{3}H_2O(s) + 2Hg(l)}$$

Its emf at t °C is given by

$$E = 1.01485 - 4.05 \times 10^{-5}(t - 20) - 9.5 \times 10^{-7}(t - 20)^2 \text{ absolute volts}$$

Thus at 20°C, $E = 1.01485$; at 25°C, $E = 1.01463$. The small temperature

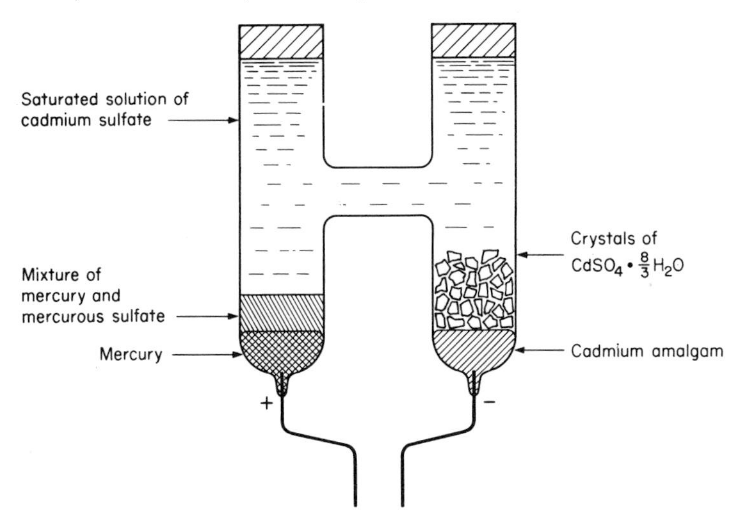

FIG. 10.3 Weston standard cell.

coefficient of E is one advantage of this cell. Since individual cells may differ slightly in emf, those used in the laboratory should be calibrated by the National Bureau of Standards, or checked against such calibrated cells.

The accuracy of the compensation method for measuring an emf is limited only by the accuracy of the standard E and of the various resistances in the circuit. The precision of the method will be determined mainly by the sensitivity of the galvanometer used to detect the balance between unknown and standard (working) emf and by the closeness of the control of temperature. Since it is not difficult to balance such a circuit so that less than 10^{-12} amperes is drawn from the cell, we can satisfy practically the condition specified by the definition, i.e., measurement of E with the cell open.

3. THE POLARITY OF AN ELECTRODE

When you connect a cell to a potentiometer and balance the potentials, you must of course connect the + and − terminals of the cell to the + and − terminals of the potentiometer, respectively. The polarity of the potentiometer terminals is determined by how the + and − terminals of the standard cell are connected. If you are to achieve a balance point, the + electrode of the standard cell must be connected so as to oppose the + electrode of the unknown.

You need not worry how to decide which electrode of a cell is + and which is −. The + electrode is the one connected to the + terminal of the potentiometer when balance is achieved. If you have connected the − of cell to the + of potentiometer, you will not be able to obtain a balance, and you will therefore not have any measurement to worry about. Thus a few minutes of experimentation tells which electrode is + and which is −.

We might ask, however, how Edward Weston knew that the cadmium electrode was negative when he made his first standard cell in 1892. The answer goes back to the choice between the vitreous and the resinous electric fluids. When Franklin proposed the one-fluid theory, he picked the vitreous fluid as *the* electrical fluid, and this kind of electricity became *positive*. The resinous kind of electricity was then considered to result from a deficiency of electrical fluid, and was called, therefore, *negative electricity*. Franklin might have made the opposite choice, since the assignment of names was quite arbitrary.

As it turned out, we live in a world which is not symmetrical where + and − electricity is concerned. The ordinary carriers of positive electricity are the massive positive ions, but the ordinary carriers of negative electricity are the much lighter electrons. A positive ion is an atom that has lost one or more electrons. If we had Franklin's choice to make over again today, we should doubtless reverse his signs to avoid the semantic difficulty of having negative carriers of a positive fluid.

In any case, the choice of + and − is consistent throughout the science of electricity. When we say that the copper wire attached to the cadmium electrode in the Weston cell is more negative than the copper wire attached to the mercury electrode, we mean that it contains an excess of the same kind of electricity found in amber rubbed with cat's fur.

4. THE CELL EMF AND THE CELL REACTION

It might have seemed reasonable to adopt a convention of writing cells so that the negative electrode was always on the left and the positive electrode always on the right. This has not been done, however, for a simple reason. We wish to associate the cell *as written* with the chemical reaction that occurs in it. Since reactions are reversible, we want to be able to write them either forwards or backwards, and we want to be able to do the same with cells.

The cell as written, therefore, indicates the direction in which the cell reaction is to be written. The cell,

$$Zn \mid Zn^{+2} \mid Cu^{+2} \mid Cu \qquad (A)$$

corresponds to the reaction,

$$Zn + Cu^{+2} \longrightarrow Zn^{+2} + Cu$$

The cell,

$$Cu \mid Cu^{+2} \mid Zn^{+2} \mid Zn \qquad (B)$$

corresponds to the reaction,

$$Cu + Zn^{+2} \longrightarrow Cu^{+2} + Zn$$

The cell is therefore written in such a way that the left hand electrode is the reactant and the right hand electrode is the product of the reaction as written.*

The definition of emf is always

$$E = E_{\text{right}} - E_{\text{left}}$$

This is consistent with the usual "Δ convention" for changes in reaction equations,

$$\Delta X = X \text{ (product)} - X \text{ (reactant)}$$

For cell (A), therefore, the emf is positive, and for cell (B) it is negative, because the zinc electrode is found by experiment to be the negative electrode of the cell.

5. REVERSIBLE CELLS

An electrode dipping into a solution is said to constitute a *half cell.* Thus $Zn|Zn^{+2}$ (0.1 m) is a half cell. The typical cell is the combination of two half cells.

We shall be interested primarily in the class of cells called *reversible cells.* These may be recognized by the following criterion: The cell is connected with a potentiometer arrangement for emf measurement by the compensation method. The emf of the cell is measured: (a) with a small current flowing through the cell in one direction; (b) then with an imperceptible flow of current; (c) and finally with a small flow in the opposite direction. If a cell is reversible, its emf changes only slightly during this sequence, and there is no discontinuity in the value of the emf at the point of balance (b). Reversibility implies that any chemical reaction occurring in the cell can proceed in either direction, depending

* This statement does not apply to all cells, since sometimes an electrode cannot be identified with a reactant or a product. This fact will be evident when different kinds of electrodes are discussed in Sec. 10.8.

on the flow of current, and at the null point the driving force of the reaction is just balanced by the compensating emf of the potentiometer. If a cell is reversible, it follows that the half cells comprising it are both reversible.

One source of irreversibility in cells is the *liquid junction*, like that in the Daniell cell of Fig. 10.1. At the junction between $ZnSO_4$ and $CuSO_4$, we have the following situation:

$$\begin{array}{r|l} Zn^{+2} & Cu^{+2} \\ (1.0\text{ m}) \qquad & \qquad (1.0\text{ m}) \\ SO_4^{=} & SO_4^{=} \end{array}$$

If we pass a small current through the cell from left to right it is carried across the junction by Zn^{+2} ions and by $SO_4^{=}$ ions. But, if we go through the balance point, and pass a small current in the opposite direction, it is carried across the junction from right to left by Cu^{+2} and $SO_4^{=}$ ions. Thus the cell with such a liquid junction is inherently not reversible.

Before we can apply reversible thermodynamics to such cells, we must eliminate the liquid junction. We can do this with considerable success by the device called the *salt bridge*. This consists of a connecting tube filled with a concentrated solution of a salt, usually KCl. The solution can be made up in a gel (for instance, agar) in order to decrease mixing with the solutions in the two half cells. Now most of the current will be carried across the junction by K^+ and Cl^- ions. There will still be some irreversible effects where the bridge enters the two solutions, but these are hopefully regarded as minimal. When the liquid junction has been "eliminated" by such a device, the cell is written with a double bar in the middle:

$$Zn \mid Zn^{+2} \parallel Cu^{+2} \mid Cu$$

A better way to avoid irreversible effects is to avoid liquid junctions altogether, by using a single electrolyte. The Weston cell does this with a solution of $CdSO_4$ which is also saturated with the sparingly soluble Hg_2SO_4. We shall discuss later other examples of cells without liquid junctions. Even in such cells, however, changes in electrolyte concentration around the electrodes, as a consequence of the cell reaction, may introduce small irreversible effects.

In order to measure the emf of a reversible cell, we must of course use a sensitive galvanometer so that no appreciable current is drawn from the cell during the measurement. If a current I passes through the cell, there is a generation of heat $q = I^2R$, where R is the internal resistance of the cell plus the resistance in the external circuit. This Joulean heat is analogous to the frictional heat generated in mechanical processes. While current I is being drawn from the cell the difference in potential measured between the electrodes must fall *below* the emf E. We can call such a difference in potential the *voltage* of the cell. Only under open-circuit conditions does the voltage equal the electromotive force, emf.

6. FREE ENERGY AND REVERSIBLE EMF

The electrical work done on a charge Q when its potential is changed by an amount ΔU is $Q\Delta U$. Consider a cell in which $|z|$ equivalents of reactant are converted to products. Then $|z|\ F$ coulombs of electric charge pass through the cell. Through the external metallic circuit, $|z|\ F$ coulombs of negative charge (electrons) are transferred. In case the emf E is positive, as in cell (A) above, these electrons are transferred from the negative to the positive electrode. Therefore, the electrical work done *on* the cell is $-|z|\ FE$.

Under reversible conditions, the work done on the cell is $w = \Delta A$. Considering the mechanical (PV) work done at constant pressure on all the different phases in the cell, we can write

$$\Delta A = -\sum_{\alpha} P^{\alpha}\Delta V^{\alpha} - |z|\ FE$$

But,

$$\Delta G = \Delta A + \sum_{\alpha} P^{\alpha}\Delta V^{\alpha}$$

Therefore,

$$\Delta G = -|z|\ FE \tag{10.2}$$

We find, therefore, the important relation that *the reversible emf is a measure of the free energy of the cell reaction.* Since $E = -\Delta G/|z|\ F$, the reversible emf E is the driving force or affinity of the reaction $-\Delta G$ per unit charge (e.g., per coulomb if the free energy is in joules).

In the case of the Daniell cell, $E = 1.100$ v at 25°C. Hence,

$$\Delta G = -2(96\,496)(1.100) = -212\,300 \qquad \text{volt coulomb [joule]*}$$

or

$$-212\,300/4.184 = -50\,780 \qquad \text{calories/mole}$$

A reaction can proceed spontaneously only if $\Delta G < 0$. Thus only if $E > 0$ can a cell reaction proceed spontaneously, and the cell serve as a source of electrical energy.

When $E > 0$, the cell reaction therefore can proceed as written. In this case, the left hand electrode becomes oxidized, and the resulting positive ions pass through the cell from left to right. The electrons flow through the external circuit from left to right. For the Daniell cell, therefore, when it acts as a galvanic cell,

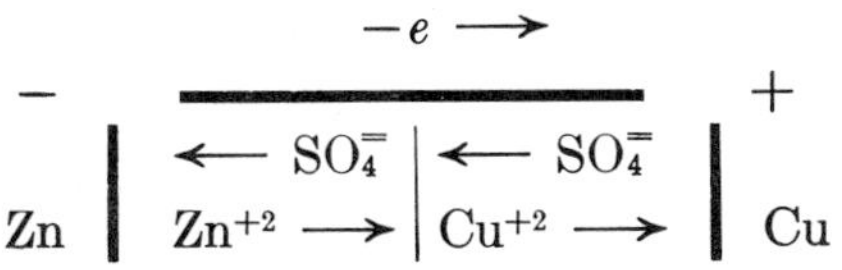

$$-e \longrightarrow$$

$$\begin{array}{c|c|c|c} - & & & + \\ & \leftarrow SO_4^{=} & \leftarrow SO_4^{=} & \\ Zn & Zn^{+2} \longrightarrow & Cu^{+2} \longrightarrow & Cu \end{array}$$

---

* Another useful unit is the *volt Faraday* (vF). $1\ vF = 96\,496$ joule $= 23\,062$ cal. Note especially that $1\ vF$ per mole $= 1$ electron volt per molecule. For the Daniell cell, $\Delta G = -2(1.100) = -2.200\ vF$ at 25°C.

7. ENTROPY AND ENTHALPY OF CELL REACTIONS

The application of the Gibbs-Helmholtz equation (3.35) to the relation $\Delta G = -|z|\, FE$ allows us to calculate the ΔH and ΔS of a cell reaction from the temperature coefficient of the reversible emf. [Note that the heat of the reaction in the *reversible cell* is $T\Delta S$, and not ΔH.]

$$\Delta S = -\left(\frac{\partial \Delta G}{\partial T}\right)_P = z\,F\left(\frac{\partial E}{\partial T}\right)_P \tag{10.3}$$

Since, at constant T,

$$\Delta H = \Delta G + T\Delta S$$

$$\Delta H = -\,|\,z\,|\,FE + |\,z\,|\,FT\left(\frac{\partial E}{\partial T}\right)_P \tag{10.4}$$

Let us apply these relations to the Weston standard cell. At 25°C,

$$E = 1.01463 \text{ volts}$$

and,

$$dE/dT = -5.00 \times 10^{-5} \text{ volts deg}^{-1}$$

Hence,

$$\Delta G = -2(96\,496)(1.01463) = -195\,815 \text{ joule}$$

$$\Delta S = 2(96\,496)(-5.00 \times 10^{-5}) = -9.65 \text{ joule deg}^{-1}$$

and,

$$\Delta H = -195\,815 - 2876 = -198\,691 \text{ joule}$$

8. TYPES OF HALF CELLS

Various kinds of chemical reactions can be carried out in cells so as to yield electric energy, and there is a corresponding variety in the types of available half cells.

One of the simplest consists of a *metal electrode* in contact with a solution containing ions of the metal, e.g., silver in silver-nitrate solution. Such a half cell is represented as $Ag \mid Ag^+(c)$, where c is the silver-ion concentration, and the vertical bar denotes the phase boundary. The reaction occurring at this electrode is the solution or deposition of the metal, according to $Ag \rightleftarrows Ag^+ + e$.

It is sometimes convenient to form a metal electrode by using an amalgam instead of the pure metal. A liquid amalgam has the advantage of eliminating nonreproducible effects due to strains in the solid metals or polarization at the electrode surface.* In some instances a dilute amalgam electrode can be successfully employed while the pure metal would react violently with the solution, for example in the sodium amalgam half cell, $NaHg(c_1) \mid Na^+(c_2)$. If the amalgam is saturated with the solute metal, the electrode is equivalent to a solid

* The high hydrogen overvoltage on mercury (Sec. 10.23) helps to eliminate polarization.

metal electrode, since the chemical potential of a component in its saturated solution equals the chemical potential of pure solute.* If the amalgam is not saturated, methods are available for calculating the emf of a pure metal electrode from a series of measurements at different amalgam concentrations.

Gas electrodes can be constructed by placing a strip of nonreactive metal, usually platinum or gold, in contact with both the solution and a gas stream. The hydrogen electrode consists of a platinum strip exposed to a current of hydrogen, and partly immersed in an acid solution. The hydrogen is probably dissociated into atoms at the catalytic surface of the platinum, the electrode reactions being

$$\tfrac{1}{2}H_2 \longrightarrow H$$
$$H \longrightarrow H^+ + e$$
$$\text{overall:} \qquad \tfrac{1}{2}H_2 \longrightarrow H^+ + e$$

The chlorine electrode operates similarly, negative chloride ions being formed in the solution: $e + \tfrac{1}{2}Cl_2 \rightarrow Cl^-$. The chlorine passes into the solution over an inert metal electrode.

In *nonmetal–nongas electrodes*, the inert metal passes into a liquid or solid phase. An example is in the bromine–bromide half cell: $Pt \mid Br_2 \mid Br^-$.

In an *oxidation–reduction electrode* an inert metal dips into a solution containing ions in two different oxidation states, e.g., ferric and ferrous ions in the half cell $Pt \mid Fe^{++}, Fe^{+++}$. When electrons are supplied to the electrode, the reaction is $Fe^{+++} + e \rightarrow Fe^{++}$. Since it is the function of electrodes either to accept electrons from, or to donate electrons to ions in the solution, they are all in a sense oxidation–reduction electrodes. The difference between the silver electrode and the ferric–ferrous electrode is that in the former the concentration of the lower oxidation state, metallic silver, cannot be varied.

Metal, insoluble-salt electrodes consist of a metal in contact with one of its slightly soluble salts; in the half cell, this salt is in turn in contact with a solution containing a common anion. An example is the silver, silver-chloride half cell: $Ag \mid AgCl \mid Cl^-(c_1)$. The electrode reaction can be considered in two steps:

$$AgCl(s) \rightleftarrows Ag^+ + Cl^-$$
$$Ag^+ + e \rightleftarrows Ag(s)$$

Or, overall,

$$AgCl(s) + e \rightleftarrows Ag(s) + Cl^-$$

Such an electrode is thermodynamically equivalent to a chlorine electrode ($Cl_2 \mid Cl^-$) in which the gas is at a pressure equal to the dissociation pressure of AgCl according to $AgCl \rightleftarrows Ag + \tfrac{1}{2}Cl_2$. This is a useful fact in view of the experimental difficulties involved in the use of reactive gas electrodes. The metal, insoluble-salt electrode is reversible with respect to the common anion.

Metal, insoluble-oxide electrodes are similar to the metal, insoluble-salt type. An example is the antimony, antimony-trioxide electrode, $Sb \mid Sb_2O_3 \mid OH^-$. An

* The solid phase may itself be an alloy of mercury with the metal, in which case the activity of metal in the liquid amalgam is definitely below that of the pure metal. The cadmium–mercury system is of this kind.

antimony rod is covered with a thin layer of oxide and dips into a solution containing OH^- ions. The electrode reaction is

$$Sb(s) + 3\,OH^- \rightleftarrows \tfrac{1}{2}Sb_2O_3 + \tfrac{3}{2}H_2O(l) + 3\,e$$

The electrode is reversible with respect to OH^- ions. Since OH^- and H^+ ions can establish rapid equilibrium, the electrode is also reversible with respect to H^+ ions.

9. CLASSIFICATION OF CELLS

When two suitable half cells are connected, we have an *electrochemical cell.* The connection is made by bringing the solutions in the half cells into contact, so that ions can pass between them. If these two solutions are the same, there is no liquid junction, and we have a *cell without transference.* If the solutions are different, the transport of ions across the junction will cause irreversible changes in the two electrolytes, and we have a *cell with transference.*

The decrease in free energy $-\Delta G$ that provides the driving force in a cell may come from a chemical reaction or from a physical change. In particular, we often study cells in which the driving force is a change in concentration (almost always a dilution process). These cells are called *concentration cells.* The change in concentration can occur either in the electrolyte or in the electrodes. Examples of changes in concentration in electrodes are found in amalgams or alloy electrodes with different concentrations of the solute metal and in gas electrodes with different pressures of the gas.

The varieties of electrochemical cells can therefore be classified as follows:

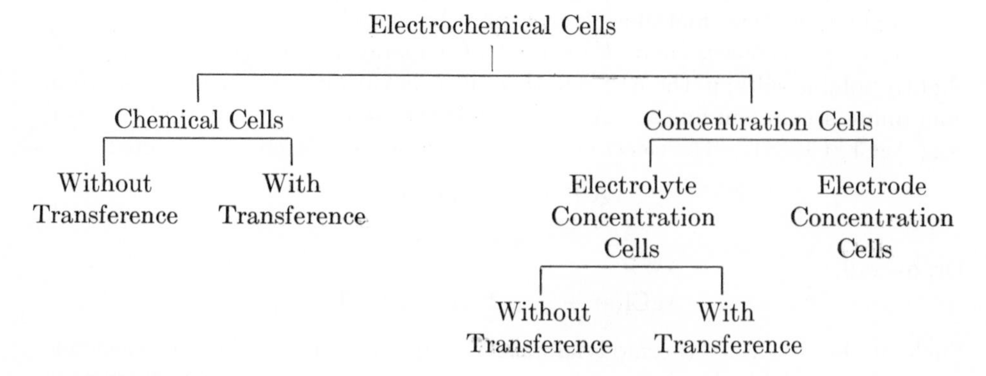

10. THE STANDARD EMF OF CELLS

Let us consider the generalized cell reaction: $aA + bB \rightleftarrows cC + dD$. By comparison with Eq. (6.11), the free-energy change in terms of the activities of the reactants is

$$\Delta G = \Delta G^\circ + RT \ln \frac{a_C^c a_D^d}{a_A^a a_B^b}$$

Since $\Delta G = -|z|\, FE$, division by $-|z|\, F$ gives

$$E = E^\circ - \frac{RT}{|z|\, F} \ln \frac{a_C^c a_D^d}{a_B^b a_A^a} \tag{10.5}$$

We shall call Eq. (10.5) the *Nernst equation.**

When the activities of all the products and reactants are unity, the value of the emf is $E^\circ = -\Delta G^\circ/|z|\, F$. This E° is called the *standard emf* of the cell. It is related to the equilibrium constant of the cell reaction, since

$$E^\circ = -\frac{\Delta G^\circ}{|z|\, F} = \frac{RT}{|z|\, F} \ln K_a \tag{10.6}$$

The determination of the standard emf's of cells is therefore one of the most important procedures in electrochemistry. We shall illustrate a useful method by means of a typical example.

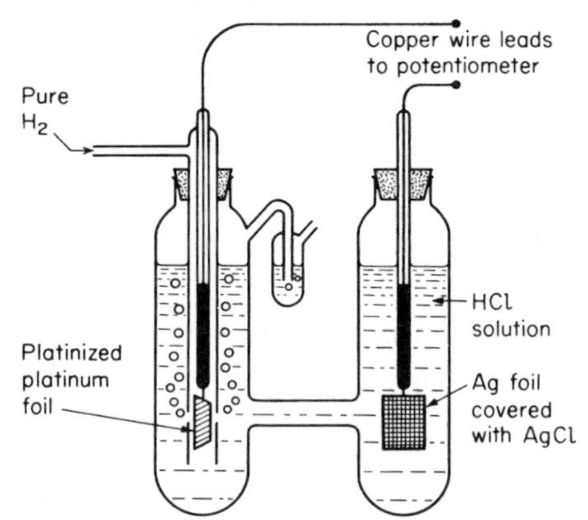

FIG. 10.4 Hydrogen electrode and silver, silver-chloride electrode in arrangement for standard emf determination.

Consider the cell shown in Fig. 10.4, consisting of a hydrogen electrode and a silver-silver chloride electrode immersed in a solution of hydrochloric acid:

$$\mathrm{Pt(H_2)} \mid \mathrm{HCl}(m) \mid \mathrm{AgCl} \mid \mathrm{Ag}$$

This is a chemical cell without a liquid junction. The electrode reactions are

$$\tfrac{1}{2}\mathrm{H_2} \rightleftharpoons \mathrm{H^+} + e$$

$$\mathrm{AgCl} + e \rightleftharpoons \mathrm{Ag} + \mathrm{Cl^-}$$

The overall reaction is accordingly

$$\mathrm{AgCl} + \tfrac{1}{2}\mathrm{H_2} \rightleftharpoons \mathrm{H^+} + \mathrm{Cl^-} + \mathrm{Ag}$$

From Eq. (10.5) the emf of the cell is

$$E = E^\circ - \frac{RT}{F} \ln \frac{a_{\mathrm{Ag}}\, a_{\mathrm{H^+}}\, a_{\mathrm{Cl^-}}}{a_{\mathrm{AgCl}}\, a_{\mathrm{H_2}}^{1/2}}$$

Setting the activities of the solid phases equal to unity, and choosing the hydrogen pressure so that $a_{\mathrm{H_2}} = 1$ (for ideal gas, $P = 1$ atm), we obtain the equation,

$$E = E^\circ - \frac{RT}{F} \ln a_{\mathrm{H^+}}\, a_{\mathrm{Cl^-}}$$

Introducing the mean activity of the ions defined by Eq. (9.24), we have

$$E = E^\circ - \frac{2RT}{F} \ln a_\pm = E^\circ - \frac{2RT}{F} \ln \gamma_\pm m \tag{10.7}$$

* A similar expression was given by Nernst in terms of concentrations instead of activities.

On rearrangement,

$$E + \frac{2RT}{F} \ln m = E^\circ - \frac{2RT}{F} \ln \gamma_\pm$$

According to the Debye-Hückel theory, in dilute solutions $\ln \gamma_\pm = Am^{1/2}$, where A is a constant. Hence the equation becomes

$$E + \frac{2RT}{F} \ln m = E^\circ - \frac{2RTA}{F} m^{1/2}$$

If the quantity on the left is plotted against $m^{1/2}$, and extrapolated back to $m = 0$, the intercept at $m = 0$ gives the value of E°.* For this cell one obtains $E^\circ = 0.2225$ volt at 25°C.

Once the standard emf has been determined in this way, Eq. (10.7) can be used to calculate mean activity coefficients for HCl from the measured emf's E in solutions of different molalities m.

11. STANDARD ELECTRODE POTENTIALS

Rather than tabulate data for all the numerous cells that have been measured, it would be much more convenient to make a list of *single-electrode potentials* of the various half cells. Cell emf's could then be obtained simply by taking differences between these electrode potentials. The status of single-electrode potentials is similar to that of single-ion activities. In 1899 Gibbs† pointed out that it is not possible to devise any experimental procedure that will measure a difference in *electrical potential* between two points in media of different chemical composition, for instance, a metal electrode and the surrounding electrolyte. What we always in fact measure is a difference in potential between two points at the same chemical composition, such as two brass terminals of a potentiometer.

Consider an ion of copper: (a) in metallic copper, (b) in a solution of copper sulfate. Its state is determined by its chemical environment, usually expressed by its chemical potential μ, and by its electrical environment, expressed by its electrical potential U. But there is no way of experimentally separating these two factors, since there is no way of separating electricity from matter and the phenomena we call "chemical" are all "electrical" in origin. Thus we can measure only the *electrochemical potential* of an ion, $\mu' = \mu + U$. It may sometimes be convenient to make an arbitrary separation of this quantity into two parts, but there is no way to give the separation an experimental meaning.

* A. S. Brown and D. A. MacInnes, *J. Am. Chem. Soc. 57*, 1356 (1935). In practice an extended form of the Debye-Hückel theory is often used to give a somewhat better extrapolation function.

† *Collected Works*, vol. 1, p. 429. See also E. A. Guggenheim, *J. Phys. Chem. 33*, 842 (1929).

Although we cannot measure absolute single-electrode potentials, we can solve the problem of reducing the cell emf's to a common basis by expressing all the values relative to the same reference electrode. The choice of a conventional reference state does not affect the values of differences between the electrode potentials, i.e., the cell emf's. The reference electrode is taken to be the *standard hydrogen electrode (SHE)*, which is assigned by convention the value $E^\circ = 0$. It is the hydrogen electrode in which (a) the pressure of hydrogen is 1 atm (strictly, unit fugacity, but the gas may be taken to be ideal), (b) the solution is a hydrogen acid in which the mean ionic activity is $a_\pm = 1$. Thus,

$$\mathrm{Pt} \mid \mathrm{H_2}\ (1\ \mathrm{atm}) \mid \mathrm{H^+}(a_\pm = 1)$$

If a cell is formed by combining any half cell X with the standard hydrogen half cell, the measured potential of the electrode in question relative to that of the standard hydrogen electrode taken as zero is called the *relative electrode potential*, or in short, the *electrode potential*, of X. Thus if the electrode X is positive with respect to the *SHE*, the electrode potential of X is positive. The sign of the electrode potential always is the observed sign of its polarity when it is coupled with a standard hydrogen electrode.* *The sign of the electrode potential is the experimentally measured sign of the cell emf if the SHE is on the left and the electrode in question on the right.*

For example,

$$\mathrm{Pt} \mid \mathrm{H_2}\ (1\ \mathrm{atm}) \mid \mathrm{H^+}(a_\pm = 1) \parallel X^+ \mid X$$

Then, the emf is

$$E = E_{\mathrm{right}} - E_{\mathrm{left}}$$
$$= E_{X/X^+} - E^\circ_{\mathrm{H_2/H^+}} = E_{X/X^+}$$

If the emf is the standard emf E°, the electrode potential is the *standard electrode potential*. When we speak of an *electrode potential*, we usually mean this standard

* The electrode potential defined here is algebraically equivalent to the electrode potential defined by the 1953 Stockholm convention. It is also similar to the definition given by Gibbs. The electrode potential so defined is a *sign invariant quantity*. By this we mean that it has a definite sign, which in no way depends on how the electrode is written on paper. The sign is the *experimental polarity* of the electrode when coupled with a *SHE*.

The electrode potential as defined is the *half-cell emf* of the electrode

$$X^+ \mid X$$

This is the emf of the cell,

$$\mathrm{Pt} \mid \mathrm{H_2} \mid \mathrm{H^+} \parallel X^+ \mid X$$

in which the cell reaction is

$$\tfrac{1}{2}\mathrm{H_2} + X^+ \rightarrow \mathrm{H^+} + X$$

Brewer and Pitzer (Second edition of Lewis and Randall *Thermodynamics*) use a special symbol $\mathcal{V}$ for the electrode potential. This device adds clarity to the first discussion of the subject but hardly seems necessary once the definitions are clearly understood.

potential, which is the one given in Tables. The electrode potential for any other choice of activities can be calculated from Eq. (10.5).

For example, in the previous section, the cell,

$$\text{Pt}(\text{H}_2) \mid \text{HCl} \mid \text{AgCl} \mid \text{Ag}$$

was found to have $E° = 0.2225$ v. The standard potential of the Ag/AgCl electrode is therefore 0.2225 volts.

A selection of electrode potentials is given in Table 10.1. Notice that the more *electropositive* elements, such as Na and K have the more *negative potentials*, since they have the greatest tendency to *lose electrons*.*

12. CALCULATION OF THE EMF OF A CELL

As a typical example, let us calculate the emf at 25°C of the cell,

$$\text{Zn} \mid \text{ZnSO}_4\ (m = 1) \parallel \text{CuSO}_4\ (m = 1) \mid \text{Cu}$$

The cell reaction is

$$\text{Zn} + \text{CuSO}_4 \longrightarrow \text{ZnSO}_4 + \text{Cu}$$

The $E°$, from Table 10.1, is $E_R^\circ - E_L^\circ = +0.337 - (-0.763) = +1.100$ v. The Nernst equation becomes

$$E = E° - \frac{RT}{2F} \ln \frac{a_{\text{ZnSO}_4} a_{\text{Cu}}}{a_{\text{CuSO}_4} a_{\text{Zn}}}$$

or

$$E = 1.100 - 0.0295 \log \frac{a_\pm^2(\text{ZnSO}_4)}{a_\pm^2(\text{CuSO}_4)}$$

From Eq. (9.30),

$$a_\pm = \gamma_\pm m$$

From Table 9.6, for $CuSO_4$ at $m = 1.00$, $\gamma_\pm = 0.047$,

$ZnSO_4$ at $m = 1.00$, $\gamma_\pm = 0.045$

Thus,

$$E = 1.100 - 0.059 \log \frac{.045}{.047} = 1.101 \text{ volt}$$

---

* The most comprehensive survey of the data on electrode reaction is *The Oxidation Potentials of the Elements and Their Values in Aqueous Solution*, by Wendell Latimer (New York: Prentice-Hall, 1952). The *oxidation potentials* tabulated are the emf's of the cells

$$X \mid X^+ \parallel \text{H}^+ \mid (\text{H}_2)\text{Pt}$$

The signs are therefore the opposite of those used in this book. Please take care in reading earlier works to be sure you know which sign convention is used.

TABLE 10.1 STANDARD ELECTRODE POTENTIALS*

Electrode	*Electrode Reaction*	$E°$ *(volts)*
	(Acid Solutions)	
$Li \mid Li^+$	$Li^+ + e \rightleftarrows Li$	−3.045
$K \mid K^+$	$K^+ + e \rightleftarrows K$	−2.925
$Cs \mid Cs^+$	$Cs^+ + e \rightleftarrows Cs$	−2.923
$Ba \mid Ba^{++}$	$Ba^{++} + 2e \rightleftarrows Ba$	−2.90
$Ca \mid Ca^{++}$	$Ca^{++} + 2e \rightleftarrows Ca$	−2.87
$Na \mid Na^+$	$Na^+ + e \rightleftarrows Na$	−2.714
$Mg \mid Mg^{++}$	$Mg^{++} + 2e \rightleftarrows Mg$	−2.37
$Al \mid Al^{+3}$	$Al^{+3} + 3e \rightleftarrows Al$	−1.66
$Zn \mid Zn^{++}$	$Zn^{++} + 2e \rightleftarrows Zn$	−0.763
$Fe \mid Fe^{++}$	$Fe^{++} + 2e \rightleftarrows Fe$	−0.440
$Cd \mid Cd^{++}$	$Cd^{++} + 2e \rightleftarrows Cd$	−0.403
$Sn \mid Sn^{++}$	$Sn^{++} + 2e \rightleftarrows Sn$	−0.136
$Pb \mid Pb^{++}$	$Pb^{++} + 2e \rightleftarrows Pb$	−0.126
$Fe \mid Fe^{+3}$	$Fe^{+3} + 3e \rightleftarrows Fe$	−0.036
$Pt \mid D_2 \mid D^+$	$2D^+ + 2e \rightleftarrows D_2$	−0.0034
$Pt \mid H_2 \mid H^+$	$2H^+ + 2e \rightleftarrows H_2$	ZERO
$Pt \mid Sn^{+2}, Sn^{+4}$	$Sn^{+4} + 2e \rightleftarrows Sn^{+2}$	+0.15
$Pt \mid Cu^+, Cu^{++}$	$Cu^{++} + e \rightleftarrows Cu^+$	+0.153
$Pt \mid S_2O_3^=, S_4O_6^=$	$S_4O_6^= + 2e \rightleftarrows 2S_2O_3^=$	+0.17
$Cu \mid Cu^{++}$	$Cu^{++} + 2e \rightleftarrows Cu$	+0.337
$Pt \mid I_2 \mid I^-$	$I_2 + 2e \rightleftarrows 2I^-$	+0.5355
$Pt \mid Fe(CN_6)^{-4}, Fe(CN)_6^{-3}$	$Fe(CN)_6^{-3} + e \rightleftarrows Fe(CN)_6^{-4}$	+0.69
$Pt \mid Fe^{+2}, Fe^{+3}$	$Fe^{+3} = e \rightleftarrows Fe^{+2}$	+0.771
$Ag \mid Ag^+$	$Ag^+ + e \rightleftarrows Ag$	+0.7991
$Hg \mid Hg^{++}$	$Hg^{++} + 2e \rightleftarrows Hg$	+0.854
$Pt \mid Hg_2^{++}, Hg^{++}$	$2Hg^{++} + 2e \rightleftarrows Hg_2^{++}$	+0.92
$Pt \mid Br_2 \mid Br^-$	$Br_2 + 2e \rightleftarrows 2Br^-$	+1.0652
$Pt \mid MnO_2 \mid Mn^{++}, H^+$	$MnO_2 + 4H^+ + 2e \rightleftarrows Mn^{++} + 2H_2O$	+1.23
$Pt \mid Cr^{+3}, Cr_2O_7^=, H^+$	$Cr_2O_7^= + 14H^+ + 6e \rightleftarrows 2Cr^{+3} + 7H_2O$	+1.33
$Pt \mid Cl_2 \mid Cl^-$	$Cl_2 + 2e \rightleftarrows 2Cl^-$	+1.3595
$Pt \mid Ce^{+3}, Ce^{+4}$	$Ce^{+4} + e \rightleftarrows Ce^{+3}$	+1.61
$Pt \mid Co^{+2}, Co^{+3}$	$Co^{+3} + e \rightleftarrows Co^{+2}$	+1.82
$Pt \mid SO_4^=, S_2O_8^=$	$S_2O_8^= + 2e \rightleftarrows 2SO_4^=$	+1.98
	(Basic Solutions)	
$Pt \mid Ca \mid Ca(OH)_2 \mid OH^-$	$Ca(OH)_2 + 2e \rightleftarrows 2OH^- + Ca$	−3.03
$Pt \mid H_2PO_2^-, HPO_3^=, OH^-$	$HPO_3^= + 2e \rightleftarrows H_2PO_2^- + 3OH^-$	−1.57
$Zn \mid ZnO_2^=, OH^-$	$ZnO_2^= + 2H_2O + 2e \rightleftarrows Zn + 4OH^-$	−1.216
$Pt \mid SO_3^=, SO_4^=, OH^-$	$SO_4^= + H_2O + 2e \rightleftarrows SO_3^= + 2OH^-$	−0.93
$Pt \mid H_2 \mid OH^-$	$2H_2O + 2e \rightleftarrows H_2 + 2OH^-$	−0.828
$Ni \mid Ni(OH)_2 \mid OH^-$	$Ni(OH)_2 + 2e \rightleftarrows Ni + 2OH^-$	−0.72
$Pb \mid PbCO_3 \mid CO_3^=$	$PbCO_3 + 2e \rightleftarrows Pn + CO_3^=$	−0.506
$Pt \mid OH^-, HO_2^-$	$HO_2^- + H_2O + 2e \rightleftarrows 3OH^-$	+0.88

* W. M. Latimer, *Oxidation Potentials* (New York: Prentice-Hall, 2nd ed., 1952).

Thus, provided activity coefficients are available for the electrolytes used, we can calculate reliable cell emf's from the tabulated electrode potentials and the Nernst equation.*

13. CALCULATION OF SOLUBILITY PRODUCTS

Standard electrode potentials can be combined to yield the E° and thus the ΔG° and equilibrium constant for the solution of salts. In this way we can calculate the solubility of a salt even if its extremely low value makes direct measurement difficult.

As an example, consider silver iodide, which dissolves according to: $AgI \rightarrow Ag^+ + I^-$. The *solubility product constant* is $K_{sp} = a_{Ag^+}a_{I^-}$. A cell whose net reaction corresponds to the solution of silver iodide can be formed by combining an Ag|AgI electrode with an Ag electrode,

$$Ag \mid Ag^+, I^- \mid AgI(s) \mid Ag$$

The electrode reactions are:

	Electrode potentials
$AgI(s) + e \longrightarrow Ag + I^-$	$E^\circ = -0.1518$ v
$Ag \longrightarrow Ag^+ + e$	$E^\circ = +0.7991$ v
Overall reaction: $AgI(s) \longrightarrow Ag^+ + I^-$	$E^\circ = -0.9509$ v $(E_{right} - E_{left})$

Then, from $\Delta G^\circ = -|z|\,FE^\circ = -RT \ln K_{sp}$,

$$\log_{10} K_{sp} = \frac{(-0.951 \times 96\,520)}{(2.303 \times 8.31 \times 298.2)} = -16.05$$

The activity coefficients will be unity in the very dilute solution of AgI, so that K_{sp} corresponds to a solubility of 2.47×10^{-6} g per liter.

14. STANDARD FREE ENERGIES AND ENTROPIES OF AQUEOUS IONS

Closely related to the standard electrode potential on the hydrogen scale is the *standard free energy of an ion.* Once again, all values are referred to a conven-

* Sometimes we may wish to use the Nernst equation to calculate the *sign invariant* electrode potential at activities other than unity. The electrode reaction in terms of the transfer of n electrons can be written:

$$Ox + ne \rightleftarrows Red$$

where Ox and Red refer to the oxidized and reduced species in the electrode. For example,

$$Zn^{+2} + 2e \rightleftarrows Zn$$

The Nernst equation for the electrode potential is

$$E = E^\circ + \frac{RT}{nF} \ln \frac{[Ox]}{[Red]}$$

tional reference standard, the hydrogen ion at $a_{\pm} = 1$, which is taken to have a standard free energy of zero. Consider the reaction,

$$\mathrm{Cd} + 2\,\mathrm{H}^+ \longrightarrow \mathrm{Cd}^{++} + \mathrm{H}_2 \qquad E^\circ = 0.403 \qquad (25^\circ\mathrm{C})$$

If all the reactants are in their standard states:*

$$-|z|\, FE^\circ = \Delta G^\circ = \bar{G}^\circ_{\mathrm{Cd}^{++}} + \bar{G}^\circ_{\mathrm{H}_2} - \bar{G}^\circ_{\mathrm{Cd}} - 2\bar{G}^\circ_{\mathrm{H}^+}$$

Now $\bar{G}^\circ_{\mathrm{H}_2}$ and $\bar{G}^\circ_{\mathrm{Cd}}$ are zero because the free energies of the elements are taken as zero in their standard states at 25°C, and $\bar{G}^\circ_{\mathrm{H}^+}$ is zero by our convention. It follows that

$$\bar{G}^\circ_{\mathrm{Cd}^{++}} = \Delta G^\circ = -|z|\, FE^\circ = \frac{-2 \times 0.403 \times 96\,520}{4.184} = -18.58 \text{ kcal per mole}$$

In addition to the standard ionic free energies, it is useful to obtain also the standard ionic entropies, $\bar{S}^\circ$. These are the partial molar entropies of the ions in solution relative to the conventionally chosen standard that sets the entropy of the hydrogen ion at unit activity equal to zero, $\bar{S}^\circ_{\mathrm{H}^+} = 0$. These ionic entropies provide a measure of the ordering effect produced by an ion on the surrounding water molecules. Small ions like Li^+ and F^- have lower entropies than larger ions like Na^+ and Cl^-. This difference is in accord with the data from transference experiments discussed on p. 337. Ions bearing a multiple charge are found to have especially low entropies in aqueous solution, as a result of their strong electrostatic attraction for the water dipoles and correspondingly large ordering effect on the solvent.

One method for calculating the ionic entropies may be illustrated in terms of our example, the Cd^{++} ion. Consider again the reaction: $\mathrm{Cd} + 2\,\mathrm{H}^+ \rightarrow \mathrm{Cd}^{++} + \mathrm{H}_2$. The standard entropy change is

$$\Delta S^\circ = \bar{S}^\circ_{\mathrm{Cd}^{++}} + \bar{S}^\circ_{\mathrm{H}_2} - 2\bar{S}^\circ_{\mathrm{H}^+} - \bar{S}^\circ_{\mathrm{Cd}}$$

Now $\bar{S}^\circ_{\mathrm{Cd}}$ and $\bar{S}^\circ_{\mathrm{H}_2}$ have been evaluated from Third-Law measurements and statistical calculations, being 12.3 and 31.23 cal deg^{-1} mole^{-1} at 25°C. By our convention, $\bar{S}^\circ_{\mathrm{H}^+}$ is zero. Therefore $\bar{S}^\circ_{\mathrm{Cd}^{++}} = \Delta S^\circ - 18.93$. The value of ΔS° can be obtained from $\Delta S^\circ = (\Delta H^\circ - \Delta G^\circ)/T$. If cadmium is dissolved in a large excess of dilute acid, the heat of solution per mole of cadmium is the standard enthalpy change ΔH°, since in the extremely dilute solution all the activity coefficients approach unity. This experiment yields the value $\Delta H^\circ = -16\,700$ cal. The ΔG° from the cell emf was found to be $-18\,580$ cal. Therefore $\Delta S^\circ = (-16\,700 + 18\,580)/298.2 = 6.22$ cal per deg. It follows that $\bar{S}^\circ_{\mathrm{Cd}^{++}} = -12.7$ cal per deg.

The methods described for determining the thermodynamic properties of ions in solution represent only a few examples of many possible ways of combining thermodynamic data. Latimer's book, *The Oxidation States of the Elements and Their Potentials in Aqueous Solutions,* should be consulted for a thorough survey of this important field and extensive tables of the thermodynamic quantities.

* The free energies are written $\bar{G}$ because for species in solution they are the partial molar free energies or chemical potentials.

15. ELECTRODE-CONCENTRATION CELLS

An example of an electrode-concentration cell would be one consisting of two hydrogen electrodes operating at different pressures and dipping into a solution of hydrochloric acid.

$$\text{Pt} \mid H_2(P_1) \mid \text{HCl}(a) \mid H_2(P_2) \mid \text{Pt}$$

At the left electrode: $\frac{1}{2} H_2(P_1) \longrightarrow H^+(a_\pm) + e$

At the right: $H^+(a_\pm) + e \longrightarrow \frac{1}{2} H_2(P_2)$

The overall change is accordingly $\frac{1}{2} H_2(P_1) \rightarrow \frac{1}{2} H_2(P_2)$, the transfer of one equivalent of hydrogen from pressure P_1 to P_2. The emf of the cell is

$$E = \frac{-RT}{F} \ln \frac{P_2}{P_1}$$

An interesting type of electrode concentration cell is one in which two amalgam electrodes of different concentrations dip into a solution containing the solute metal ions. For example:

$$\text{Cd—Hg}(a_1) \mid \text{CdSO}_4 \mid \text{Cd—Hg}(a_2)$$

The emf of this cell arises from the net work obtained in transferring cadmium from an amalgam in which its activity is a_1 to an amalgam in which its activity is a_2. The emf is therefore

$$E = \frac{-RT}{2F} \ln \frac{a_2}{a_1}$$

If the amalgams are considered to be ideal solutions, we may replace the activities by mole fractions. In Table 10.2 are some experimental data for these cells, together with the calculated emf's based on ideal solutions. Note how theoretical values are approached with increasing dilution.

TABLE 10.2 Cadmium Amalgam Electrode-Concentration Cells*

Grams Cadmium per 100 grams Mercury		Emf Observed	Emf Calculated
Electrode (1)	Electrode (2)		
1.000	0.1000	0.02966	0.02950
0.1000	0.01000	0.02960	0.02950
0.01000	0.001000	0.02956	0.02950
0.001000	0.0001000	0.02950	0.02950

* G. Hulett, *J. Am. Chem. Soc. 30*, 1805 (1908).

Electrode-concentration cells are especially useful in studying the thermodynamics of alloys.*

* J. Chipman, *Discussions of the Faraday Soc. 4*, 23 (1948).

16. ELECTROLYTE-CONCENTRATION CELLS

We shall consider a cell in which the emf is derived from the free energy of dilution of the electrolyte.

For the cell $Pt|H_2|HCl(c)|AgCl|Ag$, the cell reaction is $\frac{1}{2}H_2 + AgCl \rightarrow Ag + HCl(c)$. Measurements with two different hydrochloric acid concentrations c yielded the following results:

c(m/l)	E	$-\Delta G$ (joule)
0.0010	0.6095	58 820
0.0483	0.3870	37 340

If two such cells oppose each other, the combination constitutes a cell that can be written,

$$Ag \mid AgCl \mid HCl(c_2) \mid H_2 \mid HCl(c_1) \mid AgCl \mid Ag$$

The overall change in this cell is simply the difference between the changes in the two separate cells: for the passage of each faraday, the transfer of one mole of HCl from concentration c_2 to c_1, $HCl(c_2) \rightarrow HCl(c_1)$. Note, however, that there can be no direct transference of electrolyte from one side to the other. The HCl is removed from the left side by the reaction, $HCl + Ag \rightarrow AgCl + \frac{1}{2}H_2$. It is added to the right side by the reverse of this reaction. From the data above, if $c_1 = 0.001$ and $c_2 = 0.0483$, the free energy of dilution is $\Delta G = -21\,480$ and $E = (21\,480/96\,520) = 0.2225$ v. This cell is an example of a *concentration cell without transference.* The case of direct transfer of electrolyte across a liquid junction will be considered later.

17. CELLS WITH LIQUID JUNCTIONS

As was pointed out in Sec. 11, it is not possible to measure a difference in electrical potential between two chemically different media. Therefore liquid-junction potentials cannot be directly measured.

Attempts have been made to calculate liquid-junction potentials by solving diffusion equations for the ions in solution. Consider, for example, a junction between a solution of HCl and a solution of KCl. If the concentrations are about the same, one would expect the HCl solution to lose H^+ ions by diffusion more rapidly than the KCl solution loses K^+ ions, because the H^+ ion has a much higher mobility. Thus the HCl side of the contact would become negatively charged relative to the KCl side. Semiquantitative estimates based on this picture have led to junction potentials of from 5 to 30 millivolts, not large compared with the usual cell emf's.

Attempts have been made to eliminate the liquid-junction potential by using a salt bridge. Concentrated solutions of KCl or NH_4NO_3 are often used in the bridge. The ions in these solutions have nearly the same transport numbers, and one may hope that the two cell-to-bridge potentials will be nearly equal numerically but opposite in sign.

The most encouraging thing about cells with liquid junctions is that standard emf's obtained from them, when careful procedures are followed, often agree closely with the results from cells without liquid junctions. We thus can have considerable confidence in the necessary approximations. Cells without liquid junctions are used wherever possible, but in some applications, such as the measurement of pH, or of oxidation–reduction potentials of organic compounds, it is necessary to employ liquid junctions.

18. OXIDATION–REDUCTION REACTIONS

Cells with liquid junctions are frequently used to study the equilibrium in oxidation–reduction reactions. Special interest has been focused on the oxidations of organic substances in living cells, in view of the importance of such processes in cellular metabolism and respiration. Although the particular example is not a biological reaction, the principles involved can be illustrated by the oxidation of hydroquinone to quinone. The reaction is*

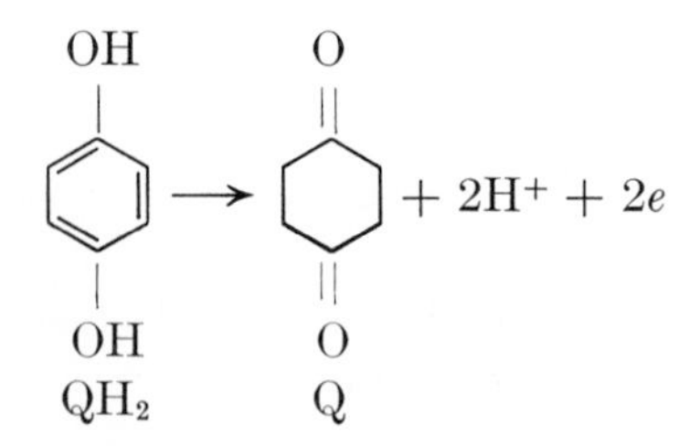

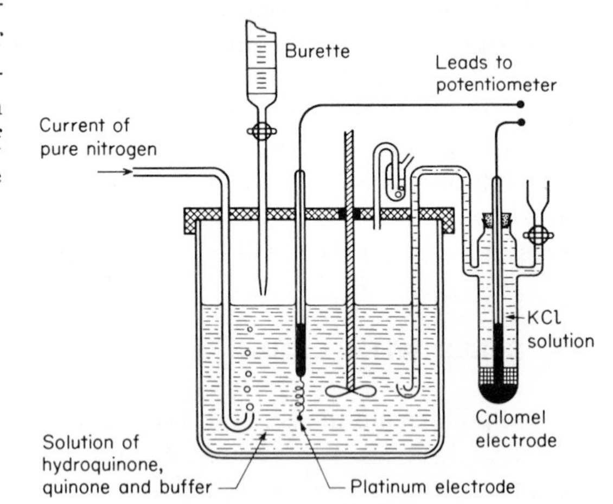

FIG. 10.5 Experimental arrangement for measuring emf of an oxidation-reduction reaction, or for a potentiometric titration.

If an inert metal electrode (Au or Pt) is placed in a solution containing a mixture of hydroquinone and quinone, the reaction can proceed in either direction as electrons are supplied or removed at the electrode. A complete cell can be formed by coupling this hydroquinone electrode with a calomel or other reference electrode. A typical experiment is shown in Fig. 10.5. The cell may be written

$$\text{Au} \mid \text{QH}_2, \text{Q (buffer: H}^+) \mid \text{KCl, Hg}_2\text{Cl}_2 \mid \text{Hg}_2\text{Cl}_2(s) \mid \text{Hg}$$

* Hydroquinone is a weak acid but in moderately acid solutions its dissociation is negligible. Under certain conditions the reaction proceeds in two steps, removal of one electron forming a highly colored *semiquinone*. See L. Michaelis, *Chem. Rev. 22*, 437 (1938).

The cell reaction is

At the left: $QH_2 \longrightarrow Q + 2H^+ + 2e$

At the right: $Hg_2Cl_2 + 2e \longrightarrow 2Hg + 2Cl^-$

Overall: $QH_2 + Hg_2Cl_2 \longrightarrow Q + 2Hg + 2H^+ + 2Cl^-$

The emf can be written

$$E = E^\circ - \frac{RT}{2F} \ln \frac{a_Q a_{H^+}^2 a_{Cl^-}^2}{a_{QH_2}}$$

$$E = E^\circ - \frac{RT}{2F} \ln \frac{a_Q}{a_{QH_2}} - \frac{RT}{F} \ln a_{HCl} \tag{10.8}$$

Since Q and QH_2 are uncharged species, it is a good approximation to replace their activity ratio by a concentration ratio. From measured values of E at known acid strengths, it is then possible to calculate E° and hence the equilibrium constant of the oxidation–reduction. Note that the E of the cell and therefore the driving force of the reaction depend on the acid concentration.

We can titrate the reduced form by adding an oxidizing agent from the buret. As the concentration of QH_2 approaches zero, it is evident from Eq. (10.8) that E approaches minus infinity. Consequently, when the amount of QH_2 remaining unoxidized becomes very small, the change in the measured cell emf becomes very steep. Of course E does not actually go to $-\infty$, because as the end point of the titration is approached the concentration of unreacted oxidizing agent (titrant) becomes appreciable, so that a new oxidation–reduction equilibrium is set up with an emf characteristic of the titrant system. The course of a typical *potentiometric titration* is shown in Fig. 10.6.. If the standard potentials of the titrated system and the titrant system are sufficiently far apart, a good end point can be readily determined.

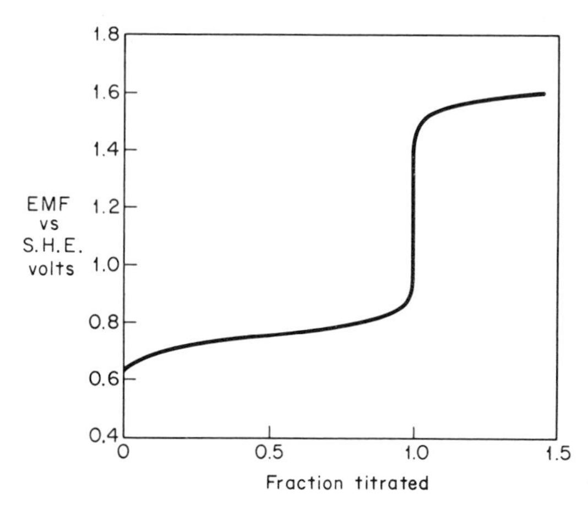

FIG. 10.6 Potentiometric titration of ferrous ion with ceric ion ($Fe^{2+} + Ce^{4+} \rightarrow Fe^{3+} + Ce^{3+}$)

19. MEASUREMENT OF *p*H

We often need to know the concentration of hydrogen ions in aqueous solution. In 1909, S. P. Sorensen invented the symbol *p*H as a convenient expression for this quantity, which he defined by $pH = -\log_{10} c_{H^+}$, where c_{H^+} is the molar concentration.

In 1909, strong electrolytes like HCl were believed to be only partially dissociated even in dilute solutions. The degree of dissociation was believed to be given by $\alpha = \Lambda/\Lambda_0$. Values of c_{H^+} were accordingly calculated from the equivalent conductivities, and Sorensen set up his pH scale on this basis. It now appears that strong electrolytes are completely dissociated in dilute solutions, so that the Sorensen pH scale is unsatisfactory.

For most practical purposes the pH is a number determined by potentiometric measurement of a cell emf. Since cell emf's depend on activities and not on concentrations it is probably wise to abandon the definition of pH by a concentration scale, except as a first approximation. It might seem logical to define pH as $-\log_{10} a_{H^+}$, but this definition has the considerable drawback that a_{H^+} is not itself an experimentally measurable quantity.

The best procedure seems to be to define a pH scale by reference to the measured emf of a cell consisting of a hydrogen electrode combined with some reference electrode. Such a cell might be

$$\text{(Pt)}H_2\text{, 1 atm} \mid H^+X^- \mid \text{KCl (saturated)} \mid Hg_2Cl_2\text{, KCl} \mid Hg_2Cl_2 \mid Hg$$

This cell contains two liquid junctions at the KCl salt bridge, so that we cannot separate the hydrogen electrode potential from the measured emf. If such a separation were possible, we could write the emf as

$$E = E_{\text{ref}} - \frac{RT}{F} \ln a_+$$

We now arbitrarily define the pH by writing

$$E = E_{\text{ref}} + 2.303 \frac{RT}{F} p\text{H} \tag{10.9}$$

We choose a value for E_{ref} that will give a pH value in accord with other thermodynamic data, such as the dissociation constants of weak acids. For the 0.1 normal KCl-calomel electrode this value at 25°C is $E_{\text{ref}} = 0.3358$ v. Therefore Eq. (10.9) defining the pH can be written

$$p\text{H} = \frac{E - 0.3358}{2.303RT/F} = \frac{E - 0.3358}{0.0592} \quad \text{(at 25°C)} \tag{10.10}$$

The hydrogen electrode is not well suited for routine pH measurements because it requires a source of gaseous hydrogen and it is sensitive to various poisons that inhibit the catalytic activity of the platinized surface. The most convenient method of measuring pH is undoubtedly by means of the *glass electrode*. The operation of this device depends upon the difference in potential across a glass membrane separating solutions of different pH.*

* M. Dole, *The Glass Electrode* (New York: Wiley, 1941).

20. CONCENTRATION CELLS WITH TRANSFERENCE

In electrolyte-concentration cells without liquid junctions, the type previously described, there is no direct transfer of electrolyte from one solution to the other. An example of a concentration cell that *does* have direct contact between the solutions is

$$\begin{array}{ccc} H_2\ (1\ \text{atm})\ |\ HCl\ (a_1) & | & HCl\ (a_2)\ |\ H_2\ (1\ \text{atm}) \\ \tfrac{1}{2}H_2 \longrightarrow H^+ & | & H^+ \longrightarrow \tfrac{1}{2}H_2 \\ & \underset{t_-Cl^-}{\overset{t_+H^+}{\rightleftarrows}} & \end{array}$$

The t's are the ionic transport numbers. For the passage of each faraday of charge, the following changes occur in the cell:

A. *At the electrodes.* (1) One equivalent of H^+ is formed at the left, by the reaction $\frac{1}{2}H_2 \rightarrow H^+(a_1)$. (2) One equivalent of H^+ is removed at the right, by the reaction $H^+(a_2) \rightarrow \frac{1}{2}H_2$. The net result of the electrode processes is $H^+(a_2) \rightarrow H^+(a_1)$.

B. *At the liquid junction.* (1) t_- equivalents of Cl^- ions pass from right to left, from the solution of activity a_2 to that of activity a_1. (2) $t_+ = (1 - t_-)$ equivalents of H^+ ions pass from left to right, from activity a_1 to a_2.

The net result of these changes at the electrodes and at the junction is

$$t_-(\text{HCl}) \text{ at } a_2 \longrightarrow t_-(\text{HCl}) \text{ at } a_1$$

Since the electrodes are reversible with respect to the cation H^+, the transport number t_- of the anion occurs in the expression for the net change.

Such a cell is called a *concentration cell with transference.* Note that it requires electrodes reversible with respect to only one of the ions. Concentration cells without transference require one electrode reversible with respect to the anion and one with respect to the cation.

The free-energy change of the cell reaction is $\Delta G = t_- RT \ln (a_1/a_2)$. The emf of the cell is accordingly

$$E_t = t_- \frac{RT}{F} \ln \frac{a_2}{a_1} \tag{10.11}$$

The same process, dilution of HCl from a_2 to a_1, can be carried out in the cell without transference whose emf is

$$E = \frac{RT}{F} \ln \frac{a_2}{a_1}$$

It follows that

$$t_- = \frac{E_t}{E} \tag{10.12}$$

From the ratio of the emf of concentration cells with and without transference, transport numbers can be obtained that are in good agreement with those measured in other ways. The result in Eq. (10.12) is, however, an approximation based on the assumption that the transport numbers do not depend on the concentration.

21. ELECTROLYSIS: DECOMPOSITION VOLTAGES

So far we have been considering electrode processes that are essentially reversible. These processes provide values for the equilibrium emf's of cells, which are related to the thermodynamic functions. The condition of reversibility is practically attained by balancing the cell emf against an external emf until only an imperceptible current flows through the cell, so that the cell reactions proceed extremely slowly. For many of the applications of electrochemistry, it is obviously necessary to consider more rapid reaction rates. Then there is necessarily a departure from the equilibrium situation. Either the cell reactions proceed spontaneously to generate electric energy, or an external source of electric energy is used to effect chemical reactions (electrolyses).

Let us consider, for example, the electrolysis of a strong solution of hydrochloric acid. Platinum electrodes are introduced into the solution and connected, through a device for varying the voltage, to an external source of electrical energy, such as a storage battery. The arrangement in (a), Fig. 10.7, may conveniently be used. If we gradually increase the applied voltage and measure the current flowing through the cell as a function of the potential difference across the electrodes, we find the typical result shown in (b), Fig. 10.7. We have plotted the current per unit area of the electrodes, called the *current density*, against the applied voltage. The current density is extremely small until a certain definite voltage is reached; thereafter the current density vs. voltage curve rises steeply. The voltage at which the current begins to flow freely corre-

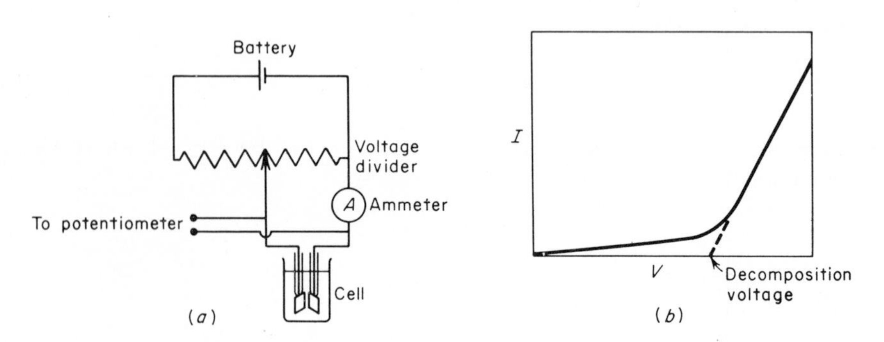

FIG. 10.7 (a) Measurement of decomposition voltage; (b) current-voltage curve.

sponds to that at which bubbles of gas are first discharged from the electrodes. It is called the *decomposition voltage* of the solution.

A definite decomposition voltage occurs for the following reason. As soon as the potential difference is set up between the electrodes, hydrogen ions migrate to the cathode and chloride ions to the anode. The ions are discharged, forming layers of adsorbed gas on the inert metal surfaces. Instead of two platinum electrodes, we now have a hydrogen electrode and a chlorine electrode. The result is a typical chemical cell:

$$\text{Pt} \mid \text{H}_2 \mid \text{H}^+\text{Cl}^-(a) \mid \text{Cl}_2 \mid \text{Pt}$$

We could have used external sources of hydrogen and chlorine to set up a cell like this, and the cell reaction would be

$$\text{H}_2 + \text{Cl}_2 \longrightarrow 2\,\text{HCl}$$

The reversible emf of such a cell is given by the Nernst equation (10.5) as

$$E = E^\circ - .059 \log (a_\pm)^2_{\text{HCl}}$$

From Table 10.1, $E^\circ = 1.3595$ v. If the solution is one molal, the mean activity coefficient of the HCl is $\gamma_\pm = 0.82$. Therefore the reversible emf of the cell is

$$E = 1.3595 - .118 \log (0.82) = 1.3697 \text{ v}$$

This is the difference in potential that we must apply from an external source to balance the driving force of the forward cell reaction. If we apply a potential difference just in excess of this value, we can reverse the cell reaction and begin the electrolysis of the HCl solution, $2\,\text{HCl} \rightarrow \text{H}_2 + \text{Cl}_2$.

If we start with two inert electrodes in the HCl solution, we can expect to find the same situation as soon as enough H^+ has discharged at the cathode and enough Cl^- at the anode to convert these electrodes into a hydrogen and a chlorine electrode respectively. In order to electrolyze the HCl solution, therefore, we must apply at least enough potential difference to overcome the reversible emf of the cell that is set up by this *polarization* of the inert electrodes. This emf is called the *back-emf* of the electrolytic cell.

In this particular case, the measured decomposition voltage was 1.370 v (with platinized platinum electrodes). In other cases the decomposition voltage may exceed the reversible back-emf, for reasons to be discussed later.

The curve in Fig. 10.7 shows that there is a small current through the cell even below the decomposition voltage. This is called the *diffusion current.* There is a slow diffusion of ions away from the polarized electrodes, and a small current of ions must flow toward the electrodes at any applied voltage in order to keep them polarized.

In the example just considered, the electrolysis of HCl solution, the ions that carry the current (H^+ and Cl^-) are also the ions that are discharged at the electrodes. In other cases, however, the principal ionic carriers of current may not be of the same species as the ions that are discharged. A good example is the electrolysis of $CuSO_4$ solution between platinum electrodes. A one molal $CuSO_4$ solution is quite acid so that the positive current carriers are both Cu^{++} and H^+ ions. The predominant negative carrier is the $SO_4^=$ ion. The solution contains, however, a small concentration of OH^- ions. To determine which ions will be discharged at the electrodes, we consider the standard electrode potentials,

$H_2 \mid H^+$	0.0
$Cu \mid Cu^{++}$	0.337
$O_2 \mid OH^-$	0.401
$S_2O_8^= \mid SO_4^=$	1.98

The electrode reactions that occur in the electrolysis of $CuSO_4$ will be those that proceed most readily, and in the absence of irreversible effects, these are the reactions which have the greatest driving force, or emf E. At the cathode the reactions possible are

$$Cu^{++} + 2e \longrightarrow Cu \quad E^\circ = 0.337$$

$$H^+ + e \longrightarrow \tfrac{1}{2}H_2 \quad E^\circ = 0$$

Thus if Cu^{++} and H^+ are present at unit activity the reduction of Cu^{++} is easier than the reduction of H^+, and Cu^{++} ions must be discharged in preference to H^+, until the Cu^{++} concentration has fallen to such a point that the E for its half cell reaction is less than that for the $H^+ \mid H_2$ half cell.

At the anode, the reactions are

$$2OH^- \longrightarrow H_2O + \tfrac{1}{2}O_2 + 2e \quad E^\circ = .401$$

$$2SO_4^= \longrightarrow S_2O_8^= + 2e \quad E^\circ = 1.98$$

In fact the oxygen electrode is not reversible, but the discharge potential for the $SO_4^=$ ion is so high that the OH^- ions are discharged preferentially even in extremely dilute $CuSO_4$ solution.

If we assume for the moment that the oxygen electrode is reversible, we can calculate from the Nernst equation the ratio of the activities of OH^- and $SO_4^=$ that must exist before $SO_4^=$ would begin to be discharged.

$$\Delta E^\circ = 1.98 - 0.40 = 1.58 = \frac{RT}{2F} \ln \frac{a_{SO_4^=}}{a_{OH^-}}$$

$$1.58 = \frac{.0592}{2} \log \frac{a_{SO_4^=}}{a_{OH^-}}$$

$$a_{SO_4^=}/a_{OH^-} \approx 10^{50}$$

Thus even with an impossibly low concentration of OH^- ions, the $SO_4^=$ ion cannot be discharged. The $SO_4^=$ ions carry almost all the negative charge across the electrolyte, but the job of giving up the electron to the anode is taken over by the OH^- ions.

Every tenfold change in concentration changes the emf by 0.0592/2 volts. It is evident that extremely large concentration charges would be needed to overcome a voltage difference of the order of one volt.

22. CONCENTRATION POLARIZATION

When an electrochemical cell is working under irreversible conditions, its emf necessarily departs from the equilibrium value. If the cell is acting as a battery or source of electricity, its voltage falls below the equilibrium value. If the cell is the site of electrolysis, the voltage supplied must exceed the equilibrium value.

Part of this voltage difference is necessary to overcome the resistance of the cell and is equal to the IR product. The corresponding electric energy I^2R is dissipated as heat. It is analogous to the frictional losses in irreversible mechanical processes.

In addition to this, we distinguish two other sources of voltage difference. One has its origin within the electrolyte of the cell, and the other is referred to rate processes occurring at the electrodes. The first is called *concentration polarization* and the second is called *overvoltage*.

As its name suggests, concentration polarization arises from concentration gradients within the electrolyte of the working cell. For example, consider a cell consisting of a copper anode and a platinum cathode in a solution of copper sulfate. When a current flows, copper is dissolved at the anode and deposited upon the cathode. If the current is appreciable, the solution around the cathode becomes relatively depleted of copper ions. Thus a concentration gradient is set up within the cell. This gradient is equivalent to a concentration cell of the type discussed in Sec. 10.16. The concentration cell produces a *back emf* opposing the applied voltage. Concentration polarization of this sort can often be reduced by vigorous stirring of the electrolyte, which destroys the concentration gradients caused by the electrolysis. Increase in temperature also tends to decrease the polarization, by accelerating the diffusion of electrolyte ions within the cell.

As the Cu^{++} plates out on the surface of the cathode, a layer of solution of thickness δ is formed in which the concentration of Cu^{++} is depleted. If the current is to continue to flow, Cu^{++} ions must diffuse into this region as a result of their random thermal motions in the solution. The flux of ions to the cathode will be governed by this slow step of diffusion of the *discharging ion* from the bulk of the solution where its concentration is c to the surface of the cathode where its concentration is c'. From Fick's first law [Eq. (9.17)], this flux will be

$$S_x = \frac{AD}{\delta}(c - c')$$

where A is the area of the electrode and D the diffusion coefficient of the ion.

For each faraday discharged, there must be a diffusion of $(1 - t_i)/|z|$ moles of ions, where t_i is the transference number of the ion. If the current density to the electrode is I_d, the diffusive flow of ions per second is

$$I_d A(1 - t_i)/|z|\, F$$

Equating this to the expression from Fick's law, we have

$$I_d = \frac{|z|\, FD}{(1 - t_i)\delta}(c - c') = \frac{|z|\, FD(c - c')}{t\delta} \qquad (10.13)$$

where t is the sum of the transference numbers of all the ions except i.

If no current is flowing through the cell, the reversible emf,

$$E = E^\circ - \frac{RT}{2F} \ln \gamma c$$

With a current I, the cell voltage must be increased to

$$E' = E^\circ - \frac{RT}{2F} \ln \gamma' c'$$

The difference in voltage due to concentration polarization becomes

$$E' - E = \Delta E = -\frac{RT}{2F} \ln \frac{\gamma' c'}{\gamma c}$$

From Eq. (10.13),

$$\Delta E = -\frac{RT}{2F} \ln \left[\frac{\gamma'}{\gamma} \left(1 - \frac{t\delta I_d}{cD|z| F} \right) \right] \tag{10.14}$$

This equation shows that as I_d approaches $cD|z| F/t\delta$, ΔE goes to infinity. Of course, before this happens some other ion will begin to be discharged. The theory shows, however, that for the discharge of each ion there will be a limiting possible current density I'_d controlled by the diffusion that follows concentration polarization at the electrode, and

$$I'_d = \frac{D|z| Fc}{t\delta} \tag{10.15}$$

In case the concentration of the discharging ions is much less than the sum of all the other ionic concentrations ($c_i \ll \sum' c_j$), $t = 1$. In this case, from Eq. (9.18),

$$I'_d = \frac{D|z| Fc}{\delta} = \frac{RT\lambda_i}{\delta F} c \tag{10.16}$$

The usual value of δ is about 0.05 cm and λ_i averages 60 ohm^{-1} cm^{-1}. Hence, approximately, $I'_d = 0.03\, c$.

23. OVERVOLTAGE

The phenomenon of *overvoltage* arises from a slow attainment of equilibrium at the electrodes, i.e., a slowness either in transfer of electrons to, or in the acceptance of electrons from, ions in the solution. Thus a free energy of activation is necessary for the reaction to proceed and the excess applied voltage serves to provide this free energy. The effect may be observed for most electrode processes, but for deposition or solution at metal electrodes it is usually small. Much more noteworthy are the overvoltages required for the liberation of gaseous hydrogen or oxygen, which may amount to a volt or more on certain metals.

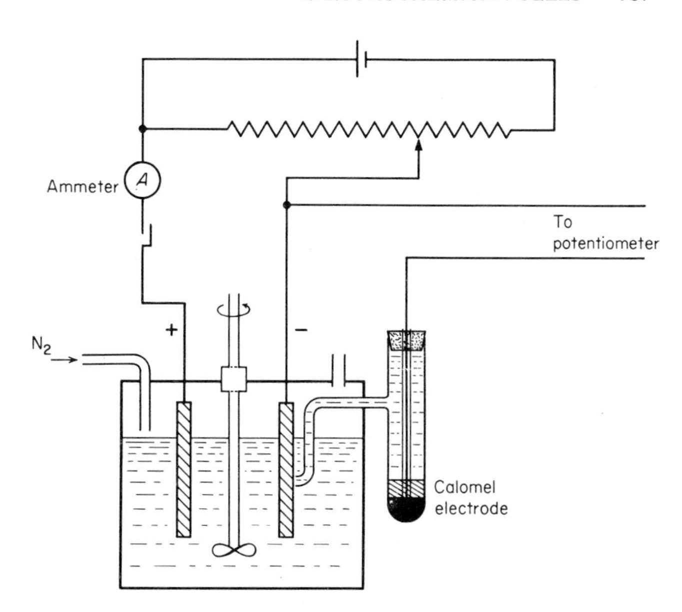

FIG. 10.8 Apparatus for measuring the overvoltage at an electrode as a function of current density.

The overvoltage can be measured with an experimental arrangement like that shown in Fig. 10.8. An auxiliary reference electrode, e.g., normal calomel, is placed close to the electrode being investigated (to minimize IR drop) and the potential of the electrode at which the gas is being discharged is measured as a function of the current density. The solution is stirred to eliminate concentration polarization. Some of the results with various metals are shown in Table 10.3. Only in the case of platinized platinum is the hydrogen overvoltage small at all current densities. The oxygen overvoltage behaves similarly, except that its value is appreciable even on platinized platinum.

TABLE 10.3 HYDROGEN OVERVOLTAGE OF METALS*

Metal	Current Density, amp cm^{-2}		
	0	0.01	0.10
Platinized platinum	0.005	0.035	0.055
Gold	0.02	0.56	0.77
Iron	0.08	0.56	0.82
Smooth platinum	0.09	—	0.39
Silver	0.15	0.76	0.90
Nickel	0.21	0.65	0.89
Copper	0.23	0.58	0.82
Lead	0.64	1.09	1.20
Zinc	0.70	0.75	1.06
Mercury	0.78	1.10	1.18

* After W. J. Hamer and R. E. Wood in *Handbook of Physics* (ed. E. U. Condon and H. Odishaw), (New York: McGraw-Hill, 1958). The values for zero current density are for lowest c.d. at which bubble formation could just be observed, usually about 5×10^{-5} amp cm^{-2}.

In many cases the overvoltage η varies with the logarithm of the current density I_d,

$$\eta = a + b \log I_d \tag{10.17}$$

In 1905, Tafel proposed Eq. (10.17) as an empirical relation. It can be derived on the basis that the overvoltage lowers the activation energy for the slow reaction that governs the discharge of H^+ ions at the cathode M.

We do not yet know which reaction is the slowest step. Several possibilities have been suggested:*

(1) $$OH_3^+ + M + e \longrightarrow H{-}M{-}H_2O$$

(2) $$2H{-}M \longrightarrow H_2 + 2M$$

(3) $$OH_3^+ + H{-}M + e \longrightarrow H_2 + M + H_2O$$

An alternative mechanism sees the slow step as the transfer of a proton from a water molecule in solution to one adsorbed at the electrode surface M,

(4) $$H_2O + H_2O{-}M \longrightarrow OH_3^+{-}M + OH^-$$

The overvoltage is important in practical applications of electrochemistry. Because of the high hydrogen overvoltage, we can plate metals from solutions in which their reversible discharge potentials are well below that of the hydrogen ion. For example, consider a cell consisting of platinum electrodes in a solution of zinc ions and hydrogen ions at unit activity. The reversible potentials of the half cells are

$$Zn \mid Zn^{++},\ E^\circ = -0.762;\ H_2 \mid H^+,\ E^\circ = 0$$

If H^+ discharged at its reversible potential, H_2 should be liberated at the cathode at a lower voltage than that required to plate out zinc. The overvoltage of hydrogen on zinc, however, amounts to about 1.0 v at 0.1 amp cm^{-2}, so that in an actual electrolysis, zinc will first be deposited on the cathode. The hydrogen ion will not be discharged rapidly until the zinc concentration has fallen to such a point that the emf of the zinc half cell lies above the hydrogen overvoltage. There will always, however, be a slow discharge in accord with the Tafel Equation (10.17).

24. THE POLAROGRAPH

Let us consider the electrolysis of a solution containing several different cations, Cu^{+2}, Tl^+, Zn^{+2}, etc. There is a certain reversible potential at which each ion is discharged at the cathode. This potential depends on the standard E° of the electrode $M|M^{+z}$, and on the concentration of M^{+z} in the solution. At 25°C,

$$E = E^\circ + \frac{.0592}{|z|} \log a_{M^{+z}}$$

Thus a tenfold change in the ionic activity changes the discharge potential of the ions by $.0592/|z|$ volts. A factor of 10^2 in activity corresponds to $0.1184/|z|$ volts.

* J. Bockris, *Chem. Rev.* *43*, 525 (1948).

If we gradually increase the potential applied to the cell, the cation with the highest value of E deposits first. As we continue to increase the applied potential, the current density also increases. As the current density rises, the concentration of the ion being discharged becomes more and more depleted in the neighborhood of the cathode, particularly if the solution is not stirred. This is the phenomenon of concentration polarization. Eventually the limiting value of I'_d is reached, given by Eq. (10.16) for the case of a stationary electrode. The I_d vs. voltage curve becomes flat and the potential rises to a value determined by the reversible discharge potential of the cation with next higher E. When this happens, the second ion begins to be discharged, even though there may still be an appreciable concentration of the first ion in the bulk of the solution. With increasing E, this process may be repeated with a third kind of ion, and so on.

Is there any way to use such a sequence of discharges of ions to identify the ions and to measure their concentrations in the solution? In 1922, Jaroslav Heyrovsky of Prague invented an elegant method. In 1924, Heyrovsky and Shikata devised an automatic instrument called the *polarograph* based on this method.

If we use the concentration polarization to differentiate reducible substances in a solution, we must have a cathode of tiny area, since otherwise the current through the cell would become impossibly high. We must eliminate transference on the part of the electroactive ion so that the current is not strongly dependent upon the mobility of the anion present. Also the cathode surface should be clean, reproducible and, preferably, readily renewable. The anode should be practically nonpolarizable. These conditions are met by the *dropping mercury electrode*, which provides a continual flow of droplets of mercury, about 0.5 mm in diameter. A pool of mercury located at the bottom of the cell can serve as a reference electrode and anode. Because of its large area it is negligibly polarized.

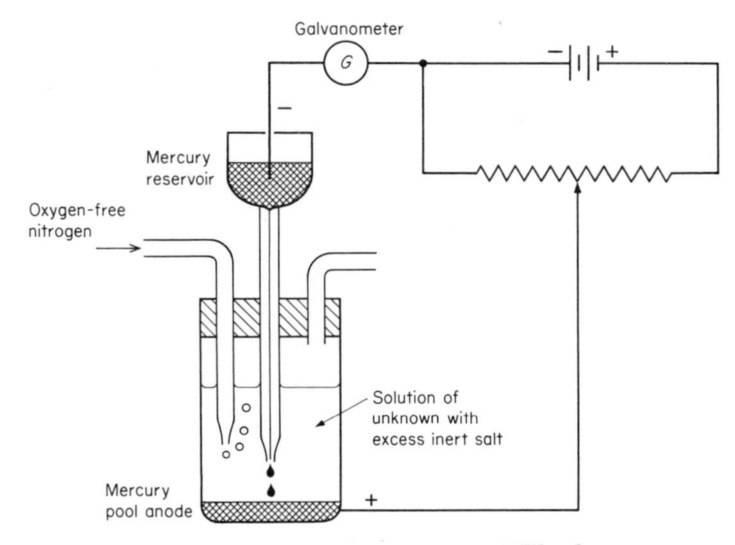

FIG. 10.9 Essential features of polarograph.

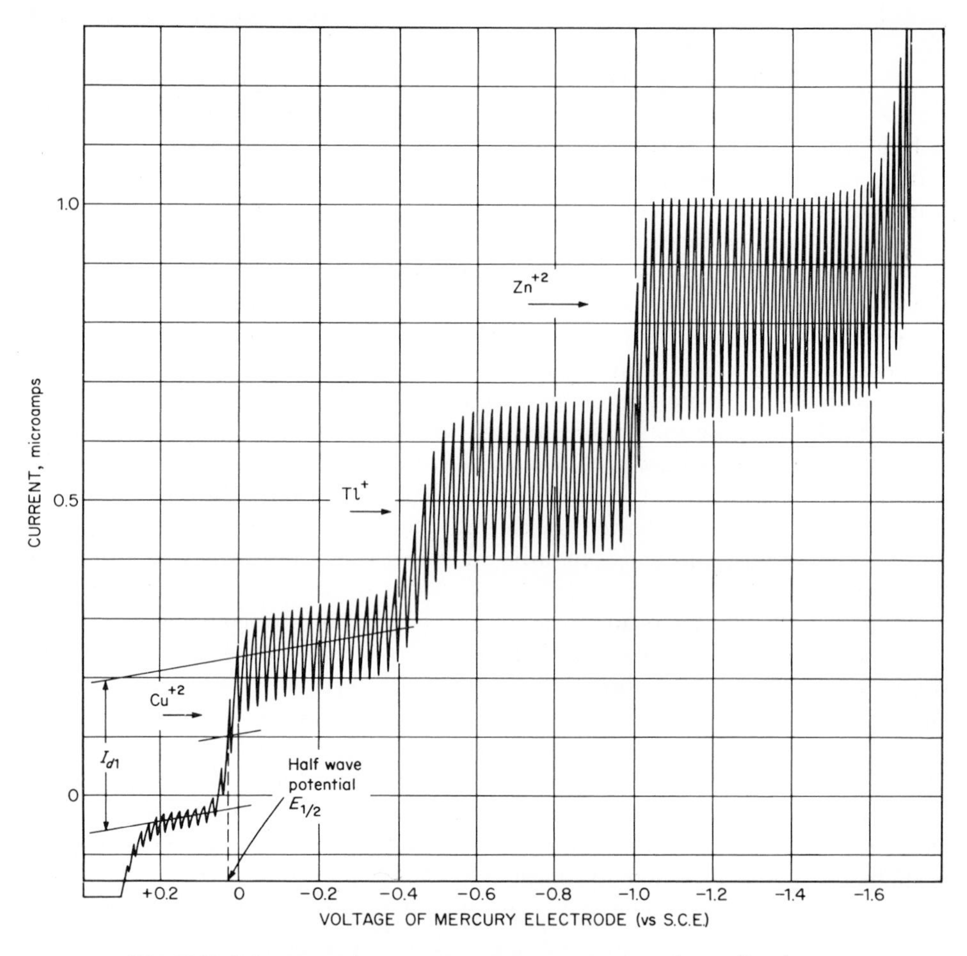

FIG. 10.10 Polarogram of an aqueous solution containing 10^{-4} M Cu^{+2}, Tl^{+} and Zn^{+2} and 0.1 M KNO_3 as supporting electrolyte. Voltages are referred to the saturated calomel electrode. [W. B. Schaap, Indiana University].

Alternatively, standard reference electrodes of large area can be used as reference anodes.

A schematic diagram of the *polarograph* is shown in Fig. 10.9. Since oxygen is reduced at a relatively low potential, it is desirable to remove dissolved oxygen from the electrolyte by bubbling an inert gas through it. A typical current density vs. voltage curve is shown in Fig. 10.10 for a solution containing 10^{-4}M Cu^{+2}, Tl^{+} and Zn^{+2} and 0.1 M KNO_3. The KNO_3 is added in large excess to carry essentially all of the cell current. Though the current will be carried by the K^{+} and NO_3^{-} ions, the K^{+} ion will not be discharged at the cathode even though its concentration greatly exceeds that of the Cu^{+2}, Tl^{+} or Zn^{+2} ion. The high overvoltage for hydrogen discharge on mercury is a great advantage in the *polarograph,* for it allows us to study many ions that have reversible electrode potentials below H_2/H^{+}. Even Na^{+} and K^{+} may be discharged before H^{+} at the dropping mercury electrode.

The current oscillates between a maximum and a minimum as each mercury drop grows and falls. The overall rise from one flat portion of the curve to the next is called the *polarographic wave.* The *half-wave potential* (shown in Fig. 10.10) serves to identify the reducible ion. The value of the diffusion limited current for each ion is proportional to the concentration of the ion.

The theoretical calculation of the diffusion current presents a nice problem since it requires a solution of the diffusion equation with an unusual boundary condition, which is determined by the change in area of the growing drop. In 1938, Ilkovic gave an approximate solution,

$$I' = 0.732F|z|\, D^{1/2}cm^{2/3}t^{1/6} \qquad (10.18)$$

where m is the mass of mercury flowing per second, D is the diffusion coefficient of the ion, t the drop time, and c the molar concentration. Note that the current is proportional to the concentration for a given capillary and for a given ion. This proportionality is the basis of quantitative applications of polarography. The Ilkovic equation can also be used to estimate $|z|$ or D under the conditions of the experiment.

Stationary microelectrodes are seldom used in practical polarography because the diffusion current decreases markedly with time as the thickness of the diffusion layer, δ, increases. This disadvantage can be overcome by moving the electrode through the solution, as in the case of the commonly used "rotating platinum electrode." Rotating the electrode keeps the diffusion layer very thin, so that a steady-state diffusion current is readily maintained. The dropping mercury electrode also maintains a constant *average* diffusion current because the surface of the rapidly growing mercury drops moves out toward the solution at least as fast as the diffusion-layer thickness can increase.

Whereas the Ilkovic equation describes the factors that control the height of the polarographic wave, i.e., the diffusion current, another equation due to Heyrovsky and Ilkovic describes the shape of the wave and its position along the potential axis. We can derive this equation from the Nernst equation for the reaction at the electrode surface and the law of diffusion.

Consider a hydrated metal ion being reduced to a soluble amalgam at the mercury drop,

$$M^{+z} + |z|e + Hg \longrightarrow M(Hg)(\text{amalgam})$$

If this reaction is reversible, we can write for the potential of the dropping mercury electrode,

$$E_{\text{d.m.e.}} = E^\circ - \frac{RT}{|z|\,F}\ln\frac{\overset{s}{a}_a}{\overset{s}{a}_M\overset{s}{a}_{Hg}} = E_a^\circ - \frac{RT}{|z|\,F}\ln\frac{\overset{s}{a}_a}{\overset{s}{a}_M} \qquad (10.19)$$

where the superscript s on the activities refers to the electrode surface. E_a° is the standard potential of the amalgam electrode $\left(= E^\circ + \dfrac{RT}{|z|\,F}\ln \overset{s}{a}_{Hg}\right)$.

In the presence of excess inert salt [*supporting electrolyte*] to eliminate transference on the part of the reducible ion, we know from Eq. (10.13) that the current at any time,

$$I = I_d A = \frac{|z|\,FAD_{\rm M}(c_{\rm M} - c^s_{\rm M})}{\delta} = k_{\rm M}(c_{\rm M} - c^s_{\rm M})$$

From Eq. (10.16), the diffusion limited current is $I' = k_{\rm M}c_{\rm M}$. Combining these two equations, we see that

$$c^s_{\rm M} = a^s_{\rm M}/\gamma_{\rm M} = (I' - I)/k_{\rm M}$$

Within the mercury drop, the concentration of reduced metal at the surface will be proportional to the current flowing, but inversely proportional to its diffusion coefficient, etc., i.e.,

$$c^s_a = a^s_a/\gamma_a = I\delta/|z|FD_aA = I/k_a$$

Substituting these last two expressions back into the Nernst equation, we obtain

$$E_{\rm d.m.e.} = E^\circ_a - \frac{RT}{|z|\,F}\ln\frac{I\gamma_a k_{\rm M}}{k_a\gamma_{\rm M}(I' - I)} \tag{10.20}$$

At 25°C,

$$E_{\rm d.m.e.} = E_{1/2} - \frac{0.0592}{|z|}\log\frac{I}{I' - I} \tag{10.21}$$

The half-wave potential, $E_{1/2}$, is a constant, independent of concentration, and is equal to $E_{\rm d.m.e.}$ at the point on the wave where $I = I'/2$, i.e., at half the

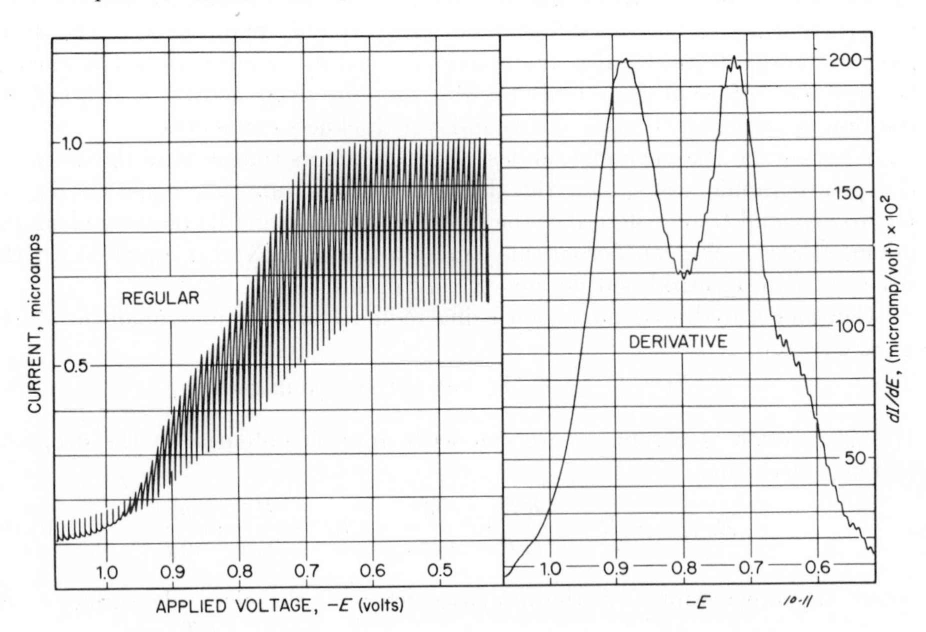

FIG. 10.11 Regular and derivative polarograms of copper (II) in anhydrous ethylene-diamine. The copper concentration = 3×10^{-4} M and 0.3 M LiCl serves as supporting electrolyte. The derivatives were obtained with automatic electronic instrumentation. [W. B. Schaap, Indiana University].

total wave height. It is useful in the qualitative identification of the electroactive species. Because the ratios of activity coefficients and diffusion coefficients occurring in Eq. (10.20) are usually not greatly different from 1, the polarographic $E_{1/2}$ is approximately equal to the standard potential of the metal-amalgam electrode, E_a°.

Equation (10.21) predicts that the plot of $E_{\text{d.m.e.}}$ vs. $\log [I/(I' - I)]$ should be linear for a reaction that behaves reversibly under diffusion controlled conditions, that the slope of this linear plot should be $RT/2.303|z|F$, and that the intercept is $E_{1/2}$.

Polarography is useful in research because it is a convenient method for measuring electrode potentials and for studying electrode reactions. As an example, the polarographic waves for the reduction of Cu^{+2} in the nonaqueous solvent, ethylenediamine, are shown in Fig. 10.11. In water, in the absence of complexing anions, Cu^{+2} is reduced to the amalgam in a single step and gives a reversible, two-electron reduction wave. In ethylenediamine, the polarographic waves show that Cu^{+2} is reduced via two one-electron reactions, giving two incompletely resolved waves. The derivatives of these waves show them to be waves of equal height. The voltage at the peak of the derivative wave is the half-wave potential in each case.

PROBLEMS

1. Devise cells in which the cell reactions are the following:
(a) $2AgBr + H_2 \longrightarrow 2Ag + 2HBr$
(b) $H_2 + I_2 \longrightarrow 2HI$
(c) $S_2O_8^{--} + 2I^- \longrightarrow I_2 + 2SO_4^{--}$
(d) $2Fe^{+3} + CH_3CHO + H_2O \longrightarrow 2Fe^{+2} + CH_3COOH + 2H^+$
(e) $Ni + 2H_2O \longrightarrow Ni(OH)_2 + H_2$
Write down the cells with proper regard for the sign convention. Calculate the E° for these cells from the standard electrode potentials. Assume any liquid-junction potentials are eliminated. The solubility of AgBr is 2.10×10^{-6} mole per liter. [*Ans.* (a) $Pt(H_2) \mid H^+ Br^- \mid AgBr \mid Ag$; $E^\circ = 0.095$ v; (b) $Pt(H_2) \mid H^+ I^- \mid I_2(Pt)$; $E^\circ = 0.5355$ v; (c) $Pt(I_2) \mid I^- \parallel SO_4^=, S_2O_8^= \mid Pt$; $E^\circ = 1.445$ v; (d) $Pt \mid CH_3CHO, CH_3COOH \parallel Fe^{+2}, Fe^{+3} \mid Pt$; $E^\circ = 0.888$ v; (e) $Ni \mid Ni(OH)_2 \mid OH^-, H^+ \mid H_2(Pt)$; $E^\circ = -0.108$ v]

2. For the cell $H_2 \mid HCl \mid AgCl \mid Ag$, $E^\circ = 0.222$ v. If the measured emf is 0.385 v what is the pH of the HCl solution? [*Ans.* 1.38]

3. Copper is being plated onto a platinum electrode from a 0.5 molar copper sulfate solution, 0.01 molar in H_2SO_4. If the hydrogen overvoltage on copper is 0.23 v, what will be the residual Cu^{++} concentration in the solution when H_2 evolution begins at cathode? [*Ans.* 5.0×10^{-24} mole l^{-1}]

4. Consider the cell: $Pt, H_2(1 \text{ atm}) \mid HCl(m) \mid Hg_2Cl_2(s) \mid Hg$, $E_{298}^\circ = 0.2676$ v. When $m = 4.48$, $E = 0.1151$ v and the partial pressure of HCl over the

solution is 0.030 mm; when $m = 0.0100$, $E = 0.5100$ v (all at 25°C). For the couple $Hg \mid Hg_2^{++}$, $E^\circ_{298} = 0.789$ v. (a) Calculate the partial pressure of HCl above the 0.0100 m solution. (b) Calculate the mean ion activity coefficient for H^+Cl^- in the 0.0100 m solution. (c) Calculate the solubility product for mercurous chloride.

5. The voltage of the cell:

$$Ag \mid Ag_2SO_4(s) \mid \text{sat'd soln of } Hg_2SO_4 \mid Hg_2SO_4(s) \mid Hg$$

is 0.140 v at 25°C, and its temperature coefficient is 0.00015 volts/°C. (a) Give the cell reaction. (b) Calculate the free energy change for the cell reaction. (c) Calculate the enthalpy change for the cell reaction. (d) Calculate the entropy change for the cell reaction. (e) Does the cell absorb or emit heat as the cell reaction occurs? (f) One mole each of Hg, $Ag_2SO_4(s)$, $Hg_2SO_4(s)$, and some saturated solution of the two salts are mixed. What solid phases finally will be present, and in what amounts?

6. The reaction $H_2 + Cl_2 + 2H_2O \rightleftarrows 2H_3O^+ + 2Cl^-$ has an equilibrium constant at 25°C of $K_a = 10^{46}$. Calculate E° at 25°C for the cell $Pt(H_2) \mid HCl\ (aq) \mid Cl_2(Pt)$.

7. The standard potentials E° of $Cu \mid Cu^{+2}$ and $Cu \mid Cu^+$ are 0.337 and 0.530 v respectively. Is it easier, in general, to oxidize Cu to the Cu^{+2} or the Cu^{+1} state? Can you suggest any structural explanation for your answer? What is the equilibrium constant for the reaction: $2\,Cu^+ \rightleftarrows Cu^{+2} + Cu$?

8. The solubility of iodine in water at 25°C is 0.00133 mole/l.

$$I_2(s) + 2e \longrightarrow 2\,I^- \qquad E^\circ = +0.5355 \text{ v}$$

$$I_3^- + 2e \longrightarrow 3\,I^- \qquad E^\circ = +0.5365 \text{ v}$$

What is the concentration of I_3^- in a saturated solution of iodine where $[I^-] = 1.000$ molar?

9. A small efficient battery for hearing aids is composed of zinc, potassium hydroxide, water, mercuric oxide, and mercury. (a) Write an overall reaction for the cell in which zinc and potassium hydroxide are consumed, mercury is deposited, and potassium zincate is formed. (b) Write the reactions occurring at the electrodes.

10. Use the standard electrode potentials to decide which chemical reactions, if any, you would expect in the following experiments: (a) ceric sulfate is added to potassium iodide solution; (b) a lead rod is immersed in silver nitrate solution; (c) a zinc rod is immersed in lead nitrate solution; (d) a lead rod is immersed in zinc nitrate solution; (e) ceric sulfate is added to chromic sulfate solution.

11. Calculate at 25°C the electrode potentials of (a) $Ag \mid 0.02\ m\ AgNO_3$; $E^\circ_{(Ag|Ag^+)} \mid = 0.80$ v; (b) $Zn \mid 0.1m\ ZnSO_4$, $E^\circ_{(Zn|Zn^{++})} = -0.76$ v; (c) $Pt \mid FeCl_3$

0.05 m, $FeCl_2$ 0.001 m, $E°(_{Fe^{+3}|Fe^{+2}}) = +0.77$ v; (d) Pt | Ce^{4+} 0.002 m, Ce^{3+} 0.1 m, $E°(_{Ce^{4+}|Ce^{3+}}) = 1.61$ v. [*Ans.* (a) 0.70 v; (b) −0.79 v; (c) 0.87 v; (d) 1.51 v]

12. A half-cell, consisting of a silver wire dipping into silver nitrate solution (0.001 m) is joined, by a capillary filled with ammonium nitrate, to a standard hydrogen electrode. The electromotive force of the cell is measured with a potentiometer. To the silver | silver nitrate half-cell is added either (a) 0.5 m silver nitrate, (b) 0.01 m sodium chloride, (c) 0.1 m ammonium nitrate, (d) 0.1 m potassium cyanide, (e) 0.1 m ammonia. What would you expect to be the qualitative effect on the potential of the silver half-cell in each case, and why?

13. Calculate the emf at 25°C of a cell consisting of a calomel electrode ($E° = +0.280$ v) on one side, and on the other a platinum wire dipping into a solution of iodine in potassium iodide. The concentration of free iodine is 0.001 m, and of KI, 0.1 m. The standard potential of the electrode Pt | I_2, I^- is +0.535 v.

14. A hydrogen electrode and a calomel half-cell are used to determine the pH of a solution on a mountain top where the pressure is 500 mm of Hg. The hydrogen is allowed to bubble out of the electrode at the atmospheric pressure prevailing there. If the pH is found to be 4.00 by a visiting scientist from the lowlands who wrongly assumed the pressure of hydrogen gas to be 760 mm, what is the correct pH? Take the temperature as 25°C. [*Ans.* 4.09]

15. Calculate the potential difference between a standard hydrogen electrode and half-cells comprising platinum foil coated with platinum black in contact with hydrogen at a pressure of 1 atmosphere and dipping into the following solutions: (a) M/1000 barium hydroxide; (b) M/10 acetic acid; (c) a mixture of 20 ml M/4 acetic acid and 30 ml M/10 sodium hydroxide; (d) a mixture of 20 ml M/4 acetic acid and 80 ml M/10 sodium hydroxide. For acetic acid, $pK_a = 4.8$. Comment briefly on any approximations used in the calculations. Assume the temperature is 25°C. [*Ans.* (a) 0.669 v; (b) 0.172 v; (c) 0.295 v; (d) 0.739 v]

16. Why are there no standard potentials more negative than about −3 volt, and more positive than about +2 volt, in aqueous solution?

17. A silver electrode is immersed in 100 ml of 0.1 M KCl. What will be the potential of the electrode after the addition of (a) 30 ml; (b) 45 ml; (c) 50 ml; (d) 55 ml; (e) 70 ml of 0.2 M $AgNO_3$ solution? Plot a titration curve of emf against volume added. How could you determine the equivalence point? The solubility product of AgCl is 2.3×10^{-10} (g-ion/liter)^2. $E°$ for Ag^+/Ag is 0.80 v. The temperature is 25°C. [*Ans.* (a) 0.32 v; (b) 0.36 v; (c) 0.52 v; (d) 0.67 v; (e) 0.70 v]

18. What is observed when a solution of sodium sulfate, to which litmus has been added, is electrolyzed between platinum electrodes? What explanation of passage of current and discharge of ions fits these observations?

19. Write the half-equation for the formation of oxygen gas at an electrode in an aqueous solution of H_2SO_4. Calculate the volume of oxygen produced (and measured at STP) if 3 amps are passed through the solution for 4 hours. [*Ans.* 2.51 liter]

---

20. The standard electrode potentials of zinc and cobalt are -0.76 volt and -0.28 volt, respectively. If a solution of an ore which contains one gram mole per liter of both zinc sulfate and cobalt sulfate is electrolyzed with platinum electrodes, what is the approximate concentration of cobalt ions when the zinc ions begin to be deposited? [*Ans.* Approximately 6×10^{-17} mole liter^{-1}]

21. What are the processes occurring at each electrode in the cell:

$$\mathrm{Cd} \mid \mathrm{CdCl_2} \parallel \mathrm{I_2, I^-} \mid \mathrm{Pt}\ (E = 0.7 \text{ volt})$$

when: (a) the electrodes are connected together externally; (b) a 2-volt storage battery is connected to the cell, with the negative terminal joined to the Cd electrode and the positive terminal to the Pt electrode; (c) the storage battery is connected to the cell the other way round?

22. Mercuric nitrate and ferrous nitrate, each in 0.01 molar solution, are mixed in equal volumes at 25°C. From the standard potentials in Table 10.1, find the equilibrium concentration of ferric ion in the solution. Activity coefficients may be estimated from the Debye-Hückel Limiting Law. [*Ans.* 0.004232 mole l^{-1}]

23. Calculate the values of the oxidation potential E of the electrode $\mathrm{Pt}|\mathrm{Fe^{++}}$, $\mathrm{Fe^{+++}}$ as a function of the per cent oxidized form. Use concentrations in place of activities. Plot the results.
[*Ans.* $E = 0.771 - 0.059 \log (\mathrm{Fe^{+3}/Fe^{+2}})$

Per cent Fe^{+3}	10	50	90	99
E	.828	.772	.716	.654]

24. The emf's of the cell $\mathrm{H_2} \mid \mathrm{HCl}(m) \mid \mathrm{AgCl} \mid \mathrm{Ag}$ at 25°C are as follows [cf. Harned and Ehlers, *J. Am. Chem. Soc. 54*, 1350 (1932)]:

m(molal conc)	E(volts)	m	E
0.01002	0.46376	0.05005	0.38568
0.01010	0.46331	0.09642	0.35393
0.01031	0.46228	0.09834	0.35316
0.04986	0.38582	0.20300	0.31774

Calculate $E°$ for the cell by the following method of graphical extrapolation. We can write $E = E° - A \log a_{\mathrm{HCl}}$ where $A = 2.303\ RT/F$. This becomes $E + 2A \log m = E° - 2A \log \gamma_{\pm}$. From Debye-Hückel theory, $\log \gamma_{\pm} =$

$-B\sqrt{m}$. Thus: $E + 2A \log m = E^\circ + 2AB\sqrt{m}$. Plot the left side of this expression vs. $\sqrt{m}$ and extrapolate to $m = 0$, the intercept giving E°. (See Harned's paper for a more precise method of extrapolation.) [*Ans.* $E^\circ = 0.224$]

25. From the value of E° obtained above and the measured emf's, calculate the mean activity coefficients $\gamma_\pm$ of HCl at the various concentrations. [*Ans.* $m = .010$, $\gamma_\pm = .906$; (0.50, .835); (.096, .795); (.203, .650)]

26. The cell, Sn(liq) | $SnCl_2$ in molten KCl + LiCl | Sn-Sb liquid solution, was measured at 905°K at various mole fractions of tin in the solution with antimony:

X_{Sn}:	0.1	0.2	0.3	0.4	0.5	0.6	0.7	0.8	0.9
E(v):	.11984	.08379	.05905	.04545	.03705	.02845	.01725	.00992	.00523

If pure liquid tin is chosen as the standard state, $\Delta G = \overline{G}_A - G_A^\circ = -zEF = RT \ln a_A$, where a_A is the activity of tin in the electrode solution. Plot γ_{Sn} and γ_{Sb} as functions of X_{Sn}.

[*Ans.*

γ_{Sn}:	0.1	0.2	0.3	0.4	0.5	0.6	0.7	0.8	0.9
γ_{Sn}:	0.47	0.59	0.74	0.78	0.77	0.80	0.92	0.97	0.97
γ_{Sb}:	0.90	0.78	0.66	0.61	0.57	0.48	0.33	0.26	0.19

The γ_{Sb} values were calculated from the γ_{Sn} by means of the Gibbs-Duhem equation in the form derived in Problem 43, Chapter 5.]

27. The emf of the cell H_2(P) | 0.1 m HCl | HgCl | Hg was studied as a function of the hydrogen pressure at 25°:

P (atm)	1.0	37.9	51.6	110.2	286.6	731.8	1035.2
E (mv)	399.0	445.6	449.6	459.6	473.4	489.3	497.5

Calculate the activity coefficients of hydrogen gas ($\gamma = f/P$) and plot them as a function of the pressure over the given range. [*Ans.*

P	1.0	37.9	51.6	110.2	286.6	731.8	1035
γ	1.000	1.003	1.011	1.043	1.15	1.53	2.11]

28. It is desired to separate Cd^{++} and Zn^{++} by electrolytic deposition of the Cd^{++}. The E° for the cadmium electrode is -0.403 v, for the zinc, -0.763 v. The overvoltages are Cd = 0.48 v; Zn = 0.70 v. Discuss the feasibility of the separation in a solution originally 0.1 molar in Zn^{++} and Cd^{++}.

11 ATOMIC STRUCTURE AND RADIOACTIVITY

In 1815–16 a London physician, William Prout, suggested that the atomic weights of the elements based on H = 1 were whole numbers, and that the atoms of the heavier elements were composed of hydrogen as a primary matter. "If the views we have ventured to advance be correct," wrote Prout, "we may almost consider the *prima materia* of the ancients to be realized in hydrogen. . . ." At that time the best atomic weights were those of Berzelius, and many of his values were certainly far from whole numbers. Yet the beautiful simplicity of Prout's idea won many supporters, since there were enough atomic weights close to whole numbers to indicate that the hypothesis might contain some basic truth.

1. PRECISE ATOMIC WEIGHTS

In an effort to solve this most important chemical problem, a great and solitary Belgian chemist, Jean-Servais Stas, undertook the determination of atomic weights of extreme accuracy. He described the origins of his researches as follows:*

> *All the analytical work undertaken for nearly a century leads us to conclude that compound substances possess a definite, constant, and invariable composition. The relations deduced from these researches have been successively called* proportional numbers, chemical proportions, chemical equivalents, *and* atoms. *The illustrious Berzelius devoted a great part of his life to the determination of the weights of chemical equivalents. His works on this subject will endure as imperishable monuments to his sagacity and his genius. The meticulous and reiterated checks to which I had the boldness, not to say the temerity, to submit them, convinced me that his analytical skill has never been surpassed, if indeed it has ever been equalled by anyone. We know that Berzelius concluded from his researches that no simple relations existed between the atomic weights; all his life he remained convinced that this was the truth.*
>
> *In 1815, Dr. William Prout . . . advanced the idea that the atomic weights that had been accurately determined at that time could be represented as integral multiples of the weight of hydrogen.*

---

* *Bull. de l'Académie de Belgique* (2) X, 208 (1860).

From the point of view of natural philosophy, the significance of Prout's idea is immense. The chemical elements which we consider as simple substances in view of their absolute immutability for us, would be themselves compounds. Those elements whose discovery made the glory of Lavoisier and immortalized his name, could then be considered as derived from the condensation of a unique matter: we are naturally led to the unity of matter, although in the real world we meet its variety and its multiplicity.

For a great number of years I have dedicated all my leisure time to the elucidation of this problem. I may say frankly that when I undertook my researches, I had confidence that was almost absolute in the correctness of the Principle of Prout.

The measurements of Stas showed, however, that many atomic weights are surely not whole numbers. Hence, he was able to state:

I have acquired a complete conviction, an entire certitude to the extent that it is possible for man to attain certitude on such a subject, that the law of Prout . . . is only an illusion, a pure hypothesis formally contradicted by experiment. . . . There does not exist a common divisor between all the weights of the elements.

Yet, after a second look, Stas concluded that pure chance could not explain why so many atomic weights were so close to whole numbers. His final remark was that after all "it is necessary to believe that there is something at the bottom of it."

2. THE PERIODIC LAW

As precise values became available, important correlations were discovered between the atomic weights of the elements and their chemical and physical properties.

In 1864, John Newlands tabulated the elements in the order of their atomic weights, and noted that every eighth element fell into a group with similar chemical properties. This regularity he unfortunately called the *Law of Octaves.* The suggested similarity to a musical scale provided an opportunity for chemical comedians, and Newlands's important observation was not studied seriously. Within a few years, however, detailed statements of what we now call the *Periodic Law* were forthcoming, one based on the chemical properties of the elements by Mendeleyev, and one based on the physical properties, by Meyer.

Dmitri Ivanovitch Mendeleyev, the youngest of fourteen children, was born in 1834 in Tobolsk, Siberia. His father was director of the college there, and his mother Maria came from a family of Siberian pioneers and merchants. When the father's health failed in 1837, Maria Mendeleyeva became the main support of her family by managing a glass factory owned by her brother. Thus Dmitri grew up in an atmosphere of industrial chemistry. Also Tobolsk was at the time the place of exile of the survivors among the Decembrists, a group that had rebelled against the Tsar in 1825, and these subversives contributed considerably to the intellectual life of the town. After the death of her husband in 1847, Maria brought Dmitri and his sister Elizabeth to Moscow. The University of

Moscow would not admit him, but he was finally allowed to enter the Central Pedagogic Institute at St. Petersburg.

The important influence of his mother is reflected in the dedication by Mendeleyev of his work on *Solutions.*

> *This investigation is dedicated to the memory of a mother by her youngest offspring. Conducting a factory, she could educate him only by her own work. She instructed by example, corrected with love, and in order to devote him to science she left Siberia with him spending thus her last resources and strength. When dying, she said 'Refrain from illusions, insist on work, and not on words. Patiently search divine and scientific truth.'*

Mendeleyev's first statement of the Periodic Table was communicated to the Russian Chemical Society in March, 1869. He went well beyond Newlands and earlier theorists. Mendeleyev emphasized that hypotheses are not theories:

> *By a theory I mean a conclusion drawn from the accumulated facts we now possess which enables us to foresee new facts which we do not yet know.*

Thus Mendeleyev was able to use his Periodic Table to predict the existence and properties of new elements which should fit into the empty spaces, and his predictions were closely confirmed when new elements were discovered. In later years he was able to write:

> *When in 1871 I wrote a paper on the application of the periodic law to the determination of the properties of the yet undiscovered elements, I did not think I should live to see the verification of the consequences of this law, but such was to be the case. Three elements were described* — eka-boron, eka-aluminum, *and* eka-silicon — *and now after the lapse of twenty years I have had the great pleasure of seeing them discovered and named after those three countries where the rare minerals containing them are found and where they were discovered, Gallia, Scandinavia and Germany.*

At the same time as the work of Mendeleyev, Julius Lothar Meyer at Karlsruhe was applying the concept of periodicity with atomic weight to the physical properties of the elements. His famous curve showing the plot of atomic volume vs. atomic weight was published in 1870* and is replotted in Fig. 11.1.

As might be expected, the Periodic Law revived interest in the hypothesis of Prout and other conceptions of a *prima materia* from which all the elements were formed. Mendeleyev himself was scornful of such speculations. In 1889 he wrote:

> *The Periodic Law, based as it is on the solid and wholesome ground of experimental research, has been evolved independently of any conception as to the nature of the elements; it does not in the least originate in the idea of a unique matter; and it has no historical connection with that relic of the torments of classical thought.*

A modern periodic table is shown in Table 11.1. There are certain defects in the arrangement of elements according to their atomic weights. Thus the most careful determinations show that tellurium has a higher atomic weight than

* *Liebig's Ann. d. Chemie. Suppl. Band 7,* 354 (1870).

TABLE 11.1 MENDELEYEV'S PERIODIC SYSTEM OF THE ELEMENTS

PERIODS	GROUPS OF ELEMENTS I	II	III	IV	V	VI	VII	VIII			0
1	1 H Hydrogen 1.0080										2 He Helium 4.0026
2	3 Li Lithium 6.939	4 Be Beryllium 9.012	5 B Boron 10.811	6 C Carbon 12.0111	7 N Nitrogen 14.007	8 O Oxygen 15.9994	9 F Fluorine 18.998				10 Ne Neon 20.183
3	11 Na Sodium 22.990	12 Mg Magnesium 24.312	13 Al Aluminium 26.982	14 Si Silicon 28.086	15 P Phosphorus 30.974	16 S Sulfur 32.064	17 Cl Chlorine 35.453				18 Ar Argon 39.948
4	19 K Potassium 39.102	20 Ca Calcium 40.08	21 Sc Scandium 44.956	22 Ti Titanium 47.90	23 V Vanadium 50.942	24 Cr Chromium 51.996	25 Mn Manganese 54.938	26 Fe Iron 55.847	27 Co Cobalt 58.933	28 Ni Nickel 58.71	
	29 Cu Copper 63.54	30 Zn Zinc 65.37	31 Ga Gallium 69.72	32 Ge Germanium 72.59	33 As Arsenic 74.9216	34 Se Selenium 78.96	35 Br Bromine 79.909				36 Kr Krypton 83.80
5	37 Rb Rubidium 85.47	38 Sr Strontium 87.62	39 Y Yttrium 88.905	40 Zr Zirconium 91.22	41 Nb Niobium 92.906	42 Mo Molybdenum 95.94	43 Tc Technetium 99	44 Ru Ruthenium 101.07	45 Rh Rhodium 102.905	46 Pd Palladium 106.4	
	47 Ag Silver 107.870	48 Cd Cadmium 112.40	49 In Indium 114.82	50 Sn Tin 118.69	51 Sb Antimony 121.75	52 Te Tellurium 127.60	53 I Iodine 126.9044				54 Xe Xenon 131.30
6	55 Cs Cesium 132.905	56 Ba Barium 137.34	57 La* Lanthanum 138.91	72 Hf Hafnium 178.49	73 Ta Tantalum 180.948	74 W Tungsten 183.85	75 Rh Rhenium 186.2	76 Os Osmium 190.2	77 Ir Iridium 192.2	78 Pt Platinum 195.09	
	79 Au Gold 196.967	80 Hg Mercury 200.59	81 Tl Thallium 204.37	82 Pb Lead 207.19	83 Bi Bismuth 208.980	84 Po Polonium 210	85 At Astatine 210				86 Rn Radon 222
7	87 Fr Francium 223	88 Ra Radium 226.05	80 Ac** Actinium 227								

6	*58-71 Lantha- nide Series	58 Ce Cerium 140.12	59 Pr Praseo- dymium 140.907	60 Nd Neody- mium 144.24	61 Pm Prome- thium 147	62 Sm Sama- rium 150.35	63 Eu Euro- pium 151.96	64 Gd Gado- linium 157.25	65 Tb Terbium 158.92	66 Dy Dyspro- sium 162.50	67 Ho Hol- mium 164.93	68 Er Erbium 167.26	69 Tm Thu- lium 168.93	70 Yb Ytter- bium 173.04	71 Lu Lute- tium 174.97
7	**90-101 Actinide Series	90 Th Thori- um 232.04	91 Pa Protac- tinium 231	92 U Urani- um 238.03	93 Np Neptu- nium 237	94 Pu Plutoni- um 239	95 Am Ameri- cium 243	96 Cm Curium 245	97 Bk Berkeli- um 249	98 Cf Califor- nium 249	99 Es Einstei- nium 255	100 Fm Fermi- um 255	101 Md Mende- levium 256	102 No Nobel- ium	103 Lw Lawrenc- ium

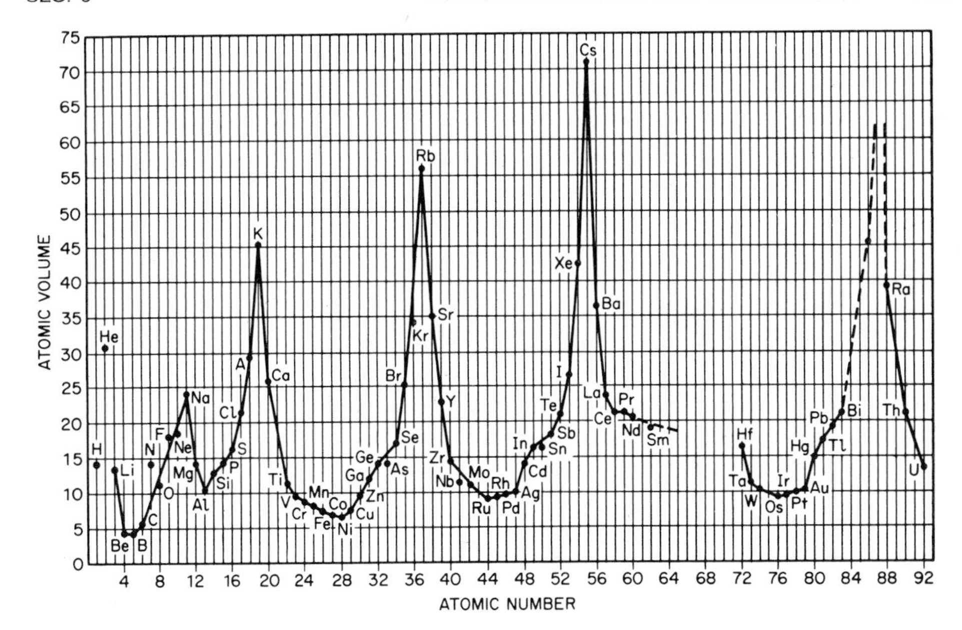

FIG. 11.1 Lothar Meyer's atomic volume curve.

iodine, despite the positions in the Table obviously required by their properties. After the discovery of the rare gases (1894–1897) by Strutt (Rayleigh) and Ramsay, it was found that argon had an atomic weight of 39.95, which was greater than that of potassium, 39.10. Such exceptions to the arrangement by weight indicated that the entire truth behind the Periodic Law was not yet understood. Perhaps the hypothesis of Prout, so often buried, was not yet dead.

3. THE DISCHARGE OF ELECTRICITY THROUGH GASES

The answer to this and many other questions about atomic structure was to be found in a quite unexpected field — the study of the discharge of electricity through gases.

William Watson,* who proposed a one-fluid theory of electricity at the same time as Franklin, was the first to describe the continuous discharge of an electrical machine through a rarefied gas (1748).

> *It was a most delightful spectacle when the room was darkened, to see the electricity in its passage: to be able to observe not, as in the open air, its brushes or pencils or rays an inch or two in length, but here the corruscations were of the whole length of the tube between the plates, that is to say, thirty-two inches.*

Progress in the study of the discharge was retarded by the lack of suitable vacuum pumps. In 1855, Geissler, the glassblower at Bonn, invented a mercury

* *Phil. Trans. Roy. Soc. 40*, 93 (1748); *44*, 362 (1752).

pump that permitted the attainment of higher degrees of vacuum. In 1858, Julius Plücker observed the deflection of the negative glow in a magnetic field and in 1869 his student, Hittorf, found that a shadow was cast by an opaque body placed between the cathode and the fluorescent walls of the tube, suggesting that rays from the cathode were causing the fluorescence. In 1876, Eugen Goldstein called these rays *cathode rays* and confirmed the observation that they traveled in straight lines and cast shadows. William Crookes (1879) regarded the rays as a torrent of negatively ionized gas molecules repelled from the cathode. The charged particle theory was contested by many who believed the rays were electromagnetic in origin, and thus similar to light waves. This group was led by Heinrich Hertz, who showed that the cathode radiation could pass through thin metal foils, which would be impossible if it were composed of massive particles.

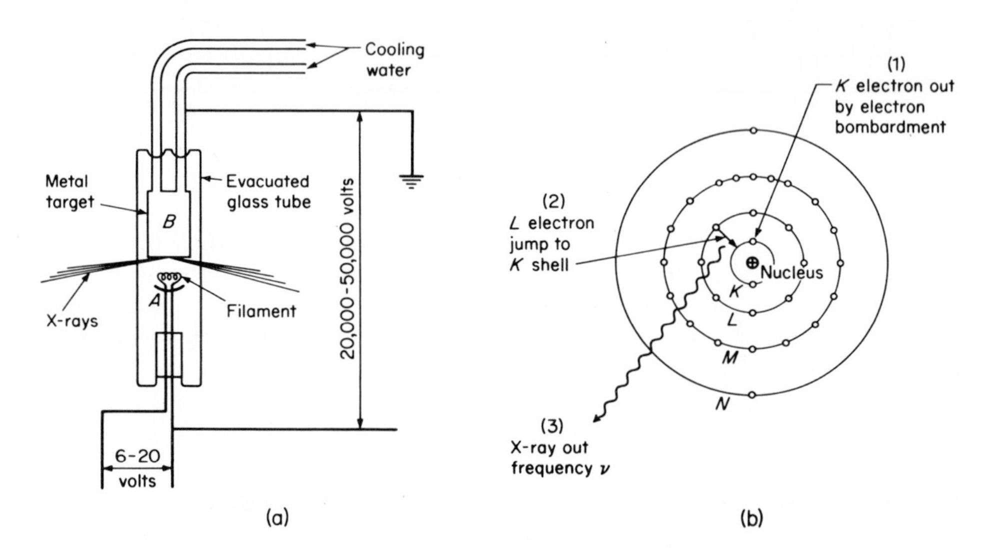

FIG. 11.2 The production of X rays. [R. L. Murray, *Introduction to Nuclear Engineering*, Prentice-Hall, 1961].

Hermann von Helmholtz, however, strongly championed the particle theory; in a lecture before the Chemical Society of London in 1881 he declared:

> *If we accept the hypothesis that the elementary substances are composed of atoms, we cannot avoid concluding that electricity also, positive as well as negative, is divided into definite elementary portions which behave like atoms of electricity.*

The breakthrough came as the consequence of an apparently accidental discovery made by Wilhelm Röntgen of Würzburg in 1895. Röntgen had been experimenting with a discharge tube completely enclosed with black cardboard. He noticed, however, that a piece of paper coated with barium platinocyanide, which was lying on the bench, fluoresced while the tube was in operation. He identified the origin of the radiation in the glass wall of the tube where it was struck by the cathode rays. The *X rays,* as he called them, were not charged particles since they were undeflected by magnetic fields. Schuster was the first to suggest that they were electromagnetic radiation of extremely short wavelength, far beyond the ultraviolet.

In order to secure an intense beam of X rays, a metal target was placed in the discharge tube. A typical arrangement is shown in Fig. 11.2. Most modern tubes are exhausted to high vacuum and permanently sealed; the electron beam is then provided by a hot filament.

For 18 years, no one knew how to measure the wavelengths of the X rays. In 1912, Max v. Laue showed that a crystal could be used as a three dimensional diffraction grating for X rays, and hence the wavelengths of the rays were of the same order of magnitude as the spacing between atoms in the crystal. In 1925, A. H. Compton measured the wavelengths with carefully ruled gratings and X rays at glancing incidence. The intensity of the X rays emitted by a given element as target depends on the wavelength. There is a broad continuous emission (so-called *white X radiation*) and superimposed upon this are sharp line emissions characteristic of the target material. The study of these *characteristic X-ray spectra* was to provide a considerable insight into the atomic structure of the elements, but this development did not occur until about twenty years after the discovery by Röntgen.

4. THE ELECTRON

In his autobiography, *Recollections and Reflections*, J. J. Thomson has described his first work with X-rays:

> *It was a most fortunate coincidence that the advent of research students at the Cavendish Laboratory came at the same time as the announcement by Roentgen of his discovery of the X rays. I had a copy of his apparatus made and set up at the Laboratory, and the first thing I did with it was to see what effect the passage of these rays through a gas would produce on its electrical properties. To my great delight I found that this made it a conductor of electricity, even though the electric force applied to the gas was exceedingly small, whereas the gas when it was not exposed to the rays did not conduct electricity unless the electric force were increased many thousandfold. . . . The X rays seemed to turn the gas into a gaseous electrolyte.*
>
> *I started at once, in the late autumn of 1895, on working at the electric properties of gases exposed to Roentgen rays, and soon found some interesting and suggestive results. . . . There is an interval when the gas conducts though the rays have ceased to go through it. We studied the properties of the gas in this state, and found that the conductivity was destroyed when the gas passed through a filter of glass wool.*
>
> *A still more interesting discovery was that the conductivity could be filtered out without using any mechanical filter by exposing the conducting gas to electric forces. The first experiments show that the conductivity is due to particles present in the gas, and the second shows that these particles are charged with electricity. The conductivity due to the Roentgen rays is caused by these rays producing in the gas a number of charged particles.*

5. THE RATIO OF CHARGE TO MASS OF THE CATHODE PARTICLES

J. J. Thomson next turned his attention to the behavior of cathode rays in electric and magnetic fields,* using the apparatus shown in Fig. 11.3.

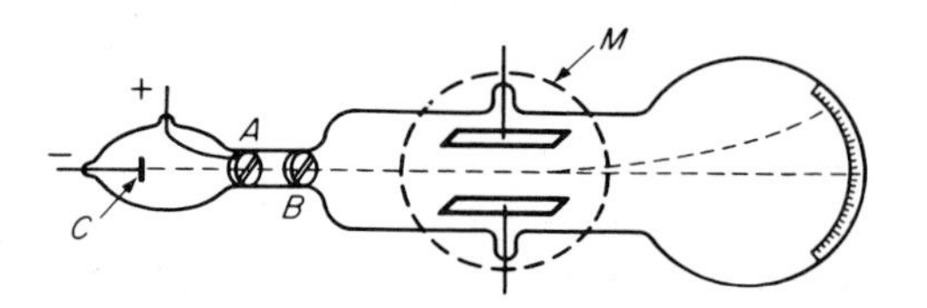

FIG. 11.3 Thomson's apparatus for determining e/m of cathode particles.

> *The rays from the cathode C pass through a slit in the anode A, which is a metal plug fitting tightly into the tube and connected with the earth; after passing through a second slit in another earth-connected metal plug B, they travel between two parallel aluminium plates about 5 cm apart; they fall on the end of the tube and produce a narrow well-defined phosphorescent patch. A scale pasted on the outside of the tube serves to measure the deflection of this patch.*
>
> *At high exhaustions the rays were deflected when the two aluminium plates were connected with the terminal of a battery of small storage cells; the rays were depressed when the upper plate was connected with the negative pole of the battery, the lower with the positive, and raised when the upper plate was connected with the positive, the lower with the negative pole.*

In an electric field of strength E, a particle with charge Q is subject to a force of magnitude EQ. The trajectory of an electron in an electric field of strength E perpendicular to its direction of motion may be illustrated by the diagram in Fig. 11.4. If m is the mass of the electron, the equations of motion may be written:

$$m\frac{d^2x}{dt^2} = 0, \qquad m\frac{d^2y}{dt^2} = EQ \tag{11.1}$$

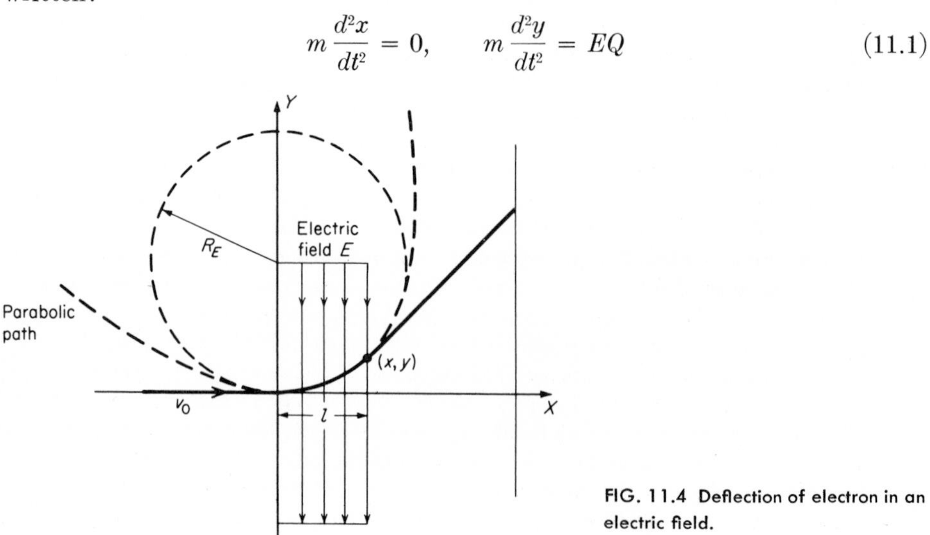

FIG. 11.4 Deflection of electron in an electric field.

* *Phil. Mag.* *44*, 293 (1897).

With $t = 0$ at the instant the particle enters the electric field, its velocity in the y direction is zero at $t = 0$. This velocity increases while the electron is in the field, while its initial velocity in the x direction, v_0, remains constant.

Integrating Eqs. (11.1), we obtain

$$x = v_0 t, \qquad y = \frac{QE}{2m} t^2 \tag{11.2}$$

Equations (11.2) define a parabolic path, as is evident when t is eliminated to give

$$y = \frac{QE}{2mv_0^2} x^2 \tag{11.3}$$

After the electron leaves the field, it travels along a straight line tangent to this parabolic path. In many experimental arrangements, its total path is considerably longer than the length of the electric field, so that the deflection in the y direction experienced while in the field is small compared to the total observed deflection. To a good approximation, therefore, the parabolic path can be considered as a circular arc of radius R_E, with the force exerted by the field equal to the centrifugal force on the electron in this circular path,

$$QE = \frac{mv^2}{R_E} \tag{11.4}$$

The time required to traverse the field of length l is simply l/v_0 so that the deflection in Eq. (11.2) becomes

$$y = \frac{QE}{2m} \frac{l^2}{v_0^2}$$

Thus

$$\frac{Q}{m} = \frac{2yv_0^2}{l^2 E} \tag{11.5}$$

The ratio of charge to mass may be calculated from the deflection in the electric field, provided the velocity of the particles is known. This v_0 may be obtained by balancing the deflection in the electric field by an opposite deflection in a magnetic field. The magnetic field is applied by the pole pieces of a magnet M mounted outside the apparatus in Fig. 11.3, so that its field is at right angles both to the electric field and to the direction of motion of the cathode rays.

A moving charged particle is equivalent to a current of electricity, the strength of the current being the product of the charge on the particle and its velocity. From Ampère's Law, therefore, the magnitude of the force on the moving charge is given by

$$f = QvB \sin \theta \tag{11.6}$$

where θ is the angle between the velocity vector v and the magnetic induction vector B. When the magnetic field is perpendicular to the direction of motion, this equation becomes

$$f = QvB \tag{11.7}$$

Fig. 11.5 illustrates the directional factors involved.

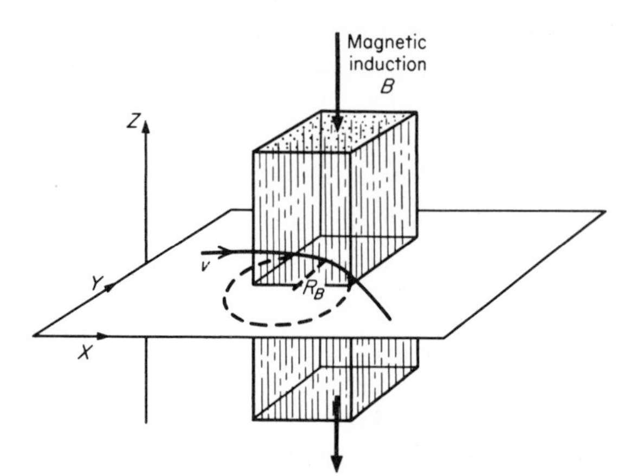

FIG. 11.5 Deflection of moving electron in magnetic field.

The force on the electron due to the magnetic field is always perpendicular to its direction of motion, and thus a magnetic field never changes the speed of a moving charge, but only its direction. As in Eq. (11.4), the force may be equated to the centrifugal force on the electron, which in this case moves in a truly circular path of radius R_B. Thus

$$BQv = \frac{mv^2}{R_B} \tag{11.8}$$

If now the force due to the magnetic field exactly balances that due to the electric field, the phosphorescent patch in Thomson's apparatus will be brought back to its initial position. When this occurs, $QvB = EQ$ and $v = E/B$. Substituting this value into Eq. (11.5) we obtain

$$\frac{Q}{m} = \frac{2yE}{l^2B^2} \tag{11.9}$$

If the units in this equation belong to the absolute practical (mks) system, the charge Q is in coulombs, the electric field E in volts per meter, the magnetic induction B in webers per square meter (1 weber per meter^2 = 10^4 gauss), lengths and masses in meters and kilograms.

Thomson found the experimental ratio of charge to mass to be of the order of 10^{11} coulombs per kilogram. The most recent value of Q/m for the electron is 1.7589×10^{11} coulomb per kilogram (5.273×10^{17} esu per gram).

The value found for the hydrogen ion H^+ in electrolysis was 1836 times less than this. The most reasonable explanation seemed to be that the mass of the cathode particle was only $\frac{1}{1836}$ that of the hydrogen ion; this presumption was soon confirmed by measurements of $-e$, the charge Q of the particle.

6. THE CHARGE OF THE ELECTRON

Thomson succeeded in measuring the charge of the cathode particles in 1898. Two years before, C. T. R. Wilson had shown that gases rendered ionizing by X rays caused the condensation of clouds of water droplets from an atmosphere supersaturated with water vapor. The ions formed acted as nuclei for the condensation of the water droplets. This principle was used in the Wilson Cloud Chamber to make visible the trajectories of individual charged corpuscles.

Thomson and Townsend observed the rate of fall of a cloud in air and from this calculated an average size for the water droplets. The number of droplets in the cloud could then be estimated from the weight of water precipitated. The total charge of the cloud was measured by collecting the charged droplets on an electrometer. The conditions of cloud formation were such that condensations occurred only on negatively charged particles. Making the assumption that each droplet bore only one charge, they could now estimate that the value of the elementary negative charge was $e = 6.5 \times 10^{-10}$ esu. This was of the same order of magnitude as the charge on the hydrogen ion, and provided further evidence that the cathode particles themselves were "atoms" of negative electricity, with mass $\frac{1}{1836}$ that of the hydrogen atom.

The exact proof of this hypothesis of the atomic nature of electricity and a careful measurement of the elementary electronic charge were obtained in 1909 by Robert A. Millikan. Millikan was able to isolate individual droplets of oil bearing an electric charge, and to observe their rate of fall under the combined influences of gravity and an electric field.

A body falls in a viscous medium with an increasing velocity until the gravitational force is just balanced by the frictional resistance, after which it falls at a constant terminal velocity, v. The frictional resistance to a spherical body is given by the Stokes equation of hydrodynamics as

$$f = 6\pi\eta rv \tag{11.10}$$

where η is the coefficient of viscosity of the medium and r the radius of the sphere. The gravitational force (weight) is equal to this at terminal velocity, so that, if ρ is the density of the body, and ρ_0 that of the fluid medium,

$$\tfrac{4}{3}\pi r^3 g(\rho - \rho_0) = 6\pi\eta rv \tag{11.11}$$

If a charged oil droplet falls in an electric field, it can be brought to rest when the upward electric force is adjusted to equal the downward gravitational force,

$$QE = \tfrac{4}{3}\pi r^3 g(\rho - \rho_0) \tag{11.12}$$

Since r may be calculated from the terminal velocity in Eq. (11.11), only the charge Q remains unknown in Eq. (11.12). Actually, somewhat better results were obtained in experiments in which the droplet was observed falling freely and then moving in an electric field. In all cases, the charge on the oil droplets was found to be an exact multiple of a fundamental unit charge e. This is the charge on the electron, whose presently accepted value is*

$$\begin{aligned} e &= (1.6021 \pm 0.00004) \times 10^{-19} \text{ coulomb} \\ &= (4.8030 \pm 0.0001) \times 10^{-10} \text{ esu} \end{aligned}$$

* Millikan's result of 4.774×10^{-10} esu was low, owing to his use of an erroneous value for the viscosity of air. J. D. Stranathan, *The Particles of Modern Physics* (Philadelphia: Blakiston, 1943), Chap. 2, gives a most interesting account of the measurements of e.

7. RADIOACTIVITY

The early workers advanced many ingenious theories for the origin of the X radiation. At first they thought that it might be connected with the fluorescence of the irradiated walls of the tubes. Henri Becquerel therefore began to investigate a variety of fluorescent substances to find out whether they emitted penetrating rays. All trials with various minerals, metal sulfides, and other compounds known to fluoresce or phosphoresce on exposure to visible light, gave negative results, until he recalled the striking fluorescence of a sample of potassium uranyl sulfate, which he had prepared 15 years previously. He exposed the uranium salt to an intense light, and placed it in the dark room under a photographic plate wrapped in "two sheets of thick black paper." After several hours exposure the plate had darkened.

Becquerel soon found that this amazing behavior had nothing to do with the fluorescence of the uranyl salt, since an equally intense darkening could be obtained from a sample of salt that had been kept for days in absolute darkness, or from other salts of uranium that were not fluorescent. The penetrating radiation had its source in the uranium itself. Becquerel called this new phenomenon *radioactivity*.*

Marya Sklodovska was born in Warsaw in 1867. Her father and mother were school teachers. The mother died of consumption in 1878, and the difficulties of Professor Sklodovski in raising his family were increased by the disfavor of the Russians who had seized his country. Despite her brilliant record in school, the possibility that Marya could continue her studies seemed slight, but with the help of her elder sister Bronya, she came to Paris, and entered the Sorbonne in 1891. She received her degree of *Licence* in physics in 1893, at the top of the class. In 1894, she took the degree also in mathematics. In the same year she met Pierre Curie, whom she married in 1895. He was 36 and had already published pioneering work in magnetism and crystal physics. At this time, Pierre was interested in radioactivity and he suggested that Marie should do her doctoral research in this field.

Marie Curie wrote in the preface to the *Collected Works* of Pierre:

> *Pierre Curie always had very restricted facilities for his work and in fact one can say he never had a conventional laboratory at his complete disposition. As director of the classes at the School of Physics he could use for his research, to the extent that the needs of the instruction permitted, the resources of the teaching laboratory; he often expressed his gratitude for the liberty allowed him in this regard. But in this laboratory for pupils no room was assigned especially to him; the place that most often served as his refuge was a narrow passage between a staircase and a preparation room; it was here that he did his extensive work on magnetism. Later he obtained authorization to use a glassed-in work shop situated on the ground floor of the school and serving as a storeroom and machine shop. It was in this shop that our researches on radioactivity began. We could not think of carrying out chemical operations there*

* *Compt. rend. 127*, 501, March 2, 1896.

without damaging the machines; these operations were organized in an abandoned shed opposite the machine shop, which had formerly sheltered the practical work of the medical school. In this shed with an asphalt floor, whose glass roof offered us only incomplete protection against the rain, which was like a greenhouse in summer and which an iron stove barely heated in winter, we passed the best and happiest years of our existence, consecrating our entire days to the work. Deprived of all the conveniences that facilitate the work of the chemist, we carried out there with great difficulty a large number of treatments on increasing quantities of material. When the operations could not be performed outside, open windows allowed the poisonous vapors to escape. The only equipment consisted of some old tables of well worn pine on which I disposed my precious fractions from the concentration of radium. Having no cabinet to enclose the radiant products obtained, we placed them on the tables or on planks, and I remember the delight we experienced when we happened to enter our domain at night and saw on all sides the palely luminescent silhouettes of the products of our work.

Pierre Curie was one of those men who made their work the principal end of their activities and the dominant preoccupation of their lives. Already fascinated by scientific research when he was still a child, he devoted to it the persevering effort and the incessant labor of his too short existence, sacrificing to it all distraction, all worldly concerns, without resting even during his vacations. Thus his life remained always in accord with the ideal of his youth, and conforming to his thought at the age of twenty, expressed in pages written by him at that time, he succeeded in 'making of life a dream, and making of the dream a reality.'

For Pierre Curie scientific production was a necessity, and the conception which he had of it was particularly pure and elevated. He did not consent to mix with it any extraneous concern, of career, of success, nor of honor and glory. He was dominated by the need to reflect on a problem, to pursue its solution without sparing either time or care, to see it hatch out little by little and then grow in precision, and finally to reach maturity in a collection of precise results, constituting a real progress in the knowledge of the question. Although constantly occupied with scientific ideas of wide interest, he brought to the execution of every work the same conscientious care, not judging any practical detail unworthy of his effort, never having as an end the splendor of the result nor the effect to be produced.

Marie Curie was one of the first to recognize that radioactivity was an atomic property, not dependent in any way on radiation from the environment. In her first experimental work she showed clearly that all uranium preparations had an activity independent of origin, history and any chemical or physical treatments. Then she discovered that some uranium minerals were four or five times as active as they should have been on the basis of their content of uranium. She concluded that the minerals must contain some new substances with a specific activity (activity per unit mass) many times greater than that of uranium itself.

At this stage, Pierre joined her in the work and by means of chemical analysis they began to separate the uranium ore, pitchblende, into fractions belonging to different groups. In July, 1898, evidence for a new element was found in the bismuth group — she called it *polonium.* In December, 1898, they found another new element in the barium group — this she called *radium.* There followed the four years of arduous work in the leaky shed to separate radium from a ton of pitchblende residues. The radium was purified by fractional crystallization of the chlorides of the barium group of metals, radium chloride being much the least soluble. In all of this research it seems that the chemical work was primarily the responsibility of Marie, while Pierre assumed major responsibilities for the physical measurements. When the concentration of radium in the barium reached one part in 8000, new spectral lines appeared. Finally in 1902, Marie obtained about 100 mg of almost pure radium chloride, with which she determined the atomic weight of radium by measuring the weight of silver required to convert the $RaCl_2$ to AgCl. Her result was 225.0 ± 1.0. In 1907, she repeated the work with 400 mg of $RaCl_2$ and obtained 226.4. The accepted present value is 226.04.

8. α-, β-, γ RAYS

Three different types of rays have been recognized and described in the radiation from radioactive substances.

The β rays are electrons moving at high velocities, as proved by measurements of their deviations in electric and magnetic fields and their ratio of charge to mass. Their velocities range from 0.3 to 0.99 that of light. The α rays are particles of mass 4 (C = 12 scale) bearing a positive charge of 2 (electron = -1 scale). Their velocity is about 0.05 that of light. The γ rays are electromagnetic radiation; they are therefore undeflected by electric and magnetic fields, being similar to X rays, but usually with shorter wave lengths.

The energies of α-, β-, and γ rays are usually measured in units based on the electron volt (ev). An electron volt is the energy acquired by an electron when it falls through a potential of one volt. Thus,

$$\begin{aligned} 1 \text{ ev} &= (\text{charge on electron}) \times (\text{one volt}) \\ &= 1.602 \times 10^{-19} \text{ coulomb volt, or joule} \\ &= 1.602 \times 10^{-12} \text{ erg} \end{aligned}$$

In terms of the chemical unit, the kilocalorie per mole,

$$1 \text{ ev} = \frac{1.602 \times 10^{-19} \times 6.02 \times 10^{23}}{4.184 \times 10^{3}} = 23.05 \text{ kcal/mole}$$

Thus if one mole (L) of particles acquire an average energy of 1 ev each, their total energy is 23.05 kcal. The energy of rays from radioactive substances is so large that the unit one million electron volts (mev) is frequently used.

The penetrating powers of α-, β-, and γ rays depend upon the kind of ray, and for a given kind upon its energy. Owing to their large mass, the α particles travel through gases in essentially straight lines, but they produce a great amount of ionization along their paths. When the paths are made visible in a cloud chamber or photographic emulsion, they are seen to be short and broad as shown in Fig. 11.6. The effectiveness of an absorber in stopping α rays depends pri-

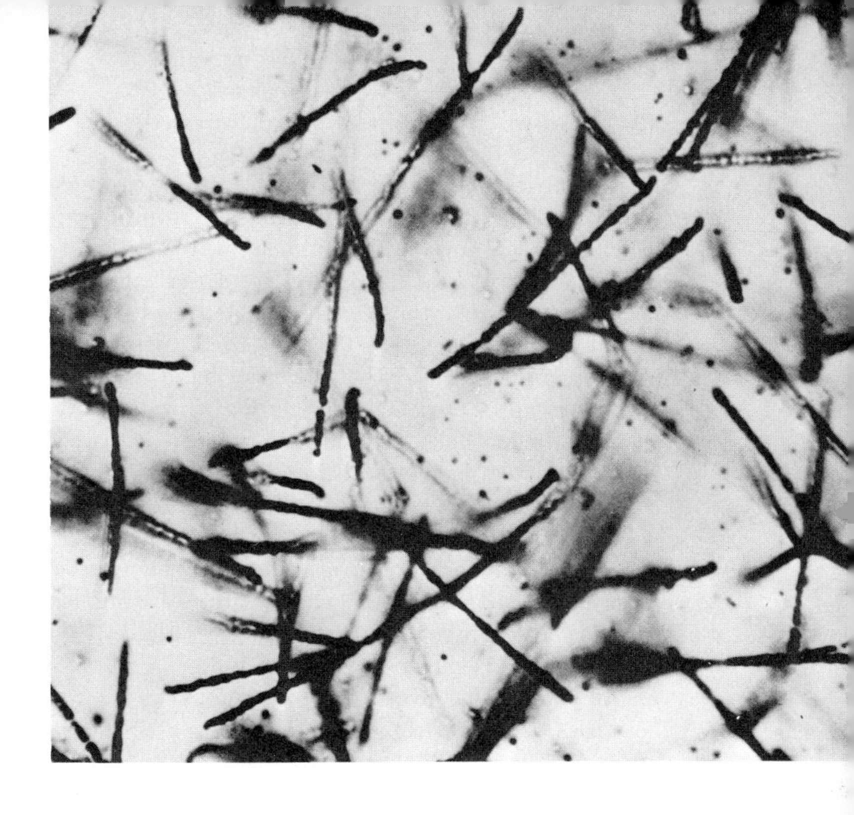

FIG. 11.6 Tracks of alpha particles in a photographic emulsion. [G. P. S. Occhialini and C. F. Powell, University of Bristol.]

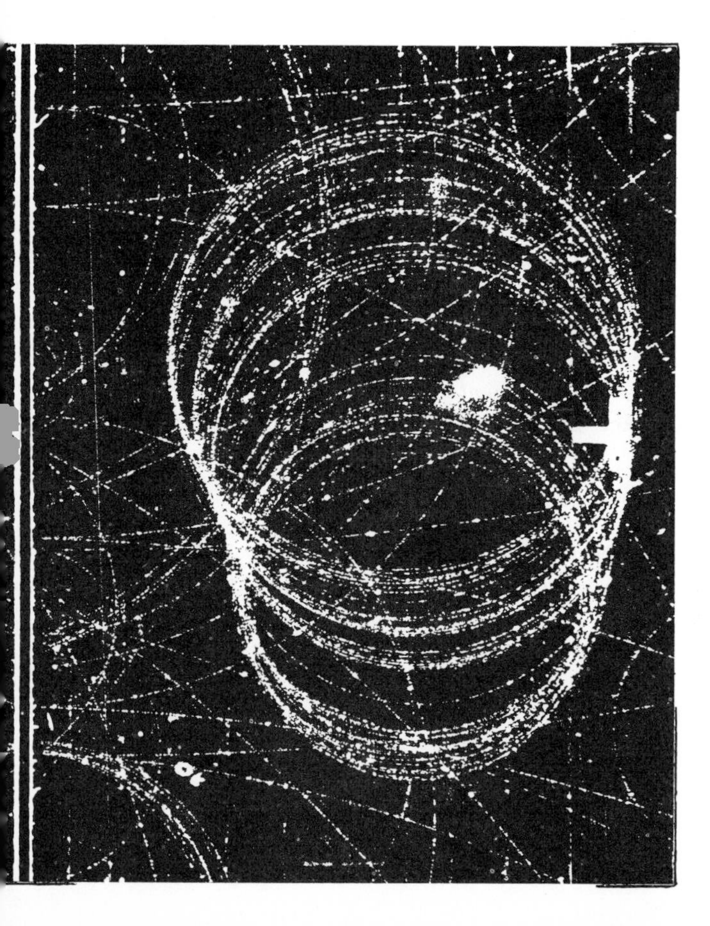

FIG. 11.7 Circular track of a 42 mev positive electron in a 12 000 gauss magnetic field. The length of the track in this photo is nearly 8 meters. [University of California–Lawrence Radiation Laboratory.]

marily on its mass per unit cross section; however, the heavier elements are somewhat less effective per unit mass. In practice, 38 mg cm^{-2} = 0.034 mm of lead or 13 mg cm^{-2} = 0.13 mm of water suffice to stop completely the most energetic α rays (about 10 mev) from radioactive sources. It follows that the radiation hazard to those exposed to α rays is readily avoided by the use of protective gloves or shields. The rays do not penetrate beyond the superficial layers of the skin in any case. On the other hand, the internal ingestion of traces of an α-emitter can be extremely dangerous, since they are heavy metals which tend to accumulate in the bones and other tissues. The chief precaution in working with α-emitters is therefore to eliminate any danger from radioactive dusts or contamination that might be accidentally taken into the body.

Having a much smaller mass than α particles, β particles travel through gases along much more erratic paths. They produce less ionization per unit track length and their tracks are readily distinguished from those of alphas by their lower densities and greater lengths (Fig. 11.7). A typical absorption curve for β particles is shown in Fig. 11.8. It may be noted that over a wide range of activities, the logarithm of the activity is a linear function of the absorber thickness. Thus,

$$\log A = \log A_0 - \kappa l$$

or

$$A = A_0 \exp(-\kappa l) \qquad (11.13)$$

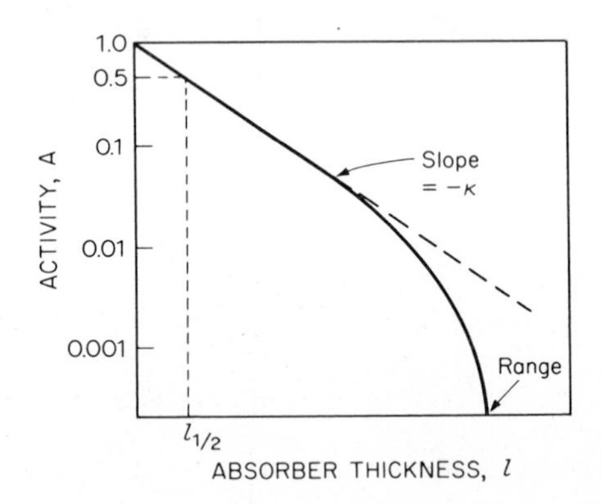

FIG. 11.8 A typical absorption curve for β particles.

Here A_0 is the activity without any absorber, and A is the activity measured through an absorber of thickness l; κ is called the *absorption coefficient*. The value of the absorption coefficient for β rays of a given energy depends almost linearly on the density ρ of the absorber. In other words, κ/ρ is practically independent of the material of the absorber; κ/ρ is called the *mass absorption coefficient*. The thickness of the absorber required to reduce the intensity by one-half is called the half-thickness, $l_{1/2}$. From Eq. (11.13),

$$l_{1/2} = \ln 2/\kappa = 0.693/\kappa \qquad (11.14)$$

The β rays emitted by a given radioactive substance have a continuous distribution of energies, called the *β-ray spectrum*. An example is shown in Fig. 11.9. The range of β particles in absorbers depends on their maximum energy. In some cases, β particles of several different ranges may be emitted from the same radioactive atom.

Even the most energetic beta rays are stopped by a few millimeters of lead, and they do not present a great hazard as far as external radiation is concerned.

They would be absorbed in the outer layers of skin and not reach the internal organs. In some applications this strong absorption is used to advantage. Beta-ray thickness gauges are widely employed for continuously measuring the thickness of thin sheets of metal, plastic, paper and textiles. Certain β-emitters are also used in the treatment of superficial lesions of the skin.

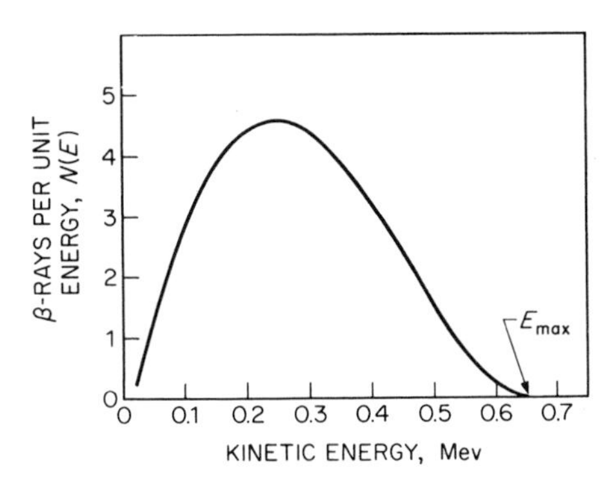

FIG. 11.9 Energy spectrum of positive β rays from ^{64}Cu.

The γ rays are extremely penetrating electromagnetic radiation ranging in wave length from 0.25 to 0.001 Å, or in energy from about 0.05 to 10.0 mev. They produce much less ionization along their paths, and the rays of higher energy are not absorbed by lead shields several centimeters thick. In Fig. 11.10 values of the half-thickness of aluminum, copper and lead are plotted as a function of the energy of the γ rays. A 2 mev γ ray has a $l_{1/2}$ of about 15 g/cm^2, corresponding to 1.3 cm of lead. To reduce the intensity of a γ-ray source to 1% of its unshielded value would require about 6.7 half thicknesses ($100 = 2^{6.7}$) or 8.8 cm of lead. It is evident that shielding for protection against γ rays is a major problem. The rays penetrate the body, affecting internal organs and bones. The dangers of external exposure to γ rays are thus in general much greater than those due to α- or β rays and cause the most difficult problems of protection for workers with radioactive substances.

In Table 11.2 we summarize the commonly used units of radioactivity and of ionizing radiation.

TABLE 11.2 Radiation Units

Name	Symbol	Unit of	Defined as
Curie	*c*	disintegration rate	3.7×10^{10} disintegrations sec^{-1}
Roentgen	*r*	radiation flux	amount of X radiation that would ionize dry air at S.T.P. to extent of 1 esu of charge per cc = release of 87.7 ergs per gram of air
Rad	—	absorbed dose	100 ergs energy released per gram of any absorber
Roentgen Equivalent Physical	r.e.p.	absorbed dose in tissue	93 ergs/cc in tissue
Roentgen Equivalent Man	rem	effective biological dose (radiation damage in human tissue)	(dose in rad) $\times$ (relative biological effectiveness)

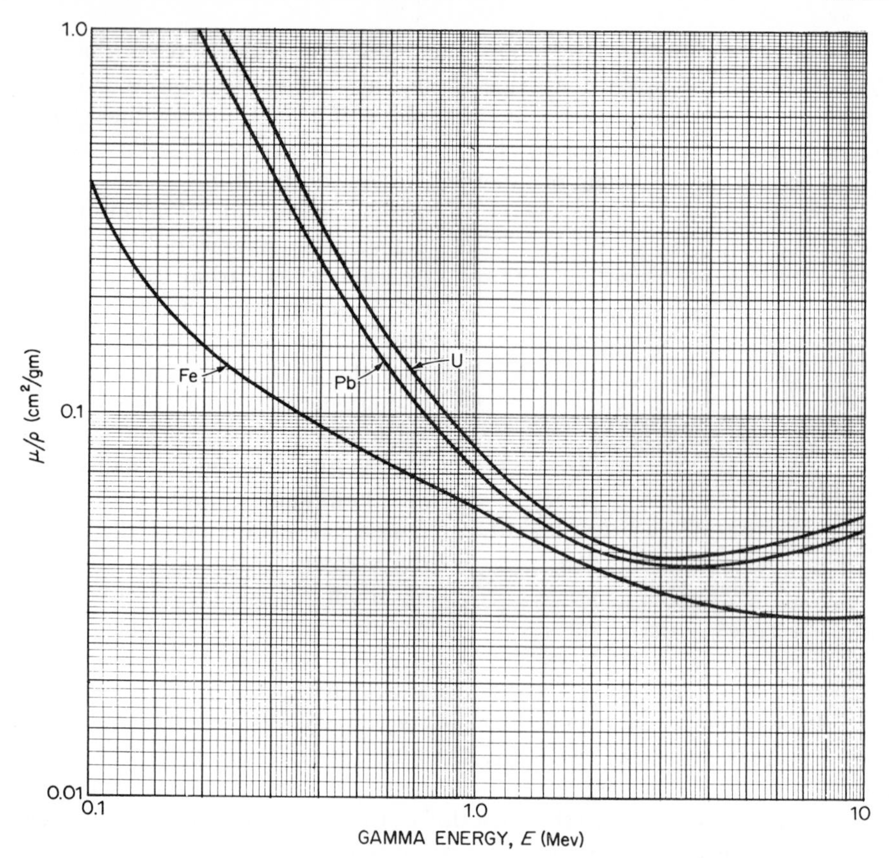

FIG. 11.10 Mass absorption coefficients of uranium, lead, and iron for γ rays. [R. L. Murray, *Introduction to Nuclear Engineering*, Prentice-Hall, 1961].

9. RADIOACTIVE TRANSFORMATIONS

After the discovery of radium, the study of radioactivity at once became one of the most important frontiers of scientific research, and many of the most capable chemists and physicists in the world devoted themselves intensely to the work. It was an unusually exciting period in the history of science — each issue of the journals brought reports of new discoveries of major importance. One man led the field for many years, an experimental physicist who achieved a Nobel prize in chemistry, perhaps the most productive experimental scientist the world has yet known —Ernest Rutherford.

Rutherford was born in 1871 in New Zealand, the son of a farmer. In 1895 he won a newly instituted scholarship to Cambridge, and on arrival there, immediately plunged into research under the direction of J. J. Thomson. In 1896 Becquerel discovered radioactivity, and in 1898 Rutherford began to study the radiations from radioactive substances, thus beginning his main life's work. He found and named the two types of rays, alpha and beta, and quickly became recognized as a young man of brilliant capabilities.

Thus, in 1898, he was appointed Professor of Physics at McGill University in Montreal at a salary of $2500 a year. He wrote to his fiancée, Mary Newton,

> *Living, I should imagine, is much the same as in New Zealand, but we should of course have to keep up a certain amount of style, and we ought to do it very comfortably on £400 [$1944] and put by the rest.*

Almost as soon as he arrived in Montreal, Rutherford had some experimental work in progress, his electrometers and electroscopes set up, and preparations of uranium and thorium under investigation. On 2 December, 1899, he wrote to Mary:

> *In your last letter you mentioned that I hadn't mentioned if I was doing any research work. My dear girl, I keep going steadily, turning up to the lab five nights out of seven till 11 or 12 o'clock, and generally make things buzz along. I sent off on Thursday another long paper for the press, which is a very good one, even if I say so, and comprises 1000 new facts which have been undreamt of, . . . suffice it to say that it is a matter of considerable moment. I have been working with the rare metals, uranium and thorium.*

He later described this research as follows:

> *Thorium compounds have about the same radioactivity weight for weight as the corresponding compounds of uranium, and, like that substance, emit alpha, beta and gamma rays. We have seen, however, that thorium differs from uranium in emitting, besides the three types of rays, an "emanation," or radioactive gas. This . . . can be readily illustrated by the simple experimental arrangement shown. [Fig. 11.11]*
>
> *A glass tube A is filled with about 50 grams of thorium oxide, or, still better, thorium hydroxide, which emits the emanation more freely than the oxide. This is connected by a narrow tube L of about a metre length with a suitable, well insulated electroscope. On charging the electroscope, the leaves converge very slowly as the thorium compound has no appreciable effect in ionizing the gas in the electroscope. If, however, a slow steady stream of air from a gas bag or gasometer is passed over the thorium, no effect is observed in the electroscope for a definite interval, which is a measure of the time taken for the air current to travel from A to the electroscope. The leaves are then seen to collapse rapidly, the rate of movement increasing for several minutes. This discharge of the electroscope is due to the ionizing effect of the thorium emanation, which has been conveyed with the current of air into the electroscope. On stopping the air current, the rate of collapse of the gold leaves is seen to diminish steadily, falling to half of its value in about one minute, or to be more accurate, in*

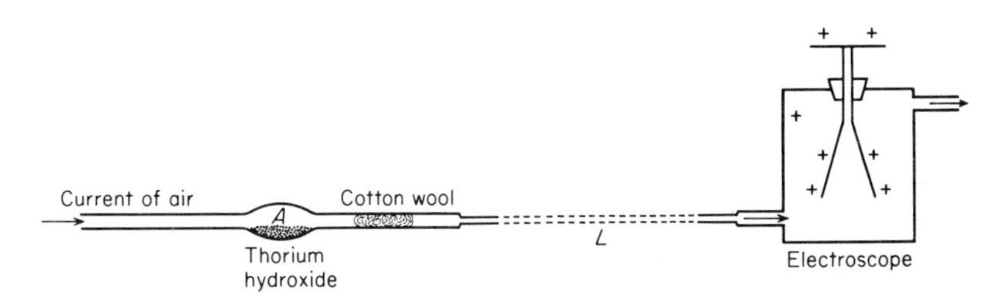

FIG. 11.11 Discharging power of the thorium emanation.

54 seconds. After about 5 minutes, the effect of the emanation is almost inappreciable. The emanation left to itself loses its activity according to an exponential law. In the first 54 seconds, the activity is reduced to half value; in twice that time, i.e., in 108 seconds, the activity is reduced to one quarter value, and in 162 seconds, one eighth value, and so on.

The period 54 seconds is the *half life* τ of the radioactive emanation Em.

In 1900, Frederick Soddy, a brilliant young chemist, came to McGill from Oxford. He at once formed a partnership with Rutherford and they worked together to unravel the complex transformations of the radioactive elements. It was found that the emanation did not come directly from thorium, but from a more active daughter, thorium-X. They dissolved $Th(NO_3)_4$ in water and added ammonia to precipitate $Th(OH)_4$. The activity stayed with the solution. Gradually the thorium recovered activity and the Th-X decayed.

Soddy has given us a good description of those days in the McGill Laboratory:

Rutherford and his radioactive emanations and active deposits got me before many weeks had elapsed and I abandoned all to follow him. For more than two years, scientific life became hectic to a degree rare in the life time of an individual, rare perhaps in the life time of an institution. The discovery that the emanations were Argon [family] gases, followed by that of Th-X as an intermediate product between Thorium and the emanation it produces, led rapidly to the complete interpretation of radioactivity as a natural process of spontaneous atomic disintegration and transmutation.

. . . The first magnetic deviation of the alpha rays by Rutherford, and then later successful electrostatic deviations were also notable events. I recall seeing him dancing like a dervish and emitting extraordinary imprecations, most probably in the Maori tongue, having inadvertently taken hold of the little deviation chamber before disconnecting the high-voltage battery and, under the influence of a power beyond his own, dashing it violently to the ground, so that its beautifully and cunningly made canalization system was strewn all in ruins over the floor.

The family of thorium products was finally found to be related as follows:

$$\mathrm{Th} \xrightarrow{\nearrow \alpha} \mathrm{Th{-}X} \xrightarrow{\nearrow \alpha} \mathrm{Em} \xrightarrow{\nearrow \alpha} \mathrm{Th{-}A} \longrightarrow \mathrm{Th{-}B} \begin{smallmatrix} \nearrow \alpha \\ \rightarrow \beta \\ \searrow \gamma \end{smallmatrix}$$

Thus they proved that in a radioactive transformation one element is changed into an entirely different element, and so on through a series of remarkable changes, each radioactive element having its own characteristic half life, which distinguishes it from the others.

10. KINETICS OF RADIOACTIVE DECAY

The decay of a radioactive species follows a rate law like that for a first-order chemical reaction. The rate of decomposition is directly proportional to the number N of atoms present at any time.

Thus,

$$-dN/dt = \lambda N \tag{11.15}$$

where λ is called the *radioactive decay constant.* If N_0 is the number of radioactive atoms present at time $t = 0$, we obtain on integration of Eq. (11.15),

$$N/N_0 = \exp(-\lambda t) \tag{11.16}$$

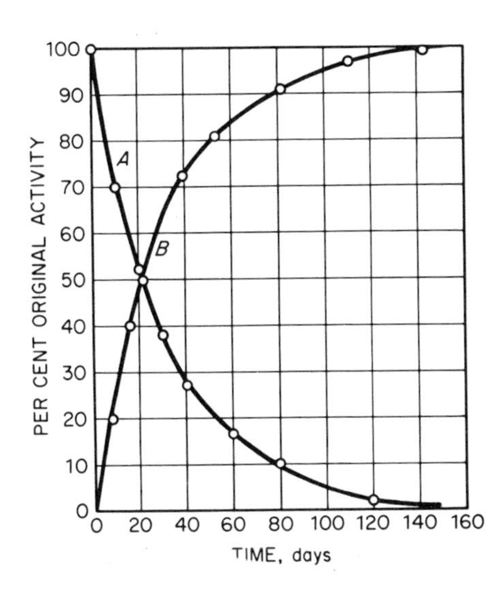

FIG. 11.12 Radioactive decay and regeneration of UX_1.

The exponential decay law of Eq. (11.16) is plotted in curve A, Fig. 11.12, the experimental points being those obtained from uranium-X_1, the first product in the uranium series. A sample of uranium or of any of its salts is found to emit both α and β particles. If an iron salt is added to a solution of a uranium salt, and the iron then precipitated as the hydroxide, it is found that the β activity is removed from the uranium and coprecipitated with the ferric hydroxide. This β activity then gradually decays according to the exponential curve A of Fig. 11.12. The original uranium sample gradually regains β activity, according to curve B. It is apparent that the sum of the activities given by curves A and B is always a constant. The amount of UX_1 (the β-emitter) decomposing per second is just equal to the amount being formed from the parent uranium.

A quantity often used instead of λ to describe the decay of a radioactive element is the *half life* τ, the time required for the activity to be reduced to one-half of its initial value. From Eq. (11.16),

$$\tfrac{1}{2} = \exp(-\lambda\tau)$$

$$\tau = \frac{\ln 2}{\lambda} = \frac{0.693}{\lambda} \tag{11.17}$$

The half life of uranium is 4.4×10^9 years, whereas that of UX_1 is 24.5 days. Because of the long life of U compared to UX_1, the number of U atoms present in a sample is effectively constant over measurable experimental periods, and the recovery curve of Fig. 11.12 reaches effectively the same initial activity after repeated separations of daughter UX_1 from the parent U. In case the radioactive atom yields a daughter atom which is itself radioactive, and so on in a radioactive series, we can treat the kinetics as a series of consecutive first-order reactions, using the method described in Sec. 8.11.

Many careful researches of this sort by Rutherford, Soddy, A. S. Russell, K. Fajans, O. Hahn, and others, are summarized in the complete *radioactive series,* such as that for the uranium family shown in Table 11.3. Examination of the properties of the elements in such series established two important general

TABLE 11.3 Radioactive Series — Uranium Family

Name	Symbol of Element	At. No. Z	Mass No. A	Particle Emitted	Half Life
Uranium I	U	92	238	α	4.56×10^9 y
Uranium X_1	Th	90	234	β	24.1 d
Uranium X_2	Pa	91	234	β, γ	1.14 m
Uranium II	U	92	234	α	2.7×10^5 y
Ionium	Th	90	230	α	8.3×10^4 y
Radium	Ra	88	226	α	1590 y
Radon	Rn	86	222	α	3.825 d
Radium A	Po	84	218	α	3.05 m
Radium B	Pb	82	214	β, γ	26.8 m
Radium C	Bi	83	214	α, β, γ	19.7 m
Radium C′ (99.96%)	Po	84	214	α	1.5×10^{-4} s
Radium C″ (0.04%)	Tl	81	210	β	1.32 m
Radium D	Pb	82	210	β, γ	22 y
Radium E	Bi	83	210	β, γ	5.0 d
Radium F	Po	84	210	α	140 d
Radium G	Pb	82	206		

principles. When an atom emits an α particle, its position shifts two places to the left in the periodic table; i.e., its atomic number decreases by two. The emission of a β particle shifts the position one place to the right, increasing the atomic number by one. It is evident, therefore, that the source of the β particles is in the nucleus of the atom, and not in the orbital electrons. No marked change in atomic weight is associated with the β-emission, whereas α-emission decreases the atomic weight by four units.

11. ISOTOPES

As more radioactive elements were discovered between uranium with atomic weight 238 and lead with atomic weight 207.3, the problem of how they could all be fitted into the periodic table became increasingly important. Cases began to appear in which two radioactive elements, distinctly different in their decay characteristics, could not be separated by any chemical method. In 1906, Bertram Boltwood at Yale discovered the parent of radium, a new element which he called *ionium*. He found that its chemical properties were those of thorium, and in fact if salts of these two elements were mixed, it was impossible to separate them by chemical methods. Marckwald and Keetman in Berlin confirmed this result after several years of the most careful work, and even Auer von Welsbach, the great expert on the separation of the rare earths, was unable to obtain the slightest separation of thorium and ionium. In 1921, A. S. Russell and R. Rossi showed that the spectra of these two elements were absolutely identical, although they put forth this conclusion with understandable caution. In the meantime, other instances of inseparable pairs among the radioactive elements had been discovered.

Soddy concluded that such inseparable elements must occupy the same position in a periodic table. In 1913, he invented for them the name *isotopes* from ισος τόπος, *the same place*.

The end product of all the natural radioactive series is lead, but the displacement law indicated that this lead should have different atomic weights in different series. Thus in the uranium series, five α particles each of mass 4 are lost between radium with an atomic weight of 226 and the product lead. This Pb therefore should have an atomic weight of 206. On the other hand, in the chain starting with thorium with an atomic weight of 232, six α particles are lost before the end product Pb is reached, and this Pb should therefore have an atomic weight of about 208. Ordinary Pb from nonradioactive sources has an atomic weight of 207.20. Soddy suggested in 1913 that Pb from thorium minerals might have a higher atomic weight than ordinary Pb. From a sample of Ceylon thorite, the Pb was found to have an atomic weight of 207.69. A sample was sent to Hönigschmid in Vienna, a great authority on atomic weights, and he obtained a weight of 207.77 as the mean of eight determinations. At about the same time, T. W. Richards at Harvard found an atomic weight of 206.08 from a uraniferous lead obtained from Norwegian clevite. The occurrence of isotopes was thus clearly demonstrated by the experts on atomic weights, the scientific descendants of Berzelius and Stas.

The ordinal number of the position of the element in the periodic table is called the *atomic number of the element*. Thus isotopes may be defined as elements having the same atomic number but different atomic weights.

The significance of atomic number was also shown by the work of H. G. J. Moseley in 1913. C. G. Barkla had discovered that in addition to the general or white radiation emitted by all the elements, there were several series of characteristic X-ray lines peculiar to each element. Moseley made systematic measurements of the vibration frequencies ν of these lines and found that they were related to the atomic number Z by

$$\nu^{1/2} = a(Z - b) \tag{11.18}$$

where for each series a and b are constant for all the elements.

When the Moseley relationship was plotted for the X-ray lines of the elements, discontinuities in the plot appeared wherever there were missing elements in the periodic table. These vacant spaces have since been filled. This work provided further convincing evidence that the atomic number and not the atomic weight governs the periodicity of the chemical properties of the elements.

12. POSITIVE-ION ANALYSIS

At this time, J. J. Thomson confirmed the existence of isotopes by an entirely different kind of experiment.

In 1886, Eugen Goldstein set up a discharge tube with a perforated cathode, and discovered rays of a new kind streaming into the space behind the cathode.

He called these *Kanalstrahlen, canal rays.* Eleven years later, W. Wien showed that these rays were composed of positively charged particles with ratios Q/m of the same magnitude as those found in electrolyses. He concluded that they were *free positive ions.*

Thomson took up the problem of the behavior of positive rays in electric and magnetic fields in 1912. He used the apparatus shown in Fig. 11.13. The positive rays generated by the ionization of the gas in a discharge tube were drawn out as a thin pencil through an elongated hole in the cathode. They were then subjected simultaneously to a magnetic and to an electric field. The electric field E deflected the beam in one direction and the magnetic induction B, in a perpendicular direction. The combined effect was to draw out the beam into a parabolic trace, which was then recorded on a photographic plate. The posi-

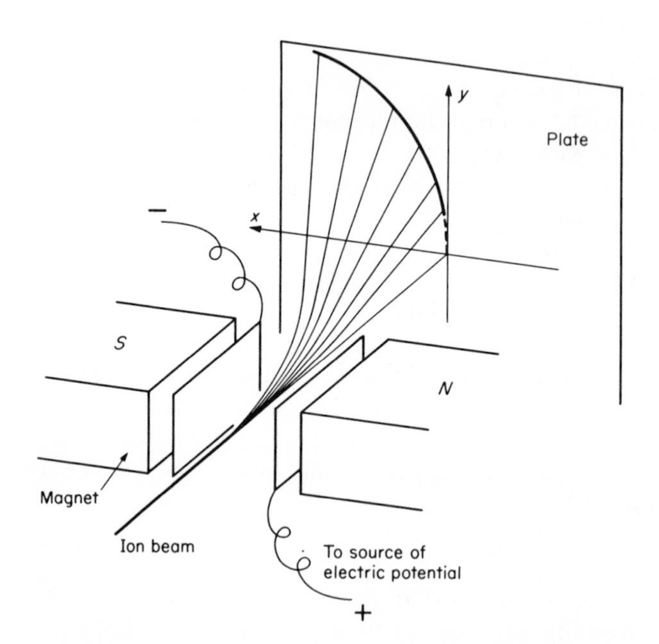

FIG. 11.13 Parabolic mass spectrograph of Thomson.

tion of the trace depended on the ratio of charge to mass Q/m of the ions in the beam, so that all ions having the same Q/m would lie on a given parabola. The actual equation for the parabola is

$$y^2 = k_1 \frac{B^2}{E} \frac{Q}{m} x \tag{11.19}$$

No remarkable results were obtained with this apparatus until November, 1912, when a sample of the lighter constituents of air was introduced. In addition to a strong line at mass 20 due to neon, an additional weak line was observed at 22. After most careful investigation, Thomson concluded that this line was probably due to an isotope of neon. Francis Aston, a research student at the Cavendish Laboratory, immediately set to work to try to obtain some separation of the neon isotopes. After 3000 fractionations of liquid neon, he could find no change in its density and no change in its positive-ray parabolas. He then tried to fractionate the neon by successive diffusions through clay pipe. A difficult and tedious set of fractional diffusions yielded two samples whose densities gave atomic weights of 20.15 and 20.28. Thus there was good confirming evidence that the two isotopes of neon really existed. By this time, the occurrence of the lead isotopes had been demonstrated, but Aston's work was interrupted by the War. On his return to the Cavendish Laboratory in 1919, he took up the problem again, and constructed a much improved apparatus for positive-ray analysis, which he called the *mass spectrograph*. With this equipment he demonstrated the existence of isotopes of many elements.

13. THE NUCLEAR ATOM

With the discovery of isotopes, the hypothesis of Prout was nearly, but not exactly, confirmed. The atomic weights of the individual isotopes are extremely close to whole numbers. The nearest whole number to an isotopic atomic weight is called the *mass number* A of the isotope. For example, the isotope of neon with an atomic weight $M = 21.9983$ has a mass number $A = 22$. The question of why the hypothesis of Prout was valid remained unanswered. The underlying theoretical model, which was ultimately to explain the occurrence of isotopes and the internal structure of atoms, had in fact been discovered by Rutherford in 1911.

After nine years crowded with epoch making researches, Rutherford had left McGill in 1907 to become professor of physics at Manchester. In 1908 he was awarded the Nobel Prize in Chemistry. In his prize address he said that he had dealt with many transformations, some occurring in extremely short periods of time, but the quickest he had ever met was his own transformation in one moment from a physicist to a chemist.

One of Rutherford's most brilliant students at Manchester was Hans Geiger who had come from Germany for postdoctoral work. Their first success was to develop a method for counting individual alpha particles. Along the axis of a partially evacuated cylinder was mounted a fine wire which could be charged to a high potential (about 1000 v). The alpha particles entered the cylinder through a tiny hole, and as they passed through the gas they produced a heavy trail of ions. As a result of this ionization, there was an electric breakdown between the wire and the shell of the cylinder, and the pulse of current which passed could be readily detected on a galvanometer or other indicator. The ionization caused by an individual particle is magnified by a factor of about 2000. This instrument for counting individual particles was later adapted to beta particles and gamma rays also, by using a different gas as the filling and providing a different method for amplifying the pulse produced. A typical arrangement is shown in Fig. 11.14. Under the name of the *Geiger counter* this was to become the archetypical instrument of a new age.

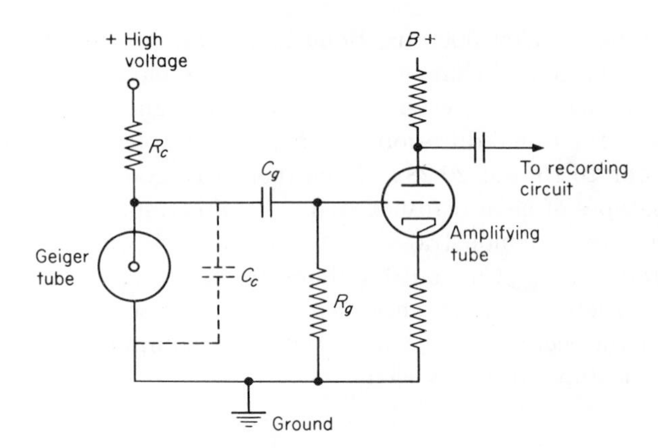

FIG. 11.14 Basic circuit of Geiger counter. When an ionizing particle passes through the Geiger tube an avalanche of electrons makes it temporarily conducting. A pulse of current passes through R_c and the tube to ground. The anode of the tube becomes more negative and this negative pulse is transmitted through C_g to the grid of the amplifying tube. The effective capacitance of the Geiger tube is denoted by C_c.

The greatest discovery of all was yet to come. The problem of the number of electrons contained in an atom had attracted the attentions of Thomson and C. G. Barkla. From measurements of the scattering of light, X rays and beams of electrons, it was possible to estimate that this number was of the same order as the atomic weight. To preserve the electrical neutrality of the atom, an equal number of positive charges would then be necessary. Thomson proposed an atomic model that consisted of discrete electrons embedded in a uniform sphere of positive charge.

Rutherford has told the story of the next great development in the problem, at the University of Manchester in 1910.

In the early days I had observed the scattering of α-particles, and Dr. Geiger in my laboratory had examined it in detail. He found in thin pieces of heavy metal that the scattering was usually small, of the order of one degree. One day Geiger came to me and said, 'Don't you think that young Marsden, whom I am training in radioactive methods, ought to begin a small research?' Now I had thought that too, so I said, 'Why not let him see if any α-particles can be scattered through a large angle?' I may tell you in confidence that I did not believe they would be, since we knew that the α-particle was a very fast massive particle, with a great deal of energy, and you could show that if the scattering was due to the accumulated effect of a number of small scatterings, the chance of an α-particle's being scattered backwards was very small. Then I remember two or three days later Geiger coming to me in great excitement and saying, 'We have been able to get some of the α-particles coming backwards.' . . . It was quite the most incredible event that has ever happened to me in my life. It was almost as incredible as if you fired a 15-inch shell at a piece of tissue paper and it came back and hit you.

On consideration I realized that this scattering backwards must be the result of a single collision and when I made calculations it was impossible to get anything of that order of magnitude unless you took a system in which the greater part of the mass of the atom was concentrated in a minute nucleus.

Marsden and Geiger passed a beam of α particles through a thin metal foil. They observed the deflections of the particles on a zinc-sulfide screen, which scintillated whenever it was struck by an α particle.

Rutherford enunciated the nuclear model of the atom in a paper published in 1911. The positive charge is concentrated in the massive center of the atom with the electrons revolving in orbits around it, like planets around the sun. Further scattering experiments indicated that the number of elementary positive charges in the nucleus of an atom is equal within experimental uncertainty to one-half its atomic weight. Thus carbon, nitrogen, and oxygen would have six, seven, and eight electrons, respectively, revolving about an equal positive charge. It follows that the charge of the nucleus, or the number of orbital electrons, may be set equal to the *atomic number* Z, of the element, the ordinal number of the position it occupies in the periodic table. Different isotopic species of an element are thus characterized by their different nuclear masses but the nuclear charge must be the same for a given element.

The scattering formula derived by Rutherford is important in many studies of the passage of charged particles through matter.*

$$\frac{dN}{d\omega} = \frac{N_0 n l Z_1^2 Z_2^2 e^4}{64\pi^2 \epsilon_0^2 m_1^2 v_0^4 \sin^4(\theta/2)} \tag{11.20}$$

This gives the number of particles dN scattered into a solid angle $d\omega$ at an angle θ to the beam direction. N_0 is the number of particles in the beam, n is the number of scattering centers per unit volume in a target of thickness l, Z_1 is the charge of the incident particles (2 for α particles), Z_2 is the atomic number of the target atoms, m_1 is the mass and v_0 the velocity of the particles in the beam. The units are in the absolute practical system so that e is in coulombs and $\epsilon_0 = 8.85434 \times 10^{-12}$ farad/meter.

It would seem to be possible to increase the mass of a nucleus by adding to it a hydrogen nucleus or proton and at the same time adding an extra electron to preserve electrical neutrality. If this model were correct, the *prima materia* of Prout and the ancients would be realized in *protons and electrons.* Actually, however, future developments were to show that there are no electrons present in the nucleus. The nucleus is composed of *protons* and neutral particles of about the same mass called *neutrons.*

14. MASS SPECTRA

The design of most modern mass spectrometers is based on a method devised by A. J. Dempster at Chicago (1918). His method, called *direction focusing,* brings all ions of the same Q/m to a sharp focus.

* A derivation is given by D. Halliday, *Introductory Nuclear Physics* [New York: John Wiley (1950)], p. 296.

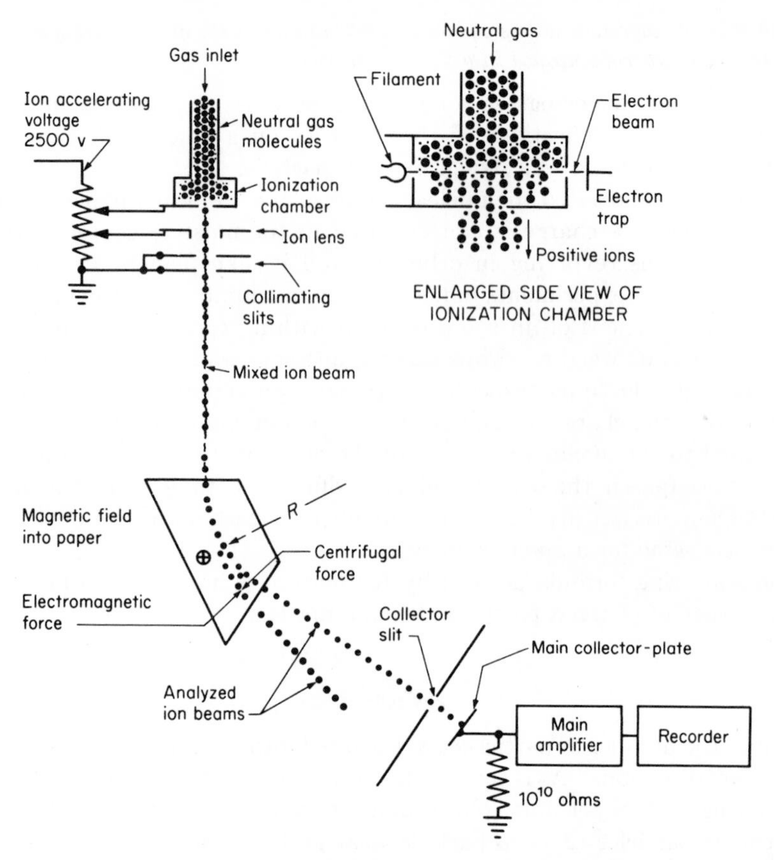

FIG. 11.15 Principles of operation of mass spectrometer. (General Electric Company)

A modern mass spectrometer of the Dempster type is outlined in Fig. 11.15. The positive ions are obtained by vaporizing atoms from a heated filament, and then ionizing them in a beam of electrons from an *electron gun.** Alternatively, ions can be formed by passing the electron beam through samples of gas. A potential difference U accelerates the ions uniformly, so that they issue from the slit with approximately the same kinetic energies,

$$\tfrac{1}{2}mv^2 = UQ \tag{11.21}$$

The accelerated beam of ions passes through the field of a powerful electromagnet. The field direction is perpendicular to the plane of the paper. The ions emerge from the collimating slits of the source in various directions, but since they all have about the same velocity, they are bent by the magnetic field into circular paths of about the same radius, given by Eq. (11.8) as $R = mv/BQ$.

* An electron gun is an arrangement by which electrons emitted from a filament are accelerated by an electric field and focused into a beam with an appropriate slit system.

Therefore, from Eq. (11.21),

$$\frac{m}{Q} = \frac{B^2R^2}{2U} \tag{11.22}$$

With m in atomic mass units, Q in multiples of the electronic charge e, B in gauss, U in volts, and R in cm,

$$m/Q = 4.79 \times 10^{-5}B^2R^2/2U$$

For any fixed value of the magnetic induction B, the accelerating potential can be adjusted to bring the ions of the same m/Q to a focus at the collector slit, through which they pass to an electrometer. The electrometer measures the charge collected or the current carried through the tube by the ions. A typical mass spectrometric curve of ion current vs. the mass number is shown in Fig. 11.16, the heights of the peaks corresponding to the relative abundances of the isotopes.

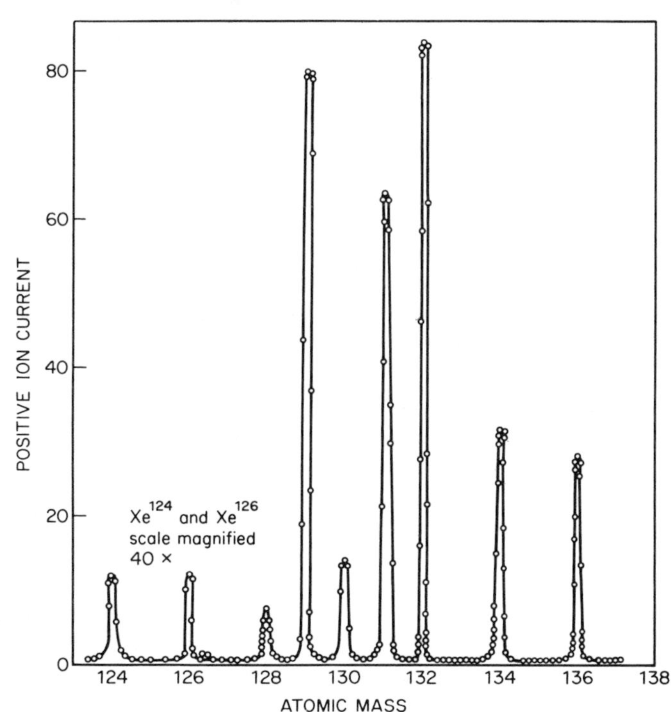

FIG. 11.16 Mass spectrometric recording of isotopes of Xenon.

15. MEASUREMENT OF ISOTOPIC MASSES

If a set of masses m_1, m_2, m_3 . . . from an ion source are separated in a mass spectrometer, the intensity and position of each ion can be recorded on the mass spectrogram, either electrically or photographically. An example of two lines at mass number 13 is shown in Fig. 11.17(a). From Eq. (11.22) the radius of

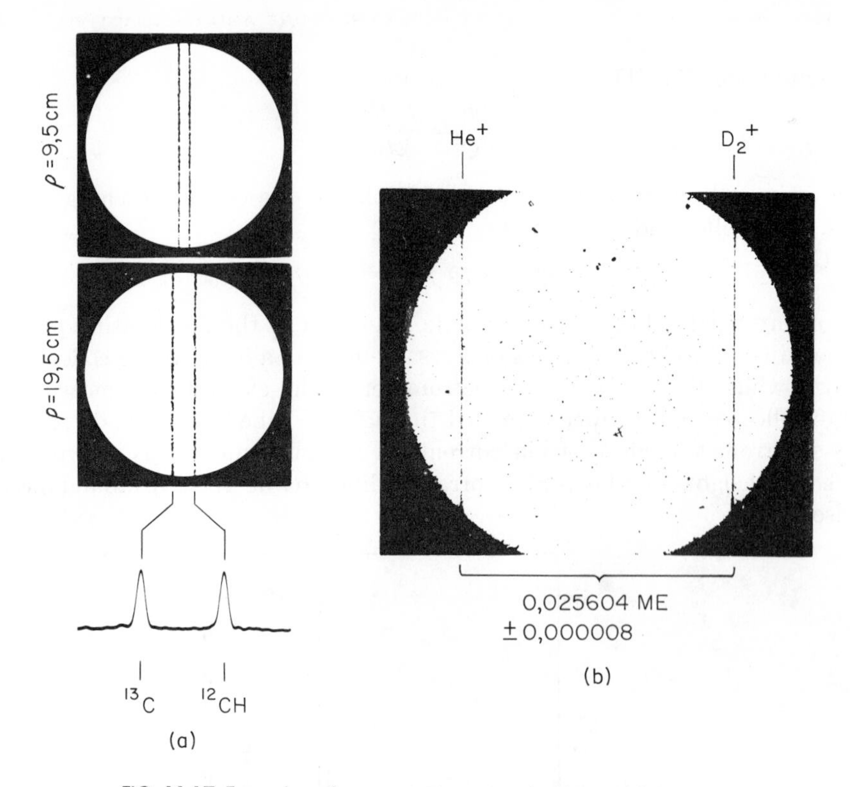

FIG. 11.17 Examples of mass spectrometer doublets used in exact determinations of atomic weights. The radius of the ionic path is ρ, ME ≡ mass units. [H. Ewald, Physikalisches Institut der Technischen Hochschule, München].

curvature of the ionic path is proportional to the square root of the mass number, and hence the displacements x_i of the lines from the origin (point of entrance of ionic beam into the magnetic field) are related as

$$x_1 : x_2 : x_3 : \ldots = m_1^{1/2} : m_2^{1/2} : m_3^{1/2} : \ldots$$

$$m_i = kx_i^2$$

where k is a constant characteristic of the dimensions of the instrument and the field strengths.

Precise isotopic masses are determined by careful measurements of the displacements of lines in closely spaced doublets or multiplets. In the example in Fig. 11.17(a) suppose we know the masses of ^{12}C and ^{1}H and wish to determine the mass cf ^{13}C.

$$^{12}\text{C} = 12.003861 \qquad m_0$$

$$^{1}\text{H} = 1.008130$$

Therefore,

$$^{12}\text{CH} = 13.011991 \qquad m_2$$

The lines ^{12}C and ^{12}CH are used as *dispersion lines* to give the Δm corresponding to a displacement Δx on the film. In this case $\Delta x = 9.9624$ mm for $\Delta m = m_2 - m_0 = 1.008130$. The unknown m_1 of ^{13}C is displaced by $\delta x = 0.0427$ mm from m_2. Hence

$$\delta m = \frac{.0427}{9.9624} \times 1.002130 = 0.004408$$

and $m_1 = m_2 - \delta m = 13.007583$ mass units.*

With such methods we can measure atomic masses to an accuracy of one part in a million in favorable cases. When accurate atomic masses are combined with accurate measurements of the relative abundance of the different stable isotopes of an element, highly accurate atomic weights are obtained.

16. ATOMIC WEIGHTS AND ISOTOPES

Table 11.4 is a partial list of naturally occurring stable isotopes and their relative abundances. Most of these isotopes were discovered by mass spectrographic analysis, but one notable exception is heavy hydrogen or deuterium, whose existence was originally demonstrated by the optical spectrum of hydrogen.

The isotopic weights in Table 11.4 are not exactly integral. Thus the hypothesis of Prout is nearly but not exactly confirmed. The nearest whole number to the atomic weight is called the *mass number* A of an atomic species. A particular isotope is designated by writing the mass number as a left-hand superscript to the symbol of the element, as ^{2}H, ^{235}U, and so on. A particular nuclear species of given mass number A and atomic number Z is called a *nuclide*.

Before 1961, the scale of atomic weights used by chemists was based on the choice of 16 (exactly) for the atomic weight of naturally occurring oxygen. This oxygen, however, contains three stable isotopes, 99.76 atom % ^{16}O, 0.04% ^{17}O and 0.20% ^{18}O. Thus the physicists were forced to adopt a scale of atomic weights based on the choice of 16 (exactly) for the nuclide ^{16}O. The atomic weight of ordinary oxygen on the physical scale would be:

$$.9976(16.00000) + 0.0004(17.00450) + 0.0020(18.00369) = 16.0044$$

Therefore, the ratio of physical to chemical atomic weights was 16.0044/-16.0000 = 1.000275.

This difference in the atomic-weight scales was a source of increasing annoyance to physical chemists and chemical physicists. In 1957, Olander and Nier independently proposed a scale based on the choice of 12 (exactly) for the nuclide ^{12}C. Although ^{12}C has a stable isotope ^{13}C with an abundance of 1.11%, the atomic weight of ^{12}C on the chemical scale is 12.00052, very close to exactly 12. Both physicists and chemists have accepted the new unified standard.† Table 11.5 gives a comparison between the two obsolete scales and the new unified scale.

* Ewald used units based on the old physical scale of atomic weights.

† It was ratified by the International Union of Physics in 1960 at Ottawa and by the International Union of Chemistry in 1961 at Montreal.

TABLE 11.4 SOME STABLE NUCLIDES

Atomic Number Z	Element	Symbol	Mass Number A	Isotopic Atomic Weight (^{12}C = 12) M	Relative Abundance (per cent)
1	Hydrogen	H	1	1.007796	99.985
		D	2	2.014068	0.015
2	Helium	He	3	3.016104	10^{-5}
			4	4.002564	100
3	Lithium	Li	6	6.014868	7.8
			7	7.015848	92.1
4	Beryllium	Be	9	9.012048	100
5	Boron	B	10	10.012992	20
			11	11.009268	80
6	Carbon	C	12	12.000000	98.9
			13	13.00332	1.1
7	Nitrogen	N	14	14.00280	99.62
			15	14.999916	0.38
8	Oxygen	O	16	15.99468	99.76
			17	16.99884	0.04
			18	17.99772	0.20
9	Fluorine	F	19	18.99816	100
10	Neon	Ne	20	19.99212	90.00
			21	20.99316	0.27
			22	21.99132	9.73
15	Phosphorus	P	31	30.97428	100
16	Sulfur	S	32	31.97244	95.1
			33	32.97168	0.74
			34	33.96852	4.2
			36		0.016
17	Chlorine	Cl	35	34.96944	75.4
			37	36.96600	24.6
82	Lead	Pb	204		1.5
			206		23.6
			207		22.6
			208	207.99096	52.3
92	Uranium	U	234		0.006
			235		0.720
			238		99.274

TABLE 11.5 COMPARISON OF ATOMIC-WEIGHT SCALES

	Old Physical Scale	Old Chemical Scale	New Unified Scale
^{16}O	16 exactly	15.99560	15.99491
O	—	16 exactly	15.9999
^{12}C	12.00382	12.00052	12 exactly
C	—	12.011	12.010
Ag	—	107.873	107.868

A mass equal to one-twelfth the mass of an atom of ^{12}C is used as an atomic mass unit m_u:

$$m_u = 1u = 1.66037 \times 10^{-24} \text{ g}$$

The *mass defect* of a nuclide is defined by

$$\text{mass defect} = \text{atomic weight} - \text{mass number} = M(Z,A) - A$$

17. SEPARATION OF ISOTOPES

We shall briefly mention several important methods. A detailed discussion can be found in standard reference works.*

(1) *Gaseous diffusion.* This was the method used to separate $^{235}UF_6$ from $^{238}UF_6$ in the plant at Oak Ridge, Tennessee. Its fundamental principle was discussed in Sec. 7.9 on the effusion of gases.

The *separation factor* f of a process of isotope separation is defined as the ratio of the relative concentration of a given species after processing to its relative concentration before processing. Thus,

$$f = (n_1'/n_2')/(n_1/n_2)$$

where (n_1, n_1') and (n_2, n_2') are the concentrations of species 1 and 2 before and after processing. Uranium-235 occurs in natural uranium to the extent of one part in 140 $(n_1/n_2 = \frac{1}{140})$. To separate 90 per cent pure ^{235}U from ^{238}U, therefore, the overall separation factor must be $f = (\frac{9}{1})/(\frac{1}{140}) = 1260$. For a single stage of diffusion the separation factor cannot exceed the ideal value α, given from Graham's Law, as $\alpha = (M_2/M_1)^{1/2}$ where M_2 and M_1 are the molecular weights of the heavy and light components, respectively. For the uranium hexafluorides, $\alpha = (\frac{352}{349})^{1/2} = 1.0043$. Actually, the value of f for a single stage will be less than this, owing to diffusion in the reverse direction, nonideal mixing at the barrier surface, and partially nondiffusive flow through the barrier. It is therefore necessary to use several thousand stages in a cascade arrangement to effect a considerable concentration of $^{235}UF_6$. The theory of a cascade is similar to that of a fractionating column with a large number of theoretical plates. The light fraction that passes through the barrier becomes the feed for the next stage, while the heavier fraction is sent back to an earlier stage.

(2) *Thermal diffusion.* This method was first successfully employed by H. Clusius and G. Dickel,† and the experimental arrangement is called a *Clusius column.* It consists of a long vertical cylindrical pipe with an electrically heated wire running down its axis. When a temperature gradient is maintained between the hot inner wire and the cold outer walls, the lighter isotope diffuses preferen-

* S. Glasstone, *Sourcebook on Atomic Energy,* 2nd ed. (Princeton: Van Nostrand, 1958); *Proceedings of the Second United Nations International Conference on the Peaceful Uses of Atomic Energy,* Vol. 4. *Production of Nuclear Materials and Isotopes* (United Nations, Geneva, 1958).

† *Naturwissenschaften 26* (1938). For the theory of the thermal diffusion separation see K. Schäfer, *Angew. Chem., 59,* 83 (1947). The separation depends not only on mass but also on difference in intermolecular forces. With isotopic molecules the mass effect predominates and the lighter molecules accumulate in the warmer regions.

tially from the cold to the warm regions. The separation is enhanced by the convection currents in the tube, which carry the molecules arriving near the warm inner wire upwards to the top of the column. The molecules at the cold outer wall are carried downwards by convection.

With columns about 30 meters high and a temperature difference of about 600°C, Clusius was able to effect a virtually complete separation of the isotopes of chlorine, ^{35}Cl and ^{37}Cl.

The cascade principle can also be applied to batteries of thermal diffusion columns, but for mass production of isotopes this operation is in general less economical than pressure-diffusion methods.

(3) *Electromagnetic separators.* This method employs large mass spectrometers with split collectors, so that heavy and light ions are collected separately. Its usefulness is greatest in applications in which the throughput of material is comparatively small.

(4) *Separation by exchange reactions.* Different isotopic species of the same element differ significantly in chemical reactivity. These differences are evident in the equilibrium constants of the so-called *isotopic exchange reactions.* If isotopes did not differ in reactivity, the equilibrium constants of these reactions would all be equal to unity. Some actual examples follow:

$$\tfrac{1}{2}S^{16}O_2 + H_2{}^{18}O \rightarrow \tfrac{1}{2}S^{18}O_2 + H_2{}^{16}O \qquad K = 1.028 \text{ at } 25°C$$

$$^{13}CO + {}^{12}CO_2 \rightarrow {}^{12}CO + {}^{13}CO_2 \qquad K = 1.086 \text{ at } 25°C$$

$$^{15}NH_3(g) + {}^{14}NH_4^+(aq.) \rightarrow {}^{14}NH_3(g) + {}^{15}NH_4^+(aq.) \qquad K = 1.023 \text{ at } 25°C$$

Such differences in affinity are most marked for the lighter elements, for which the *relative* differences in isotopic masses are greater.

Exchange reactions can be applied to the separation of isotopes. The possible separation factors in a single-stage process are necessarily small, but the cascade principle is again applicable. H. C. Urey and H. G. Thode concentrated ^{15}N through the exchange between ammonium nitrate and ammonia. Gaseous ammonia was caused to flow countercurrently to a solution of NH_4^+ ions, which trickled down columns packed with glass helices or saddles. After equilibrium was attained in the exchange columns, 8.8 grams of 70.67 per cent ^{15}N could be removed from the system, as nitrate, every twelve hours.

As a result of exchange reactions, the isotopic compositions of naturally occurring elements show small but significant variations depending on their sources. If we know the equilibrium constant of an exchange reaction over a range of temperatures, it should be possible to calculate the temperature at which a product was formed, from a measurement of the isotopic ratio in the product. Urey has applied this method, based on $^{18}O : {}^{16}O$ ratios, to the determination of the temperature of formation of calcium carbonate deposits. The exchange equilibrium is that between the oxygen in water and in bicarbonate ions. The temperature of the seas in remote geologic eras can be estimated to within 1°C from the $^{18}O : {}^{16}O$ ratio in deposits of the shells of prehistoric molluscs.

18. HEAVY HYDROGEN

In 1931, Urey, Brickwedde, and Murphy proved the existence of the hydrogen isotope of mass 2 (deuterium) by a careful examination of the spectrum of a sample of hydrogen obtained as the residue from the evaporation of several hundred liters of liquid hydrogen. Deuterium is contained in hydrogen to the extent of one part in 4500.

In 1932, Washburn and Urey discovered that an extraordinary concentration of *heavy water*, D_2O, occurred in the residue from electrolysis of water. Applications of the cascade principle to electrolytic cells, to fractional distillation of water and of hydrogen, and to various exchange reactions have been made to produce heavy water in tonnage quantities. The Savannah River plant of the U. S. Atomic Energy Commission starts with the Spevack process based on the exchange of water with H_2S,

$$HDO + H_2S \rightleftarrows HDS + H_2O$$

At 100°C equilibrium lies to the right, and at 25°C to the left. The hydrogen sulfide formed at 100° is separated and poured back into water at 25°C. Repeated cycles yield about 2% D_2O, which is concentrated to 99.8% by fractional distillation and electrolysis.

Some properties of H_2O and D_2O are compared in Table 11.6.

TABLE 11.6 PROPERTIES OF HEAVY WATER AND ORDINARY WATER

Property	Units	Ordinary Water	Heavy Water
Density at 25°C	g/cc	0.997044	1.104625
Temperature of maximum density	°C	4.0	11.6
Melting point	°C	0.000	3.802
Boiling point	°C	100.00	101.42
Heat of fusion	cal/mole	1436	1510
Heat of vaporization at 25°	cal/mole	10 484	10 743
Dielectric constant	—	81.5	80.7
Refractive index at 20° (Na D line)	—	1.33300	1.32828
Surface tension (20°C)	dynes/cm	72.75	72.8
Viscosity (10°C)	millipoise	13.10	16.85

PROBLEMS

1. Consider a mass spectrometer, as shown in Fig. 11.15, with a magnetic field of 3000 gauss and a path radius of 5.00 cm. At what accelerating voltage will (a) H^+ ions, (b) Na^+ ions be brought to focus at the ion collector? [*Ans.* (a) 5390; (b) 234]

2. Radium-226 decays by α-particle emission with a half life of 1590 years, the product being radon-222. Calculate the volume of radon evolved from 1 g of radium over a period of 50 years. [*Ans.* 2.19 cc at STP]

3. The half life of radon is 3.825 days. How long would it take for 90 per cent of a sample of radon to disintegrate? How many disintegrations per second are produced in a microgram (10^{-6} g) of radium? [*Ans.* 12.7 days; 3.68×10^4]

4. The half life of thorium-C is 60.5 minutes. How many disintegrations would occur in 15 minutes from a sample containing initially 1 mg of Th-C (at wt. 212)? [*Ans.* 4.5×10^{17}]

5. The half life of U-238 is 4.56×10^9 years. The final decay product is Pb-206, the intermediate steps being fast compared with the uranium disintegration. In Lower Pre-Cambrian minerals, lead and uranium are found associated in the ratio of approximately 1 g Pb to 3.5 g U. Assuming that all the Pb has come from the U, estimate the age of the mineral deposit. [*Ans.* 1.86×10^9 years]

6. What is the maximum velocity that a proton with an energy of 1 mev can impart to (a) another proton, (b) an oxygen atom.

7. The nuclide ^{59}Ni emits a 6.4 kv X ray (γ). What is the wavelength of this X ray in Å? In nickel oxide its linear absorption coefficient is 463.3 cm^{-1} (ρ = 7.45 g cm^{-3}). What thickness of NiO would reduce the intensity of the X radiation by 99 per cent?

8. The nuclide ^{136}Cs is a β emitter of 13.7 d half life. How much ^{136}Cs would be equivalent to 10 curies?

9. The maximum permissible dose of ^{90}Sr in the body is about 1 μC. This nuclide emits 0.61 mev β^- with τ = 19.9 y. Suppose a baby ingests 1 μC of ^{90}Sr from milk contaminated by atomic-bomb tests. Suppose further that this ^{90}Sr is concentrated in the tissues and none of it is eliminated. Calculate the total number of disintegrations of ^{90}Sr that occur in the body of the victim over a period of 20 years.

10. Potassium-40 constitutes 0.012 per cent of natural K, and K is 0.35 per cent of the weight of the body. ^{40}K emits β and γ rays with a $\tau = 4.5 \times 10^8$ yr. Estimate the number of disintegrations of ^{40}K in the body described in problem 9 over the 20 yr period, assuming an average weight of 50 kg.

---

11. Measurements of the flux of heat through the surface of the earth have shown the flux to be sensibly the same for different continents; the average value is about 1×10^{-6} cal/cm^2 sec. What fraction of this heat flux can be attributed to the radioactive decay of ^{226}Ra, ^{234}Th and ^{40}K in the earth's crust? Consider only the upper layer of the earth's crust, which is believed to consist of granitic rock extending to a depth of 15 to 20 kilometers, and assume that the distribution of Ra, Th, K is uniform in this layer. Laboratory experiments give 4×10^{-13} cal/cm^3 sec for the heat production from the decay of Ra, Th, and K in representative samples of granitic rocks.

12. An Na^+ ion is moving through an evacuated vessel in the positive x direction at a speed of 10^7 cm per sec. At $x = 0$, $y = 0$, it enters an electric field of 500 volts per cm in the positive y direction. Calculate its position (x, y) after 10^{-6} sec. [*Ans.* $x = 10.00$, $y = 10.45$ cm]

13. Make calculations as in Problem 12 except that the field is a magnetic field of 1000 gauss in the positive z direction. [*Ans.* $x = 9.76$, $y = 2.06$ cm]

14. Calculate the final position of the Na^+ ion in the above problems if the electric and magnetic fields act simultaneously. [*Ans.* $x = 11.3$, $y = 8.3$ cm]

15. Derive an expression for the average life of a radioactive atom in terms of the half life τ.

16. From the Rutherford scattering formula, calculate $dN/d\omega$ for a scattering angle of (a) 2°, (b) 10°, (c) 90° for protons of 0.5 mev incident on a gold target 1 mm thick. The ion current is 100 μA and the time 10 minutes.

17. One gram of pure radium is placed in a container. How much helium will accumulate in the container in 100 days?

18. The nuclide ^{63}Ni emits a 0.063 Mev β ray with a half life of 85 y. It was found that 0.46 mg/cm^2 of absorber reduced the intensity of the β rays by one half. Suppose that you had a slab of nickel (density 8.90 g cm^{-3}) uniformly doped with ^{63}Ni to the extent of one part in 10^9. What would be the β emission at the surface of the nickel in counts/min cm^2?

19. Cobalt-60 emits γ rays with an average energy of 1.25 Mev. What is the dosage rate in roentgens per hour to be expected at a distance of 50 cm from a 10 millicurie ^{60}Co source? The mass absorption coefficient in air of the γ rays of this energy is 12.5 g cm^{-2}. [*Ans.* 0.11 r hr^{-1}]

12 PARTICLES AND WAVES

You cannot cling to the idea that we have two sets of experiences of nature, one of primary qualities which belong to the objects perceived, and one of secondary qualities which are the products of our mental excitements. All we know of nature is in the same boat, to sink or swim together. The constructions of science are merely expositions of the characters of things perceived.

ALFRED NORTH WHITEHEAD (1920)

In the history of light two different theories were alternately in fashion, one based on the particle model and the other on the wave model. At the present time, we must regard both with equal respect. In some experiments light displays corpuscular properties: the photoelectric and Compton effects can be explained only by means of light particles, or photons, having an energy $\epsilon = h\nu$. In other experiments, just as convincing, light displays undulatory properties: polarization and interference phenomena require a wave theory.

As a result of the dual nature of light, it has become necessary to re-examine the meaning and limitations of physical measurement as applied to systems of atomic dimensions or smaller. The results of this analysis are included in what is called *quantum theory* or *wave mechanics*. Before we discuss the significant experiments that led to the new theories, we shall review the nature of vibratory and wave motions.

1. PERIODIC AND WAVE MOTION

The vibration of a simple harmonic oscillator, discussed in Sec. 7.26, is a good example of a motion that is periodic in time. The equation of motion ($f = ma$) is

$$m\, d^2x/dt^2 = -\kappa x$$

where κ is called the *force constant* of the oscillator. This is a simple linear differential equation.* It can be solved by first making the substitution $v = dx/dt$. Then $d^2x/dt^2 = dv/dt = (dv/dx)(dx/dt) = v(dv/dx)$, and the equation becomes

$$v(dv/dx) + (\kappa/m)x = 0$$

Integration gives

$$v^2 + (\kappa/m)x^2 = \text{constant}$$

The constant can be evaluated from the fact that when the oscillator is at the extreme limit of its vibration, $x = A$, the kinetic energy is zero, and hence $v = 0$. Thus the constant $= (\kappa/m)A^2$. Then

$$v^2 = \left(\frac{dx}{dt}\right)^2 = \frac{\kappa}{m}(A^2 - x^2)$$

$$\frac{dx}{dt} = \left[\frac{\kappa}{m}(A^2 - x^2)\right]^{1/2}$$

$$\frac{dx}{(A^2 - x^2)^{1/2}} = (\kappa/m)^{1/2}\,dt$$

$$\sin^{-1}\frac{x}{A} = (\kappa/m)^{1/2}t + \text{constant}$$

This integration constant $= 0$, from the initial condition that at $t = 0$, $x = 0$.

The solution of the equation of motion of the simple harmonic oscillator is accordingly

$$x = A\sin(\kappa/m)^{1/2}t \qquad (12.1)$$

If we set

$$(\kappa/m)^{1/2} = 2\pi\nu \qquad (12.2)$$

this becomes

$$x = A\sin 2\pi\nu t \qquad (12.3)$$

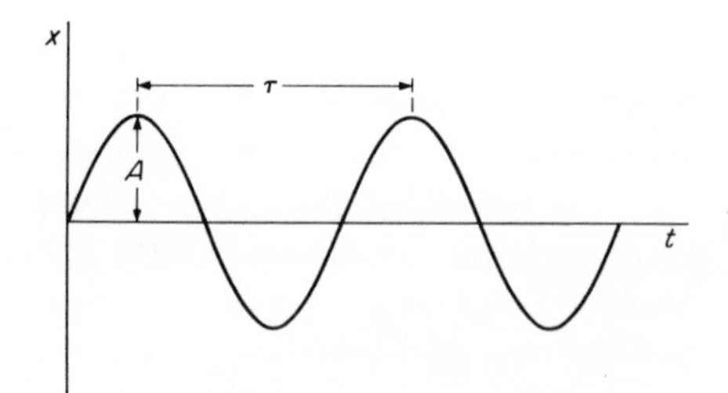

FIG. 12.1 Simple harmonic vibration.

The simple harmonic vibration can be represented graphically by this sine function, as shown in Fig. 12.1. A cosine function would do just as well. The constant ν is called the *frequency* of the motion: it is the number of vibrations in unit time. The reciprocal of the frequency, $\tau = 1/\nu$, is called the *period* of the motion, the time required for a single vibration. Whenever $t = n(\tau/2)$, where n is an integer, the displacement x passes through zero. Note that for a constant κ the frequency depends inversely on the square root of the mass.

The quantity A, the maximum value of the displacement, is called the *amplitude* of the vibration. At the position $x = A$, the oscillator reverses its direction of motion. At this point, therefore, the kinetic energy is zero, and all the energy is potential energy E_p. At position $x = 0$, all the energy is kinetic energy E_k. Since the total energy, $E = E_p + E_k$, is always a constant, it must

* See, for example, Granville, et al., *Calculus*, p. 379.

equal the potential energy at $x = A$. On page 241 the potential energy of the oscillator was shown to be equal to $\frac{1}{2}\kappa x^2$, so that the total energy is

$$E = \tfrac{1}{2}\kappa A^2 \tag{12.4}$$

The total energy is proportional to the square of the amplitude. This important relation holds true for all periodic motions.

The motion of a harmonic oscillator illustrates a displacement periodic with time, that is, temporally periodic. If such an oscillator were immersed in a fluid medium it would set up a disturbance which would travel through the medium. Such a disturbance would be not only temporally periodic but also spatially periodic. It would constitute what is called a *wave*. For example, a tuning fork vibrating in air sets up sound waves. An oscillating electric dipole sets up electromagnetic waves in space.

Let us consider a simple harmonic wave moving in one dimension x. If we took an instantaneous snapshot of the wave, it would have the form of a sine or cosine function. This snapshot is the *profile* of the wave. If the wave is displaced a distance λ along the X-axis, it will be exactly superimposed upon its original profile, and so on at 2λ, 3λ, . . . $n\lambda$. This quantity λ is called the *wavelength*. It is the measure of the periodicity of the wave in space, just as the period τ is the measure of its periodicity in time. The profile of the simple sine wave has the form:

$$\phi = A \sin 2\pi \frac{x}{\lambda} \tag{12.5}$$

Now consider the expression for the wave at some later time t. The idea of the velocity of the wave must then be introduced. If the disturbance is moving through the medium with a velocity c in the positive x direction, in a time t it will have moved a distance ct. The wave profile will have exactly the same form as before if the origin is shifted from $x = 0$ to a new origin at $x = ct$. Referred to this moving origin, the wave profile always maintains the form of Eq. (12.5). To refer the disturbance back to the stationary origin, it is necessary only to subtract the distance moved in time t from the value of x. Then the equation for the moving wave becomes

$$\phi = A \sin \frac{2\pi}{\lambda}(x - ct) \tag{12.6}$$

Now it is evident that c/λ is simply the frequency: $\nu = c/\lambda$. The number of wavelengths in unit distance is called the wave number, $\tilde{\nu} = 1/\lambda$ so that Eq. (12.6) can be written in the more convenient form,

$$\phi = A \sin 2\pi(\tilde{\nu}x - \nu t) \tag{12.7}$$

2. STATIONARY WAVES

In Fig. 12.2, two waves ϕ_1 and ϕ_2, are shown that have the same amplitude, wavelength, and frequency. They differ only in that ϕ_2 has been displaced along the X axis relative to ϕ_1 by a distance $\delta/2\pi\tilde{\nu}$. Thus they may be written

$$\phi_1 = A \sin 2\pi(\tilde{\nu}x - \nu t)$$

$$\phi_2 = A \sin [2\pi(\tilde{\nu}x - \nu t) - \delta]$$

The quantity δ is called the *phase* of ϕ_2 relative to ϕ_1.

When the displacement is exactly an integral number of wavelengths, the two waves are said to be *in phase*: this occurs when $\delta = 2\pi$, 4π, or any even multiple of π. When $\delta = \pi, 3\pi$, or any odd multiple of π, the two waves are *opposite in phase*. Interference phenomena are readily explained in terms of these phase relationships, for when two superimposed waves of equal amplitude are *opposite in phase*, the resultant disturbance is reduced to zero.

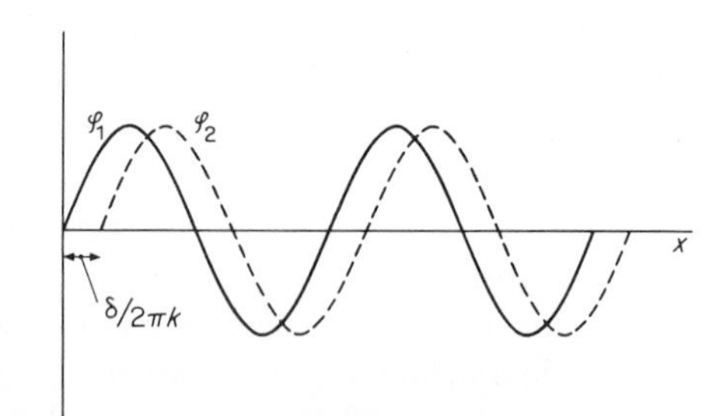

FIG. 12.2 Waves differing in phase ($\tilde{\nu} = k$).

The expression (12.7) is one solution of the general partial differential equation of wave motion, which governs all types of waves, from tidal waves to radio waves. In one dimension this equation is

$$\frac{\partial^2 \phi}{\partial x^2} = \frac{1}{c^2}\frac{\partial^2 \phi}{\partial t^2} \tag{12.8}$$

In three dimensions the equation becomes

$$\nabla^2 \phi \equiv \left(\frac{\partial^2}{\partial x^2} + \frac{\partial^2}{\partial y^2} + \frac{\partial^2}{\partial z^2}\right)\phi = \frac{1}{c^2}\frac{\partial^2 \phi}{\partial t^2} \tag{12.9}$$

The operator ∇^2 (del squared) is called the *Laplacian.*

One important property of the wave equation is apparent upon inspection. The disturbance ϕ and all its partial derivatives appear only in terms of the first degree and there are no other terms, and the coefficients of the terms are constants. This is therefore a linear differential equation with constant coefficients.* It can be verified by substitution that if ϕ_1 and ϕ_2 are any two solutions of such an equation, then a new solution can be written having the form

$$\phi = a_1\phi_1 + a_2\phi_2 \tag{12.10}$$

where a_1 and a_2 are arbitrary constants. This is an illustration of the *principle of superposition.* Any number of solutions can be added together in this way to obtain new solutions. This is essentially what we do when we break a complicated vibratory motion down into its *normal modes* (page 243), or when we represent a periodic function by a Fourier series.

* Granville, *loc. cit.*, p. 386.

An important application of the superposition principle is found in the addition of two waves of the form of Eq. (12.7) that are exactly the same except that they are going in opposite directions. Then the new solution will be

$$\phi = A \sin 2\pi(\tilde{\nu}x - \nu t) + A \sin 2\pi(\tilde{\nu}x + \nu t)$$

or

$$\phi = 2A \sin 2\pi\tilde{\nu}x \cos 2\pi\nu t \tag{12.11}$$

since

$$\sin x + \sin y = 2 \sin \frac{x+y}{2} \cos \frac{x-y}{2}$$

This new wave, which does not move either forward or backward, is a *stationary wave.* The waves of the original type [Eq. (12.7)] are called *progressive* or *traveling waves.* It will be noted that in the stationary wave represented by Eq. (12.11), the disturbance ϕ always vanishes, irrespective of the value of t, for points at which $\sin 2\pi\tilde{\nu}x = 0$ or $x = 0, 1/2\tilde{\nu}, 2/2\tilde{\nu}, 3/2\tilde{\nu} \ldots (n/2\tilde{\nu})$. These points are called *nodes.* The distance between successive nodes is $1/2\tilde{\nu}$ or $\lambda/2$, one-half a wavelength. Midway between the nodes are the positions of maximum amplitude, or *antinodes.*

Solutions of the one-dimensional type, which have just been discussed, will apply to the problem of a vibrating string in the idealized case in which there is no damping of the vibrations. In a string of infinite length one can picture the occurrence of progressive waves. Consider, however, as in Fig. 12.2, a string having a definite length a. This limitation imposes certain boundary conditions on the permissible solutions of the wave equation. If the ends of the string are held fixed: at $x = 0$ and at $x = a$, the displacement ϕ must $= 0$. Thus there must be an integral number of nodes between 0 and a, so that the allowed wavelengths are restricted to those that obey the equation

$$n\frac{\lambda}{2} = a \tag{12.12}$$

where n is an integer. This occurrence of whole numbers is typical of solutions of the wave equation under definite boundary conditions. In order to prevent destruction of the wave by interference, there must be an integral number of half wavelengths fitted within the boundary. We shall see that this principle has important consequences in quantum theory.

3. INTERFERENCE AND DIFFRACTION

The familiar construction of Huygens depicts the interference of light waves. Consider, for example, in (a) Fig. 12.3, an effectively plane wave front from a single source, incident upon a set of slits, a prototype of the diffraction grating. Each slit can now be regarded as a new light source from which spreads a semicircular wave (or hemispherical, in the three-dimensional case). If the wave-

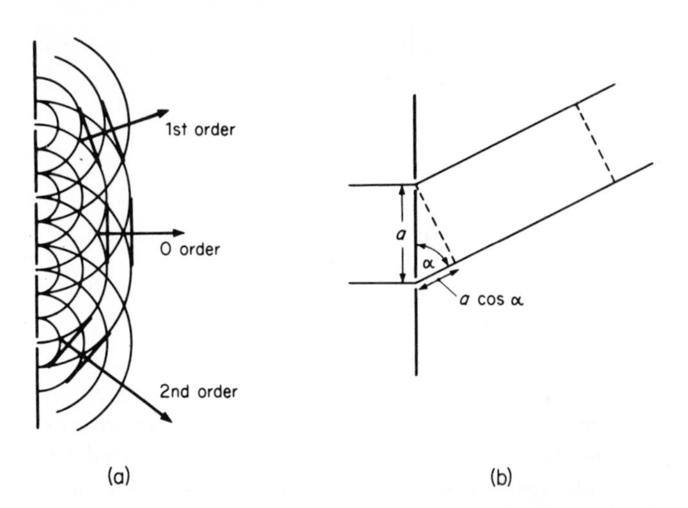

FIG. 12.3 Diffraction: (a) Huygens construction; (b) path difference.

length of the radiation is λ, a series of concentric semicircles of radii λ, 2λ, 3λ . . . may be drawn with these sources as centers. Points on these circles represent the consecutive maxima in amplitude of the new wavelets. Now, following Huygens, the new resultant wave fronts are the curves or surfaces that are simultaneously tangent to the secondary wavelets. These are called the *envelopes* of the wavelet curves and are shown in the illustration.

An important result of this construction is that there are a number of possible envelopes. The one that moves straight ahead in the same direction as the original incident light is called the *zero-order beam.* On either side of this are *first-, second-, third-, etc., order diffracted beams.* The angles by which the diffracted beams deviate from the original direction evidently depend on the wavelength of the incident radiation. The longer the wavelength, the greater is the diffraction. This is why we use a diffraction grating to measure the wavelength of radiation.

We can derive the condition for formation of a diffracted beam from Fig. 12.3 (b) where attention is focused on two adjacent slits. If the two diffracted rays are to reinforce each other, they must be in phase, otherwise the resultant amplitude is cut down by interference. The condition for reinforcement is therefore that the difference in path for the two rays must be an integral number of wavelengths. If α is the angle of diffraction and a the separation of the slits, this path difference is $a \cos \alpha$ and the condition becomes

$$a \cos \alpha = h\lambda \tag{12.13}$$

where h is an integer.

This equation applies to a linear set of slits. For a two-dimensional plane grating, there are two similar equations to be satisfied. For the case of light incident normal to the grating,

$$a \cos \alpha = h\lambda$$

$$b \cos \beta = k\lambda$$

It will be noted that the diffraction is appreciable only when the spacings of the grating are not much larger than the wavelength of the incident light. In order to obtain diffraction effects with X rays, for example, the spacings should be of the order of a few Ångstrom units.*

Max von Laue, in 1912, realized that the interatomic spacings in crystals were probably of the order of magnitude of the wavelengths of X rays. Crystal structures should therefore serve as three-dimensional diffraction gratings for X rays. This prediction was immediately verified in the critical experiment of Friedrich, Knipping, and Laue. A typical X-ray diffraction picture is shown in Fig. 16.10.

4. BLACK-BODY RADIATION

The first definite failure of the old wave theory of light was not found in the photoelectric effect, a particularly clear-cut case, but in the study of *black-body radiation*. All objects are continually absorbing and emitting radiation. Their properties as absorbers or emitters may be extremely diverse. Thus a pane of window glass does not absorb much of the radiation of visible light but absorbs most of the ultraviolet. A sheet of metal absorbs both the visible and the ultraviolet but may be reasonably transparent to X rays. In order for a body to be in equilibrium with its environment, the radiation it is emitting must be equivalent (in wavelength and energy) to the radiation it is absorbing. It is possible to conceive of objects that are perfect absorbers of radiation, the so-called *ideal black bodies*. Actually, no substances approach very closely to this ideal over an extended range of wavelengths.

The best laboratory approximation to an ideal black body is not a substance at all, but a cavity. This cavity is constructed with excellently insulating walls, in one of which a small orifice is made. When the cavity is heated, the radiation from the orifice is a good sample of the equilibrium radiation within the heated enclosure, which is practically ideal black-body radiation.

There is an analogy between the behavior of the radiation within such a cavity and that of gas molecules in a box. Both the molecules and the radiation are characterized by a density and both exert pressure on the confining walls. One difference is that the gas density is a function of the volume and the temperature, whereas the radiation density is a function of temperature alone. Analogous to the various velocities distributed among the gas molecules are the various frequencies distributed among the oscillations that comprise the radiation.

At any given temperature there is a characteristic distribution of the gas velocities given by Maxwell's equation. The corresponding problem of the spectral distribution of black-body radiation, that is, the fraction of the total energy radiated within each range of wavelength, was first explored experi-

* It is also possible to use larger spacings and work with extremely small angles of incidence. The complete equation, corresponding to Eq. (12.13) for incidence at an angle α_0, is $a(\cos\alpha - \cos\alpha_0) = h\lambda$.

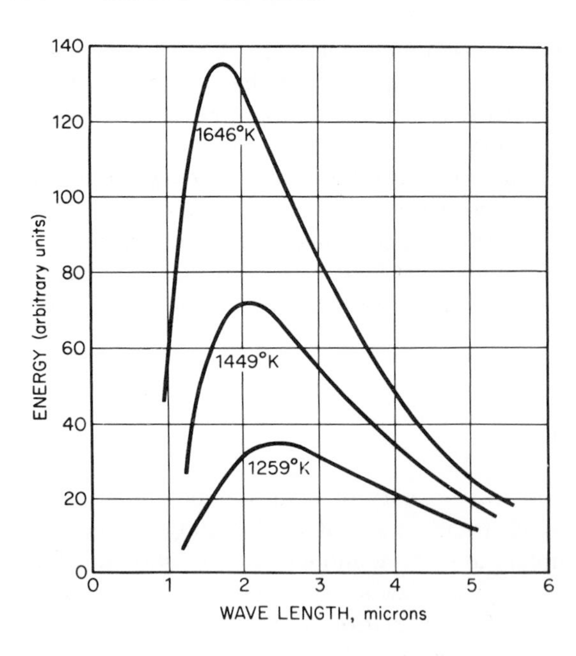

FIG. 12.4 Data of Lummer and Pringsheim on spectral distribution of radiation from a black body at three different temperatures.

mentally (1877-1900) by O. Lummer and E. Pringsheim. Some of their results are shown in Fig. 12.4. These curves indeed have a marked resemblance to those of the Maxwell distribution law. At high temperatures the position of the maximum is shifted to shorter wavelengths — an iron rod glows first dull red, then orange, then white as its temperature is raised and higher frequencies become appreciable in the radiation.

When these data of Lummer and Pringsheim appeared, attempts were made to explain them theoretically by arguments based on the wave theory of light and the principle of equipartition of energy. Without going into the details of these efforts, which were uniformly unsuccessful, it is possible to see why they were doomed to failure.

According to the principle of the equipartition of energy, an oscillator in thermal equilibrium with its environment should have an average energy equal to kT, $\frac{1}{2}kT$ for its kinetic energy and $\frac{1}{2}kT$ for its potential energy, where k is the Boltzmann constant. This classical theory states that the average energy depends in no way on the *frequency* of the oscillator. In a system containing 100 oscillators, 20 with a frequency ν_1 of 10^{10} cycles per sec and 80 with $\nu_2 = 10^{14}$ cycles per sec, the equipartition principle predicts that 20 per cent of the energy shall be in the low-frequency oscillators and 80 per cent in the high-frequency oscillators.

The radiation within a cavity can be considered to consist of standing waves of various frequencies. The problem of the energy distribution over the various frequencies (intensity I vs. ν) apparently reduces to the determination of the number of allowed vibrations in any range of frequencies.

The possible high-frequency vibrations greatly outnumber the low-frequency ones. The one-dimensional case of the vibrating string can be used to illustrate this fact. We have seen in Eq. (12.12) that in a string of length a, standing waves can occur only for certain values of the wavelength given by $\lambda = 2a/n$. It follows that the number of allowed wavelengths from any given value λ to the maximum $2a$ is equal to $n = 2a/\lambda$. We wish to find the additional number of allowed wavelengths that arise if the limiting wavelength value is decreased from λ to $\lambda - d\lambda$. The result is obtained by differentiation* as

$$dn = \frac{2a}{\lambda^2}\,d\lambda$$

This indicates that the number of allowed vibrations in a region from λ to $\lambda - d\lambda$ increases rapidly as the wavelength decreases (or the frequency increases).

5. ALLOWED VIBRATIONS IN A THREE-DIMENSIONAL ENCLOSURE†

We shall next calculate the frequency distribution of the allowed vibrations in a three-dimensional enclosure. Suppose the edges of the enclosure have lengths a, b, c. Figure 12.5 (a) shows a section of the enclosure with an allowed standing wave that makes angles α with a and β with b. If this vibration is to be a standing wave and thus not to destroy itself by destructive interference on reflection

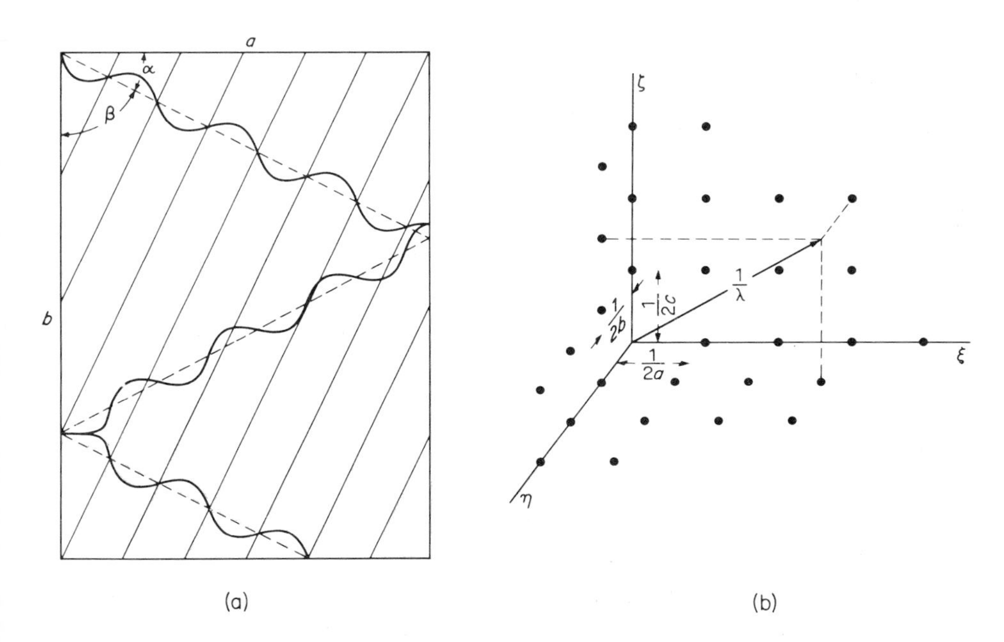

FIG. 12.5 (a) Allowed standing wave in two dimensions; (b) Representation of the standing waves in a wave number space.

* It is assumed that in a region of large a and small λ, n is so large that it can be considered to be a continuous function of λ.

† C. Zwickker, *Physical Properties of Solid Materials* (London: Pergamon, 1954), p. 144.

from the wall, it must be exactly reflected back on itself (with a difference in phase of 180°) after a number of reflections. This condition requires that

$$a \cos \alpha = h(\lambda/2)$$
$$b \cos \beta = k(\lambda/2)$$
$$c \cos \gamma = l(\lambda/2)$$

where h, k, l are integers or zero (cf. Eq. 12.13). It is therefore necessary that an integral number of half wavelengths be intercepted by each edge of the enclosure. The direction cosines must satisfy the relation*

$$\cos^2\alpha + \cos^2\beta + \cos^2\gamma = 1$$

Therefore the wavelength λ must satisfy

$$\frac{1}{\lambda^2} = \frac{h^2}{4a^2} + \frac{k^2}{4b^2} + \frac{l^2}{4c^2}$$

Each set of positive values of h, k, l gives one allowed value of λ. (Negative values do not give new waves, simply reflections.) We can see this relation graphically by plotting each set of values $(h/2a, k/2b, l/2c)$ as a point in a three-dimensional space. Then the vector from the origin to any point corresponds to a possible value of $1/\lambda$, the wave number. We therefore have a plot in *wave-number space.*

We can now readily calculate the number of allowed wavelengths greater than some definite value λ_0. This number equals the number of points within one octant of a sphere of radius $1/\lambda_0$ in the wave-number space [Fig. 12-5 (b)]. The volume occupied by one lattice point is $(1/2a)(1/2b)(1/2c)$, and the volume of the octant is $(1/8)(4/3)\pi(1/\lambda_0)^3$. Hence the required number is

$$N = \frac{(1/8)(4/3)\pi(1/\lambda_0)^3}{(1/2a)(1/2b)(1/2c)} = \frac{4}{3}\frac{\pi}{\lambda_0^3}abc = \frac{4}{3}\frac{\pi}{\lambda_0^3}V \tag{12.14}$$

where V is the volume of the solid.

The number of wavelengths between $(1/\lambda)$ and $(1/\lambda) + d(1/\lambda)$ is obtained by differentiating Eq. (12.14) as

$$dN = (4\pi V/\lambda^2)d(1/\lambda)$$

Since $\lambda = c/\nu$,

$$dN = \left(\frac{4\pi V}{c^3}\nu^2\right)d\nu \tag{12.15}$$

Since there are many more permissible high frequencies than low frequencies, and since by the equipartition principle all frequencies have the same average energy, it follows that the intensity I of black-body radiation should rise continuously with increasing frequency. This conclusion follows inescapably from classical Newtonian mechanics, yet it is in complete disagreement with the experimental data of Lummer and Pringsheim, which show that the intensity

* J. W. Cell, *Analytic Geometry*, 3rd ed. (New York: Wiley, 1960), p. 232.

of the radiation rises to a maximum and then falls off sharply with increasing frequency. This breakdown of classical mechanical principles when applied to radiation was regarded with dismay by the physicists of the time. They called it the *ultraviolet catastrophe.*

6. THE QUANTUM OF ENERGY

Max Planck was born in 1858, the son of a professor of Law at the University of Kiel. At first he was inclined to become a musician, but he soon turned to the study of physics although he had been warned that this was a closed subject in which new discoveries of any importance could scarcely be expected. Planck has given a brief account of his life and work in *A Scientific Autobiography*:

> *My original decision to devote myself to science was a direct result of a discovery which since my early youth has never ceased to fill me with enthusiasm — the comprehension of the far-from-obvious fact that the laws of human reasoning coincide with the laws that govern the sequences of impressions we receive from the world about us, and that therefore pure reasoning can enable man to gain an insight into the mechanism of the outside world. In this connection it is important to realize that the outside world is something independent from man, something absolute. The quest for the laws that apply to this absolute appeared to me to be the most sublime scientific pursuit in life.*

In 1892 Planck became professor of physics at Berlin. He attacked the interpretation of the measurements of Lummer and Pringsheim by thermodynamic methods. On October 19, 1900, he was able to announce to the Berlin Physical Society the mathematical form of the law that governs the energy distribution.* In order to obtain this law, he needed to introduce a new physical constant h, whose meaning, however, he could not deduce from his thermodynamic theories. Therefore he went back to the atomic theory in order to discover how to interpret this constant and to obtain a physical picture that would lead to his energy law.

Classical mechanics was founded on the ancient maxim, *natura non facit saltum* (nature does not make a jump). Thus an oscillator was expected to take up energy *continuously* in arbitrarily small increments. Although matter was believed to be atomic, energy was assumed to be strictly continuous. Planck discarded this precept and suggested that an oscillator could acquire energy only in discrete units, called *quanta.* The quantum theory began therefore as an *atomic theory of energy.* The magnitude ϵ of the quantum or atom of energy was not fixed, but depended on the frequency of the oscillator:

$$\epsilon = h\nu \tag{12.16}$$

Planck's constant h has the dimensions of energy $\times$ time, a quantity called *action.* In the cgs system it is $(6.6252 \pm .005) \times 10^{-27}$ erg sec. Thus an

* *Verh d. Deutsch. Phys. Ges. 2*, 237 (1900).

oscillator of fundamental frequency ν would take up energy $h\nu$, $2h\nu$, $3h\nu$, $4h\nu$, ... $nh\nu$ but it could not acquire less than a whole number of energy quanta.

7. THE PLANCK DISTRIBUTION LAW

Consider a collection of N oscillators having a fundamental vibration frequency ν. If these can take up energy only in increments of $h\nu$, the allowed energies are 0, $h\nu$, $2h\nu$, $3h\nu$, etc. Now according to the Boltzmann formula, Eq. (7.32), if N_0 is the number of systems in the lowest energy state, the number N_i having an energy ϵ_i above this ground state is given by

$$N_i = N_0 e^{-\epsilon_i/kT} \tag{12.17}$$

In the collection of oscillators, for example,

$$N_1 = N_0 e^{-h\nu/kT}$$
$$N_2 = N_0 e^{-2h\nu/kT}$$
$$N_3 = N_0 e^{-3h\nu/kT}$$

The total number of oscillators in all energy states is therefore

$$N = N_0 + N_0 e^{-h\nu/kT} + N_0 e^{-2h\nu/kT} + \ldots = N_0 \sum_{i=0}^{\infty} e^{-ih\nu/kT}$$

The total energy of all the oscillators equals the energy of each level times the number in that level.

$$E = 0N_0 + h\nu N_0 e^{-h\nu/kT} + 2h\nu N_0 e^{-2h\nu/kT} + \ldots = N_0 \sum_{i=0}^{\infty} ih\nu e^{-ih\nu/kT}$$

The average energy of an oscillator is therefore

$$\bar{\epsilon} = \frac{E}{N} = \frac{h\nu \sum i e^{-ih\nu/kT}}{\sum e^{-ih\nu/kT}}$$

Or, if $x = h\nu/kT$,

$$\bar{\epsilon} = h\nu \frac{\sum i e^{-ix}}{\sum e^{-ix}} = \frac{h\nu}{e^x - 1} = \frac{h\nu}{e^{h\nu/kT} - 1} \tag{12.18}^*$$

According to this expression, the mean energy of an oscillator whose fundamental frequency is ν approaches the classical value of kT when $h\nu$ becomes much less than kT.† Using this equation in place of the classical equipartition of energy, Planck derived an energy-distribution formula in excellent agreement with the experimental data for black-body radiation. The energy density $E(\nu)\,d\nu$ is simply the number of oscillators per unit volume between ν and $\nu + d\nu$ [from

* In Eq. (12.18) let $e^{-x} = y$, then the denominator $\sum y^i = 1 + y + y^2 + \ldots = 1/(1 - y)$, $(y < 1)$. The numerator, $\sum iy^i = y(1 + 2y + 3y^2 + \ldots) = y/(1 - y)^2$, $(y < 1)$ so that Eq. (12.18) becomes $h\nu y/(1 - y) = h\nu/(e^{h\nu/kT} - 1)$.

† When $h\nu \ll kT$, $e^{h\nu/kT} \approx 1 + (h\nu/kT)$.

Eq. (12.15)*] times the average energy of an oscillator [Eq. (12.18)]. Hence Planck's Law is

$$E(\nu)d\nu = \frac{8\pi h\nu^3}{c^3} \frac{d\nu}{e^{h\nu/kT} - 1} \tag{12.19}$$

8. SPECTROSCOPY

In 1663, Isaac Newton, at the age of 20, began his experimental work in optics by grinding lenses and studying the construction of telescopes. He was soon faced with the problem of reducing chromatic aberration. In 1666, he bought a glass prism, "to try therewith the phenomena of the colours."

> *Having darkened my chamber, and made a small hole in the window shuts, to let in a convenient quantity of the sun's light, I placed my prism at his entrance, that it might thereby be refracted to the opposite wall.*

He found that the length of the colored area was much greater than its breadth and from further experiments he deduced that the white light was split by the prism into what he called a *spectrum* of the colors, as a result of the different *refrangibility* [refractive index] of the glass for different colors of light. The phenomenon of the colors had been known for a long time, but Newton was the first to interpret it correctly.

These experiments were the beginnings of spectroscopy, but little progress was made for almost a century after Newton. In 1777, Carl Scheele studied the darkening of silver chloride by light of different colors and found that the effect was greatest toward the violet end of the spectrum. In 1803, Inglefield suggested that there might be invisible rays beyond the violet, which could also affect the salt; the existence of such *ultraviolet rays* was demonstrated by Ritter and by Wollaston. In 1800, William Herschel had discovered the *infrared rays* beyond the red by their heating effect on a thermometer bulb.

A great advance in the experimental methods for studying spectra was made by Josef Fraunhofer (1787-1826). Fraunhofer was born at Straubing, a village near Munich. His father was a glazier. The family was large and poor and Josef received practically no formal education, being apprenticed at the age of 11 to a mirror-maker in Munich. It was soon evident that young Fraunhofer was an experimental genius. At 20 he was optical foreman, at 22 a director of the company, and at 24 he had complete charge of the glass making.

In 1814 he was faced with the problem of defining more accurately the colors of the light used in measuring the properties of various glasses. He was thus led to make a detailed examination of the spectrum of sunlight. The spectroscope as used by Newton consisted merely of a slit, a prism, and a lens which was placed between the slit and the prism to focus the slit image on a screen. Fraunhofer had the excellent idea of viewing the slit with a theodolite telescope placed behind the prism, and this instrument enabled him to make exact meas-

* For electromagnetic radiation, there is an extra factor of two in Eq. (12.15) since both electric and magnetic fields are oscillating.

urements of the angles. When he viewed the spectrum from sunlight, he found that it was crossed with "an almost countless number of strong and weak vertical lines." He proved that these dark lines were really in the sunlight and measured about 700 of them. These lines provided the first precise standards for measuring the dispersion of optical glasses and this work of Fraunhofer may be said to mark the beginning of spectroscopy as an exact science.

Fraunhofer also discovered the transmission grating, and in 1823 he constructed the first glass grating by ruling lines with a diamond point. Thus he was able to measure the exact wavelengths of the lines, while previously only the angles had been used.

Of course, Fraunhofer had no idea of the origin of the black lines in the solar spectrum and their explanation was not worked out until about 35 years later. In the meantime, many workers had studied the spectra from flames and had noticed the characteristic bright lines produced by the addition of various salts. In 1848 Foucault observed that a sodium flame that emitted the D line would also absorb this same line from the light of a sodium arc placed behind it.

It remained for Kirchhoff to state the general laws connecting the emission and absorption of light. He was at that time professor of physics at Heidelberg, and in 1859 he announced his famous law which states: "The relation between the power of emission and the power of absorption for rays of the same wavelength is constant for all bodies at the same temperature." Thus an opaque body that absorbs light of all different wavelengths will emit all such wavelengths also, whereas a transparent body which absorbs little light will also emit little light when heated. If a body absorbs light of a certain wavelength, it also emits this same wavelength. Thus the Fraunhofer lines are due to the absorption of certain wavelengths by the sun's atmosphere. One can discover what elements exist in the sun if one can find what elements on earth give bright lines on emission at the same wavelengths as the dark Fraunhofer absorption lines in the solar spectrum.

At that time the professor of chemistry at Heidelberg was Robert Bunsen and he joined Kirchhoff in an extensive series of researches on the spectra of the elements. In 1861, while studying the alkali metals, Li, Na, K, they observed certain new lines which they traced to two new alkali metals, Cs and Rb. Ever since, spectroscopic identification has been the best proof for the existence of a new element.

In 1868, a monumental work on the solar spectrum was published by A. J. Ångstrom of Uppsala. He gave the wavelengths of about 1000 Fraunhofer lines to six significant figures in units of 10^{-8} cm. This unit was subsequently called the *Ångstrom unit* in his honor.

In 1885, J. J. Balmer discovered a regular relationship between the frequencies of the atomic hydrogen lines in the visible region of the spectrum. The wave numbers $\tilde{\nu}$ are given by

$$\tilde{\nu} = \mathcal{R}(1/2^2 - 1/n_1^2) \tag{12.20}$$

with $n_1 = 3, 4, 5 \ldots$. The constant $\mathcal{R}$ is called the *Rydberg constant* and has the value 109 677.581 cm^{-1}. It is one of the most accurately known physical constants.

Other hydrogen series were discovered later which obeyed the more general formula

$$\tilde{\nu} = \mathcal{R}(1/n_2^2 - 1/n_1^2) \tag{12.21}$$

Lyman found the series with $n_2 = 1$ in the far ultraviolet and others were found in the infrared. Many similar series have been observed in the atomic spectra of other elements.

Some examples of the atomic spectra are shown in Fig. 12.6.

9. THE INTERPRETATION OF SPECTRA*

Although spectroscopy developed rapidly after the work of Kirchhoff and Bunsen, there was no corresponding growth in the understanding of the origin of the spectra. Throughout the 19th century it was believed that the line spectra of the atoms were produced simultaneously by each individual atom behaving as an oscillator with a large number of different periods of vibration.

In 1907, Arthur Conway proposed that a single atom produces a single spectral line at a time. He suggested that a single electron in an atom is in an "abnormal state" which can produce vibrations of a specific frequency. In 1908, Walther Ritz showed that the observed frequencies are the differences between certain spectral terms taken in pairs. In 1911, John Nicholson at Cambridge applied the Rutherford atom model to spectra and suggested that quantum jumps take place between definite states corresponding to the term values of Ritz, but he failed to grasp Conway's idea that only a single electron is involved.

Despite this intense scientific activity and steady progress, the first correct application of quantum theory to the interpretation of spectra was not made in the field of atomic spectra but in connection with the absorption spectra of molecules. This advance was made by the Danish chemist, Niels Bjerrum, in a paper *On the Infrared Spectra of Gases* published in 1912. He showed that the infrared absorption by molecules was due to the uptake of rotational and vibrational energy in definite quanta. We shall discuss these molecular spectra in some detail in Chapter 14 since they provide the most important insight into the internal structures and motions of molecules.

10. THE WORK OF BOHR ON ATOMIC SPECTRA

The problem of the interpretation of atomic spectra was finally solved in a work of genius by a young Dane who at the time was one of Rutherford's research students at Manchester, and who was destined to become the most influential

* The historical development given here follows closely that outlined by Edmund Whittaker in his *History of Theories of Aether and Electricity*, Vol. 2. (London: Th. Nelson and Sons, Ltd., 1953).

(a)

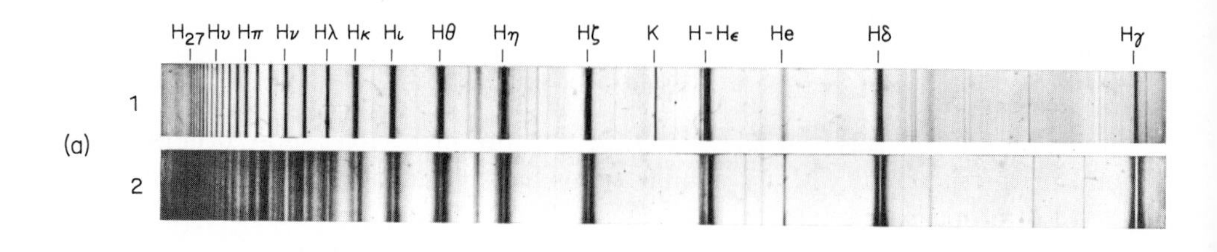

(b)

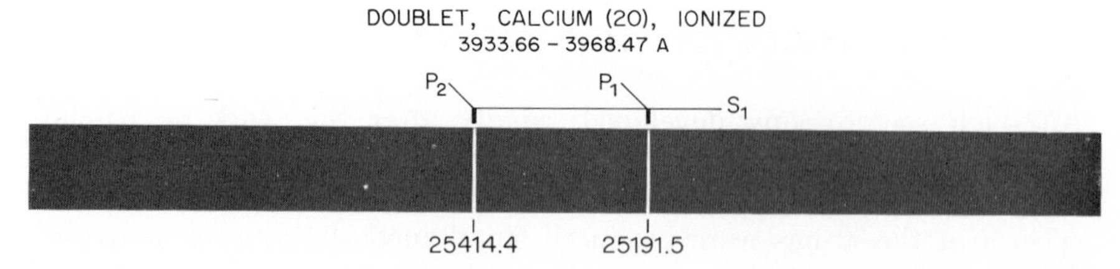

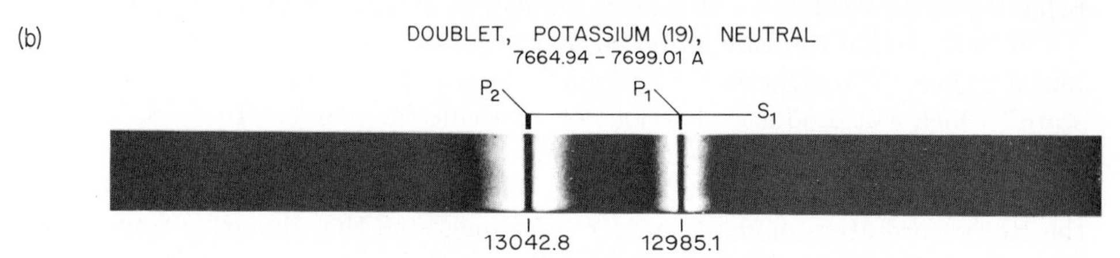

(c)

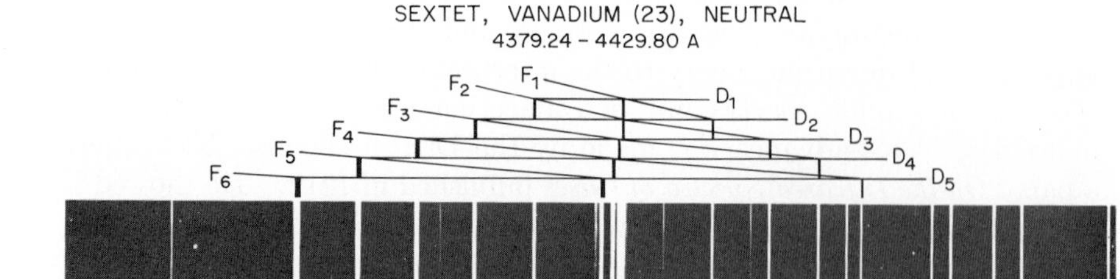

FIG. 12.6 Examples of atomic spectra [Charlotte Sitterly, National Bureau of Standards].

(a) Balmer series of hydrogen as observed in spectra of two stars. No. 1 is the spectrum from *Zeta Tauri*. Note the successive hydrogen lines converging to a series limit. No. 2 is the spectrum from *11 Camelopardalis*. Note the marked self absorption of the hydrogen lines by atomic hydrogen in the stellar atmosphere. [From observations made at the University of Michigan Observatory.]

(b) The doublets of potassium (K) and singly ionized calcium (Ca^+) at high resolution. These lines arise from transitions between the ground state $^2S_{1/2}$ and the two states $^2P_{3/2}$ and $^2P_{1/2}$ as explained in Section 12.31. [From the collection of W. F. Meggers]

(c) A section of the atomic spectrum of vanadium, showing lines arising from combinations between D and F states. [From the collection of W. F. Meggers]

physicist of our times, discovering a new way of looking at the world and founding a philosophical school which has been compared (by physicists) to that of Plato.

Niels Bohr was born in 1885; his father was Professor of Physiology at the University of Copenhagen. Niels spent many hours as a boy in his father's laboratory, but both he and his brother Harald, who became a noted mathematician, found time to become famous throughout Scandinavia as football players. "I grew up," said Bohr, "in a house with a rich intellectual life where scientific discussions were the order of the day. Indeed, for my father, there was scarcely a sharp distinction between his own scientific work and his lively interest in all the problems of human life."

Niels Bohr was destined to bring together two main streams of physics — the German school of theoretical physics exemplified by Planck and Einstein, and the English school of experimental physics of Thomson and Rutherford. The model of the nuclear atom proposed by Rutherford in 1911 had been based firmly on the facts of experiment, with little reference to the current theoretical ideas. According to the electromagnetic theory, the atom of Rutherford had no right to exist. The electrons revolving about the nucleus are accelerated charged particles; therefore, they should continuously emit radiation, lose energy, and execute descending spirals until they fall into the positive center. But the electrons were unaware of what was expected of them, and the facts of chemistry and physics pointed clearly to the Rutherford model. For Bohr there was only one conclusion: the old principles of theoretical physics must be false.

Bohr solved the problem of atomic spectra by taking what was correct in the old ideas and throwing away what was incorrect, and then adding exactly the necessary new ideas. Thus he accepted Conway's principles,

(1) *Spectral lines are produced by atoms one at a time.*
(2) *A single electron is responsible for each line.*

He retained Nicholson's principles,

(3) *The Rutherford nuclear atom is the correct model.*
(4) *The quantum laws apply to jumps between different states characterized by discrete values of angular momentum and, added Bohr, energy.*

He applied Ehrenfest's rule to the angular momentum of the electron,

(5) *The angular momentum* $p = n(h/2\pi)$, *where* n *is an integer.*

Then he advanced the distinctly new principles,

(6) *Two different states of the electron in the atom are involved. These are called* allowed stationary states, *and the spectral terms of Ritz correspond to these states.*

(7) *The Planck-Einstein equation* $\epsilon = h\nu$ *holds for the emission and absorption. Thus, if the electron makes a transition between two states with energies* E_1 *and* E_2, *the frequency of the spectral line is given by*

$$h\nu = E_1 - E_2 \tag{12.22}$$

Finally Bohr proposed a revolutionary concept, which aroused a storm of controversy among scientists and philosophers,

(8) *We must renounce all attempts to visualize or to explain classically the behavior of the active electron during a transition of the atom from one stationary state to another.*

11. BOHR ORBITS AND IONIZATION POTENTIALS

In order to specify which orbits of the electron around the nucleus are allowed, Bohr used condition (5). The angular momentum of a particle of mass m moving with velocity v in a circular path of radius r is $p_\theta = mvr$, and hence the condition becomes

$$mvr = nh/2\pi \tag{12.23}$$

The integer n is called the *principal quantum number.*

The electron is held in its orbit by the electrostatic force that attracts it to the nucleus. If the nucleus has a charge Ze, this force is Ze^2/r^2 from Coulomb's Law. For a stationary state, it must exactly balance the centrifugal force mv^2/r. Hence,

$$Ze^2/r^2 = mv^2/r$$

$$r = Ze^2/mv^2 \tag{12.24}$$

Then, from Eq. (12.23),

$$r = n^2h^2/4\pi^2me^2Z \tag{12.25}$$

In the case of hydrogen, $Z = 1$, and the smallest orbit would be that with $n = 1$, which has a radius

$$a_0 = h^2/4\pi^2me^2 = 0.529 \text{ Å} \tag{12.26}$$

The a_0 is called *the radius of the first Bohr orbit.* It has the same magnitude as values for the radius of a hydrogen atom estimated from the kinetic theory of gases, and the theoretical calculation of such a value indicated that Bohr was on the right track in his theory.

He could now demonstrate that the Balmer series arises from transitions between the orbit with $n = 2$ and outer orbits; in the Lyman series, the lower term corresponds to the orbit with $n = 1$; the other series are explained similarly. Bohr could calculate the energy of the electron in each allowed orbit, and then calculate the line frequencies from Eq. (12.22). The energy levels so obtained are plotted in Fig. 12.7, and the transitions responsible for absorption and emission of a quantum of radiation are shown as vertical lines.

The energy levels are calculated as follows. The total energy E in any state is the sum of the kinetic and potential energies,

$$E = E_k + E_p = \tfrac{1}{2}mv^2 - Ze^2/r$$

From Eq. (12.24),

$$E = -Ze^2/r + Ze^2/2r = -Ze^2/2r$$

Notice that the potential energy is twice the magnitude of the kinetic energy and opposite in sign. This result will be true at equilibrium for any system in which the forces are central, i.e., acting along the line joining two centers. Therefore, from Eq. (12.25),

$$E = (-2\pi^2 me^4/h^2)(Z^2/n^2)$$

The frequency of a spectral line due to the transitions between levels with quantum numbers n_1 and n_2 is

$$\nu = (1/h)(E_{n_1} - E_{n_2}) = (2\pi^2 me^4 Z^2/h^3)(1/n_2^2 - 1/n_1^2) \qquad (12.27)$$

This expression has exactly the form of the experimental relationship of Rydberg and hence a theoretical value for the Rydberg constant can be obtained,

$$\mathcal{R} = 2\pi^2 me^4/ch^3 = 109\,737 \text{ cm}^{-1}$$

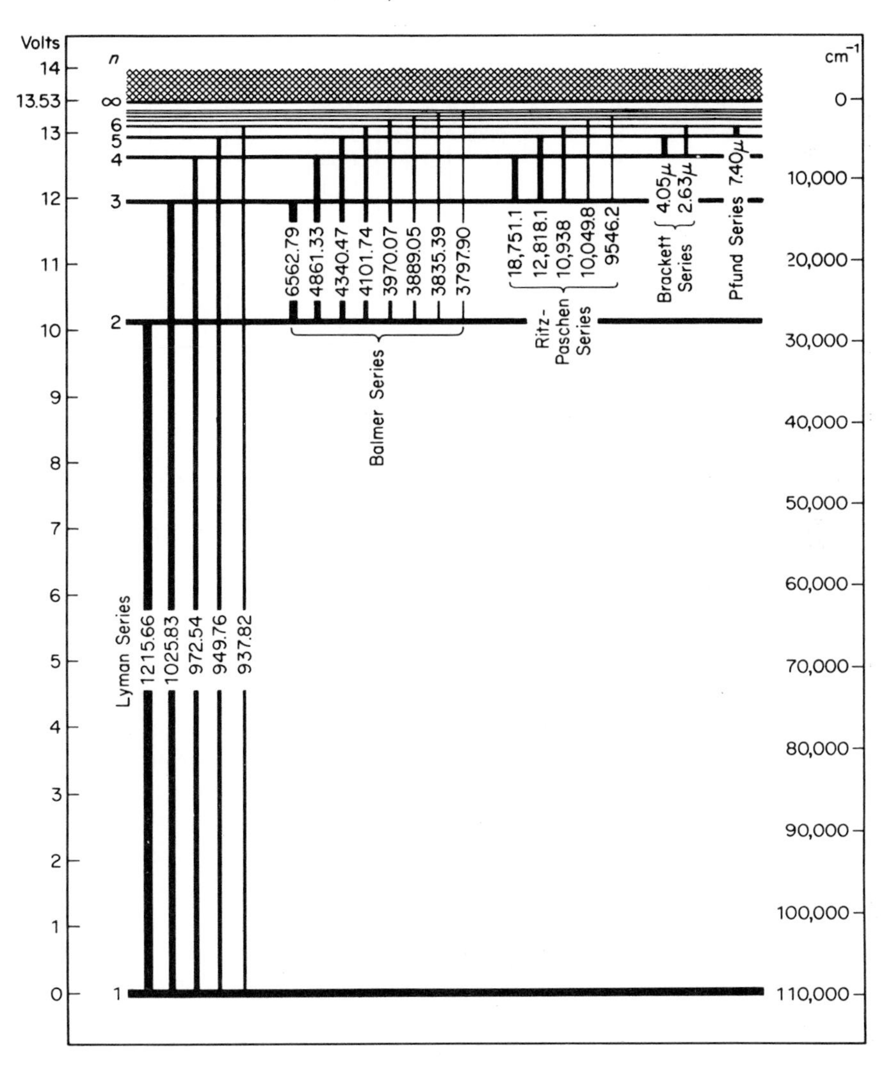

FIG. 12.7 Energy levels of the hydrogen atom.

TABLE 12.1 IONIZATION POTENTIALS RELATIVE TO THAT OF HYDROGEN (Atomic Units of Energy)

Element	Atomic Number	Configuration of outer electrons	I_1	I_2	I_3	I_4	I_5	I_6	I_7	I_8
H	1	s	0.50							
He	2	s^2	0.92	2.00						
Li	3	s	0.20	3.00	4.5					
Be	4	s^2	0.35	0.67	5.65	8.0				
B	5	s^2p	0.31	0.93	1.4	9.65	12.5			
C	6	s^2p^2	0.42	0.90	1.76	2.37	12.0	18.0		
N	7	s^2p^3	0.54	1.09	1.75	2.72	3.60	20.3	24.5	
O	8	s^2p^4	0.50	1.29	2.02	2.85	4.04	5.07	27.3	32
F	9	s^2p^5	(0.67)	1.29	2.31	3.20	3.78	5.50	6.8	35
Ne	10	s^2p^6	0.79	1.51	2.34					
Na	11	s	0.19	1.75	2.62					
Mg	12	s^2	0.28	0.55	2.95					
Al	13	s^2p	0.22	0.69	1.05	4.5				
Si	14	s^2p^2	0.30	0.60	1.23	1.66	6.24			
P	15	s^2p^3	0.40	0.73	1.11	1.77	2.39			
S	16	s^2p^4	0.38	0.86	1.29	1.74	2.47	3.24		
Cl	17	s^2p^5	0.48	0.87	1.47	1.75	2.50	(3.4)	4.0	
Ar	18	s^2p^6	0.58	1.03	1.51	6.3				
K	19	s	0.16	1.17	1.74					
Ca	20	s^2	0.23	0.44	1.88					
Sc	21	s^2d	0.25	0.48	0.91	2.67				
Ti	22	s^2d^2	0.25	0.50	1.02	1.59	3.54			
V	23	s^2d^3	0.25	0.52	0.98	1.80	2.53	4.53		
Cr	24	sd^5	0.25	0.62	(1.0)	(1.85)	(2.7)			
Mn	25	s^2d^5	0.25	0.58	(1.2)	(1.86)	(2.8)			

The excellent agreement with the experimental value of 109 677 may without exaggeration be called a triumph for the Bohr theory.

It will be noted in Fig. 12.7 that the levels become more closely packed as the height above the lowest state (called the *ground state*) increases. They finally converge to a limit whose height above the ground level is the energy necessary to remove the electron completely from the field of the nucleus. In the observed spectrum, the lines become more and more densely packed and finally merge into a *continuum*, i.e., a region of continuous absorption or emission of radiation without any line structure. The reason for the continuum is that once an electron is completely free from the nucleus, it no longer is restricted to quantized discrete energy states, but may take up energy continuously, the ordinary kinetic energy of translation corresponding to its speed in free space, $\frac{1}{2}mv^2$.

The difference in energy between the series limit and the ground level is called the *ionization potential*. If an atom contains more than one electron, there will be first, second, third, etc. ionization potentials. For example, the first ionization potential of a lithium atom is the energy required for $Li \rightarrow Li^+ + e$; the second ionization potential is the energy for $Li^+ \rightarrow Li^{+2} + e$.

The potential energy of an electron in the first Bohr orbit, $e^2/a_0 = 27.190$ ev, defines the *atomic unit of energy*. The ionization potential of the hydrogen atom is 13.595 ev = $\frac{1}{2}$ a.u. In the same way, a_0 = 0.52917 Å, the Bohr radius of the hydrogen atom, defines an *atomic unit of length.*

Examples of ionization potentials are given in Table 12.1 in atomic units. The alkali metals have low first ionization potentials. This is consistent with their tendency to form singly positive ions, and their strong electropositive character. The inert gases, however, have high ionization potentials in accord with their extreme reluctance to enter chemical reactions, which in fact they refuse to do at all in their ground states.

12. PARTICLES AND WAVES

The Bohr theory was developed intensively from 1913 to 1926 and many important successes were achieved, yet there were also some troublesome failures. The theory could not explain, for example, the spectra of helium and other more complex atoms. Also it was increasingly evident that the logical foundations of the theory were incomplete. In any theory certain postulates must be made without proof, but in the Bohr theory there were too many of these underived postulates. It seemed that there should be some way of proving some of them from more fundamental principles. This hope was to be realized in a most revolutionary way and Bohr himself was to play an important part in this work. The basic discoveries were made by three younger men — de Broglie, Heisenberg and Schrödinger.

There is one branch of physics in which, as we have seen, integral numbers occur naturally, namely in the stationary-state solutions of the equation for wave motion. This fact suggested the next great advance in physical theory: the idea that electrons, and in fact all material particles, must possess wavelike properties. It was already known that radiation exhibited both corpuscular and undulatory aspects. Now it was to be shown, first theoretically and soon afterwards experimentally, that the same must be true of matter.

This new way of thinking was first proposed in 1923 by Louis de Broglie. In his Nobel Prize Address he has described his approach as follows:*

> . . . *When I began to consider these difficulties* [*of contemporary physics*] *I was chiefly struck by two facts. On the one hand the quantum theory of light cannot be considered satisfactory, since it defines the energy of a light corpuscle by the equation* $E = h\nu$, *containing the frequency* ν. *Now a purely corpuscular theory contains nothing that enables us to define a frequency; for this reason alone, therefore, we are compelled, in the case of light, to introduce the idea of a corpuscle and that of periodicity simultaneousy.*
>
> *On the other hand, determination of the stable motion of electrons in the atom introduces integers; and up to this point the only phenomena involving integers in Physics were those of interference and of normal modes of vibration. This fact suggested to me the idea that electrons too could not be regarded simply as corpuscles, but that periodicity must be assigned to them also.*

* L. de Broglie, *Matter and Light* (New York: Dover Publications [1st ed., W. W. Norton Co.], 1946).

A simple two-dimensional illustration of this viewpoint may be seen in Fig. 12.8 which shows two possible electron waves of different wavelengths, for the case of an electron revolving around an atomic nucleus. In one case, the circumference of the electron orbit is an integral multiple of the wavelength of the electron wave. In the other case, this condition is not fulfilled and as a result the wave is destroyed by interference, and the supposed state is nonexistent. The introduction of integers associated with the permissible states of electronic motion therefore occurs quite naturally once the electron is given wave properties. The situation is analogous to the occurrence of stationary waves on a vibrating string. The necessary condition for a stable orbit of radius r_e is that

$$2\pi r_e = n\lambda \tag{12.28}$$

A free electron is associated with a progressive wave so that any energy is allowable. A bound electron is represented by a standing wave, which can have only certain definite frequencies.

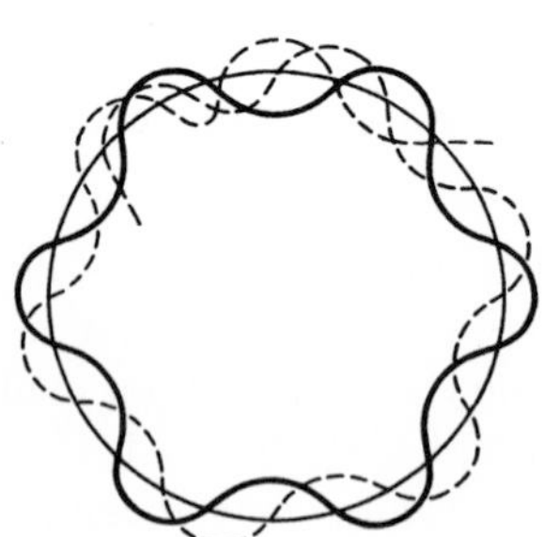

FIG. 12.8 Schematic drawing of an electron wave constrained to move around the nucleus. The solid line represents a possible stationary wave. The dashed line shows how a wave of somewhat different wavelength would be destroyed by interference.

In the case of a photon there are two fundamental equations to be obeyed: $\epsilon = h\nu$, and $\epsilon = mc^2$. When these are combined, we obtain $h\nu = mc^2$ or $\lambda = c/\nu = h/mc = h/p$, where p is the momentum of the photon. De Broglie considered that a similar equation governed the wavelength of the electron wave. Thus,

$$\lambda = \frac{h}{mv} = \frac{h}{p} \tag{12.29}$$

The original Bohr condition for a stable orbit was given by Eq. (12.23) as $2\pi mvr_e = nh$. By combination with Eq. (12.28), one again obtains Eq. (12.29) so that the de Broglie formulation gives the Bohr condition directly.

The de Broglie equation, Eq. (12.29), is the fundamental relation between the momentum of the electron considered as a particle and the wavelength of the electron considered as a wave. Consider, for example, an electron that has been accelerated through a potential difference U of 10 kilovolts. Then $U = \frac{1}{2}mv^2$, and its velocity would be 5.9×10^9 cm per sec, about one-fifth that of light. The wavelength of such an electron would be

$$\lambda = \frac{h}{mv} = \frac{6.62 \times 10^{-27}}{(9.11 \times 10^{-28})(5.9 \times 10^9)} = 0.12 \text{ Å}$$

This is about the same wavelength as that of a rather hard X ray.

Table 12.2 lists the theoretical wavelengths associated with various particles.* The wavelengths of macroscopic bodies are exceedingly short, so that any wave properties will escape our observation.

* After J. D. Stranathan, *The Particles of Modern Physics* (Philadelphia: Blakiston, 1942), p. 540.

TABLE 12.2 WAVELENGTHS OF VARIOUS PARTICLES

Particle	Mass (g)	Velocity (cm/sec)	Wavelength (Å)
1-volt electron	9.1×10^{-28}	5.9×10^{7}	12.0
100-volt electron	9.1×10^{-28}	5.9×10^{8}	1.2
10 000-volt electron	9.1×10^{-28}	5.9×10^{9}	0.12
100-volt proton	1.67×10^{-24}	1.38×10^{7}	0.029
100-volt α particle	6.6×10^{-24}	6.9×10^{6}	0.015
H_2 molecule at 200°C	3.3×10^{-24}	2.4×10^{5}	0.82
α particle from radium	6.6×10^{-24}	1.51×10^{9}	6.6×10^{-5}
22-rifle bullet	1.9	3.2×10^{4}	1.1×10^{-23}
Golf ball	45	3×10^{3}	4.9×10^{-24}
Baseball	140	2.5×10^{3}	1.9×10^{-24}

13. ELECTRON DIFFRACTION

If electrons have wave properties, a 1.0 Å electron wave should be diffracted by a crystal lattice in much the same way as an X-ray wave. Experiments along this line were first carried out by two groups of workers, who shared a Nobel prize for their efforts. C. Davisson and L. H. Germer worked at the Bell Telephone Laboratories in New York, and G. P. Thomson, the son of J. J. Thomson, and A. Reid were at the University of Aberdeen. One of the first diffraction diagrams obtained by Thomson by passing beams of electron through thin gold foils is shown in Fig. 12.9. The wave nature of the electron was unequivocally demonstrated by these researches. Fig. 12.10 shows a striking diffraction diagram recently obtained from a thin film of chromium, part of which was a single crystal and part a compact of tiny crystals. Diffraction patterns have also been obtained from crystals placed in beams of neutrons or hydrogen atoms, so that these more massive particles are also waves.

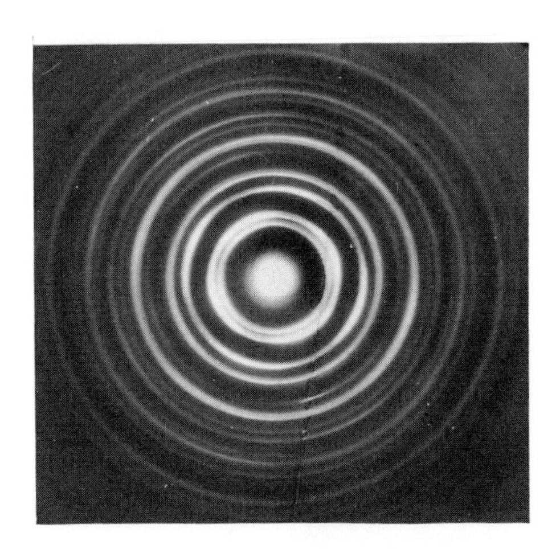

FIG. 12.9 One of the first electron diffraction pictures obtained by G. P. Thomson, which showed the wave nature of electrons.

Electron beams, owing to their negative charge, have one advantage over X rays as a means of investigating the fine structure of matter. Appropriate arrangements of electric and magnetic fields can be designed to act as lenses for electrons. These arrangements have been applied in the development of electron microscopes capable of resolving images as small as 10 Å in diameter. Fig. 12.11

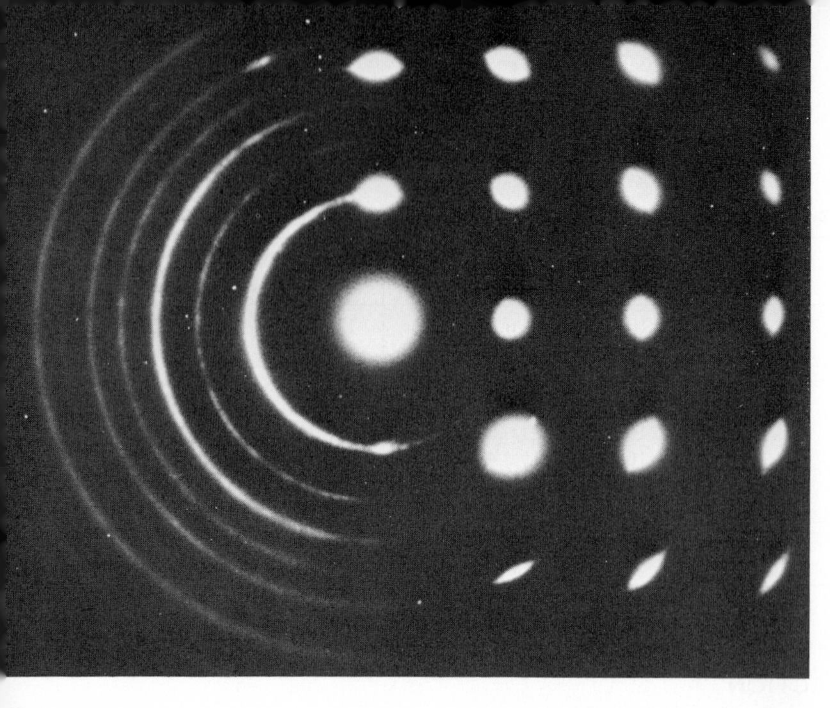

FIG. 12.10 Electron diffraction diagram of a thin chromium film, which was partly polycrystalline (rings) and partly a single crystal (spots). (I.B.M. Laboratories–Kingston, N. Y.).

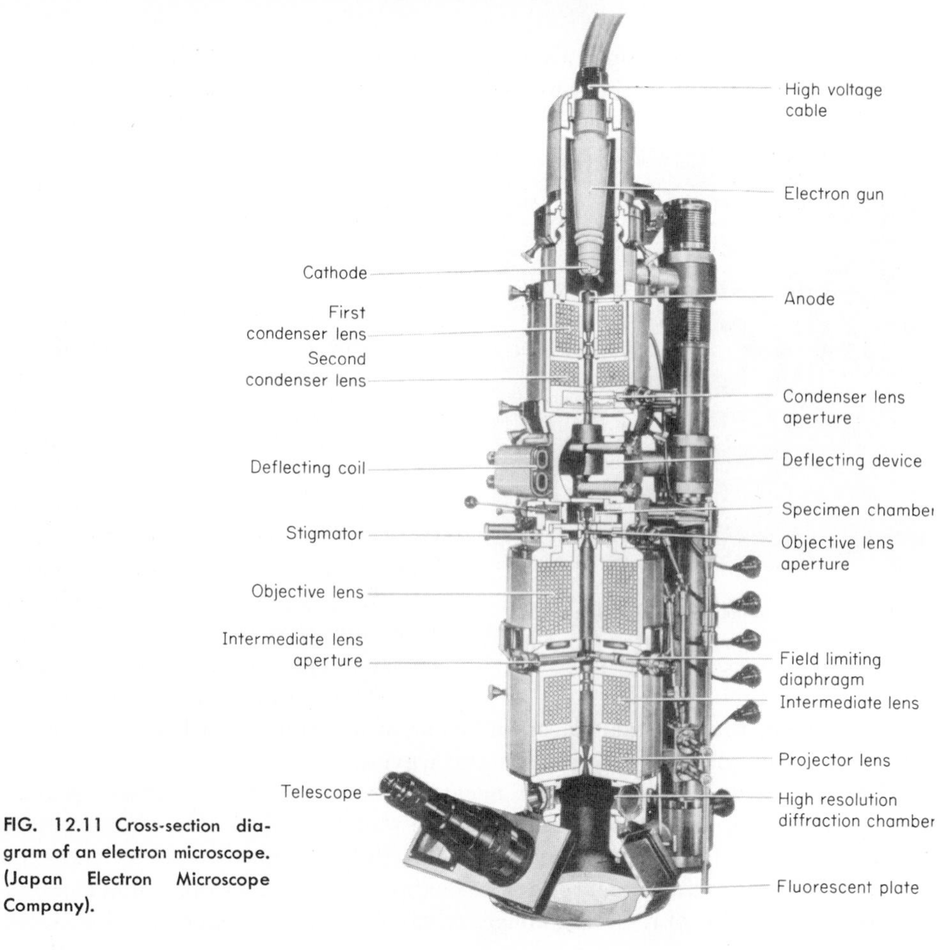

FIG. 12.11 Cross-section diagram of an electron microscope. (Japan Electron Microscope Company).

shows an electron microscope similar to one designed by E. Ruska and B. v. Borries. Several electron-microscope pictures are reproduced in this book.

14. WAVES AND THE UNCERTAINTY PRINCIPLE

In our macroscopic world, the value of the Planck constant h may be considered to be effectively zero. The de Broglie wavelengths of ordinary objects are vanishingly small, and a batter need not consider diffraction phenomena when he swings at an inside curve. But if we enter the subatomic world, h is no longer so small as to be negligible. The de Broglie wavelengths of electrons are of such a magnitude that diffraction effects occur in molecules and crystals.

A fundamental tenet of classical mechanics is that it is possible to measure simultaneously the position and the momentum of any body. The strict determinism of mechanics rested upon this principle. Knowing the position and velocity of a particle at any instant, Newtonian mechanics ventured to predict its position and velocity at any other time, past or future. Systems were completely reversible in time, past configurations being obtained simply by substituting $-t$ for t in the dynamical equations. But, if a particle has some of the properties of a wave, is it really possible to measure simultaneously its position and its momentum? The possible methods of measurement must be analyzed before an answer can be given.

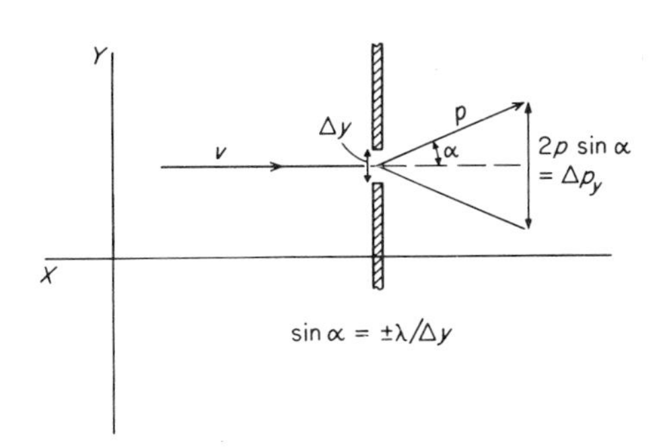

FIG. 12.12 Illustration of the uncertainty principle by the diffraction of a particle at a slit.

In Fig. 12.12, suppose a particle of mass m moves along the positive x direction with a speed v. At the point x_0 we try to determine the y coordinate of the particle by placing in its path a slit of width Δy. The wavelength of the de Broglie wave is $\lambda = h/mv$, and diffraction will occur at the slit causing the new direction of the momentum p of the particle to be within an angular spread $\pm\alpha$, where $\sin\alpha = \pm\lambda/\Delta y$.* The attempt to fix the position y within limits Δy has led to an uncertainty $\Delta p_y = 2p\sin\alpha$ in p_y, the y component of the momentum. Hence,

$$\Delta y \Delta p_y = 2p\lambda \approx 2h$$

The product of the uncertainty in momentum and the uncertainty in position is therefore of the order of h. More precisely,

$$\Delta y \Delta p_y \geq h/4\pi \qquad (12.30)$$

* Joseph Valasek, *Introduction to Theoretical and Experimental Optics* (New York: John Wiley, 1949), p. 157.

This is the famous *uncertainty principle* or *principle of indeterminacy* given by Werner Heisenberg in 1926.

As an example, consider a microscopic particle 1μ in diameter, with a mass of 6×10^{-13} g. Then

$$\Delta y \cdot \Delta v_y \approx h/m \approx 6 \times 10^{-27}/6 \times 10^{-13} \approx 10^{-14} \text{ cm sec}^{-1}$$

If we measured the position to within 10 Å, about the resolving power of an electron microscope, $\Delta y = 10^{-7}$ cm and hence $\Delta v = 10^{-7}$ cm sec^{-1}. With this indeterminacy in velocity, the position one second later would be uncertain to within 20 Å or about 0.2% of the diameter of the particle. Thus even in the case of an ordinary microscopic particle, indeterminacy may limit exact measurements. With particles of atomic or subatomic size the effect would be much greater.

Indeterminacy seems to arise from the attempt to apply two complementary but strictly incompatible models to the description of the same physical entity, for example, an electron. The wave model is derived from the basic concept of a continuous field. The particle model is derived from the concept of indivisible units of matter; it is basically an atomistic theory.

When waves are associated with particles, an uncertainty principle is a necessary consequence. If the wavelength or frequency of an electron wave is to have a definitely fixed value, the wave must have an infinite extent. Any attempt to confine a wave within boundaries requires destructive interference at the boundaries to reduce the amplitudes there to zero. It follows that an electron wave of perfectly fixed frequency, or momentum, must be infinitely extended and therefore must have a completely indeterminate position. In order to fix the position, superimposed waves of different frequencies are required, and thus as the position becomes more closely defined, the momentum becomes more fuzzy.

The uncertainty relation of Eq. (12.30) can be expressed also in terms of energy and time. Thus

$$\Delta p \Delta q = \Delta E \Delta t \geq h/4\pi \tag{12.31}$$

This equation is used to estimate the sharpness of spectral lines. In general, lines arising from transitions from the ground state of an atom are sharp. This is because the optical electron spends a long time Δt in the ground state and ΔE, the uncertainty in the energy level, is correspondingly small. The line breadth is related to ΔE by $\Delta \nu = \Delta E/h$. The lifetimes of excited states may sometimes be very short and transitions between such states give rise to diffuse lines as a result of the indeterminacy of the energy levels.*

15. ZERO-POINT ENERGY

According to the old quantum theory, the energy levels of a harmonic oscillator were given by $E_n = nh\nu$. If this were true, the lowest energy level would be

* This is not the only cause of broadening of spectral lines. There is in addition a *pressure broadening* due to interaction with the electric fields of neighboring atoms or molecules, and a *Doppler broadening*, due to motion of the radiating atom or molecule with respect to the observer.

that with $n = 0$, and would therefore have zero energy. This would be a state of complete rest, represented by the minimum in the potential-energy curve in Fig. 7.15.

The uncertainty principle does not allow such a state of completely defined position and completely defined (in this case, zero) momentum. As a result, the wave treatment shows that the energy levels of the oscillator are given by

$$E_n = (n + \tfrac{1}{2})h\nu \qquad (12.32)$$

Now, even when $n = 0$, the ground state, there is a residual *zero-point energy* amounting to

$$E_0 = \tfrac{1}{2}h\nu \qquad (12.33)$$

This must be added to the Planck expression for the mean energy of an oscillator, which was derived in Eq. (12.18).

16. WAVE MECHANICS—THE SCHRÖDINGER EQUATION

In 1926, Erwin Schrödinger and Werner Heisenberg independently laid the foundations for a distinctly new sort of mechanics which is expressive of the wave – particle duality of matter. This is called *wave* or *quantum mechanics.*

The starting point for most quantum mechanical discussions is the Schrödinger wave equation. We may recall that the general differential equation of wave motion in one dimension is given by Eq. (12.8) as

$$\frac{\partial^2 \phi}{\partial x^2} = \frac{1}{v^2}\frac{\partial^2 \phi}{\partial t^2}$$

where ϕ is the displacement and v the velocity. In order to separate the variables, let $\phi(x,t) = \psi(x) \sin 2\pi\nu t$. On substitution in the original equation, this yields

$$\frac{d^2\psi}{dx^2} + \frac{4\pi^2\nu^2}{v^2}\psi = 0 \qquad (12.34)$$

This is the wave equation with the time dependence removed. In order to apply this equation to a *matter wave,* the de Broglie relation is introduced, as follows: The total energy E is the sum of the potential energy U and the kinetic energy $p^2/2m$. $E = p^2/2m + U$. Thus, $p = [2m(E - U)]^{1/2}$, or $\lambda = h/p = h[2m(E - U)]^{-1/2}$. Substituting this in Eq. (12.34), we obtain

$$\frac{d^2\psi}{dx^2} + \frac{8\pi^2 m}{h^2}(E - U)\psi = 0 \qquad (12.35)$$

This is the famous Schrödinger equation in one dimension. For three dimensions it takes the form

$$\nabla^2\psi + \frac{8\pi^2 m}{h^2}(E - U)\psi = 0 \qquad (12.36)$$

The operator ∇^2 was defined in Eq. (12.9). The *Hamiltonian operator* H is defined as

$$H = -(h^2/8\pi^2 m)\nabla^2 + U$$

In terms of H, the Schrödinger equation can be written simply as

$$H\psi = E\psi \tag{12.37}$$

As is usual with differential equations, the solutions of Eq. (12.36) for any particular set of physical conditions are determined by the particular boundary conditions imposed upon the system. Just as the simple wave equation for a vibrating string yields a discrete set of stationary-state solutions when the ends of the string are held fixed, so in general solutions are obtained for the Schrödinger equation only for certain energy values E. In many cases the allowed energy values are discrete and separated, but in certain other cases they form a continuous spectrum of values. The allowed energy values are called the *characteristic values,* or *eigenvalues* for the system. The corresponding *wave functions* ψ are called the *characteristic functions* or *eigenfunctions.*

17. INTERPRETATION OF THE ψ FUNCTIONS

The wave function ψ is by nature a sort of amplitude function. In the case of a light wave, the intensity of the light or energy of the electromagnetic field at any point is proportional to the square of the amplitude of the wave at that point. From the point of view of the photon picture, the more intense the light at any place, the more photons are falling on that place. This fact can be expressed in another way by saying that the greater the value of ψ, the amplitude of a light wave in any region, the greater is the probability of a photon being within that region.

This interpretation is the most useful for the eigenfunctions of Schrödinger's equation. They are therefore sometimes called *probability amplitude functions.* If $\psi(x)$ is a solution of the wave equation for an electron, then the probability of finding the electron within the range from x to $x + dx$ is given* by $\psi^2(x)\,dx$.

The physical interpretation of the wave function as a probability amplitude implies that it must obey certain mathematical conditions. We require that $\psi(x)$ be single-valued, finite, and continuous for all physically possible values of x. It must be single-valued, since the probability of finding the electron at any point x must have one and only one value. It cannot be infinite at any point, for then the electron would be fixed at exactly that point, which would be inconsistent with its wave properties. The requirement of continuity is helpful in the selection of physically reasonable solutions for the wave equation.

* Since the function ψ may be a complex quantity, the probability is written more generally as $\psi^\star\psi$, where $\psi^\star$ is the complex conjugate of ψ. Thus, e.g., if $\psi = e^{-ix}$, $\psi^\star = e^{ix}$. The interpretation of ψ^2 as a probability is due to Max Born.

18. SOLUTION OF WAVE EQUATION—THE PARTICLE IN A BOX

The solution of the wave equation for any particular case may be extremely difficult. Sometimes a solution can be devised in principle that in practice would involve several decades of calculations. The recent development of high-speed computers has greatly extended the range of problems for which numerical solutions can be obtained. A computation that used to require a year's work by a careful man can now be completed in an hour by a machine.

The simplest case to which the wave equation can be applied is the free particle, i.e., one moving in the absence of any potential field. In this case we may set $U = 0$ and the one-dimensional equation becomes

$$\frac{d^2\psi}{dx^2} + \frac{8\pi^2 m}{h^2} E\psi = 0$$

A solution of this equation is readily found* to be

$$\psi = A \sin \left(\frac{8\pi^2 mE}{h^2}\right)^{1/2} x \tag{12.38}$$

where A is an arbitrary constant. This is an allowable solution as long as E is positive, since the sine of a real quantity is everywhere single-valued, finite, and continuous. Thus all positive values of E are allowable and the free particle has a continuous spectrum of energy states. This conclusion is in accord with the observed onset of the *continuum* in an atomic spectrum as the result of dissociation of an electron from the atom.

What is the effect of imposing a constraint upon the free particle by requiring that its motion be confined within fixed boundaries? In three dimensions this is the problem of a particle enclosed in a box. The one-dimensional problem is that of a particle required to move between set points on a straight line. The potential function that corresponds to such a condition is shown in Fig. 12.13 (a). For values of x between 0 and a the particle is completely free, and $U = 0$. At the boundaries, however, the particle is constrained by an infinite potential wall over which there is no escape; thus $U = \infty$ when $x = 0$, $x = a$.

The situation now is similar to that of the vibrating string considered at the beginning of the chapter. Restricting the electron wave within fixed boundaries corresponds to seizing hold of the ends of the string. In order to obtain stable standing waves, it is again necessary to restrict the allowed wavelengths so that there is an integral number of half wavelengths between 0 and a; i.e., $n(\lambda/2) = a$. Some of the allowed electron waves are shown in Fig. 12.13(b), superimposed upon the potential-energy diagram.

The allowed energy values, the *eigenvalues* of the solution to the Schrödinger equation, can be obtained from Eq. (12.38). At $x = 0$, $\psi = 0$ as required.

* The solution can be verified by substitution into the equation. The equation is the same as the one solved in detail in Section 1 of this Chapter.

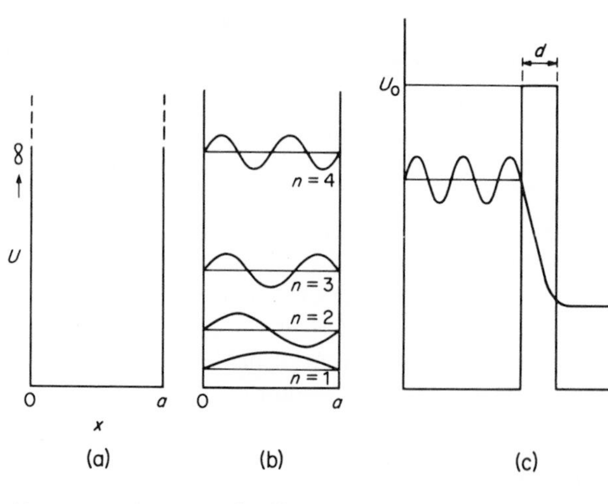

FIG. 12.13 Electron in a one-dimensional box. (a) the potential function; (b) allowed electron waves; (c) tunnel effect.

At $x = a$, $\psi = 0$ only if

$$(8\pi^2 mE/h^2)^{1/2}a = n\pi$$

or

$$E_n = \frac{n^2h^2}{8ma^2} \tag{12.39}$$

The energy levels are shown in Fig. 12.13 (b).

From this equation, two important consequences can be deduced which hold true for the energy of electrons, not only in this special case, but quite generally. First of all, it is apparent that as the value of a increases, the kinetic energy E_n decreases. Other factors being the same, the more room the electron has in which to move, the lower will be its kinetic energy. *The more localized is its motion, the higher will be its kinetic energy.* Remember that the lower the energy, the greater the stability of a system.

Secondly, the integer n is a typical *quantum number*, which now appears quite naturally and without any *ad hoc* hypotheses. It determines the *number of nodes* in the electron wave. When $n = 1$ there are no nodes. When $n = 2$ there is a node in the center of the box; when $n = 3$ there are two nodes, and so on. The value of the energy depends directly on n^2, and therefore rises rapidly as the number of nodes increases.

We can easily extend the one-dimensional result to a three-dimensional box of sides a, b, and c. The allowed energy levels for the three-dimensional case depend on a set of three integers (n_1, n_2, n_3). Since there are three dimensions, there are three quantum numbers.*

$$E = \frac{h^2}{8m}\left(\frac{n_1^2}{a^2} + \frac{n_2^2}{b^2} + \frac{n_3^2}{c^2}\right) \tag{12.40}$$

* The energy levels of a particle in a three-dimensional box provide a good illustration of *degeneracy*, the occurrence of more than one wave function with exactly the same energy level. For example if $a = b$, the wave function with $n_1 = 1$, $n_2 = 2$, has the same energy as that with $n_2 = 2$, $n_1 = 1$. The energy level is *two-fold degenerate.*

This result shows that according to wave mechanics even the translational motion of a particle in a box is quantized. Because h^2 is extremely small, these levels lie very closely packed together, except in cases where the dimensions of the box are vanishingly small.

If electron waves in one dimension are comparable with vibrations of a violin string, those in two dimensions are like the pulsations of a drumhead, whereas those in three dimensions are like the vibrations of a block of steel. The waves can then have nodes along three directions, and the three quantum numbers determine the numbers of nodes.

19. THE TUNNEL EFFECT

Let us take a baseball, place it in a well constructed box, and nail the lid down tightly. Any proper Newtonian will assure us that the ball is in the box and is going to stay there until someone takes it out. There is no probability that the ball will be found on Monday inside the box and on Tuesday rolling along outside it. Yet if we transfer our attention from a baseball in a box to an electron in a box, quantum mechanics predicts exactly this unlikely behavior.

To be more precise, consider in Fig. 12.13(c), a particle moving in a one-dimensional box with a kinetic energy E_k. It is confined by a potential-energy well; since the potential-energy barrier is higher than the available kinetic energy, the classical probability of escape is nil.

Quantum mechanics tells a different story. The wave equation (12.35) for the region of constant potential energy U_0 is

$$(d^2\psi/dx^2) + (8\pi^2 m/h^2)(E - U_0)\psi = 0$$

This equation has the general solution

$$\psi = A \exp[(2\pi i x/h) \sqrt{2m(E - U_0)}]$$

In the region within the box $E > U_0$ and this solution is simply the familiar sine or cosine wave of Eq. (12.38) written in the complex exponential form.* In the region within the potential-energy barrier, however, $U_0 > E$, so that the expression under the square-root sign is negative. One can therefore multiply out a $\sqrt{-1}$ term, obtaining the following result:

$$\psi = A \exp[-(2\pi x/h) \sqrt{2m(U_0 - E)}] \tag{12.41}$$

This exponential function describes the behavior of the wave function within the barrier. According to wave mechanics the probability of finding an electron in the region of negative energy is clearly not zero, but a certain positive number, which falls off exponentially with the distance of penetration within the barrier. The behavior of the wave function is shown in Fig. 12.13 (c). So long as the barrier is not infinitely high nor infinitely wide there is always a certain prob-

* See, for example, Courant and Robbins, *What Is Mathematics* (New York: Oxford, 1941), p. 92, for a description of notation: $e^{i\theta} = \cos\theta + i\sin\theta$.

ability that electrons (or particles in general) will leak through. This leakage is called the *tunnel effect*.

The phenomenon is not observed with baseballs in boxes or with cars in garages,† being rendered too improbable by the various parameters in the exponential. In the world of atoms, however, the effect is a common one. One of the best examples is the emission of an α particle in a radioactive disintegration. The random nature of this emission is a reflection of the fact that the position of the particle is subject to probability laws.

20. THE HYDROGEN ATOM

If we neglect the translational motion of the atom as a whole and the motion of the atomic nucleus, we can reduce the problem of the hydrogen atom to that of a single electron in a coulombic field. This is like the problem of a particle in

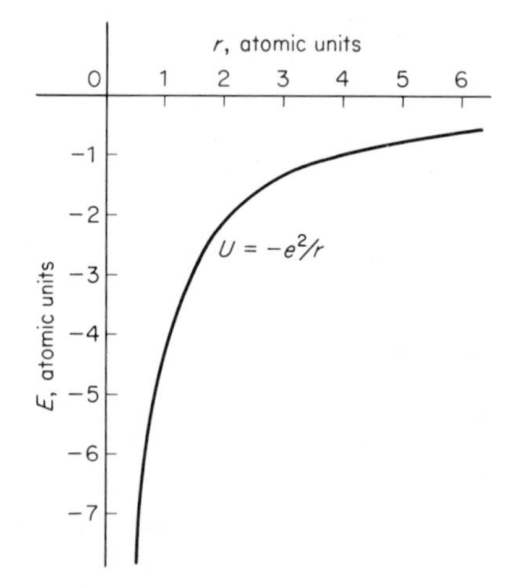

FIG. 12.14 Coulombic potential energy of negative electron in field of positive proton.

a three-dimensional box, except that now the box is spherical. Also, instead of steep walls and zero potential energy within, there is now a gradual rise in potential with distance from the nucleus: at $r = \infty$, $U = 0$; $r = 0$, $U = -\infty$. The potential energy of the electron in the field of the nucleus is given by $U = -e^2/r$, which is plotted in Fig. 12.14.

The Schrödinger equation therefore becomes

$$\frac{\partial^2\psi}{\partial x^2} + \frac{\partial^2\psi}{\partial y^2} + \frac{\partial^2\psi}{\partial z^2} + \frac{8\pi^2 m}{h^2}\left(E + \frac{e^2}{r}\right)\psi = 0 \tag{12.42}$$

† This extreme example is described by G. Gamow in *Mr. Tompkins in Wonderland* (New York: Macmillan, 1940), which is recommended as an introduction to this chapter.

In view of the spherical symmetry of the potential field, it is convenient to transform this expression into spherical coordinates,

$$\frac{1}{r^2}\frac{\partial}{\partial r}\left(r^2\frac{\partial\psi}{\partial r}\right)+\frac{1}{r^2\sin^2\theta}\frac{\partial^2\psi}{\partial\phi^2}+\frac{1}{r^2\sin\theta}\frac{\partial}{\partial\theta}\left(\sin\theta\frac{\partial\psi}{\partial\theta}\right)+\frac{8\pi^2m}{h^2}\left(E+\frac{e^2}{r}\right)\psi=0 \quad (12.43)$$

The polar coordinates r, θ and ϕ have their usual significance (Fig. 12.15). The coordinate r measures the radial distance from the origin; θ is a latitude; and ϕ a longitude. Since the electron is moving in three dimensions, three coordinates obviously suffice to describe its position at any time.

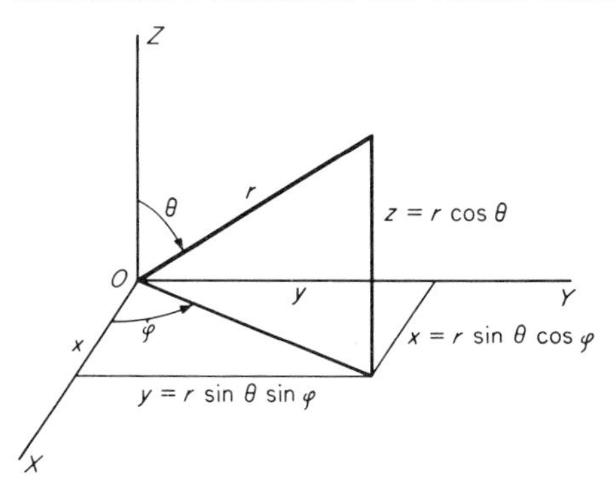

FIG. 12.15 Spherical polar coordinates.

In this equation, the variables can be separated, since the potential is a function of r alone. Let us substitute

$$\psi(r, \theta, \phi) = R(r)\Theta(\theta)\Phi(\phi) \qquad (12.44)$$

That is, the wave function is a product of three functions, one of which depends only on r, one only on θ, and the last only on ϕ. We shall skip the intervening steps in the solution and the application of the boundary conditions which permit only certain allowed eigenfunctions to be physically meaningful.* From our previous experience, however, we shall not be surprised to find that the final solutions represent a set of discrete stationary energy states for the hydrogen atom, characterized by certain quantum numbers, n, l, and m. Nor is it surprising that exactly three quantum numbers are required for this three-dimensional motion, just as one was enough for waves on a string, whereas three were needed for the particle in a box.

The allowed eigenfunctions are certain polynomials whose properties had been studied by mathematicians well before the advent of quantum mechanics. In order to give them a measure of concreteness, some examples of these hydrogen wave functions are tabulated in Table 12.3 for the lower values of the quantum numbers n, l, and m.

21. THE QUANTUM NUMBERS

The quantum number n is called the *principal quantum number*. It is the successor to the n introduced by Bohr in his theory of the hydrogen atom. The

* For the steps in the solution see, for example, L. Pauling and E. B. Wilson, *Introduction to Quantum Mechanics* (New York: McGraw-Hill, 1935), Chap. V.

TABLE 12.3 THE HYDROGENLIKE WAVE FUNCTIONS

K Shell

$n = 1, l = 0, m = 0$:

$$\psi_{1s} = \frac{1}{\sqrt{\pi}} \left(\frac{Z}{a_0}\right)^{3/2} e^{-Zr/a_0}$$

L Shell

$n = 2, l = 0, m = 0$:

$$\psi_{2s} = \frac{1}{4\sqrt{2\pi}} \left(\frac{Z}{a_0}\right)^{3/2} \left(2 - \frac{Zr}{a_0}\right) e^{-Zr/2a_0}$$

$n = 2, l = 1, m = 0$:

$$\psi_{2p_z} = \frac{1}{4\sqrt{2\pi}} \left(\frac{Z}{a_0}\right)^{3/2} \frac{Zr}{a_0} e^{-Zr/2a_0} \cos\theta$$

$n = 2, l = 1, m = \pm 1$:

$$\psi_{2p_x} = \frac{1}{4\sqrt{2\pi}} \left(\frac{Z}{a_0}\right)^{3/2} \frac{Zr}{a_0} e^{-Zr/2a_0} \sin\theta \cos\phi$$

$$\psi_{2p_y} = \frac{1}{4\sqrt{2\pi}} \left(\frac{Z}{a_0}\right)^{3/2} \frac{Zr}{a_0} e^{-Zr/2a_0} \sin\theta \sin\phi$$

total number of nodes in the wave function is equal to $n - 1$.* These nodes may be either in the radial function $R(r)$, or in the azimuthal function $\Theta(\theta)$.

The quantum number l is called the *azimuthal quantum number*. It is equal to the number of nodes in $\Theta(\theta)$, i.e., to the number of nodal surfaces passing through the origin.† Since the total number of nodes is $n - 1$, the allowed values of l are from 0 to $n - 1$. When $l = 0$, there are no nodes in the function $\Theta(\theta)$ and the wave function is spherically symmetrical about the central nucleus. The electron has an angular momentum p_θ which is quantized in such a way that

$$p_\theta = \sqrt{l(l+1)}(h/2\pi) \tag{12.45}$$

States with $l = 0$ therefore have zero angular momentum.

States with $l = 0, 1, 2, 3$ are denoted as s, p, d, and f states, respectively. In designating a state, the principal quantum number is prefixed to the letter denoting the azimuthal quantum number. For example, $n = 1$, $l = 0$ is a $1s$ state; $n = 2$, $l = 1$ is a $2p$, etc.

The quantum number m is called the *magnetic quantum number*. In order to understand its significance, we must digress to consider how a vector quantity, in particular an angular momentum, behaves in a field of force.

Figure 12.16 depicts a particle of mass M rotating in a circular orbit of radius r with a linear speed v. Its angular velocity $\omega = v/r$, and its moment of inertia $I = Mr^2$. Its angular momentum is a vector quantity of magnitude $I\omega$ directed along the axis of rotation. Now suppose that there is a gravitational field mak-

* If we consider that there is a nodal surface in the radial function at $r = \infty$, the total number of nodes equals n.

† In case $m = l$, the nodal surface becomes a nodal line.

ing an angle β with the direction of the angular momentum vector. This field exerts a torque $= Mgr \sin \beta$ which twists the angular momentum vector so that it *precesses* around the gravitational field vector. This *precession* is familiar to anyone who has ever played with tops or gyroscopes.

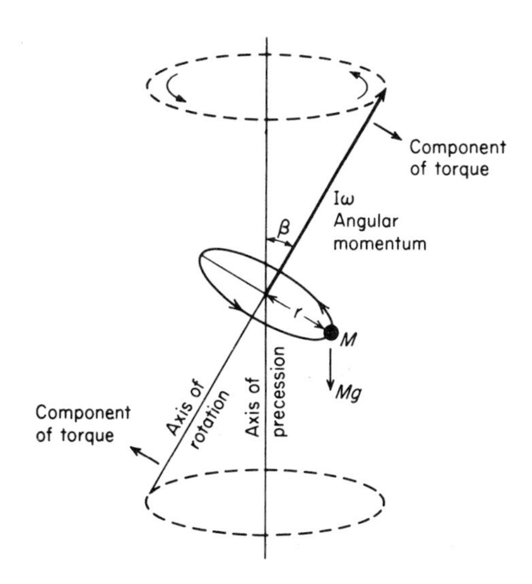

FIG. 12.16 The precession of the angular momentum vector about the direction of an external field.

If we return our attention to the electron in the hydrogen atom, we may recall that in states with $l \neq 0$, it has a certain angular momentum. In the absence of an external field, we could not expect this momentum vector to be constrained in direction. But suppose the hydrogen atom is placed in a magnetic field directed along the Z axis. A definite direction in space has now been physically established by the field, and the angular momentum vector precesses around this field direction. *The solutions of the Schrödinger equation are such that not every orientation between the angular momentum vector and the field direction is allowed.* The only allowed directions are those at which the components of the angular momentum along the Z-axis have certain quantized values given by

$$p_{\theta,z} = m(h/2\pi) \tag{12.46}$$

This behavior is called *space quantization.* It is illustrated in Fig. 12.17 for the case in which the azimuthal quantum number $l = 2$. The magnetic quantum number m can then have the values $-2, -1, 0, 1, 2$. For any value of l, which specifies the total angular momentum, there are $2l + 1$ values of m, which specify the allowed components of the angular momentum in the field direction.

We should not think that *space quantization* implies a "quantization of space." The energy quanta involved are those of the precessional motion. Like other periodic motions of an electron, this precessional motion must be quantized. In a magnetic field B the frequency of precession of the angular momentum vector of the electron is $\nu = eB/4\pi m_e c$. The allowed energy levels are spaced such that $\epsilon = mh\nu$. These energy levels are indicated in Fig. 12.17.

22. THE RADIAL WAVE FUNCTIONS

In Fig. 12.18 (a) we have plotted the radial parts of the wave functions for a few values of n and l. These plots show clearly the nodes in the waves, and the fact that the number of nodes in the radial function equals $n - l - 1$. We

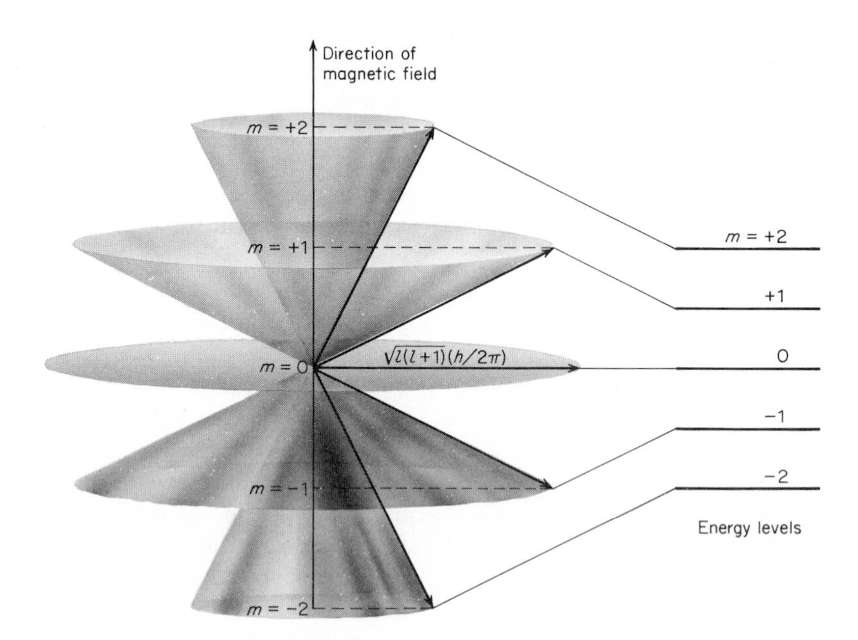

FIG. 12.17 Space quantization of the angular momentum in a magnetic field *B*. for the case $l = 2$.

recall, however, that ψ is the amplitude of the wave and it can be either positive or negative. In order to obtain the probability of finding the electron in the region between r and $r + dr$ we must take the square of the amplitude. Often we wish to know the probability of finding the electron at a given distance r from the nucleus, irrespective of direction: in other words, the probability that the electron lies between two spheres, one having a radius of r and the other of $r + dr$. The volume of this spherical shell is $4\pi r^2\, dr$, if we neglect terms in which the very small quantity dr is squared or cubed. Hence the probability of finding the electron somewhere within this shell is $4\pi r^2\psi^2$. The function $4\pi r^2\psi^2$ is called the *radial distribution function* $D(r)$. It has been plotted in Fig. 12.18 (b) for the values of n and l previously used in Fig. 12.18 (a).

Consider first the case of $n = 1$, $l = 0$, called the 1*s* state of the electron in the hydrogen atom. This is the lowest or *ground state* of hydrogen. In the old Bohr theory, the electron in this state revolved in a circular orbit of radius $a_0 = 0.529$ Å. The new wave mechanical picture shows that the electron has a certain probability of being anywhere from $r = 10^{-13}$ cm, smack in the center of the nucleus, to r 10^{22} cm, out in the Milky Way. Nevertheless, the position of *maximum probability* for the electron does correspond to the value $r = a_0$, and the chance that the electron is very far away from the nucleus is comfortingly small. For example, what is the probability that the electron is at a distance of 10 a_0 or 5.29 Å? From the expression for $\psi_{1s} = (\pi a_0^3)^{-1/2}\, e^{-r/a_0}$, the relative probability ($r^2\psi^2$) compared to that of finding the electron at a_0 is $10^2(e^{-10}/e^{-1})^2 = 1.52 \times 10^{-6}$. This is a rather small but far from negligible number. Another

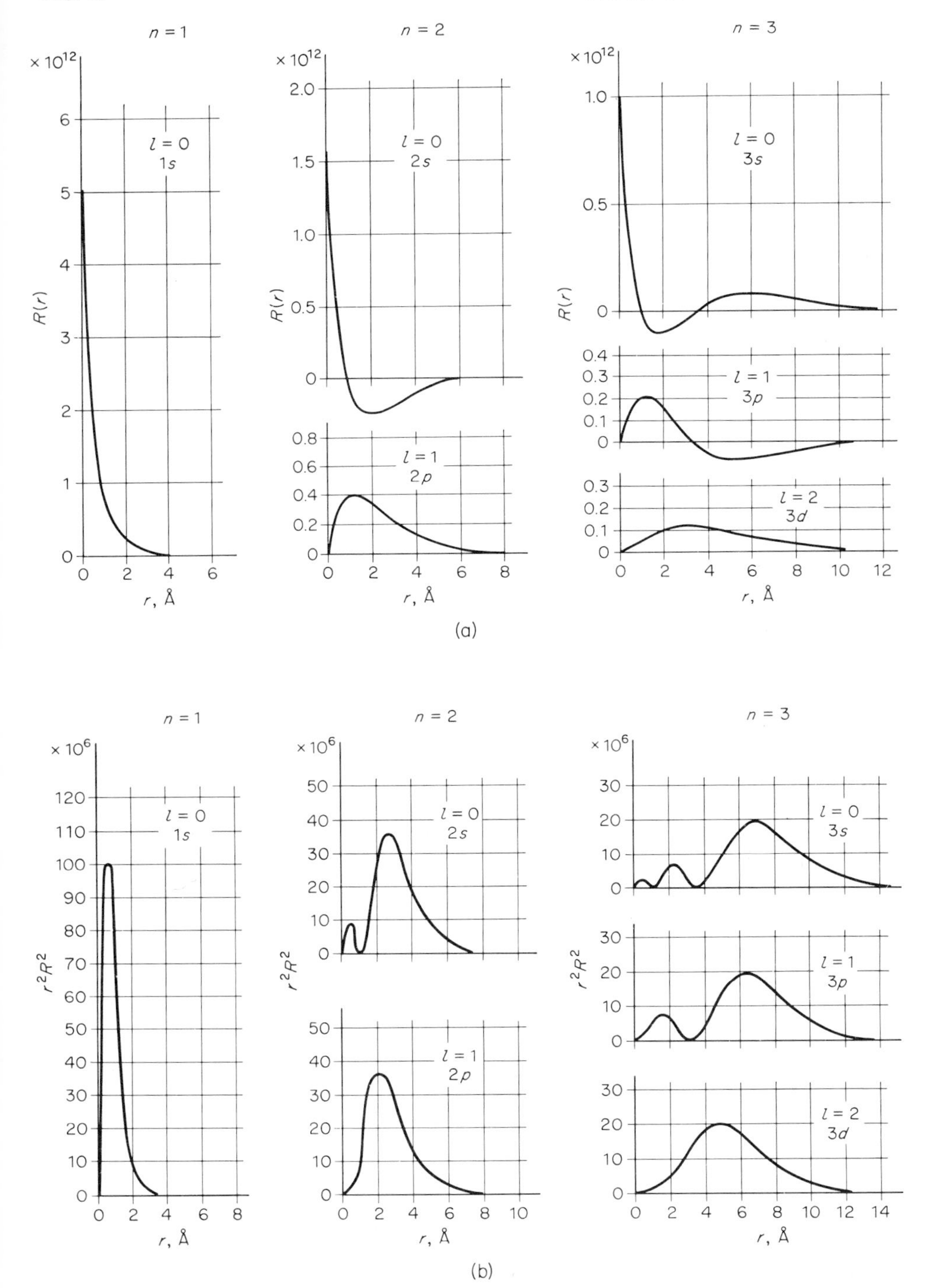

FIG. 12.18 (a) Radial part of wave functions for hydrogen atom; (b) Radial distribution functions — giving probability of finding electrons at a given distance from nucleus. [After G. Herzberg, *Atomic Spectra* (New York, Dover, 1944)].

way of looking at it is to say that if we had 10^6 hydrogen atoms, at any instant the electron in one of them might be expected to be at a distance 10 a_0 from the nucleus. If an ordinary hydrogen atom were the size of a golf ball, this exceptional hydrogen atom would be the size of a basketball. Of course it does not stay so big for very long, and if we took our snapshot an instant later, we might find the basketball back to its usual size while another hydrogen atom had shrunk to the size of a pea. Thus the hydrogen atom of wave mechanics is not a static rigid structure of fixed size.

Let us consider the state $2s$, that is, $n = 2$, $l = 0$. We find, in addition to the main peak in the radial distribution function at $r = 2.5\ a_0$, another little peak in probability at a much smaller value, $r = 0.4\ a_0$. This unexpected effect, called *penetration*, gives an important new insight into the behavior of electrons in the atomic shells. It shows that in certain states the electron spends a small proportion of its time very close to the nucleus. This penetration is important for states with low values of l, the azimuthal quantum number. Since the electron close to the nucleus is held by an exceptionally high electrostatic attraction, the penetration effect makes a considerable contribution to the bonding energy of the electron and thus tends to increase the stability (lower the energy) of states in which it occurs.

The wave function of an electron is called an *orbital*. The old theory spoke of the *orbits* of electrons and pictured them like tiny planets revolving around the nucleus as a sun. In the new theory there are no orbits and all the information about the position of an electron is summarized in its orbital.

The orbitals with $l = 0$ are called s orbitals and are always spherically symmetrical. In this case, ψ is a function of r alone, and does not depend on θ or ϕ. The orbitals with $l = 1$, called p orbitals, have a marked directional character since the ψ function depends on θ and ϕ. The d orbitals, with $l = 2$, are also directional.

23. ANGULAR DEPENDENCE OF HYDROGEN ORBITALS

There are several ways to illustrate the angular dependence of the orbitals. One of the most pictorial is to draw in perspective a picture of the angular part of the wave functions in three dimensions. These pictures show the product $\Theta\Phi$ of Eq. (12.44). Such surfaces are shown in Fig. 12.19 for the orbitals with $l = 0$ (s orbitals), and $l = 1$ (p orbitals). We also show the square of the angular wave functions $\Theta^2\Phi^2$ which determine the electron densities. In order to obtain the actual amplitudes of the wave functions we must multiply the angular parts $\Theta(\theta)\Phi(\phi)$ shown in Fig. 12.19 by the radial parts $R(r)$ shown in Fig. 12.18. In the same way, we can obtain the electron densities by multiplying $\Theta^2\Phi^2$ in Fig. 12.19 by R^2. The angular dependence is the same for all values of r. Thus the solid shapes in Fig. 12.19 do *not* imply that the orbitals are sharply defined in space. They simply depict the angular dependence of the orbitals for any value of r.

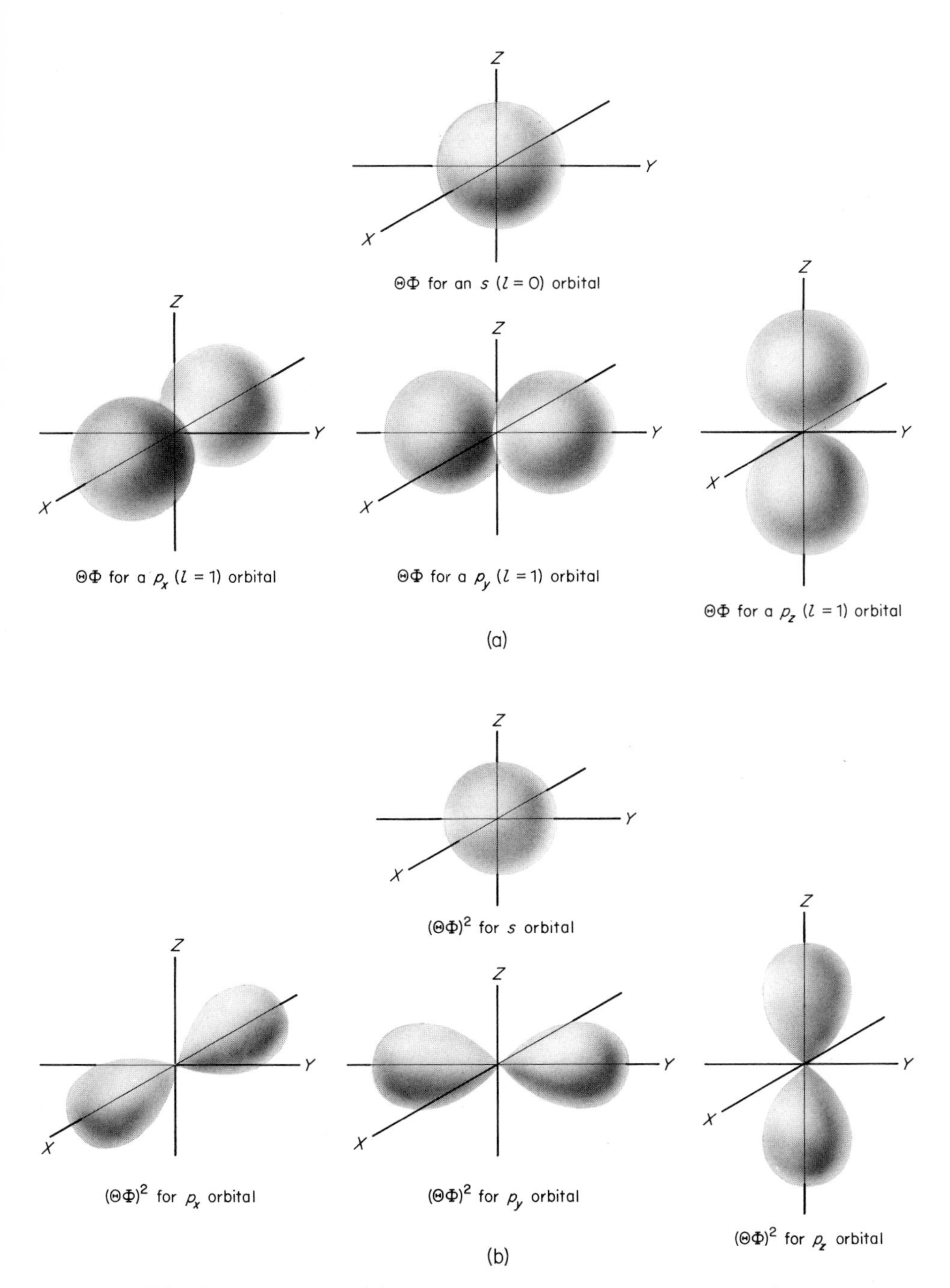

FIG. 12.19 Polar graphs: (a) the absolute values of $\Theta\Phi$, the angular part of the hydrogen-atom wave functions for $l = 0(s)$ and $l = 1(p)$ orbitals; (b) $(\Theta\Phi)^2$ which is proportional to the electron densities.

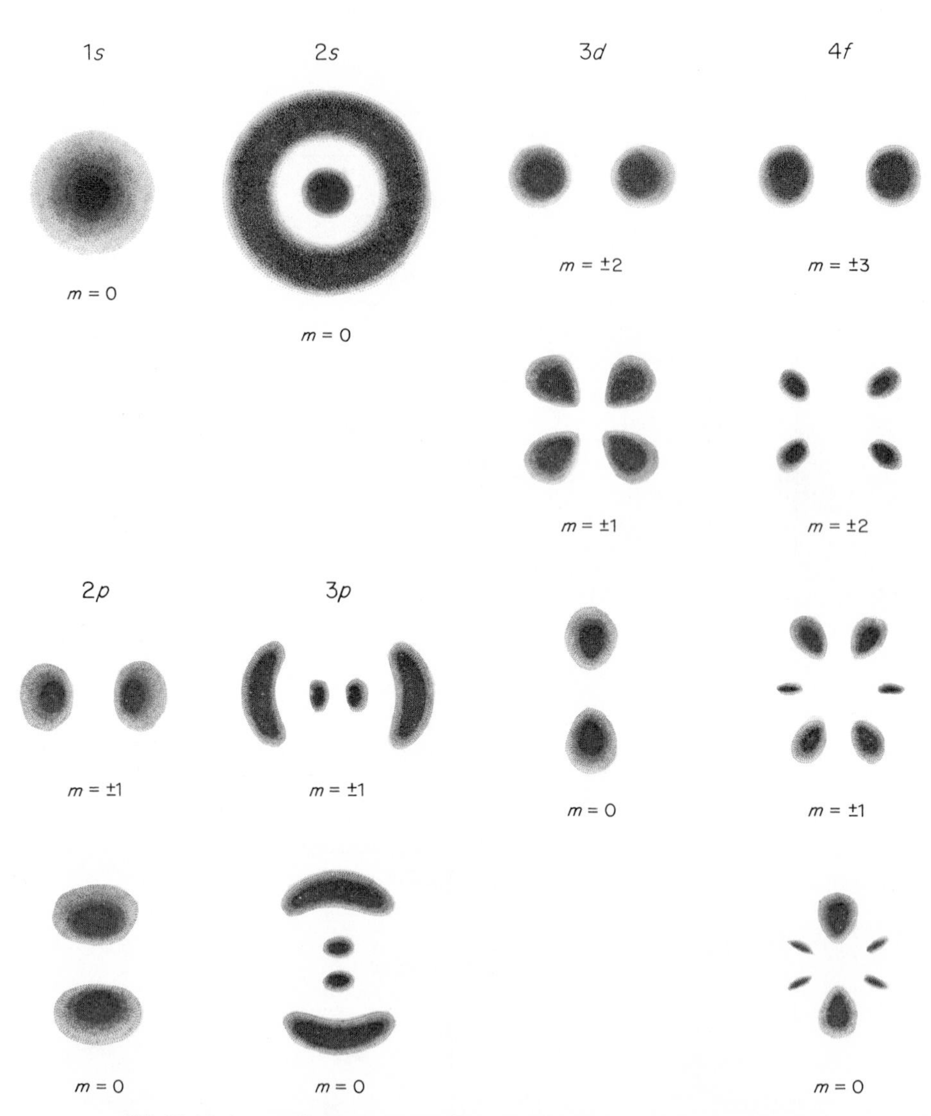

FIG. 12.20 Sections (not to same scale) of electron probability densities in various states of the hydrogen atom. The Z axis is in plane of paper.

The three p orbitals shown are plots of the angular functions given in Table 12.3.* They differ only with respect to their orientations along a specific axis, for instance, the Z axis.

There are five d orbitals, with $l = 2$, and $m = -2, -1, 0, 1, 2$. There are different ways of choosing a set of these five orbitals so that they are independent. The set usually used* is shown in Fig. 13.15 on p. 548. Three of the orbitals,

* These orbitals do not correspond directly with the different m values, and a different set (in the complex notation) is used when we wish to show the different m values explicitly.

d_{xy}, d_{xz} and d_{yz} have alternating + and − lobes directed at 45° to the axes of reference. There are also three possible quatrefoil orbitals pointing directly along pairs of axes, but only two of these can be independent. Thus we choose one, $d_{x^2-y^2}$, directed along the X and Y axes, and take a linear combination of the other two, which gives the orbital d_{z^2}, which is directed mainly along the Z axis, but also has a little doughnut of charge density at the XY plane.

Although we cannot conveniently draw $\psi = R(r)\Theta(\theta)\Phi(\phi)$, the complete wave functions, or ψ^2, the density functions, in three dimensions, we can show a section through them. Such sections are shown in Fig. 12.20. In these *cloud pictures* the intensity of the light shading is proportional to the value of ψ^2, the probability of finding the electron in a given region. It should be clearly understood that wave mechanics does not say that the electron itself is smeared out into a cloud; it can still be considered to be a charge located at a point. Its position and momentum cannot, however, be fixed simultaneously and all that the theory can predict with physical meaning is the *probability* that the electron is in a certain region.

24. ATOMIC ORBITALS AND ENERGIES—THE VARIATION METHOD

Quantum mechanics gives an exact solution for the hydrogen atom. The calculated energy levels and electron distributions are exact. Any experimental measurement of these quantities can hope only to be nearly as good as the theoretical values. But when we consider the next atom, helium with two electrons and a nuclear charge of +2, the situation is not so rosy. Already in this case we must face the hard truth that although we can write down the Schrödinger equation for the system, we cannot solve it exactly by analytic methods.

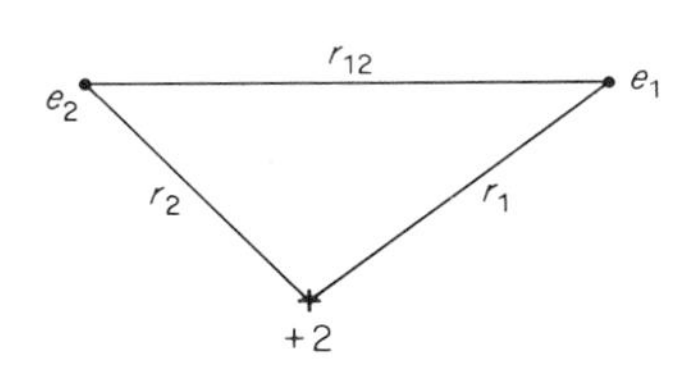

FIG. 12.21 Coordinates for the helium atom.

The helium system is shown in Fig. 12.21. In atomic units, the potential energy is

$$U = -\frac{2}{r_1} - \frac{2}{r_2} + \frac{1}{r_{12}}$$

The Schrödinger equation is therefore

$$\left[\nabla_1^2 + \nabla_2^2 + 2\left(E + \frac{2}{r_1} + \frac{2}{r_2} - \frac{1}{r_{12}}\right)\right]\psi = 0 \qquad (12.47)$$

The difficulty lies in the term $1/r_{12}$, the interaction between the two electrons. This term makes it impossible to separate the variables, i.e., the coordinates of electrons (1) and (2).

Fortunately we have powerful approximation methods which allow us to obtain useful (and in some cases practically exact) solutions in cases like this. We shall describe the *Variation Method*. It is important for every student of chemistry to understand this mathematical method, because it lies at the heart of modern theoretical approaches to atomic and molecular structure.

We write the Schrödinger equation in the operator form of Eq. (12.37),

$$H\psi = E\psi$$

Let us multiply each side of the equation by $\psi^\star$, and integrate over all space, to obtain

$$\int \psi^\star H\psi\, d\tau = \int \psi^\star E\psi\, d\tau$$

Since E is a constant, we can remove it from the integral to find

$$E = \frac{\int \psi^\star H\psi\, d\tau}{\int \psi^\star \psi\, d\tau} \tag{12.48}$$

This expression gives us the energy of the system provided we have the correct wave function ψ, which is the solution to the Schrödinger equation. (If you like, you can test this for the example of the hydrogen atom by putting in $\psi_{1s} = \pi^{-1/2}\, e^{-r}$).

But what use is Eq. (12.48) if we do not know the correct ψ? Suppose we guess (more politely, estimate) an approximate $\psi^{(1)}$, using our knowledge of what a reasonable electron distribution might be. If we put this trial $\psi^{(1)}$ into Eq. (12.48), we find

$$E^{(1)} = \frac{\int \psi^{\star(1)} H\psi^{(1)}\, d\tau}{\int \psi^{\star(1)}\psi^{(1)}\, d\tau}$$

The *variation principle* states that for any $\psi^{(1)}$ we may choose, $E^{(1)} \geq E$. The energy calculated from the trial $\psi^{(1)}$ can never be less than the true energy E.*

Our procedure is now clear. We must keep trying new estimated ψ's until we no longer get any further lowering of the calculated energy (or until we are satisfied that the particular kind of trial function we are using has reached the limit of its capabilities). Of course, systematic mathematical methods are available for getting the best trial ψ of any particular form. We might think of the variation method as a systematic effort to discover the electron distribution chosen by Nature for a particular atom or molecule. This distribution is naturally the one with the *lowest possible energy*.

25. THE HELIUM ATOM

Armed with the variation method, we return to the attack on the helium atom. If we simply neglected the effect of one electron on the motion of the other we could assume that each electron moved in the field of an He^+ ion and had a hydrogenlike atomic orbital. Then,†

$$\psi = e^{-Zr_1}\, e^{-Zr_2} \tag{12.49}$$

* The variation method is not limited to the Schrödinger equation and was in fact invented by Rayleigh and Ritz for vibration problems. A proof of the principle can be found in *Quantum Chemistry* by W. Kauzmann, (New York: Academic Press, (1957)), p. 119.

† The wave function for electron (1) is $1s(1) = e^{-Zr_1}$, that for electron (2) is $1s(2) = e^{-Zr_2}$. The function that expresses the probability for simultaneously finding (1) in $1s(1)$ and (2) in $1s(2)$ is the product.

where Z is the nuclear charge ($Z = 2$). The corresponding energy is $-11/4$ a. u. $= -74.81$ ev, compared to the experimental -78.99 ev.

The large discrepancy indicates that the effect of the interaction of the two electrons is important and cannot be neglected. The entire distribution of electron density is altered by the interaction between the two electrons. The resultant change in the energy of the system is called the *correlation energy*.

We try next the wave function

$$\psi^{(2)} = e^{-Z'r_1} e^{-Z'r_2} \tag{12.50}$$

This is like the zero-order function except that Z' is a variable parameter, which is adjusted until the minimum energy is found. (How would you do this mathematically?) This use of an adjustable Z' is common in the variation treatment of atoms and molecules. The effect of changing Z' is to cause the electron distribution to expand ($Z' < Z$) or contract ($Z' > Z$). We therefore call this operation the adjustment of the *scale factor*. We find the minimum energy when $Z' = Z - (\frac{5}{16})$. The corresponding energy is $E^{(2)} = -77.47$ ev.

We can interpret the wave function of Eq. (12.50) by saying that one electron partially screens the nucleus from the other, reducing the effective charge from $+2$ to $+(\frac{27}{16})$. One might think that the lower effective charge would cause a higher instead of a lower energy, since the lower the effective nuclear charge, the less negative is the energy of the electron in the field of the nucleus. The lower effective charge, therefore, must result in a *lower kinetic energy* for the electron, which more than compensates for the higher potential energy. The lower effective charge results in an expansion of the "electron cloud" about the nucleus. The electron has more space in which to move. Accordingly, as we pointed out in connection with the particle in a box, the delocalization causes a lowering of the kinetic energy.

It is evident that we have not achieved the best stability for this system simply by including the scale factor. As a matter of fact, we have probably allowed the trial helium atom to expand too much. What we would really like to do is to allow it to expand somewhat less and to put in an expression that would explicitly tell one electron to stay away from the other as much as possible. We therefore try a wave function

$$\psi^{(3)} = (1 + br_{12})\, e^{-Z'r_1} e^{-Z'r_2} \tag{12.51}$$

Notice that this function is larger as r_{12} becomes larger. Hence it is weighted in the right direction. The values for b and Z' that give the minimum energy are

$$b = 0.364$$

and

$$Z' = 2 - 0.151$$

The energy is -78.64 ev. We are now very close to the experimental -78.99 ev. Hylleraas in 1930 used a variation function with 14 parameters to obtain a calculated energy in agreement with the experimental one.

High speed digital computers have extended the frontiers of this kind of computational work, so that now the theoretical chemist can calculate a wide variety of properties of atoms and molecules more easily than the experimentalist can measure them. A calculation that in 1950 required two man years of work can now be done in an hour with a high speed computer such as the IBM 7090. As the computers become faster and gain larger memories, the range of computations becomes vastly enlarged. An important difficulty for the chemist will be to translate the language of the variation method, with its many parametered wave functions, back into a chemical language of effective charges, electron distributions and chemical bonds.

26. THE SPINNING ELECTRON

In 1921, while doing research in Rutherford's laboratory at Cambridge, Arthur H. Compton, a young American physicist, had the idea that an electron might possess an intrinsic angular momentum or spin, and thus act as a little magnet. In 1925, Wolfgang Pauli investigated the problem of why the lines in the spectra of the alkali metals are not single as predicted by the Bohr theory, but actually made up of two closely spaced components. An example was shown in Fig. 12.6. He showed that the doublet in the fine structure could be explained if the electron could exist in two distinct states. G. E. Uhlenbeck and S. Goudsmit of Leiden identified these states as two states of different angular momentum. They showed that the spectral multiplets could be explained by introducing a new quantum number s, which could have either of two values, $+\frac{1}{2}$ or $-\frac{1}{2}$, so that the intrinsic angular momentum of the electron could be $\frac{1}{2}(h/2\pi)$ or $-\frac{1}{2}(h/2\pi)$. The spinning electron acts like a tiny magnet with a magnetic moment $eh/4\pi m_e c$.

The most convincing experimental demonstration of the fact that the electron acts like a magnet was given by the famous *Stern-Gerlach experiment.* If a beam of atoms of an alkali metal is passed between the poles of a powerful magnet arranged so as to give an inhomogeneous field, the beam is split into two parts which make two separate deposits on a collector plate. Analysis shows that the effect can only be due to the outermost electron in the atom, which may have the spin quantum number of $+\frac{1}{2}$ or $-\frac{1}{2}$. The field splits the atoms into two beams corresponding to the two different spins.

The concept of the electron spin first appeared as an extra hypothesis, which needed to be tacked onto the rest of the theory. We then obtained four quantum numbers n, l, m and s. Since we expect a quantum number in wave theory for each dimension in which the electron can move, we might think that the four quantum numbers correspond to four dimensions. The *fourth dimension* is a phrase made famous by Einstein's relativity theory, in which events are described in a four-dimensional world of three space coordinates and one time coordinate. When Paul Dirac, an English theoretical physicist, worked out a relativistic form of wave mechanics for the electron, he found that the property of spin fell out naturally from his theory, and no separate hypothesis was necessary.

27. THE PAULI EXCLUSION PRINCIPLE

An exact solution of the Schrödinger wave equation for an atom has been obtained only in the case of the hydrogen atom — a single electron in the field of a positive charge. Nevertheless, even in the most complex atoms, the allowed stationary states of the electrons can be referred to the same four quantum numbers n, l, m and s.

An important rule governs the quantum numbers allowed for an electron in an atom. This is the *Exclusion Principle*, first enunciated by Pauli in a restricted form in 1924 and later given in a more general form. Pauli was born and educated in Vienna, his father being professor of physical chemistry there. He has recalled the story of his work on the Exclusion Principle as follows.

> *The history of the discovery of the Exclusion Principle, for which I have received the honor of the Nobel Prize award this year, goes back to my student days in Munich. While, in school in Vienna, I had already obtained some knowledge of classical physics and the then-new Einstein relativity theory, it was at the University of Munich that I was introduced by Sommerfeld to the structure of the atom — somewhat strange from the point of view of classical physics. I was not spared the shock which every physicist accustomed to the classical way of thinking experienced when he came to know of Bohr's "basic postulate of quantum theory" for the first time . . .*
>
> *The series of whole numbers 2, 8, 18, 32, giving the lengths of the periods in the natural system of chemical elements, was zealously discussed in Munich . . . Sommerfeld tried especially to connect the number 8 and the number of corners of a cube.*
>
> *When in 1923 Bohr made his first trip to United States, I returned, as an assistant, to the University of Hamburg, where soon after I gave my inaugural lecture as Privatdozent on the periodic system of elements. The contents of this lecture appeared very unsatisfactory to me, since the problem of the closing of the electronic shells had been clarified no further. The only thing that was clear was that a closer relation of this problem to the theory of multiplet structure must exist. I therefore tried to examine again critically the simplest case, the doublet structure of the alkali spectra. I arrived at the result that the point of view then orthodox — according to which a finite angular momentum of the atomic core was the cause of the doublet structure — must be given up as incorrect. In the fall of 1924 I published some of my arguments that, instead of the angular momentum of the closed shells of the atomic core, a new quantum theoretic property of the electron had to be introduced, which I called a two-valuedness not describable classically.*

At this time, the English physicist Stoner published an important paper, which pointed out that the number of energy levels of the same principal quantum number is the same as the number of electrons in the closed shells of the rare gases. "On the basis of my earlier results on the classification of spectral terms in a strong magnetic field," said Pauli, "the general formulation of the Exclusion Principle became clear to me."

The Pauli Exclusion Principle declares that no two electrons can exist in the same quantum state. Thus no two electrons in a given atom can have all four quantum numbers, n, l, m and s, the same.

28. ANTISYMMETRY OF WAVE FUNCTIONS

Consider in Fig. 12.22 two electrons A and B. Each electron can be denoted by a set of three space coordinates (x, y, z) [of which only x and y are shown here] and a spin coordinate, which can have either of two values, shown by an arrow in the diagram. We can exchange the spacial and/or the spin coordinates of the two electrons, as shown in the diagram. Since the electrons are indistinguishable particles, when we make such an exchange, the wave function of the system ψ must either remain the same $(\psi \rightarrow \psi)$ or simply change in sign $(\psi \rightarrow -\psi)$. In the first case we call the ψ *symmetric* for the exchange; in the second case, we call the ψ *antisymmetric* for the exchange. The total wave function for one electron can be written as a product of a spin part σ and a coordinate part ϕ,

$$\psi = \phi(x, y, z)\,\sigma$$

The general statement of the Pauli Principle is: A wave function for a system of electrons must be *antisymmetric* for the exchange of the spacial and the spin coordinates of any pair of electrons. (If, therefore, $\phi \rightarrow -\phi$, $\sigma \rightarrow \sigma$; if $\phi \rightarrow \phi$, $\sigma \rightarrow -\sigma$, so that $\psi \rightarrow -\psi$ always.)

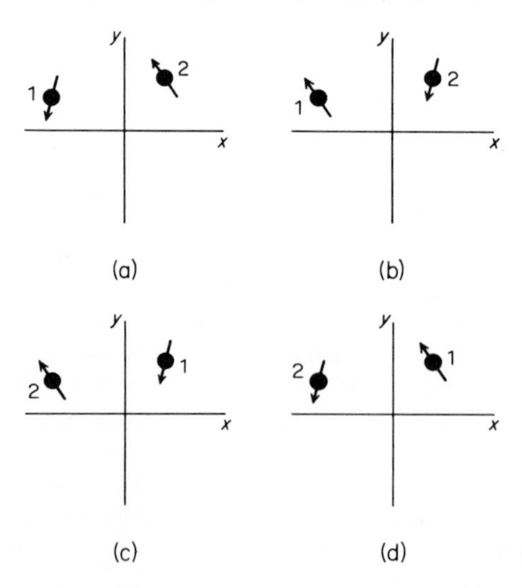

FIG. 12.22 Exchange of space and spin coordinates for two electrons. (a) original configuration; (b) spin coordinates exchanged; (c) space coordinates exchanged; (d) spin and space coordinates exchanged.

We can show that the original statement of the principle is a special case of the general statement. Consider two electrons, 1 and 2, in states specified by n_1, l_1, m_1, s_1, and n_2, l_2, m_2, s_2. An antisymmetric function would be

$$\psi = \psi_{n_1,l_1,m_1,s_1}(1)\,\psi_{n_2,l_2,m_2,s_2}(2) - \psi_{n_1,l_1,m_1,s_1}(2)\,\psi_{n_2,l_2,m_2,s_2}(1)$$

If we exchange (1) and (2), $\psi \rightarrow -\psi$ as is necessary. Suppose, however, all four quantum numbers were the same for the two electrons. Then $\psi = 0$, i.e., no such state can exist. It is impossible, therefore, to satisfy the requirement of antisymmetry and to have all four quantum numbers the same.

If we had a system of N particles, we could write the antisymmetric wave function most conveniently as a determinant:

$$\psi(1, 2, \ldots N) = A \begin{vmatrix} \psi_a(1) & \psi_a(2) & \ldots & \psi_a(N) \\ \psi_b(1) & \psi_b(2) & \ldots & \psi_b(N) \\ \cdot & & & \\ \cdot & & & \\ \cdot & & & \\ \psi_n(1) & \psi_n(2) & \ldots & \psi_n(N) \end{vmatrix}$$

The subscripts on the ψ's may denote the four quantum numbers specifying an orbital. If we exchange any two columns we change the sign of the determinant. Hence the antisymmetry requirement holds. If any set of four quantum numbers becomes the same, for example $a = b$, then two rows would become the same and the determinant would vanish.

29. ATOMIC ENERGY LEVELS

The Pauli Exclusion Principle provides the key to one of the greatest problems in chemistry — the explanation of the structure of the periodic table of the elements.

We recall that in a complex atom the electronic energy states can be enumerated by means of the four quantum numbers, n, l, m and s. The Exclusion Principle requires that no two electrons in an atom can have the same values for all four numbers. The most stable state or *ground state* of an atom will be that in which all the electrons are in the lowest possible energy levels that are consistent with the Exclusion Principle. We arrange the different orbitals, each specified by its unique set of four quantum numbers, in the order of increasing energy and then feed the electrons one by one into the lowest open orbitals until all the electrons, equal in number to the nuclear charge Z of the atom, are safely accommodated. This process was called by Pauli the *Aufbau Prinzip* or *Building Principle*.

In Table 12.4 the assignment of electrons to their orbitals is shown for all the elements, in accordance with our best present knowledge as derived from chemical and spectroscopic data.

TABLE 12.4 Electron Configurations of the Elements as Gaseous Atoms

Shell:	*K*	*L*		*M*			*N*			
Element	1*s*	2*s*	2*p*	3*s*	3*p*	3*d*	4*s*	4*p*	4*d*	4*f*
1. H	1									
2. He	2									
3. Li	2	1								
4. Be	2	2								
5. B	2	2	1							
6. C	2	2	2							
7. N	2	2	3							

TABLE 12.4 *(Cont.)*

Shell:	*K*	*L*		*M*			*N*			
Element	1*s*	2*s*	2*p*	3*s*	3*p*	3*d*	4*s*	4*p*	4*d*	4*f*
8. O	2	2	4							
9. F	2	2	5							
10. Ne	2	2	6							
11. Na	2	2	6	1						
12. Mg	2	2	6	2						
13. Al	2	2	6	2	1					
14. Si	2	2	6	2	2					
15. P	2	2	6	2	3					
16. S	2	2	6	2	4					
17. Cl	2	2	6	2	5					
18. A	2	2	6	2	6					
19. K	2	2	6	2	6		1			
20. Ca	2	2	6	2	6		2			
21. Sc	2	2	6	2	6	1	2			
22. Ti	2	2	6	2	6	2	2			
23. V	2	2	6	2	6	3	2			
24. Cr	2	2	6	2	6	5	1			
25. Mn	2	2	6	2	6	5	2			
26. Fe	2	2	6	2	6	6	2			
27. Co	2	2	6	2	6	7	2			
28. Ni	2	2	6	2	6	8	2			
29. Cu	2	2	6	2	6	10	1			
30. Zn	2	2	6	2	6	10	2			
31. Ga	2	2	6	2	6	10	2	1		
32. Ge	2	2	6	2	6	10	2	2		
33. As	2	2	6	2	6	10	2	3		
34. Se	2	2	6	2	6	10	2	4		
35. Br	2	2	6	2	6	10	2	5		
36. Kr	2	2	6	2	6	10	2	6		

Shell:	*K*	*L*	*M*	*N*				*Q*					*P*			*Q*
Element				4*s*	4*p*	4*d*	4*f*	5*s*	5*p*	5*d*	5*f*	5*g*	6*s*	6*p*	6*d*	7*s*
37. Rb	2	8	18	2	6			1								
38. Sr	2	8	18	2	6			2								
39. Y	2	8	18	2	6	1		2								
40. Zr	2	8	18	2	6	2		2								
41. Nb	2	8	18	2	6	4		1								
42. Mo	2	8	18	2	6	5		1								
43. Tc	2	8	18	2	6	(5)		(2)								
44. Ru	2	8	18	2	6	7		1								
45. Rh	2	8	18	2	6	8		1								
46. Pd	2	8	18	2	6	10										
47. Ag	2	8	18	2	6	10		1								
48. Cd	2	8	18	2	6	10		2								
49. In	2	8	18	2	6	10		2	1							
50. Sn	2	8	18	2	6	10		2	2							
51. Sb	2	8	18	2	6	10		2	3							
52. Te	2	8	18	2	6	10		2	4							
53. I	2	8	18	2	6	10		2	5							
54. Xe	2	8	18	2	6	10		2	6							

TABLE 12.4 *(Cont.)*

Shell:	K	L	M	N				O					P			Q
Element				$4s$	$4p$	$4d$	$4f$	$5s$	$5p$	$5d$	$5f$	$5g$	$6s$	$6p$	$6d$	$7s$
55. Cs	2	8	18	2	6	10		2	6				1			
56. Ba	2	8	18	2	6	10		2	6				2			
57. La	2	8	18	2	6	10		2	6	1			2			
58. Ce	2	8	18	2	6	10	2	2	6				2			
59. Pr	2	8	18	2	6	10	3	2	6				2			
60. Nd	2	8	18	2	6	10	4	2	6				2			
61. Pm	2	8	18	2	6	10	5	2	6				2			
62. Sm	2	8	18	2	6	10	6	2	6				2			
63. Eu	2	8	18	2	6	10	7	2	6				2			
64. Gd	2	8	18	2	6	10	7	2	6	1			2			
65. Tb	2	8	18	2	6	10	8	2	6	1			2			
66. Dy	2	8	18	2	6	10	9	2	6	1			2			
67. Ho	2	8	18	2	6	10	10	2	6	1			2			
68. Er	2	8	18	2	6	10	11	2	6	1			2			
69. Tu	2	8	18	2	6	10	13	2	6				2			
70. Yb	2	8	18	2	6	10	14	2	6				2			
71. Lu	2	8	18	2	6	10	14	2	6	1			2			
72. Hf	2	8	18	2	6	10	14	2	6	2			2			
73. Ta	2	8	18	2	6	10	14	2	6	3			2			
74. W	2	8	18	2	6	10	14	2	6	4			2			
75. Re	2	8	18	2	6	10	14	2	6	5			2			
76. Os	2	8	18	2	6	10	14	2	6	6			2			
77. Ir	2	8	18	2	6	10	14	2	6	7			2			
78. Pt	2	8	18	2	6	10	14	2	6	9			1			
79. Au	2	8	18	2	6	10	14	2	6	10			1			
80. Hg	2	8	18	2	6	10	14	2	6	10			2			
81. Tl	2	8	18	2	6	10	14	2	6	10			2	1		
82. Pb	2	8	18	2	6	10	14	2	6	10			2	2		
83. Bi	2	8	18	2	6	10	14	2	6	10			2	3		
84. Po	2	8	18	2	6	10	14	2	6	10			2	4		
85. At	2	8	18	2	6	10	14	2	6	10			2	5		
86. Rn	2	8	18	2	6	10	14	2	6	10			2	6		
87. Fr	2	8	18	2	6	10	14	2	6	10			2	6		1
88. Ra	2	8	18	2	6	10	14	2	6	10			2	6		2
89. Ac	2	8	18	2	6	10	14	2	6	10			2	6	1	2
90. Th	2	8	18	2	6	10	14	2	6	10			2	6	2	2
91. Pa	2	8	18	2	6	10	14	2	6	10	2		2	6	1	2
92. U	2	8	18	2	6	10	14	2	6	10	3		2	6	1	2
93. Np	2	8	18	2	6	10	14	2	6	10	5		2	6		2
94. Pu	2	8	18	2	6	10	14	2	6	10	6		2	6		2
95. Am	2	8	18	2	6	10	14	2	6	10	7		2	6		2
96. Cm	2	8	18	2	6	10	14	2	6	10	7		2	6	1	2
97. Bk	2	8	18	2	6	10	14	2	6	10	8		2	6	1	2
98. Cf	2	8	18	2	6	10	14	2	6	10	9		2	6	1	2
99. E	2	8	18	2	6	10	14	2	6	10	10		(2	6	1	2)
100. Fm	2	8	18	2	6	10	14	2	6	10	11		(2	6	1	2)
101. Mv	2	8	18	2	6	10	14	2	6	10	12		(2	6	1	2)
102. No	2	8	18	2	6	10	14	2	6	10	13		(2	6	1	2)
103. Lw	2	8	18	2	6	10	14	2	6	10	14		(2	6	1	2)

In the element following argon, potassium with $Z = 19$, the last electron enters the 4*s* orbital. This is required by its properties as an alkali metal, and the fact that its spectral ground state is the same as that in Li and Na. We may well ask, however, why the 4*s* orbitals are lower than the 3*d* orbitals, which provide 10 vacant places. We can give a qualitative answer to this question which should help to clarify the structure of the remainder of the periodic table and the properties of the elements in the transition series. Quantum mechanical calculations of the energy levels should provide more quantitative data.

The reason why the 4*s* orbital for K has a lower energy than a 3*d* arises from the fundamental difference in form of *s*, *p*, and *d* orbitals. The electron distributions in the 3*s*, 3*p*, and 3*d* orbitals for the hydrogen atom were shown in Fig. 12.18. Of course these hydrogen wave functions are not an accurate picture of the orbitals in a more complex atom with many electrons, but they provide a satisfactory approximation for the valence electrons, which move in the hydrogen-like field of the nucleus shielded by inner electrons.

The 4*s* and 3*p* orbitals predict a considerable concentration of the charge close to the nucleus, whereas the 3*d* orbital predicts an extremely low probability of finding the electron close to the nucleus. As a result of this *penetration* of the 4*s* orbital toward the nucleus, a 4*s* electron will be more tightly bound by the positive nuclear charge, and will be in a lower energy state than a 3*d* electron, whose orbital does not penetrate, and which is therefore more shielded from the nucleus by the intermediate shells. It is true that the most probable position for a 4*s* electron is farther from the nucleus than that for a 3*d* electron; the penetration effect more than makes up for this, since the coulombic force of attraction decreases as the square of the distance from the nucleus. Since the 4*s* lies lower than 3*d*, the nineteenth electron in K enters the 4*s* rather than the 3*d* level, and K is a typical alkali metal.

Following Ca, the 3*d* orbitals begin to be filled rather than the 4*p*. One obtains the first transition series of metals, Sc, Ti, V, Cr, Mn, Fe, Co, Ni. These are characterized by variable valence and strongly colored compounds. Both these properties are associated with the closeness of the 4*s* and 3*d* levels, which provide a variable number of electrons for bond formation, and possible excited levels at separations corresponding with the energy available in visible light (around 2 ev).

The filling of the 3*d* shell is completed with Cu, which has the configuration $1s^2\ 2s^2\ 2p^6\ 3s^2\ 3p^6\ 3d^{10}\ 4s^1$. Copper is not an alkali metal despite the outer 4*s* electron, because the 3*d* level is only slightly below the 4*s* and Cu^{+2} ions are readily formed.

The next electrons gradually fill the 4*s* and 4*p* levels, the process being completed with Kr. The next element Rb is a typical alkali with one 5*s* electron outside the $4s^2\ 4p^6$ octet. Strontium, with two 5*s* electrons, is a typical alkaline earth of the Mg, Ca, Sr, Ba series. Now, however, the 4*d* levels become lowered sufficiently to be filled before the 5*p*. This causes the second transition series, which is completed with Pd. Silver follows with the copper-type structure and the filling of the 5*s* and 5*p* levels is completed with Xe. A typical alkali (Cs) and alkaline earth (Ba) follow with one and two 6*s* electrons.

The next electron, in lanthanum, enters the $5d$ level, and one might suspect that a new transition series is underway. Meanwhile, however, with increasing nuclear charge, the $4f$ orbitals have been drastically lowered and these are filled before the $5d$. The $4f$ levels can hold exactly 14 electrons as follows:

$$n = 4$$

$$l = 3$$

$$m = -3, -2, -1, \quad 0, +1, +2, +3$$

$$s = \pm\tfrac{1}{2}, \pm\tfrac{1}{2}, \pm\tfrac{1}{2}, \pm\tfrac{1}{2}, \pm\tfrac{1}{2}, \pm\tfrac{1}{2}, \pm\tfrac{1}{2}$$

As these levels are filled, we obtain the 14 rare earths with their remarkably similar chemical properties, determined by the common $5s^2\ 5p^6$ outer configuration of their ions. This process is complete with lutecium.

The next element is hafnium, with $5d^2\ 6s^2$. Its properties are very similar to those of zirconium with $4d^2\ 5s^2$. After Hf the $5d$ shell is filled, and then the filling of the $6p$ levels is completed, the next $s^2\ p^6$ octet being attained with radon. The long missing halogen (85-astatine) and alkali (87-francium) below and above radon were found as artificial products from nuclear reactions.

Radium is a typical alkaline earth metal with two $7s$ electrons. In the next element, actinium, the extra electron enters the $6d$ level, so that the outer configuration is $6d^1\ 7s^2$; this is to be compared to lanthanum with $5d^1\ 6s^2$. It was formerly thought that the filling of the $6d$ levels continued in the elements following Ac. As a result of studies of the properties of the transuranium elements it now appears that Ac marks the beginning of a new rare-earth group, successive electrons entering the $5f$ shell. Successive electrons added to the f shell are more tightly bound as the nuclear charge increases. Thus the trivalent state becomes more stable compared to the quadrivalent state as one proceeds through Ac, Th, Pa, U, Np, Pu, Am, Cm, just as it does in the series La, Ce, Pr, Nd, Pm, Sm, Eu, etc. The *actinide rare earths* therefore resemble the *lanthanide rare earths* rather than the elements immediately above themselves in the periodic table. It was the knowledge of this basic chemistry as predicted from the electronic structures which made possible the isolation of transuranium elements such as neptunium and plutonium.

This explanation of the structure of the periodic table solved one of the greatest problems of chemistry. As we look back, the historical development has been long and difficult, based on much painstaking experimental and theoretical work by chemists and physicists. The final result, however, has the beautiful simplicity that we have come to recognize as the aesthetic criterion of a satisfying explanation in the world of nature.

Fig. 12.23 shows the best available calculation of the energy levels of the orbitals as a function of nuclear charge Z (atomic number). These curves were calculated* from an approximate quantum mechanical treatment of complex atoms adapted for numerical solution with a high speed computer. In the

* R. Latter, *Phys. Rev.* *99*, 510 (1955).

limit of low Z all orbitals having the same principal quantum number fall together at the same energy, because there are too few electrons to cause splitting of levels due to interelectronic interactions. In the limit of high Z, inner orbitals having the same principal quantum number again fall together in energy. This convergence occurs because the nuclear attraction is now so great that any inter-

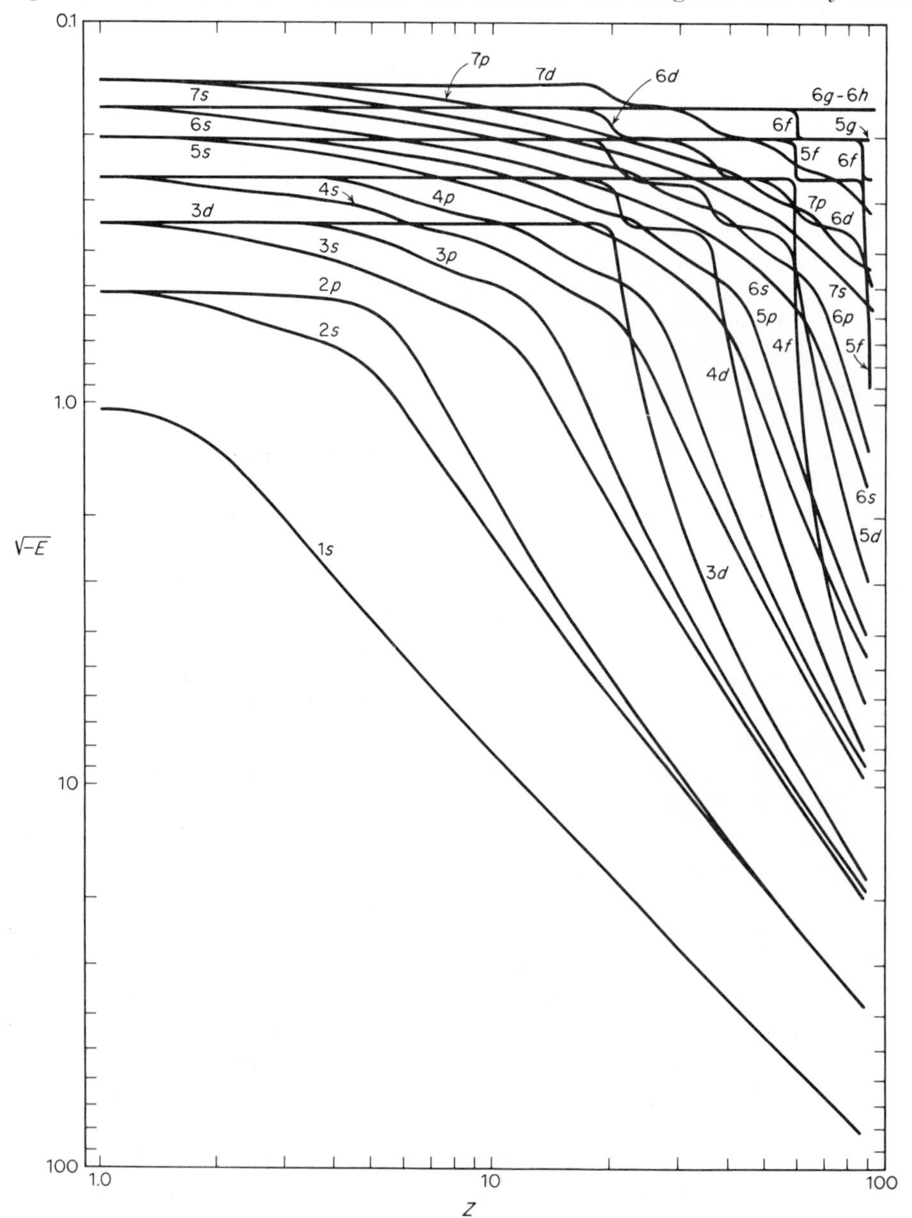

FIG. 12.23 Energy levels of atomic orbitals calculated as functions of nuclear charge (atomic number) [Redrawn by M. Kasha from paper of R. Latter].

actions between the electrons in the same shell are practically overwhelmed. These are the energy levels observed in X-ray spectra. A hole in the shell with $n = 1$ gives the K series; a hole in the shell with $n = 2$ gives the L series; and so on.

At intermediate Z, the sequence of energy levels can become much more tangled. This is the region in which interelectronic interactions, such as penetration effects, can lead to departures from the sequence of principal quantum numbers. Consider, for example, the $3d$ orbital. Owing to the shielding of the nucleus by inner electrons, a $3d$ electron experiences an almost constant nuclear attraction until about $Z = 20$ (Ca). Its energy then begins to fall with Z. According to the calculation the $3d$ crosses the $4s$ at $Z = 28$ (Ni). Actually we know from chemical and spectroscopic evidence that the crossover occurs at about $Z = 21$ (Sc). Compared with experiment, all the calculated curves in Fig. 12.23 are displaced somewhat toward higher Z.

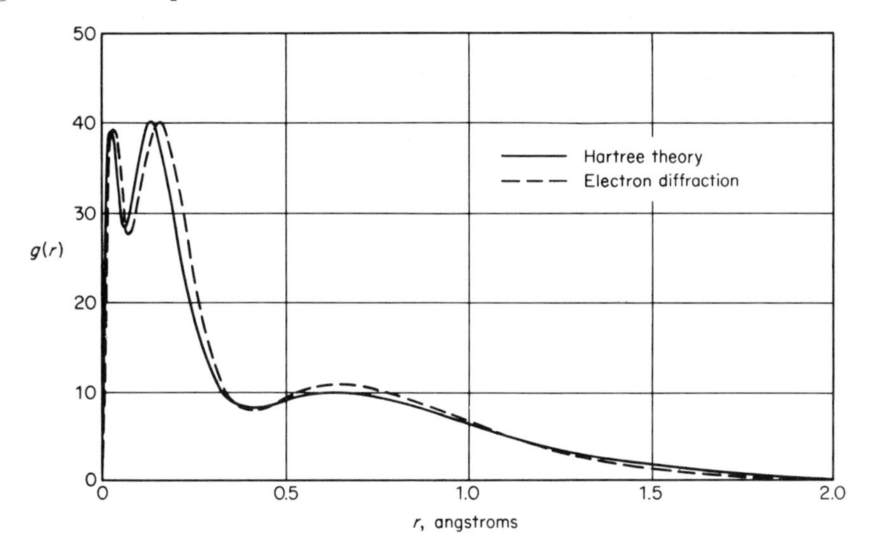

FIG. 12.24 Experimental radial distribution of electrons in argon from electron diffraction compared with the quantum mechanical calculation.

In a complex atom, the electrons lose their identities and all that can be measured experimentally is the density of negative electronic charge $\rho(r)$ as a function of distance r from the nucleus. We can calculate this charge density from quantum mechanics by the method of the self consistent field approximation invented by D. Hartree.* We can also measure the distribution experimentally by means of the diffraction of X-ray or electron beams by atomic gases. A comparison of the experimental† and theoretical distributions for argon is shown in Fig. 12.24. These results provide a beautiful confirmation of the *shell structure* of the electron density distribution.

* D. Hartree, *Reports on Progress in Physics*, *11*, 113 (1947).
† L. S. Bartell and L. O. Brockway, *Phys. Rev. 90*, 833 (1953).

30. THE VECTOR MODEL OF THE ATOM

The spectrum of atomic hydrogen as explained by the Bohr theory is particularly simple because there is one electron only. When there is more than one electron, the number of energy states increases, and the spectra arising from transitions between these states become more complex. We need to solve the problem of how the electric and magnetic fields of the different electrons interact with one another to produce the final pattern of energy levels.

A most useful method is based on the *vector model* of the atom. We have seen how an angular momentum vector interacts with an external field and precesses around its direction. In a similar way the angular momentum vectors of two different electrons within an atom can couple together to form a resultant total angular momentum, and each of the individual vectors then precesses around the resultant vector. We must consider, however, the two different kinds of angular momentum, the intrinsic angular momentum or spin of the electron, and the orbital angular momentum due to the motion of the electron about the nucleus.

The way in which these angular momenta interact is summarized in the scheme called *Russell-Saunders coupling*.*

(a) The individual spins s_i combine to form a resultant spin S

$$\sum_i s_i = S$$

The resultant must have integral or half integral values. For example, three spins of $+\frac{1}{2}$ could couple to give $S = \frac{3}{2}$ or $\frac{1}{2}$. Two spins of $+\frac{1}{2}$ could couple to give $S = 1$ or 0. The coupling between spins is caused by electrostatic forces acting between the negatively charged electrons. Consider two electrons with the same quantum numbers n, l and m. They would be in the same orbital and able to move in the same general region about the nucleus. Consequently, they would repel each other strongly and the energy of the state would be raised. To obey the Pauli principle, two electrons with the same n, l and m must have different spins, one $s = +\frac{1}{2}$, the other $s = -\frac{1}{2}$. If they have the same spin, they cannot have the same n, l and m and thus cannot tend to occupy the same region about the nucleus. Electrostatic interaction between spins is thus the result of a powerful indirect effect based ultimately on the Pauli principle. Electrons can lower their energies by staying as far away from each other as possible. When they have the same spin, the Pauli principle forces them to stay away from each other by occupying different orbitals. The vector model denotes this effect as an electrostatic coupling of the spin vectors to give a resultant S.

(b) The individual orbital angular momenta couple to form a resultant L:

$$\sum_i l_i = L$$

* The Russell-Saunders scheme applies to most atoms, but begins to break down in the heavier atoms. In these the large nuclear charge leads to a strong coupling between the s_i and l_i of each electron to give a resultant j_i.

Through space quantization, the quantum number L is restricted to integral values. The coupling of the l_i can be considered as a vector addition of the corresponding angular momenta which precess about the resultant L. This is shown in Fig. 12.25. The coupling is due to electrostatic forces acting between the different electron clouds in the different orbitals.

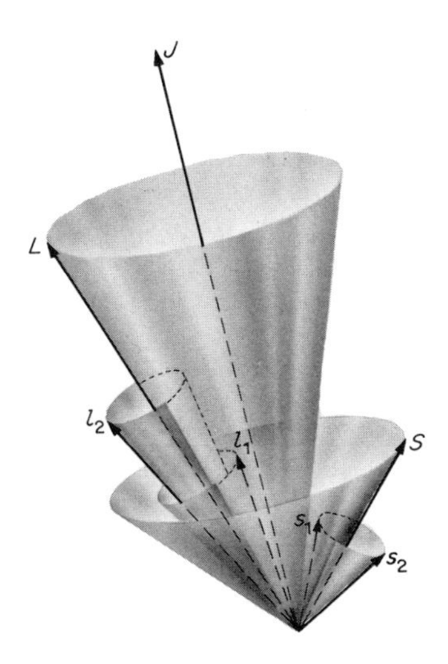

FIG. 12.25 An example of Russell-Saunders coupling. The l_1 and l_2 combine to form a resultant L. The s_1 and s_2 form a resultant S. L and S precess about their resultant J.

(c) The two resultants L and S represent the total orbital and the total spin angular momenta of all the electrons in the atom. The angular momentum vectors correspond to magnetic field vectors which exert magnetic forces on each other, and hence may couple magnetically to form a resultant J. This gives the total resultant angular momentum of all the electrons in the atom and it is quantized in values $\sqrt{J(J+1)}\,(h/2\pi)$. J is called the *inner quantum number*.

In the absence of an external field the total angular momentum of the atom must be constant. Hence L and S precess around their resultant J as shown in Fig. 12.25.

The various energy levels or spectral terms of an atom are denoted by symbols based on this model. The symbol can be expressed as

$$^{2S+1}L_J$$

The values of $L = 0, 1, 2, 3, \ldots$ are denoted by capital letters S, P, D, F. Thus the symbol $^2S_{1/2}$ would denote a state with $2S + 1 = 2$, or $S = \frac{1}{2}$, $L = 0$, $J = \frac{1}{2}$. The lefthand superscript $2S + 1$ is called the *multiplicity* of the state. It is read as "singlet," "doublet," "triplet," etc. When $L > S$ the multiplicity gives the number of J values for the given state.

31. ATOMIC SPECTRA

We shall apply these ideas to the energy levels in the lithium atom and hence to the interpretation of its spectrum. The electron configuration of Li in the ground state is $1s^2\,2s^1$. Closed shells (e.g., $1s^2$ in Li) with all states of a given n occupied, have zero angular momentum and spin, and need not be considered in the assignment of term values. The $2s$ electron has $l = 0$ and $s = \frac{1}{2}$. Hence, $L = 0$, $S = \frac{1}{2}$, $J = \frac{1}{2}$. The ground state in lithium is therefore $1s^2\,2s - {}^2S_{1/2}$. Suppose the optical electron is excited to give the configuration $1s^2\,2p$. Now, $L = 1$, $S = \frac{1}{2}$, and $J = \frac{3}{2}$ or $\frac{1}{2}$. The states are $1s^2\,2p - {}^2P_{3/2,1/2}$. These states differ slightly in energy and hence the line corresponding to a transition between the ground state ^2S and the first higher state ^2P is a closely spaced doublet. It was the occurrence of such doublets in the spectra of the alkali metals that first led to the recognition of electron spin. The absorption spectrum of potassium vapor was shown in Fig. 12.6.

The various energy levels of the lithium atom are summarized in Fig. 12.26. Transitions are permitted between these levels only if they obey certain *selection rules*. These are

$$\Delta J = 0, \pm 1$$

$$\Delta L = \pm 1$$

Some of the lower transitions are shown on the diagram, each one corresponding to a line observed in the spectrum of lithium.

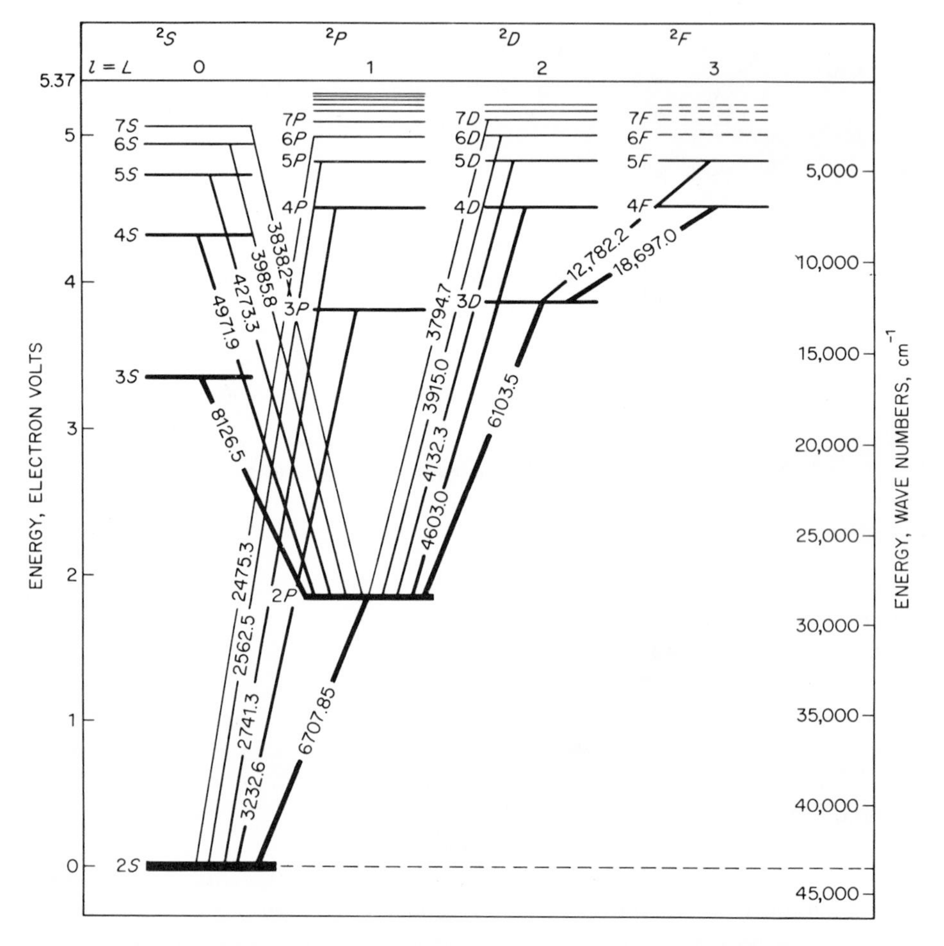

FIG. 12.26 Energy level diagram of the Li atom. The wavelengths of the spectral lines are written on the connecting lines representing the transitions. Doublet structure is not included. Some unobserved levels are indicated by dotted lines.

PROBLEMS

1. What is the average energy, $\bar{\epsilon}$, of a harmonic oscillator of frequency 10^{13} sec^{-1} at 0°, 200°, 1000°C? What is the ratio $\bar{\epsilon}/kT$ at each temperature? [*Ans.* (a) 1.39×10^{-14}; 3.77×10^{-14}; 3.77×10^{-14}; 11.8×10^{-14} ergs; (b) 0.370, 0.577, 0.670]

2. The K_α X-ray line of iron has a wavelength of 1.932 Å. A photon of this wavelength is emitted when an electron falls from the L shell into a vacancy in the K shell. Write down the electronic configuration of the ions before and after emission of this line. What is the energy difference in kcal per mole between these two configurations? [*Ans.* 1.48×10^5 kcal $mole^{-1}$]

3. The fundamental vibration frequency of N_2 corresponds to a wave number of 2360 cm^{-1}. What fraction of N_2 molecules possess no vibrational energy (except their zero-point energy) at 25°C? [*Ans.* 0.999989]

4. An excited energy level has a lifetime of 10^{-10} sec. What is the minimum width of the spectral line arising in a transition from the ground state to this level? [*Ans.* 0.053 cm^{-1}]

5. Calculate the wavelengths of (a) a proton, (b) an electron, accelerated through a potential difference of 1 mev. (Neglect relativity effect on velocity.)

6. For a particle of mass 9×10^{-28} g confined to a one-dimensional box 100 Å long, calculate the number of energy levels lying between 9 and 10 ev. [*Ans.* $n = 3$]

7. Write an account of the probable inorganic chemistry of Np, Pu, Am, Cm, in view of their probable electron configurations. Compare the chemistry of astatine and iodine, francium and cesium.

8. Calculate the approximate minimum uncertainty in the position or velocity for the following cases: (a) an automobile moving at 60 mph $\pm$ 0.001 mph (mass = 1 ton); (b) a bullet whose position at time t is known to ± 0.01 mm (mass = 10 g); (c) a hydrogen atom whose velocity is known to ± 1 cm/sec; (d) an electron whose position is known to ± 1 Å.

9. Calculate the separation of the lowest two energy levels for a particle of mass equal to that of a hydrogen molecule confined to a cubical box 1 mm on a side (express result in ergs). Compare the result with kT for $T = 300$°K.

10. The human eye, when completely adapted to darkness, is able to perceive a point source of light against a dark background when the rate of incidence of radiation on the retina is 2×10^{-16} watt. Find the minimum rate of incidence of quanta of radiation on the retina necessary to produce vision, assuming a wavelength of 5500 Å.

11. What are the wavelengths in Å of (a) an electron, (b) a photon, each with kinetic energies of 1 ev?

12. Calculate from Planck's law the relative intensities of the radiation from a black body at 2000°K at wavelength 4000 ± 10 Å and 8000 ± 10 Å.

13. Consider an electron in a one dimensional box 10 Å long. (a) What is the zero-point energy of the electron in ev? (b) What is the wavelength of the radiation absorbed when the electron makes a transition from the state $n = 1$ to the state $n' = 2$?

14. What is the Bohr radius of He^+, Li^{2+}?

15. What is the velocity of an electron in the ground state of the H atom according to the Bohr theory? What would be the de Broglie wavelength of this electron?

16. The diameter of a typical small nucleus is about 10^{-13} cm. Suppose that a proton is held in a one-dimensional potential well with infinite walls and a width of 10^{-13} cm. Calculate the first three energy levels in ev. Suppose you placed an electron in this box. What would the lowest energy level be? From this result, what would you say about the likelihood that an electron can exist within the nucleus?

17. In the photoelectric effect, if the energy of the quantum incident on a solid surface exceeds the photoelectric work function ϕ, an electron is driven from the surface. Calculate the kinetic energy of the photoelectron emitted from a surface of potassium ($\phi = 2.26$ ev) when illuminated by light of wavelength 4000 Å.

18. A snail of 1 g mass is traveling at a velocity of 0.1 mm/s. What is the uncertainty in its position?

19. An atom of mass m is inside a spherical container of radius R. Estimate from the uncertainty principle its minimum possible energy. Apply the result to an electron in a sphere with $R = 1$ Å. What about an electron *inside* a nucleus of $R = 10^{-13}$ cm?

20. Explain how each of the following properties of an element is related to the position of the element in the periodic classification: (a) the valence; (b) the melting point of the chloride; (c) the specific heat; (d) the electrical conductivity; (e) the atomic weight; (f) the existence of oxyacids.

21. Explain the structures of the hydrides of the elements of groups 4 and 5 in terms of their electronic configurations, and comment on their stabilities. Discuss the stability of the halides of silicon, tin and lead.

22. For each of the following elements give *two* compounds in which the element displays different valences: phosphorus, copper, bromine, bismuth. How does valence theory explain this variation in valence?

23. Explain the following:
    (a) Chemical inertness of rare gases.
    (b) Variable valence of lead.
    (c) The reactions occurring when ammonia is added to copper sulfate solution.
    (d) The comparative stabilities of the pentachlorides of nitrogen and phosphorus.
    (e) The variable valence of chromium.
    (f) The solubility in water of compounds of the alkali metals.

---

24. A positive and negative electron can form a short lived complex called *positronium*. Assume that the Bohr theory of the hydrogen atom could be applied to positronium and calculate the energy difference between its ground state and first excited state.

25. Strictly speaking, the electron in a hydrogen atom and the proton should be considered to revolve about their center of mass. We can introduce the effect into the Bohr theory by using the reduced mass $\mu(1/\mu = 1/m_1 + 1/m_2)$, instead of the electronic mass. On this basis calculate the Rydberg constant for H and D atoms. What would be the predicted difference in wavelength of the first Balmer lines in H and D spectra?

26. Write down the Schrödinger equation for an electron moving in a 3-dimensional box of sides a, b, c, with infinite walls. Show how it can be separated into three one-dimensional equations. Give the solutions for these equations. Write down the wave function $\psi_{n_1n_2n_3}$ and the energy levels $E_{n_1n_2n_3}$ for the first five energy levels for this system.

27. Consider a helium atom at 1°K in a cubical box with side $a = 1$ mm. If the kinetic energy is $\frac{1}{2}mv^2 = \frac{3}{2}kT$, find the value of n in the wavefunction $\psi_{n,n,n}$ which would correspond to this energy.

28. Two functions ψ_1 and ψ_2 are said to be *orthogonal* when $\int \psi_1\psi_2 \, d\tau = 0$ where the integral is taken over all space. Show that the ψ_{1s} function for the H atom is orthogonal to the ψ_{2s} and the ψ_{2p}.

29. Show that in the ground state of the H atom as given by wave mechanics the *most probable value* of the distance r of the electron from the nucleus is a_0. Show that the *average value* of $1/r$ is $1/a_0$.

30. Apply the Heisenberg uncertainty principle to estimate the kinetic energy of the electron in the H atom, at a distance r from the nucleus. Then calculate the equilibrium distance r_e by minimizing the total energy E (kinetic + potential) with respect to r. Calculate the total E. Compare with experiment.

31. Repeat the calculation in problem 30 for the two electrons in a He atom, taking account of the interelectronic repulsion. [*Ans.* Minimum energy at $r_1 = r_2 = (h^2/4\pi^2me^2)(4/7)$, $E = -2(7/4)^2(4\pi^2me^4/h^2)$]

32. Suppose an electron with kinetic energy of 9.00 ev is held in a one-dimensional box, with a barrier of height $U_0 = 10$ ev. If the width of the barrier is 10 Å estimate the chance that the electron will tunnel through the barrier. (This situation is similar to that of an electron tunneling through a thin insulating oxide layer at a metallic contact.)

33. Consider an electron in a hydrogenlike $2p$ orbital. What is the relative probability that it will be at $\theta = 90°$, $\theta = 45°$ (i.e., on the x-axis and 45° to it)?

34. On the basis of Russell-Saunders coupling, what can you say about the ground states of the helium atom, the carbon atom?

35. According to Stefan's law, the rate R of emission of radiant energy per unit area is given by $R = e\sigma T^4$ where T is the absolute temperature, e the emissivity of the body, and $\sigma = 5.672 \times 10^{-5}$ ergs sec^{-1} cm^{-2} deg^{-4}. The earth receives energy from the sun on a surface normal to the incoming rays at the rate of 1.94 cal/cm^2 min. What is the temperature of a black body which radiates energy at the same rate?

36. For the Bohr model of a hydrogen atom, calculate: (a) the velocity of the electron in the first orbit and the ratio of this velocity to the velocity of light; (b) the radial acceleration, $a_r = v^2/r$, of this electron and the ratio of this acceleration to that due to gravity; (c) the rate of radiation of electromagnetic energy, assuming the electron were to behave classically; (d) an approximate upper limit to the radiative lifetime of a "classical" hydrogen atom.

37. Consider an electron moving in a circular path around the lines of force in a magnetic field. Apply the Bohr quantum condition eq. (12.23) to this rotation. What is the radius of the orbit of quantum number $n = 1$ in a magnetic field of 10^5 gauss? [*Ans.* 81 Å]

38. The $K_{\alpha 1}$ X-ray line is emitted when an electron falls from an L level to a hole in the K level. Assume that the Rydberg formula holds for the energy levels in a complex atom, with an effective nuclear charge Z' equal to the atomic number minus the number of electrons in shells between the given electron and the nucleus. On this basis, estimate the wavelength of the $K_{\alpha 1}$ X-ray line in chromium. The experimental value is 2.285 Å. [*Ans.* 2.003 Å]

39. The wave function for the electron in the ground state of the hydrogen atom is $\psi_{1s} = (\pi a_0^3)^{-1/2} e^{-r/a_0}$, where a_0 is the radius of the Bohr orbit. Calculate the probability that an electron will be found somewhere between 0.9 and 1.1 a_0. What is the probability that the electron will be beyond 2 a_0? [*Ans.* 0.108, 0.238]

13 THE CHEMICAL BOND

Compare a concept with a style of painting. For is even our style of painting arbitrary? Can we choose one at pleasure? (The Egyptian, for instance). Is it a mere question of pleasing and ugly?

LUDWIG WITTGENSTEIN (1953)

The electrical discoveries at the beginning of the nineteenth century strongly influenced the concept of the chemical bond. Indeed, Berzelius proposed in 1812 that all chemical combinations were caused by electrostatic attractions. As it turned out 115 years later, this theory happened to be true, though not in the sense supposed by its originator. It did much to postpone the acceptance of diatomic structures for the common gaseous elements, such as H_2, N_2 and O_2. Most organic compounds also fitted poorly into the electrostatic scheme, but until 1828 it was widely believed that these were held together by *vital forces*, arising by virtue of their formation from living things. In that year, Wöhler's synthesis of urea from ammonium cyanate destroyed this distinction between organic and inorganic compounds, and the vital forces slowly retreated to their present refuge in living cells.

1. THE DEVELOPMENT OF VALENCE THEORY

Two classes of compounds came to be distinguished, with an assortment of uncomfortably intermediate specimens. The *polar* compounds, of which NaCl was a prime example, could be described as structures of positive and negative ions held together by coulombic attraction. The nature of the chemical bond in the *nonpolar* compounds, such as CH_4, was obscure. Nevertheless, the relations of valence with the periodic table, which were demonstrated by Mendeleyev, emphasized the remarkable fact that the valence of an element in a definitely polar compound was usually the same as that in a definitely nonpolar compound, e.g., O in K_2O and $(C_2H_5)_2O$.

In 1904, Abegg pointed out the *rule of eight:* To many elements in the periodic table he could assign a *negative valence* and a *positive valence* the sum of which was eight, for example, Cl in LiCl and Cl_2O_7, N in NH_3 and N_2O_5. Drude suggested that positive valence was the number of loosely bound electrons an atom could give away, and that negative valence was the number of electrons an atom could accept.

Once Moseley had clearly established the concept of atomic number (1913), further progress was possible, for then the number of electrons in an atom became known. The special stability of a complete outer octet of electrons was at once noted. For example: He, 2 electrons; Ne, $2 + 8$ electrons; A, $2 + 8 + 8$ electrons.

In 1916, W. Kossel made an important contribution to the theory of the electrovalent bond, and in the same year G. N. Lewis proposed a theory for the nonpolar bond. Kossel explained the formation of stable ions by a tendency of the atoms to gain or lose electrons until they achieved an inert-gas configuration. Thus argon has a completed octet of electrons. Potassium has $2 + 8 + 8 + 1$, and it tends to lose the outer electron, becoming the positively charged K^+ ion with the argon configuration. Chlorine has $2 + 8 + 7$ electrons and tends to gain an electron, becoming Cl^- with the argon configuration. If an atom of Cl approaches one of K, the K donates an electron to Cl, and the resulting ions combine as K^+Cl^-, the atoms displaying their valences of one. G. N. Lewis proposed that the links in nonpolar compounds resulted from the *sharing of pairs* of electrons between atoms in such a way as to form stable octets to the greatest possible extent. Thus carbon has an atomic number of 6, i.e., 6 electrons, or 4 less than the stable neon configuration. It can share electrons with hydrogen as follows:

$$\begin{array}{c} \mathrm{H} \\ {\scriptstyle \times\ \circ} \\ \mathrm{H} \,{\scriptstyle \overset{\times}{\circ}}\, \mathrm{C} \,{\scriptstyle \overset{\times}{\circ}}\, \mathrm{H} \\ {\scriptstyle \times\ \circ} \\ \mathrm{H} \end{array}$$

Each pair of shared electrons constitutes a single *covalent bond.* The Lewis theory explained why the covalence and electrovalence of an atom are usually identical, for an atom usually accepts one electron for each covalent bond that it forms.

2. THE IONIC BOND

The simplest type of molecular structure to understand is formed from two atoms, one of which is strongly electropositive (low ionization potential) and the other, strongly electronegative (high electron affinity), for example, sodium and chlorine. In crystalline sodium chloride, one should not speak of an NaCl molecule since the stable arrangement is a three-dimensional crystal structure of Na^+ and Cl^- ions. In the vapor, however, a true NaCl molecule exists, in which the binding is due mainly to the electrostatic attraction between an Na^+ and a Cl^- ion. Spectra of this molecule are observed in the vapor of sodium chloride.

The attractive force between two ions with charges Q_1 and Q_2 can be represented at moderate distances of separation by the coulombic force Q_1Q_2/r^2 or by a potential $U = -Q_1Q_2/r$. If the ions are brought so close together that their electron clouds begin to overlap, a mutual repulsion between the positively charged nuclei becomes evident. Born and Mayer suggested a repulsive potential having the form $U = be^{-r/a}$, where a and b are constants.

The net potential for two ions is therefore

$$U = \frac{-Q_1Q_2}{r} + be^{-r/a} \tag{13.1}$$

This function is plotted in Fig. 13.1 for NaCl; the minimum in the curve represents the stable internuclear separation for the molecule. Note, however, that at large separations Na + Cl is a more stable system than $Na^+ + Cl^-$, and thus we find that the molecule NaCl dissociates into atoms.

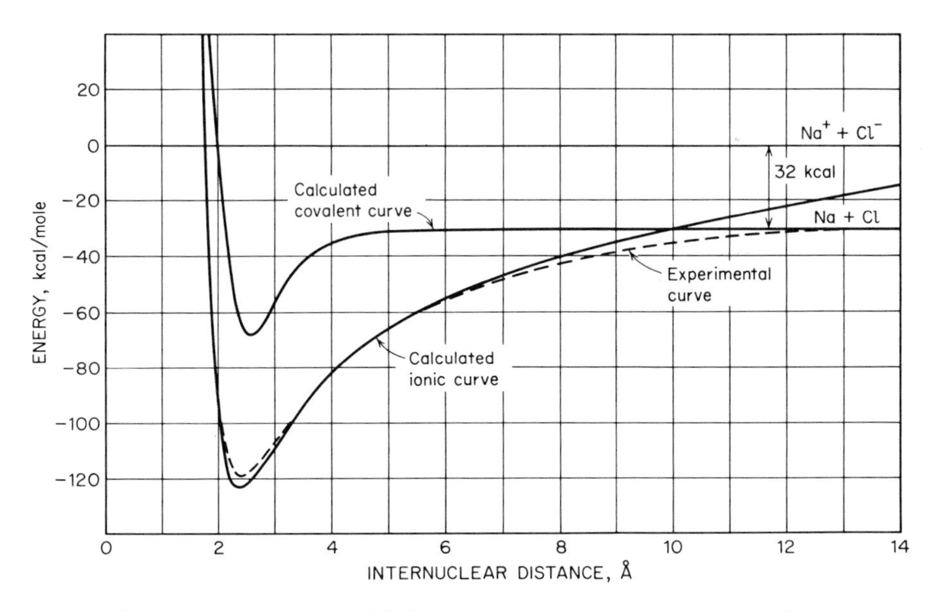

FIG. 13-1 Potential energy of NaCl as a function of internuclear separation. The ionic curve was calculated from Eq. (13.1).

3. THE COVALENT BOND

The most important application of quantum mechanics to chemistry has been its explanation of the nature of the covalent bond. The simplest example of such a bond is found in the H_2 molecule. Lewis, in 1918, declared that this bond consists of a shared pair of electrons. In 1927, W. Heitler and F. London applied the new quantum mechanics to give the first quantitative theory of the bond.

If two H atoms are brought together, the system consists of two positively charged protons and two negatively charged electrons. If the atoms are far apart their mutual interaction is effectively nil. In other words, the energy of interaction $U \to 0$ as the internuclear distance $r \to \infty$. At the other extreme, if the two atoms are forced closely together, there is a large repulsive force between the positive nuclei, so that as $r \to 0$, $U \to \infty$. Experimentally we know that two hydrogen atoms can unite to form a stable hydrogen molecule, whose dissociation energy is 109.5 kcal per mole. The equilibrium internuclear separation in the molecule is 0.740 Å.

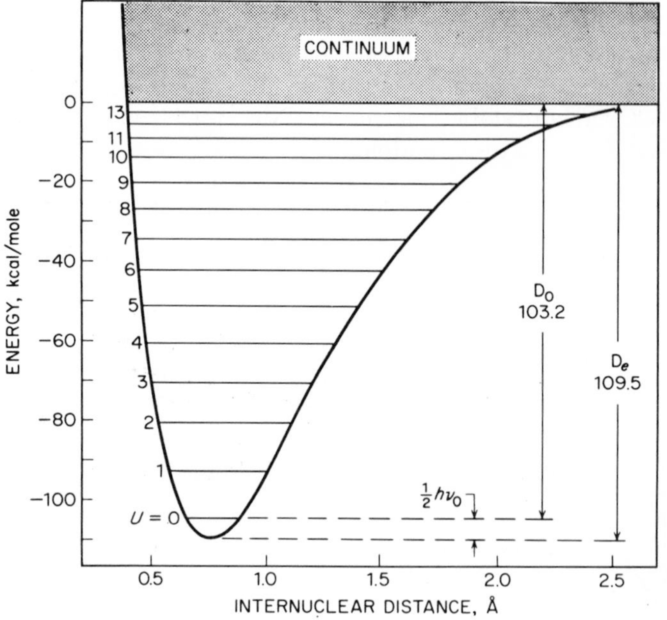

FIG. 13.2 Potential energy curve for hydrogen molecule. The vibrational energy levels are shown. [Note the shorter range of bonding in H_2 compared to ionic molecule NaCl in Fig. 13.1].

These facts about the interaction of two H atoms are summarized in the potential-energy curve* of Fig. 13.2. Our problem is to explain the minimum in the curve. This is another way of asking why a stable molecule is formed, or what is the essential nature of the covalent bond in H_2.

We can obtain an understanding of the chemical bond from the wave properties of electrons. Let us consider two H atoms A and B each with an electron in a $1s$ orbital. These orbitals were shown in Fig. 12.18. Along the line of centers between the two nuclei, the orbitals overlap. If both the orbitals are positive

* We call this a *potential-energy* curve, because the nuclei are stationary at each value of R for which the energy of the system is calculated. This energy is the sum of the *kinetic and potential* energies of the electrons and nuclei relative to a zero level which is that of the atoms at infinite separation.

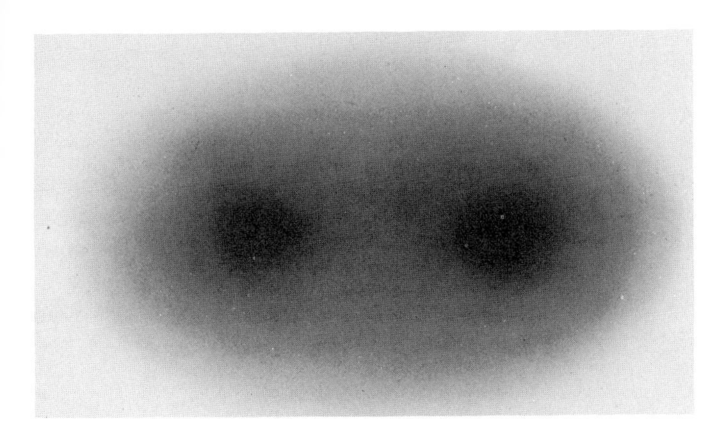

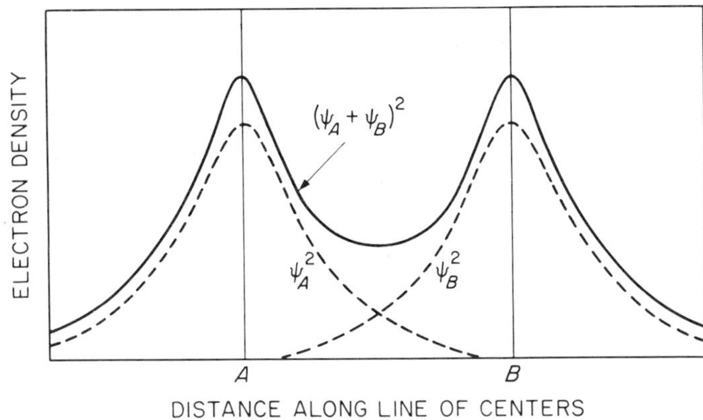

FIG. 13.3 Estimated electron densities along the line of centers between two hydrogen atoms.

in sign, the electron waves enhance each other by constructive interference and there is a region between the nuclei in which the probability of finding an electron is thereby increased. The probability of finding an electron in any region of space $d\tau$ is $\psi^2\, d\tau$. We must therefore square the amplitudes ψ to get a measure of the electron density. This behavior is typical of waves; it would not happen if the electrons behaved merely as particles. In Fig. 13.3 we have drawn ψ_A^2 and ψ_B^2 along the line of centers A—B, and also $(\psi_A + \psi_B)^2$ as it appears when the two H atoms are brought quite close to each other. The negative electron density builds up between and around the protons and is strongly attracted by their positive charges. The negative charge therefore *bonds together* the two protons, forming the bond, H—H.

In this way the wave properties of electrons lead to an interpretation of the nature of chemical bonding. A picture is shown in Fig. 13.3, in which the darkness of the shading is proportional to the electron density. The origin of the covalent bond is the extra electron density close to the positive nuclei due to the superposition of the electron waves. The bonding is primarily caused by the decrease in electrostatic potential energy as the two atoms are brought together. The mathematical calculation of the energy of the bond is quite difficult, but the underlying physical picture never changes.

4. QUANTUM MECHANICS OF H_2–MOLECULAR ORBITALS

The system of two protons and two electrons is shown in Fig. 13.4, with coordinates appropriately labeled. We notice at once that this system is quite similar to that for the helium atom, shown in Fig. 12.21. The difference is that we now have two nuclei with charges of +1 each, instead of one nucleus with charge +2. Thus, instead of the expression in Eq. (12.47), the potential energy becomes now (in atomic units):

$$U = r_{12}^{-1} - r_{1a}^{-1} - r_{2b}^{-1} - r_{1b}^{-1} - r_{2a}^{-1} + R^{-1} \tag{13.2}$$

The terms in the potential energy are the following:

$U_1 = r_{12}^{-1}$	electron (1) repels electron (2)
$U_2 = -r_{1a}^{-1}$	electron (1) attracts nucleus (a)
$U_3 = -r_{2b}^{-1}$	electron (2) attracts nucleus (b)
$U_4 = -r_{1b}^{-1}$	electron (1) attracts nucleus (b)
$U_5 = -r_{2a}^{-1}$	electron (2) attracts nucleus (a)
$U_6 = R^{-1}$	nucleus (a) repels nucleus (b)

In order to compare the theoretical energy with the experimental curve of Fig. 13.2, we must calculate the energy of the system for a number of different values of the internuclear distance R. The repulsion between the nuclei always contributes a term $U_6 = R^{-1}$. To calculate the energy of the electrons, we apply the variation method, just as we did in the case of the He atom. To begin the calculation, we must make some reasonable choice as to the form of the wave function for an electron in the molecule. A wave function for a single electron in an atom was called an *atomic orbital*. By analogy, a wave function for a single electron in a molecule is called a *molecular orbital*.

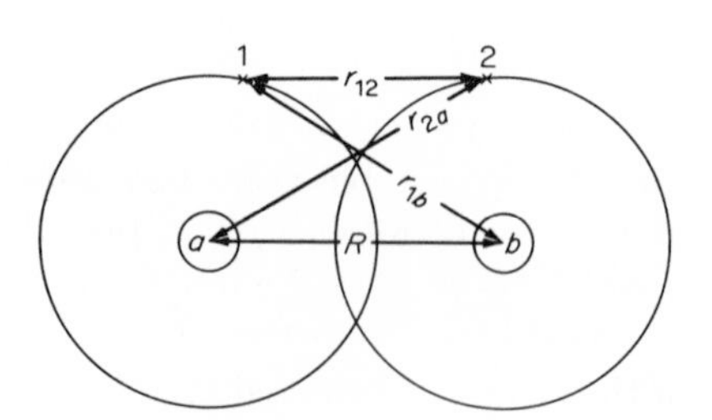

FIG. 13.4 Interaction of two hydrogen atoms.

What shall we take as the first order approximation for a molecular orbital in the H_2 molecule? If we pull the nuclei far apart, one electron will go with each nucleus, and the system can be represented as the sum of two H atoms. The molecular orbital accordingly would become the sum of two 1s atomic orbitals for H atoms, one centered on nucleus (a) and the other on nucleus (b).

$$\psi^{(1)} = 1s_a(1) + 1s_b(1) \tag{13.3}$$

We recall that in atomic units $1s_a = e^{-r_{1a}}$ and $1s_b = e^{-r_{2b}}$, hence $\psi^{(1)} = e^{-r_{1a}} + e^{-r_{1b}}$. Eq. (13.3) is an example of the formation of a molecular orbital as a linear combination of atomic orbitals. It is called an M.O.–L.C.A.O. approximation.

Our first trial wave function for the H_2 molecule can therefore be written as

$$\psi_{MO}^{(1)} = [1s_a(1) + 1s_b(1)][1s_a(2) + 1s_b(2)] \tag{13.4}$$

We have placed both the electrons into the same molecular orbital, which was formed as the sum of two $1s$ atomic orbitals. We can put two electrons into such an orbital, in accord with the Pauli Exclusion Principle, provided they have antiparallel spins.

In order to calculate the energy, we substitute $\psi^{(1)}$ from Eq. (13.4) into Eq. (12.48). We shall not go into the details of the calculation here; it involves several rather difficult integrations.* The calculated dissociation energy D_e ($H_2 \rightarrow 2H$) is 61.8 kcal and the calculated equilibrium internuclear distance r_e is 0.850 Å. The experimental values are 109.5 kcal and 0.740 Å. The quantitative agreement is therefore poor, but the fact that the calculation yields a very stable molecule indicates that our model must contain elements of truth.

The next step, as in the treatment of the He atom, is to introduce the scale factor. The molecular orbital then becomes

$$\psi^{(2)} = e^{-Zr_a} + e^{-Zr_b} \tag{13.5}$$

The lowest energy is found when $Z = 1.197$, and gives $D_e = 80$ kcal with $r_e = 0.732$ Å. In this case, unlike that of the He atom, the effective charge is greater than the charge on the individual nucleus. The electrons are thus squeezed into a smaller volume, closer to the nuclei, and their potential energy is lowered. True, the kinetic energy must be raised, but the total energy is still lowered by pulling the electrons closer to the nuclei. The resulting improvement in D_e, however, is rather disappointing. The source of the trouble is obvious. We have not included properly the effect of the interaction between the two electrons. In fact the M.O. of Eq. (13.5) places both electrons on the same nucleus for a considerable proportion of the time, and thus greatly enhances the interelectronic repulsion energy.

One way to write a wave function that keeps electrons away from each other is to include what is called a *configuration interaction*. The M.O. of Eq. (13.5) is an L.C.A.O. formed entirely of $1s$ orbitals of atomic hydrogen. If we include terms from $2s$ and other higher states, we give the electrons some additional place to go to get out of each other's way. This treatment at best improves D_e to 92.3 kcal.

So far we have avoided any wave functions that include explicitly the interelectronic distance r_{12}. Even the most complicated functions, if they neglect this factor, will not yield a value of D_e greater than 98 kcal, about 10 per cent below the experimental value. Once we include such r_{12} terms, however, the energy again begins to improve. James and Coolidge devised a very complicated function of the form

$$\psi = e^{-\delta(\mu_1+\mu_2)} \sum_{m,n,j,k,p} C_{mnjkp}[\mu_1^m \mu_2^n \nu_1^j \nu_2^k + \mu_1^n \mu_2^m \nu_1^k \nu_2^j] r_{12}^p \tag{13.6}$$

The exponents m, n, j, k, p are integers and $\delta = 0.75$. The C_{mnjkp} are variable

* C. A. Coulson, *Trans. Faraday Soc.*, *33*, 1479 (1937).

parameters. They finally tried an expression with 13 terms, including 5 terms in r_{12}. They calculated $D_e = 108.8$ kcal, which is within 0.7 kcal of the experimental value. Kolos and Roothaan* extended the calculation to 50 terms, obtaining $D_e = 109.426$ kcal and $r_e = .741$. Fig. 13.5 shows how the electrons tend to avoid each other in the wave functions used by these workers.

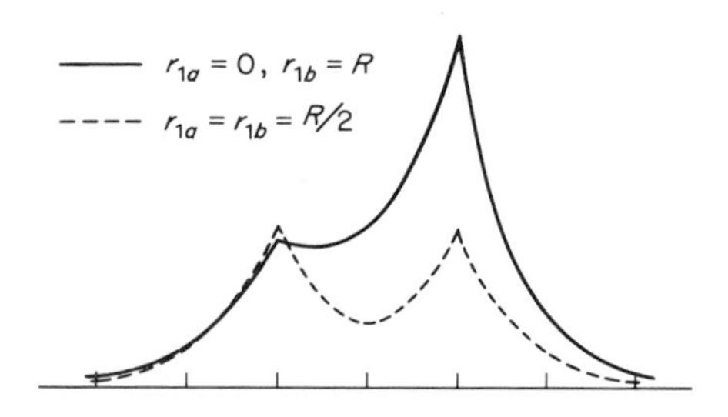

FIG. 13.5 Probability density of the second electron along the axis for two fixed locations of the first electron.

A wave function like that of Kolos and Roothaan must represent a spacial distribution of electronic charge practically identical with that which actually occurs in the H_2 molecule. Yet the function is so complicated that we cannot hope to obtain any simple physical interpretation of its terms. *Simple physical pictures of the covalent bond are possible only at the level of simple approximate wave functions.* The cause of the bonding is clear — the electron density builds up around two nuclei and the resultant electrostatic potential energy stabilizes the system — but the bond itself as a simple conceptual model has disappeared into the impenetrable complexity of the wave function.

5. THE VALENCE-BOND METHOD

The procedure used by Heitler and London to calculate the energy of the H_2 molecule was different from the molecular-orbital method just outlined. It was the first example of what is now called the *valence-bond method* in molecular quantum mechanics. The method is closely related to the classical structure theory of organic chemistry, which considers molecules to be constructed of *atoms* held together by *chemical bonds*. More precisely, the atoms contribute some of their outer or valence electrons to form bonds with other atoms, so that the molecule consists of atomic cores [atoms which may have provided valence electrons] and bonds between these cores. In the case of the H_2 molecules, each atom provides one valence electron, and the cores are simply the protons.

The approximate wave function chosen by Heitler and London was

$$\psi_{VB}^{(1)} = 1s_a(1)1s_b(2) + 1s_a(2)1s_b(1) \tag{13.7}$$

The argument by which they arrived at this choice is very interesting. They started by considering two H atoms, each with its own electron. The wave function that places electron 1 on nucleus a and electron 2 on nucleus b is then the product

$$\phi_1 = 1s_a(1)1s_b(2)$$

They then pointed out that the electrons are indistinguishable particles and therefore when the atoms are close together, the wave function must express this

* *Rev. Mod. Phys.*, *32*, 226 (1960).

fact. There are two simple wave functions of this type:

$$\begin{aligned} \psi_s &= 1s_a(1)1s_b(2) + 1s_a(2)1s_b(1) = \phi_1 + \phi_2 \\ \psi_a &= 1s_a(1)1s_b(2) - 1s_a(2)1s_b(1) = \phi_1 - \phi_2 \end{aligned} \tag{13.8}$$

The function ψ_s, called *symmetric* in the coordinates of the electrons, does not change if the indices (1) and (2) are interchanged. The function ψ_a, called *antisymmetric* in the coordinates of the electrons, changes to $-\psi_a$ if we interchange (1) and (2). Since the electron density depends on ψ^2 the change from ψ_a to $-\psi_a$ does not affect the electron distribution.

If we introduce the wave functions in Eq. (13.8) into the formula for the variation method, Eq. (12.48), we obtain

$$E = \frac{\int (\phi_1 \pm \phi_2) H (\phi_1 \pm \phi_2)\, d\tau}{\int (\phi_1 \pm \phi_2)^2\, d\tau} \tag{13.9}$$

6. THE EFFECT OF ELECTRON SPINS

So far we have not included the spin properties of the electrons, which we must do in order to obtain a correct wave function. The electron-spin quantum number s, with allowed values of either $+\frac{1}{2}$ or $-\frac{1}{2}$, determines the magnitude and orientation of the spin. We introduce two spin functions α and β corresponding to $s = +\frac{1}{2}$ and $s = -\frac{1}{2}$. For the two-electron system there are then four possible complete spin functions:

Spin Function	*Electron 1*	*Electron 2*
$\alpha(1)\alpha(2)$	$+\frac{1}{2}$	$+\frac{1}{2}$
$\alpha(1)\beta(2)$	$+\frac{1}{2}$	$-\frac{1}{2}$
$\beta(1)\alpha(2)$	$-\frac{1}{2}$	$+\frac{1}{2}$
$\beta(1)\beta(2)$	$-\frac{1}{2}$	$-\frac{1}{2}$

When the spins have the same direction they are said to be *parallel*; when they have opposite directions, *antiparallel*.

Once again, however, the fact that the electrons are indistinguishable, forces us to choose either symmetric or antisymmetric linear combinations for the two-electron system. There are three possible symmetric spin functions:

$$\left.\begin{aligned} \alpha(1)\alpha(2) \\ \beta(1)\beta(2) \\ \alpha(1)\beta(2) + \alpha(2)\beta(1) \end{aligned}\right\} \text{symmetric}$$

There is one antisymmetric spin function:

$$\alpha(1)\beta(2) - \alpha(2)\beta(1) \quad \text{antisymmetric}$$

The possible complete wave functions for the H—H system are obtained by combining these four possible spin functions with the two possible orbital wave functions. This leads to eight functions in all.

At this point in the argument the Pauli Exclusion Principle enters in an important way. "Every allowable wave function for a system of two or more electrons must be antisymmetric for the simultaneous interchange of the position and spin coordinates of any pair of electrons.'' As a consequence, the only allowable wave functions are those made up either of symmetric orbitals and antisymmetric spins or of antisymmetric orbitals and symmetric spins. There are four such combinations for the H—H system:

Orbital	*Spin*	*Total Spin*	*Term*
$a(1)b(2) + a(2)b(1)$	$\alpha(1)\beta(2) - \alpha(2)\beta(1)$	0 (singlet)	$^1\Sigma$
$a(1)b(2) - a(2)b(1)$	$\begin{cases}\alpha(1)\alpha(2)\\ \beta(1)\beta(2)\\ \alpha(1)\beta(2) + \alpha(2)\beta(1)\end{cases}$	1 (triplet)	$^3\Sigma$

The term symbol Σ expresses the fact that the molecular state has an angular momentum of zero about the internuclear axis, since it is made up of two atomic S terms. The multiplicity of the term, or number of wave functions corresponding with it, is added as a left-hand superscript. This multiplicity is always $2S + 1$ where S is the total spin.*

7. RESULTS OF THE HEITLER-LONDON METHOD

When we calculate the energy from Eq. (13.9) and the valence-bond wave functions of Eq. (13.8), we find that the function $\phi_1 + \phi_2$ (i.e., the $^1\Sigma$) leads to a deep minimum in the potential-energy curve, but the function $\phi_1 - \phi_2$ (i.e., the $^3\Sigma$) leads to repulsion at all values of R. The results are shown in Fig. 13.6 together with the experimental curve.

The covalent bond is formed between atoms that share a pair of electrons with opposite spins. Only when the spins are antiparallel can the two electron waves reinforce each other in the region between the nuclei so as to cause an attractive interaction. If the spins are parallel, there is a destructive interference between the electron waves in the region between the two protons. Then little electron cement remains to hold together the protons, and there is a strong net repulsion between the relatively bare positive charges. It is interesting to note that if two H atoms are brought together, there is only one chance in four that they will attract each other, since the stable state is a singlet and the repulsive state is a triplet.

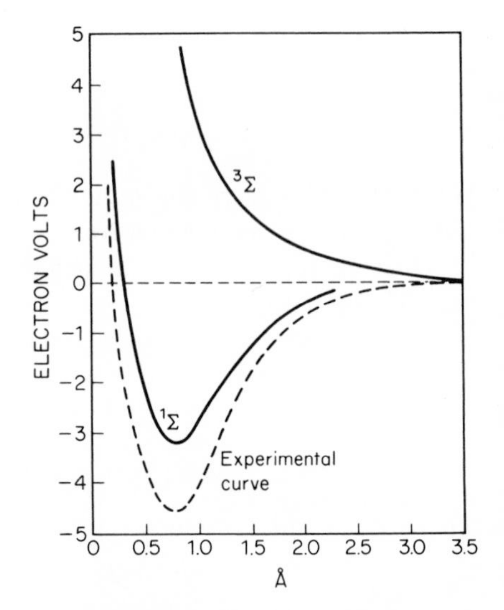

FIG. 13.6 Heitler-London treatment of the H_2 molecule.

* Note that S denotes total spin and also denotes an atomic state with $L = 0$. There is little reason to confuse these two usages.

The calculated binding energy is 72.5 kcal and the calculated r_e is 0.80 Å. This result is actually a little better than the result from the simple molecular orbital approach. The reason is that the valence-bond wave function does not give so much weight to configurations which place both electrons on the same nucleus. Unfortunately, the physical picture of the simple Heitler-London theory is not correct. It results in a binding energy which is mostly due to the greater space available for the electrons and hence to a lowering of the *kinetic energy* of the system. As we saw before, the bond is really due, however, to a lowered electrostatic *potential energy*.

The next step is therefore to apply the scale factor to the Heitler-London functions, by using the modified atomic orbitals, $e^{-Z' r_a}$. With $Z' = 1.166$ the electron distribution is pulled in more closely. The kinetic energy rises, but the potential energy falls more drastically. The calculated bonding energy is then 86.8 kcal at $r_e = 0.743$ Å. As with the molecular orbital method, further improvements require among other things the introduction of terms for the electron correlation.

8. COMPARISON OF M. O. AND V. B. METHODS

The molecular-orbital and the valence-bond methods are the two basic approaches to the quantum theory of molecules. How do they compare?

The V. B. treatment starts with individual atoms and considers the interaction between them. Consider two atoms a and b with two electrons (1) and (2). A possible wave function is $\psi_1 = a(1)b(2)$. Equally possible is $\psi_2 = a(2)b(1)$, since the electrons are indistinguishable. Then the valence-bond wave function is

$$\psi_{VB} = a(1)b(2) + a(2)b(1)$$

The M. O. treatment of the molecule starts with the two nuclei. If $a(1)$ is a wave function for electron (1) on nucleus (a), and $b(1)$ is a wave function for electron (1) on nucleus (b), the wave function for the single electron moving in the field of the two nuclei can be written as an L. C. A. O., $\psi_1 = c_1a(1) + c_2b(1)$. Similarly for the second electron, $\psi_2 = c_1a(2) + c_2b(2)$. The combined wave function is the product of these two, or

$$\psi_{MO} = \psi_1\psi_2 = c_1^2a(1)a(2) + c_2^2b(1)b(2) + c_1c_2[a(1)b(2) + a(2)b(1)]$$

Comparing the ψ_{VB} with the ψ_{MO}, we see that ψ_{MO} gives a large weight to configurations that place both electrons on one nucleus. In a molecule AB, these are the ionic structures A^+B^- and A^-B^+. The ψ_{VB} neglects these ionic terms. Actually, for most molecules, the simple M. O. considerably overestimates the ionic terms, whereas the simple V. B. considerably underestimates them. The true structure is usually some compromise between these two extremes, but the mathematical treatment of such a compromise is more difficult. It is necessary to add further terms to the expressions for the wave functions, for instance, ionic terms to the V. B. function.

9. CHEMISTRY AND MECHANICS

"The underlying physical laws necessary for the mathematical theory of a large part of physics and the whole of chemistry are thus completely known, and the difficulty is only that the exact application of these laws leads to equations much too complicated to be soluble." This much quoted statement was written by Dirac in 1929, about three years after the discovery of quantum mechanics, but it remains just as true and exasperating today. Despite the development of high speed computers, which can perform in a few minutes what used to be a year's computation, "it looks as if somewhere around 20 electrons there is an upper limit to the size of a molecule for which accurate calculations are ever likely to become practicable."*

The nature of the problem may be illustrated by considering the iron atom. It has 26 electrons. If we were to tabulate the values of the wave functions for the ground state with sufficiently small intervals for all the coordinates of the electrons, we should need a whole library to house the books in which they were printed. Thus the conclusion that "Chemical questions are problems in applied mathematics,"† seems a little premature.

We can hope to obtain exact information from quantum mechanical calculations about electron distributions in light atoms and molecules. Such information should give us a much deeper understanding of the nature of the factors responsible for molecular structures. We can then try to translate this quantum mechanical information into concepts such as the nature of chemical bonds, electronegativities, classes of excited states, and so on, which can help us to interpret the chemical behavior of more complex molecules.

Einstein once wrote that "*Being* is always something which is mentally constructed by us. The nature of such constructs does not lie in their derivation from what is given by the senses. Such a type of derivation is nowhere to be had. The justification of these constructs, which represent 'reality' for us, lies above all in the quality of making intelligible what is sensually given." The *chemical bond* is a good example of a specifically *chemical construct* which makes intelligible the results of chemical experimentation and makes possible the design of new chemical experiments. For a chemist engaged in working out a synthesis of chlorophyll, we can be sure that the chemical bond will be more "real" than the James and Coolidge wave function for H_2.

Out of the undifferentiated continuum of experience man crystallizes certain entities. Whether he creates them or discovers them is a paradoxical question. Does nature imitate art or art depict nature? The elementary individual entity is always incompatible in some sense with the continuous field from which it was

* C. A. Coulson, "Present State of Molecular Structure Calculations," *Rev. Mod. Phys.*, *32*, 170 (1960). "Ever," however, is a long time, and other experts would not agree with Coulson on this point.

† H. Eyring, J. Walter, G. Kimball, *Quantum Chemistry*, (New York: Wiley, 1944), p. iii.

drawn. Kant expressed this with regard to the atom by saying that the notion of an indivisible atom and the intuition of space are incompatible. Weizsäcker* expressed it by saying that chemistry and mechanics are *complementary*. If we push the mechanics as far as we can, the chemistry disappears. If we push the chemistry to its far reaches, the mechanics disappears. In exemplary terms, the James and Coolidge calculation of the H_2 structure is mechanics without chemistry, the synthesis of chlorophyll or the elucidation of the structure of insulin is chemistry without mechanics. To say "chemistry is applied mathematics" is something like saying "poetry is applied music."

We departed from the historical development of the chemical bond to give a quantum mechanical analysis of chemical bonding. As a result we found our chemical bond had disappeared. The purpose of this philosophic digression was to bring it back again to "reality."†

10. NOTATION FOR THE MOLECULAR ORBITALS

The V. B. method was based on the chemical concept that, in some sense, atoms exist within molecules, and that the structure of a molecule can be interpreted in terms of its constituent atoms and the *bonds* between them. The M. O. method would like to discard the idea of atoms within molecules, and to start with the bare positive nuclei arrayed in definite positions in space. The total number of electrons would be fed one by one into this electrostatic field. The M. O. theory is more physical than chemical in its view of a molecular structure, which it sees not as atoms connected by bonds, but as an electronic pudding of varying density, interspersed with some positive nuclear plums.

Just as the electrons in an atom have definite atomic orbitals characterized by quantum numbers, n, l, m, and occupy the lowest levels consistent with the Pauli Principle, so the electrons in a molecule have definite *molecular orbitals* and quantum numbers, and only two electrons having opposite spins can occupy any particular molecular orbital. For diatomic molecules, the molecular quantum numbers include a principal quantum number n, with $n - 1$ equal to the number of nodes in the wave function, and a quantum number λ, which gives the component of angular momentum in the direction of the internuclear axis. This λ takes the place of the atomic quantum number m which gave the component of angular momentum along the Z axis. We have states designated σ, π, δ, . . . as $\lambda = 0, 1, 2, \ldots$.

We shall consider now the *molecular orbitals of the hydrogen molecule.* If H_2 is pulled apart, it separates into two hydrogen atoms, H_a and H_b, each with a single 1s atomic orbital. If the process is reversed and the hydrogen atoms are squeezed together, these atomic orbitals coalesce into the molecular orbital

* C. F. Weizsäcker, *The World View of Physics*,(Chicago: U. Chicago Press, 1952.)

† It is only fair to add that it would be difficult to find a scientist who would accept all the statements in this section, and not too easy to find one who would accept any of them.

occupied by the electrons in H_2. We therefore adopt the principle that the molecular orbital can be constructed from a linear combination of atomic orbitals (L. C. A. O.). Thus

$$\psi = c_1(1s_a) + c_2(1s_b) \tag{13.10}$$

Since the molecules are completely symmetrical, c_1 must be $\pm c_2$. Then there are two possible molecular orbitals,

$$\begin{aligned} \psi_g &= 1s_a + 1s_b \\ \psi_u &= 1s_a - 1s_b \end{aligned} \tag{13.11}$$

The subscript g (*gerade*, even) means that the orbital does not change sign on inversion through the *center of symmetry* at the midpoint between the two nuclei. The subscript u (*ungerade*, uneven) means that it does change sign under this operation.

These molecular orbitals are given a pictorial representation in Fig. 13.7 (a). The $1s$ A. O.'s are spherically symmetrical (see p. 494). If two of these A. O.'s are brought together until they overlap, the resulting M. O.'s can be represented as shown. The additive one, ψ_g, leads to a building up of electronic charge density between the nuclei. The subtractive one, ψ_u, makes a space relatively free of charge between the nuclei. Both these M. O.'s are completely symmetrical about the *internuclear axis*; the angular momentum about the axis is zero, $\lambda = 0$, and they are called *σ orbitals*. The first one is designated as a $1s\sigma_g$ orbital. It is called a *bonding orbital*, because the concentration of charge between the nuclei bonds them together. The second one is written as $1s\sigma_u$, and it is called an *antibonding orbital*, corresponding to a net repulsion, since there is no shielding between the positively charged nuclei.

11. ORBITALS FOR HOMONUCLEAR DIATOMIC MOLECULES

The homonuclear diatomic molecules contain two identical nuclei, as in H_2, Li_2, N_2 or O_2. Although the molecular orbitals we have described are those for H_2, we can use the same description for the other homonuclear diatomic molecules. In a similar way, when we discussed the electronic structures of the heavier atoms, we used the atomic orbitals derived from the exact treatment of the hydrogen atom. In the series of homonuclear diatomic molecules, an increase in nuclear charge will tend to lower the equilibrium distance R.

The building-up principle for the molecules is now exactly like that for atoms. We imagine the nuclei to be fixed and feed the electrons one by one into the available molecular orbitals of lowest energy. The Pauli Exclusion Principle requires that only two electrons with antiparallel spins can be placed in any orbital.

In the case of H_2, the two electrons enter the $1s\sigma_g$ orbital. The configuration is $(1s\sigma_g)^2$ and corresponds to a single electron pair bond between the H atoms.

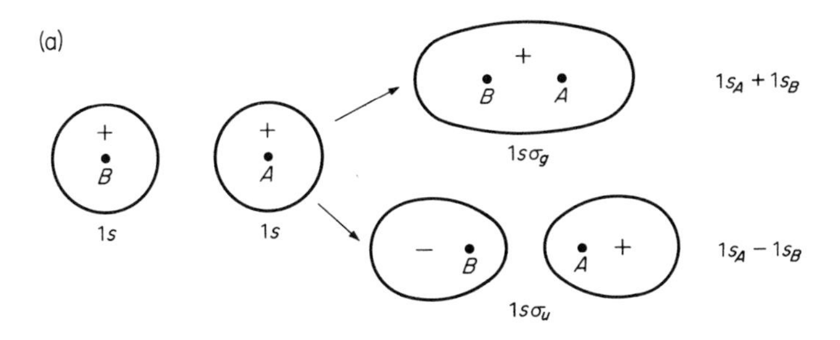

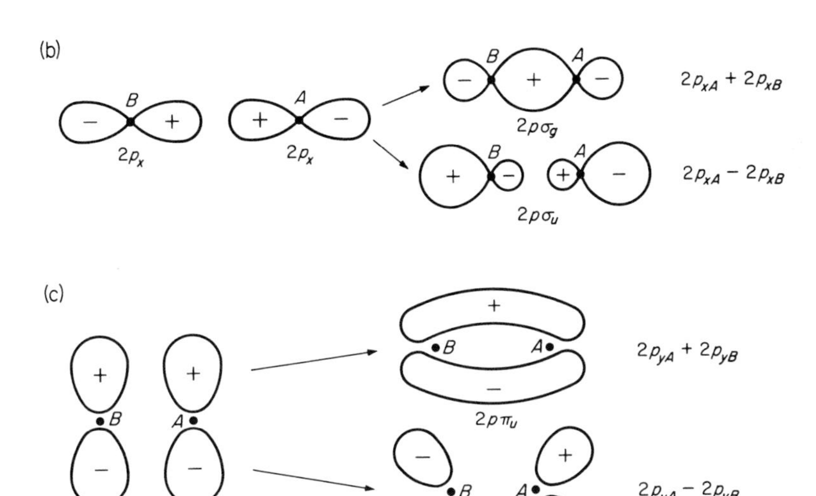

FIG. 13.7 Formation of molecular orbitals by linear combinations of atomic orbitals.

The next possible molecule would be one with three electrons, He_2^+. This has the configuration $(1s\sigma_g)^2(1s\sigma_u)^1$. There are two bonding electrons and one antibonding electron, so that a net bonding is to be expected. The molecule has, in fact, been observed spectroscopically; it has a dissociation energy of 3.0 ev.

If two helium atoms are brought together, the result is $(1s\sigma_g)^2(1s\sigma_u)^2$. Since there are two bonding and two antibonding electrons, there is no tendency to form a stable He_2 molecule.

The next possible A. O.'s are the $2s$, and these behave just like the $1s$ providing $2s\sigma_g$ and $2s\sigma_u$ M. O.'s with accommodations for four more electrons. If we bring together two lithium atoms with three electrons each, the molecule Li_2 is formed. Thus

$$Li[1s^2 2s^1] + Li[1s^2 2s^1] \longrightarrow Li_2[(1s\sigma_g)^2(1s\sigma_u)^2(2s\sigma_g)^2]$$

Actually, only the outer-shell or valence electrons need be considered, and the M. O.'s of inner K-shell electrons need not be explicitly designated. The Li_2 configuration is therefore written as $[KK(2s\sigma_g)^2]$. The molecule has a dissociation energy of 1.14 ev. The hypothetical molecule Be_2, with eight electrons, does not occur, since the configuration would be $[KK(2s\sigma_g)^2(2s\sigma_u)^2]$ with no net bonding electrons.

The next atomic orbitals are the $2p$'s shown in Fig. 13.7. There are three of these, p_x, p_y, p_z, mutually perpendicular and with characteristic wasp-waisted figures. The most stable M. O. that can be formed from the atomic p orbitals is one with the maximum overlap along the internuclear axis. This M. O. is shown in Fig. 13.7 (b). This bonding orbital and the corresponding antibonding orbital can be written,

$$\psi_g = \psi_a(2p_x) + \psi_b(2p_x) \qquad 2p\sigma_g$$

$$\psi_u = \psi_a(2p_x) - \psi_b(2p_x) \qquad 2p\sigma_u$$

These orbitals have the same symmetry around the internuclear axis as the σ orbitals formed from atomic s orbitals; thus they also have zero angular momentum about the axis, so that $\lambda = 0$ and they are σ orbitals.

The M. O.'s formed from the p_y and p_z A. O.'s have a distinctly different form, as shown in Fig. 13.7 (c). As the nuclei are brought together, the sides of the p_y or p_z orbitals coalesce, and lead to two streamers of charge density, one above and one below the internuclear axis. These orbitals have an angular momentum of one unit, so that $\lambda = 1$ and they are called π orbitals.

We can summarize the available M. O.'s as follows, in order of increasing energy:

$$1s\sigma_g < 1s\sigma_u < 2s\sigma_g < 2s\sigma_u < 2p\sigma_g < 2p_y\pi_u = 2p_z\pi_u < 2p_y\pi_g = 2p_z\pi_g < 2p\sigma_u$$

We can obtain a good understanding of the relative energy levels of these orbitals by means of the model of the *united atom*. We imagine that we start with two H atoms both in a given quantum state ($1s$, for example) and squeeze them gradually together until they coalesce to form the united atom of helium. In this way, we can correlate the initial atomic orbitals in the hydrogen atoms with the final atomic orbitals in the helium atom. The molecular orbitals of the H_2 molecule will lie somewhere on the line joining these two extremes, at the correct internuclear distance for H_2.

Such a *correlation diagram* is shown in Fig. 13.8. We can usually see how the orbitals of the isolated atoms must correlate with those of the united atom by looking at the symmetry properties of the orbitals. Examples are shown in Fig. 13.8. The lines for orbitals of the same symmetry cannot cross on the correlation diagram; thus a σ_g can never cross a σ_g, etc. (*non-crossing rule*).

We can tell whether a molecular orbital is bonding or antibonding by examining the correlation diagram to see whether the energy rises or falls as the atoms are brought together to form this orbital. In the diagram of Fig. 13.8, the following are bonding orbitals: $1s\sigma_g$, $2s\sigma_g$, $2p\sigma_g$, $2p\pi_u$, $3s\sigma_g$, $3p\sigma_g$, $3p\pi_u$, $3d\sigma_g$, $3d\pi_u$, $3d\sigma_g$.

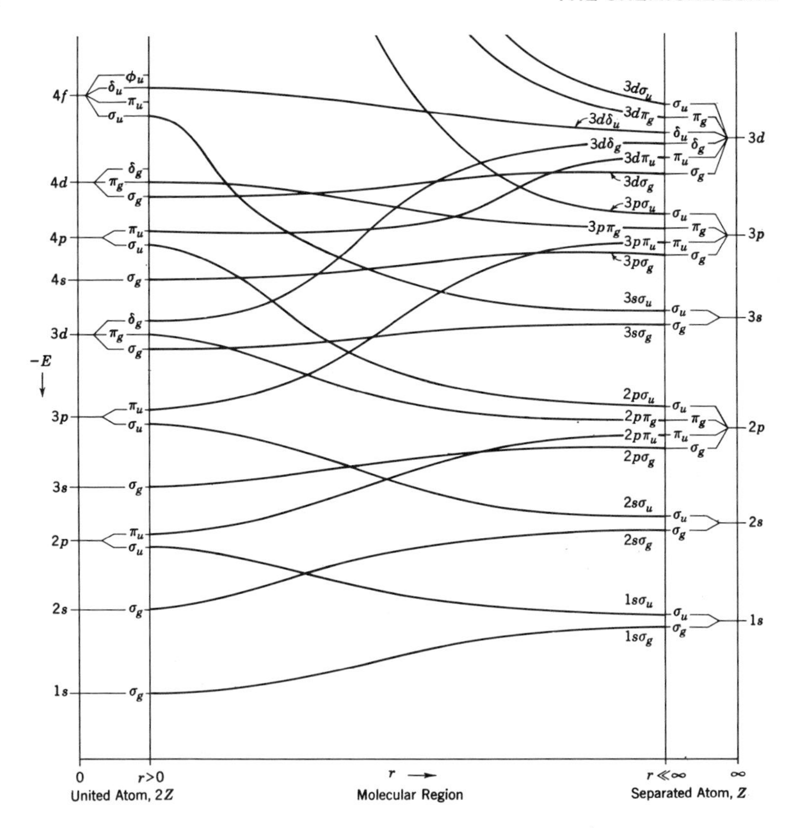

FIG. 13.8 Correlation diagram to show how molecular orbitals are formed from atomic orbitals of separated atoms and correlate with atomic orbitals of the united atom formed as nuclei come together [M. Kasha, *Molecular Electronic Structure*, to be published].

With the good supply of M. O.'s now available, the configurations of other homonuclear diatomic molecules can be determined, by feeding pairs of electrons with opposite spins into the orbitals.

The formation of N_2 proceeds as follows:

$$N[1s^2 2s^2 2p^3] + N[1s^2 2s^2 2p^3] \longrightarrow N_2[KK(2s\sigma_g)^2(2s\sigma_u)^2(2p\sigma_g)^2(2p\pi_u)^4]$$

Since there are six net bonding electrons, it can be said that there is a triple bond between the two N's. One of these bonds is a σ bond; the other two are π bonds at right angles to each other. (It is also possible, however, to form three identical *equivalent bond orbitals* which can be considered to have a mixture of σ and π characters.)

Molecular oxygen is an interesting case:

$$O[1s^2 2s^2 2p^4] + O[1s^2 2s^2 2p^4] \longrightarrow O_2[KK(2s\sigma_g)^2(2s\sigma_u)^2(2p\sigma_g)^2(2p\pi_u)^4(2p\pi_g)^2]$$

There are four net bonding electrons, or a double bond consisting of a σ and a π bond. A single bond is usually a σ bond, but a double bond is not formed from two σ bonds, but from a σ plus a π. In O_2, the $2p\pi_g$ orbital, which can hold 4 electrons, is only half filled. Because of electrostatic repulsion between the electrons, the most stable state will be that in which the electrons occupy separate orbitals and have parallel spins. Thus the two electrons are assigned as $(2p_y\pi_g)^1(2p_z\pi_g)^1$. The total spin of O_2 is therefore $S = 1$, and its multiplicity, $2S + 1 = 3$. The ground state of oxygen is $^3\Sigma$. Because of its unpaired electron spins, O_2 is paramagnetic (Sec. 14.10).

In the M. O. method, all the electrons outside closed shells make a contribution to the binding energy of the molecule. The shared electron pair bond is not particularly emphasized. The way in which the excess of bonding over antibonding electrons determines the tightness of binding may be seen by reference to the molecules in Table 13.1.

TABLE 13.1 PROPERTIES OF HOMONUCLEAR DIATOMIC MOLECULES

Molecule	Binding Energy (kcal/mole)	Internuclear Separation (Å)	Vibration Frequency (sec^{-1})	Bonding − Antibonding Electrons
B_2	83	1.59	3.15×10^{13}	2
C_2	127	1.31	4.92×10^{13}	4
N_2	170	1.09	7.08×10^{13}	6
O_2	118	1.20	4.74×10^{13}	4
F_2	69	1.30	3.40×10^{13}	2

12. HETERONUCLEAR DIATOMIC MOLECULES

If the two nuclei in a diatomic molecule are different, it is still possible to build up molecular orbitals by L. C. A. O., but now the symmetry of the homonuclear case is lost. Consider, for example, the molecule HCl. The bond between the atoms is caused mainly by electrons in an M. O. formed from the 1*s* A. O. of H and a 3*p* A. O. of Cl.

The M. O. can be written as

$$\psi = c_1(1s_H) + c_2(3p_{Cl})$$

Now c_1 is no longer $\pm c_2$; the chlorine has a greater tendency than the hydrogen to hold electrons, and the resulting M. O. partakes more of the chlorine A. O. than of the hydrogen A. O. The larger the ratio c_2/c_1, the more unsymmetrical is the orbital, and the more polar is the bond. Thus in the series HI, HBr, HCl, HF, the value of c_2/c_1 increases as the halogen becomes more electronegative.

13. DIRECTED VALENCE

In the case of polyatomic molecules, a rigorous M. O. treatment would simply set up the nuclei in their equilibrium positions and pour in the electrons. It is, however, desirable to preserve the idea of definite chemical bonds, and to do this we utilize *bond orbitals*, or *localized molecular orbitals*.

For example, in the water molecule, the A. O.'s that take part in bond formation are the 1*s* orbitals of hydrogen, and the $2p_x$ and $2p_y$ of oxygen. The stable structure will be that in which there is maximum overlap of these orbitals. Since p_x and p_y are at right angles to each other, the situation in Fig. 13.9 is obtained. The observed valence angle in H_2O is not exactly 90° but actually 105°. The difference can be ascribed in part* to the polar nature of the bond; the electrons are drawn toward the oxygen, and the residual positive charge on the hydrogens causes their mutual repulsion. In H_2S the bond is less polar and the angle is 92°. The important point is the straightforward fashion in which the directed valence is explained in terms of the shapes of the atomic orbitals.

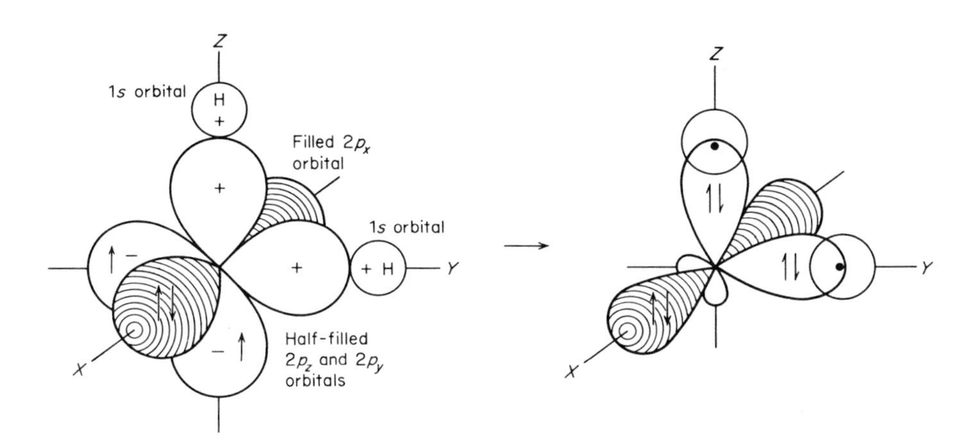

FIG. 13.9 Formation of a molecular orbital for H_2O by overlap of 2*p* orbitals of oxygen and 1*s* orbitals of hydrogen.

We see an example of directed valence in the tetrahedral orientation of the bonds formed by carbon in aliphatic compounds. To explain these bonds, we need to introduce a new principle, the formation of *hybrid orbitals*. The ground state of the carbon atom is $1s^22s^22p^2$. There are two uncoupled electrons $2p_x$, $2p_y$, and we should therefore expect the carbon to be bivalent. In order to display a valence of four, the carbon atom must have four electrons with uncoupled spins. The simplest way to obtain this condition is to *excite* or *promote* one of the 2*s* electrons into the 2*p* state, and to have all the resulting 2*p* electrons with uncoupled spins. Then the outer configuration would be $2s2p^3$, with $2s^12p_x^12p_y^12p_z^1$. This excitation requires an energy investment of about 65 kcal per mole, but the extra binding energy of the four bonds which are formed more than compensates for the promotion energy, and carbon is normally quadrivalent rather than bivalent.

* A more detailed theory shows that the 2*s* electrons of the oxygen also take part in the bonding, forming hybrid orbitals like those discussed below for carbon.

TABLE 13.2 TYPES OF HYBRIDIZATION OF s AND p ORBITALS
[R. Daudel, R. Lefebvre, C. Moser, *Quantum Chemistry* (New York: Interscience, 1959]

Tetrahedral Hybridization

(Four hybrids, t_1, t_2, t_3 and t_4 pointing toward the vertices of a regular tetrahedron centered at the origin of the coordinates; the first hybrid points along the axis of the triad of x, y, z.)

$$t_1 = (1/2)(s + p_x + p_y + p_z)$$
$$t_2 = (1/2)(s + p_x - p_y - p_z)$$
$$t_3 = (1/2)(s - p_x + p_y - p_z)$$
$$t_4 = (1/2)(s - p_x - p_y + p_z)$$

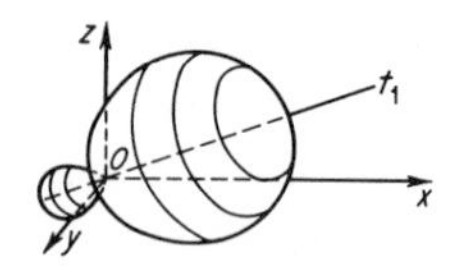

Polar representation of tetrahedral hybridization.

Trigonal Hybridization

(Three hybrids, T_1, T_2 and T_3 pointing along the xy plane; the first points along the x-axis, the other two along the directions forming an angle of 120° with the x-axis.)

$$T_1 = (1/\sqrt{3})s + (\sqrt{2}/\sqrt{3})p_x$$
$$T_2 = (1/\sqrt{3})s - (1/\sqrt{6})p_x + (1/\sqrt{2})p_y$$
$$T_3 = (1/\sqrt{3})s - (1/\sqrt{6})p_x - (1/\sqrt{2})p_y$$

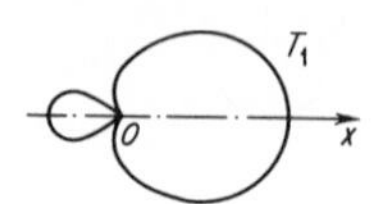

Polar representation of trigonal hybridization.

Digonal Hybridization

(Two hybrids, D_1 and D_2, pointing along the z-axis in opposite directions.)

$$D_1 = (1/\sqrt{2})(s + p_z)$$
$$D_2 = (1/\sqrt{2})(s - p_z)$$

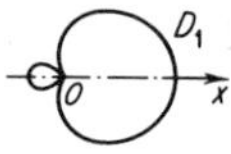

Polar representation of digonal hybridization.

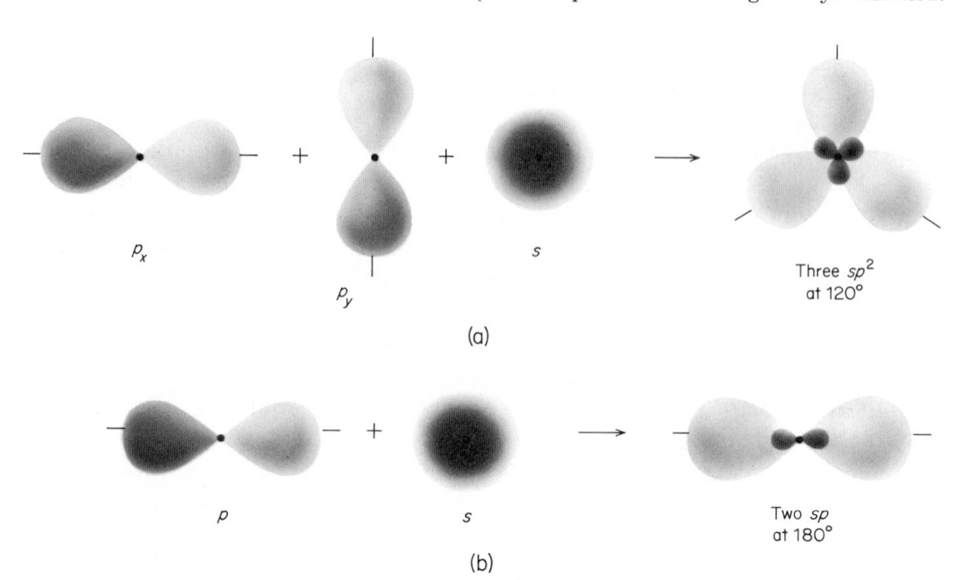

FIG. 13.10 Hybridization of s and p orbitals. (a) trigonal (b) digonal.

If these four $2s2p^3$ orbitals of carbon were coupled with the $1s$ orbitals of hydrogen to yield the methane molecule, we might think at first that three of the bonds should be different from the remaining one. Actually, of course, the symmetry of the molecule is such that all the bonds must be exactly the same.

In such a case it is possible to form sets of four *hybrid orbitals*, which are linear combinations of the s and p orbitals. One set consists of hybrid orbitals spacially directed from the carbon atom towards the corners of a regular tetrahedron. These are called *tetrahedral orbitals*, t_1, t_2, t_3, t_4. They are shown in Table 13.2. The tetrahedral orbitals are exceptionally stable since they allow the electron pairs to avoid one another to the greatest possible extent. The hybrid t orbitals of the carbon then combine with the $1s$ orbitals of four hydrogen atoms to form a set of four localized molecular orbitals for methane, $\psi_1 = c_1(t_1) + c_2(1s_1)$, etc.

In addition to the tetrahedral hybrids, the orbitals of carbon can be hybridized in other ways. The so-called *trigonal hybrids* sp^2 mix $2s$, $2p_x$ and $2p_y$ to form three orbitals at an angle of 120°. These hybrids are also shown in Table 13.2. The fourth A. O., $2p_z$, is perpendicular to the plane of the others. This kind of hybridization is used in ethylene. The double bond consists of an sp^2 hybrid σ bond with a π bond formed by overlapping p orbitals, as shown in Fig. 13.10(a).

If one $2s$ is mixed with a $2p$, we obtain the *digonal hybrids sp*. These are also shown in Table 13.2. This kind of hybridization is used in acetylene as shown in Fig. 13.10(b).

The use of hybrid orbitals is by no means restricted to carbon atoms. The hybrid orbital will almost always make it possible to form a stronger covalent bond between two atoms, since the strongly directed character of the orbital will allow the best overlap of the orbital of one atom with the orbital of its partner.

Fig. 13.11 shows how different hybrid bonds can provide different angles

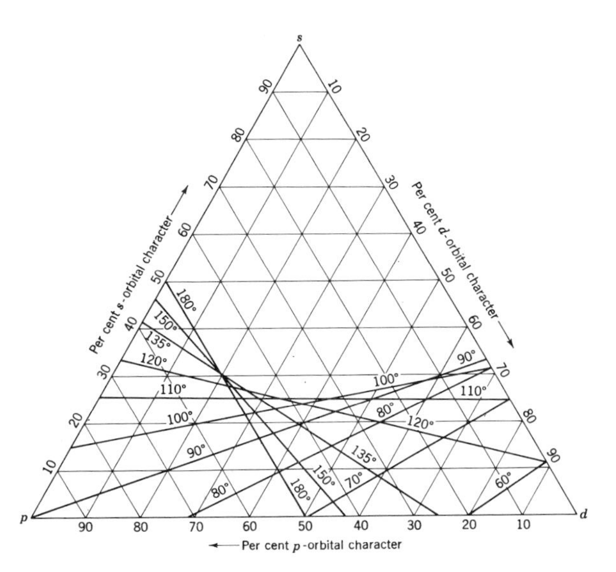

FIG. 13.11 Directional properties of hybrid orbitals from s, p and d atomic orbitals. [M. Kasha, *Molecular Electronic Structure, to be published*].

between the bonds. We see, for example, that the 105° bond angle in H_2O could be produced by mixing about 20 per cent s character and 80 per cent p character. This would provide stronger bonds for H_2O than the pure p bonds shown in Fig. 13.8.

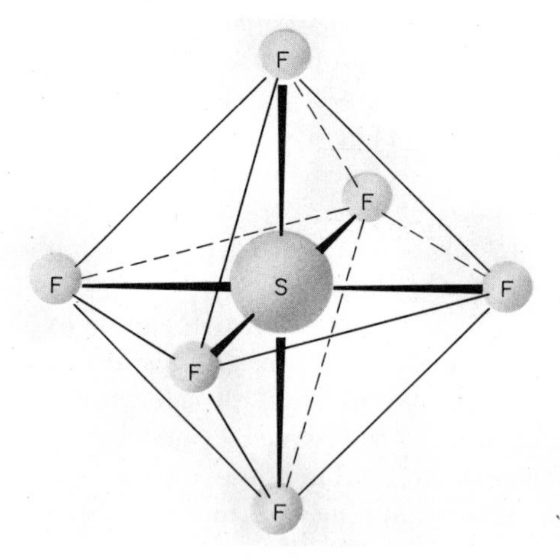

FIG. 13.12 The octahedral molecule SF_6. The sulfur atom provides six hybrid d^2sp^3 orbitals.

As an example of the use of Fig. 13.11 let us predict the bond angle of the hybrids d^2sp^3, which are so important in the coordination compounds of the transition metals. For $33\frac{1}{3}\%$ d, $16\frac{2}{3}\%$ s, 50% p the diagram shows that the bond angles are 90° and 180°, i.e., the configuration of a regular octahedron. An example is shown in Fig. 13.12.

14. NONLOCALIZED MOLECULAR ORBITALS

It is not always possible to assign the electrons in molecules to molecular orbitals localized between two nuclei. Important examples of *delocalization* are found in conjugated and aromatic hydrocarbons.

Consider, for example, the structure of butadiene, usually written $CH_2{=}CH{-}CH{=}CH_2$. The molecule is coplanar, and the C—C—C bond angles are close to 120°. The M. O.'s are evidently formed from hybrid carbon A. O.'s of the sp^2 trigonal type. Three of these trigonal orbitals lie in a plane and are used to form localized bonds with C and H as follows: $CH_2{-}CH{-}CH{-}CH_2$. The fourth orbital is a p-shaped one, perpendicular to the others. These orbitals line up as shown in (a), Fig. 13.13, for the individual atoms. When the atoms are pushed together, the orbitals overlap to form a continuous sheet above and below the carbon nuclei as in (b). There are two of these nonlocalized π orbitals, and they each can hold two electrons.

It is important to note that the four π electrons are not localized in particular bonds, but are free to move anywhere within the region in the figure. Since a larger volume is available for the motion of the electrons, their energy levels are lowered, just as in the case of the particle in a box (p. 485). Thus delocalization

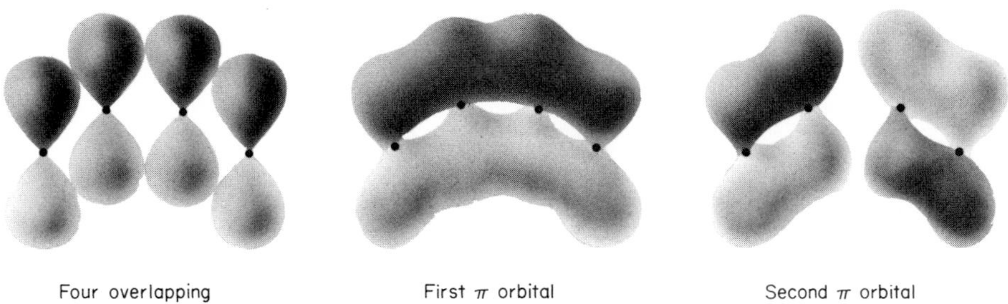

FIG. 13.13 Molecular orbitals of butadiene. [This figure and Fig. 13.14 are from *Organic Chemistry* by Donald Cram and George Hammond. McGraw Hill Book Company, New York, 1959.]

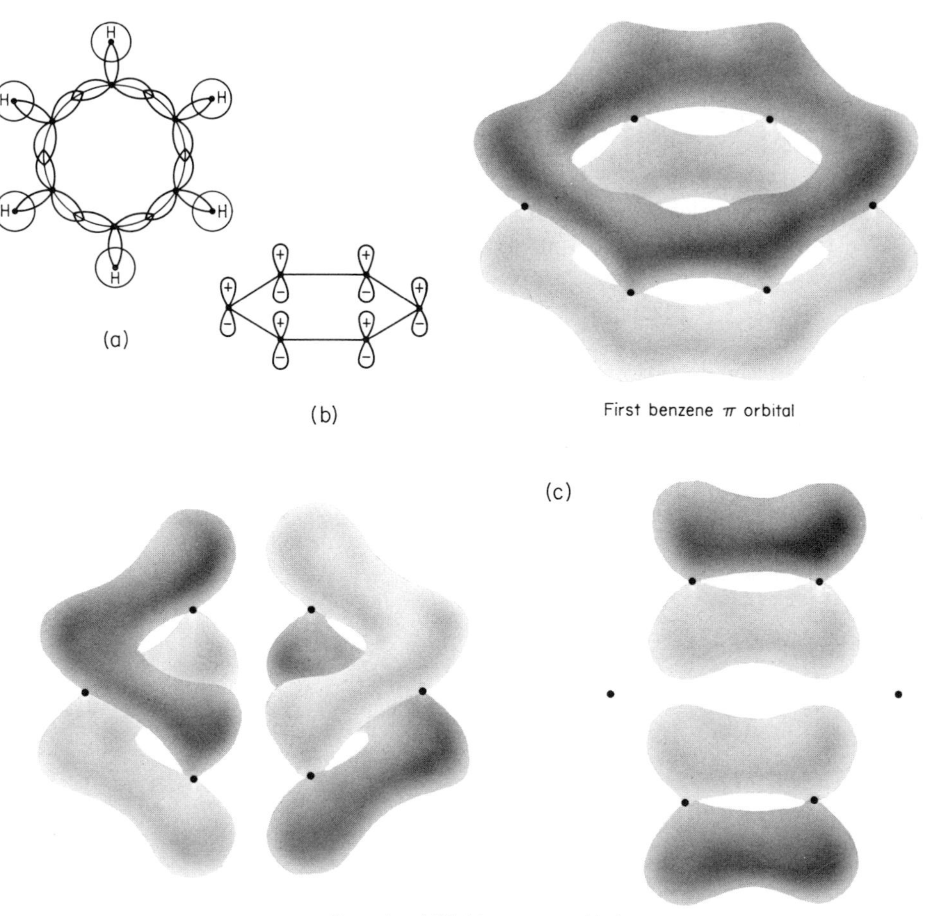

FIG. 13.14 Molecular orbitals for benzene.

results in an extra binding energy, greater than would be achieved in the classical structure of alternating double and single bonds. In the case of butadiene, this *delocalization energy*, often called the *resonance energy*, amounts to about 7 kcal per mole.

15. MOLECULAR ORBITALS OF BENZENE

Benzene and other aromatic molecules use nonlocalized orbitals. The discussion of benzene proceeds similarly to that of butadiene. First the carbon A. O.'s are prepared as trigonal sp^2 hybrids and then brought together with the hydrogens. These localized σ orbitals lie in a plane, as shown in Fig. 13.14(a). The atomic p-orbitals extend their sausage-shaped sections above and below the plane [Fig. 13.14(b)] and when they overlap they form molecular π orbitals, above and below the plane of the ring. These orbitals hold six mobile delocalized electrons. The shapes of the π orbitals are shown in Fig. 13.14(c). The orbitals π_1, π_2, π_3 are bonding orbitals, while $\pi_4^\star$, $\pi_5^\star$ and $\pi_6^\star$ are antibonding orbitals.

We can write a π molecular orbital in benzene as a linear combination of six atomic p orbitals.

$$\psi = c_1\psi_1 + c_2\psi_2 + c_3\psi_3 + c_4\psi_4 + c_5\psi_5 + c_6\psi_6 \tag{13.12}$$

This ψ is a one electron wave function or orbital that expresses the fact that the electron can move around the benzene ring. We calculate the ground state by variation of the coefficients c_1, c_2, etc. until we find the ψ that gives the lowest energy.

When we substitute the wave function of Eq. (13.12) into the basic energy formula of the variation method, Eq. (12.48), we obtain*

$$E = \frac{\int (\Sigma c_j\psi_j)H(\Sigma c_j\psi_j)d\tau}{\int (\Sigma c_j\psi_j)^2 d\tau} \tag{13.13}$$

The summations run from $j = 1$ to $j = 6$. For convenience, we now introduce the notation

$$\begin{aligned} H_{jk} &= \int \psi_j H \psi_k d\tau \\ S_{jk} &= \int \psi_j \psi_k d\tau \end{aligned} \tag{13.14}$$

We can show that $S_{jk} = S_{kj}$ and $H_{jk} = H_{kj}$. Then Eq. (13.13) can be written as

$$E = \frac{\sum_j \sum_k c_j c_k H_{jk}}{\sum_j \sum_k c_j c_k S_{jk}} \tag{13.15}$$

* To obtain familiarity with the mathematical operations of this theory, you should work through an example without the summation signs, taking $\psi = c_1\psi + c_2\psi_2$. We use in Eq. (13.13) the real form of wave functions ψ_j.

In order to minimize the energy E with respect to the variable coefficients c_i, we set the derivatives of E with respect to the c_i, $\partial E/\partial c_i$, equal to zero, and solve the resultant set of [six] simultaneous equations for the values of c_i. For example, the differentiation of

$$E\sum_j\sum_k c_j c_k S_{jk} = \sum_j\sum_k c_j c_k H_{jk}$$

with respect to c_i, with $\partial E/\partial c_i = 0$, gives

$$E\sum_k c_k S_{ik} + E\sum_j c_j S_{ji} = \sum_k c_k H_{ik} + \sum_j c_j H_{ji}$$

Since $S_{ij} = S_{ji}$ and $H_{ij} = H_{ji}$, this becomes

$$E\sum_j c_j S_{ji} = \sum_j c_j H_{ji}$$

or

$$\sum_j c_j(H_{ji} - ES_{ji}) = 0 \qquad (13.16)$$

We have a set of six equations like this as the value of i runs from 1 to 6, corresponding to the process of minimizing the energy with respect to each of the six coefficients c_i. If we write out the set of six simultaneous equations, it looks as follows:

$$\begin{array}{l}
c_1(H_{11} - S_{11}E) + c_2(H_{21} - S_{21}E) + \cdots\cdots + c_6(H_{61} - S_{61}E) = 0 \\
c_1(H_{12} - S_{12}E) + c_2(H_{22} - S_{22}E) + \cdots\cdots + c_6(H_{62} - S_{62}E) = 0 \\
\quad\vdots \\
c_1(H_{16} - S_{16}E) + c_2(H_{26} - S_{26}E) + \cdots\cdots + c_6(H_{66} - S_{66}E) = 0
\end{array}$$

These are *linear homogeneous equations.* If we tried to solve them in the usual way by setting up the determinant of the coefficients, and dividing it into the same determinant in which a given row was replaced by the constant terms, we would get only the trivial solutions $c_j = 0$. Only in case the determinant of the coefficients itself equals 0 can we obtain nontrivial solutions, and then only for certain values of E, called the *eigenvalues* of the problem. We therefore write the condition for nontrivial solutions as the vanishing of the determinant of the coefficients:

$$\begin{vmatrix}
H_{11} - S_{11}E & H_{21} - S_{21}E & \cdots\cdots & H_{61} - S_{61}E \\
H_{12} - S_{12}E & H_{22} - S_{22}E & \cdots\cdots & H_{62} - S_{62}E \\
H_{13} - S_{13}E & H_{23} - S_{23}E & \cdots\cdots & H_{63} - S_{63}B \\
H_{14} - S_{14}E & H_{24} - S_{24}E & \cdots\cdots & H_{64} - S_{64}E \\
H_{15} - S_{15}E & H_{25} - S_{25}E & \cdots\cdots & H_{65} - S_{65}E \\
H_{16} - S_{16}E & H_{26} - S_{26}E & \cdots\cdots & H_{66} - S_{66}E
\end{vmatrix} = 0 \qquad (13.17)$$

Equation (13.17), when multiplied out, is an equation of the sixth degree in E, and therefore possesses six roots. It is called the *secular equation.* Clearly, we need not restrict this method to the benzene problem, which is merely a typical example. We can handle all variation-theory problems by this powerful general method.

Because of the difficulties in evaluating the integrals in the secular equation, an approximate treatment, developed by E. Hückel, has been widely used.† The approximations are the following:

1) $H_{jj} = \alpha$, the *coulombic integral* for all j.

2) $H_{jk} = \beta$, the *resonance integral* for atoms which are bonded together.

3) $H_{jk} = 0$ for atoms which are not bonded together.

4) $S_{jj} = 1$

5) $S_{jk} = 0$ for $j \neq k$.

With these approximations, the secular equation is greatly simplified, and becomes

$$\begin{vmatrix} \alpha - E & \beta & 0 & 0 & 0 & \beta \\ \beta & \alpha - E & \beta & 0 & 0 & 0 \\ 0 & \beta & \alpha - E & \beta & 0 & 0 \\ 0 & 0 & \beta & \alpha - E & \beta & 0 \\ 0 & 0 & 0 & \beta & \alpha - E & \beta \\ \beta & 0 & 0 & 0 & \beta & \alpha - E \end{vmatrix} = 0$$

The roots of this equation of the sixth degree are:

$$E_1 = \alpha + 2\beta \qquad E_{2,3} = \alpha + \beta \text{ (twice)} \qquad E_{4,5} = \alpha - \beta \text{ (twice)} \qquad E_6 = \alpha - 2\beta$$

Since β is negative, they are given in order of ascending energy. When the values of E are put back into the system of linear equations, they can be solved for the coefficients c_j and thus we can get explicit expressions for the molecular orbitals (wave functions).

It turns out that the lowest M. O. is

$$\psi_A = (6)^{-1/2}(\psi_1 + \psi_2 + \psi_3 + \psi_4 + \psi_5 + \psi_6)$$

This orbital, which can hold two electrons with antiparallel spins, is shown in Fig. 13.14(c). There are two next lowest molecular orbitals ψ_B and $\psi_{B'}$, which together hold four electrons. The six π electrons of benzene occupy these three orbitals of low energy, so that the exceptional stability of the structure is explained by the theory.

† A. Streitwieser, *Molecular Orbital Theory for Organic Chemists* (New York: John Wiley, 1961) gives a complete account of the applications of the Hückel method.

The total energy, in this approximate treatment, would be

$$2(\alpha + 2\beta) + 4(\alpha + \beta) = 6\alpha + 8\beta$$

If we had three localized π bonds the energy would have been $6(\alpha + \beta)$. Hence the *delocalization energy* amounts to 2β. The observed value of the delocalization energy of benzene is 41 kcal. This figure is computed by subtracting the observed ΔH of formation from the ΔH based on three single and three double C—C bonds.

The properties of benzene confirm the existence of these mobile electrons. All the C—C bonds in benzene have the same length, 1.39 Å compared to 1.54 in ethane and 1.30 in ethylene. The benzene ring is like a little loop of wire containing electrons; if a magnetic field is applied normal to the planes of the rings in solid benzene, the electrons are set in motion, and experimental measurements show that a magnetic field is induced opposed to the applied field.

16. RESONANCE BETWEEN VALENCE-BOND STRUCTURES

Instead of the M. O. method it is often convenient to imagine that the structure of a molecule is made up by the superposition of various distinct valence-bond structures. Applying this viewpoint to the case of benzene, we would say that the actual structure is formed principally by *resonance* between the two Kekulé structures,

with smaller contributions from the three Dewar structures,

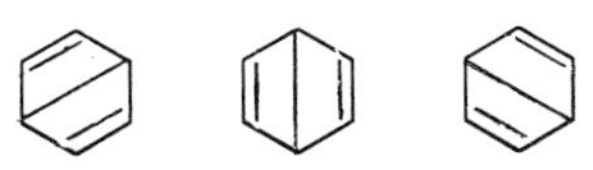

According to the resonance theory, the wave function ψ describing the molecular structure is a linear combination of the functions for possible valence bond structures,

$$\psi = c_1\psi_1 + c_2\psi_2 + c_3\psi_3 + \cdots$$

This is an application of the general superposition principle for wave functions. Each wave function ψ corresponds to some definite value E for the energy of the system. The problem is to determine the values of c_1, c_2, c_3, etc., in such a way as to make E a minimum. The relative magnitude of these coefficients when E is a minimum is then a measure of the contribution to the overall structure of the different special structures represented by $\psi_1, \psi_2, \psi_3, \ldots$. Note that $\psi_1, \psi_2, \psi_3, \ldots$ each corresponds to a complete valence bond structure. In the M. O. treatment of benzene, the ψ_1 in Eq. (13.12) were atomic orbitals. It must be clearly understood that the resonance description does *not* mean that some molecules have one structure and some another. The structure of each molecule can only be described as a sort of weighted average of the resonance structures.

Two rules must be obeyed by possible resonating structures: (1) The structures can differ only in the position of electrons. Substances that differ in the arrangement of the atoms are ordinary isomers and are chemically and physically distinguishable as distinct compounds. (2) The resonating structures must have the same number of paired and unpaired electrons, otherwise they would have different total spins and could be physically distinguished by their magnetic properties.

In substituted benzene compounds, the contributions of various ionic structures must be included. For example, aniline has the following resonance structures:

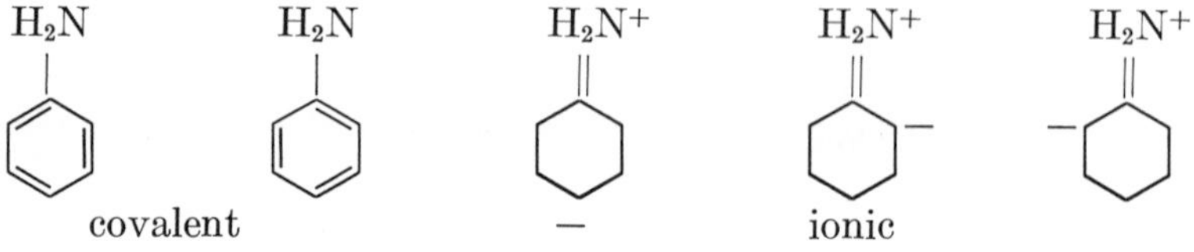

H_2N H_2N H_2N^+ H_2N^+ H_2N^+

covalent — ionic

The ionic structures give aniline an additional resonance energy of 7 kcal, compared to benzene. The increased negative charge at the *ortho* and *para* positions in aniline accounts for the fact that the NH_2 group in aniline directs positively charged approaching substituents (NO_2^+, Br^+) to these positions.

The way in which the V. B. method would treat the hydrogen halides is instructive. Two important structures are postulated, one purely covalent and one purely ionic:

$$\mathrm{H:\ddot{\underset{..}{Cl}}:} \qquad \text{and} \qquad \mathrm{H^+ :\ddot{\underset{..}{Cl}}:^-}$$

The actual structure is visualized as a resonance hybrid between these two extremes. Its wave function is

$$\psi = \psi_{\text{covalent}} + a\psi_{\text{ionic}} \tag{13.18}$$

The value of a is adjusted until the minimum energy is obtained. Then $100a^2/(1 + a^2)$ is called the *per cent ionic character* of the bond. For the various halides the following results are found:

Molecule	HF	HCl	HBr	HI
Ionic Character	45	17	11	5

The bond in HI is predominantly covalent; in HF, it is about midway between ionic and covalent. The distinction between the different bond types is seldom clear cut, and most bonds have an intermediate character. After our experience with the calculation of the energy of the H—H bond, we must recognize that the description of a structure by a simple wave function like that of Eq. (13.18) has at best a qualitative significance.

17. ELECTRONEGATIVITY

The tendency of a pair of atoms to form an ionic bond is measured by the difference in their abilities to attract an electron, or in their *electronegativities*. Fluorine is the most, and the alkali metals are the least electronegative of the elements. The fractional ionic character of a bond depends upon the difference in the electronegativities of its constituent atoms.

Electronegativity is a concept that the chemist frequently uses in an intuitive way, but it is somewhat difficult to put it on a quantitative basis. Pauling devised an electronegativity scale based on bond energies. He considered that the energy of a bond $A—B$ would exceed the geometric mean of the energies of $A—A$ and $B—B$ by an amount proportional to the difference in the electronegativities X of A and B. Thus

$$X_A - X_B = E_{AB} - (E_{AA}E_{BB})^{1/2} = \Delta' \qquad (13.19)$$

Mulliken suggested that the average of the first ionization potential I of an atom and its electron affinity A would be a measure of the attraction of a neutral atom for an electron, and hence of its electronegativity.

$$A \longrightarrow A^+ + e \qquad I_A$$

$$e + A \longrightarrow A^- \qquad A_A$$

$$\text{Electronegativity} = (I + A)/2.$$

There is an empirical relationship between the electronegativity values of Pauling and of Mulliken. If I_A and A_A are expressed in kilocalories per mole,

$$X_A \simeq \frac{I_A + A_A}{30}$$

Table 13.3 shows the electronegativities of the elements arranged in the periodic table.*

Several attempts have been made to obtain a single equation relating partial ionic character to difference in electronegativity. The empirical relation of Hannay and Smyth† is quite satisfactory:

$$\% \text{ ionic character} = 16(X_A - X_B) + 3.5(X_A - X_B)^2 \qquad (13.20)$$

18. COORDINATION COMPOUNDS

As the theory of valence developed during the nineteenth century, chemists recognized many compounds in which the normal rules failed to apply. Among such substances were the so-called complex compounds, including salt hydrates,

* E. J. Little and M. M. Jones, *J. Chem. Ed.*, *37*, 231 (1960).

† *J. Am. Chem. Soc.*, *68*, 171 (1946).

TABLE 13.3 Electronegativities of the Elements

	H																	He
	2.1																	—
	Li	Be											B	C	N	O	F	Ne
	0.97	1.47											2.01	2.50	3.07	3.50	4.10	—
	Na	Mg											Al	Si	P	S	Cl	A
	1.01	1.23											1.47	1.74	2.06	2.44	2.83	—
	K	Ca	Sc	Ti	V	Cr	Mn	Fe	Co	Ni	Cu	Zn	Ga	Ge	As	Se	Br	Kr
	0.91	1.04	1.20	1.32	1.45	1.56	1.60	1.64	1.70	1.75	1.75	1.66	1.82	2.02	2.20	2.48	2.74	—
	Rb	Sr	Y	Zr	Nb	Mo	Tc	Ru	Rh	Pd	Ag	Cd	In	Sn	Sb	Te	I	Xe
	0.89	0.99	1.11	1.22	1.23	1.30	1.36	1.42	1.45	1.35	1.42	1.46	1.49	1.72	1.82	2.01	2.21	—
	Cs	Ba	*	Hf	Ta	W	Re	Os	Ir	Pt	Au	Hg	Tl	Pb	Bi	Po	At	Rn
	0.86	0.97		1.23	1.33	1.40	1.46	1.52	1.55	1.44	1.42	1.44	1.44	1.55	1.67	1.76	1.90	—
	Fr	Ra	**															
	0.86	0.97																
*	La	Ce	Pr	Nd	Pm	Sm	Eu	Gd	Tb	Dy	Ho	Er	Tm	Yb	Lu			
	1.08	1.08	1.07	1.07	1.07	1.07	1.01	1.11	1.10	1.10	1.10	1.11	1.11	1.06	1.14			
**	Ac	Th	Pa	U	Np	Pu	Am	Cm	Bk	Cf	Es	Fm	Md	No	Lw			
	1.00	1.11	1.14	1.22	1.22	1.22	(1.2)	(1.2)	(1.2)	(1.2)	(1.2)	(1.2)	(1.2)	(1.2)	(1.2)			

Values in parentheses are estimates.

metal ammines and double salts. In 1893, Alfred Werner suggested that an element might have a secondary valence in addition to its normal valence. The secondary valence bonds were also directed in space, so that geometrical and optical isomerism might occur. Typical of such compounds are two cobalt-ammine chlorides,

$$[Co(NH_3)_6]^{+3}(Cl^-)_3$$

$$[Co(NH_3)_3(Cl)_3]$$

G. N. Lewis (1916) included Werner's complex compounds in his electronic theory of valence, with the suggestion that each bond consists of a pair of electrons, *both* of which are donated by a group coordinated to the metal ion. Therefore the bond was called a *dative bond* and sometimes written with an arrow to denote the origin of the electrons. For instance,

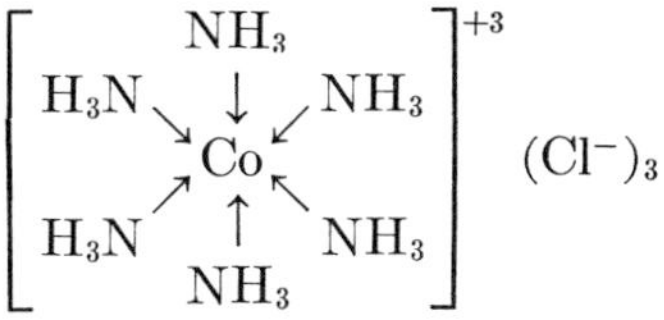

$$\left[\begin{array}{ccccc} & & NH_3 & & \\ H_3N & \searrow & \downarrow & \swarrow & NH_3 \\ & & Co & & \\ & \nearrow & \uparrow & \nwarrow & \\ H_3N & & & & NH_3 \\ & & NH_3 & & \end{array}\right]^{+3} (Cl^-)_3$$

One way to describe these bonds is to construct hybrid orbitals from the available atomic orbitals and to examine their stereochemistry. The bare cobaltic ion Co^{+3} has an electron configuration:

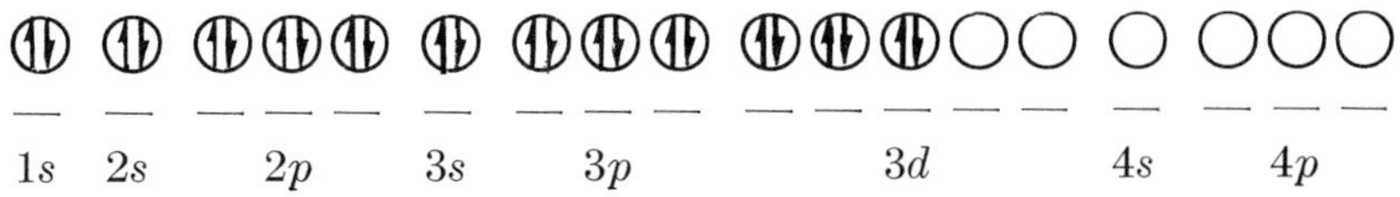

$1s$	$2s$	$2p$	$3s$	$3p$	$3d$	$4s$	$4p$
(↑↓)	(↑↓)	(↑↓)(↑↓)(↑↓)	(↑↓)	(↑↓)(↑↓)(↑↓)	(↑↓)(↑↓)(↑↓)( )( )	( )	( )( )( )

If we take two $3d$, one $4s$, and three $4p$ orbitals, we can make six hybrid orbitals d^2sp^3 directed to the corners of a regular octahedron. The valence bond model of the hexamminocobaltic ion would use these six hybrid orbitals to accommodate six pairs of electrons from the six NH_3 molecules. The strong covalent bonds so formed would have considerable ionic character, but in this model they would not differ in kind from the sp^3 tetrahedral hybrids used in the CH_4 molecule.

A different way of looking at these structures starts with the idea that the bonding is essentially due to electrostatic interaction between the positive central ion and the dipoles or ions of the coordinated groups. The groups attached to the central ion are called *ligands*. These ligands create an electrostatic field around the central ion which produces an additional bonding effect called the *ligand field stabilization energy* (L. F. S. E.). The L. F. S. E. arises as a consequence of the action of the field of the ligands on the d-orbitals of the central ion.

In order to understand this important effect, we must first look again at the properties of the d-orbitals, as shown in Fig. 13.15. In the absence of an external field, the five $3d$ orbitals are all equal in energy (fivefold degeneracy). As soon as these orbitals are placed in an electrostatic ligand field that is not spherically

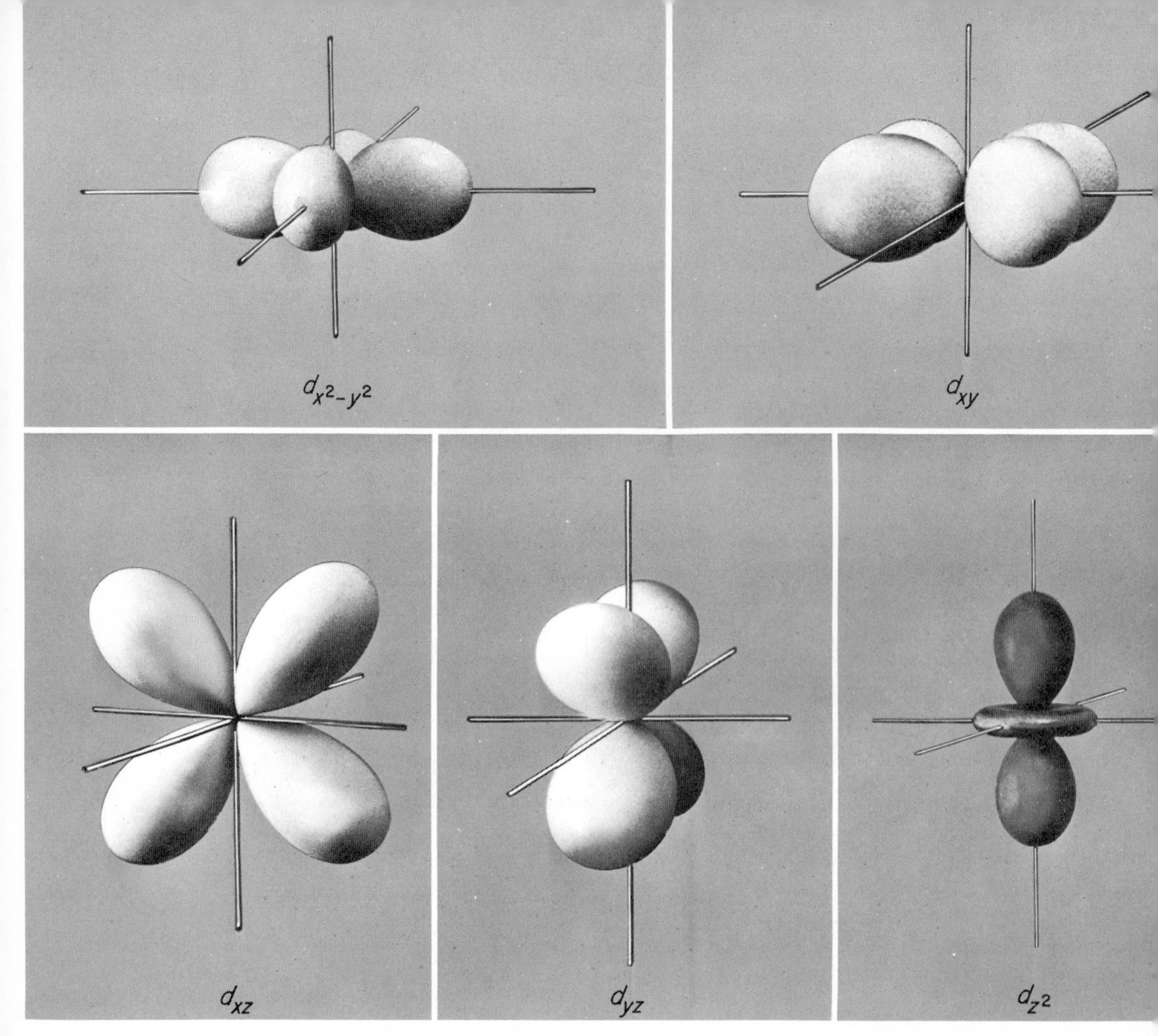

FIG. 13.15 The atomic *d*-orbitals (hydrogenlike) [R. G. Pearson, Northwestern University — American Chemical Society].

symmetrical, their energies are no longer exactly equal. Those orbitals which point in the direction of the ligands are raised in energy owing to the repulsion between the negative charge density in the *d*-orbitals and that in the ligands. The *d*-orbitals of lowest energy are those which point away from the ligands. This effect is shown schematically in Fig. 13.16 for the case of an octahedral field (for example, six NH_3 at the corners of a regular octahedron). We see that the $d_{x^2-y^2}$ and d_{z^2} orbitals are raised in energy, whereas the d_{xy}, d_{xz} and d_{yz} are lowered.

The electron configuration of the complex will depend on the magnitude of the splitting produced by the ligand field. The case of $(FeF_6)^{3-}$ is typical of the effect of a weak field, with a splitting of about 10 000 cm^{-1}, whereas the case of $[Fe(CN)_6]^{3-}$ shows the effect of a strong field, with a splitting five times as great.

In accord with Hund's rule, the *d* electrons tend to occupy orbitals which allow them to keep their spins parallel, because in this way they are forced to stay away from one another and thus to decrease the electrostatic repulsive energy. On the other hand, if the splitting of the *d* levels by the ligand field is too great, this electrostatic effect will not be large enough to compensate for the energy needed to promote the electrons into the higher orbitals.

We see examples of two different situations in Fig. 13.16. The five d electrons in $(FeF_6)^{-3}$ have the configuration $t_{2g}^3 e_g^2$ with completely uncoupled spins. In $[Fe(CN)_6]^{3-}$ the configuration is t_{2g}^5, with four spins coupled. Each uncoupled spin acts as a little magnet so that we can distinguish these configurations experimentally by measuring the magnetic susceptibility of the complexes. (See Sec. 14.10.)

In Fig. 13.17 we show how the five d orbitals are split by fields of various symmetries. Of course, the extent of the splitting depends on the intensity of the electrostatic field of the ligands. Sometimes a situation occurs in which one d orbital is filled with a pair of electrons but another d orbital of equal energy

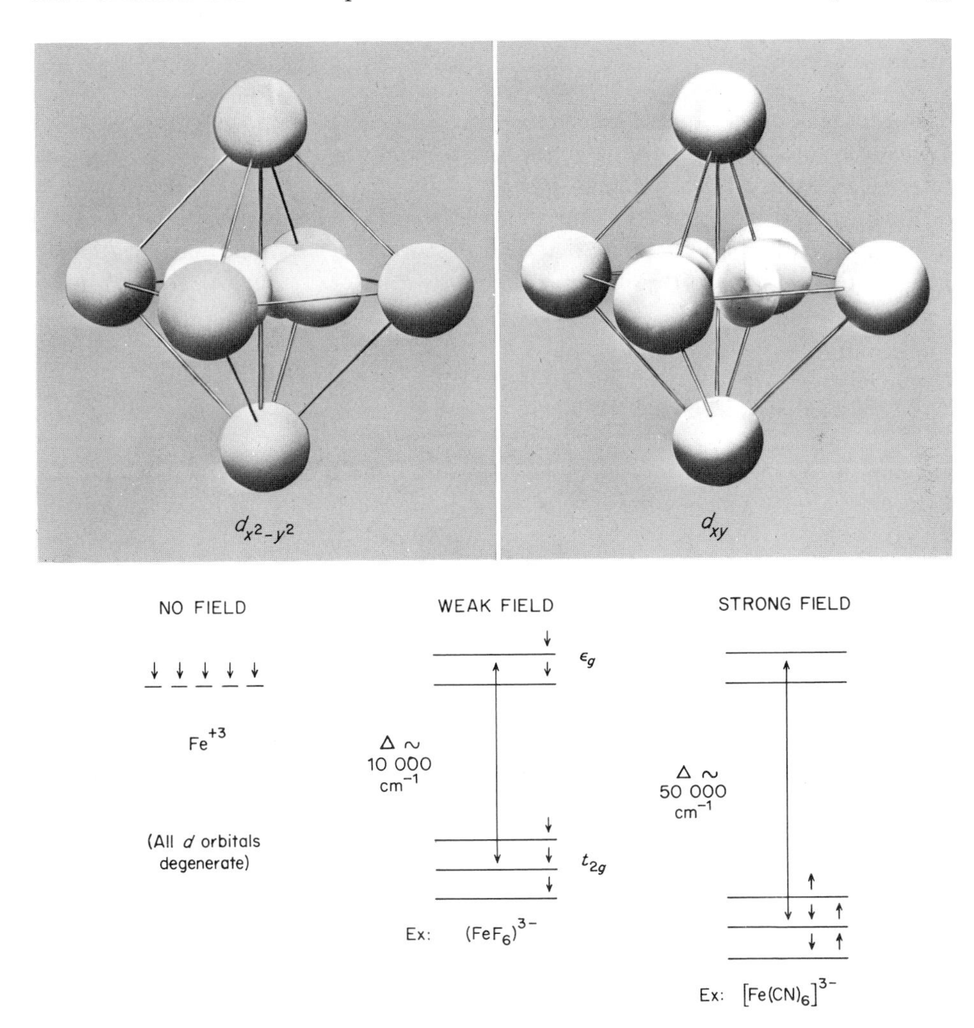

FIG. 13.16 Effect of octahedral ligand field on d-orbitals [R. G. Pearson].

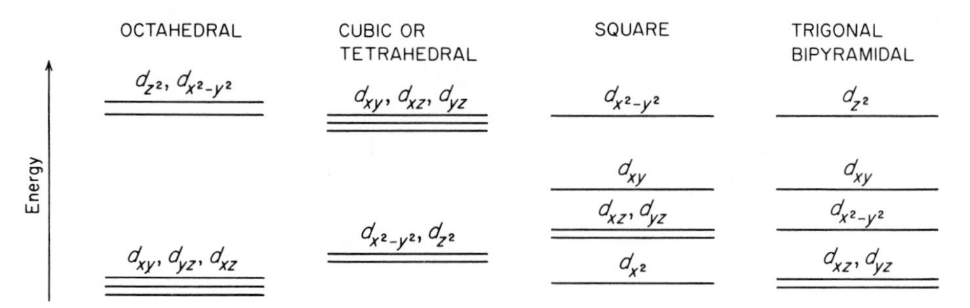

FIG. 13.17 The energy levels of *d*-orbitals in ligand fields with various symmetries.

is only half filled. This configuration would be degenerate. For example, the electrons in the ion Cu^{+2} might be assigned as

$$\textit{either} \qquad t_{2g}^6 d_{z^2}^2 d_{x^2-y^2}^1$$

$$\textit{or} \qquad t_{2g}^6 d_{z^2}^1 d_{x^2-y^2}^2$$

In such a case there may be a change in the geometry of the complex which serves to break the degeneracy, producing a lower and an upper level somewhat different in energy. This change is called the *Jahn-Teller effect*. In the case of Cu^{+2} complexes, we often find that the regular octahedral arrangement does not occur, but instead an irregular octahedral structure, in which four ligands lie in a square about the Cu^{+2} and two others at a greater distance above and below the central ion.

19. THE HYDROGEN BOND

In some situations a hydrogen atom can form a bond to two other atoms instead of to only one. A typical example is the dimer of formic acid, which has the structure

O—H . . . . O
H—C C—H
O . . . . H—O

This *hydrogen bond* is not very strong, usually having a dissociation energy of about 5 kcal, but it is important in many structures, such as the proteins. It occurs in general between hydrogen and the electronegative elements N, O, F, of small atomic volumes. Besides intermolecular H-bonds, like those in formic acid, we can have intramolecular H-bonds. An example of the latter type is found in salicylaldehyde,

O—H
O
HC

We know that hydrogen can form only one normal covalent electron-pair bond, since it has only the single 1*s* orbital available for bond formation. Since the proton is extremely small, its electrostatic field is intense, and a bonding can occur due to the attraction of the positive proton for the electrons on the bonded atom.

An interesting hydrogen-bonded structure is the ion $(HF_2)^-$, which occurs in hydrofluoric acid and in crystals of KHF_2. It can be represented as a resonance hybrid of three structures,

$$F{-}HF^- \qquad F^-H{-}F \qquad F^-H^+F^-$$

The ionic $F^-H^+F^-$ structure is the most important.

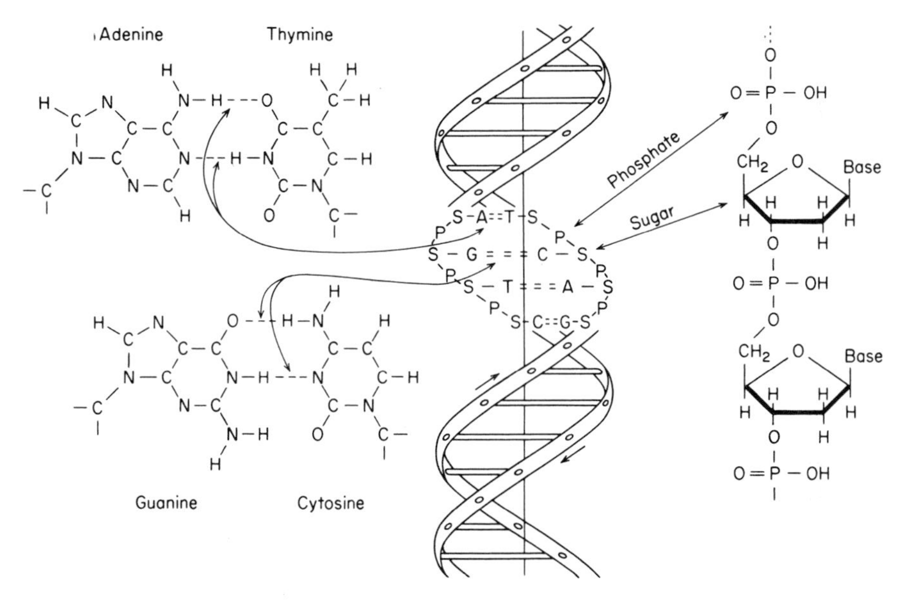

FIG. 13.18 The model of Watson and Crick for the structure of deoxyribonucleic acid (DNA). A double helix of sugar phosphate chains is held together by hydrogen bonded pairs of bases.

Hydrogen bonds extended through three dimensions can cause the formation of polymeric structures, as in water and ice (cf. Sec. 16.16). They can hold molecules together in certain definite arrays or orientations. An important example of this kind of function is found in the structure proposed for the nucleic acids by Watson and Crick,* as shown in Fig. 13.18. The two intertwined helical ribbons represent sugar phosphate chains. The bars binding them together represent pairs of purine and pyrimidine bases, one from each chain, held together in a specific orientation by hydrogen bonds. One example of such a linkage by base pairs is shown in Fig. 13.18.

* J. D. Watson and F. H. C. Crick, *Nature 17*, 964 (1953).

PROBLEMS

1. The dissociation energy for the H_2 molecule is $D_0 = 4.46$ ev and the zero point energy is 0.26 ev. Calculate the D_0 and $h\nu_0$ for the D_2 molecule.

2. Describe the molecular orbitals that would be used in the molecules HeH^+, LiH, CO, CN.

3. Estimate the per cent ionic character of the following bonds from the Hannay-Smyth equation: HF, HCl, HBr, HI, Hg—C, Zn—C.
   Describe the nature of the hybrid bonds formed to the metal atom in the following structures:

   $[SbBr_6]^-$ (octahedral)
   $[SbBr_6]^{-3}$ (octahedral)
   $[PtCl_4]^{-2}$ (square)
   GeF_4 (tetrahedral)

4. The complex ion $[Co(CN)_6]^{4-}$ has an octahedral structure. Predict its magnetic moment.

5. Write down possible resonance forms contributing to the structure of the following:
   CO_2, CH_3COO^-, $CH_2{:}CH.CH{:}CH_2$, CH_3NO_2, C_6H_5Cl, $C_6H_5NH_2$, naphthalene.

---

6. On the basis of molecular-orbital theory, how would you explain the following? The binding energy of N_2^+ is 6.35 and that of N_2 7.38 ev, whereas the binding energy of O_2^+ is 6.48 and that of O_2, 5.08 ev.

7. The heats of sublimation of benzene, phenol, benzoic acid, and *p*-hydroxybenzoic acid are 10.5, 16.1, 21.8, and 27.7 kcal mole^{-1}, respectively. Discuss these values from the point of view of the hydrogen bonding in the crystals.

8. Cyclooctatetraene $(CH)_8$ has an eight membered puckered ring containing four short C—C distances and four long ones. Describe the hybridization and molecular orbitals used in forming this ring, contrasting this situation with that in benzene. To what do you ascribe the difference?

9. Consider the molecular orbital for H_2 to be $2^{-1/2}(\psi_{1sA} + \psi_{1sB})$, although this is not exactly normalized. Calculate the charge density at various points in the plane of the two nuclei. Assume the internuclear distance to be 0.74 Å. Make a plot to show lines of constant density of charge.

10. Ferrocene is biscyclopentadienyl iron. Its structure can be written

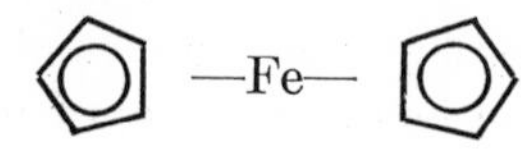

to indicate that the metal is bound to the rings as a whole. The cyclopentadienyl rings are planar pentagons with all the C—C distances the same, 1.40 Å. Discuss the nature of the bonding in this substance.

14 MOLECULAR STRUCTURE AND MOLECULAR SPECTRA

In this chapter we shall describe important methods for the study of the structure of molecules. The first problem is to find the positions of all the atomic nuclei in a molecule, and thus to obtain a complete description of its geometrical structure. The geometrical structure can also be described in terms of the bonds between the different atoms, the lengths of these bonds and the angles between them. We should like to know also how the electrons are distributed about the nuclei. In the past we had to be content with semiquantitative information about such electronic distributions, expressed, for example, in partial ionic characters of bonds. More sensitive methods are now available: we can measure properties of the nuclei which depend on their electronic environments, for example, nuclear magnetic resonance and quadrupole coupling. The powerful methods of spectroscopy also provide detailed data on the structures of molecules in both the ground and excited states.

1. DIPOLE MOMENTS

If a bond is formed between two atoms that differ in electronegativity, there is an accumulation of negative charge on the more electronegative atom, leaving a positive charge on the more electropositive atom. The bond then constitutes an electric dipole, which is by definition an equal positive and negative charge, $\pm Q$, separated by a distance r. A dipole, as in Fig. 14.1 (a), is characterized by its *dipole moment*, a vector having the magnitude Qr and the direction of the line joining the negative to the positive charge. The dimensions of a dipole moment are charge times length. Two charges with the magnitude of e (4.80×10^{-10} esu) separated by a distance of 1 Å would have a dipole moment of 4.80×10^{-18} esu cm. The unit 10^{-18} esu cm is called the debye (d).

If a polyatomic molecule contains two or more dipoles in different bonds, the net dipole moment of the molecule is the resultant of the vector addition of the individual bond moments. An example of this is shown in Fig. 14.1 (b).

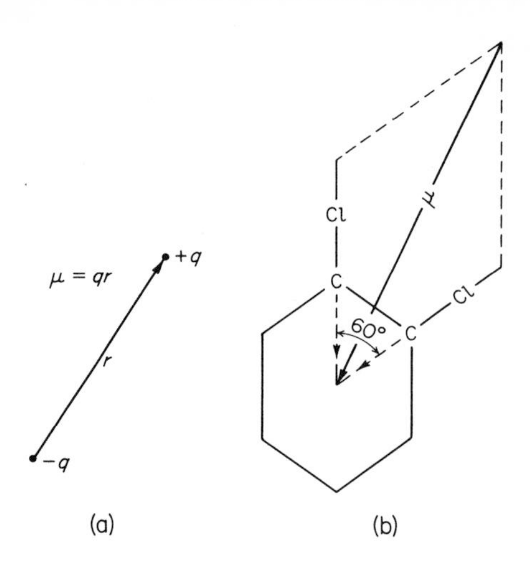

FIG. 14.1 (a) Definition of dipole moment; (b) Vector addition of bond dipole moments in orthodichlorobenzene.

The measurement of the dipole moments of molecules provides an insight into their geometric structures and into the character of their valence bonds. Before we can discuss the determination of dipole moments, however, it is necessary to review some aspects of the theory of dielectrics.

2. POLARIZATION OF DIELECTRICS

Consider a parallel-plate capacitor with the region between the plates evacuated, and let the charge on one plate be $+\sigma$ and on the other $-\sigma$ per square centimeter. The electric field within the capacitor is then directed perpendicular to the plates and has the magnitude* $E_0 = 4\pi\sigma$. The capacitance is

$$C_0 = \frac{Q}{U} = \frac{\sigma A}{4\pi\sigma d} = \frac{A}{4\pi d}$$

where A is the area of the plates, d the distance, and U the potential difference between them.

Now consider the space between the plates to be filled with some material substance. In many cases we can say that this substance is a conductor or is an insulator. Under the influence of small fields, electrons move quite freely through conductors, whereas in insulators or *dielectrics* these fields displace the electrons only slightly from their equilibrium positions.

An electric field acting on a dielectric thus causes a separation of positive and negative charges. The field is said to *polarize* the dielectric. This *polarization* is shown pictorially in Fig. 14.2 (a). The polarization can occur in two ways: the *induction effect* and the *orientation effect*. An electric field always induces dipoles in molecules whether or not they contain dipoles to begin with.

* See, for example, G. P. Harnwell, *Electricity and Magnetism* (New York: McGraw-Hill, 1949), p. 26.

If the dielectric does contain molecules that are permanent dipoles, the field also tends to aline these dipoles along its own direction. The random thermal motions of the molecules oppose this orienting action. Our main interest is in the permanent dipoles, but before these can be studied, effects due to the induced dipoles must be clearly distinguished.

When a dielectric is introduced between the plates of a capacitor, the capacitance is increased by a factor ϵ, called the *dielectric constant*. Thus if C_0 is the capacitance with a vacuum, the capacitance with a dielectric is $C = \epsilon C_0$. Since the charges on the capacitor plates are unchanged, the field between the plates is reduced by the factor ϵ, so that $E = E_0/\epsilon$.

The reason the field is reduced is clear from the picture of the polarized dielectric: all the induced dipoles are alined so as to produce an overall dipole moment that cuts down the field strength. Consider in Fig. 14.2 (b), a unit cube of dielectric between the capacitor plates, and define a vector quantity P called the *dielectric polarization*, which is the dipole moment per unit volume. Then the

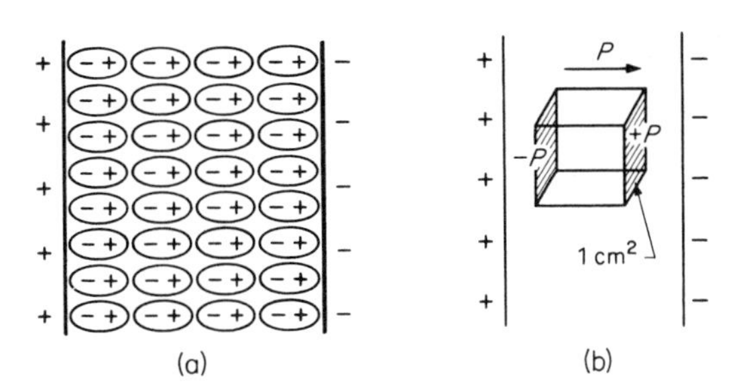

FIG. 14.2 (a) Polarization of a dielectric; (b) definition of the polarization vector, P.

effect of the polarization is equivalent to that which would be produced by a charge of $+P$ on one face and $-P$ on the other face (1 cm²) of the cube. The field in the dielectric is now determined by the net charge on the plates, so that

$$E = 4\pi(\sigma - P) \tag{14.1}$$

A new vector has been defined, called the *electric displacement* D, which depends only on the charge σ, according to $D = 4\pi\sigma$. From Eq. (14.1),

$$D = E + 4\pi P, \qquad \text{and} \qquad D/E = \epsilon \tag{14.2}$$

It follows

$$\epsilon = 1 + \frac{4\pi P}{E}$$

In a vacuum, where $\epsilon = 1$ and $P = 0$, $D = E$.

3. THE INDUCED POLARIZATION

We have seen that the polarization is the sum of two terms, $P = P_d + P_o$. P_d is the *induced* or *distortion polarization* caused by the separation of positive and negative charges due to the action of the electric field on the dielectric. P_o is the *orientation polarization* caused by the preferential alinement of permanent dipoles in the direction of the electric field.

To compute P_d we must consider the magnitude of the dipole moment m induced in a molecule by the field acting on it. We can assume that this induced moment is proportional to the strength of the field, F, so that

$$m = \alpha F \tag{14.3}$$

The proportionality factor α is called the *polarizability.* It is the induced moment per unit field strength. Note that α has the dimensions of volume, since $Qr/(Q/r^2) = r^3$. The polarizability of a hydrogen atom is $4.5a_0^3$, which is close to the volume of a sphere of radius equal to that of the Bohr orbit, $\frac{4}{3}\pi a_0^3 = 4.19a_0^3$. The polarizability of an atom or ion is a good measure of its volume.

In the case of a gas at low pressure, the molecules are so far apart that they do not exert appreciable electrical forces on one another. Therefore, the field that polarizes a molecule [F in Eq. (14.3)] is simply the external field E. We can therefore calculate immediately the induced polarization in a gas. If M is the molecular weight and ρ the density, M/ρ is the volume of one mole and this contains L molecules. Hence the polarization

$$P_d = \frac{\text{molecules}}{\text{unit volume}} \times \frac{\text{dipole moment}}{\text{molecule}} = \frac{L\rho}{M}(\alpha E)$$

From Eq. (14.3),

$$(\epsilon - 1)\frac{M}{\rho} = 4\pi L\alpha \tag{14.4}$$

If the dielectric is not a gas, we must consider the influence of the surrounding molecules in order to estimate the field that acts to polarize a given molecule. This difficult problem has not yet been completely solved, but approximate formulas have been obtained for different special cases. For gases at high pressures, for nonpolar liquids, and for dilute solutions of polar solutes in nonpolar solvents, the effective field F is often taken to be*

$$F = E + \frac{4\pi}{3}P \tag{14.5}$$

It follows that $m = \alpha\left(E + \frac{4\pi}{3}P\right)$, and instead of Eq. (14.4), we obtain

$$P_M = \frac{\epsilon - 1}{\epsilon + 2}\frac{M}{\rho} = \frac{4\pi L\alpha}{3} \tag{14.6}$$

The quantity P_M is called the *molar polarization.*† So far it includes only the contribution from induced dipoles, and a term due to permanent dipoles must be

* A derivation is given by Slater and Frank, *Introduction to Theoretical Physics* (New York: McGraw-Hill, 1933), p. 278; also, Syrkin and Dyatkina, *The Structure of Molecules* (New York: Interscience, 1950), p. 471.

† The polarization P is an electric dipole moment per unit volume, but the *molar polarization* P_M has the dimensions of volume and is really a *molar polarizability*.

added to give the total molar polarization. Eq. (14.6) was first derived by O. F. Mossotti in 1850.

4. DETERMINATION OF THE DIPOLE MOMENT

Having examined the effect of induced dipoles on the dielectric constant, we are in a position to consider the effect of permanent dipoles. If the bonds in a molecule are ionic or partially ionic, the molecule has a permanent moment, unless the individual bond moments add vectorially to zero.

There will always be an induced moment. It is evoked almost instantaneously in the direction of the electric field. It is independent of the temperature, since if the position of the molecule is disturbed by thermal collisions, the dipole is immediately induced again in the field direction. The contribution to the polarization caused by permanent dipoles, however, is less at higher temperatures, since the random thermal collisions of the molecules oppose the tendency of their dipoles to line up in the electric field.

It is necessary to calculate the average component of a permanent dipole in the field direction as a function of the temperature. Consider a dipole with random orientation. If there is no field, all orientations are equally probable. This fact can be expressed by saying that the number of dipole moments directed within a solid angle $d\omega$ is simply $A\,d\omega$, where A is a constant depending on the number of molecules under observation.

If a dipole moment μ is oriented at angle θ to a field of strength F its potential energy* is $U = -\mu F \cos\theta$. According to the Boltzmann equation, the number of molecules oriented within the solid angle $d\omega$ is then

$$A \exp(-U/kT)\, d\omega = A \exp(\mu F \cos\theta/kT)\, d\omega$$

The average value of the dipole moment in the direction of the field, by analogy with Eq. (7.47), can be written

$$\overline{m} = \frac{\int_0^{4\pi} A \exp(\mu F \cos\theta/kT)\mu \cos\theta\, d\omega}{\int_0^{4\pi} A \exp(\mu F \cos\theta/kT)\, d\omega}$$

To evaluate this expression, let $\mu F/kT = x$, $\cos\theta = y$; then $d\omega = 2\pi \sin\theta\, d\theta = 2\pi dy$. Thus

$$\frac{\overline{m}}{\mu} = \frac{\int_{-1}^{+1} e^{xy} y\, dy}{\int_{-1}^{+1} e^{xy}\, dy}$$

Since

$$\int_{-1}^{+1} e^{xy}\, dy = (e^x - e^{-x})/x$$

$$\frac{\overline{m}}{\mu} = \frac{e^x + e^{-x}}{e^x - e^{-x}} - \frac{1}{x} = \coth x - \frac{1}{x} \equiv L(x)$$

* Harnwell, *op. cit.*, p. 64.

Here $L(x)$ is called the *Langevin function*, in honor of the inventor of this treatment.

In most cases $x = \mu F/kT$ is a small fraction* so that on expanding $L(x)$ in a power series, only the first term need be retained, leaving $L(x) = x/3$ or

$$\overline{m} = (\mu^2/3kT)F \tag{14.7}$$

The orientation polarization due to permanent dipoles is now added to the induced polarization. Instead of Eq. (14.6), the total molar polarization is therefore

$$\frac{\epsilon - 1}{\epsilon + 2}\frac{M}{\rho} = P_M = \frac{4\pi}{3} L\left(\alpha + \frac{\mu^2}{3kT}\right) \tag{14.8}$$

This equation was derived by P. Debye.

It is now possible to evaluate both α and μ from the intercept and slope of P_M vs. $1/T$ plots, as shown in Fig. 14.3. The necessary experimental data are values of the dielectric constant over a range of temperatures. These can be obtained by measuring the capacitance of a parallel plate capacitor in which the vapor or solution under investigation is the dielectric between the plates. Some values for dipole moments are collected in Table 14.1.†

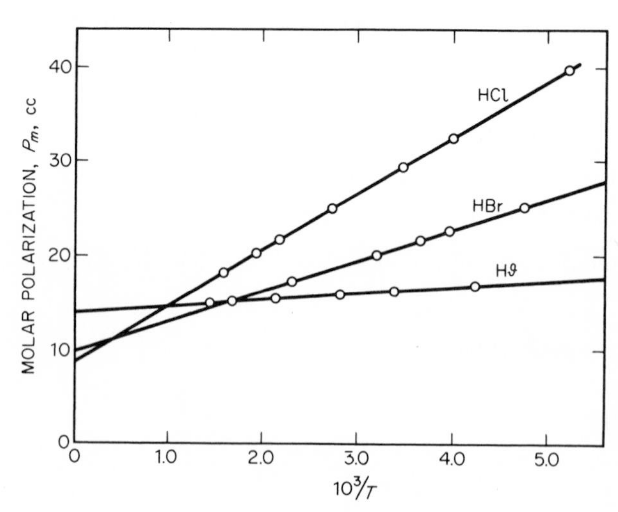

FIG. 14.3 Application of the Debye equation (14.8) to the molar polarizations of the hydrogen halides.

5. DIPOLE MOMENTS AND MOLECULAR STRUCTURE

Dipole moments provide two kinds of information about molecular structure: (1) The extent to which a bond is permanently polarized, or its per cent ionic

* Values of μ range around 10^{-18} (esu)(cm). If a capacitor with 1 cm between plates is charged to 3000 volts, $\mu F = 10^{-18}[(3 \times 10^3)/(3 \times 10^2)] = 10^{-17}$ erg, compared to $kT = 10^{-14}$ erg at room temperature.

† Accurate dipole moments can also be obtained from an analysis of the effect of electric fields on molecular spectra (Stark effect) and from the *electric resonance method* applied to molecular beams.

TABLE 14.1 DIPOLE MOMENTS

Compound	Moment (debyes)	Compound	Moment (debyes)
HCN	2.93	CH_3F	1.81
HCl	1.03	CH_3Cl	1.87
HBr	0.78	CH_3Br	1.80
HI	0.38	CH_3I	1.64
H_2O	1.85	C_2H_5Cl	2.05
H_2S	0.95	n-C_3H_7Cl	2.10
NH_3	1.49	i-C_3H_7Cl	2.15
SO_2	1.61	CHF_3	1.61
CO_2	0.00	CH_2Cl_2	1.58
CO	0.12	$CH{\equiv}CCl$	0.44
NO	0.16	CH_3COCH_3	2.85
KF	2.55	CH_3OH	1.69
KCl	2.667	C_2H_5OH	1.69
KBr	2.821	C_6H_5OH	1.70
LiH	5.883	$C_6H_5NO_2$	4.08
B_2H_6	0.00	CH_3NO_2	3.50
H_2O_2	2.20	$C_6H_5CH_3$	0.37

character, and (2) an insight into the geometry of the molecule, especially the angles between the bonds. Only a few typical applications will be mentioned.*

Carbon dioxide has no dipole moment, despite the difference in electronegativity between carbon and oxygen. We can conclude that the molecule is linear, O—C—O; the moments due to the two C—O bonds, which are surely present owing to the difference in electronegativity of the atoms, exactly cancel each other by vector addition.

On the other hand, water has a moment of 1.85 d, and must have a triangular structure. It has been estimated that each O—H bond has a moment of 1.60 d and the bond angle is therefore about 105°, as shown by a vector diagram.

Consider the substituted benzene derivatives:

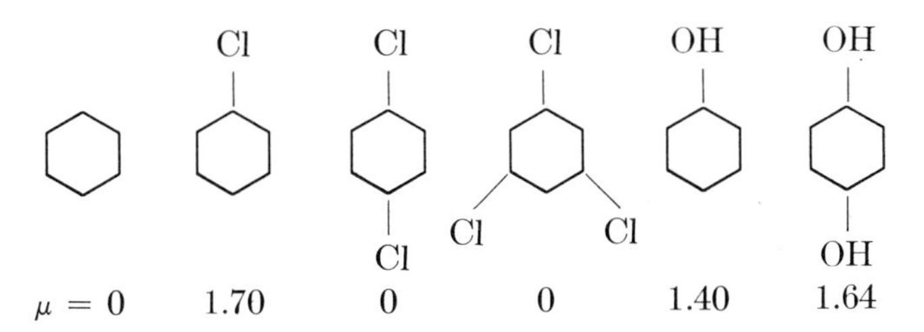

The zero moments of p-dichloro- and sym-trichlorobenzene indicate that benzene is planar and that the C—Cl bond moments are directed in the plane of the ring, thereby adding to zero. The moment of p-di-OH benzene, on the other hand, shows that the O—H bonds are not in the plane of the ring, but directed at an angle to it, thus providing a net moment.

* R. J. W. LeFevre, *Dipole Moments* (London: Methuen, 1948) gives many interesting examples.

The dipole moment of ethyl chloride (2.05 d) is considerably larger than that of chlorobenzene (1.70 d). We might have expected that the electronegative Cl atom would draw electrons away from the π orbitals of benzene and thus place a higher effective negative charge on the Cl by an inductive effect. There must evidently be some more powerful influence that tends to decrease the negative charge on the aromatic Cl. We are thus led to consider resonance structures such as:

:Cl+ :Cl+ :Cl+

The internuclear distance in HCl is 1.26 Å (found by methods described in Sec. 22). If the structure is H^+Cl^-, the dipole moment should be

$$\mu = (1.26)(4.80) = 6.05 \text{ d}$$

The actual moment of 1.03 suggests therefore that the ionic character of the bond is equivalent to a separation of charges of about $e/6$.

How does this separation of charge arise? The most naive interpretation would be that the different electronegativities of the H and Cl atoms cause the center of negative charge of the *pair of electrons* in the H—Cl bond to be displaced toward the Cl. This model is shown in Fig. 14.4(a). The bond is shown as the pairing of the $1s$ electron of the H with one of the $3p$ electrons of the Cl. In such a model the remaining nonbonding electrons in Cl are symmetrically disposed about the Cl nucleus and make zero net contributions to the dipole. We know

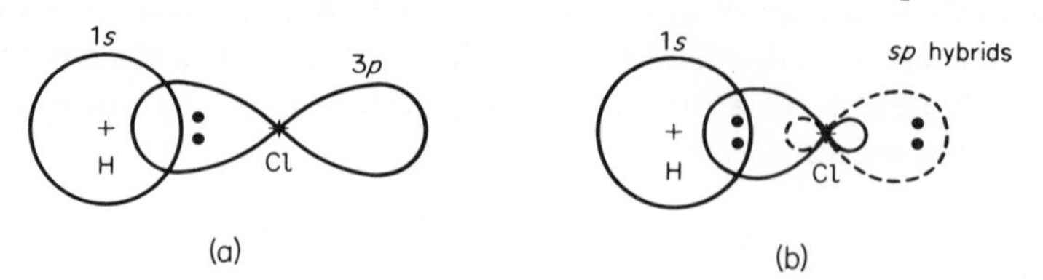

FIG. 14.4 Two models for the origin of the dipole moment in HCl.

however, that a greater overlap of the bonding orbitals and hence a stronger bond can be obtained if we first form hybrid *sp* orbitals with the chlorine $3s$ and $3p_x$. One of these hybrid orbitals then overlaps the hydrogen $1s$ orbital to form the bonding orbital that holds the electron pair. Fig. 14.4(b) shows this model. Now, however, the pair of electrons in the nonbonding *sp* hybrid orbital are not symmetrically disposed about the Cl nucleus and thus must make a substantial contribution to the dipole moment $H^+ \leftarrow Cl^-$. It is highly probable that such *atomic dipoles* contribute to the total dipole moment in many cases, so that we must abandon the older model by which a dipole moment was explained entirely in terms of the displacements of pairs of bonding electrons.

6. POLARIZATION AND REFRACTIVITY

It may be recalled that one of the most interesting results of Maxwell's electromagnetic theory of light* was the relationship $\epsilon = n^2$, where n is the index of refraction.

The physical reason for this relationship can be understood without going into the details of the electromagnetic theory. The refractive index of a medium is the ratio of the speed of light in a vacuum to its speed in the medium, $n = c/c_m$. Light always travels more slowly through a material substance than it does through a vacuum. A light wave is a rapidly alternating electric and magnetic field. This field acts to polarize the dielectric through which it passes, pulling the electrons back and forth in rapid alternation. The greater the polarizability of the molecules, the greater is the field induced in opposition to the applied field, and the greater therefore is the "resistance" to the transmission of the light wave. We have already seen that increasing the polarization increases the dielectric constant. The detailed theory leads to the Maxwell relation, $\epsilon = n^2$.

This relation is experimentally confirmed only under certain conditions: (1) The substance contains no permanent dipoles, (2) the measurement is made with radiation of long wavelength, in the infrared region, (3) the refractive index is not measured in the neighborhood of a wavelength where the radiation is absorbed.

The first restriction is due to the fact that dielectric constants are measured at low frequencies (500 to 5000 kc), whereas refractive indices are measured with radiation of frequency about 10^{12} kc. A permanent dipole cannot line up quickly enough to follow an electric field alternating with such high frequency. Permanent dipoles therefore contribute to the dielectric constant but *not* to the refractive index.

The second restriction is due to the effect of high frequencies on the induced polarization. With high-frequency radiation (in the visible) only the electrons in molecules can adjust themselves to the rapidly alternating electric field; the more sluggish nuclei stay practically in their equilibrium positions. With the lower-frequency infrared radiation the nuclei are also displaced.

It is customary, therefore, to distinguish, in the absence of permanent dipoles, an electronic polarization P_E and an atomic polarization P_A. The total polarization, $P_A + P_E$, is obtained from dielectric-constant measurements or infrared determinations of the refractive index. The latter are hard to make, but sometimes results with visible light can be successfully extrapolated. The electronic polarization P_E can be calculated from refractive-index measurements with visible light. Usually P_A is only about 10 per cent of P_E, and it may often be neglected.

When the Maxwell relation is satisfied, we obtain from Eq. (14.6) the Lorenz-Lorentz equation,

$$R_M \equiv \frac{n^2 - 1}{n^2 + 2}\frac{M}{\rho} = P_M \tag{14.9}$$

* G. P. Harnwell, *op. cit.*, p. 579.

The quantity at the left of Eq. (14.9) is called the *molar refraction* R_M. When the Maxwell relation holds, $R_M = P_M$.

The molar refraction R_M has the dimensions of volume. It can indeed be shown from simple electrostatic theory* that a sphere of conducting material of radius r, in an electric field F, has an induced electric moment of $m = r^3F$. According to this simple picture, the molar refraction should be equal to the true volume of the molecules contained in one mole. A comparison of some values of molecular volume obtained in this way from refractive index measurements with those obtained from the van der Waals b was shown in Table 7.5.

7. DIPOLE MOMENTS FROM DIELECTRIC CONSTANTS AND REFRACTIVE INDICES

The Lorenz-Lorentz equation also provides an alternative method of separating the orientation and the distortion polarizations, and thereby determining the dipole moment. A solution of the dipolar compound in a nonpolar solvent, e.g., nitrobenzene in benzene, is prepared at various concentrations. The dielectric constant is measured and the apparent molar polarization calculated from Eq. (14.8). This quantity is made up of the distortion polarizations of both solute and solvent plus the orientation polarization of the polar solute. The molar polarizations due to distortion can be set equal to the molar refractions R_M, calculated from the refractive indices of the pure liquids. When these R_M are subtracted from the total apparent P_M, the remainder is the apparent molar orientation polarization P_M° for the solute alone. This polarization is plotted against the concentration in the solution and extrapolated to zero concentration.† A value of P_M° is obtained in this way from which the effect of interaction between the dipoles has been eliminated. From Eq. (14.8), therefore, it is equal to $(4\pi/3)L(\mu^2/3kT)$ and the dipole moment of the polar solute molecules can be calculated.

8. MAGNETIC PROPERTIES

The theory for the magnetic properties of molecules resembles in many ways that for the electric polarization. Thus a molecule can have a permanent magnetic moment and also a moment induced by a magnetic field.

Corresponding to Eq. (14.2), we have

$$B = H + 4\pi I \tag{14.10}$$

where B is the magnetic induction, H is the field strength, and I is the intensity of magnetization or magnetic moment per unit volume. These quantities are

* Slater and Frank, *Theoretical Physics*, p. 275.

† E. A. Guggenheim, *Trans. Faraday Soc.* 47, 573 (1951), gives an improved method for extrapolation.

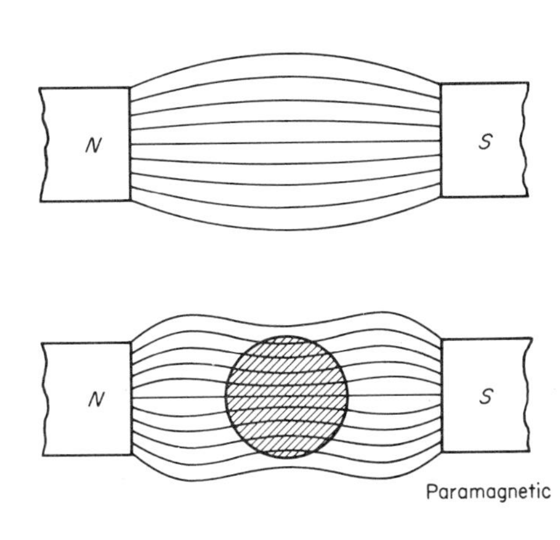

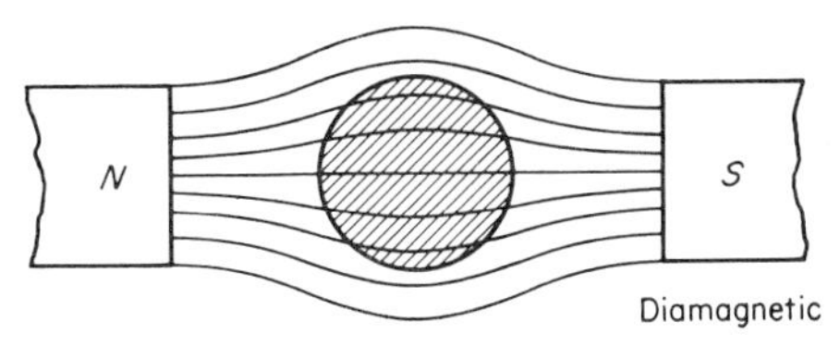

FIG. 14.5 The magnetic lines of force are drawn into a paramagnetic substance, so that the field in it is greater than in free space. The lines of force are pushed out of a diamagnetic substance, so that the field in it is less than in free space.

the magnetic counterparts of the electrical D, E, and P. In a vacuum $B = H$, but otherwise $B = \epsilon' H$, where ϵ', the *permeability*, is the magnetic counterpart of the dielectric constant ϵ. Usually, however, magnetic properties are discussed in terms of

$$\frac{I}{H} = \chi \tag{14.11}$$

where χ is called the *magnetic susceptibility* per unit volume of the medium. (Electric susceptibility would be P/E.) The susceptibility per mole is

$$\chi_M = (M/\rho)\chi \tag{14.12}$$

The magnetic analog of Eq. (14.8) is

$$\chi_M = L\left(\alpha + \frac{\mu^2}{3kT}\right) \tag{14.13}$$

where χ_M is the molar susceptibility, α is the induced magnetic moment, and μ is the permanent magnetic dipole moment. As in the electrical case, the two contributions can be separated by measurements of the dependence of χ_M on temperature. Pierre Curie showed in 1895 that for gases, solutions, and some crystals

$$\chi_M = D + \frac{C}{T} \tag{14.14}$$

where D and C are constants. The theoretical analysis by Langevin in 1905 led to Eq. (14.13) and hence to the value $C = L\mu^2/3k$ for the *Curie constant.*

An important difference from the electrical case now appears in that χ, or χ_M, can be either negative or positive. If χ_M is negative, the medium is called *diamagnetic.* If χ_M is positive, it is called *paramagnetic.* Examples of these two types of magnetic behavior are shown in Fig. (14.5), together with a representation of the paths of magnetic lines of force passing through the two kinds of substances. The magnetic field in a diamagnetic medium is less than in a vacuum; in a paramagnetic medium, it is greater than in a vacuum.

An experimental measurement of susceptibility can be made with the *magnetic balance*. The specimen is suspended from a balance beam so that it is half inside and half outside the region between the poles of a strong magnet (about 5000 gauss). When the magnet is turned on, a paramagnetic sample is drawn into the field region, whereas a diamagnetic sample is pushed out. The force necessary to restore the original balance point is

$$mg = \frac{(\chi_1 - \chi_2)}{2} AH^2 \tag{14.15}$$

where A is the cross sectional area of the specimen, χ_1 is its susceptibility and χ_2 is the susceptibility of the surrounding atmosphere.

9. DIAMAGNETISM

Diamagnetism is the counterpart of the distortion polarization in the electrical case. The effect is exhibited by all substances and is independent of temperature. A simple interpretation is obtained if one imagines the electrons moving about the nuclei to be like currents in a wire. If a magnetic field is applied, the velocity of the electrons is changed, inducing a magnetic field, which in accord with Lenz's Law is opposed in direction to the applied field. The diamagnetic susceptibility is therefore always negative. In the case of an electric current in a wire, if the applied field is kept constant the induced field quickly dies out owing to the atomic resistance. Inside an atom, however, there is no resistance to the electronic current, so that the opposing field persists as long as the external magnetic field is maintained.

The molar diamagnetic susceptibility contributed by electrons in an atom has been calculated as

$$\chi_M = \frac{-Le^2}{6mc^2} \sum \overline{r_i^2} \tag{14.16}$$

where $\overline{r_i^2}$ is the average value of the square of the distance of the i'th electron from the nucleus. The summation is taken over all the electrons in the atom. Eq. (14.16) would not apply exactly to molecules, since r_i would not be properly defined. It does show, however, that the diamagnetic effect will be small because of the small orbits of electrons in atoms. It is of the order of -10^{-6} per gram.

10. PARAMAGNETISM

When paramagnetism occurs, χ is usually 10^{-3} to 10^{-4} per gram, so that the small diamagnetic effect is overwhelmed. Paramagnetism is associated with the orbital angular momentum and spin.

An electron revolving in an orbit is like an electric current in a loop of wire or a turn in a solenoid. The magnetic moment of a current loop is defined as $\mu = AI$ where A is the area of the loop and I is the current. If the current is due to an electron of charge e moving with velocity v, $I = ev/2\pi r$ so that $\mu = (ev/2\pi r)\pi r^2 = evr/2$, where r is the radius of the loop. The angular momentum of the electron of mass m is $p = mvr$. Hence

$$\mu/p = g = e/2m \tag{14.17}$$

The ratio of magnetic moment to angular momentum is the *gyromagnetic ratio g*. Both μ and p are vectors, directed along an axis normal to the plane of the current loop.

The angular momentum can have only quantized values $\sqrt{l(l+1)}(h/2\pi)$. If the atom is in an external field, the frequency of precession of the angular momentum vector is also quantized, so that the component of p in the field direction is restricted to values $m_l(h/2\pi)$ (space quantization). The allowed values of the component in the field direction of the orbital magnetic moment of the electron are

$$\mu_z = m_l(eh/4\pi m) \tag{14.18}$$

We see, therefore, that there is a natural unit of magnetic moment, $\beta = eh/4\pi m$. It is called the *Bohr magneton*. The electromagnetic system of units is based on the definition of the magnetic moment of a current loop as used in this analysis. In these units, $\beta = 0.9273 \times 10^{-20}$ emu.* In electrostatic units, $\beta = eh/4\pi mc = 0.927 \times 10^{-20}$ erg gauss^{-1}.

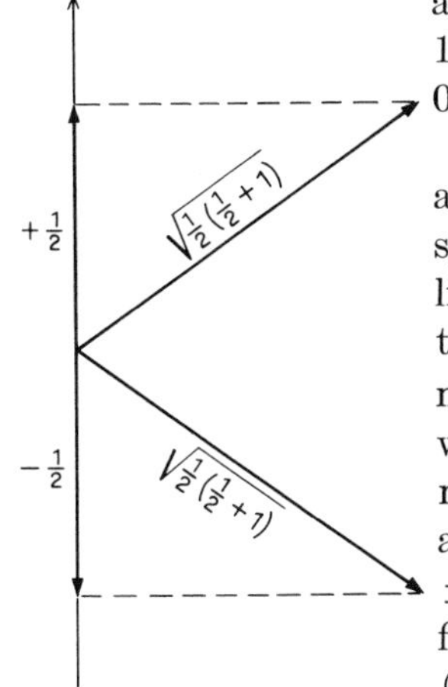

FIG. 14.6 Space quantization of electron spin.

As we have seen, the electron also has an intrinsic angular momentum or spin, which gives rise to a corresponding magnetic moment. A spinning electron is a little magnet. For the electron spin, however, $g = e/m$, twice the value for orbital motion. The spin angular momentum is quantized in units of $\sqrt{s(s+1)}(h/2\pi)$, where $s = \frac{1}{2}$. In an external field, the spin angular momentum is also subject to space quantization, and the allowed values of its component in the field direction are $\pm\frac{1}{2}(h/2\pi)$. The corresponding magnetic moment in the field direction of one unpaired electron spin is $(e/m)(\frac{1}{2})(h/2\pi) = eh/4\pi m$, one Bohr magneton. The quantization of the spin is shown in Fig. 14.6.

In the case of molecules, only the contributions due to spin are important. Within a molecule there are strong internal electric fields, directed along the chemical bonds. In a diatomic molecule, for example, such a field is directed along the internuclear axis. This internal field holds the orbital angular momenta of the electrons in fixed orientations. They cannot line up with an external magnetic field, and thus the contri-

* 1.165×10^{-29} weber meter.

bution they would normally make to susceptibility is ineffective. It is said to be *quenched.* Only the effect due to electron spin remains, and this is not influenced by the internal field. Thus a measurement of the permanent magnetic moment of a molecule tells us how many unpaired spins are in its structure. The magnetic moment for n unpaired spins is $\sqrt{n(n+2)}$ Bohr magnetons.

11. TYPES OF MAGNETIC BEHAVIOR

Especially in the solid state various other types of magnetic behavior occur. The more important types are summarized in Table 14.2.

TABLE 14.2 TYPES OF MAGNETIC BEHAVIOR
(After R. S. Nyholm)

Type	Caused by	Magnitude at 20°C	Temperature Dependence	Example
1. Diamagnetism	Induced magnetic field of orbital electrons	−, very small $\chi \sim 10^{-6}$	Nil	H_2, KCl
2. Normal Paramagnetism	Spin and (usually) orbital angular momentum of electrons	+, small $\chi \sim 10^{-5}$	T^{-1} Curie, or $(T + \Delta)^{-1}$ Curie-Weiss	O_2 $K_3Fe(CN)_6$
3. Temperature independent or Van Vleck Paramagnetism	Atoms with upper state separated by $\Delta E \gg kT$ from ground state	+, very small $\chi \sim 10^{-6}$	Nil	$KMnO_4$ Co^{+2}
4. Free Electron or Pauli Paramagnetism	Paramagnetism of electron	+, very small	very slight	Metals: K, Na
5. Ferromagnetism	Particles arranged on lattice — electrons with parallel spins	+, very large $\chi \sim 10^{-2}$	complicated big decline at Curie T	Metals: Fe
6. Antiferromagnetism	Particles arranged on two lattices with spins on A antiparallel to those on B	+, very small $\chi \sim 10^{-7}$ to 10^{-4}	positive below transition T	$KMnF_3$ MnSe
7. Ferrimagnetism	Particles on interpenetrating lattices with unequal numbers of electrons with spin antiparallel	+, small $\chi \sim 10^{-5}$	positive	Fe_3O_4

12. NUCLEAR PROPERTIES AND MOLECULAR STRUCTURE

An experimental investigation of the structure of a molecule seeks first of all to learn how the nuclei of the atoms in the molecule are arranged in space. This information consists of the bond distances and bond angles in the structure. We are seldom content, however, with such a structure. We want to know also how the electrons are distributed among the nuclei. The distribution of electronic charges tells us the nature of the bonding and should ultimately explain the chemical reactivity of the molecule. Measurements of dipole moments, magnetic susceptibility, optical spectra, and X-ray and electron diffraction yield information about electronic structure. These methods are all based on the interaction of the molecule with an external probe consisting of some kind of electromagnetic field. In most cases, however, these probes are not delicate enough to reveal the finer details of the electron distribution.

In recent years an important breakthrough has been achieved in this field. The idea is *to use the nuclei themselves as probes* to reveal the electron distribution which surrounds them. Nuclei are not unfeeling point charges. They have definite characters of their own which make them sensitive to the electrical environment in which they may be placed. The study of effects caused by the interaction of nuclei with their surroundings can sometimes give us a detailed picture of the distribution of electrical charge within a molecule.

The significant properties of the nuclei are their *magnetic moments* and their *electric quadrupole moments*. A nucleus may possess an intrinsic *nuclear spin* and thus act as a little magnet with magnetic moment μ_n. Although a nucleus cannot have an intrinsic dipole moment, it may have a quadrupole moment* eQ. If a nucleus has a quadrupole moment, the distribution of charge in the nucleus must depart from perfect sphericity. We can represent such nuclei as ellipsoids.

We thus classify the nuclei as shown in Fig. 14.7. Nuclei with quadrupole moments and/or magnetic moments different from zero can act as delicate probes which report on the electromagnetic field that surrounds them.

---

* The electric potential U, due to any cluster of charges obeys the Poisson equation,

$$\nabla^2 U = 0$$

The solution to this equation, obtained in a way similar to that mentioned for the Schrödinger equation on p. 488, is

$$\begin{aligned} U = \frac{A_0}{r} &+ \frac{1}{r^2}(A_{1x}p_x + A_{1y}p_y + A_{1z}p_z) \\ &+ \frac{1}{r^3}(A_{2z}d_{z^2} + A_{2xz}d_{xz} + A_{2yz}d_{yz} + A_{2xy}d_{xy} + A_{2(x^2-y^2)}d_{x^2-y^2} \\ &+ \frac{1}{r^4}(\text{Sum of } f \text{ modes}) + \ldots, \text{etc.} \end{aligned}$$

We note that the potential can be represented as a power series in $(1/r)$. The first term is the coulombic potential due to the net charge of the cluster. The second term is the potential due to the dipole moment of the cluster. The third term defines the contribution due to the quadrupole moment, and the fourth term that due to the octupole moment, etc. The coefficients are written as proportional to p, d, f, etc., orbitals since they have the same form as these functions, being in fact the Legendre functions or spherical harmonics that we find in the problem of the hydrogen atom.

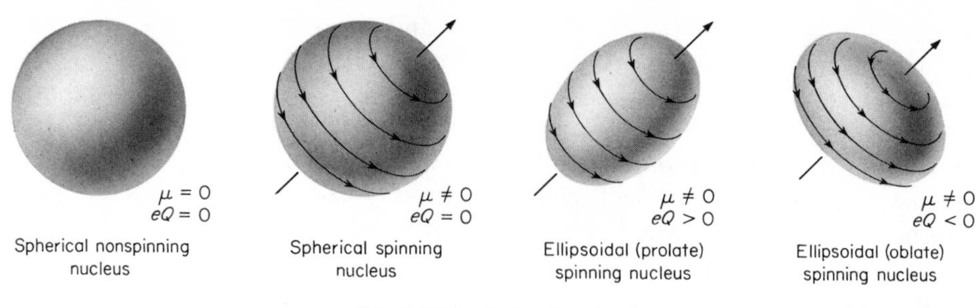

FIG. 14.7 Varieties of nuclei.

13. NUCLEAR PARAMAGNETISM

A nucleus is composed of protons and neutrons, and both these *nucleons* have intrinsic angular momenta or spins, and hence act as elementary magnets. In most nuclei these spins add to give a nonzero resultant nuclear spin. It was first predicted that the magnetic moment of the proton would be one *nuclear magneton*, $\beta_n = eh/4\pi M$, where M is the proton mass. Actually, however, the proton has a magnetic moment of 2.79245 nuclear magnetons, and the neutron has a magnetic moment of -1.9135. The minus sign indicates that the moment behaves like that of a negatively charged particle.* Since M is almost 2000 times the electronic mass m, nuclear magnetic moments are less than electronic magnetic moments by a factor of about 1000.

The nuclear magneton β_n is related to the electronic (or Bohr) magneton β by

$$\beta_n = \beta(m/M); \quad \beta_n = \beta/1835.98 = 5.0504 \times 10^{-24} \text{ erg gauss}^{-1} \tag{14.19}$$

If a nucleus has a spin I, the nuclear angular momentum is $[I(I + 1)]^{1/2}(h/2\pi)$, where I has integral or half-integral values. The magnitude of the nuclear magnetic moment is given by

$$\mu_n = g_n[I(I + 1)]^{1/2}\beta_n \tag{14.20}$$

where g_n is the *nuclear g factor*.

The properties of a number of important nuclei are summarized in Table 14.3.

Nuclear magnetism was first revealed in the *hyperfine structure* of spectral lines. As an example, consider the hydrogen atom, a proton with one orbital electron. The nucleus can have a spin $I = \pm\frac{1}{2}$ and the electron can have a spin $S = \pm\frac{1}{2}$. The nuclear and electron spins can be either parallel or antiparallel to each other, and these two different alinements differ slightly in energy, the parallel state being higher. Thus the ground state of the hydrogen atom is a closely spaced doublet, and this splitting can be observed in the atomic spectrum of hydrogen, if a spectrograph of high resolving power is employed. The spacing between the two levels, $\Delta E = h\nu$, corresponds to a frequency ν of 1420 megacycles. After the prediction of the astrophysicist van der Hulst, an intense

* See the charge distribution in the neutron in Fig. 20.5.

TABLE 14.3 PROPERTIES OF REPRESENTATIVE NUCLEI*

Nuclide	Natural Abundance %	Spin I $(h/2\pi)$	Magnetic Moment μ (nuclear magnetons)	Quadrupole Moment $e \times 10^{-24}$ cm^2	NMR frequency mc at 10 kG field
^{1}H	99.9844	$\frac{1}{2}$	2.79270	—	42.577
^{2}H	0.0156	1	0.85738	2.77×10^{-3}	6.536
^{10}B	18.83	3	1.8006	0.111	4.575
^{11}B	81.17	$\frac{3}{2}$	2.6880	3.55×10^{-2}	13.660
^{13}C	1.108	$\frac{1}{2}$	0.70216	—	10.705
^{14}N	99.635	1	0.40357	2×10^{-2}	3.076
^{15}N	0.365	$\frac{1}{2}$	−0.28304	—	4.315
^{17}O	0.07	$\frac{5}{2}$	−1.8930	-4.0×10^{-3}	5.772
^{19}F	100	$\frac{1}{2}$	2.6273	—	40.055
^{31}P	100	$\frac{1}{2}$	1.1305	—	17.235
^{33}S	0.74	$\frac{3}{2}$	0.64272	-6.4×10^{-2}	3.266
^{39}K	93.08	$\frac{3}{2}$	0.39094	—	1.987

* A complete table is given by J. A. Pople, W. G. Schneider and H. J. Bernstein, *High Resolution Nuclear Magnetic Resonance*, (New York: McGraw-Hill, 1959), p. 480.

emission of radiation at this frequency was observed from clouds of interstellar dust. The study of this phenomenon is an important part of the rapidly developing subject of radioastronomy, which is providing much information about hitherto uncharted regions of the universe.

14. NUCLEAR MAGNETIC RESONANCE

If a nucleus with spin I is placed in a magnetic field, space quantization occurs. The magnetic moment vector must precess about the field direction, and its component in the direction of the field is restricted to values

$$\mu = m_n g_n \beta_n \tag{14.21}$$

where $m_n = I, I-1, I-2, \ldots -I$. Fig. 14.8 shows an example of the space quantization of the nuclear spin of a nucleus with $I = 4$ (e.g., ^{40}K). In the magnetic field the states with different values of m_n have slightly different energies. The potential energy of the magnet with a component of moment μ in the direction of the field H_o is

$$U_m = -\mu H_o = -m_n g_n \beta_n H_o \tag{14.22}$$

The energy spacing between two adjacent levels ($\Delta m_n = \pm 1$) is

$$\Delta E = g_n \beta_n H_o$$

As an example, consider the case of the nucleus ^{19}F for which $g_n = 5.256$. In a field of 10^4 gauss,

$$\Delta E = (5.256)(5.0504 \times 10^{-24})(10^4) = 2.653 \times 10^{-19} \text{ erg}$$

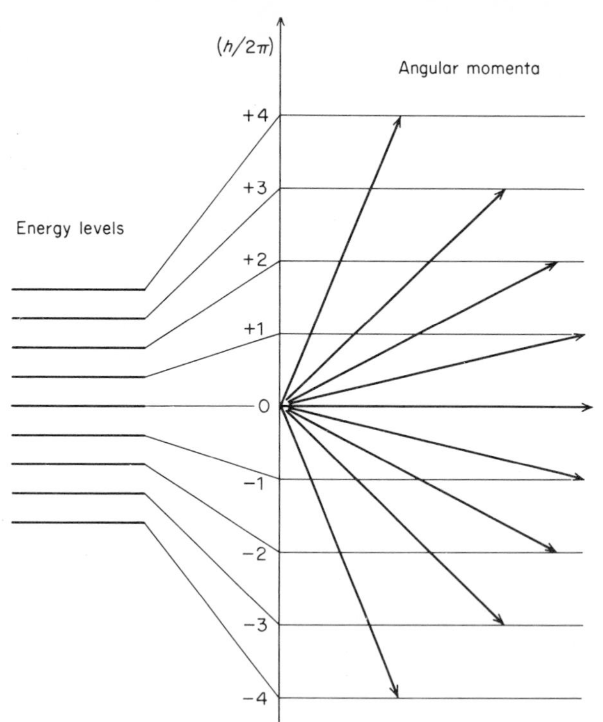

FIG. 14.8 Space quantization of the nuclear spin for the case $I = 4$.

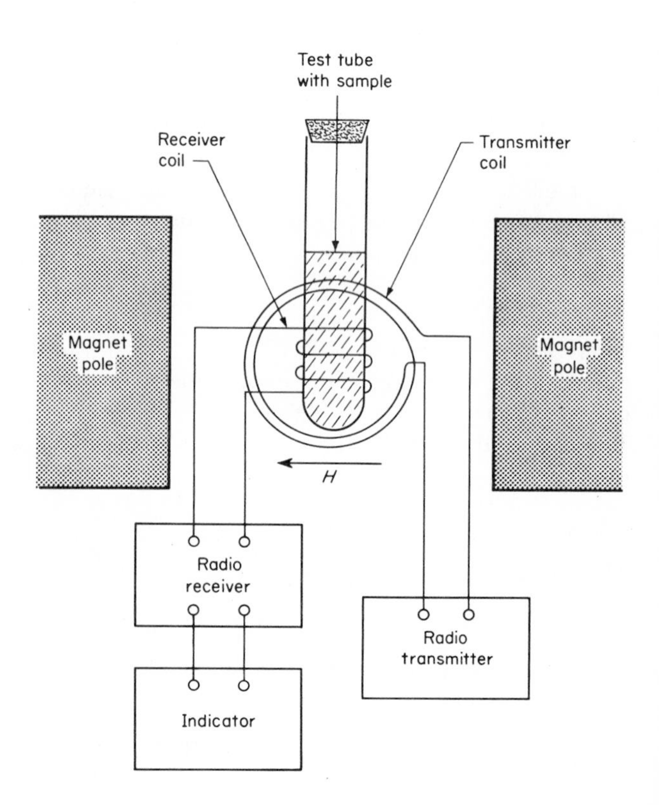

FIG. 14.9 Simplified apparatus for basic nuclear-magnetic-resonance experiment. (Varian Associates)

The frequency of radiation corresponding to this ΔE would be

$$\nu = \frac{\Delta E}{h} = 19.85 \times 10^6 \text{ hz} = 19.85 \text{ mc}$$

which lies in the shortwave region. This frequency would be the same as that of the classical Larmor precession of the magnetic moment about the field direction. The earlier attempts to detect transitions between energy levels of different nuclear-spin components in a magnetic field were unsuccessful. In 1946, however, E. M. Purcell and Felix Bloch independently developed the method of *nuclear magnetic resonance.*

The principle of this method is shown in Fig. 14.9. The field H_o of the magnet is variable from 0 to 10 000 gauss. This field produces an equidistant splitting of the nuclear energy levels which arise as a result of space quantization. The low-power radiofrequency transmitter operates at, for example, 60 megacycles. It causes a small oscillating electromagnetic field to be applied to the sample. This field induces transitions between the energy levels, by a resonance effect, when the frequency of the oscillating field equals that of the transitions. When such transitions occur in the sample, the resultant oscillation in the field induces a voltage oscillation in the receiver coil, which can be amplified and detected. In the instrument shown, the magnetic field of the large magnet is fixed and the radiofrequency of the oscillator is fixed; the resonance condition is achieved by superimposing a small variable *sweep field* on the field of the large magnet.

Figure 14.10 shows an oscillographic trace of the voltage fluctuations over a small range of magnetic sweep field (38 milligauss) around 7050 gauss, with ethyl alcohol as the sample. Note that each different kind of proton in the molecule CH_3CH_2OH appears at a distinct value of H. The reason for this splitting is that the different protons in the molecule have slightly different magnetic environments, and hence slightly different resonant frequencies. The areas under the peaks are in the ratio 3:2:1, corresponding to the relative numbers of protons in the different environments. Each peak also has a fine structure. The structural information that can be provided by this method is thus almost unbelievably detailed, and a new and deep insight into the nature of the chemical bond is provided.

When the frequency of the oscillatory field of the transmitting coil in Fig. 14.9 is the same as the natural precession frequency of the nuclear magnet in the strong external field, energy is absorbed from the oscillatory field. In other words, quanta of microwave radiation are absorbed as the nuclear magnetic quantum number m_n increases by one unit. To have continuous absorption of energy from the oscillating field, however, there must be some effective mechanism by which the nuclear magnet can lose this energy again and return from the "excited state" to the ground state and thus be able to take part in another quantum jump with absorption of energy.

We should mention also that the resonance effect measures the *net* absorption of energy (i.e., the difference between the energy absorbed in going from the

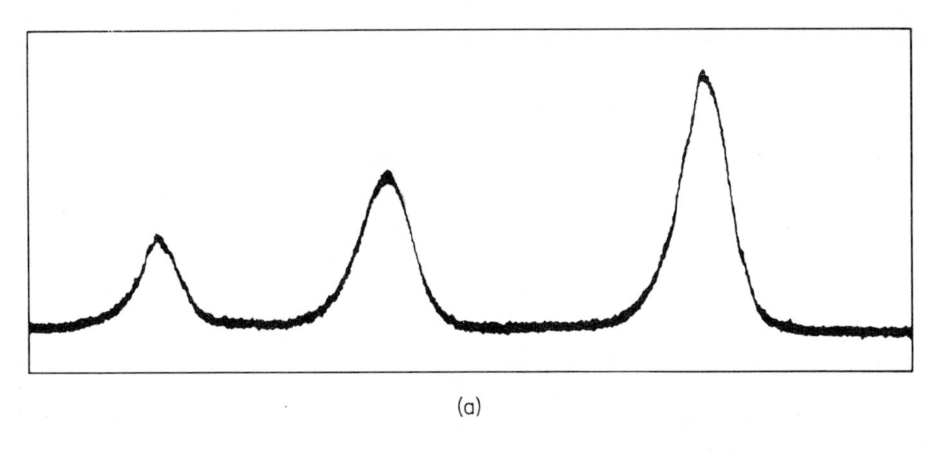

(a)

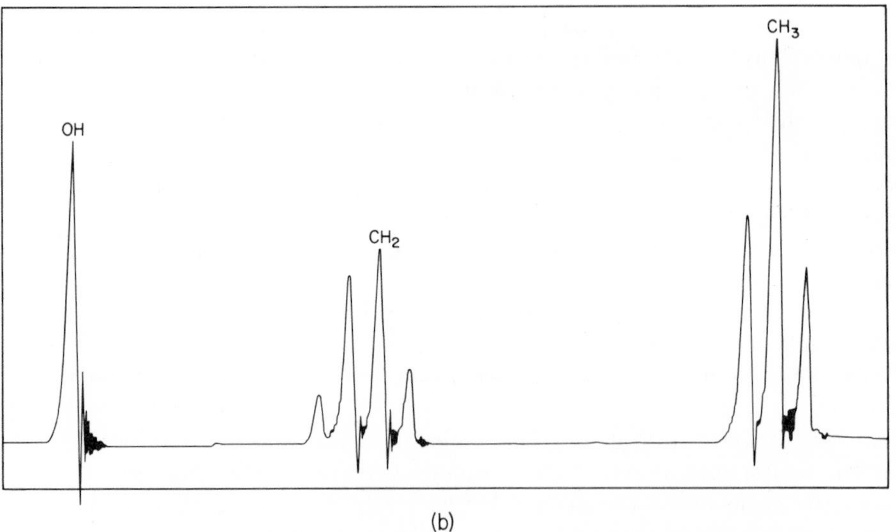

(b)

FIG. 14.10 (a) Nmr spectrum of ethanol at low resolution (40 mc); (b) Spectrum of ethanol at high resolution (40 mc).

lower to the upper state and the energy emitted in going from the upper to the lower state). Since there are more systems in the lower state (in accord with the Boltzmann factor $e^{-\Delta E/kT}$), there is a net absorption of energy.

The system can return to the lower state not only by emission of radiation, but also by various radiationless mechanisms, which are called *relaxation processes.* If it were not for these relaxation processes, nuclear resonance would be impossible in practice, since there would be no way to maintain the thermal equilibrium which keeps the lower states less populated than the upper ones.

There are two kinds of relaxation to be distinguished. The relaxation that establishes the equilibrium value of the nuclear magnetization along the direction of the external field is called *longitudinal relaxation.* It follows a kinetic law which is first order, in that the rate of relaxation depends on the first power of the

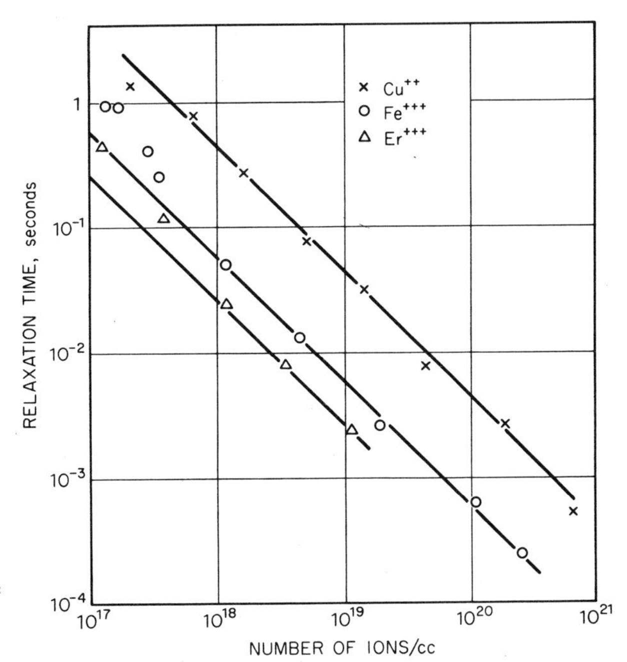

FIG. 14.11 Relaxation time T_1 for solutions of paramagnetic ions, measured at 29 mc/sec.

excess (over the equilibrium value) of the number of nuclei in the upper state. From Eq. (8.11),

$$n - n_e = (n - n_e)_0 \, e^{-k_1 t} = (n - n_e)_0 \, e^{-t/T_1}$$

where the reciprocal of the rate constant k_1 is called T_1, the *longitudinal relaxation time*. This process is also called *spin-lattice relaxation*. It is due to the interaction of various fluctuating local fields in the matter surrounding the oriented nuclei. As one example of many mechanisms, it is found that the addition of paramagnetic ions to water greatly reduces the relaxation time T_1 of the proton, as a consequence of the strong magnetic fields of the unpaired electrons in the ions. Fig. 14.11 shows this effect for three different ions in water.

The other kind of relaxation process is called *transverse relaxation* (time T_2). If the nuclei precessing about a field direction are in phase with one another, there will be a net component of magnetic moment in a plane XY normal to the axis Z of the magnetic field. Any disturbing field that tends to destroy this phase coherence will cause relaxation of the XY component of magnetic moment. One such process is *spin-spin relaxation*, in which a nucleus in a higher spin state transfers energy to a neighboring nucleus by exchanging spins with it.

15. CHEMICAL SHIFTS AND SPIN-SPIN SPLITTING

The environment surrounding the nucleus can have a slight effect on the field sensed by the nucleus. On this fact depends the usefulness of *nmr* in studying the structure of molecules and the nature of chemical bonds. The electrons surrounding a nucleus are acted upon by the external field to produce an induced diamagnetism which partially shields the nucleus. This shielding effect amounts to only about ten parts per million of the external field, but the precision of *nmr* measurements is so great that the effect is readily measured to within 1%. The result is called the *chemical shift.* We saw in Fig. 14.10 an example in which the frequency of proton resonance in CH_3CH_2OH was somewhat different for each of the three different kinds of H atom in the structure. Since the chemical shift is due to the diamagnetism induced by the external field, its absolute magnitude depends on the field strength.

The chemical shift is expressed relative to that of some standard substance. In the case of proton resonance, the standard is usually water. We define the chemical shift parameter δ as

$$\delta = \frac{H(\text{sample}) - H(\text{reference})}{H(\text{reference})} \times 10^6 \tag{14.23}$$

Some examples of δ for different kinds of H atoms in organic molecules are given in Table 14.4. The chemical shift parameter itself can be very useful in determining an unknown molecular structure. The proton *nmr* spectrum of a molecule thus provides a sort of catalog of the different locations of hydrogen atoms in the structure.

When the *nmr* spectrum shown in Fig. 14.10(a) was studied at higher resolution, the peak for CH_2 was split into four lines and that for CH_3 into three lines. The spectrum obtained at high resolution is shown in Fig. 14.10(b). The effect which splits the CH_2 and CH_3 peaks is not a chemical shift due to shielding of

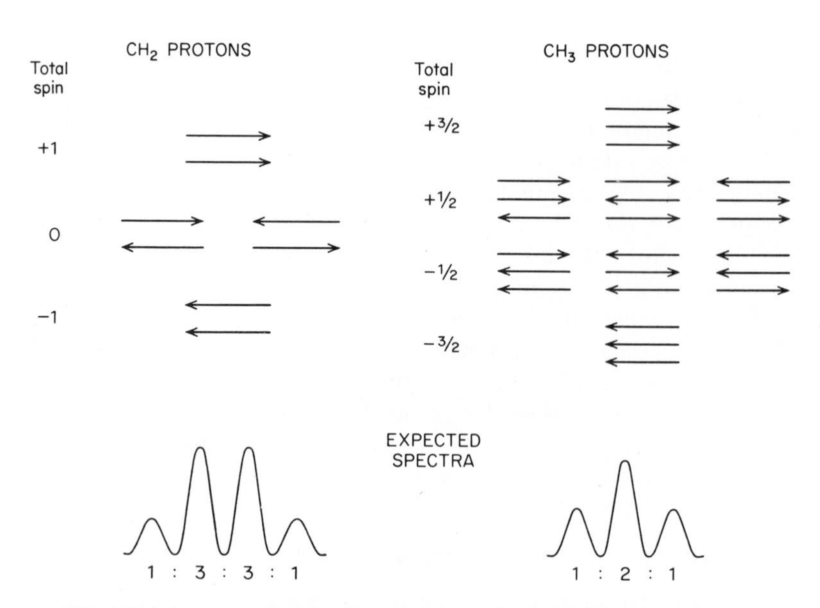

FIG. 14.12 Spin-spin splittings of nmr spectrum of $CH_3 \cdot CH_2OH$. Each proton in CH_2 "feels" four different spin arrangements of CH_3 and each proton of CH_3 "feels" three different spin arrangements of CH_2.

TABLE 14.4 Chemical Shifts of Proton Resonances Relative to Water as Zero

$—SO_3H$	-6.7 ± 0.3	H_2O	(0.00)
$—CO_2H$	-6.4 ± 0.8	$—OCH_3$	$+1.6 \pm 0.3$
RCHO	-4.7 ± 0.3	$\equiv C—H$	$+2.4 \pm 0.4$
$RCONH_2$	-2.9	RSH	$+3.3$
ArOH	-2.3 ± 0.3	$—CH_2—$	$+3.5 \pm 0.5$
ArH	-1.9 ± 1.0	RNH_2	$+3.6 \pm 0.7$
$=CH_2$	-0.6 ± 0.7	$\geqslant C—CH_3$	$+4.1 \pm 0.6$
ROH	-0.1 ± 0.7	R_2NH	$+4.4 \pm 0.1$

After J. D. Roberts, *Nuclear Magnetic Resonance* (New York: McGraw-Hill, 1959). Data from H. S. Gutowsky, L. H. Meyer and A. Saika, *J. Am. Chem. Soc.*, *75*, 4567 (1953).

nuclei by surrounding electrons; this conclusion is proved by the fact that the observed splitting does not depend on the strength of the applied field. The effect is caused by the interaction of the nuclear spins (magnetic moments) of one set of protons with those of another. It is therefore called *spin-spin splitting.*

Consider first the two protons A and B of the CH_2 group. How can the spins of protons A and B be arranged in relation to the spin of a given proton in the CH_3 group. There are four possible ways:

(1) Spin parallel to both A and B
(2) Spin antiparallel to both A and B
(3) Spin parallel to A, antiparallel to B
(4) Spin antiparallel to A, parallel to B

The last two arrangements clearly have the same energy. The result of the spin-spin interaction is that a proton in the CH_3 group can feel three slightly different magnetic fields, depending on its relation to the spins of the CH_2 protons. The resonance signal thus splits into three components, as shown in Fig. 14.12. In the same way a proton in the CH_2 group feels slightly different fields depending on how its spin is related to those of the CH_3 group. There are four energetically different arrangements possible, as shown in Fig. 14.12.

The analysis of the spin-spin coupling in various structures has also provided much important information about the detailed nature of chemical bonds in molecules and in crystals.*

16. ELECTRON DIFFRACTION OF GASES

One of the most useful methods for measuring bond distances and bond angles has been the study of the diffraction of electrons by gases and vapors. The wavelength of 40000 volt electrons is 0.06 Å, about one-twentieth the magnitude of interatomic distances in molecules, so that diffraction effects are expected.

On p. 462 diffraction by a set of slits was discussed in terms of the Huygens construction. In the same way, if a collection of atoms at fixed distances apart

* J. A. Pople, W. G. Schneider, and H. T. Bernstein, *op. cit.*, give complete details.

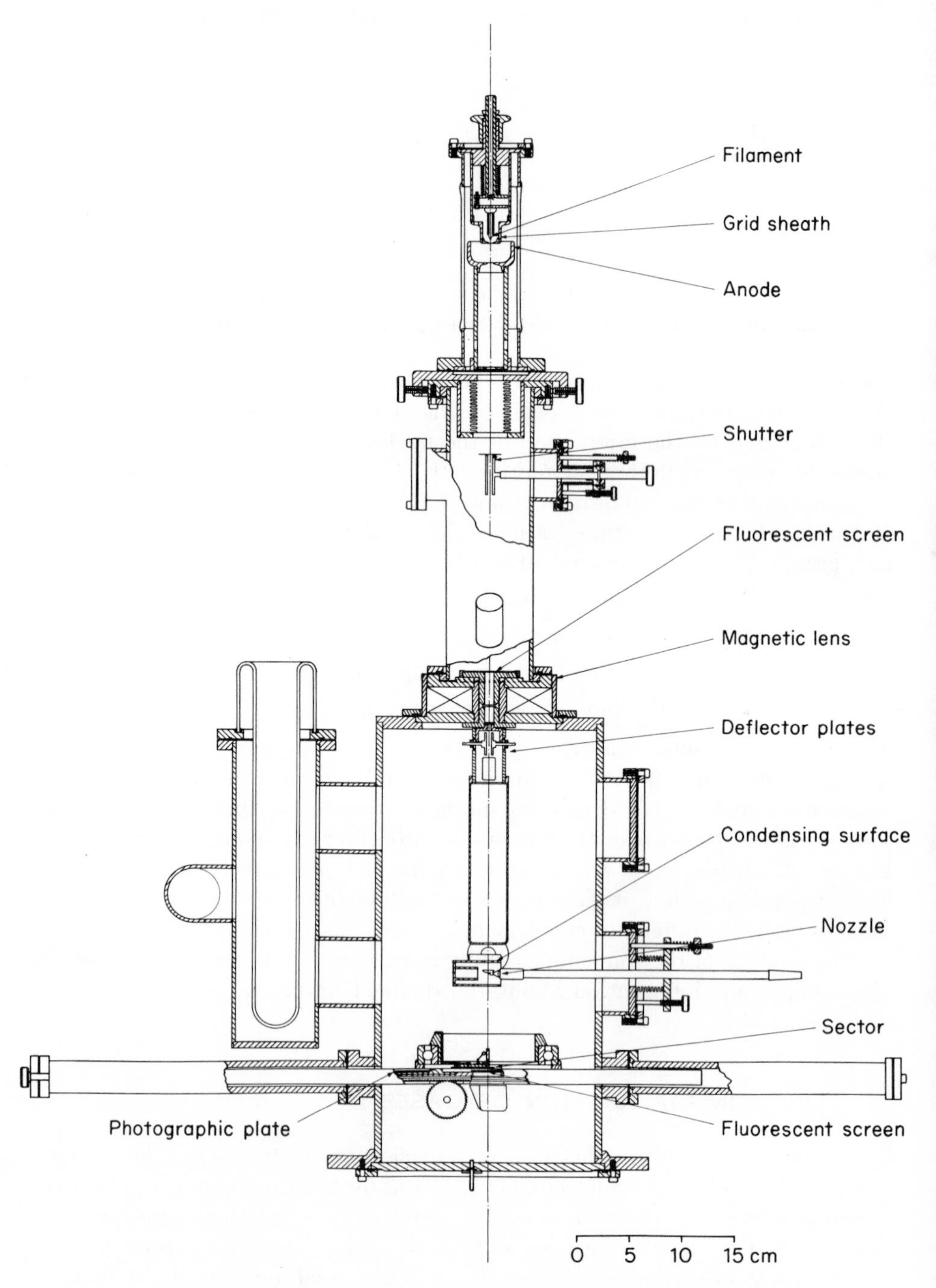

FIG. 14.13 Apparatus for electron diffraction of gases. [L. O. Brockway. University of Michigan]

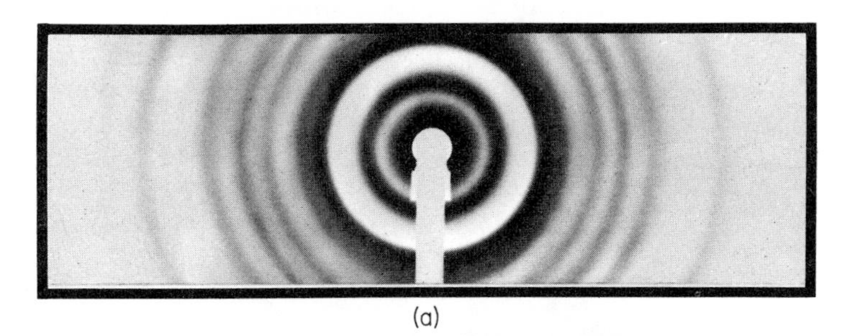
(a)

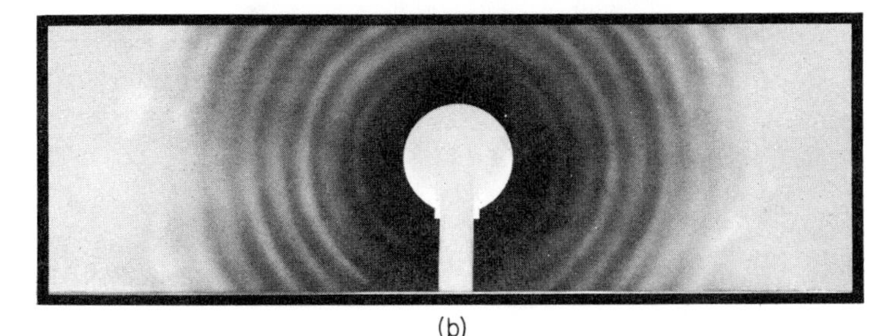
(b)

FIG. 14.14 Electron diffraction patterns from gases. (a) coronene; (b) phosphorus trichloride [Otto Bastiansen, Norges Tekniske Høgskole, Trondheim]

(i.e., a molecule) is placed in a beam of radiation, each atom can be regarded as a new source of spherical wavelets. From the interference pattern produced by these wavelets, the spacial arrangement of the scattering centers can be determined. An experimental apparatus for electron diffraction of gases is illustrated in Fig. 14.13. The rotating heart-shaped sector is placed in front of the photographic plate in order to provide an exposure time that increases with angle of scattering, and thus to compensate for the sharp decrease of scattering intensity with angle. The type of pattern found is shown in Fig. 14.14.

The electron beam traverses a collection of many gas molecules, oriented at random to its direction. Maxima and minima occur in the diffraction pattern despite the random orientation of the molecules. This is because the scattering centers occur as groups of atoms with the same definite fixed arrangement within every molecule. A collection of individual atoms, e.g., argon gas, would give no diffraction rings. Diffraction by gases was treated theoretically (for X rays) by Debye in 1915, but electron-diffraction experiments were not carried out until the work of Wierl in 1930.

We can show the essential features of the diffraction theory by considering the simplest case, that of a diatomic molecule.

Consider in Fig. 14.15 the molecule AB, with atom A at the origin and B a distance r away. The orientation of the molecule AB is specified by the angles α and ϕ. The incident electron beam enters parallel to the Y axis and diffraction occurs through an angle θ. The interference between the waves scattered from A and B depends on the difference between the lengths of the paths they traverse. The calculation of the path difference δ requires that we recognize points on the diffracted and undiffracted beams which are in phase with each other. Hence drop from B a perpendicular BN onto the diffracted direction, and a perpendicular BM onto the undiffracted direction. Now M and N are in phase and the path difference $\delta = AN - AM$.

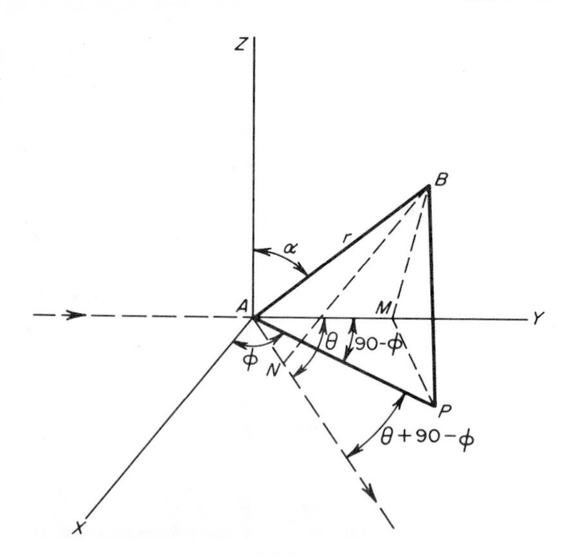

FIG. 14.15 Scattering of electrons by a diatomic molecule.

Since PM is $\perp AY$ and PN is $\perp$ the diffracted beam,

$$\delta = AN - AM = AP \cos (\theta + \phi - 90) - AP \cos (90 - \phi)$$

But $AP = r \sin \alpha$, so that

$$\delta = r \sin \alpha \, [\sin (\theta + \phi) - \sin \phi]$$

$$\delta = 2\, r \sin \alpha \cos \left(\phi + \frac{\theta}{2}\right) \sin \frac{\theta}{2}$$

In order to add waves that differ in phase and amplitude, it is convenient to represent them in the complex plane and to add vectorially.* The difference in phase between the two scattered waves is $(2\pi/\lambda)\delta$. We shall assume for simplicity that the atoms A and B are identical. Then the resultant amplitude at P is $A = A_0 + A_0 e^{2\pi i\delta/\lambda}$. A_0, called the *atomic form factor for electron scattering*,† depends on the nuclear charge of the atom. The intensity of radiation is proportional to the square of the amplitude, or in this case to $A\bar{A}$, the amplitude times its complex conjugate. Thus,

$$\begin{aligned} I \sim A\bar{A} &= A_0^2(1 + e^{-2\pi i\delta/\lambda})(1 + e^{2\pi i\delta/\lambda}) \\ &= A_0^2(2 + e^{-2\pi i\delta/\lambda} + e^{2\pi i\delta/\lambda}) \\ &= 2A_0^2\left(1 + \cos \frac{2\pi\delta}{\lambda}\right) = 4A_0^2 \cos^2 \frac{\pi\delta}{\lambda} \end{aligned}$$

---

* See Courant and Robbins, *What is Mathematics?* (New York: Oxford Univ. Press, 1941) p. 94.

† Whereas X rays are scattered primarily by the electrons in atoms, fast electrons are scattered primarily by the nuclei.

In order to obtain the required formula for the intensity of scattering of a randomly oriented group of molecules, it is necessary to average the expression for the intensity at one particular orientation (α, ϕ) over all possible orientations. The differential element of solid angle is $\sin \alpha \, d\alpha \, d\phi$, and the total solid angle of the sphere around AB is 4π. Hence the required average intensity becomes

$$I_{av} \sim \frac{4A_0^2}{4\pi} \int_0^{2\pi} \int_0^{\pi} \cos^2 \left[2\pi \frac{r}{\lambda} \sin \frac{\theta}{2} \sin \alpha \cos \left(\phi + \frac{\theta}{2} \right) \right] \sin \alpha \, d\alpha \, d\phi$$

On integration,*

$$I_{av} = 2A_0^2 \left(1 + \frac{\sin sr}{sr} \right) \tag{14.24}$$

where

$$s = \frac{4\pi}{\lambda} \sin \frac{\theta}{2}$$

In Fig. 14.16(a), I/A_0^2 is plotted against s, and the maxima and minima in the intensity are clearly evident.

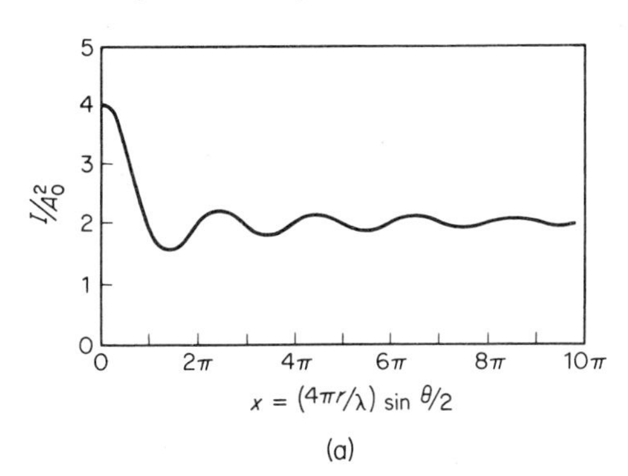

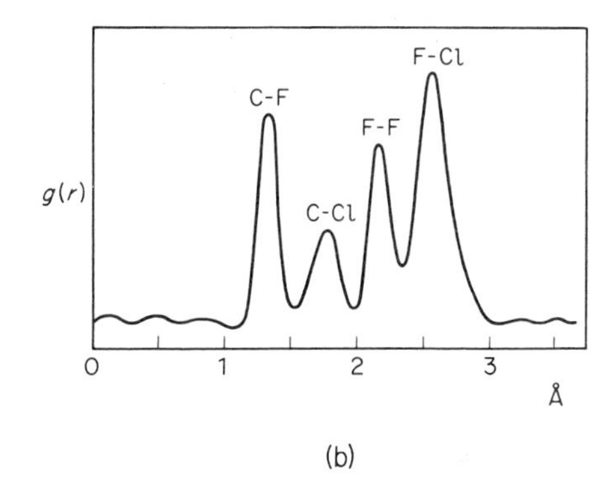

FIG. 14.16 (a) Scattering curve for diatomic molecule-plot of Eq. 14.24; (b) Radial distribution function for the compound CF_3Cl.

---

* Let

$$I_{av} = \frac{A_0^2}{\pi} \int_0^{\pi} \int_0^{2\pi} \cos^2 (A \cos \beta) \, d\beta \sin \alpha \, d\alpha$$

where

$$A = (2\pi r/\lambda) \sin \frac{\theta}{2} \sin \alpha \qquad \text{and} \qquad \beta = \phi + (\theta/2)$$

Since $\cos^2 \beta = (1 + \cos 2\beta)/2$,

$$I_{av} = \frac{A_0^2}{\pi} \int_0^{\pi} \int_0^{2\pi} \left(\frac{d\beta}{2} + \cos (2 A \cos \beta) \, d\beta \right) \sin \alpha \, d\alpha$$

The integral can be evaluated by a series expansion of the cosine $\left[\cos x = 1 - \frac{x^2}{2!} + \frac{x^4}{4!} - \ldots \right]$ followed by a term by term integration first over β and then over α.

In a more complex molecule with atoms j, k (having scattering factors A_j, A_k) a distance r_{jk} apart, the resultant intensity would be

$$I(\theta) = \sum_j \sum_k A_j A_k \frac{\sin sr_{jk}}{sr_{jk}} \tag{14.25}$$

This is called the *Wierl equation*. The summation must be carried out over all pairs of atoms in the molecule.

17. INTERPRETATION OF ELECTRON-DIFFRACTION PICTURES

In electron diffraction it is the scattering by the nuclei that provides information about the structure of molecules. The scattering by the diffusely distributed electrons is less intense, and the observed scattering curves can be corrected for it. The general incoherent background scattering can also be eliminated from the total scattering before the data are used for the determination of structure. One thus uses a molecular scattering $M(s) = (I_t/I_b) - 1$ where I_t is the total intensity and I_b is a suitably chosen background.

This M_s can be related to a radial distribution function $g(r)$ which gives the probability that a nucleus j will be found at a distance r from a nucleus k in the molecule.

$$g(r) = \int_0^{s(\max)} sM(s) \exp(-bs^2) \sin sr \, ds \tag{14.26}$$

Thus $g(r)$ will have a maximum for each value of r corresponding to an internuclear distance in the molecule. The integral is taken from $s = 0$ to the maximum angle of scattering measured. The factor $\exp(-bs^2)$ is a weighting factor introduced to improve the convergence of the integral. The computation of these integrals can now be done quickly on a machine.* An example of a radial distribution function is shown in Fig. 14.16(b) for the molecule CF_3Cl, but peaks are not always so completely resolved. Bond angles in a molecule can also be computed if enough neighboring internuclear distances are known.

Electron-diffraction data can also be analyzed by a direct comparison between the experimental $M(s)$ curve and curves computed from the Wierl equation for selected values of molecular parameters (distances and angles).

Some results of electron diffraction studies are collected in Table 14.5. As molecules become more complicated, it becomes increasingly difficult to determine an exact structure, since usually only a dozen or so maxima are visible, which obviously will not permit the exact calculation of more than five or six parameters. Each distinct interatomic distance or bond angle constitutes a parameter. It is possible, however, from measurements on simple compounds, to obtain reliable values of bond distances and angles, which may be used to estimate the structures of more complex molecules.

* R. A. Bonham and L. S. Bartell, *J. Chem. Phys. 31*, 702 (1959).

TABLE 14.5 THE ELECTRON DIFFRACTION OF GAS MOLECULES

Diatomic Molecules			
Molecule	Bond Distance Å	Molecule	Bond Distance Å
NaCl	2.51 ± .03	N_2	1.095 ± .005
NaBr	2.64 ± .01	F_2	1.435 ± .010
NaI	2.90 ± .02	Cl_2	2.009 ± .015
KCl	2.79 ± .02	Br_2	2.289 ± .015
RbCl	2.89 ± .01	I_2	2.660 ± .005

Polyatomic Molecules			
Molecule	Configuration	Bond	Bond Distance Å
$CdCl_2$	Linear	Cd—Cl	2.235 ± .030
$HgCl_2$	Linear	Hg—Cl	2.27 ± .03
BCl_3	Planar	B—Cl	1.73 ± .02
SiF_4	Tetrahedral	Si—F	1.55 ± .02
$SiCl_4$	Tetrahedral	Si—Cl	2.01 ± .02
P_4	Tetrahedral	P—P	2.21 ± .02
Cl_2O	Bent, 111 ± 1°	Cl—O	1.70 ± .02
SO_2	Bent, 120°	S—O	1.43 ± .01
CH_2F_2	mm (cf. p. 651)	C—F	1.360 ± .005
CO_2	Linear	C—O	1.162 ± .010
C_6H_6	Planar	C—C	1.393 ± .005
		C—H	1.08 ± .02

18. MOLECULAR SPECTRA

The spectra of atoms consist of sharp lines, and those of molecules appear to be made up of bands in which a densely packed line structure is sometimes revealed under high resolving power. The study of molecular spectra is the most useful of all methods for investigating molecular structure. It affords information not only about the dimensions of molecules but also about the possible molecular energy levels. While other methods pertain to the ground state of the molecule alone, the analysis of spectra also elucidates the nature of excited states.

Spectra arise from the emission or absorption of definite quanta of radiation when transitions occur between certain energy levels. In an atom the energy levels represent different allowed states for the orbital electrons. A molecule too can absorb or emit energy in transitions between different electronic energy levels. Such levels would be associated, for example, with the different molecular orbitals discussed in Sec. 13.10. In addition a molecule can change its energy level in two other possible ways, which do not occur in atoms. These are by changes in the vibrations of the atoms within the molecule and by changes in the rotational energy of the molecule. These energies, like the electronic, are quantized, so that only certain distinct levels of vibrational and rotational energy are permissible.

In the theory of molecular spectra it is customary, as a good first approximation, to consider that the energy of a molecule can be expressed simply as the sum of electronic, vibrational, and rotational contributions.

$$E = E_{\text{elec}} + E_{\text{vib}} + E_{\text{rot}} \tag{14.27}$$

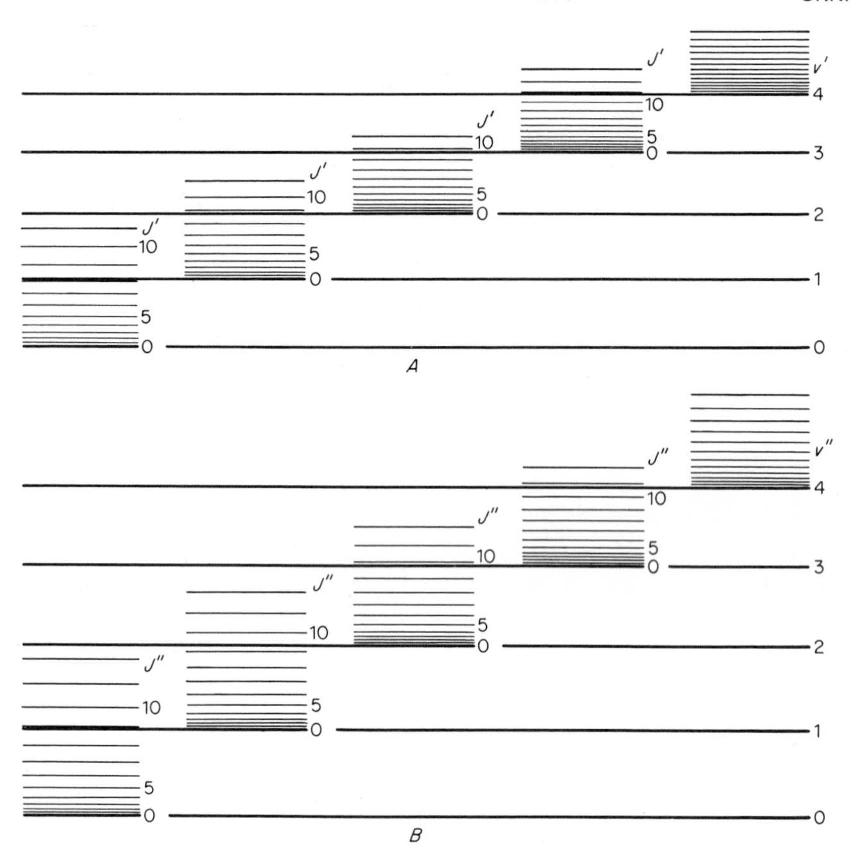

FIG. 14.17 Energy-level diagram for a molecule. Two electronic levels *A* and *B*, with their vibrational levels (*v*) and rotational levels (*J*).

This separation of the energy into three distinct categories is not strictly correct. For example, the atoms in a rapidly rotating molecule are pushed apart by centrifugal forces, which thereby affect the character of the vibrations. Nevertheless, the approximation of Eq. (14.27) suffices to explain many of the observed characteristics of molecular spectra.

As we shall see, the separations between electronic energy levels are usually much larger than those between vibrational energy levels, which in turn are much larger than those between rotational levels. The type of energy-level diagram that results is shown in Fig. 14.17. Associated with each electronic level is a series of vibrational levels, each of which is in turn associated with a series of rotational levels. The close packing of the rotational levels is responsible for the banded structure of molecular spectra.

Transitions between different electronic levels give rise to spectra in the visible or ultraviolet region; these are called *electronic spectra*. Transitions between vibrational levels within the same electronic state are responsible for spectra in the near infrared ($<20\mu$), called *vibration-rotation spectra*. Finally, spectra are observed in the far infrared ($>20\mu$) arising from transitions between rotational levels belonging to the same vibrational level; these are called *pure rotation spectra.*

19. EMISSION AND ABSORPTION OF RADIATION

So far we have discussed applications of quantum mechanics to the structures of atoms and molecules in stationary states, in which the systems do not change with time. If an atom or molecule absorbs or emits quanta of radiation, however, it changes with time from one stationary state to another. Certain general relations can be derived, which will apply to all such changes and will govern the intensities of all kinds of spectra.

The method used is called the *perturbation theory* of quantum mechanics. We consider the atom or molecule in a stationary state as an *unperturbed system* and investigate theoretically what happens when it is *perturbed* by some field, which may vary with time. Such a field might, for example, be the periodic electric or magnetic field of a ray of light passing through the system.

In the absence of any perturbation, the atom or molecule is represented by a wave equation

$$(ih/2\pi)\frac{\partial\Psi}{\partial t} = H_0\Psi \tag{14.28}$$

where H_0 is the Hamiltonian operator (p. 484) of the unperturbed system. The solution of this equation gives a set of allowed wave functions corresponding to allowed energy levels E_n of the stationary states, with

$$\Psi_n^\circ = \psi_n \exp\,(2\pi i E_n t/h)$$

In the presence of the perturbing field there will be an additional term U in the Hamiltonian, so that the wave equation thus becomes

$$(ih/2\pi)\frac{\partial\Psi}{\partial t} = (H_0 + U)\Psi \tag{14.29}$$

Let us suppose that initially ($t = 0$) the state of the system is given by Ψ_0. Eq. (14.29) then allows us to calculate the wave function at any later time t, $\Psi(q, t)$. We expand $\Psi(q, t)$ as a series in terms of $\Psi_n^\circ(q, t)$, the time dependent wave functions of the imperturbed system.

$$\Psi(q, t) = \sum_n a_n(t)\Psi_n^\circ(q, t) \tag{14.30}$$

where the Ψ_n° are wave functions for the unperturbed system.

To solve for the coefficients a_n, we substitute Eq. (14.30) into Eq. (14.29). Making use of Eq. (14.28), we obtain

$$(ih/2\pi)\sum\frac{da_n}{dt}\Psi_n^\circ(q, t) = U\Psi(q, t)$$

We multiply each side by $\Psi_n^{\circ\star}(q, t)$ the complex conjugate of Ψ_n°, and integrate over all q,

$$\left(\frac{ih}{2\pi}\right)\frac{da_n}{dt} = \int \Psi_n^{\circ\star}(q, t)U\Psi(q, t)\, dq$$

We now assume that the perturbation is small so that the change in the wave function is small, and $\Psi(q, t)$ can be replaced by its initial value $\Psi_0(q, t)$, to yield

$$\left(\frac{ih}{2\pi}\right)\frac{da_n}{dt} = \int \Psi_n^{\circ\star}(q, t)U\Psi_0(q, t)\, dq$$

Setting

$$\int \psi_n(q)U\psi_0(q)\, dq \equiv U_{n0} \tag{14.31}$$

we obtain,

$$a_n(t) = \frac{2\pi}{ih}\int_0^t U_{n0} \exp\left[2\pi i(E_0 - E_n)t/h\right] dt \tag{14.32}$$

We can derive immediately an important consequence from Eq. (14.32). If the perturbing potential U varies periodically with time with a frequency ν, the coefficient a_n will not increase unless

$$\nu = (E_0 - E_n)/h$$

Otherwise the two periodic terms under the integral sign in Eq. (14.32) will cancel each other by destructive interference. This is the Bohr condition for a spectral transition.

Once this condition is met, the intensity of the transition will be governed by the value of the quantity U_{n0}, which is called the *transition moment matrix element.*

The probability that at time t, the system is in the state n is given by

$$P_n = |a_n(t)|^2$$

The transition probability per unit time is

$$P_n/t = |a_n|^2/t = \frac{4\pi^2}{h}|U_{n0}|^2$$

20. THE EINSTEIN COEFFICIENTS

Consider in Fig. 14.18 two states of an atom or molecule designated by m and n. If the atom or molecule is placed in a beam of electromagnetic radiation it can undergo transitions between these states under the influence of the perturbing field of the incoming radiation. The number of atoms going from n to m by absorption of a quantum $h\nu_{nm}$ will be proportional to the number N_n in the state n, and to the density of radiation at that frequency $\rho(\nu_{nm})$. Thus,

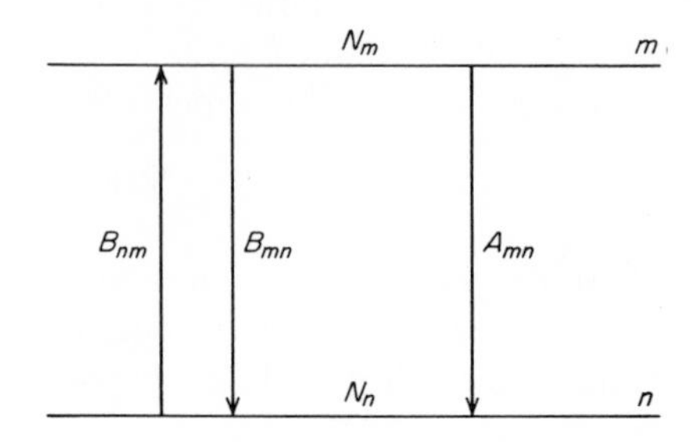

FIG. 14.18 Transitions between two states of a molecule, $E_m - E_n = h\nu_{nm}$.

$$\text{Number of atoms passing from } n \text{ to } m = B_{nm}N_n\rho_n(\nu_{nm})$$

The B_{nm} is called the *Einstein transition probability for absorption.* The transition from m to n caused by the perturbing beam of radiation will be given by

$$\begin{matrix}\text{Number of atoms passing from } m \\ \text{to } n \text{ caused by perturbing radiation}\end{matrix} = B_{mn}N_m\rho(\nu_{nm})$$

In addition to the transition from m to n induced by the field of the beam of radiation there will be a spontaneous emission, with an Einstein transition probability for spontaneous emission given by A_{mn}. We cannot, in fact, calculate this A_{mn} by simple radiation theory, but we can calculate the relation between A_{mn} and B_{mn}, and hence get A_{mn} indirectly. In a steady state the number of atoms or molecules passing from n to m equals the number passing from m to n. Thus

$$N_m[A_{mn} + \rho(\nu_{nm})B_{mn}] = N_nB_{nm}\rho(\nu_{nm})$$

We know that $B_{mn} = B_{nm}$ from the general property of the matrix element $U_{n0} = U^{\star}_{0n}$.* Furthermore, from the Boltzmann relation,

$$N_m/N_n = \exp\left(-h\nu_{nm}/kT\right)$$

Planck's radiation law, Eq. (12.19), was

$$\rho(\nu) = \frac{8\pi h\nu^3}{c^3}\left(e^{h\nu/kT} - 1\right)^{-1}$$

It follows that

$$A_{mn}/B_{mn} = \frac{8\pi h\nu_{nm}^3}{c^3} \tag{14.33}$$

Thus we can calculate A_{mn} if we know B_{mn}. The Dirac theory of radiation also allows us to calculate A_{mn} directly.

Let us consider a collection of atoms or molecules in which some have been raised to excited states and then the radiation or other source of excitation has been turned off. The Einstein coefficient for spontaneous emission is similar to the rate constant of a first-order reaction whose rate can be written

$$-dN_m/dt = A_{mn}N_m$$

If N°_m is the number of atoms or molecules initially in the upper state at $t = 0$, at any time t,

$$N_m = N^{\circ}_m\, e^{-A_{mn}t}$$

After a time $\tau = 1/A_{mn}$ the number of atoms or molecules in the excited state will have declined to $1/e$ of its initial value. For allowed transitions τ is usually

* For any solutions ψ_n, ψ_m of the Schrödinger equation and any Hermitian operator M,

$$\int \psi^{\star}_n M\, \psi_m d\tau = \int \psi^{\star}_m M\, \psi_n d\tau$$

This *Hermitian property* of the matrix elements is the quantum mechanical foundation of the principle of microscopic reversibility. See Norman Davidson, *Statistical Mechanics* (New York: McGraw-Hill, 1962), pp. 222-238.

of the order of 10^{-8} sec. There are some excited states, however, for which τ is much higher ($\sim 10^{-3}$ sec). These are called *metastable states.*

We shall now examine more closely the expression in the *transition probability,* U_{n0} in Eq. (14.31), to see how its value is determined. Consider the case of an atom or molecule subjected to an electric field E_x directed along the X axis. Each electron in the molecule will experience a force $-E_x e$, which corresponds to a potential energy $E_x ex$ $(f = -\partial U/\partial x)$. For all the electrons in the atom or molecule, therefore, this perturbing potential will be

$$U = E_x \sum_j ex_j$$

where the summation is made over all the x coordinates of the electrons, x_j. Note that $ex_j = \mu_j$, the contribution of the j electron to the x component of the dipole movement of the atom or molecule. The contribution to U_{n0} is

$$\int \psi_n(q)(E_x \sum ex_j)\psi_0(q)\, dq = \mu_{x,n0} E_x \tag{14.34}$$

The transition probability depends on the dipole moment of the atom or molecule averaged between the lower and upper states. Thus $\mu_{x,n0}$ is called the *transition moment.* The final result for B_{nm} is

$$B_{nm} = \frac{8\pi^3}{3h^2}(\mu^2_{x,mn} + \mu^2_{y,mn} + \mu^2_{z,mn}) \tag{14.35}$$

where the squares of the three different components of the transition moment are added.

From Eq. (14.34) we derive the various *selection rules* for spectral transitions. If we are interested in pure rotational spectra we insert the rotational wave function into Eq. (14.34); for vibrational spectra, we use the vibrational wave function; for electronic spectra, we use wave functions for different electronic states.

It should be mentioned, however, that even when no transition is allowed by this *electric dipole mechanism,* other smaller terms may contribute to the perturbing potential and lead to transitions with much lower intensities. Such effects can be quadrupole interactions, or magnetic dipole interactions with the magnetic field of the light wave.

21. ROTATIONAL LEVELS—FAR-INFRARED SPECTRA OF DIATOMIC MOLECULES

In Sec. 7.26 we described the model of the *rigid rotor.* For a diatomic molecule, the rotation of the two atoms of masses m_1 and m_2 about their center of mass was seen to be equivalent to the rotation of a *reduced mass* μ at the internuclear distance r from the rotation axis. The moment of inertia $I = \mu r^2$. For a rigid rotor, the potential energy is zero, and the Schrödinger equation becomes simply

$$\nabla^2\psi + \frac{8\pi^2\mu}{h^2}E\psi = 0 \tag{14.36}$$

Since r is a constant, the wave functions ψ are functions only of θ and ϕ. The equation is in fact the same as that for the angular part of the wave functions of the hydrogen atom, which was discussed in Chapter 12.

The allowed energy levels of the diatomic rigid rotor are given by

$$E_r = \frac{h^2 J(J+1)}{8\pi^2 I} = BhJ(J+1) \tag{14.37}$$

where B is called the *rotational constant.* The quantum number J can have only integral values. The wave functions *are

$$\psi_r = N_r P_J^k (\cos\theta)\, e^{ik\phi} \tag{14.38}$$

where N_r is a normalization factor. For each value of J there are $2J + 1$ wave functions characterized by the allowed values of k which run from $-J$ to $+J$. Each rotational energy level specified by J therefore has a degeneracy of $2J + 1$.

The value of J gives the allowed values of the rotational angular momentum p,

$$p = (h/2\pi)\sqrt{J(J+1)} \tag{14.39}$$

This expression is exactly similar to the one for the orbital angular momentum of an electron in the hydrogen atom, as specified by the quantum number l.

To investigate whether a rotating molecule can absorb or emit radiation quanta in passing from one rotational level to another, we consider our general theoretical expression for the transition moment, Eq. (14.34). Substituting the rotational wave functions, we find

$$\mu_{nm} = \int \psi_n(\theta, \phi)\, \vec{\mu}\, \psi_m(\theta, \phi)\, d\tau$$

Let us consider, for example, the z component of the dipole moment (the argument holds for all components).

$$\mu_z = ez = er\cos\theta = \mu^\circ \cos\theta$$

where μ° is the magnitude of the dipole moment. Thus

$$\mu_{nm} = \mu^\circ \int \psi_n^\star(\theta, \phi) \cos\theta\, \psi_m(\theta, \phi)\, d\tau \tag{14.40}$$

It is clear that unless the permanent dipole moment μ° differs from zero, the transition probability will be zero, and no emission or absorption of radiation can occur. We thus have proved that *in order to have a pure rotation spectrum a molecule must have a permanent dipole moment.* For example, HCl displays an absorption spectrum in the far infrared, but N_2 does not.

If we substitute the rotational wave function into Eq. (14.40) and evaluate the transition probability, we find that it vanishes except for the case in which the quantum number J changes by one unit, $\Delta J = \pm 1$.

Thus an expression for ΔE for the rigid-rotor model is readily derived from Eq. (14.37). We obtain for two levels with quantum numbers J and J':

$$\Delta E = h\nu = hB[J(J+1) - J'(J'+1)].$$

* See K. S. Pitzer, *Quantum Chemistry* (New York: Prentice-Hall, 1953), Chapter 3, for a discussion of solution of the angular equation and properties of the wave functions.

Since $\nu = (\Delta E/h)$, and $J - J' = 1$,

$$\nu = 2BJ \tag{14.41}$$

The spacing between energy levels increases linearly with J, as shown in Fig. 14.19. The absorption spectra due to pure rotation arise from transitions from each of these levels to the next higher one. By means of a spectrograph of good resolving power, the absorption band will be seen to consist of a series of equidistant lines. From Eq. (14.41) the spacing is

$$\Delta\nu = \nu - \nu' = 2B$$

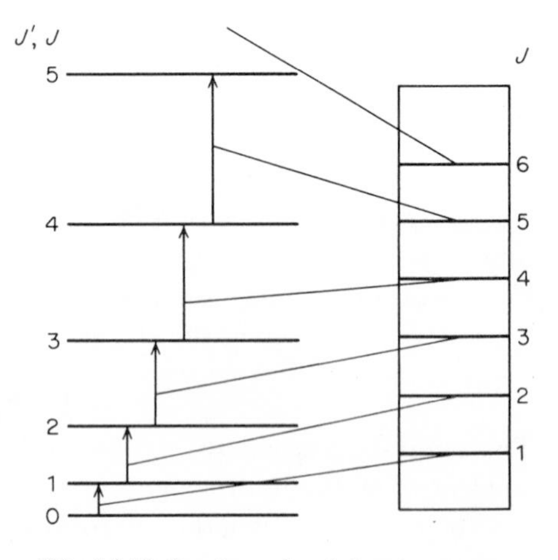

FIG. 14.19 Spacing of rotational energy levels and the lines of a pure rotational spectrum from transitions between levels J and levels $J' = J - 1$.

The model of the rigid rotor is an approximation. There is always a tendency for a bond to stretch at high rotation speed by a centrifugal effect. As a result, the moment of inertia increases at higher rotational energies, causing the levels to be somewhat closer together than for a rigid rotor. The equation for the levels corrected for this effect becomes

$$E_r = B_0 hJ(J+1) - D_0 h[J(J+1)]^2 \tag{14.42}$$

where D_0 is called the *centrifugal distortion constant.* It is about $10^{-4}B$.

22. INTERNUCLEAR DISTANCES FROM ROTATION SPECTRA

The analysis of rotation spectra can give accurate values of the moments of inertia, and hence of internuclear distances and shapes of molecules. Let us consider the example of HCl.

Absorption by HCl has been observed in the far infrared, around $\lambda = 50$ microns or $\tilde{\nu} = 200\ \text{cm}^{-1}$. The spacing between successive lines is $\Delta\tilde{\nu} = 20.1$ to $20.7\ \text{cm}^{-1}$. Analysis shows that the transition from $J = 0$ to $J = 1$ corresponds to a wave number of $\tilde{\nu} = 1/\lambda = 20.6\ \text{cm}^{-1}$. The frequency is therefore

$$\nu = \frac{c}{\lambda} = (3.00 \times 10^{10})(20.6) = 6.20 \times 10^{11}\ \text{sec}^{-1}$$

The first rotational level, $J = 1$, lies at an energy of

$$h\nu = (6.20 \times 10^{11})(6.62 \times 10^{-27}) = 4.10 \times 10^{-15}\ \text{erg}$$

From Eq. (14.37),

$$E = \frac{h^2}{4\pi^2 I} = 4.10 \times 10^{-15}$$

so that

$$I = 2.72 \times 10^{-40} \text{ g cm}^2$$

Since $I = \mu r^2$, where μ is the reduced mass, we can now determine the internuclear distance r for HCl:

$$\mu = \frac{(35.0)1}{35.0 \times 1} \times \frac{1}{6.02 \times 10^{23}} = 1.61 \times 10^{-24} \text{ g}$$

Hence

$$r = \left(\frac{2.72 \times 10^{-40}}{1.61 \times 10^{-24}}\right)^{1/2} = 1.30 \times 10^{-8} \text{ cm} = 1.30 \text{ Å}$$

23. ROTATIONAL SPECTRA OF POLYATOMIC MOLECULES

The rotational energy levels of linear polyatomic molecules are given by Eq. (14.37). The moment of inertia, however, may depend on two or more different internuclear distances. Consider, for example, the molecule chloroacetylene, Cl—C≡C—H. The moment of inertia depends on three internuclear distances Cl—C, C—C, and C—H. Clearly, we cannot calculate these three parameters from a single moment of inertia, obtained from the rotational spectrum.

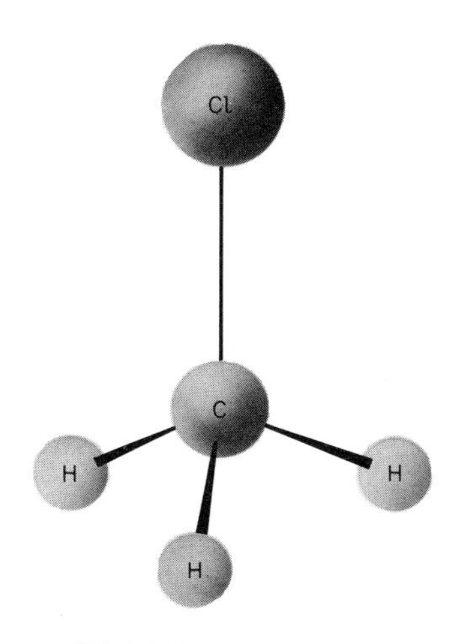

FIG. 14.20 Methyl chloride. A typical symmetric-top molecule.

In such cases, the *method of isotopic substitution* is used. The internuclear distances are determined by the electrostatic configuration of the nuclei and electrons in the structure; they do not depend on the masses of the nuclei. Thus isotopic substitution gives new moments of inertia but unchanged internuclear distances. A study of the rotational spectra of isotopically substituted chloroacetylenes gave the results in Table 14.6. It is possible to calculate precise interatomic distances by means of this valuable method of isotopic substitution.

For nonlinear molecules, the formulas for the rotational energy levels become more complex, and the spectra, correspondingly, become more difficult to unravel. If a molecule has three moments of inertia of which two are equal it is called a *symmetric top*. An example is CH_3Cl, shown in Fig. 14.20. The rotational energy levels of the symmetric top as a rigid rotor are

$$E_r = \frac{h^2}{8\pi^2 I_b} J(J+1) - \frac{h^2}{8\pi^2}\left(\frac{1}{I_a} - \frac{1}{I_b}\right) K^2 \qquad (14.43)$$

TABLE 14.6 ROTATIONAL SPECTRA OF ISOTOPICALLY SUBSTITUTED MOLECULES

Molecule	Frequency (J = 1 → J = 2) mc	Computed Bond Distances Å	
H—C≡C—^{35}Cl	22736.97	H—C	1.052 ± .001
H—C≡C—^{37}Cl	22289.51	C≡C	1.211 ± .001
D—C≡C—^{35}Cl	20748.05	C—Cl	1.632 ± .001
D—C≡C—^{37}Cl	20336.94		

Rotation about the axis C—Cl does not change the dipole moment and hence the selection rule is $\Delta K = 0$. A molecule with three different moments of inertia is an *asymmetric top*. Its rotational energy levels do not follow any simple formula.

24. VIBRATIONAL ENERGY LEVELS

Investigations in the far infrared are difficult to make, and a much greater amount of useful information has been obtained from the near-infrared spectra, arising from transitions between different vibrational energy levels.

The simplest model for a vibrating molecule is that of the harmonic oscillator, whose potential energy is given by $U = \frac{1}{2}\kappa x^2$, the equation of a parabola. The Schrödinger equation is therefore

$$\frac{d^2\psi}{dx^2} + \frac{8\pi^2\mu}{h^2}\,(E - \tfrac{1}{2}\kappa x^2)\,\psi = 0 \tag{14.44}$$

The solution to this equation can be obtained exactly by quite simple methods.* The result has already been mentioned as a consequence of uncertainty-principle arguments (p. 483), being

$$E_v = (v + \tfrac{1}{2})\,h\nu \tag{14.45}$$

The energy levels are equally spaced, and the existence of a zero-point energy, $E_0 = \frac{1}{2}h\nu_0$ when $v = 0$, will be noted.

Actually, the harmonic oscillator is not a very good model for molecular vibrations except at low energy levels, near the bottom of the potential-energy curve. It fails, for example, to represent the fact that a molecule can dissociate if the amplitude of vibration becomes sufficiently large. The sort of potential-energy curve that should be used is one like that pictured for the H_2 molecule in Fig. 13.2.

In harmonic vibration the restoring force is directly proportional to the displacement r. The potential-energy curve is parabolic and dissociation can never take place. Actual potential-energy curves, like that in Fig. 13.2, correspond to *anharmonic vibrations*. The restoring force is no longer directly proportional to the displacement. The force is given by $-\partial U/\partial r$, the slope of the

* Pauling and Wilson, *op. cit.*, p. 68. A student might well study this as a typical quantum mechanical problem.

potential curve, and this decreases to zero at large values of r, so that dissociation can occur as the result of vibrations of large amplitude.

Two *heats of dissociation* may be defined by reference to a curve like Fig. 13.2. The *spectroscopic heat of dissociation* D_e is the height from the asymptote to the minimum. The *chemical heat of dissociation* D_0 is measured from the ground state of the molecule, at $v = 0$, to the onset of dissociation. Therefore,

$$D_e = D_0 + \tfrac{1}{2}h\nu_0 \tag{14.46}$$

The energy levels corresponding to an anharmonic potential-energy curve can be expressed as a power series in $(v + \frac{1}{2})$,

$$E_v = h\nu[(v + \tfrac{1}{2}) - x_e(v + \tfrac{1}{2})^2 + y_e(v + \tfrac{1}{2})^3 - \ldots]$$

Considering only the first anharmonic term, with *anharmonicity constant* x_e, we have

$$E_v = h\nu(v + \tfrac{1}{2}) - h\nu x_e(v + \tfrac{1}{2})^2 \tag{14.47}$$

The energy levels are not evenly spaced, but lie more closely together as the quantum number increases. This fact is illustrated in the levels superimposed on the curve in Fig. 13.2. Since a set of closely packed rotational levels is associated with each of these vibrational levels, it is sometimes possible to determine with great precision the energy level just before the onset of the continuum, and so to calculate the heat of dissociation from the vibration-rotation spectra.

25. VIBRATION-ROTATION SPECTRA OF DIATOMIC MOLECULES

A diatomic molecule has only one degree of vibrational freedom and hence one fundamental vibration frequency ν_0. To absorb or emit quanta $h\nu_0$ of vibrational energy the molecule must possess a permanent dipole moment, since otherwise the transition probability in Eq. (14.34) must vanish. Thus molecules like NO and HCl display a spectrum in the near infrared due to transitions between vibrational energy levels, but molecules like H_2 and Cl_2 display no infrared spectra.

The selection rule governing vibrational transition is $\Delta v = \pm 1$. The vibrational spectrum, however, arises from transitions between definite rotational energy levels belonging to definite vibrational levels. Therefore it is called a vibration-rotation spectrum. The expression for an energy level is

$$E_{vr} = (v + \tfrac{1}{2})h\nu_0 + BhJ(J + 1) \tag{14.48}$$

For a transition between an upper level v', J' and a lower level v'', J'',

$$E_{vr} = (v' - v'')h\nu_0 + B'hJ'(J' + 1) - B''hJ''(J'' + 1) \tag{14.49}$$

Note that we must use different rotational constants B' and B'' for the upper and lower states, since the moment of inertia of the molecule is not exactly the same in different vibrational states.

The selection rules for transitions between the vibration-rotation levels are $\Delta v = \pm 1$, $\Delta J = \pm 1$. In the exceptional case that the diatomic molecule has a

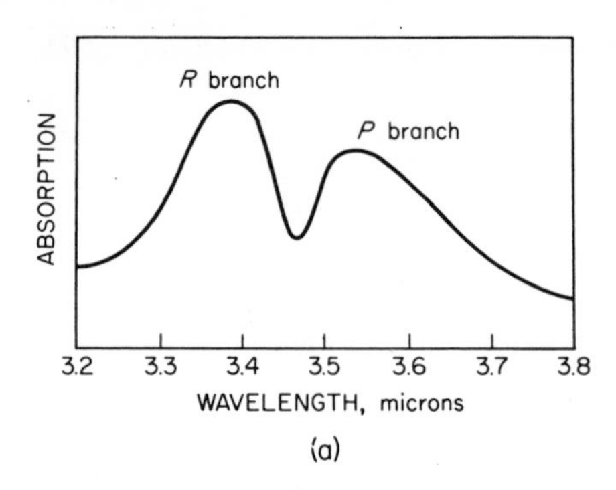

(a)

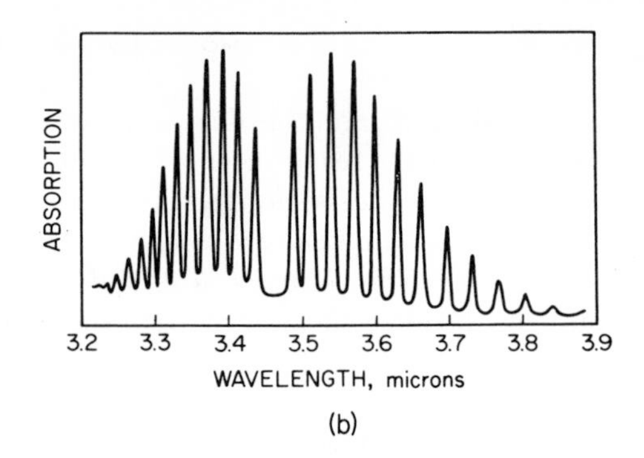

(b)

FIG. 14.21 (a) Fundamental vibration band of HCl in near infrared at low resolution. (b) Fundamental vibration band of HCl with resolved rotation spectrum.

$\Lambda \neq 0$ (i.e., has a moment of inertia about the internuclear axis) we can also have $\Delta J = 0$. The only molecule of this type studied so far is NO which has a $^2\Pi$ ground state.

A vibration-rotation band may display three sections corresponding to the three cases:

$$J' - J'' = \Delta J = +1 \qquad R \text{ branch}$$
$$J' - J'' = \Delta J = -1 \qquad P \text{ branch}$$
$$J' - J'' = \Delta J = 0 \qquad Q \text{ branch}$$

As an example, the fundamental infrared absorption spectrum of HCl at 2886 cm^{-1} is shown in Fig. 14.21. This band occurs from transitions between $v' = 0$ and $v = 1$. The appearance of the band at low resolution is shown in (a). The rotational fine structure is not resolved, but we can see the P and R branches. The band is shown in (b) at high resolution. Each line corresponds to a distinct value of J' or J''. Note that the lines of greatest intensity do not correspond to $J = 0$ but to J about 4. Why is this so?

For the $v = 1$ band in HCl, we have,

$$\nu = c\tilde{\nu} = (3 \times 10^{10})(2886) = 8.65 \times 10^{13} \text{ sec}^{-1}$$

as the fundamental vibration frequency. This is about one hundred times the rotation frequency found from the far-infrared spectra.

The force constant of a harmonic oscillator with this frequency, from Eq. (12.2), would be

$$\kappa = 4\pi^2\nu^2\mu = 4.81 \times 10^5 \text{ dyne cm}^{-1}$$

If the chemical bond is thought of as a spring, the force constant is a measure of its tightness.

Potential-energy curves of the type shown in Fig. 13.2 are so useful in chemical discussions that we need a convenient analytical expression for them. An empirical function that fits well was suggested by P. M. Morse:

$$U = D_e[1 - \exp - \beta(r - r_0)]^2 \tag{14.50}$$

Here β is a constant, evaluated in terms of molecular parameters as $\beta = \nu_0\sqrt{2\pi^2\mu D_e}$.

26. INFRARED SPECTRA OF POLYATOMIC MOLECULES

A polyatomic molecule need not have a permanent dipole moment in order to have a vibrational spectrum in the infrared, but any vibration which emits or absorbs radiation must cause a changing dipole moment. For example, CO_2 is a linear molecule which has no permanent dipole. There are $3n - 5 = 4$ normal modes of vibration shown in Fig. 7.16. The symmetrical stretching vibration ν_1 cannot cause a changing dipole moment, and therefore this vibration is said to be *inactive in the infrared.* The twofold degenerate bending vibration ν_2 causes a changing dipole moment, and is therefore active in the infrared, causing a fundamental absorption band at 667 cm^{-1}. The antisymmetric stretching mode ν_3 also causes a changing dipole and is observed in the fundamental absorption band at 2349 cm^{-1}. Notice that the stretching frequency is much higher than the bending. This is a general result: it is easier to distort a molecule by bending than by stretching, and the force constant κ is lower for bending modes.

In addition to the fundamental absorption bands, many combination and overtone bands occur in the infrared spectrum of CO_2, but these have lower intensities than the fundamental. [Their occurrence shows the failure of the harmonic oscillator selection rule $\Delta v = 1$.] The analysis of an infrared spectrum consists in sorting out the bands and correctly assigning the fundamental frequencies to their particular normal modes. As we shall see, some vibrations inactive in the infrared region may be active in the Raman spectrum, so that comparisons of data from these two methods may facilitate the analysis. The assignment of some of the bands in the CO_2 spectrum is shown in Table 14.7.

TABLE 14.7 THE INFRARED VIBRATION BANDS OF CO_2*

Wavelength in μ	Vibrational Quantum Numbers $v_1\ v_2\ v_3$		Significance of Bands
	Initial State	Final State	
14.986	0 0 0	0 1 0	Fundamental vibration δ
10.4	1 0 0	0 0 1	Combination vibration $\nu(a) - \nu(s)$
9.40	0 2 0	0 0 1	Combination vibration $\nu(a) - 2\delta$
5.174	0 0 0	0 3 0	Overtone vibration 3δ
4.816	0 0 0	1 1 0	Combination vibration $\nu(s) + \delta$
4.68	0 1 0	2 0 0	Combination vibration $2\nu(s) - \delta$
4.25	0 0 0	0 0 1	Fundamental vibration $\nu(a)$
2.27	0 0 0	0 2 1	Combination vibration $2\delta + \nu(a)$
2.006	0 0 0	1 2 1	Combination vibration $\nu(s) + 2\delta + \nu(a)$
1.957	0 0 0	2 0 1	Combination vibration $2\nu(s) + \nu(a)$
1.574	0 0 0	2 2 1	Combination vibration $2\nu(s) + 2\delta + \nu(a)$
1.433	0 0 0	0 0 3	Overtone vibration $3\nu(a)$
0.8698	0 0 0	0 0 5	Overtone vibration $5\nu(a)$

* Data from *Landolt-Bornstein Tables,* 6th edition, Berlin 1951.

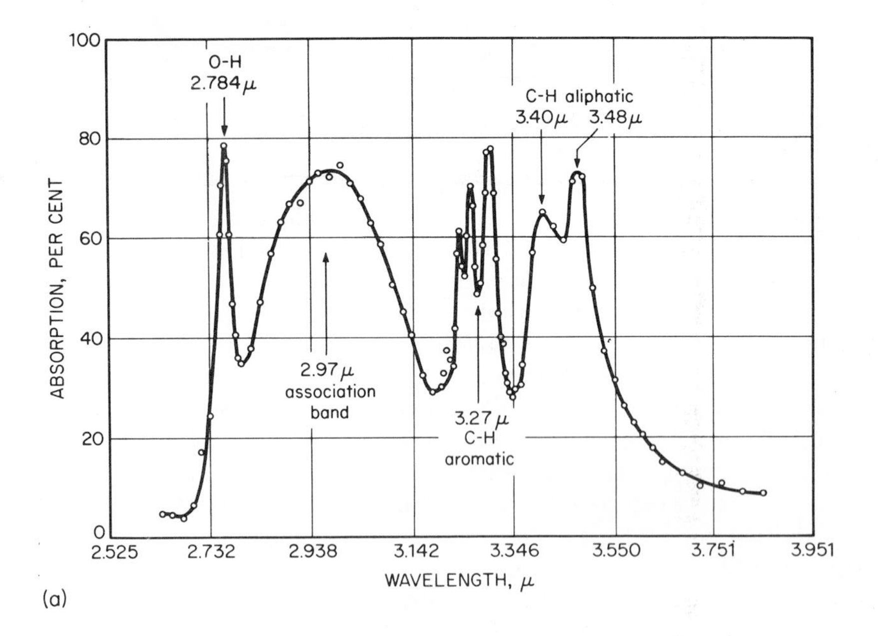

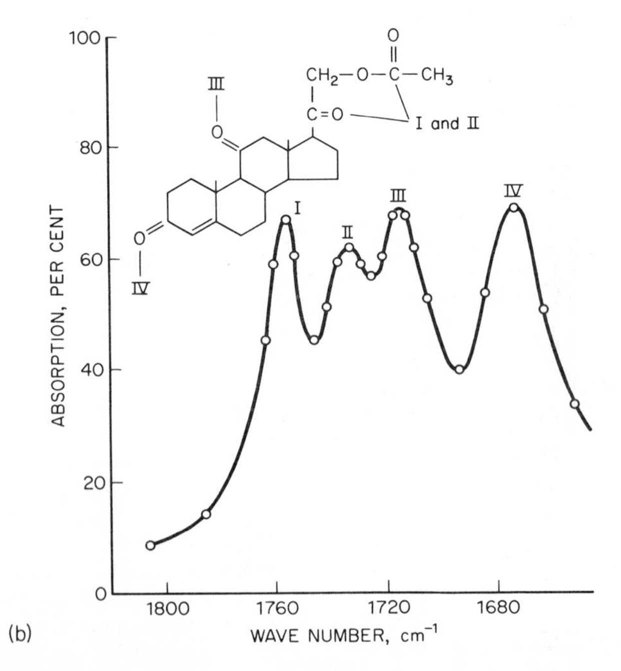

FIG. 14.22 (a) Absorption of a solution of benzyl alcohol in carbon tetrachloride at 18°C (0.169 mole/lit). Thickness 1.3 mm. [J. J. Fox and A. E. Martin, *Nature* *139,* 507 (1937)]; (b) Absorption by the carbonyl groups in a complex molecule, showing how the position of the group in the molecule influences the frequency of the bond.

When a molecule becomes quite complex, the analysis of its infrared spectrum becomes difficult. It is exactly with such complex molecules, however, that the IR spectrum proves most useful to the chemist who wishes to identify compounds and to determine structures. By empirical comparisons of many spectra, we can isolate frequencies characteristic of certain bonds, i.e., nearly the same for these bonds in a wide variety of structures. Examples of these *IR group frequencies* are given in Table 14.8. A fairly typical IR spectrum of a complex molecule with some of the group frequencies identified is shown in Fig. 14.22.

TABLE 14.8 CHARACTERISTIC BOND FREQUENCIES*

Bond	Group	Type of Vibration	Frequency, cm^{-1}
C—H	CH_3, alkane	stretching	2962 ± 10, 2872 ± 10
C—H	CH_2, alkane	stretching	2926 ± 10, 2853 ± 10
C—H	CH, alkane	stretching	2890 ± 10
C—H	—CH=CH⁻	stretching	3040 – 3010
C—H	≡CH	stretching	3300
C—H	=CH—, aromatic	stretching	3030
C—H	—C—CH_3, alkane	bending	1450 ± 20
C—H	—CH_2—, alkane	bending	1465 ± 20
C—H	—CH=CH— (trans)	out of plane, bending	970 – 960
C—H	—CH=CH— (trans)	in plane, bending	1310 – 1295
C—H	—CH=CH— (cis)	out of plane, bending	~690
C—C	$CH_3)_3$—C—R	skeletal	1250, ~415
C—C	—$(CH_2)_4$⁻	skeletal	750 – 720
C—C	—C=C—	stretching	1680 – 1620
C–C	—C≡C—, monosubstituted	stretching	2140 – 2100
C—C	—C≡C—, disubstituted	stretching	2260 – 2190
O—H	—O—H free	stretching	3650 – 3590
S—H	—S—H free	stretching	2650 – 2550
O—C	O=C <	stretching	1850 – 1700
F—C	—	stretching	1300 – 1100
Cl—C	—	stretching	800 – 700
Br—C	—	stretching	600 – 500
I—C	—	stretching	500 – 400

* L. J. Bellamy, *The Infrared Spectra of Complex Molecules* (2nd ed.) (London: Methuen' 1958).

27. MICROWAVE SPECTROSCOPY

Microwaves have a wavelength in or about the range from 1 mm to 1 cm. In ordinary absorption spectroscopy, the source of radiation is usually a hot filament or a high-pressure gaseous-discharge tube, giving in either case a wide distribution of wavelengths. This radiation is passed through the absorber and the intensity of the transmitted portion at different wavelengths is measured after analysis by means of a grating or prism. In microwave spectroscopy, the source

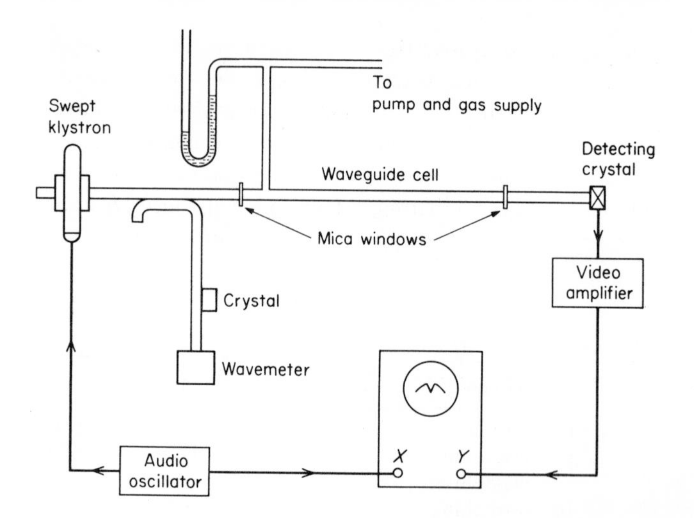

FIG. 14.23 Schematic diagram of a microwave spectrometer.

is monochromatic, at a well defined single wavelength which can, however, be rapidly varied (frequency modulation). It is provided by an electronically controlled oscillator employing a klystron or magnetron tube. After passage through the cell containing the substance under investigation, the microwave beam is picked up by a receiver, often of the crystal type, and after suitable amplification is fed to a cathode-ray oscillograph acting as detector or recorder. The resolving power of this arrangement is 100 000 times that of the best infrared grating spectrometer, so that wavelength measurements can be made to seven significant figures. The set-up of a typical microwave spectrograph is shown in Fig. 14.23.

An intensively investigated microwave spectrum has been that of the "umbrella inversion" of the ammonia molecule, the vibration in which the nitrogen atom passes back and forth through the plane of the three hydrogen atoms. The rotational fine structure of this transition is beautifully resolved, over 40 lines

TABLE 14.9 BOND LENGTHS AND ANGLES FROM MICROWAVE SPECTRA*

Linear Molecules

Molecule	Bond	r_0, Å	Bond	r_0, Å
ClCN	C—Cl	1.629	C—N	1.163
BrCN	C—Br	1.790	C—N	1.159
HCN	C—H	1.064	C—N	1.156
OCS	C—O	1.161	C—S	1.560
NNO	N—N	1.126	N—O	1.191

Symmetric Tops

Molecule	Bond Angle	Bond	r_0, Å	Bond	r_0, Å
$CHCl_3$	Cl—C—Cl 110° 24′	C—H	1.073	C—Cl	1.767
CH_3F	H—C—H 110° 0°	C—H	1.109	C—F	1.385
SiH_3Br	H—Si—H 111° 20′	Si—H	1.57	Si—Br	2.209

* W. Gordy, W. V. Smith and R. F. Trambarulo, *Microwave Spectroscopy*, (New York: Wiley, 1953).

being catalogued for $^{14}NH_3$ and about 20 for $^{15}NH_3$. Such detailed data make it possible to construct extremely detailed theories for the molecular energy levels.

Pure rotational transitions in heavier molecules are inaccessible to ordinary infrared spectroscopy because, in accord with Eq. (14.37), the large moments of inertia would correspond to energy levels at excessively long wavelengths. Microwave techniques have made this region readily accessible. With the moments of inertia obtained from microwave spectra, we can calculate internuclear distances to better than ± 0.002 Å. A few examples are shown in Table 14.9. The spectra under the influence of an electric field (Stark effect) yield precise values of the dipole moments of gas molecules. Microwave measurements also afford one of the best methods for finding nuclear spins.

28. ELECTRONIC BAND SPECTRA

The energy differences ΔE between electronic states in a molecule are in general much larger than those between successive vibrational levels. Thus the band spectra due to transitions between two different electronic states are observed in the visible or ultraviolet region. The ΔE between molecular electronic levels is usually of the same order of magnitude as that between atomic energy levels, ranging therefore from 1 to 10 ev.

Figure 14.24 shows the ground state of a molecule (curve A), and two distinctly different possibilities for an excited state. In one (curve B), there is a minimum in the potential-energy curve, so that the state is a stable configuration for the molecule. In the other (curve C) there is no minimum, and the state is unstable for all internuclear separations.

A transition from ground state to unstable state would be followed immediately by dissociation of the molecule. Such a transition gives rise to a continuous

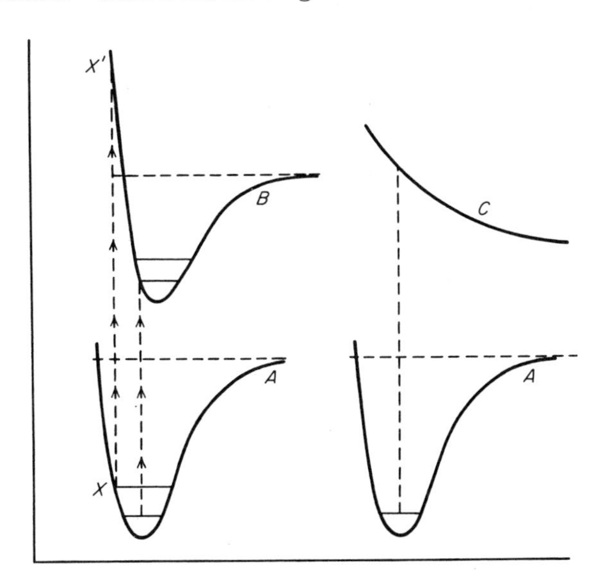

FIG. 14.24 Transitions between electronic levels in molecules.

absorption band. Transitions between different vibrational levels of two stable electronic states also lead to a band in the spectrum, but in this case the band can be analyzed into closely packed lines corresponding to the different upper and lower vibrational and rotational levels. The task of the spectroscopist is to measure the wavelengths of the various lines and interpret them in terms of the energy levels from which they arise.

A rule known as the *Franck-Condon principle* helps us to understand electronic transitions. An electron jump takes place very quickly, much more quickly than the period of vibration of the atomic nuclei ($\sim 10^{-13}$ sec), which are heavy and sluggish compared to electrons. Therefore the positions and velocities of the nuclei are almost unchanged during an electronic transition.* Thus we can represent a transition by a vertical line drawn on the potential-energy curves, Fig. 14.24.

The Franck-Condon principle shows how transitions between stable electronic states may sometimes lead to dissociation. For example, in Curve A of Fig. 14.24, the transition XX' goes in the upper state to a vibrational level that lies above the asymptote to the potential-energy curve. Such a transition leads to dissociation of the molecule during the period of one vibration.

If a molecule dissociates from an excited electronic state, the fragments formed (atoms in the case of a diatomic molecule) are not always in their ground states. In order to obtain the heat of dissociation into atoms in the ground states we must therefore subtract the excitation energy of the atoms. For example, in the ultraviolet absorption spectrum of oxygen there is a series of bands corresponding to transitions from the ground state to an excited state. These bands converge to the onset of a continuum at 1959 Å, equivalent to 6.34 ev. The two atoms formed by the dissociation are found to be a normal atom (^3P state) and an excited atom (^1D state). The atomic spectrum of oxygen reveals that this ^1D state lies at 1.97 ev above the ground state. Thus the heat of dissociation of molecular oxygen into two normal atoms $[O_2 \rightarrow 2O(^3P)]$ is $7.05 - 1.97 = 5.08$ ev or 117 kcal per mole.

The vibrational and rotational fine structure of electronic bands in the visible and ultraviolet region of the spectrum can provide detailed information about the structure of the molecule in its ground state and in electronically excited states. These electronic spectra are of course more complex and more difficult to analyze than the IR and Raman spectra. On the other hand, it is especially important that they be understood by chemists, since they determine the paths followed by photochemical reactions. Fig. 14.25 shows portions of one vibrational band in the electronic absorption spectrum of NH_2. The individual rotational lines have been well resolved.

---

* It may be noted that the vertical line for an electronic transition is drawn from a point on the lower curve corresponding to the midpoint in the internuclear vibration. This is done because the maximum in ψ in the ground state lies at the midpoint of the vibration. This is not true in higher vibrational states, for which the maximum probability lies closer to the extremes of the vibration. Classical theory predicts a maximum probability at the extremes of the vibration.

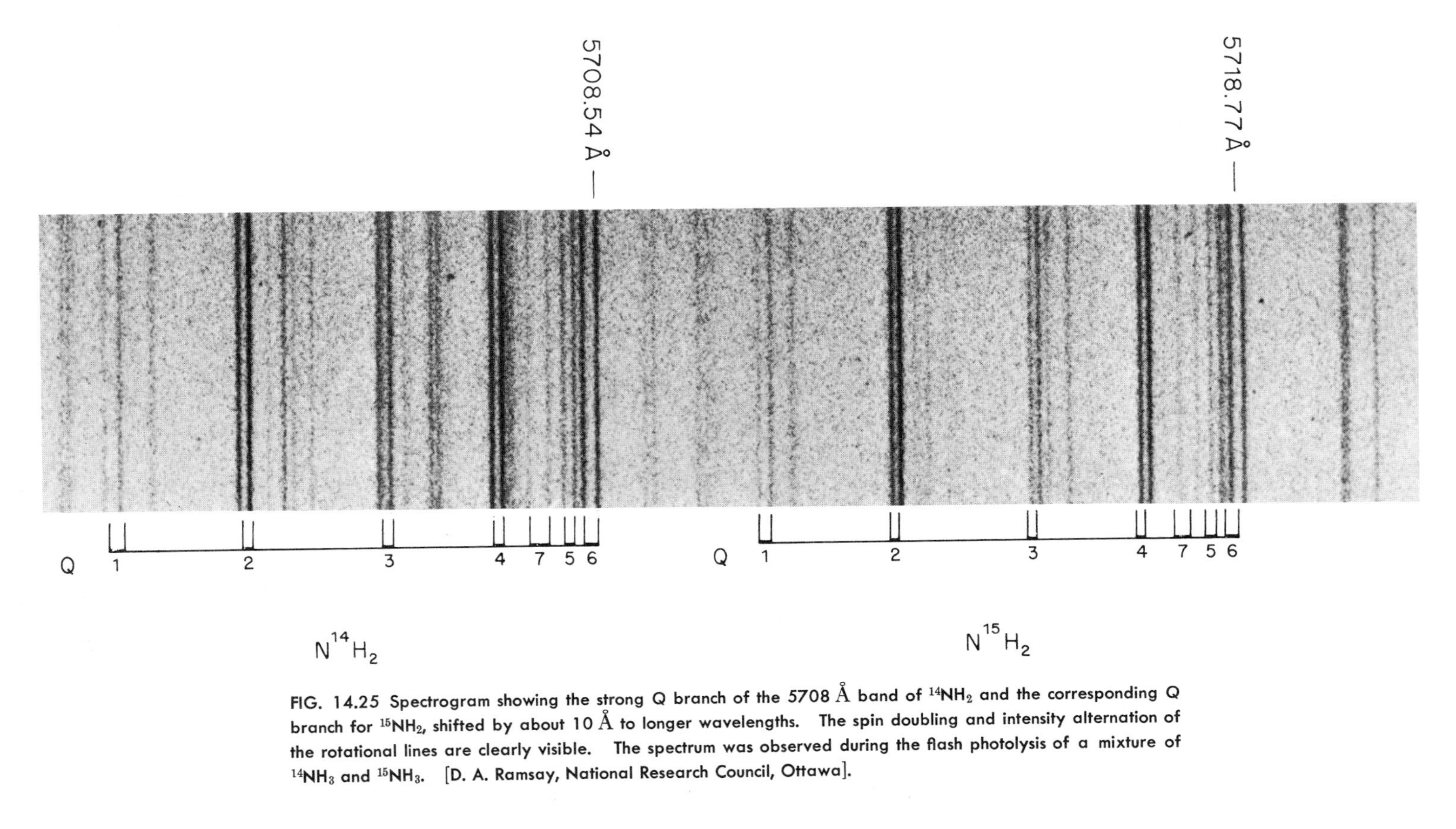

FIG. 14.25 Spectrogram showing the strong Q branch of the 5708 Å band of $^{14}NH_2$ and the corresponding Q branch for $^{15}NH_2$, shifted by about 10 Å to longer wavelengths. The spin doubling and intensity alternation of the rotational lines are clearly visible. The spectrum was observed during the flash photolysis of a mixture of $^{14}NH_3$ and $^{15}NH_3$. [D. A. Ramsay, National Research Council, Ottawa].

The range of wavelengths from the red end of the visible spectrum at 8000 Å to the violet at 4000 Å corresponds to a range of energies from 35 to 70 kcal per mole. Somewhat more energy than this is necessary to excite an electron from a typical covalent band in a small molecule. Most stable compounds of low molecular weight are therefore colorless, although many of them display an absorption in the near ultraviolet. Color indicates the existence of a relatively low excited state, from 35 to 70 kcal mole^{-1} above the ground state. For example, molecules containing an unpaired electron (NO_2, ClO_2, triphenylmethyl, etc.) are usually colored. Groups such as $-NO_2$, $-C{=}O$, or $-N{=}N$, often cause a compound to be colored, since they contain electrons in π orbitals, which are readily raised to excited orbitals.

In an excited electronic state a molecule may have a quite different shape from that in the ground state. For example, the dimensions of acetylene in the ground state and first excited state are as follows:

	Normal	*Excited*
C—C length	1.208 Å	1.385 Å
C—H length	1.058 Å	1.080 Å
C—C—H angle	180°	120°

In the ground state H—C≡C—H is linear; in the excited state it has swollen to a larger size and it has become bent. In the electronic excitation an electron is removed from a π orbital and placed in a σ orbital. This excitation can be written as follows:

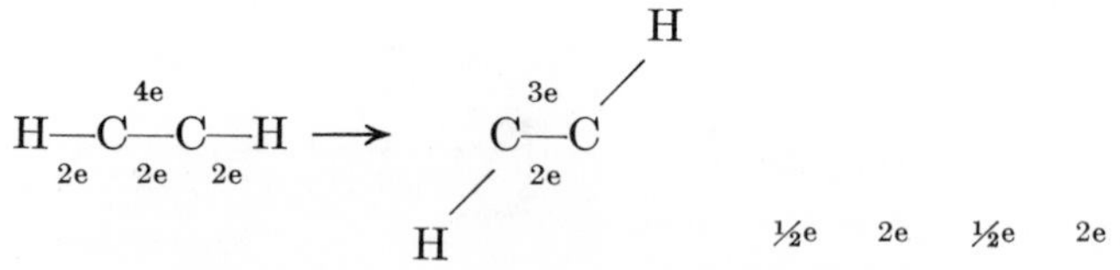

```
                                      H
       4e                     3e     /
   H—C—C—H   ——>            C—C
   2e  2e  2e               / 2e
                           H                ½e   2e   ½e   2e
```

29. TYPES OF ORBITAL EXCITATION

The main types of molecular orbitals that occur in polyatomic molecules can be seen in the simple example of the formaldehyde molecule, $H_2{=}C{=}O$. Fig. 14.26 shows the five lowest orbitals, following a notation given by Michael Kasha.* The lines represent the outlines of the regions of appreciable electron probability density. The solid line indicates positive amplitude of ψ function, the dotted line indicates negative amplitude of ψ function.

The σ orbital is symmetric with respect to the molecular axis with its center of gravity displaced toward the more electronegative atom O. The $\sigma^\star$-orbital is also axially symmetric, but it contains an excitation node perpendicular to the C—O axis. This node makes the orbital antibonding relative to the atomic orbitals from which it is formed. The π-orbital is antisymmetric with respect to the plane of the molecule; the positive ψ region above the plane is denoted by the

* M. Kasha, "Paths of Molecular Excitation," *Conference on Bioenergetics*, U. S. Atomic Energy Commission, Brookhaven, N. Y., October, 1959.

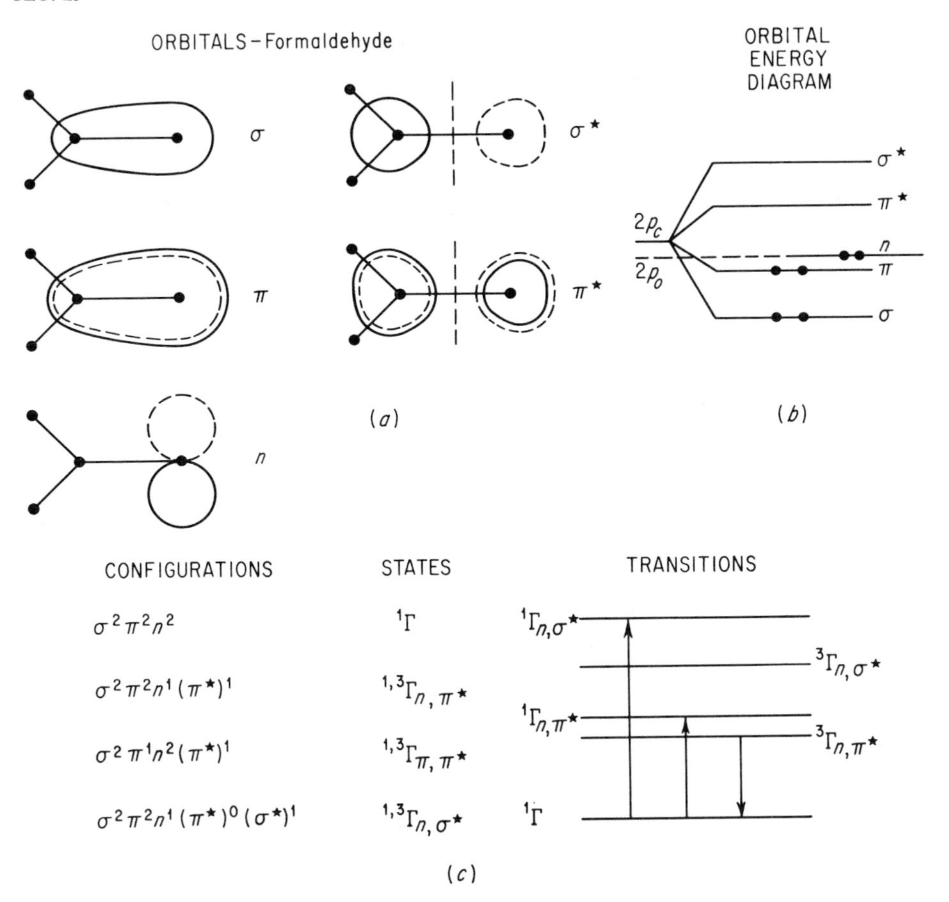

FIG. 14.26 Classification of types of molecular orbitals important in electronic spectra for the typical case of H_2CO [Michael Kasha, Florida State University].

solid contour; the negative ψ region below the plane, by the dashed contour. The π-orbital is a bonding orbital. The π^*-orbital is also antisymmetric with respect to the plane, but it has an excitation node perpendicular to the C—O axis. The n-orbital is essentially the $2p$ orbital of an oxygen atom. (The $2s$ orbitals are more closely bound and need not be considered.) The n-orbital is nonbonding.

The relative energies of the orbitals are shown in Fig. 14.26(b). The six electrons of interest enter the orbitals in the ground state as shown; two form a σ bond between C and O; two form a π bond; the last two form a *lone pair* on the O atom. If this molecule absorbs light, a number of different promotions are possible, as shown on the diagram. These give rise to the different excited electronic states which are shown. Note particularly the order of increasing energy jumps ΔE for the electronic promotions. These results were obtained from theoretical calculations* for aldehydes and ketones.

An electron in an orbital in the ground state has its spin coupled with that of the other electrons in the orbital. When one electron is promoted to an excited

* H. L. McMurry and R. S. Mulliken, *Proc. Nat. Acad. Sci.* *26*, 312 (1940).

state orbital, it may either have its spin parallel or antiparallel to that of the electron left behind. Thus every promotion will lead to two possible states, one with total spin $S = \frac{1}{2} + \frac{1}{2} = 1$, a triplet state $(2S + 1 = 3)$; the other with total spin $S = \frac{1}{2} - \frac{1}{2} = 0$, a singlet state $(2S + 1 = 1)$. The triplet always lies somewhat lower, in accord with Hund's rule.

The important electronic transitions that occur in the near ultraviolet spectrum of CH_2CO are shown in Fig. 14.26(c). Transitions between pure singlet and pure triplet states are strictly forbidden, but the states are never pure, so that such transitions can occur with much diminished intensity. The singlet state has a little triplet character and the triplet has a little singlet character, and this mixing permits the transitions.

The important absorption in CH_2O is the singlet-singlet transition shown. If the molecule reemits a quantum in returning from the $^1\Gamma'$ to the $^1\Gamma$ state, we have a typical *fluorescence*. There is an excited triplet state, $^3\Gamma n\pi^\star$, close to $^1\Gamma n\pi^\star$, and the system sometimes slips over into this by a *radiationless transition.* It is then in a metastable state, since it is forbidden to revert to the $^1\Gamma$ ground state by emission of a quantum. Nevertheless, sometimes it does so, and the resultant emission of light is a typical *phosphorescence*. Since phosphorescent emission occurs through a forbidden transition, the lifetime of the metastable state may sometimes be quite long, and hence phosphorescence may continue for an appreciable time after the exciting light is switched off. This feature is not essential, and any triplet-singlet emission following a singlet-singlet absorption is called *phosphorescence.*

30. RAMAN SPECTRA

When a beam of light passes through a medium, a certain amount is absorbed, a certain amount transmitted, and a certain amount scattered. The scattered light can be studied by observations perpendicular to the direction of the incident beam. Most of the light is scattered without change in wavelength (Rayleigh scattering); but there is in addition a small amount of scattered light whose wavelength has been altered. If the incident light is monochromatic, e.g., an isolated atomic spectral line, the scattered spectrum will exhibit a number of lines displaced from the original wavelength. An example is shown in Fig. 14.27. This effect was first observed by C. V. Raman and K. S. Krishnan in 1928.

The origin of the Raman effect can be seen as follows. A quantum $h\nu$ of incident light strikes a molecule. If it is scattered *elastically* its energy is not changed and the scattered light has the same frequency as the incident light. If it is scattered *inelastically*, it can give up energy to the molecule or take up energy from the molecule. This energy exchanged must naturally be in quanta $h\nu'$, where $h\nu' = E_1 - E_2$ is the energy difference between two stationary states E_1 and E_2 of the molecule, for example, two definite vibrational energy levels. The frequency of the radiation that has undergone Raman scattering will therefore be

$$\nu'' = \nu \pm \nu' \tag{14.51}$$

The Raman frequency ν' is completely independent of the frequency of the incident light ν. We can observe pure rotational and vibrational-rotational Raman spectra, which are the counterparts of the absorption spectra in the far and near infrared. The Raman spectra, however, are studied with light sources in the visible or ultraviolet. In many cases the Raman and *IR* spectra of a molecule complement each other, since vibrations and rotations that are not observable in the *IR* may be active in the Raman. Thus, the spectrum of oxygen in Fig. 14.27 gives the spacing of the vibrational energy levels in O_2, although O_2 has no spectrum in the infrared because it has no dipole moment.

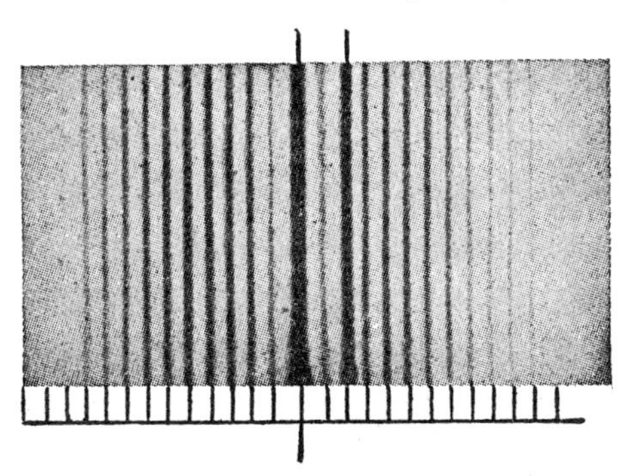

Fig. 14.27 Raman spectrum of O_2 excited by Hg 2536.5-Å line. [F. Rasetti]. The strong line to right of exciting line is the Hg 2534.8 line.

We should understand the distinction between *Raman scattering* and *fluorescence.* In both cases a light quantum is produced which has a frequency different from that of the incident quantum. In fluorescence the system first absorbs the quantum $h\nu$ and then re-emits a quantum $h\nu''$; the incident light must therefore be at an absorption frequency. In Raman scattering, the incident light can be of any frequency.

Raman scattering occurs as a result of the dipole moment induced in the molecule by incident light. The induced dipole m depends on the strength of the electric field F through Eq. (14.3),

$$m = \alpha F$$

where α is the polarizability.

The transition probability for the Raman effect, from Eq. (14.34) therefore becomes

$$|m|^{nm} = |F| \int \psi_n^\star \alpha \psi_m \, d\tau \tag{14.52}$$

If α is constant, this integral vanishes because of the orthogonality of the wave functions. In order that a vibration or rotation be active in the Raman, therefore, the polarizability must change during the rotation or vibration.

The polarizability changes during rotation of any nonspherical molecule. Recent developments in experimental techniques, particularly by Boris Stoicheff, have led to some excellent rotational Raman spectra. In Fig. 14.28 is shown the rotational Raman spectrum of CS_2 extending out to values of the rotational quantum number of about $J = 90$.

An example of how data from *IR* and Raman spectra can be combined to permit the analysis of the vibration spectrum of a molecule is the spectrum of acetylene. The observed frequencies have been assigned as shown in Table 14.10. The normal modes of vibration of this molecule are shown below the Table.

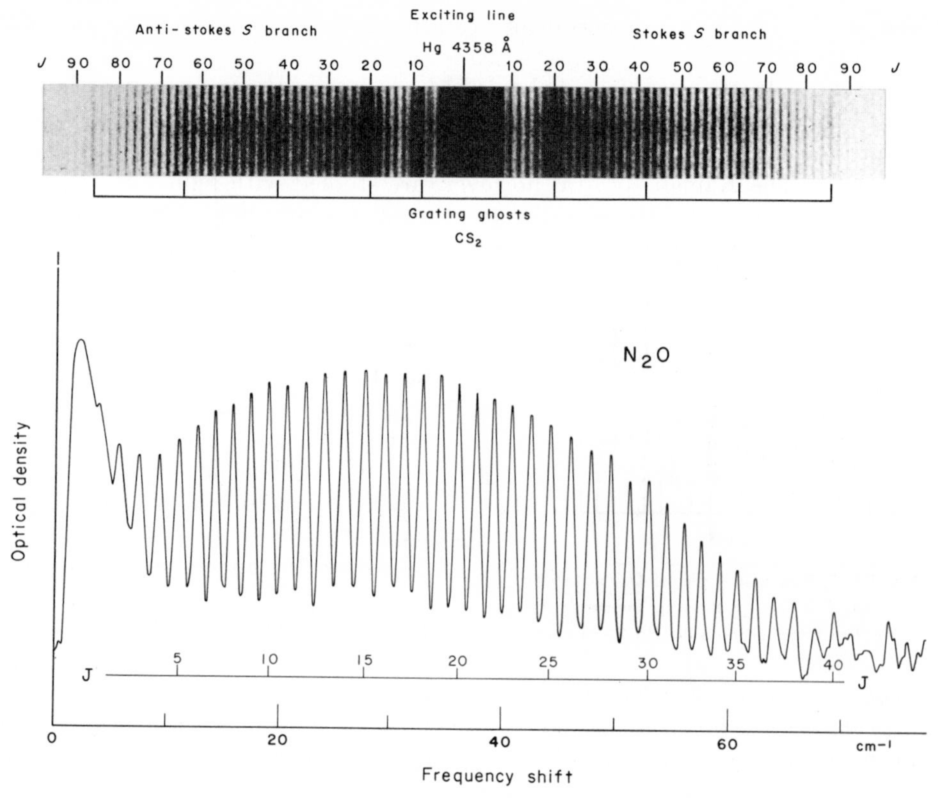

FIG. 14.28 Examples of rotational Raman spectra. The photograph shows the spectrum of CS_2 and the drawing is a microphotometer curve of a photographic plate of the spectrum of N_2O. The rotational quantum numbers *J* are shown [Boris Stoicheff, National Research Council, Ottawa].

TABLE 14.10 SPECTRUM OF ACETYLENE

Assignment	Frequency cm^{-1}	Infra Red		Raman Intensity
		Branches	Intensity	
4	612	—	—	v. weak
5	729	PQR	v. strong	—
4 and 5	1328	PR	s.	—
$5 + (2 \times 4)$	1956	PQR	w.	—
2	1974	—	—	v.s.
$2 + 5$	2712	PQR	med	—
3	3287	PR	med	—
1	3374	—	—	s.

1) $\leftarrow$ H C C H $\rightarrow$
2) $\leftarrow$ H $\leftarrow$ C C $\rightarrow$ H $\rightarrow$
3) $\leftarrow$ H C $\rightarrow$ C $\rightarrow \leftarrow$ H
4) $\uparrow$ H $\downarrow$ C $\uparrow$ C $\downarrow$ H $(2\times)$
5) $\uparrow$ H $\downarrow$ C $\downarrow$ C $\uparrow$ H $(2\times)$

Notice, for example, that the high-frequency vibrations at 1974 and at 3374 cm^{-1} are strong in the Raman and inactive in the *IR*. These are therefore certainly the symmetric stretching vibrations, which do not cause an oscillating dipole. We assign the higher frequency to the C—H stretching from our knowledge of bond frequencies. The antisymmetric stretching frequency (3) is active in the *IR* and hence is assigned to the strong band at 3287 cm^{-1}.

31. MOLECULAR DATA FROM SPECTROSCOPY

Table 14.11 is a collection of data derived from spectroscopic observations on a number of molecules.

TABLE 14.11 SPECTROSCOPIC DATA ON THE PROPERTIES OF MOLECULES*

Diatomic Molecules

Molecule	Equilibrium Internuclear Separation, r_e (Å)	Heat of Dissociation, D_0(ev)	Fundamental Vibration Frequency (ω_e cm^{-1})	Moment of Inertia, (g $cm^2 \times 10^{-40}$)
Cl_2	1.989	2.481	564.9	114.8
CO	1.1284	9.144	2168	14.48
H_2	0.7414	4.777	4405	0.459
HD	0.7413	4.513	3817	0.611
D_2	0.7417	4.556	3119	0.918
HBr	1.414	3.60	2650	3.30
HCl^{35}	1.275	4.431	2989	2.71
I_2	2.667	1.542	214.4	748
Li_2	2.672	1.14	351.3	41.6
N_2	1.095	7.384	2360	13.94
$NaCl^{35}$	2.51	4.25	380	75.5
NH	1.038	3.4	3300	1.68
O_2	1.2076	5.082	1580	19.34
OH	0.971	4.3	3728	1.48

Triatomic Molecules

Molecule, X-Y-Z	Internuclear Separation (Å)		Bond Angle (deg)	Moments of Inertia (g $cm^2 \times 10^{-40}$)			Fundamental Vibration Frequencies (cm^{-1})		
	r_{xy}	r_{yz}		I_A	I_B	I_C	ω_1	ω_2	ω_3
O=C=O	1.162	1.162	180	—	71.67	—	1320	668	2350
H—O—H	0.96	0.96	105	1.024	1.920	2.947	3652	1595	3756
D—O—D	0.96	0.96	105	1.790	3.812	5.752	2666	1179	2784
H—S—H	1.35	1.35	92	2.667	3.076	5.845	2611	1290	2684
O=S=O	1.40	1.40	120	12.3	73.2	85.5	1151	524	1361
N=N=O	1.15	1.23	180	—	66.9	—	1285	589	2224

* From G. Herzberg, *Molecular Spectra and Molecular Structure*, Vols. I and II (New York: D. Van Nostrand Co., 1950).

PROBLEMS

1. The following results are found for the dielectric constant ϵ of gaseous sulfur dioxide at 1 atm as a function of temperature:

°K	267.6	297.2	336.9	443.8
ϵ	1.009918	1.008120	1.005477	1.003199

Estimate the dipole moment of SO_2, assuming ideal gas behavior. [*Ans.* 1.67 debye]

2. M. T. Rogers [*J. Am. Chem. Soc. 69*, 457 (1947)] found the following values for the dielectric constant ϵ and density ρ of isopropyl cyanide at various mole fractions X in benzene solution at 25°C:

X	0.00301	0.00523	0.00956	0.01301	0.01834	0.02517
ϵ	2.326	2.366	2.422	2.502	2.598	2.718
ρ	0.87326	0.87301	0.87260	0.87226	0.87121	0.87108

For pure C_3H_7NC, $\rho = 0.76572$, refractive index $n_D = 1.3712$; for pure benzene, $\rho = 0.87345$, $n_D = 1.5016$. Calculate the dipole moment μ of isopropyl cyanide. [*Ans.* 2.65 debye]

3. Chlorobenzene has $\mu = 1.55$ d, nitrobenzene $\mu = 3.80$ d. Estimate the dipole moments of: metadinitrobenzene, orthodichlorobenzene, metachloronitrobenzene. The observed moments are 3.90, 2.25, 3.40 d. How would you explain any discrepancies?

4. The moment of inertia of the NH radical is 1.68×10^{-40} g cm². At what frequency in the microwave region would you expect to detect the transition $J = 2$ to $J = 3$?

5. The frequency of the O—H stretching in CH_3OH is 3300 cm⁻¹ in the IR spectrum. Predict the frequency of the O—D bond in CH_3OD.

6. In the far infrared spectrum of HBr is a series of lines having a separation of 16.94 cm^{-1}. Calculate the moment of inertia and the internuclear separation in HBr from this datum. [*Ans.* 3.30×10^{-40} g cm²; 1.42 Å]

7. The angular velocity of rotation $\omega = 2\pi\nu_{\text{rot}}$ where ν_{rot} is the rotation frequency of a diatomic rotor. The angular momentum is $(h/2\pi)\sqrt{J(J+1)}$. Calculate the rotation frequency of the HBr molecule for the state with $J = 5$. Calculate the frequency of the spectral line corresponding to the transition $J = 5$ to $J = 4$. [Cf. problem 6]

8. In the near infrared spectrum of carbon monoxide there is an intense band at 2144 cm^{-1}. Calculate (a) the fundamental vibration frequency of CO; (b) the period of the vibration; (c) the force constant; (d) the zero-point energy of CO in cal per mole. [*Ans.* (a) 6.43×10^{13} sec^{-1}; (b) 1.54×10^{-14} sec; (c) 18.5×10^5 dyne cm^{-1}; (d) 3065]

9. With data from Table 14.11, draw to scale the first five rotational levels in the molecule NaCl. At what frequency would the transition $J = 4$ to $J = 5$ be observed? In NaCl vapor at 1000°C what would be the relative numbers of molecules in the states with $J = 0$, $J = 1$, and $J = 2$? [*Ans.* 11.14×10^{10} sec^{-1}; 1.00, 2.99, 4.98]

10. In ions of the first transition series, the paramagnetism is due almost entirely to the unpaired spins, being approximately equal to $\mu = 2\sqrt{S(S+1)}$ magnetons where S is the total spin. On this basis, estimate μ for V^{+3}, Mn^{+2}, Co^{+2}, and Cu^{+}. [*Ans.* 2.83; 5.92; 3.88; 0.00 magnetons]

11. Show that the time dependent solution of the wave equation

$$\psi(x, t) = \exp[i(Et/h - kx)]$$

represents a wave traveling in the positive x-direction with phase velocity E/hk. What is the group velocity? What is the momentum associated with the wave in accord with the de Broglie relation?

12. By means of the concept of hybrid bond orbitals, predict the configuration of CH_3. Would you expect the molecule to have a pure rotational spectrum in far infrared? Give a reason for your answer.

13. Suppose that at 300°K, 10^6 protons were subjected to a magnetic field of 10^4 gauss. How many of the protons would have their magnetic moments alined in the direction of the field? The magnetic moment of the proton is 2.79 μ_M where $\mu_M = e/4\pi Mc$, M being the mass of the proton.

14. In the microwave spectrum of carbon monoxide [$^{12}C^{16}O$] the $J = 0 \rightarrow 1$ rotational transition has been measured at 115 271.204 Mc/sec. Calculate the moment of inertia (in units amu Å^2) and the internuclear separation in CO. (Note: The accuracy of the derived internuclear distance will be considerably less than that of the microwave measurement; although the rigid rotor approximation can be corrected for, the accuracy obtainable is limited by the uncertainty of about 1 part in 10 000 in our present knowledge of Planck's constant.)

15. Roughly sketch the absorption spectrum of a molecule such as CH_3Cl on the following scale. Above the scale label the various types of processes which give rise to the absorptions: (a) vibrational, (b) electronic, (c) rotational transitions, (d) ionization and gross molecular decomposition, (e) predissociation and dissociation. Indicate below the scale the positions of the various spectral regions: (f) radiofrequency, (g) visible, (h) microwave, (i) ultraviolet, (j) infrared.

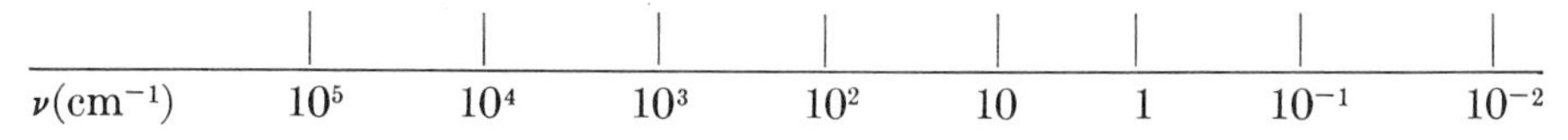

16. Qualitatively, how will the intensity of absorption in the microwave region compare with that in the infrared or the visible region and what are the fundamental physical reasons for this?

17. Pictured below are some normal modes of vibration of several molecules. Indicate which are active and which inactive as infrared fundamentals.

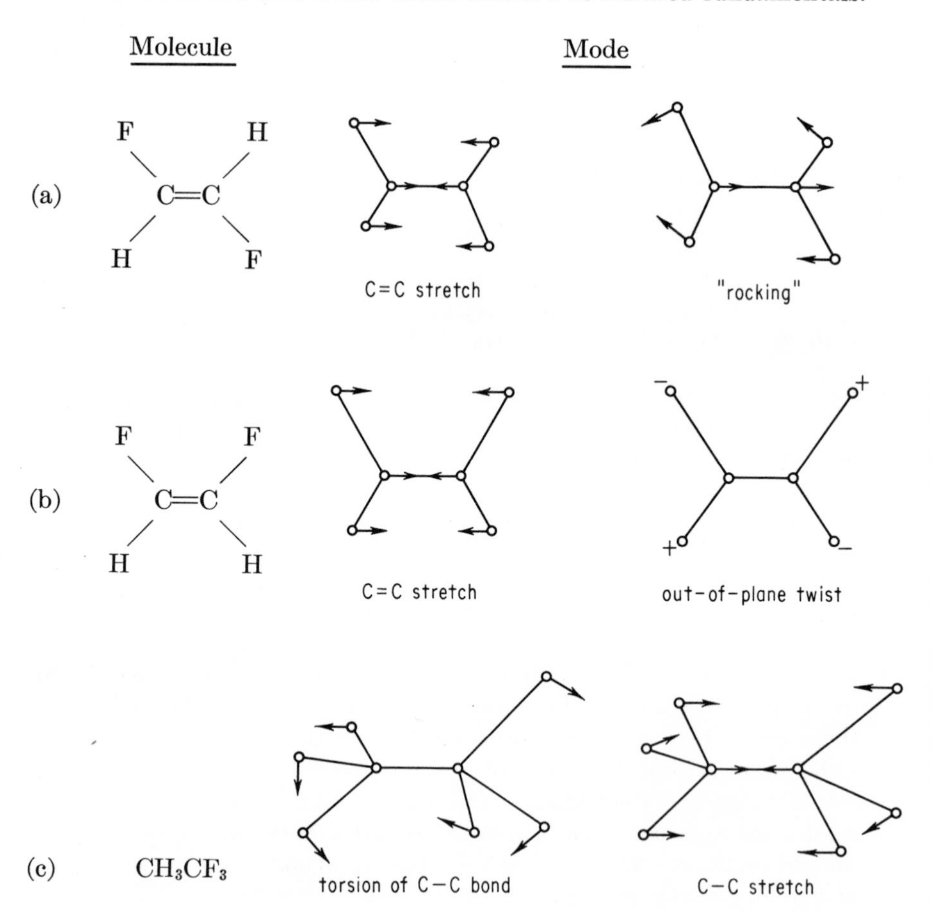

18. In the ultraviolet spectrum of the O_2 molecule there appears a series of bands, called the Schumann-Runge bands, which converges to a well defined limit at 1759 Å. The products of the dissociation are an O atom in the ground state, ^3P, and an excited atom. Atomic spectroscopy has shown that there are two low-lying excited atomic states, ^1D and ^1S, at 1.967 and 4.190 ev above the ground state. From thermodynamic studies the equilibrium constant of O_2 is known to be 1.4×10^{-37}, 8.0×10^{-16}, and 1.7×10^{-8} at 600°K, 1200°K, and 1800°K, respectively. Decide which excited atomic state is formed, and then calculate the spectroscopic dissociation energy of O_2 into two O atoms in the ground state.

19. Below are the two equivalent resonance structures of the singly ionized anion of a common type of organic dye molecule.

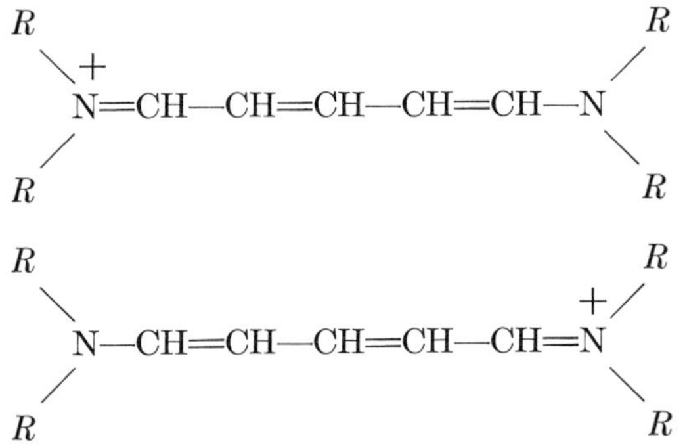

```
R                                    R
 \+                                 /
  N=CH—CH=CH—CH=CH—N
 /                                  \
R                                    R

R                                    R
 \                                 +/
  N—CH=CH—CH=CH—CH=N
 /                                  \
R                                    R
```

(R may be various organic groups: CH_3 for example.) Note that the two structures differ only in the positions of the double bonds, much like the resonance forms of benzene. When two such structures exist, involving a series of conjugated double bonds, it is a good approximation to assume that the two π electrons associated with each double bond are free to move the length of the molecule in a field of constant potential energy but are prevented from leaving the molecule by an infinite potential energy barrier. This is similar to the quantum mechanical problem of a particle in a box where the potential energy is zero inside the box and rises to infinity at the walls. The length of the box here is L, the distance between the two nitrogen atoms. (a) Derive the formula $E_n = n^2h^2/8mL^2$ for the energy levels of an electron in such a box of length L (one-dimensional), starting from either the Schrödinger equation or de Broglie's relation. (b) From the result of part (a) draw an energy level diagram showing the five lowest energy states with their respective quantum numbers, n, and sketch the associated wave functions. (c) The six π electrons occupy the lowest energy states, subject to the Pauli exclusion principle which requires that no two electrons have the same values of both n and the spin quantum number, s. ($s = +\frac{1}{2}$ or $-\frac{1}{2}$) Indicate on your energy level diagram where the electrons would be. (d) Light absorption raises an electron from the highest filled energy level to the lowest unfilled level. Compute the energy difference between these levels and the wavelength in Å of the absorbed light. For this you need to know L, which is 8.4 Å. (e) How much will the wavelength increase for a dye containing one additional vinylene group, —CH=CH—, for which L is increased by about 1.4 Å?

20. Sketch the proton NMR spectra you would expect to find for (a) Isopropyl alcohol; (b) *t*-Butyl alcohol. Indicate the estimated chemical shifts, fine structure due to spin-spin splitting, and relative intensities of the lines, and discuss briefly.

21. The fluorine NMR spectrum of 1,1-difluoro-1,2-dibromo-2,2-dichloroethane

at 40 Mc is shown below as a function of temperature:

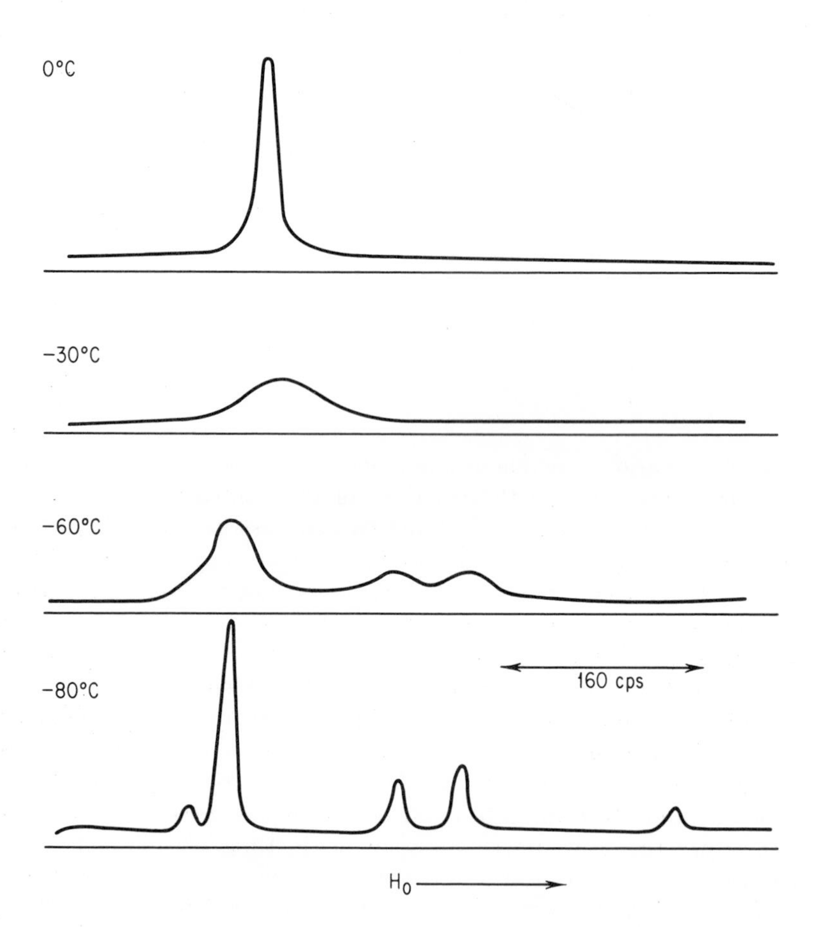

Explain qualitatively what is happening and correlate the lines observed at −80°C with the three rotational isomers of the molecule. Calculate an upper limit to the average rate of rotation about the C—C bond at −80°C and −60°C.

22. How would you expect the intensities of the C≡C stretching vibration to compare in the infrared and in the Raman spectrum of these compounds: (a) HC≡CH; (b) HC≡CCl.

23. In an electron diffraction study of the structure of CS_2, the photographs showed four strong maxima (labeled 1, 2, 3, 4 here) each followed closely by a weak maximum (labeled 1a, 2a, . . .) and a deep minimum (labeled 2′, 3′, 4′). This appearance, as can be seen from the Wierl equation, is due to the fact

that one of the two different interatomic distances in the molecule is just twice the other. The values of s at which the maxima and minima appear are:

1	1a	2′	2	2a	3′	3	3a	4′	4
4.713	6.312	7.623	8.698	10.63	11.63	12.65	14.58	15.54	16.81

40 kev electrons were used. (a) Assuming CS_2 is a linear molecule, plot the Wierl equation versus sr using the approximation that the scattering factor is equal to the atomic number Z, and locate the values of $(sr)_{calc}$ which give maxima and minima. (b) Calculate the CS bond distance by averaging the values derived from each of the observed maxima and minima. (c) Qualitatively, how would the theoretical intensity curve (I_m) versus (sr) change on going to CO_2 and CSe_2? [Cross and Brockway, *J. Chem. Phys.* **3**, 821 (1935)].

24. Given that a typical value of the radiative lifetime of an allowed electronic transition (at 2500 Å, say) is $\tau = 10^{-8}$ sec, predict the order of magnitude of the τ's to be expected for an infrared transition (at 1000 cm^{-1}) and a microwave transition (at 30 000 Mc/sec).

25. Sketch the NMR spectra you would expect to find for (a) the protons in isopropyl bromide; (b) the protons in dimethylethylamine, $(CH_3)_2C_2H_5N$; (c) the ^{19}F nuclei in PF_3; (d) the ^{31}P nucleus in PF_3. In each case show qualitatively the line positions and relative intensities and indicate with suitable labels the origin of the various features shown in the spectra. Assume a 40 Mc spectrometer and room temperature; if you need to make additional assumptions, mention them explicitly.

26. The proton NMR spectrum of dimethylformamide at 40 Mc and room temperature is shown below:

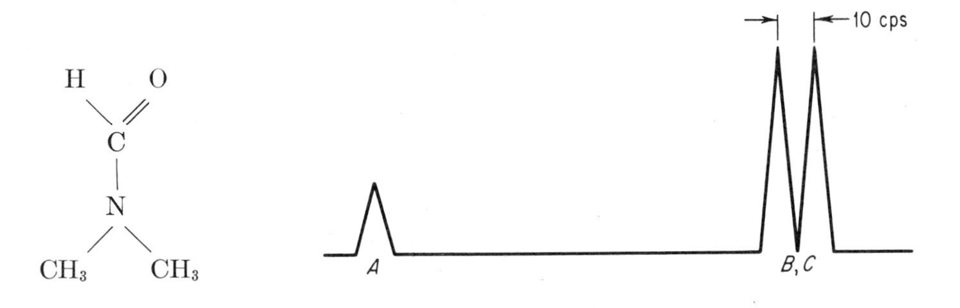

The doublet B, C might arise either from chemically different groups or from spin-spin coupling. (a) What feature of the spectrum immediately rules out one of these explanations in this case? (b) What experimental operation offers a general method for distinguishing between chemical shifts and spin-spin splittings? (c) Explain the origin of the lines A, B, C, and how you expect the spectrum to appear at a higher temperature.

27. Sketch the potential-energy curve for the molecule Li_2 according to the Morse function, given $D_0 = 1.14$ ev, $\nu_0 = 351.35$ cm^{-1}, $r_e = 2.672$ Å.

---

28. A diatomic rotor, $m_1 \overset{}{\underset{r}{\text{———}}} m_2$ is equivalent to a reduced mass $m^\star = m_1m_2/(m_1 + m_2)$ rotating about a fixed point, x ——$m^\star$. For the NaCl molecule, (a) calculate the moment of inertia I (amu A^2) and rotational constant B(cm^{-1} and Mc/sec). (b) Draw to scale the rotational energy levels for the first five rotational states (kcal/mole), and polar diagrams showing the magnitude and allowed orientations of the angular momentum vector **J** for these states. (c) List the rotational transitions that would be expected to appear in the convenient microwave range of 10 000 to 30 000 Mc/sec. (d) Prepare a rough graph showing the relative number of molecules, N_J/N, in the various rotational states J of NaCl vapor at 800°C. The rotational energy of the most populous level is approximately $\frac{1}{2}$ kT.

29. In classical mechanics, the rotation frequency ν, the angular velocity of rotation ω, the tangential velocity v, and radial acceleration a_r experienced by a particle rotating about a fixed point are connected by the relations

$$\omega = 2\pi\nu$$

$$v = r\omega$$

$$a_r = r\omega^2 = v^2/r$$

and the angular momentum is given by $I\omega$. (a) Calculate the classical rotational frequency ν(sec^{-1}) of NaCl for the states with $J = 1$ and $J = 10$. How does this compare with the quantum mechanical frequency of the $J = 0 \rightarrow 1$ and $J = 9 \rightarrow 10$ transitions? (b) The vibration frequency of NaCl observed in the infrared spectrum is 366.1 cm^{-1}. How many vibrations does an NaCl molecule execute during each rotational cycle in the $J = 1$ and $J = 10$ states? (c) Calculate the tangential velocity v and radial acceleration a_r for the $J = 1$ and $J = 10$ states. (d) Estimate the rate of emission of electromagnetic energy and radiative lifetime of NaCl in the $J = 1$ and $J = 10$ states. Assume the molecule is a dipole μ fluctuating with the rotational frequency ν of part (a) and use the result of the classical treatment,

$$\text{energy loss/sec} = \frac{64\pi^4\nu^4}{3c^3}\,\mu^2$$

The dipole moment of NaCl is 8.5 d (where 1 Debye unit $= 10^{-18}$ esu). Since quantum mechanics gives energy loss/sec $= h\nu_{nm}A^{nm}$, one may compare this with the classical result in order to estimate the Einstein coefficient A^{nm} for a transition and hence obtain the radiative lifetime for the transition, $\tau_{nm} = a/A^{nm}$.

30. The following microwave absorption lines were observed for NaCl vapor at 800°C:

Frequency (mc/sec)	Rough relative intensity
26051.1	1.0
25847.6	0.6
25666.5	0.3_5
25493.9	0.3_0
25473.9	0.2_3
25307.5	0.1_8
25120.3	0.1_0

The probable error in these frequencies is ± 0.75 mc/sec (about ten times worse than usual in microwave spectroscopy, owing to difficulties associated with the high temperature.) (a) Assign rotational (J) and vibrational (v) quantum numbers to these transitions. (b) Determine from these lines the values of B_v and r_v for each vibrational state, and derive B_e and r_e, for both isotopic molecules. Handy conversion factor: $B(\text{mc/sec}) = (h/8\pi^2 I) = (5.05531 \times 10^5)/I(\text{amu Å}^2)$. Atomic masses are as follows:

NaCl	22.997139 gm/mole, 100 per cent abundance
^{35}Cl	34.97993 gm/mole, 75.4 per cent abundance
^{37}Cl	36.97754 gm/mole, 24.6 per cent abundance

31. The moment of inertia of a rigid linear molecule

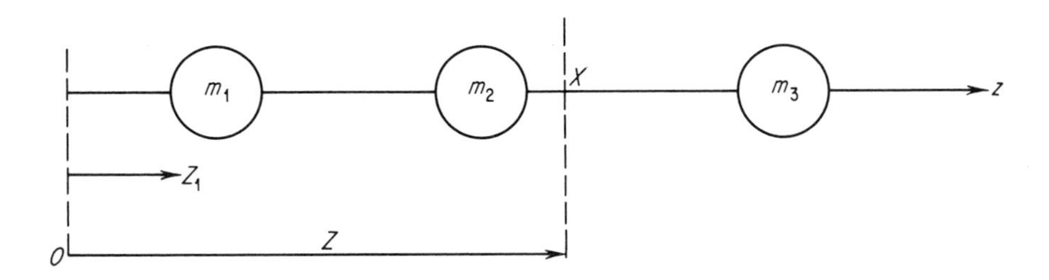

is given by $I = \sum_i m_i z_i^2 - MZ^2$ where $M = \sum_i m_i$ is the total mass and $Z = (\sum_i m_i z_i)/M$ is the coordinate of the center of mass. Here I refers to an axis through the center of mass, although the coordinates z_i and Z may be measured from any arbitrary origin ("parallel axis" theorem). (a) Show that if an isotopic substitution is made on an atom j, the distance of this atom from the center of mass of the original molecule is given by $z_j^2 = \gamma \Delta I$, where $\gamma = (M + \Delta m)/(M\Delta m)$, $\Delta M = m_j' - m_j$, $\Delta I = I' - I$. Show also that if the error in ΔI is δ, the corresponding uncertainty in the derived coordinate is $(\gamma/2z_j)\delta$ and consequently becomes large when the substitution is near the center of mass. (b) The observed rotational constants for four isotopic species of OCS are:

Isotope	B_0, Mc/sec	I_0, amu A^2
$^{16}O^{12}C^{32}S$	6081.490	83.12617
$^{16}O^{13}C^{32}S$	6061.886	83.39500
$^{18}O^{12}C^{32}S$	5704.83	88.61456
$^{16}O^{12}C^{34}S$	5932.816	85.20928

Calculate the coordinates of the atoms and the bond lengths by the substitution method. Atomic masses are as follows:

^{16}O	15.99468
^{18}O	17.99772
^{12}C	12.00000
^{13}C	13.00332
^{32}S	31.97244
^{34}S	33.96852

Note that the coordinates found by the substitution method will not reproduce the observed effective moments of inertia I_0 and will not quite satisfy the center of mass condition.

32. In the far infrared spectrum of HCl is a series of lines having a separation of 21.18 cm^{-1}. (a) Calculate from this the moment of inertia and bond length for the principal isotopic species, $H^{35}Cl$. (b) How would the spacing and intensity of the corresponding lines of the $H^{37}Cl$ isotope compare with those of $H^{35}Cl$?

33. If we were suddenly to multiply the dimensions of a molecule, HCl, for example, by a factor of 100 (without changing its mass or electrical properties), how would this affect its spectrum in the infrared and microwave regions?

34. In Raman spectra, how do the corresponding Stokes and Antistokes lines compare in intensity? Explain briefly.

35. Consider the vibrational fine structure on an electronic transition. (a) Suppose that substitution of an atom by a heavier isotope is found to cause a band corresponding to a given $v'' \rightarrow v'$ to shift to the red (that is, to longer

wavelength). Use suitable diagrams to show that one may conclude from this that the atom vibrates more strongly in the upper than in the lower electronic state involved in the transition. (b) What would one conclude if a shift toward the violet were observed? These shifts are to be measured with respect to the $0 \rightarrow 0$ band of each isotopic molecule. (c) It is usually observed that the $0 \rightarrow 0$ band moves to the violet if heavier isotopes are substituted. Show that this is to be expected whenever the vibrational frequencies are higher in the initial than in the final electronic state involved in the absorption.

36. Suppose a biochemist friend, who professed to be quite ignorant about *nmr*, comes to you for advice. He would like to study, if possible, the transformation ATP $\rightarrow$ ADP which occurs in muscle metabolism by monitoring the *nmr* of the ^{31}P nuclei. He is rather wealthy, and has a complete *nmr* apparatus including oscillators at 40, 30, 20, 10, and 3 mc/sec and a magnet which will go up to about 12 000 gauss. Which oscillator would you suggest he use to study the ^{31}P spectra and why? Calculate the value of the magnetic field at which the resonance would appear.

15 CHEMICAL STATISTICS

If anyone has ever maintained that the universe is a pure throw of the dice, the theologians have abundantly refuted him. "How often," says Archbishop Tillotson, "might a man, after he had jumbled a set of letters in a bag, fling them out upon the ground before they would fall into an exact poem, yea, or so much as make a good discourse in prose! And may not a little book be as easily made by chance as this great volume of the world?"

CHARLES S. PEIRCE (1878)

If you take a deck of cards, shuffle it well, and draw a single card at random, it is not possible to predict what the card will be, unless you happen to be a magician. Nevertheless, a number of significant statements can be made about the result of the drawing. For example the probability of drawing an ace is one in thirteen, the probability of drawing a spade is one in four, the probability of drawing the ace of spades is one in fifty-two.

In such instances it is impossible to foretell the outcome of an individual event, but if a large number of similar events are considered, a statement based on probability laws becomes possible. An example from physics is found in the disintegration of radioactive elements. No one can determine *a priori* whether an isolated radium atom will disintegrate within the next 10 minutes, the next 10 days, or the next 10 centuries. If a milligram of radium is studied, however, we know that very close to 2.23×10^{10} atoms will explode in any 10-minute period.

1. THE STATISTICAL METHOD

Some applications of statistical principles to chemical systems were discussed in Chapter 7. We pointed out that since atoms and molecules are extremely small, any large-scale body contains an enormous number of elementary particles. Any theory that attempts to interpret the behavior of macroscopic systems in terms of atoms and molecules must therefore rely on statistical considerations. But just because such systems contain so many particles, their actual behaviors will be practically indistinguishable from those predicted by statistics. If a man tossed 10 coins, the result might deviate widely from 50 per cent heads; if he tossed a thousand, the percentage deviation would be fairly small; but if some tireless player were to toss 10^{23} coins, the results would be for all practical purposes exactly 50 per cent heads.

Now that we have considered the structures and energy levels of atoms and molecules, we can see how the behavior of macroscopic systems is determined by these atomic and molecular parameters. At first, we shall confine our attention to systems in equilibrium, those usually treated by thermodynamics. This is not, however, a necessary restriction for the statistical method, which is competent to handle also situations in which the system is changing with time. These are sometimes called *rate processes*, and include transport phenomena, such as diffusion and thermal conductivity, as well as the kinetics of chemical reactions.

2. PROBABILITY OF A DISTRIBUTION

The question to be answered is this: given a macroscopic physical system, composed of molecules (and/or atoms), and knowing from quantum mechanics the allowed energy levels for these molecules, how shall we distribute the large number of molecules among the energy levels? The problem has already been discussed for certain special cases, the answers being expressed in the form of *distribution laws*, for example, the Maxwell distribution law for the kinetic energies of molecules, the Planck distribution law for the energies of harmonic oscillators. We wish now to obtain a more general formulation.

The statistical treatment is based on an important principle: the most probable distribution in a system can be taken to be the equilibrium distribution. In a system containing a very large number of particles, deviations from the most probable distribution need not be considered in defining the equilibrium condition.*

We first require an expression for the probability p of a distribution. Then the expression for the maximum probability is obtained by setting the variation of p equal to zero, subject to certain restraining conditions imposed on the system.

The method of defining the probability may be illustrated by an example that is possibly familiar to some students, the rolling of dice. The probability of rolling a certain number N will be defined as the number of different ways in which N can be obtained, divided by the total number of combinations that can possibly occur. There are six faces on each of two dice so that the total number of combinations is $6^2 = 36$. There is only one way of rolling a twelve; if the

* See J. E. Mayer and M. Mayer, *Statistical Mechanics* (New York: Wiley, 1940), for a good discussion of this point.

dice are distinguished as a and b, this way can be designated as $a(6) - b(6)$. Its probability $p(12)$ is equal to one in 36. For a seven, there are six possibilities:

$$a(6) - b(1) \qquad a(1) - b(6)$$
$$a(5) - b(2) \qquad a(2) - b(5)$$
$$a(4) - b(3) \qquad a(3) - b(4)$$

Therefore, $p(7) = \frac{6}{36} = \frac{1}{6}$.

Just as with the dice, the probability of a given distribution of molecules among energy levels could be defined as the number of ways of realizing the particular distribution divided by the total number of possible arrangements. For a given system, this total number is some constant, and it is convenient to omit it from the definition of the probability of the system. The new definition therefore is: the thermodynamic probability W of a distribution is equal to the number of ways of realizing the distribution. This was the definition introduced by Boltzmann to relate probability and entropy in $S = k \ln W$ (cf. Sec. 7.31).

3. THE BOLTZMANN DISTRIBUTION

Let us consider a system that has a fixed energy E and contains a fixed number N of identical particles. Such a collection of units is called a *microcanonical ensemble*. Let us assume that the allowed energy levels for the particles (atoms, molecules, etc.) are known from quantum mechanics and are specified as ϵ_1, ϵ_2, ϵ_3, . . . ϵ_j, . . . , etc. How will the total energy E be distributed among the energy levels of the N particles?

For the time being, we shall assume that each particle is distinguishable from all the others and that there are no restrictions on how the particles may be assigned to the various energy levels. These assumptions lead to the "classical" or Boltzmann distribution law. It will be seen later that this law is only an approximation to the correct quantum mechanical distribution law, but the approximation is often completely satisfactory.

Now the N distinguishable particles are assigned to the energy levels in such a way that there are N_1 in level ϵ_1, N_2 in ϵ_2, or in general N_j in level ϵ_j. The probability of any particular distribution, characterized by a particular set of occupation numbers N_j, is by definition equal to the number of ways of realizing that distribution. Since permuting the particles within a given energy level does not produce a new distribution, the number of ways of realizing a distribution is the total number of permutations $N!$, divided by the number of permutations of the particles within each level, $N_1!\ N_2!\ \ldots\ N_j!\ \ldots$. The required probability is therefore

$$W = \frac{N!}{N_1!\ N_2!\ \ldots\ N_j!\ \ldots} = \frac{N!}{\Pi_j N_j!} \tag{15.1}$$

As an example of this formula, consider four particles a, b, c, d distributed so that two are in ϵ_1, none in ϵ_2, and one each in ϵ_3 and ϵ_4. The possible arrangements are as follows:

ϵ_1	ϵ_2	ϵ_3	ϵ_4
ab	—	*c*	*d*
ab	—	*d*	*c*
ac	—	*b*	*d*
ac	—	*d*	*b*
ad	—	*b*	*c*
ad	—	*c*	*b*
bc	—	*a*	*d*
bc	—	*d*	*a*
bd	—	*a*	*c*
bd	—	*c*	*a*
cd	—	*a*	*b*
cd	—	*b*	*a*

There are twelve arrangements as given by the formula [$0! = 1$]:

$$W = \frac{4!}{2!\,0!\,1!\,1!} = \frac{4 \cdot 3 \cdot 2 \cdot 1}{2 \cdot 1 \cdot 1 \cdot 1} = 12$$

Note that interchanges of the two particles *within* level ϵ_1 are not significant.

The equilibrium distribution is the one for which the probability in Eq. (15.1) is a maximum. The maximum is subject to two conditions, the constancy of the number of particles and the constancy of the total energy. These conditions can be written

$$\begin{aligned} \sum N_j &= N \\ \sum N_j \epsilon_j &= E \end{aligned} \tag{15.2}$$

By taking the logarithm of both sides of Eq. (15.1), the continued product is reduced to a summation.

$$\ln W = \ln N! - \sum_j \ln N_j!$$

The condition for a maximum in W is that the variation of W, and hence of $\ln W$, be zero. Since $\ln N!$ is a constant,

$$\delta \ln W = 0 = \sum \delta \ln N_j! \tag{15.3}$$

Stirling's formula* for the factorials of large numbers is

$$\ln N! = N \ln N - N \tag{15.4}$$

Therefore Eq. (15.3) becomes

$$\delta \sum N_j \ln N_j - \delta \sum N_j = 0$$

or

$$\sum \ln N_j \, \delta N_j = 0 \tag{15.5}$$

* For derivation see D. Widder, *Advanced Calculus* (New York: Prentice-Hall, 1947), p. 317.

The two restraints in Eq. (15.2), since N and E are constants, can be written

$$\delta N = \sum \delta N_j = 0$$

$$\delta E = \sum \epsilon_j \delta N_j = 0 \qquad (15.6)$$

These two equations are multiplied by two arbitrary constants,* α and β, and added to Eq. (15.5), yielding

$$\sum \alpha\, \delta N_j + \sum \beta \epsilon_j\, \delta N_j + \sum \ln N_j\, \delta N_j = 0 \qquad (15.7)$$

The variations δN_j may now be considered to be perfectly arbitrary (the restraining conditions having been removed) so that for Eq. (15.7) to hold, each term in the summation must vanish. As a result,

$$\ln N_j + \alpha + \beta \epsilon_j = 0$$

or

$$N_j = \exp\,(-\alpha - \beta \epsilon_j) \qquad (15.8)$$

This equation has the same form as the Boltzmann Distribution Law previously obtained and suggests that the constant β equals $1/kT$. It could have been calculated anew.† Thus

$$N_j = \epsilon^{-\alpha}\, e^{-\epsilon_j/kT} \qquad (15.9)$$

It is convenient at this point to make one extension of this distribution law. It is possible that there may be more than one state corresponding with the energy level ϵ_j. If this is so, the level is said to be *degenerate* and is assigned a *statistical weight* g_j, equal to the number of superimposed levels. The distribution law in this more general form is accordingly

$$N_j = g_j\, e^{-\alpha}\, e^{-\epsilon_j/kT} \qquad (15.10)$$

The constant α is evaluated from the condition

$$\sum N_j = N$$

whence

$$\sum e^{-\alpha}\, g_j\, e^{-\epsilon_j/kT} = N$$

$$e^{-\alpha} = \frac{N}{\sum g_j\, e^{-\epsilon_j/kT}}$$

Therefore Eq. (15.10) becomes

$$\frac{N_j}{N} = \frac{g_j\, e^{-\epsilon_j/kT}}{\sum\limits_j g_j\, e^{-\epsilon_j/kT}} \qquad (15.11)$$

This is the Boltzmann distribution law in its most general form. The expres-

* This is an application of Lagrange's method of undetermined multipliers, the standard treatment of constrained maxima problems. See, for example, D. Widder, *op. cit.*, p. 113.

† See T. L. Hill, *Introduction to Statistical Thermodynamics* (Reading, Mass.: Addison-Wesley, 1960), p. 26.

sion $\sum g_j e^{-\epsilon_j/kT}$ in the denominator of Eq. (15.11) is important in statistical mechanics. It is called the *partition function*, and will be denoted by the symbol z for the microcanonical ensemble.

$$z \equiv \sum_j g_j e^{-\epsilon_j/kT} \tag{15.12}$$

The ratio of the number of particles in any two states k and l is

$$N_k/N_l = g_k e^{-\epsilon_k/kT}/g_l e^{-\epsilon_l/kT}$$

Thus the terms in the summation for z indicate how the particles are *partitioned* among the various energy states.

The average energy $\bar{\epsilon}$ of a particle is given by (see Eq. 7.46).

$$\bar{\epsilon} = \frac{\sum N_j \epsilon_j}{\sum N_j} = \frac{\sum g_j \epsilon_j e^{-\epsilon_j/kT}}{\sum g_j e^{-\epsilon_j/kT}}$$

or

$$\bar{\epsilon} = kT^2 \frac{\partial \ln z}{\partial T} \tag{15.13}$$

4. INTERNAL ENERGY AND HEAT CAPACITY

Thermodynamics deals not with individual particles, but with large-scale systems containing very many particles. The usual thermodynamic measure is the mole, 6.02×10^{23} molecules.

Instead of considering a large number of individual particles, let us consider an ensemble of a large number of systems, each containing a mole of the substance being studied. The temperature and volume are constant. The average energy of these systems will be the ordinary molar internal energy $\overline{E}$. A collection of systems of this kind is called a *canonical ensemble.* The basic idea of Gibbs which underlies the application of statistical mechanics to thermodynamics was that an instantaneous average of a property taken over the systems of such an ensemble would be equivalent to the time average of the property taken for the one system of interest. We again use Eq. (15.13), except that now a whole system takes the place of each particle. If the allowed energies of the whole system are $E_1, E_2, \ldots E_j, \ldots$, the average energy will be

$$\overline{E} = \frac{\sum N_j E_j}{\sum N_j} = \frac{\sum g_j E_j e^{-E_j/kT}}{\sum g_j e^{-E_j/kT}}$$

Writing

$$Z \equiv \sum g_j e^{-E_j/kT} \tag{15.14}$$

then,

$$E = kT^2 \frac{\partial \ln Z}{\partial T} \tag{15.15}$$

We write Z for the *partition function* of the canonical ensemble.

From Eq. (15.15) the molar heat capacity at constant volume is

$$\overline{C}_V = \left(\frac{\partial \overline{E}}{\partial T}\right)_V = \frac{\partial}{\partial T}\left(kT^2 \frac{\partial \ln Z}{\partial T}\right)$$

or

$$\overline{C}_V = \frac{k}{T^2} \cdot \frac{\partial^2 \ln Z}{\partial (1/T)^2} \tag{15.16}$$

5. ENTROPY AND THE THIRD LAW

Equation (15.16) can be employed to calculate the entropy in terms of the partition function Z. Thus:

$$S - S_0 = \int_0^T \frac{C_V}{T}\, dT = \int_0^T \frac{1}{T}\frac{\partial}{\partial T}\left(kT^2 \frac{\partial \ln Z}{\partial T}\right)_V dT$$

Integrating by parts, we find

$$S - S_0 = kT\left(\frac{\partial \ln Z}{\partial T}\right)_V + k\int_0^T \left(\frac{\partial \ln Z}{\partial T}\right)_V dT$$

$$S - S_0 = \frac{E}{T} + k \ln Z - k \ln Z \mid {}^{\text{at}}_{T=0} \tag{15.17}$$

In this equation, only S_0 and $|k \ln Z|_{T=0}$ are temperature-independent terms. The constant term S_0, the entropy at the absolute zero, is therefore

$$S_0 = k \ln Z|_{T=0} = k \ln g_0 \tag{15.18}$$

Here g_0 is the statistical weight of the lowest possible energy state of the system. Equation (15.18) is the statistical-mechanical formulation of the Third Law of Thermodynamics.

If we consider, for example, a perfect crystal at the absolute zero, there will usually be one and only one equilibrium arrangement of its constituent atoms, ions, or molecules. In other words, the statistical weight of the lowest energy state is unity: the entropy at 0°K becomes zero. This formulation ignores the possible multiplicity of the ground state due to nuclear spin. If the nuclei have different nuclear-spin orientations, there will be a residual entropy at 0°K. In chemical problems such effects are of no importance, since in any chemical reaction the nuclear-spin entropy would be the same on both sides of the reaction equation. It is thus conventional to set $S_0 = 0$ for the crystalline elements and hence for all crystalline solids.

Many statistical calculations on this basis have been quantitatively checked by experimental Third-Law values based on heat-capacity data. Examples are given in Table 15.1.

TABLE 15.1 COMPARISON OF STATISTICAL (SPECTROSCOPIC) AND THIRD-LAW (HEAT-CAPACITY) ENTROPIES

Gas	Entropy as Ideal Gas at 1 atm, 298.2°K (Calories per deg nole)	
	Statistical	Third Law
N_2	45.78	45.9
O_2	49.03	49.1
Cl_2	53.31	53.32
H_2	31.23	29.74
HCl	44.64	44.5
HBr	47.48	47.6
HI	49.4	49.5
H_2O	45.10	44.28
N_2O	52.58	51.44
NH_3	45.94	45.91
CH_4	44.35	44.30
C_2H_4	52.47	52.48

In certain cases, however, the particles in a crystal may persist in more than one geometrical arrangement even at absolute zero. An example is nitrous oxide. Two adjacent molecules of N_2O can be oriented either as (ONN NNO) or as (NNO NNO). The energy difference ΔE between these alternative configurations is so slight that their relative probability, exp $(\Delta E/RT)$, is practically unity even at low temperatures. When the crystal has cooled to the *extremely low* temperature at which even a tiny ΔE might produce considerable reorientation at equilibrium, the *rate* of rotation of the molecules within the crystal has become vanishingly slow. Thus the random orientations are effectively frozen. As a result, heat-capacity measurements will not include a residual entropy S_0 equal to the entropy of mixing of the two arrangements. From Eq. (5.18) this amounts to

$$S_0 = -R \sum X_i \ln X_i = -R(\tfrac{1}{2} \ln \tfrac{1}{2} + \tfrac{1}{2} \ln \tfrac{1}{2}) = R \ln 2 = 1.38 \text{ cal deg}^{-1}$$

It is found that the entropy calculated from statistics is actually 1.14 cal deg^{-1} higher than the Third-Law value; this difference checks the calculated 1.38 within the experimental uncertainty of ± 0.25 in S_0. A number of examples of this type have been carefully studied.*

Another source of residual entropy of mixing at 0°K arises from the isotopic constitution of the elements. This effect can usually be ignored since in most chemical reactions the isotopic ratios change very slightly.

As a result of this discussion, we shall set $S_0 = 0$ in Eq. (15.18), obtaining

$$S = \frac{E}{T} + k \ln Z \tag{15.19}$$

* For the interesting case of ice, see L. Pauling, *J. Am. Chem. Soc.* *57*, 2680 (1935).

6. ENTROPY AND PROBABILITY

Although we obtained the statistical expression for the entropy through the heat capacity equations, we could have proceeded directly from Boltzmann's famous $S = k \ln W$ (p. 247). From Eq. (15.1) and the Stirling approximation,

$$S = k(N \ln N - N) - k \sum (N_j \ln N_j - N_j)$$

Substituting,

$$N_j = Ne^{-\epsilon_j/kT}/z$$

we find

$$S = k(N \ln N - N) - kN (\ln N - \ln z - 1 - \bar{\epsilon}/kT)$$
$$S = N\bar{\epsilon}/T + kN \ln z$$

If we now let N equal L, the Avogadro Number, the molar entropy is

$$\overline{S} = \overline{E}/T + k \ln z^L$$

We see that this expression is the same as Eq. (15.19) provided $Z = z^L$. In Section 8 the limitations of this relation are considered.

7. FREE ENERGY AND PRESSURE

From the relation $A = E - TS$ and Eqs. (15.15) and (15.19), the Helmholtz free energy becomes

$$A = -kT \ln Z \tag{15.20}$$

The pressure, $-(\partial A/\partial V)_T$, is then

$$P = kT \left(\frac{\partial \ln Z}{\partial V}\right)_T \tag{15.21}$$

The Gibbs free energy is simply $G = A + PV$, and from $\Delta G°$ the equilibrium constant for a reaction can be calculated.

Expressions have now been obtained that enable us to calculate all thermodynamic properties of interest, once we know how to evaluate the partition function Z.

8. EVALUATION OF PARTITION FUNCTIONS

The evaluation of the partition function Z has not yet been accomplished for all types of systems, which is of course hardly surprising, for Z contains the answers to all the equilibrium properties of a substance. If we can calculate Z from the properties of individual particles, we can then readily calculate the energies, entropies, free energies, specific heats, and so forth, as may be desired.

In many cases, it is a good approximation to consider that E_j, an energy of the system, can be represented simply as the sum of energies ϵ_j of noninteracting individual particles. This would be the case, for example, of a crystal composed of independent oscillators, or of an almost perfect gas in which the intermolecular forces were negligible. In such instances we can write

$$E_j = \epsilon_1(1) + \epsilon_2(2) + \epsilon_3(3) + \ldots \epsilon_L(L) \tag{15.22}$$

This expression indicates that particle (1) occupies an energy level ϵ_1, particle (2) an energy level ϵ_2, etc. Each different way of assigning the particles to the energy levels determines a distinct state of the system, E_j.

The partition function then becomes

$$Z = \sum_j \exp(-E_j/kT) = \sum_j \exp(-[\epsilon_j(1) + \epsilon_j(2) + \ldots \epsilon_j(L)]/kT)$$

(The statistical weights g_j are omitted for convenience in writing the expressions.) The second summation must be taken over all the different ways of assigning the particles to the energy levels ϵ_j. It can be rewritten as

$$\sum_j e^{-\epsilon_j(1)/kT} \cdot e^{-\epsilon_j(2)/kT} \ldots e^{-\epsilon_j(L)/kT}$$

Since each particle has the same set of allowed energy levels, this sum is equal* to

$$Z = (\sum_j e^{-\epsilon_j/kT})^L = z^L$$

The relation $Z = z^L$ applies to the case in which rearranging the particles among the energy levels in Eq. (15.22) actually gives rise to different states that must be included in the summation for Z. This is the situation in a perfect crystal: the different particles (oscillators) occupy distinct sites at different locations in the crystal structure. In the case of a gas, on the other hand, there are no such distinct labeled sites; each particle is free to move throughout the whole available volume. States in the gas that differ merely by the interchange of two particles are not distinguishable and should be counted only once. If

* It may be rather hard to see this equality at first. Consider therefore a simple case in which there are only two particles (1) and (2) and two energy levels ϵ_1 and ϵ_2. The ways of assigning the particles to the levels are:

$$E_1 = \epsilon_1(1) + \epsilon_2(2), \qquad E_2 = \epsilon_1(2) + \epsilon_2(1)$$
$$E_3 = \epsilon_1(1) + \epsilon_1(2), \qquad E_4 = \epsilon_2(1) + \epsilon_2(2)$$

The sum over states is

$$Z = e^{-E_1/kT} + e^{-E_2/kT} + e^{-E_3/kT} + e^{-E_4/kT}$$

which is equal to

$$e^{-2\epsilon_1/kT} + 2e^{-\epsilon_1/kT}e^{-\epsilon_2/kT} + e^{-2\epsilon_2/kT}$$

Now it is evident that this is identical with

$$z^L = (\sum e^{-\epsilon_j/kT})^2 = (e^{-\epsilon_1/kT} + e^{-\epsilon_2/kT})^2$$

each level in Eq. (15.22) contains only one particle,* the number of permutations of the particles among the levels is $L!$. We therefore divide the expression for Z by this factor, obtaining for the ideal gas case, $Z = (1/L!)z^L$.

Thus the relations between z and Z in the two extreme cases are

$$\text{Ideal crystals} \qquad Z = z^L$$
$$\text{Ideal gases} \qquad Z = \frac{1}{L!} z^L \tag{15.23}$$

Intermediate kinds of systems, such as imperfect gases and liquids, are much more difficult to evaluate, since they cannot be treated as ensembles of non-interacting particles.

To calculate the partition functions for an ideal gas, we find it convenient to use a simplifying assumption. We express the energy of a molecule as the sum of translational, rotational, vibrational and electronic terms. Thus

$$\epsilon = \epsilon_t + \epsilon_r + \epsilon_v + \epsilon_e \tag{15.24}$$

It follows that the partition function is the product of corresponding terms,

$$z = z_t \, z_r \, z_v \, z_e \tag{15.25}$$

The simplest case is the monatomic gas, in which there are no rotational or vibrational degrees of freedom, and rarely any electronic excitation except at very high temperatures.

9. MONATOMIC GASES—TRANSLATIONAL PARTITION FUNCTION

In Section 12.17 it was shown that the translational energy levels for a particle in a one-dimensional box are given by

$$\epsilon_n = \frac{n^2h^2}{8ma^2}$$

The statistical weight of each level is unity, $g_n = 1$. Therefore the partition function z becomes

$$z = \sum \exp\left(\frac{-n^2h^2/8ma^2}{kT}\right)$$

The energy levels are so closely packed together that they can be taken to be continuous, and the summation can be replaced by an integration,

$$z = \int_0^\infty \exp\left(\frac{-n^2h^2/8ma^2}{kT}\right) dn$$

* When the volume is large and the temperature not very low, there will be many more energy levels than there are particles. This will be evident on examination of Eq. (12.40) for the levels of a particle in a box. Since there is no housing shortage, there is no reason for the particles to "double-up" and hence the assumption of single occupancy is a good one. For a further discussion, see Tolman, *Principles of Statistical Mechanics* (Oxford Univ. Press, 1938), pp. 569–572.

Letting
$$x^2 = \frac{n^2h^2}{8ma^2kT}$$
we have
$$z = \frac{a}{h}(8mkT)^{1/2}\int_0^\infty e^{-x^2}dx = \frac{(2\pi mkT)^{1/2}a}{h} \tag{15.26}$$

For three degrees of translational freedom this expression is cubed, and since $a^3 = V$, we obtain
$$z = \frac{(2\pi mkT)^{3/2}V}{h^3} \tag{15.27}$$

The partition function Z is
$$Z = \frac{1}{L!}z^L = \frac{1}{L!}\left[\frac{(2\pi mkT)^{3/2}V}{h^3}\right]^L \tag{15.28}$$
The energy is therefore
$$\overline{E} = LkT^2\frac{\partial \ln z}{\partial T} = RT^2\frac{\partial \ln z}{\partial T} = RT^2\frac{3}{2}\cdot\frac{1}{T} = \frac{3}{2}RT$$
This is, of course, the simple result to be expected from the principle of equipartition.

We evaluate the entropy from Eq. (15.19), with the help of the Stirling formula, $L! = (L/e)^L$. Thus,
$$Z = \left[\frac{(2\pi mkT)^{3/2}eV}{Lh^3}\right]^L$$
$$\ln Z = L\ln\left[\frac{eV}{Lh^3}(2\pi mkT)^{3/2}\right]$$
The entropy is therefore
$$\overline{S} = \tfrac{3}{2}R + R\ln\frac{eV}{Lh^3}(2\pi mkT)^{3/2}$$
$$\overline{S} = R\ln\frac{e^{5/2}V}{Lh^3}(2\pi mkT)^{3/2} \tag{15.29}$$

This is the famous equation that Sackur and Tetrode first obtained by somewhat unsatisfactory arguments in 1913. As an example, we shall use it to calculate the entropy of argon at 273.2°K and at one atmosphere pressure.

$R = 1.99$ cal per °C $\qquad \pi = 3.1416$

$e = 2.718 \qquad m = 6.63 \times 10^{-23}$g

$V = 22\,414$ cc $\qquad k = 1.38 \times 10^{-16}$ erg °K^{-1}

$L = 6.02 \times 10^{23} \qquad T = 273.2$°K

$h = 6.62 \times 10^{-27}$ erg sec

Substituting these quantities into Eq. (15.29), we calculate the entropy to be 36.99 ± 0.01 cal deg^{-1} mole^{-1}. The Third-Law value is 36.95 ± 0.2.

10. DIATOMIC MOLECULES—ROTATIONAL PARTITION FUNCTION

The energy levels for diatomic molecules, according to the rigid-rotor model, were given in Eq. (14.37) as

$$\epsilon_r = \frac{J(J+1)h^2}{8\pi^2 I}$$

If the moment of inertia I is sufficiently high, these energy levels become so closely spaced as to be practically continuous. This condition is, in fact, realized for all diatomic molecules except H_2, HD, and D_2. Thus for F_2, $I = 25.3 \times 10^{-40}$ g cm^2; for N_2, 13.8×10^{-40}; but for H_2, $I = 0.47 \times 10^{-40}$. These values are calculated from the interatomic distances and the masses of the molecules. (cf. p. 240).

Now the multiplicity of the rotational levels requires some consideration. The number of ways of distributing J quanta of rotational energy between *two* axes of rotation equals $2J + 1$, for in every case except $J = 0$ there are *two* possible alternatives for each added quantum. The statistical weight of a rotational level J is therefore $2J + 1$.

The rotational partition function now becomes

$$z_r = \sum (2J+1) \exp\left[-J(J+1)h^2/8\pi^2 IkT\right] \tag{15.30}$$

Replacing the summation by an integration, since the levels are closely spaced, we obtain

$$z_r = \int_0^\infty (2J+1) \exp\left[-J(J+1)h^2/8\pi^2 IkT\right] dJ$$

$$z_r = \frac{8\pi^2 IkT}{h^2} \tag{15.31}$$

One further complication remains. In homonuclear diatomic molecules ($^{14}N^{14}N$, $^{35}Cl^{35}Cl$, etc.) only all odd or all even J's are allowed, depending on the symmetry properties of the molecular eigenfunctions. If the nuclei are different ($^{14}N^{15}N$, HCl, NO, etc.) there are no restrictions on the allowed J's. A symmetry number σ is therefore introduced, which is either $\sigma = 1$ (heteronuclear) or $\sigma = 2$ (homonuclear). Then

$$z_r = \frac{8\pi^2 IkT}{\sigma h^2} \tag{15.32}$$

As an example of the application of this equation, consider the calculation of the molar entropy of F_2 at 298.2°K, assuming translational and rotational contributions only. From Eq. (15.29), the translational entropy is calculated to be 36.88 cal deg^{-1}. Then the rotational entropy is

$$\overline{S}_r = RT\frac{\partial \ln z_r}{\partial T} + k \ln z_r^L = R + R \ln z_r = R + R \ln \frac{8\pi^2 IkT}{2h^2}$$

Note that the rotational energy is simply RT in accordance with the equipartition principle. Substituting $I = 32.5 \times 10^{-40}$, $\bar{S}_r = 11.50$ cal deg^{-1}. Adding the translational term, we have

$$\bar{S} = \bar{S}_r + \bar{S}_t = 11.50 + 36.88 = 48.38 \text{ cal deg}^{-1}$$

This compares with a total entropy of $\bar{S}^\circ_{298} = 48.48$ cal deg^{-1} from heat-capacity data. The vibrational contribution is therefore small at 25°C, but of course it becomes appreciable at higher temperatures.

11. POLYATOMIC MOLECULES—ROTATIONAL PARTITION FUNCTION

The partition function in Eq. (15.32) holds also for linear polyatomic molecules, with $\sigma = 2$ if the molecule has a plane of symmetry (such as O=C=O), and $\sigma = 1$ if it has not (such as N≡N=O).

For a nonlinear molecule, the classical rotational partition function has been calculated* to be

$$z_r = \frac{8\pi^2(8\pi^3 ABC)^{1/2}(kT)^{3/2}}{\sigma h^3} \tag{15.33}$$

In this equation A, B, C are the three principal moments of inertia of the molecule. The symmetry number σ is equal to the number of indistinguishable positions into which the molecule can be turned by simple rigid rotations. For example: H_2O, $\sigma = 2$; NH_3, $\sigma = 3$; CH_4, $\sigma = 12$; C_6H_6, $\sigma = 12$.

12. VIBRATIONAL PARTITION FUNCTION

In evaluating a partition function for the vibrational degrees of freedom of a molecule, it is often sufficient to use the energy levels of the harmonic oscillator [Eq. (14.45)],

$$\epsilon_v = (v + \tfrac{1}{2})h\nu \tag{15.34}$$

At low temperatures, vibrational contributions are usually small and this approximation is adequate. For reasonably exact calculations at higher temperatures the anharmonicity of the vibrations must be considered. Sometimes the summation for z can be made with energy levels obtained directly from molecular spectra.

Corresponding to Eq. (15.12), the partition function for each vibrational degree of freedom is

$$z_v = \sum_v \exp\left[-(v + \tfrac{1}{2})h\nu/kT\right] = \exp(-h\nu/2kT) \sum_v \exp(-vh\nu/kT)$$

$$z_v = \exp(-h\nu/2kT)(1 - e^{-h\nu/kT})^{-1} \tag{15.35}$$

* J. E. Mayer and M. Mayer, *Statistical Mechanics* (New York: Wiley, 1940), p. 191.

The total vibrational partition function is the product of terms like Eq. (15.35), one for each of the normal modes of vibration of the molecule

$$z_v = \prod_j z_{v,j} \tag{15.36}$$

For the purposes of tabulation and facility in calculations, the vibrational contributions can be put into more convenient forms.

The vibrational energy, from Eqs. (15.15), (15.23), and (15.35), is

$$\overline{E} = RT^2 \frac{\partial \ln z}{\partial T} = L\frac{h\nu}{2} + \frac{Lh\nu e^{-h\nu/kT}}{1 - e^{-h\nu/kT}}$$

Now $Lh\nu/2$ is the zero point energy per mole $\overline{E}_0$, whence, writing $h\nu/kT = x$, we have

$$\frac{\overline{E} - \overline{E}_0}{T} = \frac{Rxe^{-x}}{1 - e^{-x}} \tag{15.37}$$

Then the heat capacity,

$$\left(\frac{\partial E}{\partial T}\right)_V = C_{V(\text{vib})} = \frac{Rx^2}{2(\cosh x - 1)} \tag{15.38}$$

From Eq. (15.20), since for the vibrational contribution* $A = G$,

$$\frac{\overline{G} - \overline{E}_0}{T} = R \ln (1 - e^{-x}) \tag{15.39}$$

Finally, the contribution to the entropy is

$$\overline{S} = \frac{\overline{E} - \overline{E}_0}{T} - \frac{\overline{G} - \overline{E}_0}{T} \tag{15.40}$$

An excellent tabulation of these functions has been given by J. G. Aston.† An abridged set of values is given in Table 15.2. If the vibration frequency is obtainable from spectroscopic observations, these tables can be used to calculate the vibrational contributions to the energy, entropy, free energy, and heat capacity. For precise work correction must be made for the anharmonicity of the vibrations.§

Let us calculate the vibrational contribution to the entropy of F_2 at 25°C. The fundamental vibration frequency is $\tilde{\nu} = 892.1 \text{ cm}^{-1}$. Hence

$$x = (h\nu/kT) = (hc\tilde{\nu}/kT) = \frac{(6.62 \times 10^{-27})(3.00 \times 10^{10})(892.1)}{(1.38 \times 10^{-16})(298.2)} = 4.305$$

From Table 15.2 and Eq. (15.40)

$$\overline{S} = \frac{\overline{E} - \overline{E}_0}{T} - \frac{\overline{G} - \overline{E}_0}{T} = .1196 + .0279 = .1475 \text{ cal deg}^{-1}$$

* This is evident from Eq. (15.21) since z_v is not a function of V, $P = 0$, $F = A + PV = A$.

† H. S. Taylor and S. Glasstone, *Treatise on Physical Chemistry*, 3rd ed., vol. 1, p. 655 (New York: Van Nostrand, 1942).

§ Lewis and Randall (Pitzer and Brewer), *op. cit.*, p. 430.

The statistical entropy is therefore 48.38 + 0.15 = 48.53 compared to $\overline{S}^{\circ}_{298} =$ 48.48 from the Third Law (heat-capacity data).

TABLE 15.2 THERMODYNAMIC FUNCTIONS OF A HARMONIC OSCILLATOR

$x = \frac{h\nu}{kT}$	C_V	$\frac{(E - E_0)}{T}$	$\frac{-(G - E_0)}{T}$	$x = \frac{h\nu}{kT}$	C_V	$\frac{(E - E_0)}{T}$	$\frac{-(G - E_0)}{T}$
0.10	1.985	1.891	4.674	1.70	1.571	0.7551	0.4008
0.15	1.983	1.842	3.917	1.80	1.528	0.7070	0.3591
0.20	1.981	1.795	3.394	1.90	1.484	0.6640	0.3219
0.25	1.977	1.749	2.999	2.00	1.439	0.6221	0.2889
0.30	1.972	1.704	2.683	2.20	1.348	0.5448	0.2333
0.35	1.967	1.660	2.424	2.40	1.256	0.4758	0.1890
0.40	1.961	1.616	2.206	2.60	1.164	0.4145	0.1534
0.45	1.954	1.574	2.017	2.80	1.074	0.3603	0.1246
0.50	1.946	1.532	1.853	3.00	0.9860	0.3124	0.1015
0.60	1.929	1.450	1.581	3.50	0.7815	0.2166	0.0610
0.70	1.908	1.372	1.364	4.00	0.6042	0.1483	0.0367
0.80	1.884	1.297	1.186	4.50	0.4571	0.1005	0.0223
0.90	1.858	1.225	1.037	5.00	0.3393	0.0674	0.0133
1.00	1.830	1.157	0.9120	5.50	0.2477	0.0449	0.0081
1.10	1.798	1.091	0.8044	6.00	0.1782	0.0296	0.0050
1.20	1.765	1.028	0.7128	6.50	0.1266	0.0195	0.0030
1.30	1.729	0.9678	0.6321	7.00	0.0890	0.0127	0.0018
1.40	1.692	0.9106	0.5628	8.00	0.0427	0.0053	0.0006
1.50	1.653	0.8561	0.5016	9.00	0.0199	0.0022	0.0004
1.60	1.612	0.8043	0.4481	10.00	0.0090	0.0009	0.0001

13. INTERNAL ROTATIONS

When certain polyatomic molecules are studied, it is found that the strict separation of the internal degrees of freedom into vibration and rotation is not valid. Let us compare, for example, ethylene and ethane, $CH_2{=}CH_2$ and $CH_3{-}CH_3$.

The orientation of the two methylene groups in C_2H_4 is fixed by the double bond, so that there is a torsional or twisting vibration about the bond but no complete rotation. In ethane, however, there is an *internal rotation* of the methyl groups about the single bond. Thus one of the vibrational degrees of freedom is lost, becoming an internal rotation. Such a rotation would not be difficult to treat if it were completely free and unrestricted, but usually there are potential-energy barriers, which must be overcome before rotation occurs.

Let us consider first the case of free internal rotation, which corresponds to a potential barrier much less than kT. The energy levels are

$$\epsilon = h^2K^2/8\pi^2I_r \tag{15.41}$$

where K is a quantum number and I_r is the *reduced moment of inertia*. For the case of two coaxial symmetrical tops, such as $CH_3{-}CCl_3$,

$$I_r = \frac{I_A I_B}{I_A + I_B}$$

where I_A and I_B are the moments of the tops about the common axis of internal rotation. For other structures I_r is more complicated.* The partition function for free internal rotation is obtained as

$$z_{fr} = \frac{1}{\sigma'} \int_{-\infty}^{+\infty} \exp\left(-K^2h^2/8\pi^2 I_r kT\right) dK$$

$$z_{fr} = \frac{1}{\sigma'} \left(\frac{8\pi^2 I_r kT}{h^2}\right)^{1/2}$$

An example of a free internal rotation was found in cadmium dimethyl,

$$H_3C—Cd—CH_3$$

The various contributions to the entropy were computed as follows:

Translation and Rotation	60.66
Vibration	8.76
Free internal rotation	2.93
Total statistical	72.35 cal deg^{-1} mole^{-1}

The third-law entropy was 72.40 ± 0.20; the excellent agreement with the statistical value confirms the hypothesis of free internal rotation in this case.

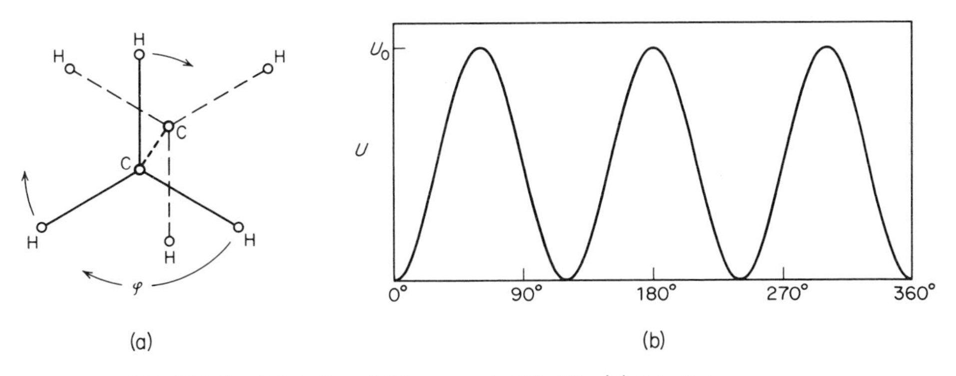

FIG. 15.1 (a) Orientation of CH_3 groups in $CH_3–CH_3$; (b) Potential energy as a function of CH_3 orientation.

When the entropy calculated on the assumption of free rotation deviates from the third-law value, we must examine the consequence of *restricted internal rotation*, with a potential energy barrier $> kT$. Consider for example the case of ethane, shown in Fig. 15.1(a) as viewed along the C—C bond axis. The position shown is that of minimum potential energy $U = 0$; when the CH_3 group is rotated through 60° we have the H atoms alined and a position of maximum

* Lewis and Randall (Pitzer and Brewer), *op. cit.*, p. 440.

potential energy $U = U_0$. The variation of U with angle ϕ is shown in Fig. 15.1(b). The potential-energy curve is represented by

$$U = \tfrac{1}{2}U_0(1 - \cos \sigma'\phi) \qquad (15.42)$$

Some barriers to internal rotation are listed in Table 15.3. Much theoretical work has been done in an effort to explain the origin of these barriers.

TABLE 15.3 POTENTIAL ENERGY BARRIERS TO INTERNAL ROTATION ABOUT SINGLE BONDS

Molecule	Bond	Barrier, cal
$CH_3)_2O$	C—O	2570
CH_3—CH_3	C—C	2750
CH_3CCl_3	C—C	2700
$CH_3)_2S$	C—S	2100
$CH_3)_3SiH$	C—Si	1830
CH_3SiH_3	C—Si	1670
$CH_3)_2SiH_2$	C—Si	1660
CH_3SH	C—S	1280
CH_3OH	C—O	1070
CH_3COF	C—C	1040

There is no simple formula for the partition function for restricted internal rotation. It is necessary to solve the quantum mechanical problem for the energy levels and then to carry out the summation for z. The results have been summarized in Tables.*

14. THE ELECTRONIC PARTITION FUNCTION

The electronic term in the partition function is calculated directly from Eq. (15.12) and the observed spectroscopic data for the energy levels. Often the smallest quantum of electronic energy is so large compared to kT that at moderate temperatures the electronic energy acquired by the gas is negligible. In other cases, the ground state may be a multiplet, but have energy differences so slight that it may be considered simply as a degenerate single level.

There are, however, certain intermediate cases in which the multiplet splitting is of the order of kT at moderate temperatures. A notable example is NO, with a doublet splitting of around 120 cm^{-1} or 2.38×10^{-14} erg. An electronic contribution to the heat capacity is well marked in NO. Complications arise in these cases, however, owing to an interaction between the rotational angular momentum of the nuclei (quantum number J) and the electronic angular momentum (quantum number λ). The detailed analysis is therefore more involved than a simple separation of the internal energy into vibrational, rotational, and electronic contributions would indicate.†

* An excellent set of Tables is given by Pitzer and Brewer, *op. cit.*, p. 441.

† R. H. Fowler and E. A. Guggenheim, *Statistical Thermodynamics* (Cambridge Univ. Press, 1939), p. 102.

15. EQUILIBRIUM CONSTANT FOR IDEAL GAS REACTIONS

We can calculate the equilibrium constant K_p of a chemical reaction from the partition functions of the reactants and products by means of the relation

$$\Delta G^\circ = -RT \ln K_p$$

From Eqs. (15.20) and (15.23), the work function per mole is

$$\bar{A} = -kT \ln Z = -kT \ln (z^L/L!)$$

Since $\bar{G} = \bar{A} + P\bar{V} = \bar{A} + RT$, and $L! = (L/e)^L$ [Stirling formula],

$$\bar{G} = -RT \ln (z/L) \tag{15.43}$$

Let us write

$$z = z_{\text{int}} \frac{(2\pi mkT)^{3/2}\bar{V}}{h^3} \tag{15.44}$$

where z_{int} designates $z_r z_v z_e$, the product of the nontranslational contributions to z. If we consider one mole of ideal gas in its standard state of $P = 1$ atm,

$$\bar{V} = RT/P = RT$$

and Eq. (15.44) becomes, for the partition function of an ideal gas in the standard state,

$$z^\circ = z_{\text{int}} \frac{(2\pi mkT)^{3/2}}{h^3} (RT) \tag{15.45}$$

Then, from Eq. (15.43)

$$\bar{G}^\circ = -RT \ln (z^\circ/L) \tag{15.46}$$

Let us consider the application of this theory to a very simple reaction,

$$A \rightleftarrows B$$

A and B might represent two isomers, for example, butane and isobutane.

In Fig. 15.2, we show two sets of energy levels $\epsilon_j(A)$ belonging to A and $\epsilon_j(B)$ belonging to B. In each case the zero level of energy in this diagram corresponds to complete dissociation of the molecule into atoms in the ground state. The difference in the lowest energy levels, $j = 0$ of the two compounds,

$$\Delta\epsilon_0 = \epsilon_0(B) - \epsilon_0(A) \tag{15.47}$$

When the reaction $A \rightleftarrows B$ has come to equilibrium the molecules of A will be distributed in accord with a Boltzmann distribution in the energy levels $\epsilon_j(A)$, and the molecules of B similarly distributed in their levels $\epsilon_j(B)$.

If we take the zero level of energy for the entire system as the lowest energy level of the A molecules, the partition function for A is simply

$$z_A = \sum_{j=0}^{\infty} \exp\,[-\epsilon_j(A)/kT]$$

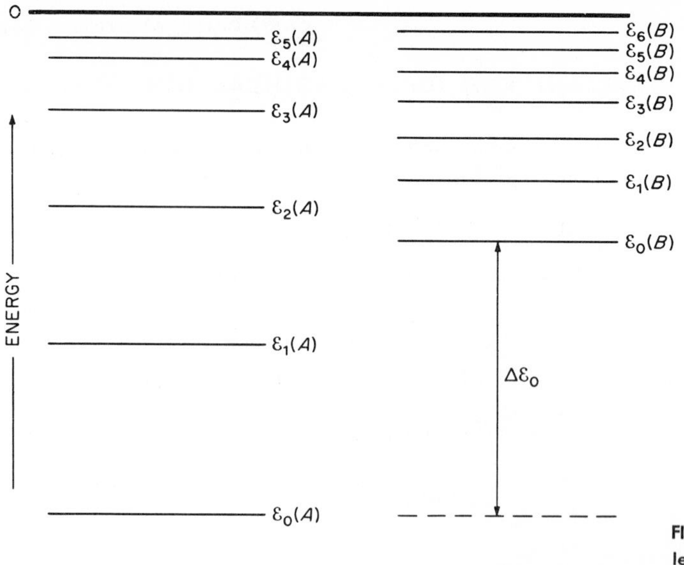

FIG. 15.2 Sets of energy levels for two different molecules A and B.

In order to discuss equilibrium between A and B we must reckon the energy levels of B from the same zero level as that used for A. Thus,

$$z_B = \sum_{j=0}^{\infty} \exp\left(-[\epsilon_j(B) + \Delta\epsilon_0]/kT\right) = \exp\left(-\Delta\epsilon_0/kT\right) \sum_{j=0}^{\infty} \exp\left[-\epsilon_j(B)/kT\right]$$

Having made such an assignment of a common zero level for the energies, we can obtain the statistical expression for the equilibrium constant from Eq. (15.46). For the reaction $A \rightleftarrows B$,

$$-RT \ln K_p = \Delta G^\circ = -RT \ln \frac{(z_B^\circ/L)}{(z_A^\circ/L)} \exp\left(-\Delta\epsilon_0/kT\right)$$

or

$$K_p = \frac{z_B^\circ}{z_A^\circ} \exp\left(-\Delta\epsilon_0/kT\right)$$

We can thus give the equilibrium constant a simple statistical interpretation. It is the sum of the probabilities that the system be found at equilibrium in one of the energy levels of B divided by the sum of the probabilities that it be found in one of the levels of A.

The reaction $A \rightleftarrows B$ was a special case, in that Δn, the change in the number of moles on reaction, was zero. Consider now the general reaction,

$$aA + bB \rightleftarrows cC + dD$$

From Eq. (15.46),

$$\Delta G^\circ = -RT \ln \frac{(z_C^\circ/L)^c (z_D^\circ/L)^d}{(z_A^\circ/L)^a (z_B^\circ/L)^b} \exp\left(-\Delta\epsilon_0/kT\right)$$

and

$$K_p = \frac{(z_C^\circ/L)^c (z_D^\circ/L)^d}{(z_A^\circ/L)^a (z_B^\circ/L)^b} \exp\left(-\Delta\epsilon_0/kT\right) \tag{15.48}$$

16. EXAMPLE OF A STATISTICAL CALCULATION OF K_p

We shall calculate K_p at 1000°K for the dissociation reaction,

$$Na_2 \rightleftharpoons 2\, Na$$

The energy of dissociation of Na_2 was measured spectroscopically as $\Delta\epsilon_0^\circ = 0.73$ ev. The fundamental vibration frequency of Na_2 is $\tilde{\nu} = 159.23\ \text{cm}^{-1}$, and the internuclear distance is 3.078 Å. From Eq. (15.48)

$$K_p = \frac{[z^\circ(\text{Na})]^2}{z^\circ(\text{Na}_2)} \cdot \frac{1}{L} \exp\left(-\Delta\epsilon_0^\circ/kT\right)$$

From Eq. (15.45),

$$K_p = \frac{(2\pi m_{Na} kT)^3/h^6}{(2\pi m_{Na_2} kT)^{3/2}/h^3} \cdot \frac{(RT)}{L} \cdot \frac{\sigma h^2}{8\pi^2 IkT} (1 - e^{-h\nu_0/kT}) \exp\left(-\Delta\epsilon_0^\circ/kT\right) \qquad (15.49)$$

$$m_{Na} = \tfrac{1}{2} m_{Na_2} = 23/6.02 \times 10^{23} = 3.82 \times 10^{-23}\ \text{g}$$

$$I = \mu r^2 = (1.91 \times 10^{-23})(3.078 \times 10^{-8})^2 = 1.81 \times 10^{-38}\ \text{cm}^2\ \text{g}$$

$$h\nu_0/kT = \frac{6.62 \times 10^{-27} \times 3 \times 10^{10} \times 159.23}{1.38 \times 10^{-16} \times 10^3} = 0.229$$

$$(1 - e^{-h\nu_0/kT}) = 1 - 0.795 = 0.205$$

$$\exp\left(-\Delta\epsilon_0^\circ/kT\right) = \exp\left(-0.73 \times 1.602 \times 10^{-12}/1.38 \times 10^{-16} \times 10^3\right)$$

$$= \exp(-8.47) = 2.09 \times 10^{-4}$$

Notice that the R in Eq. (15.49) has the dimensions cc atm deg^{-1}, since it was introduced in connection with the definition of the standard state of 1 atm. Making the substitutions, we find

$$K_p = 0.607$$

17. EXAMPLE OF AN ISOTOPIC EXCHANGE REACTION

A type of equilibrium problem conveniently treated by the statistical theory is the calculation of K_p for isotopic exchange reactions. For example, consider

$$^{16}O_2 + {}^{18}O_2 \rightleftharpoons 2\ {}^{16}O^{18}O$$

From Eq. (15.48),

$$K_p = \frac{[z^\circ(^{16}O^{18}O)]^2}{[z^\circ(^{16}O_2)][z^\circ(^{18}O_2)]} \exp\left(-\Delta\epsilon_0/kT\right) \qquad (15.50)$$

The zero-point vibration frequencies are:

$^{16}O^{18}O$	$\tilde{\nu}_0 = 1535.8\ \text{cm}^{-1}$
$^{16}O_2$	$\tilde{\nu}_0 = 1580.4\ \text{cm}^{-1}$
$^{18}O_2$	$\tilde{\nu}_0 = 1490.0\ \text{cm}^{-1}$

Thus $\Delta\epsilon_0 = \frac{1}{2}hc[2(1535.8) - 1580.4 - 1490.0] = 1.19 \times 10^{-15}$ erg and $\Delta\epsilon_0/kT = 0.029$.

Inserting the expressions for the partition functions into Eq. (15.50) we obtain,

$$K_p = \frac{m^3(^{16}O^{18}O)}{m^{3/2}(^{16}O_2)m^{3/2}(^{18}O_2)} \cdot \frac{\mu^2(^{16}O^{18}O)4}{\mu(^{18}O_2)\mu(^{16}O_2)} \cdot \frac{z_v(^{16}O^{18}O)}{z_v(^{18}O_2)z_v(^{16}O_2)} \exp(-\Delta\epsilon_0/kT) \tag{15.51}$$

The internuclear distances in the isotopic molecules are the same. Note especially, however, the symmetry number $\sigma = 2$ which occurs in the rotational partition functions for the homonuclear diatomic molecules, but not in $^{16}O^{18}O$. This leads to the factor of 4 in the term from the ratio of rotational partition functions. Introducing numerical values into Eq. (15.51) we find for K_p at 25°C,

$$K_p = \frac{34^3}{32^{3/2}\,36^{3/2}} \cdot \frac{[(16 \times 18)/34]^2 4}{9 \times 8} \cdot \frac{(.99951)(.99924)}{(.99940)} e^{-0.029}$$

$$K_p = (1.0045) \qquad (3.96) \qquad (1.00) \qquad (0.971)$$

$$K_p = 3.98$$

We see that the vibrational, translation, and zero-point energies contribute in a minor way to the K_p for the reaction. The important term is the ratio of rotational partition functions and in this ratio the effect of the symmetry number predominates.

18. THE HEAT CAPACITY OF GASES

The statistical theory provides a satisfactory interpretation of the temperature dependence of the heat capacity of gases.

The translational energy is effectively nonquantized. It makes a constant contribution $\overline{C}_V = \frac{3}{2}R$, for all types of molecules.

Except in the molecules H_2, HD, and D_2, the rotational energy quanta are small compared to kT at temperatures greater than about 80°K. There is therefore a constant rotational contribution of $\overline{C}_V = R$ for diatomic and linear polyatomic molecules or $\overline{C}_V = \frac{3}{2}R$ for nonlinear polyatomic molecules. For example, with nitrogen at 0°C, $\epsilon_r = 8 \times 10^{-16}$ erg compared to $kT = 377 \times 10^{-16}$ erg. At temperatures below 80°K the rotational heat capacity can be calculated from the partition function in Eq. (15.30) and the general formula, Eq. (15.16).

The magnitude of the quantum of vibrational energy $h\nu$ is usually quite large compared to kT at room temperatures. For example, the fundamental vibration frequency in N_2 is 2360 cm^{-1}, corresponding to ϵ_v of 46.7×10^{-14} erg, whereas at 0°C, $kT = 3.77 \times 10^{-14}$. Such values are quite usual and the vibrations therefore make relatively small contributions to low-temperature energies, entropies, and specific heats. In Fig. 15.3, the heat-capacity curve for a typical harmonic oscillator is shown as a function of T/θ_v, where $\theta_v = h\nu/k$ is called the *characteristic temperature of the vibration.* As the temperature is raised, vibrational excitation becomes more appreciable. If we know the fundamental vibration frequencies of a molecule, we can determine from Fig. 15.3 or Table 15.2 the corresponding contribution to $\overline{C}_V$ at any temperature. The sum of these contributions for the normal modes of vibration is the total vibrational heat capacity on the harmonic oscillator model.

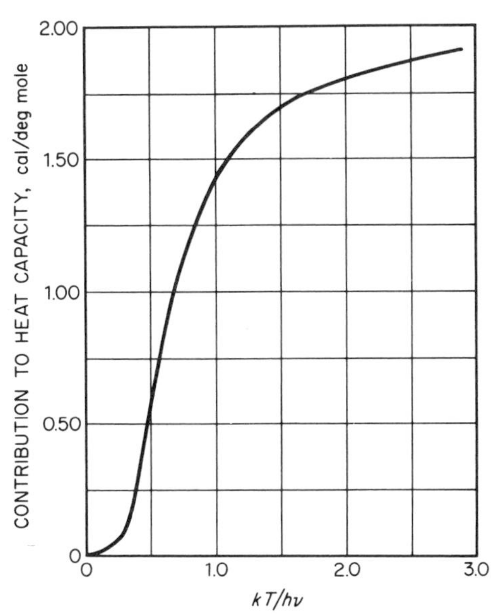

FIG. 15.3 Heat-capacity contribution of a harmonic oscillator.

19. THE HYDROGEN MOLECULES

Since the moment of inertia of the hydrogen molecule, H_2, is only 0.47×10^{-40} g cm^2, the quantum of rotational energy is too large for a classical treatment. To evaluate the partition function, the complete summation must be carried out. When this was first done, using Eq. (15.30), modified with a symmetry number $\sigma = 2$, the calculated specific heats were in poor agreement with the experimental values. It was recognized later that the discrepancy must be due to the existence of the two nuclear-spin isomers for H_2.

The proton (nucleus of the H atom) has a nuclear spin $I = \frac{1}{2}$ in units of $h/2\pi$. The spins of the two protons in the H_2 molecule may either parallel or oppose each other. These two spin orientations give rise to the two spin isomers:

ortho H_2	spins parallel	resultant spin = 1
para H_2	spins antiparallel	resultant spin = 0

Spontaneous transitions between the *ortho* and *para* states are strictly prohibited. The *ortho* states are associated with only odd rotational levels ($J = 1$,

3, 5, . . .), and *para* states have only even rotational levels ($J = 0, 2, 4, \ldots$). The nuclear-spin weights are $g = 3$ for *ortho*, corresponding to allowed directions $+1, 0, -1$, and $g = 1$ for *para*, whose resultant spin is 0. At ordinary temperatures (~0°C), therefore, an equilibrium mixture of hydrogen consists of three parts *ortho* and one part *para*. At quite low temperatures (around 80°K, liquid-air temperature) the equilibrium condition is almost pure *para* hydrogen, with the molecules in the lowest rotational state, $J = 0$.

The equilibrium is attained very slowly in the absence of a suitable catalyst, such as oxygen adsorbed on charcoal, or other paramagnetic substance. It is thus possible to prepare almost pure p-H_2 by adsorbing hydrogen on oxygenated charcoal at liquid-air temperatures, and then warming the gas in the absence of catalyst.

The calculated heat capacities of pure p-H_2, pure o-H_2 and of the 1:3 normal H_2, are plotted in Fig. 15.4. Mixtures of o- and p-H_2 are conveniently analyzed by measuring their thermal conductivities, since these are proportional to their heat capacities.

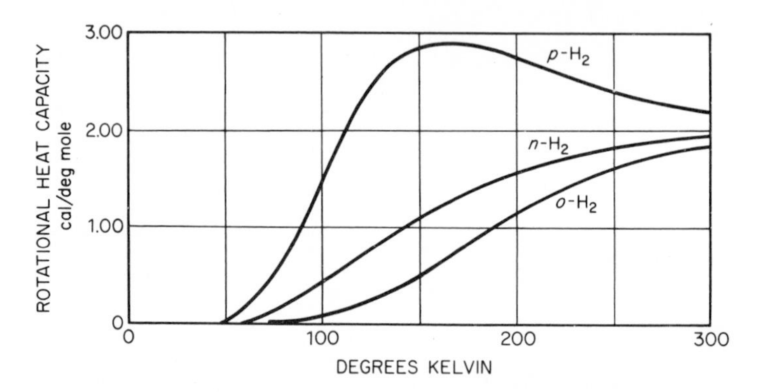

FIG. 15.4 Heat capacities of pure para-hydrogen, pure ortho-hydrogen and 3-o to 1-p normal hydrogen.

A similar situation arises with deuterium, D_2. The nuclear spin of the D atom is 1. The possible resultant values for D_2 are therefore 0, 1, and 2. Of these, $I = 0$ and 2 belong to the *ortho* modification and $I = 1$ to the *para*. The weights $(2I + 1)$ are $1 + 5 = 6$, and 3, respectively. The high-temperature equilibrium mixture therefore contains two parts *ortho* to one part *para*.

In the molecule HD, which is not homonuclear, there are no restrictions on the allowed rotational energy levels. The partition function of Eq. (15.30) is directly applicable.

Other diatomic molecules composed of like nuclei with nonzero nuclear spins may also be expected to exist in both *para* and *ortho* modifications. Any thermodynamic effects due to such isomers would be confined to extremely low temperatures, because their rotational energy quanta are so small. The energy levels are so close together that in calculating heat capacities it is unimportant whether all odds or all evens are taken. It is necessary only to divide the total number of levels by $\sigma = 2$. Spectroscopic observations, however, will often reveal an alternating intensity in rotational lines caused by the different nuclear-spin statistical weights.

20. QUANTUM STATISTICS

In deriving the Boltzmann statistics, we assumed that the individual particles were distinguishable and that any number of particles could be assigned to one energy level. We know from quantum mechanics that the first of these assumptions is invalid. (Why?) The second assumption is also incorrect if one is dealing with elementary particles or particles composed of an odd number of elementary particles. In such cases, the Pauli Exclusion Principle requires that no more than one particle can go into each energy level. If the particles considered are composed of an even number of elementary particles, any number can be accommodated in a single energy level.

Two different quantum statistics therefore arise, which are characterized as follows:

Name	*Obeyed by*	*Restrictions on N*
(1) Fermi-Dirac	Odd number of elementary particles (e.g., electrons, protons)	Only one particle per state, $N \leq g$
(2) Bose-Einstein	Even number of elementary particles (e.g., deuterons, photons)	Any number of particles per state

It is interesting to note that photons follow the Bose-Einstein statistics, suggesting that they are complex particles and recalling the formation of electron-positron pairs from X-ray photons.

A schematic illustration of the two types of distribution would be

⊗ ○ ⊗ ⊗ ○ ⊗   ⊗ ○ ○ ⊗ ⊗ ○

Fermi-Dirac   Bose-Einstein

We can calculate distribution laws for these two cases by exactly the same procedure we used for the Boltzmann statistics.* The results are found to be

$$N_j = \frac{g_j}{\exp(\alpha + \beta\epsilon_j) \pm 1} \tag{15.52}$$

Fermi-Dirac case is +

Bose-Einstein case is −

Now in many cases the exponential term is large compared to unity, and the Boltzmann statistics is a perfectly good approximation for such systems. This

* For these calculations, see, for example, R. C. Tolman, *The Principles of Statistical Mechanics* (Oxford Univ. Press, 1938) p. 388.

can be seen by using the value of $e^\alpha = z/N$ from Eq. (15.10). The condition for the Boltzmann approximation is then

$$e^\alpha e^{\beta\epsilon_j} \gg 1, \qquad \text{or} \qquad \frac{e^{\epsilon/kT} z}{N} \gg 1$$

Using the translational partition function z in Eq. (15.27), we have

$$\frac{e^{\epsilon/kT}(2\pi mkT)^{3/2}V}{Nh^3} \gg 1 \tag{15.53}$$

This condition is obviously realized for a gas at room temperature. It is interesting to note, however, the circumstances under which it would fail. If N/V, proportional to the density, became very high, the classical statistics would eventually become inapplicable. This is the situation in the interior of the stars. A more mundane case occurs in the electron gas in metals. In this case the density term in Eq. (15.53) is exceptionally high, and in addition the mass term m is lower by about 2×10^3 than in any molecular case. Thus the electron gas will not obey Boltzmann statistics; it must indeed follow the Fermi-Dirac statistics since electrons obey the Pauli Principle.

The Fermi-Dirac distribution law can be rewritten as

$$N_j = \frac{g_j}{\exp\left[(\epsilon_j - \mu)/kT\right] + 1}$$

In the electron theory of metals μ is called the *Fermi level*. It is simply the chemical potential of the electrons. At 0°K, $N_j = g_j = 2$ and each energy level is *completely* filled by two electrons with opposite spins, until all the levels up to the Fermi level contain two electrons each.

PROBLEMS

1. Starting from Eqs. (15.19) and (15.27), show that the equation of state of a perfect gas is $PV = LkT$.

2. From Eq. (15.29) calculate the change in entropy of one mole of a perfect gas heated from 300°K to 500°K at constant pressure.

3. Calculate the partition function z in Eq. (15.27) for hydrogen at a volume of 1 cc and $T = 298$°K.

4. Calculate the partition function Z of Eq. (15.28) for hydrogen at 298°K and 1 atm.

5. Calculate the rotational partition function Z_r at 298°K for $^{14}N^{14}N$ and for $^{14}N^{15}N$ molecules.

6. Calculate the rotational partition function for NH_3 at 298°K. The NH bond length is 1.014 Å, the bond angle is 107.3°.

7. Plot the potential function for internal rotation of the CH_3 groups in ethane, given that the barrier height is 2750 cal.

8. Estimate the equilibrium constant of the reaction $Cl_2 \rightarrow 2Cl$ at 1000°K. The fundamental vibration frequency of Cl_2 is 565 cm^{-1} and the equilibrium Cl—Cl distance is 1.99 Å. The D_0 for Cl_2 is 2.48 ev. The ground state of Cl_2 is a doublet ($^2P_{3/2,1/2}$) with a separation of 881 cm^{-1}. [*Ans.* 6.9×10^{-7}]

9. The isotopic composition of zinc is: ^{64}Zn 50.9 atom per cent, ^{66}Zn 27.3, ^{67}Zn 3.9, ^{68}Zn 17.4, ^{70}Zn 0.5. Calculate the entropy of mixing per mole of zinc at 0°K. [*Ans.* 2.29 cal deg^{-1}]

10. In a star at a temperature of 10^6 °K calculate the density of matter at which the classical statistics would begin to fail. [*Ans.* About 10^8 g cm^{-3}]

11. The vibrational frequency of H_2 is 4262 cm^{-1} and that of I_2 is 214 cm^{-1}. (a) Calculate the separation of the vibrational levels (in calories). (b) Calculate the ratio of the number of molecules in the first excited vibrational state to the number in the ground state, for each at 100°C. (c) Would you expect the vibrational contribution to the heat capacities to be large or small at 100°C for these molecules?

---

12. In the far infrared spectrum of HCl, there is a series of lines with a spacing of 20.7 cm^{-1}. In the near infrared there is an intense band at 3.46 micron. Use these data to calculate the entropy of HCl as an ideal gas at 1 atm and 298°K. [*Ans.* 44.6 cal deg^{-1} mole^{-1}]

13. The Ni^{+2} ion in an octahedral field at low temperatures is in a nearly degenerate threefold ground state with energies $E_i = -2D/3$, $D/3$, $D/3$, with $D = -2.0$ cm^{-1} in a typical case. Write down the electronic contribution to the partition function for this system. Hence calculate the electronic contribution to the heat capacity C_V. Show that $C_V \rightarrow 0$ as $T \rightarrow 0$ and as $T \rightarrow \infty$, and is only appreciable when kT is comparable to D. [Hint: Expand Z and C_V in a power series in T^{-1}. Calculate maximum value of C_V].

14. Thallium forms a monatomic vapor. The normal electronic state of the atom is $^2P_{1/2}$ but there is a $^2P_{3/2}$ state lying 0.96 ev above the ground state. The statistical weights of the states are 2 and 4, respectively. Calculate the electronic contribution to E, S and C_V at 2000°K.

15. Calculate the equilibrium constant of the reaction $H_2 + D_2 \rightarrow 2\,HD$ at 300°K given:

	H_2	HD	D_2
ω_e, cm^{-1}	4371	3786	3092
Reduced mass, μ, at. wt. units	0.5038	0.6715	1.0065
Moment of inertia, I, g cm^2 $\times 10^{40}$	0.458	0.613	0.919

[*Ans.* 3.25]

16. The ionization potential of Na is 5.14 ev. Calculate the degree of dissociation, $Na \rightarrow Na^+ + e$ at 10^3 °K and 1 atm.

17. The ionization potential of atomic hydrogen is 13.60 ev. Estimate the temperature at which gaseous hydrogen at 10^{-3} torr pressure would be at least 99 per cent dissociated into protons and electrons.

18. Calculate the translational partition function z for helium with $V = 100$ cc and $T = 300$°K. Considering the allowed states of the helium atom to be given by the energy levels of the particle in a box, estimate the number of states that contribute appreciably to z.

19. The ground state of the $^{14}N^1H$ radical is $^3\Sigma$ (degenerate) with $\omega_e = 3300$ cm^{-1} and $r_e = 1.038$ Å. Calculate E and S of the NH radical at 1000°K.

20. Calculate the equilibrium constant at 1000°K for the reaction $^7Li_2 + {}^6Li_2 \rightarrow 2\ {}^6Li^7Li$. For $^7Li_2$, $\omega_e = 351.4$ cm^{-1}. Assume the vibrational force constants and the $r_e = 2.672$ Å are the same for all these molecules.

21. In Problem 6.24, heat-capacity data were listed for a calculation of the Third-Law entropy of nitromethane. From the following molecular data, calculate the statistical entropy S°_{298}. Bond distances (Å): N—O 1.21, C—N, 1.46; C—H, 1.09. Bond angles: O—N—O 127°; H—C—N $109\frac{1}{2}$°. From these distances, calculate the principal moments of inertia, $I = 67.2$, 76.0, 137.9×10^{-40} g cm^2. The fundamental vibration frequencies in cm^{-1} are: 476, 599, 647, 921, 1097, 1153, 1384, 1413, 1449, 1488, 1582, 2905, 3048 (2). One of the torsional vibrations has become a free rotation around the C—N bond with $I = 4.86 \times 10^{-40}$. [*Ans.* 65.7 cal deg^{-1} mole^{-1}. See Pitzer and Gwinn, *J. Am. Chem. Soc. 63*, 3313 (1941)]

16 THE SOLID STATE

It has been said that the beauty of crystals lies in the planeness of their faces. Crystallography began when the relations between the plane faces became a subject for scientific measurement. In 1669, Niels Stensen, Professor of Anatomy at Copenhagen and Vicar Apostolic of the North, compared the interfacial angles in specimens of quartz crystals. An interfacial angle is defined as the angle between lines drawn normal to two faces. He found that the corresponding angles in different crystals were always equal. After the invention of the contact goniometer in 1780, this conclusion was checked and extended to other substances, and the constancy of interfacial angles has been called the *first law of crystallography*.

1. THE GROWTH AND FORM OF CRYSTALS

A crystal grows from solution or melt by the deposition onto its faces of molecules or ions from the liquid. If molecules deposit preferentially on a certain face, that face will not extend rapidly in area, compared with faces at angles to it on which deposition is less frequent. The faces with the largest area are therefore those on which added molecules deposit most slowly.

Sometimes an altered rate of deposition can completely change the form, or *habit*, of a crystal. Sodium chloride grows from water solution as cubes, but from 15% aqueous urea as octahedra. It is believed that urea is preferentially adsorbed on the octahedral faces, preventing deposition of sodium and chloride ions, and therefore causing these faces to develop rapidly in area.

Some of the most ornate crystals are formed by *dendritic growth*. The snow crystals in Fig. 16.1 all display the symmetry of ice, but with many variations on the hexagonal theme. In such dendritic growth a definite crystallographic axis coincides with the axis of each growing branch; the tips are positions from which heat is most rapidly removed from the crystal.*

* Bruce Chalmers, in *Growth and Perfection of Crystals* (New York: John Wiley, 1958), pp. 291–302.

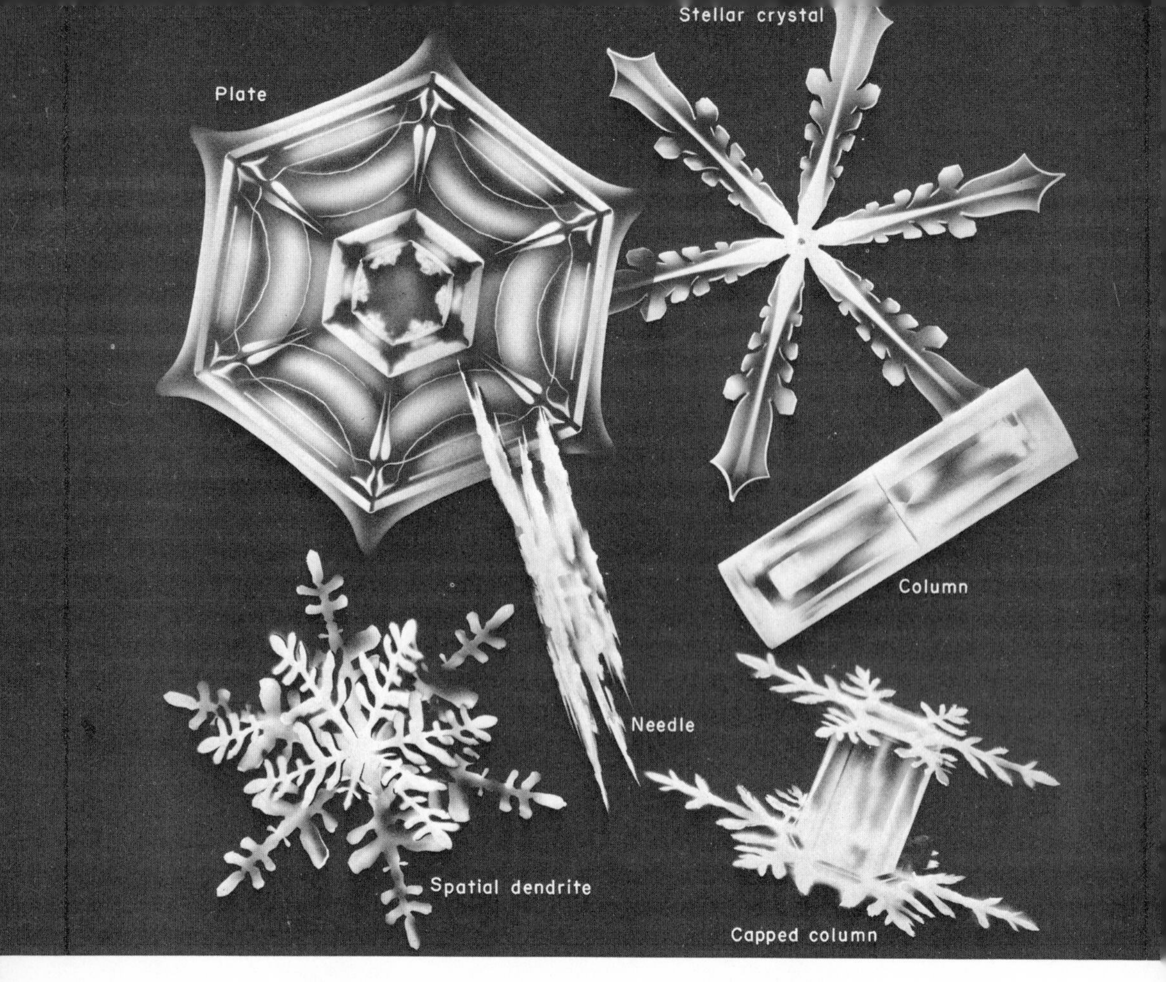

FIG. 16.1 Six typical habits of snow crystals. The different forms are characteristic of growth at different altitudes, the major determinant factor being the temperature. This drawing was made by H. Wimmer for an article "Wintry Art in Snow" by John A. Day, *Natural History, 71*, 24 (1962), [American Museum of Natural History, New York].

Already in 1665, Robert Hooke* had speculated on the reason for the regular forms of crystals, and decided that they were the consequence of a regular packing of small spherical particles:

> . . . *So I think, had I time and opportunity, I could make probable that all these regular Figures that are so conspicuously* various *and* curious, *and do so adorn and beautify such multitudes of bodies . . . arise only from three or four several positions or postures of* Globular *particles. . . . And this I have* ad oculum *demonstrated with a company of bullets, and some few other very simple bodies, so that there was not any regular Figure, which I have hitherto met withal . . . that I could not with the composition of bullets or globules, and one or two other bodies, imitate, and even almost by shaking them together.*

In 1784, René Just Haüy, Professor of the Humanities at the University of Paris, proposed that the regular external form of crystals was the result of a

* *Micrographia*, p. 85.

regular internal arrangement of little cubes or polyhedra, which he called the *molécules intégrantes* of the substance. A model of a crystal structure drawn by Haüy is shown in Fig. 16.2(a). Figure 16.2(b) is an electron minograph of a crystal of tobacco necrosis virus.* Thus, the Haüy model has been confirmed by direct observation.

* *J. Ultrastructure Research* 2, 8 (1958).

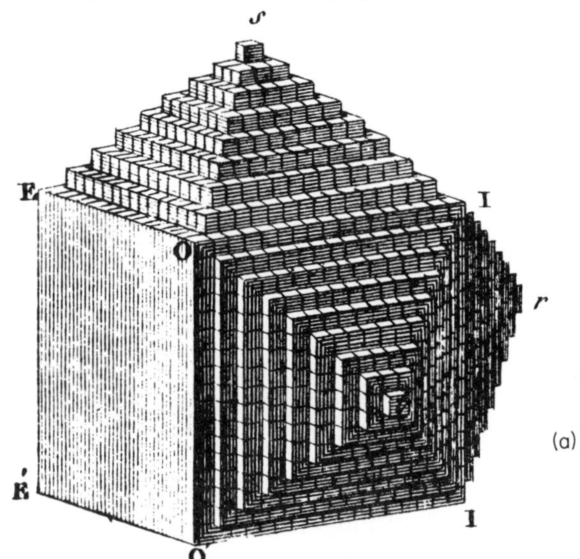

FIG. 16.2 (a) Model of a crystal structure proposed by René Haüy in *Traite elémentaire de Physique,* Vol. I, [Paris: De L'Imprimerie de Delance et Lesueur, 1803]; (b) A crystal of the rhombic type of tobacco necrosis virus in which the molecular order is unusually good. Magnification (X42000) [Ralph W. G. Wyckoff and L. W. Labaw, National Institutes of Health, Bethesda, Md.]

(b)

2. THE CRYSTAL SYSTEMS

The faces of crystals, and also planes within crystals, can be characterized by means of a set of three noncoplanar axes. Consider in Fig. 16.3(a) three axes having lengths a, b, and c, which are cut by the plane ABC, making intercepts OA, OB and OC. If a, b, c are chosen as unit lengths, the lengths of the intercepts may be expressed as OA/a, OB/b, OC/c. The reciprocals of these lengths will then be a/OA, b/OB, c/OC. Now it has been established that it is always possible to find a set of axes on which the reciprocal intercepts of crystal faces are small whole numbers. Thus, if h, k, l are small integers,

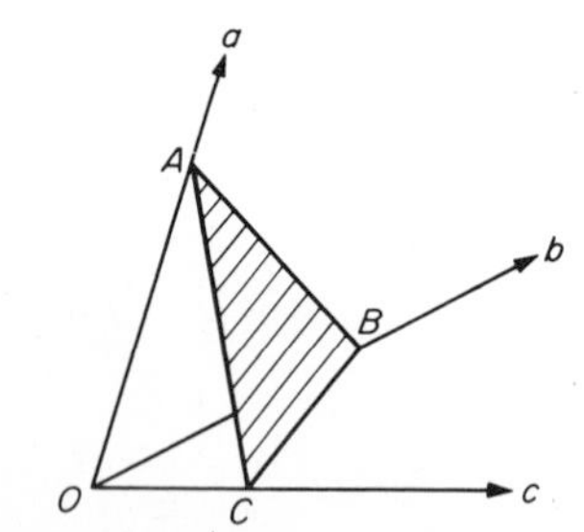

FIG. 16.3(a) Crystal axes intercepted by a crystal plane.

$$\frac{a}{OA} = h, \qquad \frac{b}{OB} = k, \qquad \frac{c}{OC} = l$$

This is equivalent to the *law of rational intercepts*, first enunciated by Haüy. The use of the reciprocal intercepts (hkl) as indices to define the crystal faces was proposed by W. H. Miller in 1839. If a face is parallel to an axis, the intercept is at ∞, and the Miller index becomes $1/\infty$ or 0. The notation is also applicable to planes drawn within the crystal. As an illustration of the Miller indices, some of the planes in a cubic crystal are shown in Fig. 16.3(b). A direction in a crystal is specified by a line perpendicular to a crystal plane. Thus $[hkl]$ denotes the direction perpendicular to the planes (hkl).

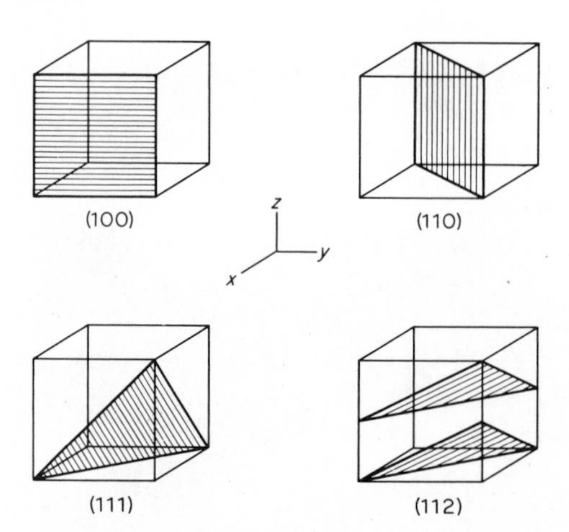

FIG. 16.3(b) Miller indices of planes in cubic lattice.

According to the set of axes used to represent their faces, crystals may be divided into seven systems. These are summarized in Table 16.1. They range from the completely general set of three unequal axes (a, b, c) at three unequal angles (α, β, γ) of the triclinic system, to the highly symmetrical set of three equal axes at right angles of the cubic system.

TABLE 16.1 THE SEVEN CRYSTAL SYSTEMS

System	Axes	Angles	Example
Cubic	$a = b = c$	$\alpha = \beta = \gamma = 90°$	Rock salt
Tetragonal	$a = b; c$	$\alpha = \beta = \gamma = 90°$	White tin
Orthorhombic	$a; b; c$	$\alpha = \beta = \gamma = 90°$	Rhombic sulfur
Monoclinic	$a; b; c$	$\alpha = \gamma = 90°; \beta$	Monoclinic sulfur
Rhombohedral	$a = b = c$	$\alpha = \beta = \gamma$	Calcite
Hexagonal	$a = b; c$	$\alpha = \beta = 90°; \gamma = 120°$	Graphite
Triclinic	$a; b; c$	$\alpha; \beta; \gamma$	Potassium dichromate

3. LATTICES AND CRYSTAL STRUCTURES

Instead of considering, as Haüy did, that a crystal is made of elementary material units, it is helpful to introduce a geometrical idealization, consisting only of a regular array of points in space. This is called a *lattice*. An example in two dimensions is shown in Fig. 16.4.

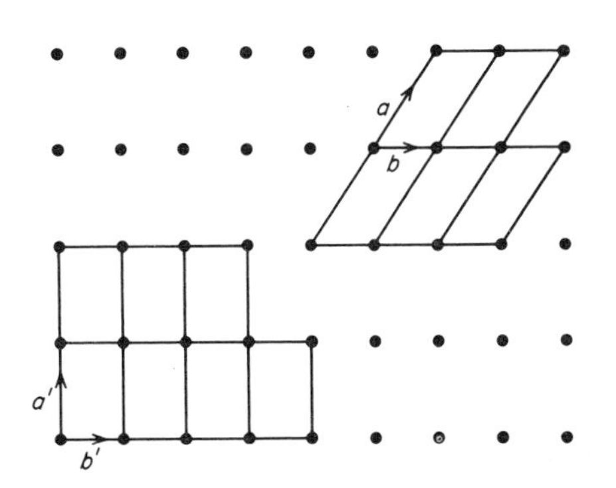

FIG. 16.4. Two-dimensional lattice with unit cells.

The lattice points can be connected by a regular network of lines in various ways. Thus the lattice is broken up into a number of *unit cells*. Some examples are shown in the figure. Each cell requires two vectors, a and b, for its description. A three-dimensional *space lattice* can be similarly divided into unit cells described by three vectors.

If each point in a space lattice is replaced by an identical atom or group of atoms there is obtained a *crystal structure*. The lattice is an array of points; in the crystal structure each point is replaced by a material unit. The positions of atoms in unit cells are denoted by coordinates which are fractions of the unit cell dimensions. For example, if a unit cell has sides a, b, c, an atom at $(\frac{1}{2}, \frac{1}{4}, \frac{1}{2})$ would be at $(a/2, b/4, c/2)$ relative to the origin $(0, 0, 0)$ at a corner of the cell.

In 1848, A. Bravais showed that all possible space lattices could be assigned to one of only 14 classes.* The 14 Bravais lattices are shown in Fig. 16.5. They give the allowed different translational relations between points in an infinitely extended regular three-dimensional array. The choice of the 14 lattices is somewhat arbitrary, since in certain cases alternative descriptions are possible.

* A lattice that contains body-, face-, or end-centered points can always be reduced to one that does not (*primitive lattice*). Thus the face-centered cubic can be reduced to a primitive rhombohedral. The centered lattices are chosen when possible because of their higher symmetry.

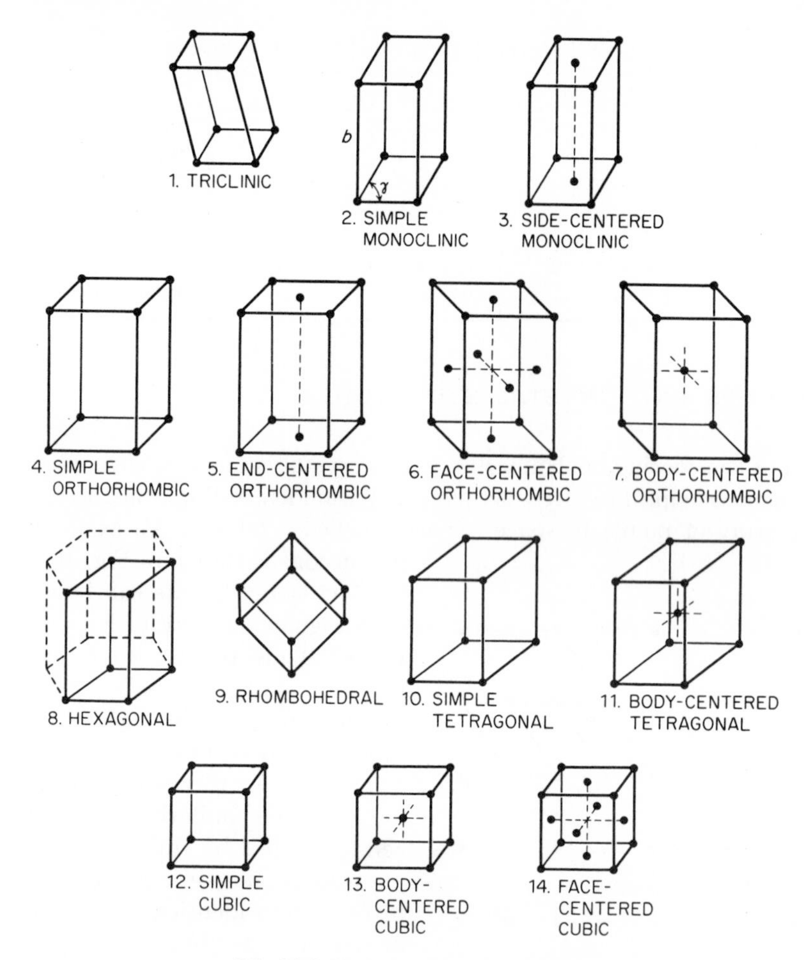

FIG. 16.5 The fourteen Bravais lattices.

4. SYMMETRY PROPERTIES

The word *symmetry* has been used in referring tc the arrangement of crystal faces. It is now desirable to consider the nature of this symmetry in more detail. If an actual crystal of a substance is studied, some of the faces may be so poorly developed that it is difficult or impossible to see its full symmetry just by looking at it. It is necessary therefore to consider an ideal crystal in which all the faces of the same kind are developed to the same extent. It is not only in face development that the symmetry of the crystal is evident but also in all of its physical properties, e.g., electrical and thermal conductivity, piezoelectric effect, and refractive index.

Symmetry is described in terms of certain *symmetry operations*, which transform the crystal into an image of itself. The operations are the result of certain *symmetry elements*. The possible *symmetry elements* of finite figures, for example, crystals or molecules, are listed in Table 16.2, with the international symbols

TABLE 16.2 THE SYMMETRY ELEMENTS OF CRYSTALS

No symmetry (identity element)	1	Fourfold rotation axis (rotor)	4
Mirror plane of symmetry	m	Fourfold rotatory inverter	$\bar{4}$
Twofold rotation axis (rotor)	2	Sixfold rotation axis (rotor)	6
Threefold rotation axis (rotor)	3	Sixfold rotatory inverter	$\bar{6}$
Threefold rotatory inverter	$\bar{3}$	Center of symmetry (inverter)	$\bar{1}$

devised by Hermann and Mauguin. Examples of the operations of the symmetry elements are shown in Fig. 16.6. An axis of rotary inversion is the combination of a rotation axis with a center of symmetry; it is denoted by placing a bar over the symbol for the axis.

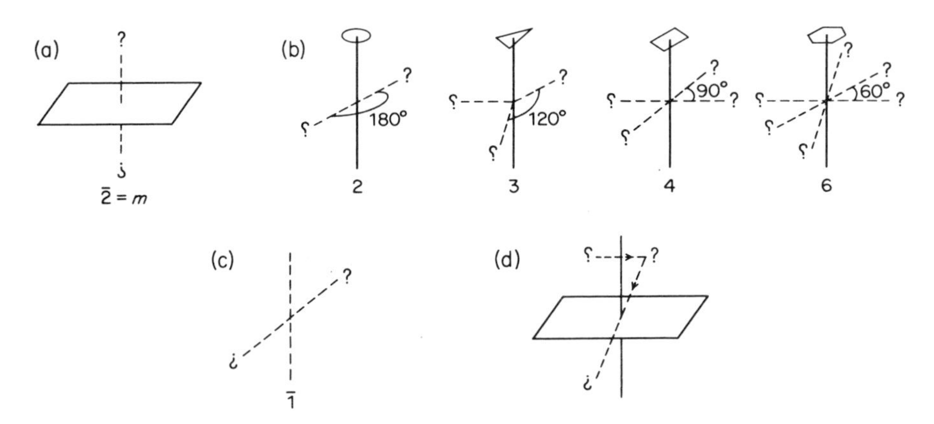

FIG. 16.6 Examples of symmetry elements: (a) mirror plane m; (b) rotation axes; (c) symmetry center $\bar{1}$; (d) twofold rotary inversion axis $\bar{2} = m$.

Exactly 32 possible combinations of these symmetry elements can occur in crystals. These define the 32 *crystallographic point groups**, which determine the 32 *crystal classes*.

The symbol for a crystal class is derived by writing down the symmetry elements associated with three important directions in the crystal.†

* A set of symmetry operations forms a *group* when the consecutive application of any two operations in the set is equivalent to an operation belonging to the set (Law of Multiplication). It is understood that the identity operation, leaving the crystal unchanged, is included in each set; that the operations are reversible; and that the associative law holds, $A(BC) = (AB)C$.

† Monoclinic: the axis normal to the other two.
Orthorhombic: the three axes a, b, c.
Tetragonal: the c axis; the a axis; an axis $\perp$ c and 45° to a.
Hexagonal: the c axis, the a axis $\perp$ c, and an axis $\perp$ c and 30° to a.
Rhombohedral: the body diagonal and an axis normal to it. (Or principal and secondary axes of hexagonal system.)
Cubic: the directions [001], [111], and [110].

When a mirror plane is normal to a rotation axis it is written as the denominator of a fraction. For example: 4/mmm is the holohedral class of the tetragonal system having a 4 along the c axis with an m normal to it, and m's normal to each the other two standard directions.

All crystals necessarily fall into one of the *seven systems*, but there are several *classes* in each system. Only one of these, called the *holohedral class*, possesses the complete symmetry of the system. For example, consider two crystals belonging to the cubic system, rock salt (NaCl) and iron pyrites (FeS_2). Crystalline rock salt, Fig. 16.7, possesses the full symmetry of the cube: three 4-fold axes, four 3-fold axes, six 2-fold axes, three mirror planes perpendicular to the 4-fold axes, six mirror planes perpendicular to the 2-fold axes, and a center of inversion. The cubic crystals of pyrites might at first seem to possess all these symmetry elements too. Closer examination reveals, however, that the pyrites crystals have characteristic striations on their faces, as shown in the picture, so that all the faces are not equivalent. These crystals therefore do not possess the six 2-fold axes with the six planes normal to them, the 4-fold axes have been reduced to 2-fold axes, and the 3 have become $\bar{3}$.

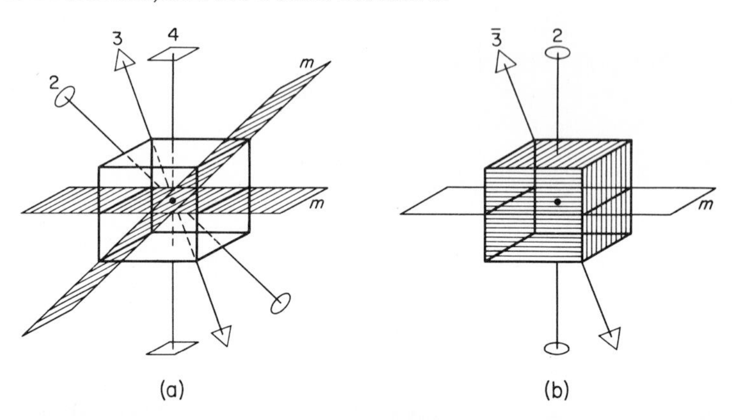

FIG. 16.7 Symmetry elements of two cubic crystals: (a) Rock salt. (b) Pyrites.

In other cases, such departures from full symmetry are only revealed, as far as external appearance goes, by the orientation of etch figures formed on the surfaces. Sometimes the phenomenon of pyroelectricity provides a useful symmetry test. When a crystal that contains no center of symmetry is heated, a difference in potential is developed across its faces. This can be observed by the resultant electrostatic attraction between individual crystals.

All these differences in symmetry are caused by the fact that the full symmetry of the point lattice has been modified in the crystal structure, as a result of replacing the geometrical points by groups of atoms. Since these groups need not have so high a symmetry as the original lattice, classes of lower than holohedral symmetry can arise within each system.

5. SPACE GROUPS

The crystal classes are the various groups of symmetry operations of finite figures, e.g., actual crystals. They are made up of operations by symmetry elements that leave at least one point in the crystal invariant. This is why they are called *point groups*.

In a crystal structure, considered as an infinitely extended pattern in space, new types of symmetry operation are admissible, which leave no point invariant. These are called *space operations*. The new symmetry operations involve *translations* in addition to rotations and reflections. Clearly only an infinitely extended pattern can have a space operation (translation) as a symmetry operation.

The possible groups of symmetry operations of infinite figures are called *space groups*. They may be considered to arise from combinations of the 14 Bravais lattices with the 32 point groups.* A space group may be visualized as a sort of crystallographic kaleidoscope. If one structural unit is introduced into the unit cell, the operations of the space group immediately generate the entire crystal structure, just as the mirrors of the kaleidoscope produce a symmetrical pattern from a few bits of colored paper.

The space group expresses the sum total of the symmetry properties of a crystal structure, and mere external form or bulk properties do not suffice for its determination. The inner structure of the crystal must be studied and this is made possible by the methods of X-ray diffraction.

6. X-RAY CRYSTALLOGRAPHY

At the University of Munich in 1912, there was a group of physicists interested in both crystallography and the behavior of X rays. P. P. Ewald and A. Sommerfeld were studying the passage of light waves through crystals. At a colloquium discussing some of this work, Max von Laue pointed out that if the wavelength of the radiation became as small as the distance between atoms in the crystals, a diffraction pattern should result. There was some evidence that X rays might have the right wavelength, and W. Friedrich agreed to make the experimental test.

On passing an X ray beam through a crystal of copper sulfate, they obtained a definite diffraction pattern. Fig. 16.8 shows a modern example of an X-ray diffraction pattern obtained by the Laue method. The wave properties of X rays were thus definitely established and the new science of X-ray crystallography began.

The conditions for diffraction maxima from a regular three-dimensional array of scattering centers are given on p. 463:

$$\begin{aligned} a(\cos\alpha - \cos\alpha_0) &= h\lambda \\ b(\cos\beta - \cos\beta_0) &= k\lambda \\ c(\cos\gamma - \cos\gamma_0) &= l\lambda \end{aligned} \qquad (16.1)$$

* A good example of the construction of space groups is given by Lawrence Bragg, *The Crystalline State* (London: G. Bell and Sons, 1933), p. 82. The space-group notation is described in *International Tables for the Determination of Crystal Structures*, Vol. I. There are exactly 230 possible crystallographic space groups.

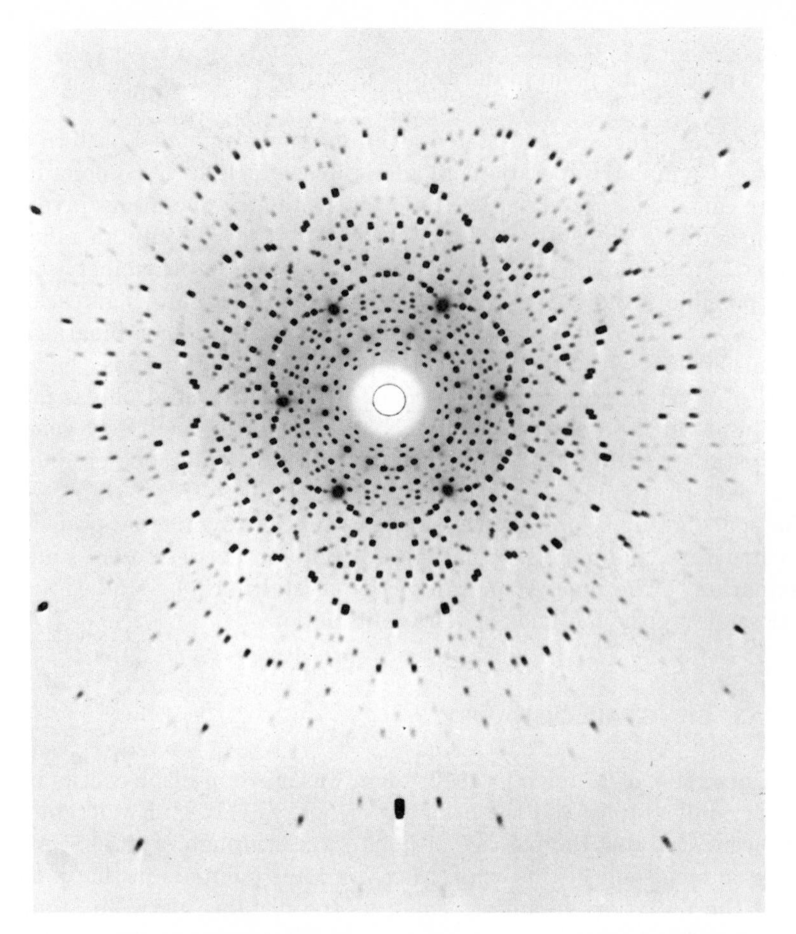

FIG. 16.8 X-ray diffraction by the Laue method of a crystal of beryl. [Eastman Kodak Research Laboratories]

In these equations α_0, β_0, and γ_0 are the incident angles of the X-ray beam with the rows of scattering centers parallel to each of the three axes of the crystal, and α, β, γ are the corresponding angles of diffraction.

If monochromatic X rays are used, there is only a slim chance that the orientation of the crystal is fixed in such a way as to yield diffraction maxima. The Laue method, however, uses a continuous spectrum of X-radiation with a wide range of wavelengths, the so-called *white radiation*, conveniently obtained from a tungsten target at high voltages. In this case, at least some of the radiation is at the proper wavelength to experience interference effects, no matter what the orientation of crystal to beam.

7. THE BRAGG TREATMENT

When the news of the Munich work reached England, it was immediately taken up by William Bragg and his son Lawrence who had been working on a corpuscular theory of X rays. Lawrence Bragg, using Laue-type photographs, analyzed the structures of NaCl, KCl, and ZnS (1912, 1913). In the meantime (1913), the elder Bragg devised a spectrometer that measured the intensity of an X-ray beam by the amount of ionization it produced, and he found that the characteristic X-ray line spectrum could be isolated and used for crystallographic work. Thus the Bragg method uses a monochromatic (single wavelength) beam of X rays.

The Braggs developed a treatment of X-ray scattering by a crystal that was much easier to apply than the Laue theory, although the two are essentially equivalent. It was shown that the scatterings of X rays could be represented as a "reflection" by successive planes of atoms in the crystal.* Consider, in Fig. 16.9, a set of parallel planes in the crystal structure and a beam of X-rays incident at an angle θ. Some of the rays will be "reflected" from the upper layer of atoms, the angle of reflection being equal to the angle of incidence. Some of the rays will be absorbed, and some will be "reflected" from the second layer, and so on with successive layers. All the waves "reflected" by a single crystal plane will be in phase. Only under certain strict conditions will the waves "reflected" by different underlying planes be in phase with one another. The condition is that the difference in length of path between the waves scattered from successive planes must be an integral number of wavelengths, $n\lambda$. If we consider the "reflected" waves at the point P, this path difference for the first two planes is $\delta = \overline{AB} + \overline{BC}$. Since triangles AOB and COB are congruent, $\overline{AB} = \overline{BC}$ and $\delta = 2\overline{AB}$. Therefore $\delta = 2d \sin \theta$. The condition for reinforcement or Bragg "reflection" is thus

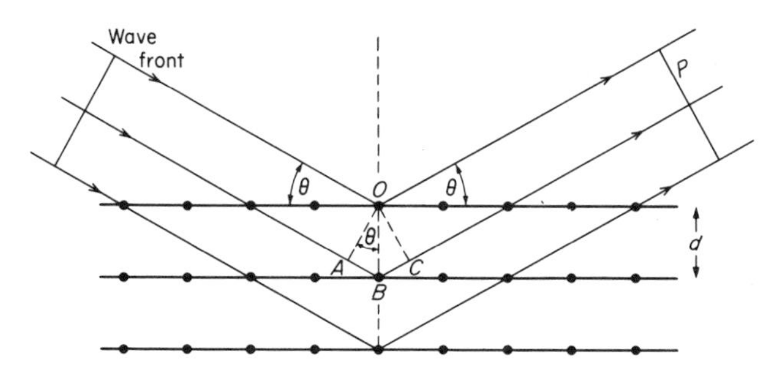

FIG. 16.9 Bragg scattering condition.

$$n\lambda = 2d \sin \theta \tag{16.2}$$

According to this viewpoint, there are different *orders* of "reflection" specified by the values $n = 1, 2, 3, \ldots$. The second order diffraction maxima from (100) planes may then be regarded as a "reflection" due to a set of planes (200) with half the spacing of the (100) planes.

* For a proof of this equivalence, see C. W. Bunn, *Chemical Crystallography* (Oxford Univ. Press, 1945), p. 114. An elegant proof in vector notation is given by G. Wannier, *Solid State Theory* (Cambridge Univ. Press, 1959), p. 39.

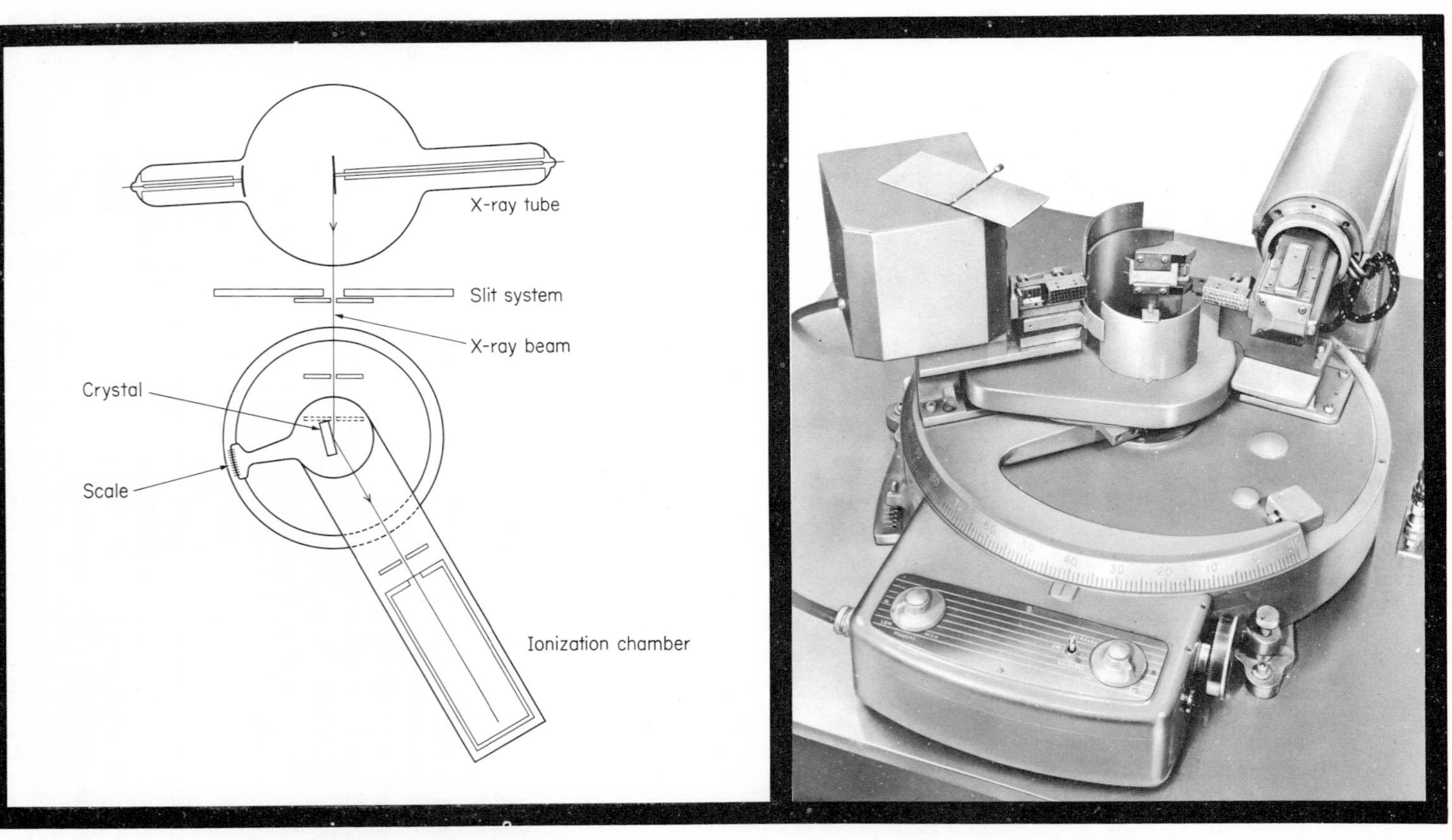

FIG. 16.10(a) Bragg X-ray spectrometer.

FIG. 16.10(b) A modern X-ray spectrometer. The head of the X-ray tube is at right. The diffracted beam is measured by the counter tube at left. [General Electric Company].

The Bragg equation indicates that for any given wavelength of X-rays there is a lower limit to the spacings that can give observable diffraction spectra. Since the maximum value of $\sin\theta$ is 1, this limit is given by

$$d_{\min} = \frac{n\lambda}{2\sin\theta_{\max}} = \frac{\lambda}{2}$$

8. STRUCTURES OF SODIUM AND POTASSIUM CHLORIDES

Among the first crystals to be studied by the Bragg method were sodium and potassium chlorides. A single crystal was mounted on the spectrometer, as shown in Fig. 16.10, so that the X-ray beam was incident on one of the important crystal faces, (100), (110), or (111). The apparatus was arranged so that the "reflected" beam entered the ionization chamber, which was filled with methyl bromide. Its intensity was measured by the charge built up on an electrometer.

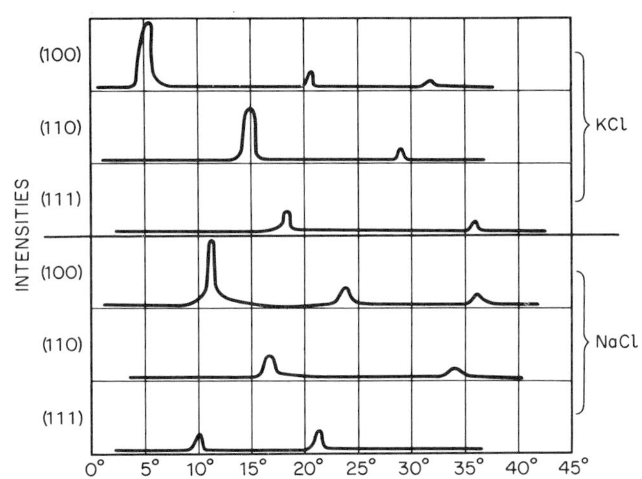

FIG. 16.11 Bragg spectrometer data, I vs. 2θ.

The experimental data are shown plotted in Fig. 16.11 as "intensity of scattered beam" *vs.* "twice the angle of incidence of beam to crystal." As the crystal is rotated, successive maxima "flash out" as the angles are passed conforming to the Bragg condition, Eq. (16.2). In these first experiments the monochromatic X-radiation was obtained from a palladium target.

To begin with, Bragg knew neither the wavelength of the X rays nor the structure of the crystals. He did know, from external form, that both NaCl and KCl could be based on one of the cubic lattices, simple, body-centered, or face-centered. By comparing the spacings calculated from the X-ray data with those expected for these lattices, he could decide the proper assignment.

The distance between the planes (hkl) in a cubic lattice is*

$$d_{hkl} = \frac{a_0}{(h^2 + k^2 + l^2)^{1/2}}$$

* Bunn, *op. cit.*, p. 376.

When this is combined with the Bragg equation, we obtain

$$\sin^2\theta = (\lambda^2/4a_0^2)(h^2 + k^2 + l^2)$$

Thus each observed value of $\sin\theta$ can be indexed by assigning to it the value of (hkl) for the set of planes responsible for the "reflection." For a simple cubic lattice, the following spacings are allowed:

(hkl)	100	110	111	200	210	211	220	221, 300	etc.
$h^2 + k^2 + l^2$ . .	1	2	3	4	5	6	8	9	etc.

If the observed X-ray pattern from a simple cubic crystal was plotted as intensity *vs.* $\sin^2\theta$ we should obtain a series of six equidistant maxima. Then the seventh should be missing, since there is no set of integers hkl such that $h^2 + k^2 + l^2 = 7$. There would then follow seven more equidistant maxima, with the 15th missing; seven more, the 23rd missing; four more, the 28th missing; and so on.

In Fig. 16.12(a) we see the (100), (110), and (111) planes for a simple cubic lattice. A structure may be based on this lattice by replacing each lattice point

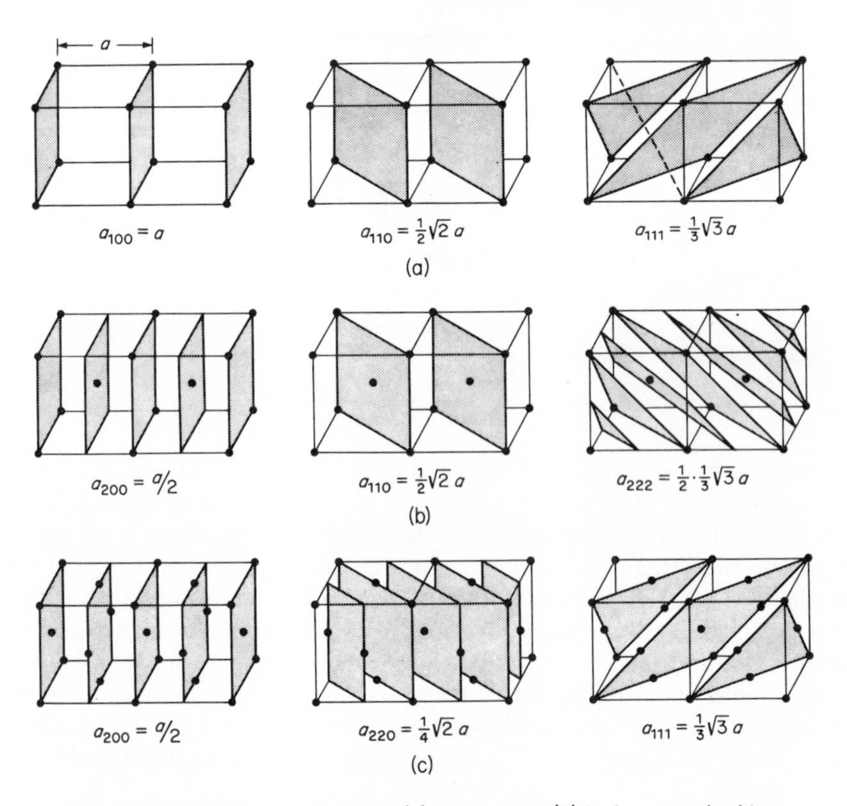

FIG. 16.12 Spacings in cubic lattices: (a) simple cubic; (b) body-centered cubic; (c) face-centered cubic.

by an atom. If an X-ray beam strikes such a structure at the Bragg angle, $\theta = \sin^{-1}(\lambda/2a)$, the rays scattered from one (100) plane will be exactly in phase with the rays from successive (100) planes. The strong scattered beam may be called the "first-order reflection from the (100) planes." A similar result is obtained for the (110) and (111) planes. With a structure based on a simple cubic lattice, we should obtain a diffraction maximum from each set of planes (hkl), since for any given (hkl) all the atoms are included in the planes.

Figure 16.12(b) shows a structure based on a body-centered cubic lattice. The (110) planes, as in the simple-cubic case, pass through all the lattice points, and thus a strong first-order (110) reflection occurs. In the case of the (100) planes, however, we find a different situation. Exactly midway between any two (100) planes, there lies another layer of atoms. When X-rays scattered from the (100) planes are in phase and reinforce one another, the rays scattered by the interleaved atomic planes will be retarded by half a wavelength, and hence will be exactly out of phase with the others. The observed intensity will therefore be the difference between the scattering from the two sets of planes. If the atoms all have identical scattering powers, the resultant intensity will be reduced to zero by the destructive interference, and no first-order (100) reflection will appear. If, however, the atoms are different, the first-order (100) will still appear, but with a reduced intensity given by the difference between the scatterings from the two interleaved sets of planes.

The second-order diffraction from the (100) planes, occurring at the Bragg angle with $n = 2$ in Eq. (16.2), can equally well be expressed as the scattering from a set of planes, called the (200) planes, with just half the spacing of the (100) planes. In the body-centered cubic structure, all the atoms lie in these (200) planes, so that all the scattering is in phase, and a strong scattered beam is obtained. The same situation holds for the (111) planes: the first-order (111) will be weak or extinguished, but the second-order (111), i.e., the (222) planes, will give strong scattering. If we examine successive planes (hkl) in this way, we find for the body-centered cubic structure the results shown in Table 16.3, in which planes missing due to extinction are indicated by dotted lines.

TABLE 16.3 CALCULATED AND OBSERVED DIFFRACTION MAXIMA

(hkl)	100	110	111	200	210	211	—	220	300 221	310
$h^2 + k^2 + l^2$	1	2	3	4	5	6	—	8	9	10
simple cubic	|	|	|	|	|	|	—	|	|	|
body-centered cubic	⋮	|	⋮	|	⋮	|	—	|	⋮	|
face-centered cubic	⋮	⋮	|	|	⋮	⋮	—	|	⋮	⋮
Sodium Chloride	⋮	⋮	|	|	⋮	⋮	—	|	⋮	⋮
Potassium Chloride	200 |	220 |	222 |	400 |	420 |	422 |	—	440 |	600 422 |	620 |

In the case of the face-centered cubic structure, Fig. 16.12(c), reflections from the (100) and (110) planes are weak or missing, and the (111) planes give intense "reflection." The results for subsequent planes are included in Table 16.3.

In the first work on NaCl and KCl, the X-ray wavelength was not known, so that the spacings corresponding to the diffraction maxima could not be calculated. The values of $\sin^2\theta$, however, could be used directly. The observed maxima are compared in Table 16.3 with those calculated for the different cubic lattices. The curious result is noted that apparently NaCl is face centered while KCl is simple cubic. The reason why the KCl structure behaves toward X-rays like a simple cubic array is that the scattering powers of K^+ and Cl^- ions are indistinguishable since they both have an argon configuration with 18 electrons.

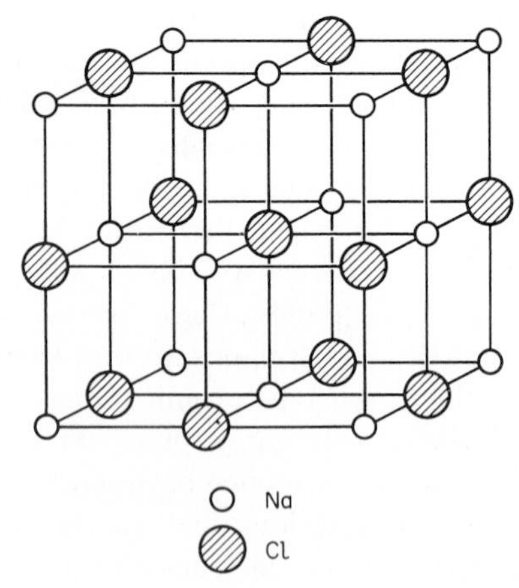

FIG. 16.13 Sodium-chloride structure.

In the NaCl structure, the Na^+ and Cl^- ions differ in scattering power, and the face-centered structure is revealed. The observed maxima from the (111) face of NaCl include a weak peak at an angle of about 10°, in addition to the stronger peak at about 20°, corresponding to that observed with KCl. These results are all explained by the NaCl structure shown in Fig. 16.13, which consists of a face-centered cubic array of Na^+ ions and an interpenetrating face-centered cubic array of Cl^- ions. Each Na^+ ion is surrounded by six equidistant Cl^- ions and each Cl^- ion by six equidistant Na^+ ions. The (100) and (110) planes contain an equal number of both kinds of ions, but the (111) planes consist of either all Na^+ or all Cl^- ions. Now if X rays are scattered from the (111) planes in NaCl, whenever scattered rays from successive Na^+ planes are exactly in phase, the rays scattered from the interleaved Cl^- planes are retarded by half a wavelength and are therefore exactly out of phase. The first-order (111) reflection is therefore weak in NaCl since it represents the difference between these two scatterings. In the case of KCl, where the scattering powers are the same, the first-order reflections are altogether extinguished by interference. Thus the postulated structure is in complete agreement with the experimental X-ray evidence.

Once the NaCl structure was well established, it was possible to calculate the wavelength of the X rays used. From the density of crystalline NaCl, $\rho =$ 2.163 g per cm^3, the molar volume is $M/\rho = 58.45/2.163 = 27.02$ cc per mole. Then the volume occupied by each NaCl unit is $27.02/(6.02 \times 10^{23}) = 44.88 \times 10^{-24}$ cc. In the unit cell of NaCl, there are eight Na^+ ions at the corners of the cube, each shared between eight cubes, and six Na^+ ions at the face centers, each shared between two cells. Thus, per unit cell, there are $\frac{8}{8} + \frac{6}{2} = 4$ Na^+ ions. There is an equal number of Cl^- ions, and therefore four NaCl units per unit cell ($Z = 4$). The volume of the unit cell is therefore $4 \times 44.88 \times 10^{-24} = 179.52$ Å^3. The interplanar spacing for the (200) planes is $\frac{1}{2}a = \frac{1}{2}(179.52)^{1/3} = 2.82$ Å. When this value and the observed diffraction angle are put into the Bragg equation, $\lambda = 2(2.82) \sin 5° 58' = 0.586$ Å.

The wavelength measured in this way can be used to determine the interplanar spacings in other crystal structures. Conversely, crystals with known spacings can be used to measure the wavelengths of other X-ray lines. The most generally useful target material is copper, with $\lambda = 1.537$ Å ($K\alpha_1$), a convenient length relative to interatomic distances. When short spacings are of interest, molybdenum (0.708) is useful, and chromium (2.285) is often employed for study of longer spacings.

The Bragg spectrometer method is generally applicable but most crystal investigations have used photographic methods to record the diffraction patterns. Improved spectrometers are widely used which incorporate a Geiger counter tube in place of the electrometer and ionization chamber.

9. THE POWDER METHOD

The simplest technique for obtaining X-ray diffraction data is the powder method, first used by P. Debye and P. Scherrer. Instead of a single crystal with a definite orientation to the X-ray beam, a mass of finely divided crystals with random orientations is taken. The experimental arrangement is illustrated in Fig. 16.14(a). The powder is contained in a thin-walled glass capillary, or deposited on a fiber. Polycrystalline metals are studied in the form of fine wires. The sample is rotated in the beam to average as well as possible the orientations of the crystallites.

Out of many random orientations of the little crystals, there will be some at the proper angle for X-ray "reflection" from each set of planes. The direction of the reflected beam is limited only by the requirement that the angle of reflection equal the angle of incidence. Thus if the incident angle is θ, the reflected beam makes an angle 2θ with the direction of the incident beam, Fig. 16.14(b). This angle 2θ may itself be oriented in various directions around the central beam direction, corresponding to the various orientations of the individual crystallites. For each set of planes, therefore, the reflected beams outline a cone of scattered radiation. This cone, intersecting a cylindrical film surrounding the specimen, gives rise to the observed lines. On a flat plate film the observed pattern consists of a series of concentric circles. Fig. 16.14 shows the Debye-Scherrer (powder) diagrams obtained from several examples of important types of cubic crystal structures. The observed patterns may be compared with the theoretical predictions in Table 16.3.

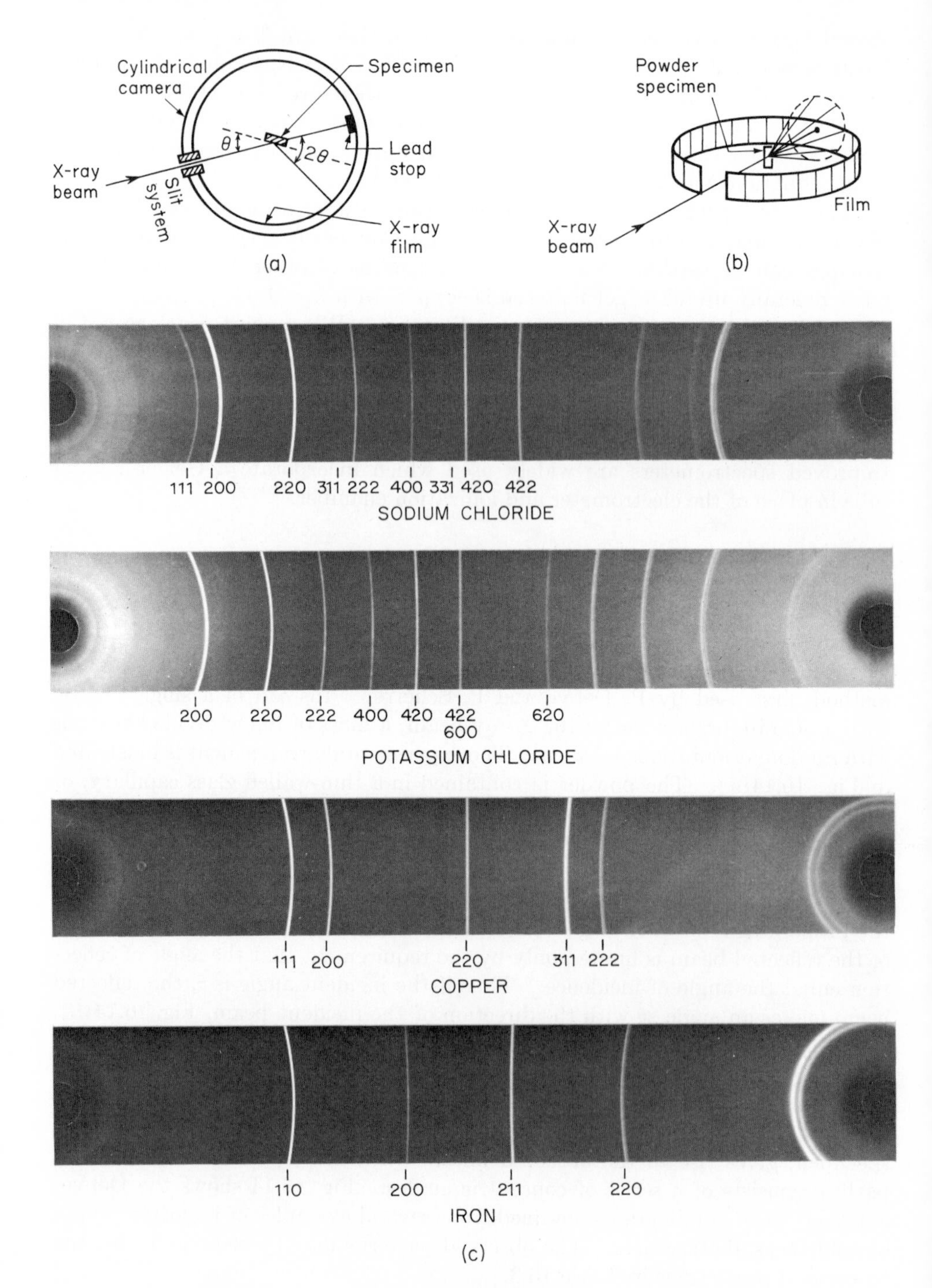

FIG. 16.14 X-ray diffraction by the powder method. [A. Lessor, I.B.M. Laboratories]

After we obtain a powder diagram, our next step is to index the lines, assigning each to the responsible set of planes. The distance x of each line from the central spot is measured carefully, usually by halving the distance between the two reflections on either side of the center. If the film radius is r, the circumference $2\pi r$ corresponds to a scattering angle of 360°. Then, $x/2\pi r = 2\theta/360°$. Thus we calculate θ and, from Eq. (16.2), the interplanar spacing.

To index the reflections, we must know the crystal system to which the specimen belongs. This can sometimes be determined by microscopic examination. Powder diagrams of monoclinic, orthorhombic, and triclinic crystals may be almost impossible to index. For the other systems straightforward methods are available. Once we have found the dimensions of the unit cell by calculation from a few large spacings (100, 110, 111, etc.), we can calculate all the interplanar spacings and compare them with those observed, thus completing the indexing. Then more precise unit-cell dimensions can be calculated from high-index spacings. The general formulae giving the interplanar spacings are derived from analytic geometry.*

10. ROTATING-CRYSTAL METHOD

The rotating-single-crystal method, with photographic recording of the diffraction pattern, was developed by E. Schiebold about 1919. It has been, in one form or another, the most widely used technique for precise structure investigations.

The crystal, which is preferably small and well formed, perhaps a needle a millimeter long and a half-millimeter wide, is mounted with a well defined axis perpendicular to the beam which bathes it in X-radiation. The film may be held in a cylindrical camera. As the crystal is rotated slowly during the course of the exposure, successive planes pass through the orientation necessary for Bragg reflection, each producing a spot on the film. Sometimes only part of the data is recorded on a single film, by oscillating the crystal through some smaller angle instead of rotating it through 360°. In the Weissenberg and other moving-camera methods, the film is moved back and forth with a period synchronized with the rotation of the crystal. Thus the position of a spot on the film immediately indicates the orientation of the crystal at which the spot was formed.

We cannot give here a detailed interpretation of these several varieties of rotation pictures.† An example is shown in Fig. 16.15, taken from a crystal of sperm-whale myoglobin. The spots are indexed and their intensities are measured. These data are the raw materials for the determination of the crystal structure. Even structures of complex molecules such as the proteins can be worked out from the information concealed in these data.

* Bunn, *op. cit.*, p. 376.

† See Bragg, *op. cit.*, p. 30. Also Bunn, *op. cit.*, p. 137.

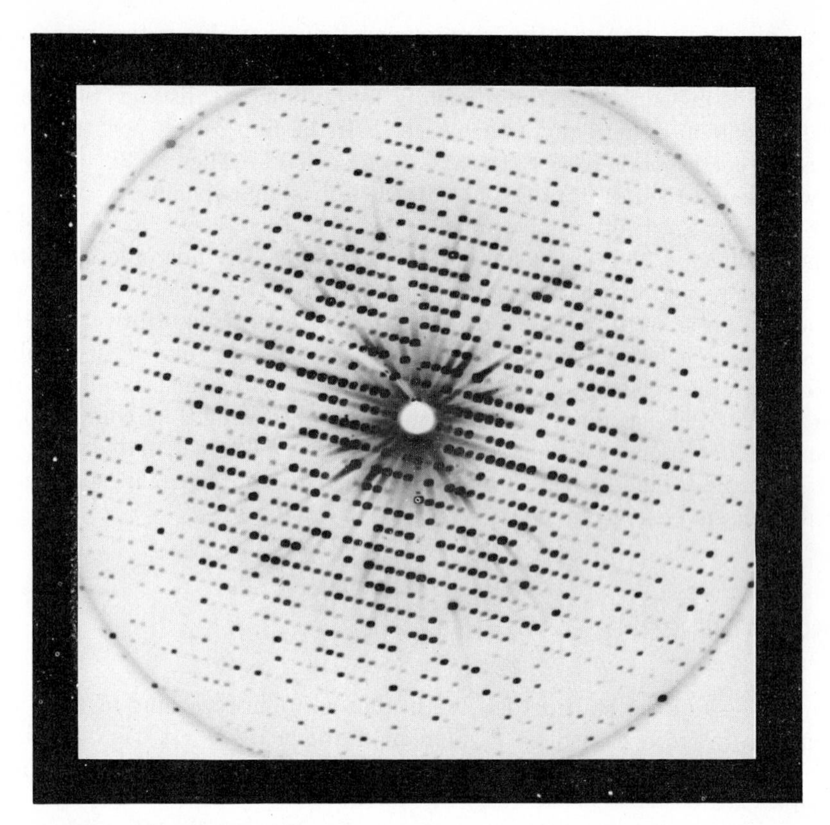

FIG. 16.15 X-ray diffraction pattern from a crystal of sperm whale myoglobin. Taken with a Buerger precession camera [J. C. Kendrew, Cambridge University].

11. CRYSTAL-STRUCTURE DETERMINATIONS

The reconstruction of a crystal structure from the intensities of the various X-ray diffraction maxima is analogous to the formation of an image by a microscope. According to Abbe's theory of the microscope, the objective gathers various orders of light rays diffracted by the specimen and resynthesizes them into an image. This synthesis is possible because two conditions are fulfilled in the optical case: the phase relationships between the various orders of diffracted light waves are preserved at all times, and optical glass is available to focus and form an image with radiation having the wavelengths of visible light. Electron beams can be focused with electrostatic and magnetic lenses, but we have no such lenses for forming X-ray images. Also, the way in which the diffraction data are necessarily obtained (one by one) means that all the phase relationships are lost. The essential problem in determining a crystal structure is to regain this lost information in some way or other, and to resynthesize the structure from the amplitudes and phases of the diffracted waves.

We shall return to this problem in a little while, but first let us see how the intensities of the various spots in an X-ray picture are governed by the crystal structure.* The Bragg relation fixes the angle of scattering in terms of the interplanar spacings, which are determined by the arrangement of points in the crystal lattice. In an actual structure, each lattice point is replaced by a group of atoms. The arrangement and composition of this group primarily controls the intensity of the scattered X-rays, once the Bragg condition has been satisfied.

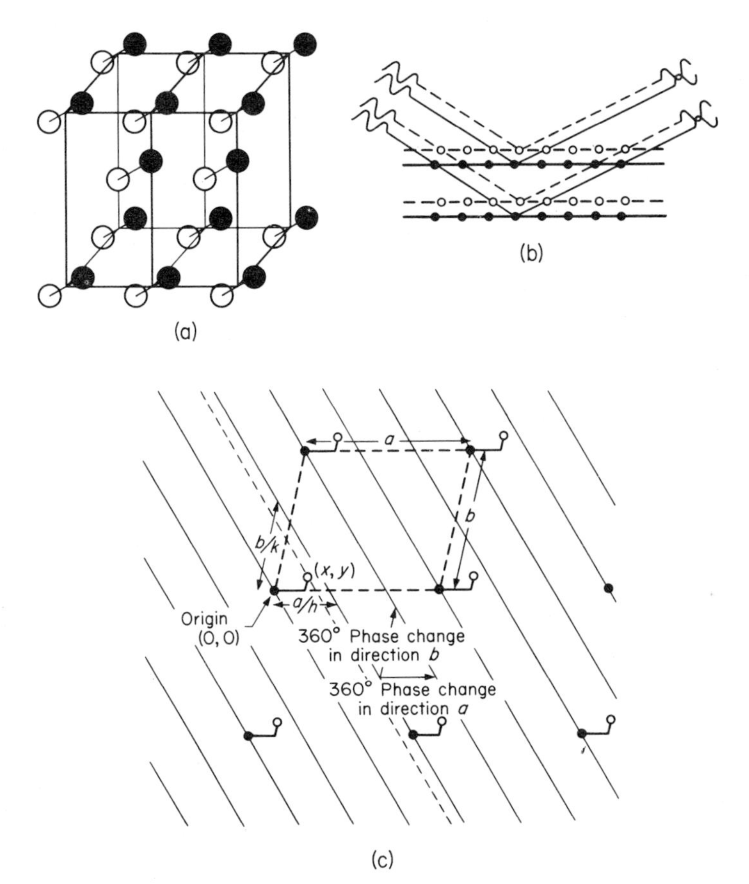

FIG. 16.16 X-ray scattering from a typical structure.

As an example, consider in (*a*), Fig. 16.16, a structure formed by replacing each point in a body-centered orthorhombic lattice by two atoms (e.g., a diatomic molecule). If a set of planes is drawn through the black atoms, another parallel but slightly displaced set can be drawn through the white atoms. When the Bragg condition is met, as in (*b*), Fig. 16.16, the reflections from all the black atoms are in phase, and the reflections from all the white atoms are in phase.

* This treatment follows that given by M. J. Buerger in *X-Ray Crystallography* (New York: Wiley, 1942), which should be consulted for more details.

The radiation scattered from the blacks is slightly out of phase with that from the whites, so that the resultant amplitude, and therefore intensity, is diminished by interference.

The problem is to obtain a general expression for the phase difference. An enlarged view of a section through the structure is shown in (*c*), Fig. 16.16, with the black atoms at the corners of a unit cell with sides a and b, and the whites at displaced positions. The coordinates of a black atom may be taken as (0, 0) and those of a white as (x, y). A set of planes (hk) is shown, for which the Bragg condition is fulfilled; these are actually the (32) planes in the figure. Now the spacings a/h along a and b/k along b correspond to positions from which scattering differs in phase by exactly 360° or 2π radians, i.e., scattering from these positions is exactly in phase. The phase difference between these planes and those going through the white atoms is proportional to the displacement of the white atoms. The phase difference P_x for displacement x in the a direction is given by $x/(a/h) = P_x/2\pi$, or $P_x = 2\pi h(x/a)$. The total phase difference for displacement in both a and b directions becomes

$$P_x + P_y = 2\pi\left(h\frac{x}{a} + k\frac{y}{b}\right)$$

By extension to three dimensions, the total phase change that an atom at (xyz) in the unit cell contributes to the plane (hkl) is

$$P = 2\pi\left(\frac{hx}{a} + \frac{ky}{b} + \frac{lz}{c}\right) \qquad (16.3)$$

We may recall (p. 578) that the superposition of waves of different amplitude and phase can be accomplished by vectorial addition. If f_1 and f_2 are the amplitudes of the waves scattered by atoms (1) and (2), and P_1 and P_2 are the phases, the resultant amplitude is $F = f_1e^{iP_1} + f_2e^{iP_2}$. For all the atoms in a unit cell:

$$F = \sum_j f_j e^{iP_j} \qquad (16.4)$$

When this is combined with Eq. (16.3), we obtain an expression for the resultant amplitude of the waves scattered from the (hkl) planes by all the atoms in a unit cell:

$$F(hkl) = \sum_j f_j e^{2\pi i(hx/a+ky/b+lz/c)} \qquad (16.5)$$

The expression $F(hkl)$ is called the *structure factor* of the crystal. Its value is determined by the exponential terms, which depend on the positions of the atoms, and by the *atomic scattering factors* f_j, which depend on the number and distribution of the electrons in the atom and on the scattering angle θ. Structure-factor expressions have been tabulated for all the space groups.*

* *International Tables for the Determination of Crystal Structures* (1952). It is usually possible to narrow the choice of space groups to two or three by means of study of missing reflections (hkl) and comparison with the tables.

The intensity of scattered radiation is proportional to the absolute value of the amplitude squared, $|F(hkl)|^2$. The crystal structure problem is to obtain agreement between the observed intensities and those calculated from a postulated structure.

As an example of the use of the structure factor, let us calculate $F(hkl)$ for the (100) planes in a face-centered cubic structure, e.g., metallic gold. In this structure there are four atoms in the unit cell ($Z = 4$), which may be assigned coordinates (x/a, y/b, z/c) as follows: (000), ($\frac{1}{2}\frac{1}{2}0$), ($\frac{1}{2}0\frac{1}{2}$) and ($0\frac{1}{2}\frac{1}{2}$). Therefore, from Eq. (16.5),

$$F(100) = f_{\mathrm{Au}}(e^{2\pi i\cdot 0} + e^{2\pi i\cdot 1/2} + e^{2\pi i\cdot 1/2} + e^{2\pi i\cdot 0})$$

$$= (2 + 2e^{\pi i}) = 0$$

since

$$e^{\pi i} = \cos\pi + i\sin\pi = -1$$

Thus the structure factor vanishes and the intensity of scattering from the (100) planes is zero. This is almost a trivial case, since inspection of the face-centered cubic structure immediately reveals that there is an equivalent set of planes interleaved midway between the (100) planes, so that the resultant amplitude of the scattered X-rays must be reduced to zero by interference. In more complicated instances, however, it is essential to use the structure factor to obtain quantitative estimation of the scattering intensity expected from any set of planes (hkl) in any postulated crystal structure.

12. FOURIER SYNTHESES

It is the electrons in a crystal structure that scatter the X-rays. Thus a crystal structure examined by X-rays may be regarded simply as a periodic three-dimensional distribution of electron density, $\rho(xyz)$. Any such density function can be expressed as a Fourier series, a summation of sine and cosine terms.* It is more concisely written in the complex exponential form. Thus the electron density in a crystal may be represented as

$$\rho(xyz) = \sum_{p=-\infty}^{+\infty}\sum_{q=-\infty}^{+\infty}\sum_{r=-\infty}^{+\infty} A_{pqr}\, e^{-2\pi i(px/a+qy/b+rz/c)} \tag{16.6}$$

It is not hard to show† that the Fourier coefficients A_{pqr} are equal to the structure factors divided by the volume of the unit cell. Thus

$$\rho(xyz) = \frac{1}{V}\sum F(hkl)e^{-2\pi i(hx/a+ky/b+lz/c)} \tag{16.7}$$

The summation is carried out over all values of h, k, l, so that there is one term for each set of planes (hkl), and hence for each spot on the X-ray diffraction diagram.

* See, for example, Widder, *Advanced Calculus*, p. 324.

† Bragg, *op. cit.*, p. 221.

Equation (16.7) summarizes the whole problem involved in structure determinations, since the crystal structure is simply $\rho(xyz)$. Positions of individual atoms are peaks in the electron density function ρ, with heights proportional to the atomic numbers (number of electrons). Thus if we knew the $F(hkl)$'s we could immediately plot the crystal structure. All we know, however, are the intensities of the spots which are proportional to $|F(hkl)|^2$. As stated earlier, we know the amplitudes but we have lost the phases in taking the X-ray pattern.

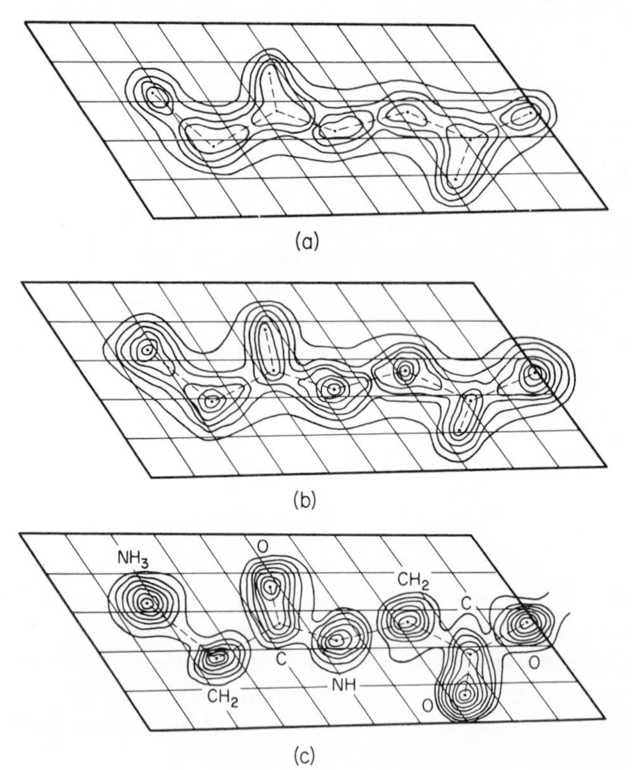

FIG. 16.17 Fourier map of electron density in glycylglycine projected on base of unit cell: (a) 40 terms; (b) 100 terms; (c) 160 terms.

In one method of solution, we assume a trial structure and calculate the intensities. If the assumed structure is even approximately correct, the most intense observed reflections should have large calculated intensities. We then compute the Fourier series by taking the *observed* F's for these reflections with the *calculated* phases. If we are on the right track, the graph of the Fourier summation should give new positions of the atoms, from which new F's can be calculated which allow more of the phases to be correctly determined. Sometimes we can introduce into the structure a heavy atom whose position is known from symmetry arguments. The large contribution of the heavy atom makes it possible to determine the phases of many of the F's.

As more terms are included in the Fourier syntheses, the resolution of the structure improves, just as the resolution of a microscope improves with objectives that catch more orders of diffracted light. Fig. 16.17 shows three Fourier

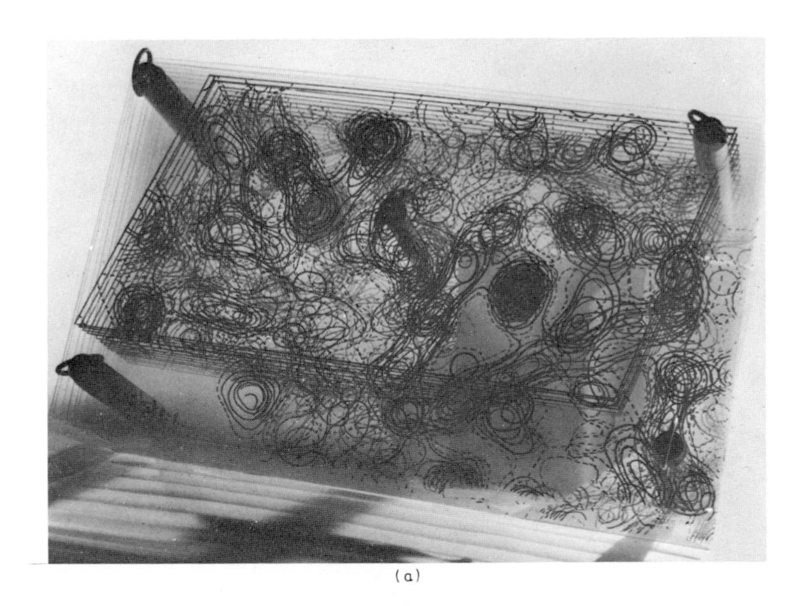

(a)

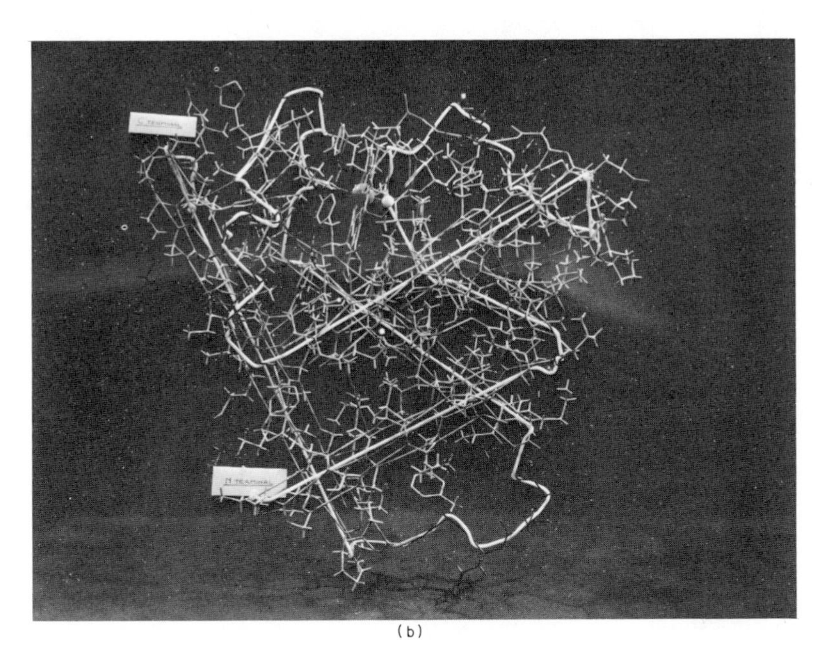

(b)

FIG. 16.18(a) (above) Three dimensional Fourier synthesis of myoglobin at 6Å resolution; (b) (below) The molecule of myoglobin at 2Å resolution. The white cord shows the course of the main chain. The grey sphere is an iron atom; the white sphere is a water molecule attached to the Fe in the position occupied by O_2 in oxymyoglobin. [J. C. Kendrew, Cambridge University].

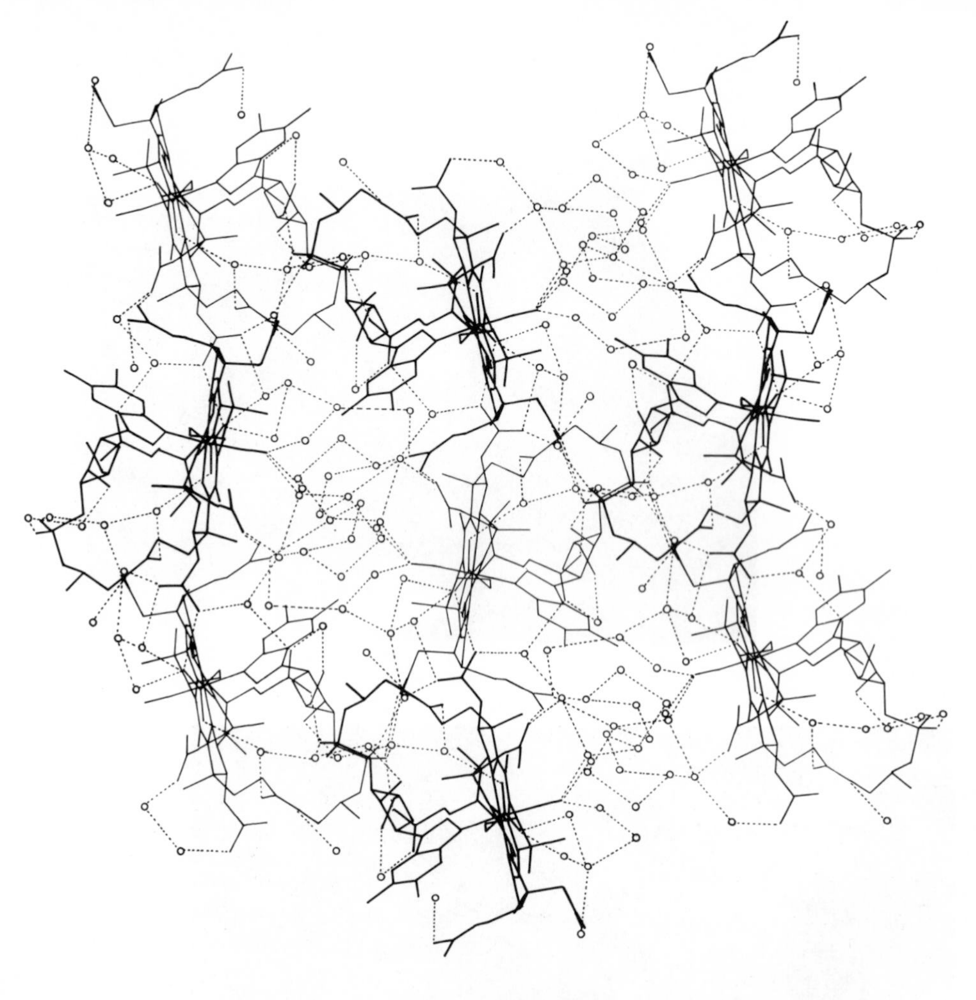

HOOC — CH_2
CH_2 CH_3 CH_3 CH_2 — C=O
CH C C NH
HOOC — CH_2 C C C
CH_3 C N Cl N=C CH_2 — CH_2 — COOH
CH_3 C Co CH
CH N C N C
HOOC — CH_2 — CH N C CH_3
C C C CH_3
CH_3 C C CH
CH_2 CH_3 CH_2
CH_2 CH_2
COOH COOH

FIG. 16.19 The crystal structure of wet vitamin B12 projected along the [001] direction. Open circles are water molecules and dotted lines are hydrogen bonds. Only some of the possible sites for water molecules are shown. [Dorothy Hodgkin, Oxford University].

syntheses for the structure of glycylglycine. The first (a) included 40 terms in the summation and gave a resolution of about 2.5 Å; the second (b) with 100 terms gave a resolution of about 1.5 Å; the third (c) with 160 terms gave a resolution of about 1.1 Å. The more atomic positions we need to determine, the more terms we must include in the summation to achieve a given resolution. For a complex protein structure, like myoglobin, about 10 000 terms are needed to give a resolution of 2 Å. Fig. 16.18(a) shows a three dimensional Fourier density map of the structure of myoglobin as determined by J. C. Kendrew, and his associates at the Cavendish Laboratory.* Within each rod-shaped unit, the peptide chain is wound in precisely the configuration of the right-handed α-helix, which had been suggested earlier† as a basic pattern in protein structure. Fig. 16.18(b) shows a model of the myoglobin structure. The exact situation of each amino-acid residue can be determined by combining the X-ray data with chemical studies based on paper chromatographs.

One of the most complex structures that has yet been completely elucidated by X-ray analysis is vitamin B_{12}, shown in Fig. 16.19.§ The description of this structure by Dorothy Hodgkin may give some feeling for the fascination of this kind of research:

> *In outline, the crystal structure is simple.‡ The roughly spherical molecules are arranged in approximately hexagonally close packed layers, the two layers in each crystal unit being slid a little distance from the formal positions required by close-packing, with the spaces between the layers occupied by water molecules. But in detail, the atomic arrangement is very intricate, a consequence of the exact molecular geometry. In wet B12, where the crystals are suspended in their mother liquor, the acetamide and propionamide groups all make direct intermolecular hydrogen-bonded contacts — the B12 molecules are in contact with one another on every side. Between these, the water molecules, approximately 22 per B12 molecule, make additional hydrogen bonds with the active groups, particularly with the amide and phosphate groups and with one another. Along particular lines in the crystal structure, water is continuous from one side of the crystal to another and is probably trickling through it during X-ray photography in narrow streams, one molecule deep. . . .*

13. NEUTRON DIFFRACTION

Not only X-ray and electron beams, but also beams of heavier particles may exhibit diffraction patterns when scattered from the regular array of atoms in a crystal. Neutron beams are sometimes especially useful. The wavelength is related to the mass and velocity by the de Broglie equation, $\lambda = h/mv$. Thus a neutron with a speed of 3.9×10^5 cm sec^{-1} (kinetic energy 0.08 ev) would have a

* J. C. Kendrew, *Scientific American, 205*, 96 (1961).

† L. Pauling, R. Corey and H. R. Branson, *Proc. Nat. Acad. Sci. U. S. 37*, 241 (1951).

§ Dorothy Hodgkin, Jenny Pickworth, J. H. Robertson, R. J. Prosen, R. A. Sparks and K. N. Trueblood, *Proc. Roy. Soc. A 251*, 306 (1959).

‡ The elucidation of the structure was the result of eight years' work by one of the best teams in the field.

wavelength of 1.0 Å. The diffraction of X rays is caused by the orbital electrons of the atoms in the material through which they pass; the atomic nuclei contribute practically nothing to the scattering. The diffraction of neutrons, on the other hand, is primarily caused by two other effects: (a) *nuclear scattering* due to interaction of the neutrons with the atomic nuclei, (b) *magnetic scattering* due to interaction of the magnetic moments of the neutrons with permanent magnetic moments of atoms or ions.

In the absence of an external magnetic field, the magnetic moments of atoms in a paramagnetic crystal are arranged at random, so that the magnetic scattering of neutrons by such a crystal is also random. It contributes only a diffuse background to the sharp maxima occurring when the Bragg condition is satisfied for the nuclear scattering. In *ferromagnetic materials*, however, the magnetic moments are regularly alined, so that the resultant spins of adjacent atoms are parallel, even in the absence of an external field. In *antiferromagnetic materials*, the magnetic moments are also regularly alined, but in such a way that adjacent spins along certain directions are opposed. The neutron diffraction patterns distinguish experimentally between these different magnetic structures, and indicate the direction of alinement of spins within the crystal.

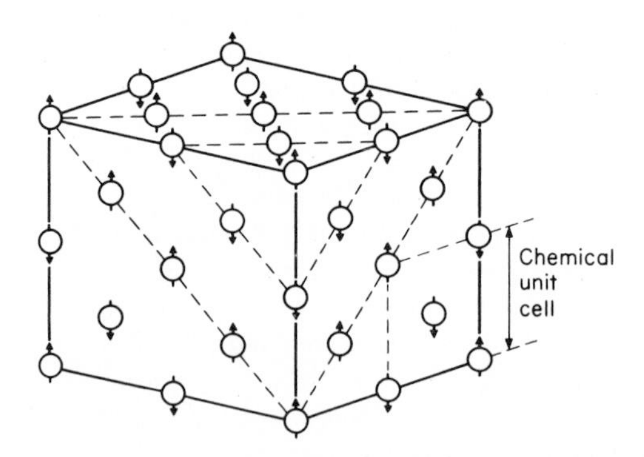

FIG. 16.20 Magnetic structure of MnO as found by neutron diffraction. Note that the "magnetic unit cell" has twice the length of the "chemical unit cell." [From C. G. Shull, E. O. Wollan, and W. A. Strauser, *Phys. Rev.*, 81, 483 (1951).]

For example, manganous oxide, MnO, has the rock-salt structure (Fig. 16.13), and is antiferromagnetic. The detailed magnetic structure as revealed by neutron diffraction is shown in Fig. 16.20. The manganous ion Mn^{+2} has the electronic structure $3s^2 3p^6 3d^5$. The five $3d$ electrons are all unpaired, and the resultant magnetic moment is $2\sqrt{\frac{5}{2}(\frac{5}{2}+1)} = 5.91$ Bohr magnetons. If we consider Mn^{+2} ions in successive (111) planes in the crystal, the resultant spins are oriented so that they are directed positively and negatively along the [100] direction.

Neutron diffraction can also be used to locate hydrogen atoms in crystal structures. It is usually difficult to locate these by means of X-ray or electron diffraction, because the small scattering power of the hydrogen is overshadowed by that of heavier atoms. The hydrogen nucleus, however, is a strong scatterer of neutrons. Thus it has been possible to work out the structures of such compounds as UH_3 and KHF_2 by neutron-diffraction analysis.*

* S. W. Peterson and H. A. Levy, *J. Chem. Phys.*, *20*, 704 (1952).

14. CLOSEST PACKING OF SPHERES

Quite a while before the first X-ray structure analyses, some shrewd theories about the arrangement of atoms and molecules in crystals were developed from purely geometrical considerations. From 1883 to 1897, W. Barlow discussed a number of structures based on the packing of spheres.

There are two simple ways in which spheres of the same size can be packed together so as to leave a minimum of unoccupied volume, in each case 26 per cent voids. These are the hexagonal-closest-packed (*hcp*) and the cubic-closest-packed (*ccp*) arrangements depicted in Fig. 16.21.

In these closest packed structures, each sphere is in contact with twelve others, a hexagon of six in the same plane, and two triangles of three, one above

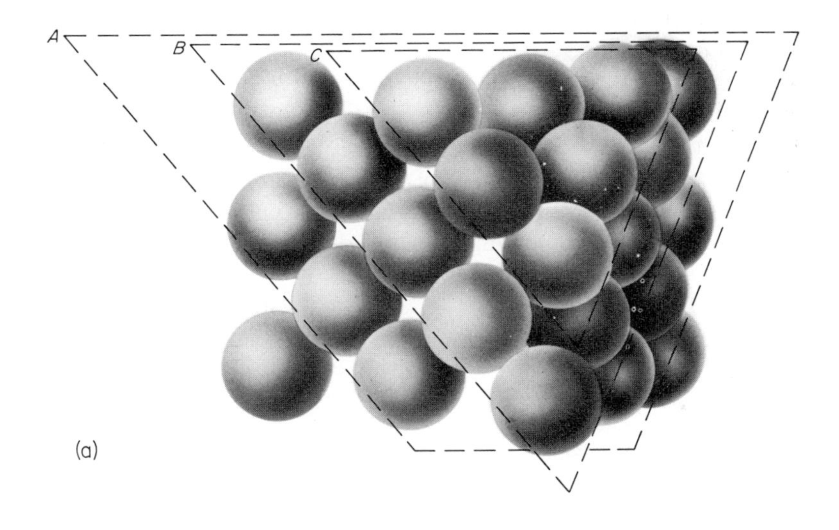

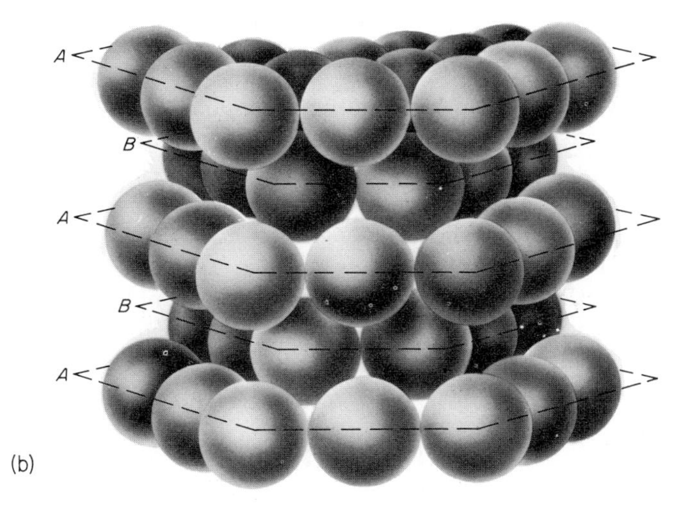

FIG. 16.21 Structures that arise from the closest packing of uniform spheres. (a) Cubic closest packing. The closest packed layers are the (111) planes in the face centered cubic structure. (b) Hexagonal closest packing. The closest packed layers are the (001) planes [L. V. Azaroff, *Introduction to Solids* (New York: McGraw-Hill, 1960].

and one below. In the *hcp* structure the spheres in the upper triangle lie directly over those in the lower triangle; thus the layers repeat in the order *AB*, *AB*, *AB*, *AB*. In the *ccp* structure the orientation of the upper triangle is rotated 60° from that of the lower. Thus the repeat order is *ABC*, *ABC*, *ABC*.

The *ccp* structure is based on a face-centered cubic unit cell. The closest packed layers form the (111) planes of this structure, and they are thus stacked normal to the [111] directions. The *hcp* structure is based on a hexagonal unit cell. The closest packed layers form the (001) planes, which are stacked normal to the sixfold *c*-axis.

The *ccp* structure is found in the solid state of the inert gases, in crystalline methane, etc. — symmetrical atoms or molecules held together by van der Waals forces. The high-temperature forms of solid H_2, N_2, and O_2 occur in *hcp* structures.

The great majority of the typical metals crystallize in the *ccp*, the *hcp*, or a body-centered-cubic structure. Some examples are collected in Table 16.4. Other structures include the following:* the diamond-type cubic of grey tin and germanium; the face-centered tetragonal, a distorted *fcc*, of γ-manganese and indium; the rhombohedral layered structures of bismuth, arsenic, and antimony; the body-centered tetragonal of white tin; the simple cubic of polonium. It will be noted that many of the metals are polymorphic (allotropic), with two or more structures depending on conditions of temperature and pressure.

TABLE 16.4 Structures of the Metals

Cubic Closest Packed (*fcc*) or (*ccp*)		Hexagonal Closest Packed (*hcp*)		Body-Centered Cubic (*bcc*)	
Ag	γFe	αBe	Os	Ba	Mo
Al	Ni	γCa	αRu	αCr	Na
Au	Pb	Cd	βSc	Cs	Ta
αCa	Pt	αCe	αTi	αFe	βTi
βCo	Sr	αCo	αTl	δFe	V
Cu	Th	βCr	Zn	K	βW
		Mg	αZr	Li	βZr

The nature of the binding in metal crystals will be discussed later. For the present, we may think of them as a network of positive metal ions packed primarily according to geometrical requirements, and permeated by mobile electrons. This so-called *electron gas* is responsible for the high conductivity and for the cohesion of the metal.

The *ccp* metals, such as Cu, Ag, Au, Ni, are all very ductile and malleable. The other metals, such as V, Cr, Mo, W, are harder and more brittle. This distinction in physical properties reflects a difference between the structure types. When a metal is hammered, rolled, or drawn, it deforms by the gliding of planes of atoms past one another. These *slip planes* are those that contain the most

*For descriptions see R. W. G. Wyckoff, *Crystal Structures* (New York: Interscience, 1948).

densely packed layers of atoms. In the *ccp* structure, the slip planes are therefore usually the (111), which occur in sheets normal to all four of the cube diagonals. In the *hcp* and other structures there is only one set of slip planes, those perpendicular to the hexagonal axis. Thus the *ccp* metals are characteristically more ductile than the others, since they have many more glide ways.

15. BINDING IN CRYSTALS

Two different theoretical approaches to the nature of the chemical bond in molecules have been described in Chapter 13. In the method of atomic orbitals, the point of departure is the individual atom. We bring together two atoms, each with the electrons that "belong to it," and consider the effect of exchanging electrons between the orbitals. In the second approach, the electrons in a molecule are no longer assigned possessively to the individual atoms. We arrange a set of nuclei at the proper final distances and feed the electrons into the available molecular orbitals.

For studying the nature of binding in crystals, these two different treatments are again available. In one case, the crystal structure is pictured as an array of regularly spaced atoms, each possessing electrons which are used to form bonds with neighboring atoms. These bonds may be ionic, covalent, or intermediate in type. Extending throughout three dimensions, they hold the crystal together. The alternative approach is again to consider the nuclei at fixed positions in space and gradually to pour the electron cement into the periodic array of nuclear bricks.

Both these methods yield useful and distinctive results, displaying complementary aspects of the nature of the crystalline state. We shall call the first treatment, growing out of the atomic-orbital theory, the *bond model* of the solid state. The second treatment, an extension of the method of molecular orbitals, we shall call, for reasons to appear later, the *band model* of the solid state. The bond model is sometimes called the *tight binding approximation*, and the band model, the *collective electron approximation*.

16. THE BOND MODEL

If we consider that a solid is held together by chemical bonds, it is useful to classify the bond types. Even though the classes are, as usual, somewhat frayed at the edges, we can distinguish the following.

(1) *The van der Waals bonds*. These bonds result from forces between inert atoms or essentially saturated molecules. The forces are the same as those responsible for the *a* term in the van der Waals equation. Crystals held together in this way are sometimes called *molecular crystals*. Examples are nitrogen, carbon tetrachloride, benzene. The molecules tend to pack together as closely

as their geometry allows. The binding between the molecules in van der Waals structures represents a combination of factors such as dipole-dipole and dipole-polarization interactions, and the quantum mechanical *dispersion forces*, first elucidated by F. London, which are often the principal component. (*Cf.* Sec. 17.9).

(2) *The ionic bonds.* These bonds are familiar from the case of the NaCl molecule in the vapor state (p. 519). In a crystal, the coulombic interaction between oppositely charged ions leads to a regular three-dimensional structure. In rock salt, each positively charged Na^+ ion is surrounded by six negatively charged Cl^- ions, and each Cl^- is surrounded by six Na^+. There are no sodium-chloride molecules unless you wish to regard the entire crystal as a giant molecule. The ionic bond is spherically symmetrical and undirected; an ion will be surrounded by as many oppositely charged ions as can be accommodated geometrically, provided that the requirement of overall electrical neutrality is satisfied.

(3) *The covalent bonds.* These bonds are the result of the sharing of electrons by atoms. When extended through three dimensions, they may lead to a

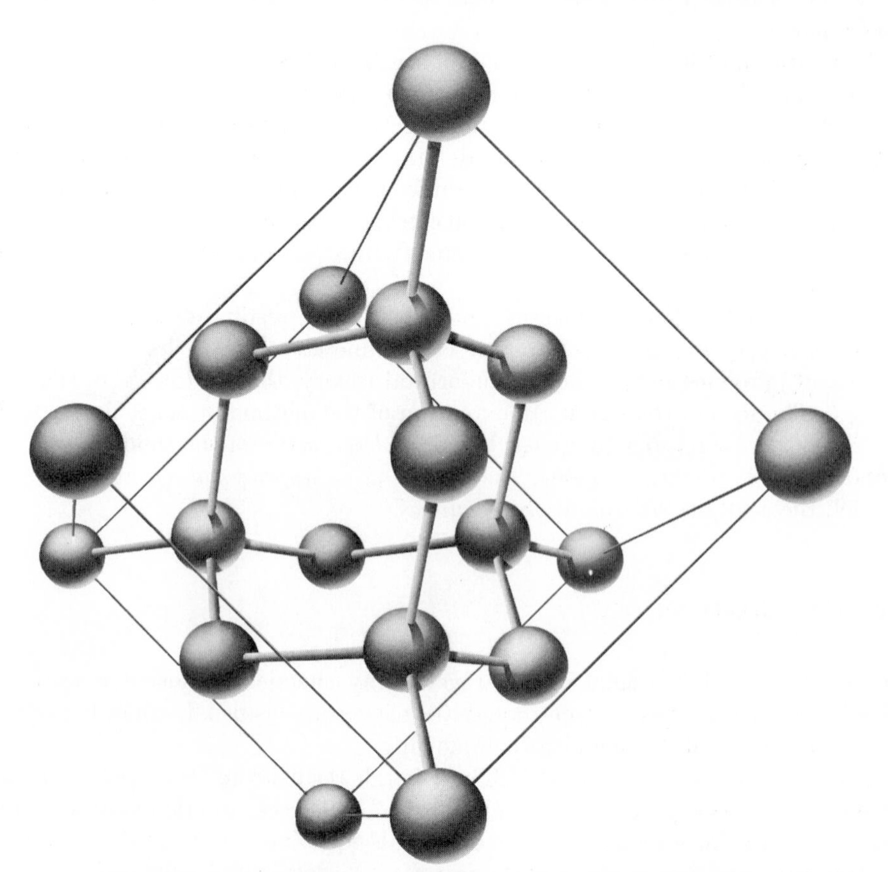

FIG. 16.22 Cubic unit cell of the diamond structure (drawn by F. M. Thayer). [G. H. Wannier, *Solid State Theory,* Cambridge University Press, 1959].

variety of crystal structures, depending on the valence of the constituent atoms, or the number of electrons available for bond formation.

A good example is the diamond structure in Fig. 16.22. The structure can be based on two interpenetrating face-centered cubic lattices. Each atom on one lattice is surrounded tetrahedrally by four equidistant atoms on the other lattice. This arrangement constitutes a three-dimensional polymer of carbon atoms joined together by tetrahedrally oriented sp^3 bonds. Thus the configuration of the carbon bonds in diamond is similar to that in aliphatic compounds such as ethane. The C—C bond distance is 1.54 Å in both diamond and ethane. Germanium, silicon and grey tin also crystallize in the diamond structure.

A similar structure is assumed by compounds such as ZnS (zinc blende), AgI, AlP and SiC. In all these structures, each atom is surrounded by four unlike atoms oriented at the corners of a regular tetrahedron. In every case the binding is primarily covalent. It is interesting to note that it is not necessary that each atom provide the same number of valence electrons; the structure can occur whenever the total number of outer-shell electrons is just four times the total number of atoms.

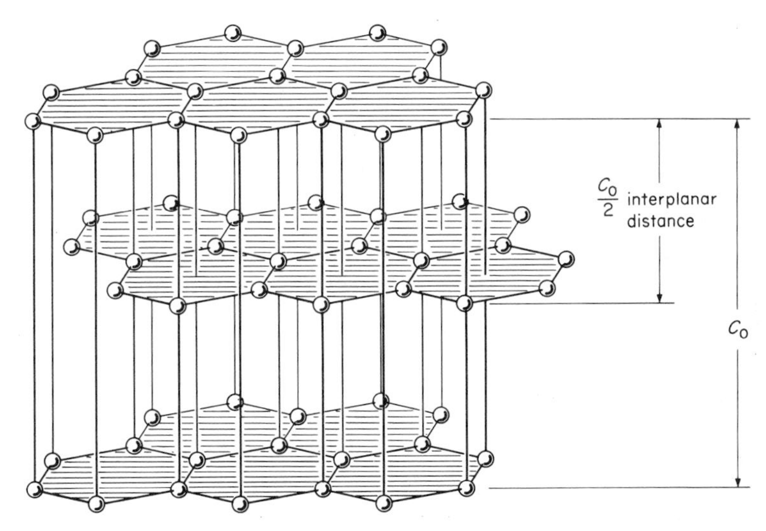

FIG. 16.23 The hexagonal structure of graphite.

In graphite, the more stable allotrope of carbon, the bonds resemble those in the aromatic series of compounds. The structure is shown in Fig. 16.23. Strong bonds operate within each layer of carbon atoms, whereas much weaker binding joins the layers; hence the slippery and flaky nature of graphite. The C—C distance within the layers of graphite is 1.34 Å, identical with that in anthracene. As in the aromatic hydrocarbons (p. 538), we can distinguish two types of electrons within the graphite structure. The σ electrons are paired to form localized-pair (sp^2) bonds, and the π electrons are free to move throughout the planes of the C_6 rings.

Atoms with a valence of only 2 cannot form isotropic three-dimensional structures. Thus we have the interesting structures of selenium (Fig. 16.24) and tellurium, which consist of endless chains of atoms extending through the crystal, the individual chains being held together by much weaker forces. Another way of solving the problem is illustrated by the structure of rhombic sulfur, Fig. 16.25. Here there are well defined, puckered, eight-membered rings of sulfur atoms. The bivalence of sulfur is maintained and the S_8 molecules are held together by van der Waals attractions. Elements like arsenic and antimony, which in their compounds display a covalence of 3, tend to crystallize in structures containing well defined *layers* or sheets of atoms.

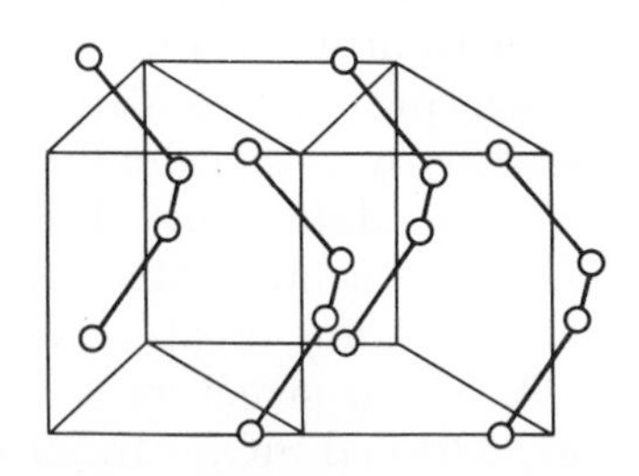
FIG. 16.24 Structure of selenium.

(4) *The intermediate-type bonds.* As in individual molecules, such bonds arise from resonance between covalent and ionic contributions. Alternatively, we may consider the polarization of one ion by an oppositely charged ion. An ion is said to be polarized when its "electron cloud" is distorted by the presence of the oppositely charged ion. The larger an ion the more readily is it polarized, and the smaller an ion the more intense is its electric field and the greater its polarizing power. Thus the larger anions are more strongly polarized by the smaller cations. Even apart from the size effect, cations are less polarizable than anions because their net positive charge tends to hold their electrons in place. The structure of the ion is also important: rare-gas cations such as K^+ have less polarizing power than transition cations such as Ag^+, since their positive nuclei are more effectively shielded.

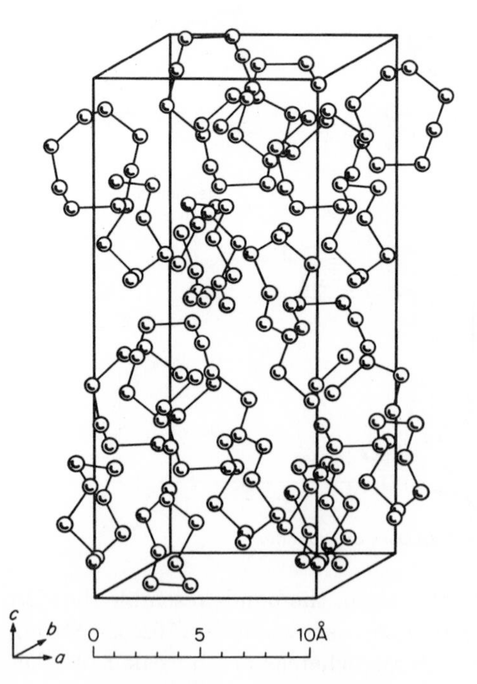

FIG. 16.25 Structure of rhombic sulfur.

We can see the effect of polarization in the structures of the silver halides. AgF, AgCl and AgBr have the rock-salt structure, but as the anion becomes larger it becomes more strongly polarized by the small Ag^+ ion. Finally, in AgI the binding has little ionic character and the crystal has the zinc-blende structure. It has been confirmed spectroscopically that crystalline silver iodide is composed of atoms and not ions.

(5) *The hydrogen bonds.* The hydrogen bond, discussed on p. 550, is important in many crystal structures, e.g., inorganic and organic acids, salt hydrates, ice. The structure of ice is shown in Fig. 16.26. The coordination is similar to that in wurtzite, the hexagonal form of zinc sulfide. Each oxygen is surrounded tetrahedrally by four nearest neighbors at a distance of 2.67 Å. The hydrogen bonds hold the oxygens together, leading to a very open structure. By way of contrast, hydrogen sulfide has a *ccp* structure, each molecule having twelve nearest neighbors.

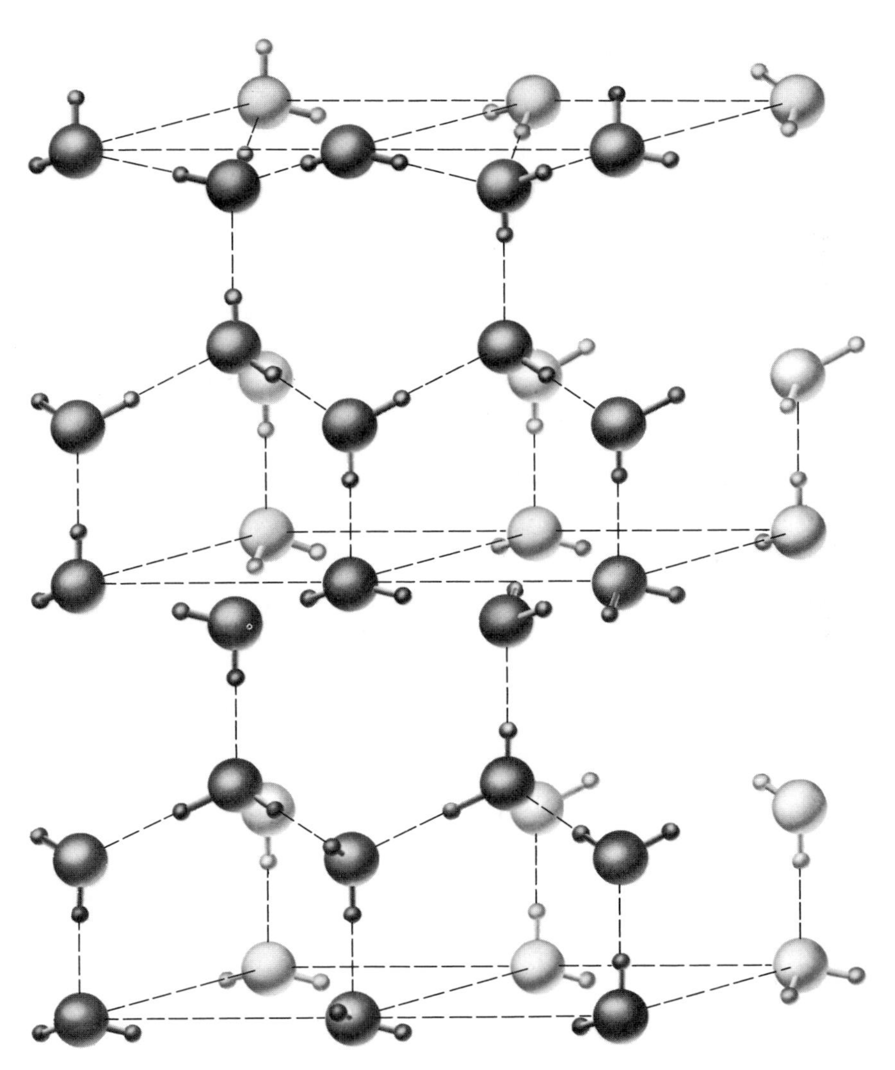

FIG. 16.26 The arrangement of molecules in the ice crystal. The orientation of the water molecules as represented in the drawing is arbitrary; there is one proton along each oxygen-oxygen axis, closer to one or the other of the two oxygen atoms. [Linus Pauling, The Nature of the Chemical Bond, Cornell University Press, 1960].

(6) *The metallic bonds.* The metallic bond is closely related to the ordinary covalent electron-pair bond. Each atom in a metal forms covalent bonds by sharing electrons with its nearest neighbors, but there are more orbitals available for bond formation than electrons to fill them. As a result the covalent bonds resonate among the available interatomic positions. In the case of a crystal this resonance extends throughout the entire structure, thereby producing great stability. The empty orbitals permit a ready flow of electrons under the influence of an applied electric field, leading to metallic conductivity.

17. THE BAND MODEL

The high thermal and electrical conductivities of metals focused attention on the electrons as important entities in their structures. Based on the behavior of electrons, three classes of solids could be distinguished:

(1) Conductors or metals, which offer a low resistance to the flow of electrons, an electric current, when a potential difference is applied. The resistivities of metals lie in the range 10^{-4} to 10^{-6} ohm cm at room temperature, and increase with the temperature.

(2) Insulators, which have high resistivities, from 10^{10} to 10^{22} ohm cm at room temperature.

(3) Semiconductors, whose resistivities are intermediate between those of typical metals and typical insulators, and decrease with rising temperature, usually as $e^{\epsilon/kT}$.

The starting point of the band theory is a collection of nuclei arrayed in space at their final crystalline internuclear separations. The total number of available electrons is poured into the resultant field of force, a regularly periodic field. What happens?

Consider in Fig. 16.27 a simplified model of a one-dimensional structure. For concreteness, think of the nuclei as those of sodium, with a charge of +11. The

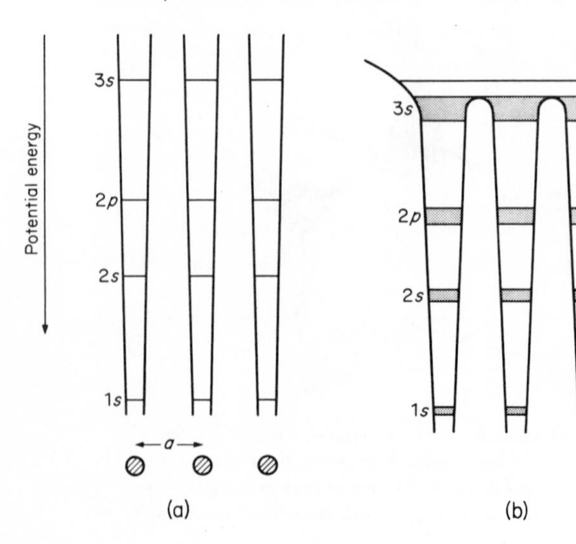

FIG. 16.27 Energy levels in sodium: (a) isolated atoms; (b) section of crystal.

position of each nucleus represents a deep potential-energy well for the electrons. If these wells were infinitely deep, the electrons would all fall into fixed positions on the sodium nuclei, giving rise to $1s^22s^22p^63s^1$ configurations, typical of isolated sodium atoms. This is the situation shown in Fig. 16.27(a). But the wells are not infinitely deep, and the actual situation is more like that shown in Fig. 16.27(b). The electrons can tunnel through the barriers, an electron on one nucleus slipping through to occupy a position on a neighboring nucleus. We are thus no longer concerned with the energy levels of single sodium atoms but with levels of the crystal as a whole. The Pauli Principle tells us that no more than two electrons can occupy exactly the same energy level. Once the possibility of electrons moving through the structure is admitted, we can no longer consider the energy levels to be sharply defined. The sharp $1s$ energy level in an individual sodium atom is broadened in crystalline sodium into a band of closely packed energy levels. A similar situation arises for the other energy levels, each becoming a band of levels as shown in Fig. 16.27(b).

Each atomic orbital contributes one level to a band. In the lower bands ($1s$, $2s$, $2p$) there are therefore just enough levels to accommodate the number of available electrons, so that the bands are completely filled. If an external electric field is applied, the electrons in the filled bands cannot move under its influence, for to be accelerated by the field they would have to move into somewhat higher energy levels. This is impossible for electrons in the interior of a filled band, since all the levels above them are already occupied, and the Pauli Principle forbids their accepting additional tenants. Nor can the electrons at the very top of a filled band acquire extra energy, since there are no higher levels for them to move into. Occasionally, it is true, an electron may receive a relatively terrific jolt of energy and be knocked completely out of its band into a higher unoccupied band.

So much for the electrons in the lower bands. The situation is different in the uppermost band, the $3s$, which is only half filled. An electron in the interior of the $3s$ band still cannot be accelerated because the levels directly above are already filled. Electrons near the top of the filled zone, however, can readily move up into unfilled levels within the band. The topmost band has actually broadened sufficiently to overlap the peaks of the potential-energy barriers, so that electrons in the top upper levels can move quite freely throughout the crystal structure. According to this idealized model, in which the nuclei are always arranged at the points of a perfectly periodic lattice, no resistance at all would oppose the flow of an electric current. The resistance is caused by departures from the perfect periodicity. One important loss of periodicity results from the thermal vibrations of the atomic nuclei. These vibrations destroy the perfect resonance between the electronic energy levels and cause a resistance to the flow of electrons. As would be expected, the resistance therefore increases with the temperature. Another illustration of the same principle is found in the increased resistance that results when an alloying constituent is added to a pure metal, and the regular periodicity of the structure is diminished by the foreign atoms.

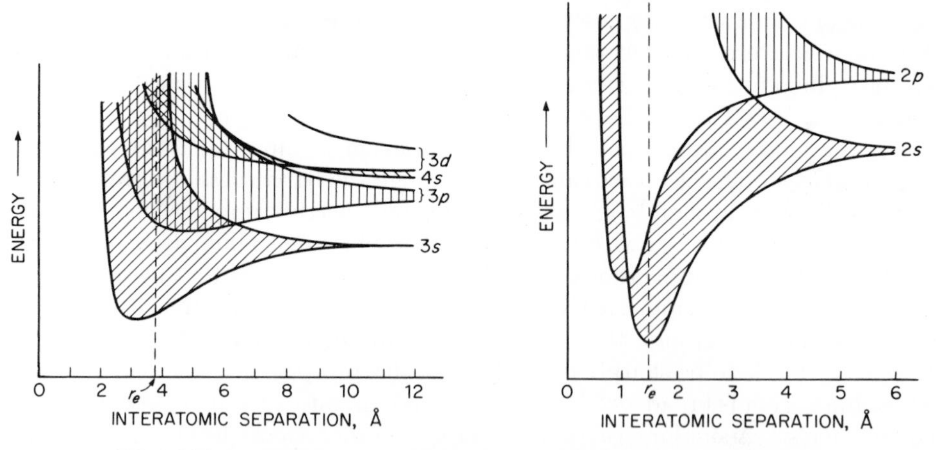

FIG. 16.28 Approximate quantum mechanical calculation of the formation of energy bands as atoms are brought together into a crystal. (a) sodium (b) diamond.

At this point the reader may well be thinking that this is a pretty picture for a univalent metal like sodium, but what of magnesium with its two 3*s* electrons and therefore completely filled 3*s* bands? Why is it not an insulator instead of a metal? More detailed calculations show that in such cases the 3*p* band is low enough to overlap the top of the 3*s* band, providing a large number of available empty levels. Actually, this happens for the alkali metals also. The way in which the 3*s* and 3*p* bands in sodium broaden as the atoms are brought together is shown in Fig. 16.28. The interatomic distance in sodium at one atmosphere pressure and 25°C is $r = 4.0$ atomic units. At this distance there is no longer any gap between the 3*s* and 3*p* bands. In the case of diamond, on the other hand, there is a large energy gap between the filled *valence band* and the empty *conduction band.*

Thus conductors are characterized either by partial filling of bands or by overlapping of the topmost bands. Insulators have completely filled lower bands with a wide energy gap between the topmost filled band and the lowest empty band. These models are represented in Fig. 16.29.

The energy bands in solids can be studied experimentally by the method of

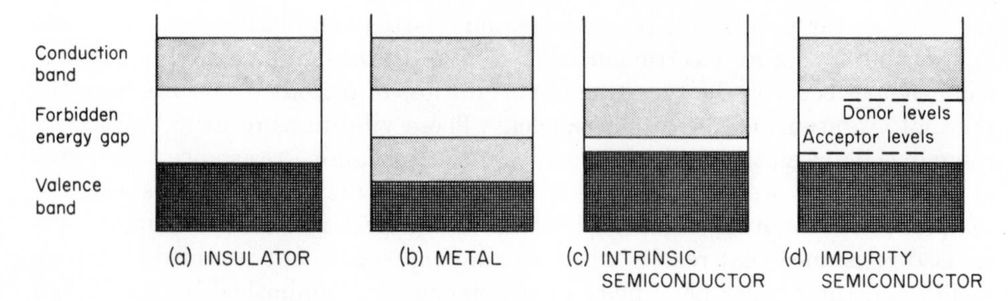

FIG. 16.29 Schematic band models of solids classified by electronic behavior.

X-ray emission spectroscopy.* For example, if an electron is driven out of the 1*s* level in sodium metal the K_β X-ray emission occurs when an electron from the 3*s* band falls into the hole in the 1*s* level. Since the 3*s* electron can come from anywhere within the band of energy levels, the X rays emitted will have a spread of energies (and hence frequencies) exactly corresponding with the spread of allowed energies in the 3*s* band. The following widths (in ev) were found for the conduction bands in a few of the solids investigated:

Li	Na	Be	Mg	Al
4.1	3.4	14.8	7.6	13.2

18. SEMICONDUCTORS

Band models for semiconductors are also included in Fig. 16.29. These are of two kinds, *intrinsic semiconductors* and *impurity semiconductors.*

In an intrinsic semiconductor, as in Fig. 16.29(c), the gap in energy between the filled valence band and the empty conduction band is so narrow that an appreciable number of electrons (n) can be raised into the conduction band by thermal excitation from the valence band. This process leaves positive holes (p) in the valence band. These holes and the electrons will both be mobile under an applied electric field, and thereby contribute to the electrical conductivity. Germanium with an energy gap of 0.72 ev and grey tin with 0.10 ev are examples of intrinsic semiconductors at moderate temperatures. As a matter of fact, any solid that can be raised to a sufficiently high temperature should show intrinsic semiconduction, for even a large energy gap ϵ can be overcome by a high T in the $e^{-\epsilon/kT}$ Boltzmann factor.

Figure 16.30 represents a section of the structure of a germanium crystal. Each line between atoms denotes one electron in a covalent bond. Two such electrons are shown separated from the bonds. These represent mobile electrons in the conduction band. The positive holes left in the band structure are also mobile: a jump of an electron from a bond to a hole in an adjacent bond corresponds exactly to the jump of a positive hole in the opposite direction. This model therefore illustrates the mobility of positive holes in the valence band. Sometimes a free electron meets a positive hole and recombination occurs. Equilibrium is reached when the rate of thermal generation of electrons and holes just equals their rate of recombination.

The model of the impurity conductor is shown in Fig. 16.29(d). The energy gap is large — a pure and perfect crystal of such a substance would be an insulator. It is possible, however, to introduce imperfections into such a crystal so as to create empty levels closely above the valence bands, or filled levels closely below the conduction band. Electrons can then be tossed thermally from the filled or *donor* levels into the conduction band. Similarly, electrons can be

* A review by N. F. Mott gives further references. *Prog. Metal Phys. 3*, 76–114 (1952), "Recent Advances in the Electron Theory of Metals."

raised thermally from the valence band into the empty *acceptor* levels, leaving mobile positive holes. In this way the presence of the impurity levels leads to appreciable concentrations of mobile carriers of charge — substances with such levels are called *impurity semiconductors.*

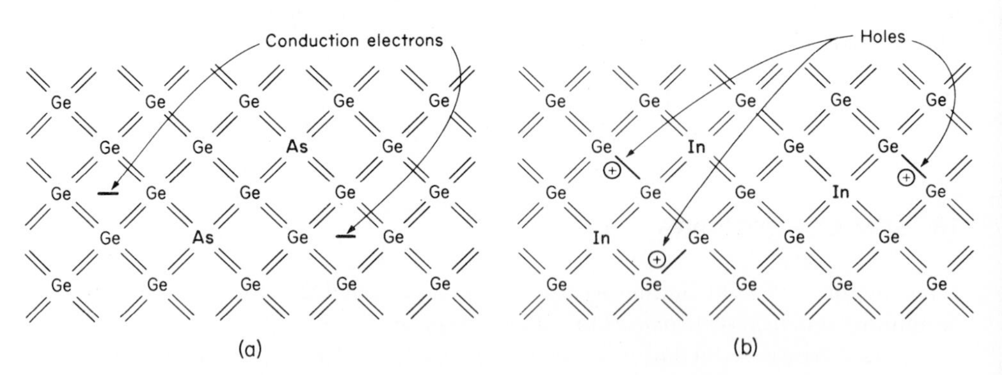

FIG. 16.30 (a) Donors produced by Group V impurities in germanium; (b) Acceptors produced by Group III impurities.

An example is shown in Fig. 16.30(a) in which a small concentration of arsenic has been dissolved in the germanium structure. The As atom contains one electron more than the Ge atom. This electron cannot be accommodated in the normal quadricovalent structure that represents the valence band. It therefore must go into a higher energy level, such as one of the donor levels shown in Fig. 16.29(d). Hence germanium *doped* with arsenic is a good semiconductor, in which the carriers of charge are electrons from the donor levels of the arsenic. It is called an n-type semiconductor, because the carriers are the *negative electrons.*

If the germanium is doped with *indium,* we find the situation shown in Fig. 16.30(b). The In atom contains one less electron than Ge, and hence whenever In replaces Ge, an *acceptor level* is created. When an electron is thermally excited from a normal Ge—Ge bond into such a level, it leaves behind a mobile positive hole in the valence band. Thus germanium doped with indium is a typical p-type semiconductor, because the carriers are the *positive holes.*

19. NONSTOICHIOMETRY

Another kind of crystalline defect that leads to semiconductivity is the departure of a compound from chemical stoichiometry. Thus zinc oxide, ZnO, normally contains more Zn than O, whereas nickel oxide, NiO, normally contains more O than Ni. Such *nonstoichiometry* may be due to the incorporation of extra atoms into the crystal at interstitial sites, or to vacancies caused by the absence of atoms from normal sites.

The evidence suggests that the excess zinc in ZnO is largely interstitial Zn, whereas the excess oxygen in NiO is largely due to vacant Ni^{+2} sites. In NiO and ZnO the departures from stoichiometry, even at temperatures up to 1000°C, are quite small, about 0.1 atom per cent excess of Zn or O. In other metallic oxides and chalcogenides, however, the departures from stoichiometric composition may be much wider.

We may note that the excess Zn in ZnO acts as a typical donor and leads to n-type semiconductivity. In NiO, the Ni^{+2} vacancies, each associated with two Ni^{+3} to preserve electrical neutrality, provide typical acceptor levels leading to p-type semiconductivity. [We distinguish in nomenclature between a *vacancy*, the absence of an atom from a normal structural site, and a *hole*, the absence of an electron from a normal band or bond orbital.]

20. POINT DEFECTS

In 1896, the English metallurgist Roberts-Austen showed that gold diffused faster in lead at 300°C than sodium chloride diffused in water at 15°C. This is one example of the surprising ease with which atoms can sometimes move about in the solid state. Rate processes such as diffusion, sintering, and tarnishing reactions provide further evidence. It was difficult to believe that atoms usually moved in solids simply by changing places with one another: the energetic requirement would be too high.

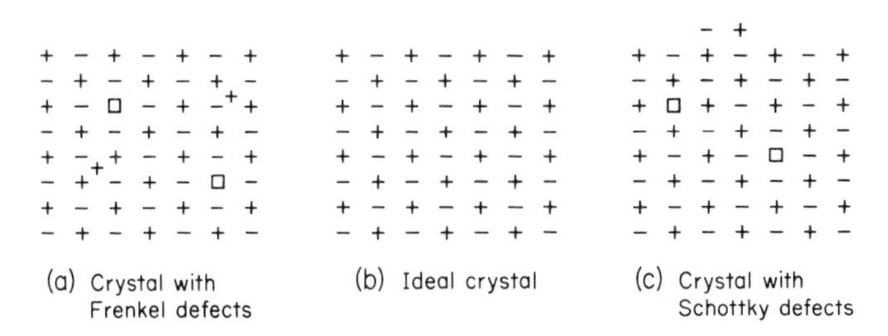

FIG. 16.31 Intrinsic point defects in crystals.

More reasonable mechanisms were finally suggested by the Russian, Frenkel, in 1926, and by the German, Schottky, in 1930. They proposed the first exact models for what are now called *point defects* in crystals. The Frenkel defect is shown in Fig. 16.31(a) as originally proposed for silver chloride. It consists of an Ag^+ ion that has left its lattice site and moved to an interstitial position. The Frenkel defect consists of the vacancy plus the interstitial. The Schottky defect is shown in Fig. 16.31(c), for the case of sodium chloride. It consists of a pair of vacancies of opposite sign. Frenkel and Schottky defects are called *intrinsic defects*. They do not alter the exact stoichiometry of the crystal, but they provide a facile mechanism by which atoms can move within the crystal. It is much easier for an atom to move from an occupied site into a vacancy than it would be for two atoms in occupied sites to change places directly.

We can calculate the concentration of such defects from simple statistical considerations. It costs an energy E to make a defect but we gain entropy S due to the disorder associated with the entropy of mixing of the defects with the normal lattice sites. If n imperfections are distributed among the total of N crystal sites, the entropy of mixing is

$$S = k \ln N!/(N - n)!n!$$

If E is the increase in energy per defect and if we neglect contributions to the energy caused by changes in vibration frequencies in the neighborhood of the defect, we can write for the change in the Helmholtz free energy

$$\Delta A = \Delta E - T\Delta S$$

$$\Delta A = nE - kT \ln N!/(N - n)!n!$$

At equilibrium,

$$\partial A/\partial n = 0$$

Applying the Stirling formula ($\ln X! = X \ln X - X$) we find,

$$\ln \frac{n}{N - n} = -E/kT$$

And thus if $n \ll N$,

$$n = Ne^{-E/kT}$$

As an example, if E is about 1 ev and T is 1000°K,

$$n/N \approx 10^{-5}$$

For a pair of vacancies the expression for the number of ways of forming the defect is squared and we get finally, for the Schottky defects,

$$n = Ne^{-E/2kT} \qquad (16.8)$$

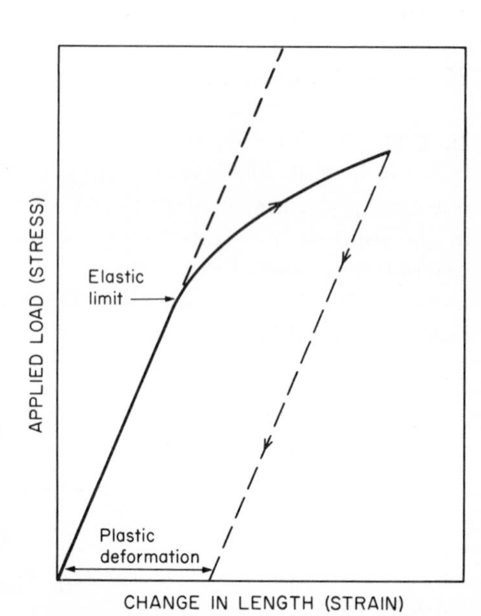

FIG. 16.32 Stress vs. strain behavior of a typical metal rod.

For Frenkel defects,

$$n = (NN')^{1/2} e^{-E/2kT} \qquad (16.9)$$

where N' is the number of interstitial sites available.

21. LINEAR DEFECTS: DISLOCATIONS

The stress-strain curve for a typical solid is traced in Fig. 16.32. The linear region of the curve, where strain is proportional to stress, represents an *elastic deformation;* if the stress is released in such a region, the solid springs back to its original length. It is true that a low stress maintained for a long time may produce some permanent deformation of a solid, a phenomenon called *creep.* But the rapid irreversible deformation of a solid, which we call *plastic deformation,* begins only when a certain critical stress is exceeded. The stamping of sheets of steel into car fins is an example of plastic deformation.

The big problem with metals under deformation is not why they are so strong, but why they are so weak. The calculated elastic limit of a perfect crystal would be 10^2 to 10^4 times that actually observed. There must be some imperfections or defects in the actual crystals, which cause them to deform plastically under quite small loads.

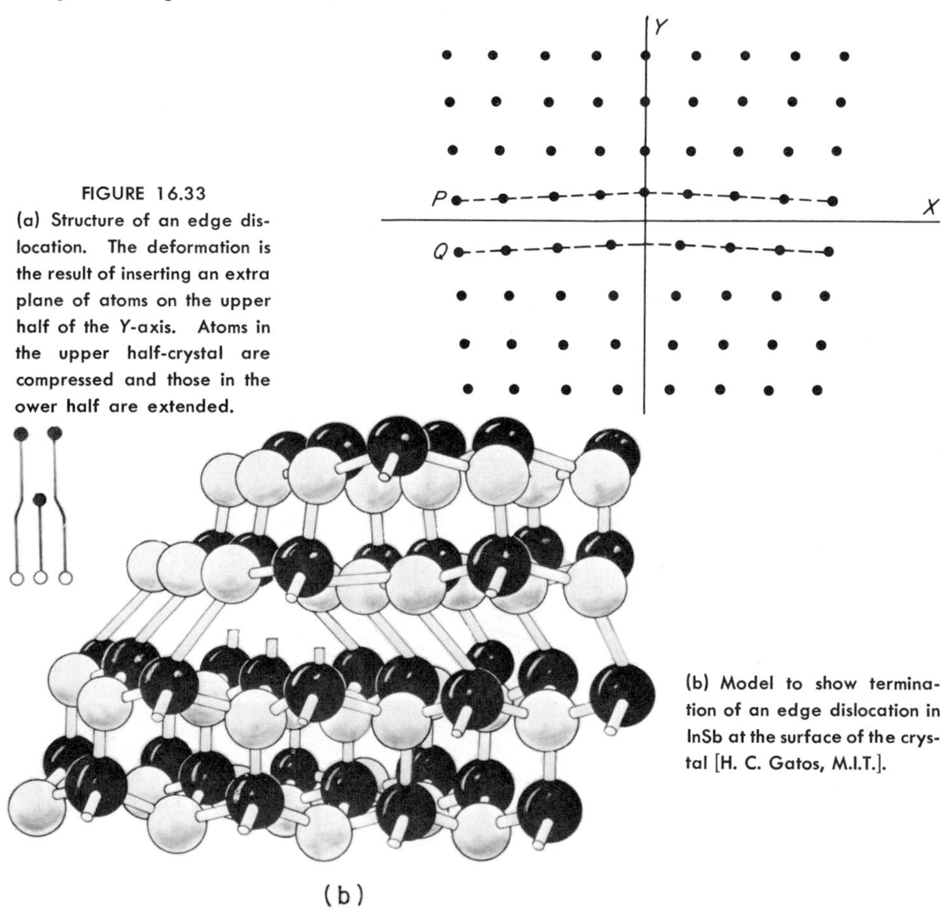

FIGURE 16.33

(a) Structure of an edge dislocation. The deformation is the result of inserting an extra plane of atoms on the upper half of the Y-axis. Atoms in the upper half-crystal are compressed and those in the ower half are extended.

(b) Model to show termination of an edge dislocation in InSb at the surface of the crystal [H. C. Gatos, M.I.T.].

(c) Electron microscope picture of a thin crystal of platinum phthalocyanine (direct transmission) showing crystal planes and the presence of an edge dislocation. Magnification (300 000X). [J. W. Menter, Tube Investments Research Laboratories].

(c)

A solution to this problem was worked out quite independently in 1934 by three different scientists, Taylor, Orowan and Polanyi.*

> *We all have experience of pulling carpets over floors and know that there are two ways of doing it. One can take hold of one end and tug, or one can make a ruck in one end of the carpet and gently edge it to the other end. For a big heavy carpet, the second way is the way to do it which involves least effort.*

This analogy was given by N. F. Mott.† Crystals contain defects something like rucks in carpets. These are called *dislocations*. The type most like a *ruck* is the edge dislocation shown in Fig. 16.33(a), which represents a section through the three dimensional crystal structure. The *dislocation line* is perpendicular to the plane of the section shown, at the point of origin. The presence of the dislocation allows the crystal to deform readily by the slipping of one plane of atoms at a time. Fig. 16.33(b) shows a three-dimensional model of the dislocation in a crystal of the zinc blende structure. Fig. 16.33(c) shows the direct observation of a dislocation by electron microscopy.

The other basic kind of dislocation is the *screw dislocation*. You can visualize this defect by cutting a rubber stopper parallel to its axis, and then pushing on one end so as to create jog at the other end. If you suppose that initially your stopper contained atoms at regular lattice points, the resulting displacement of these atoms constitutes a *screw dislocation*; the dislocation line is along the axis of the stopper. A model of the emergence of a screw dislocation at the surface of a crystal is shown in Fig. 16.34.

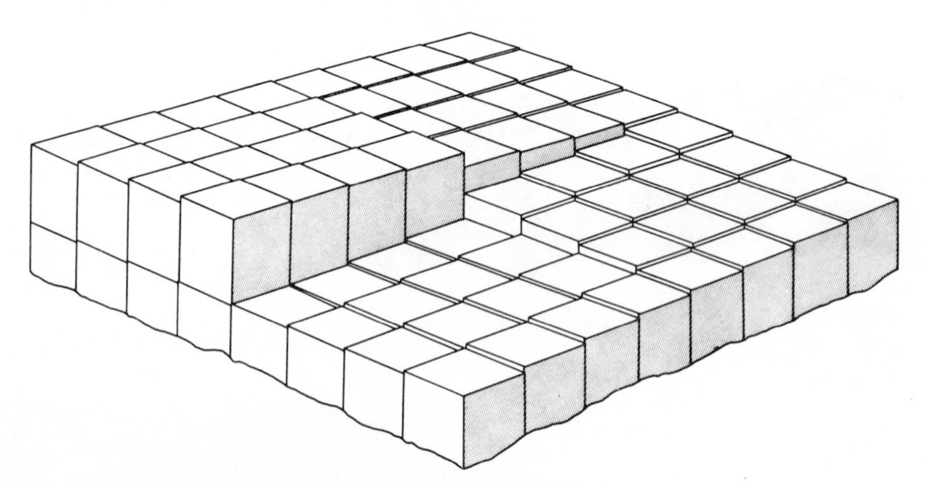

FIG. 16.34 An emergent screw dislocation at the surface of a crystal. The atoms (or molecules) are represented by small cubes.

---

* G. I. Taylor, *Proc. Roy. Soc. A 145*, 362 (1934). E. Orowan, *Z. Physik 89*, 604, 634 (1934). M. Polanyi, *Z. Physik 89*, 660 (1934).
(The idea of the defects now called *dislocations* was discussed earlier, especially in the work of Prandtl, Masing and Dehlinger.)

† N. F. Mott, *Atomic Structure and the Strength of Metals* (London: Pergamon Press, 1956).

FIG. 16.35 Direct transmission electron micrograph of a thin flake (~ 1000 Å) of talc showing a crossed grid of dislocation ribbons. (10 000X) [S. Amelinckx, Centre d'Etude de L'Energie Nucleaire, Mol-Donk, Belgium].

22. EFFECTS DUE TO DISLOCATIONS

Dislocations provide mechanisms for many of the processes which occur in the solid state. We have already seen how they determine the mechanical strength of crystals. They also provide sites within crystals at which chemical reactions and physical changes (such as phase transformation and precipitation) can occur

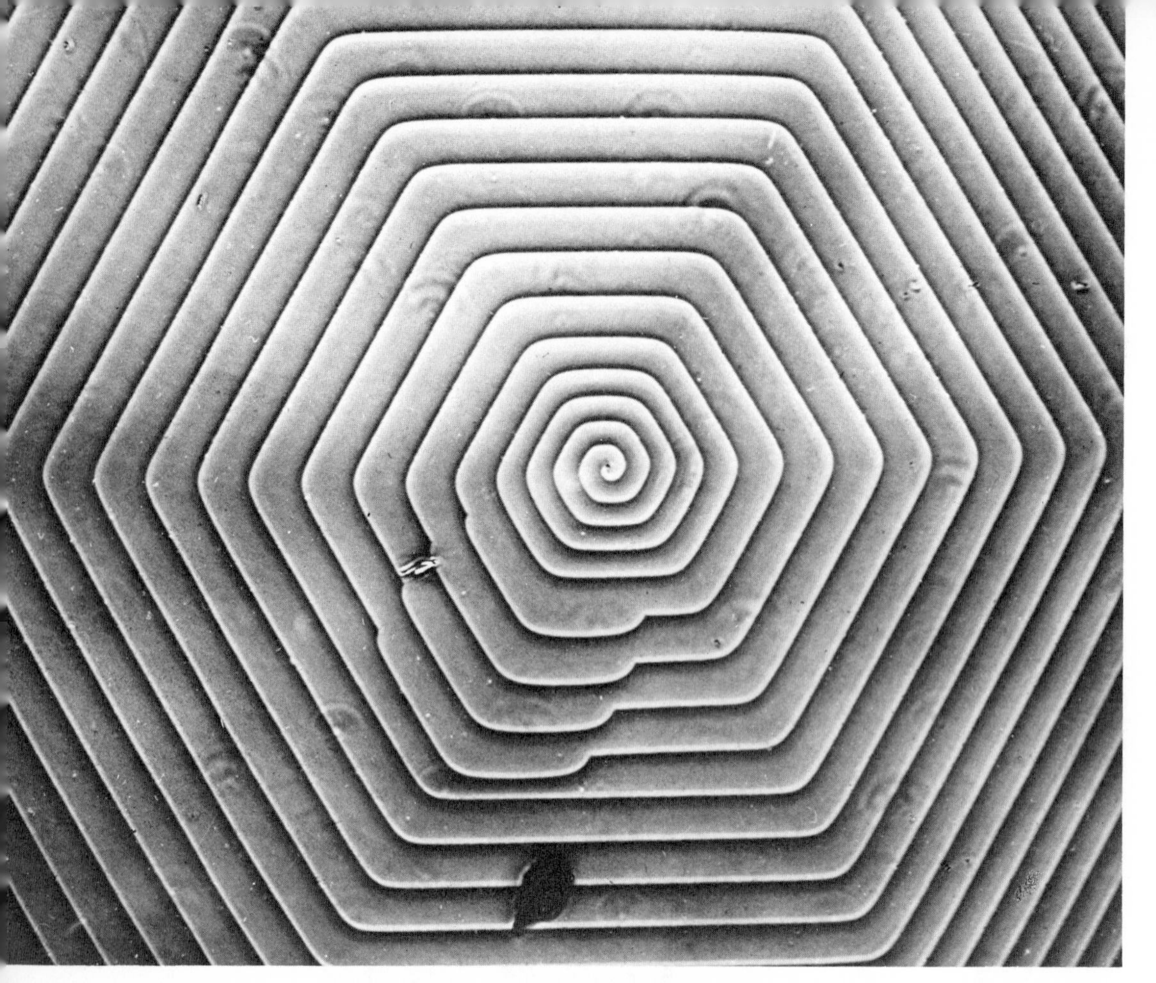

FIG. 16.36 Spiral growth pattern of a crystal due to an emergent screw dislocation. Phase contrast micrograph (300X). [S. Tolansky, London University].

most readily. An excellent example is the work of Hedges and Mitchell* on mechanisms of photographic sensitivity. They took thin single crystals of silver bromide, stressed them, and exposed them to light. Careful development then revealed the preferential deposition of the silver along dislocation lines within the crystal. A process which makes a dislocation visible in this way is called the *decoration* of the dislocation. The pattern of dislocation lines can also be seen by direct transmission electron microscopy.† An example is shown in Fig. 16.35.

The point of emergence of a dislocation at the surface of a crystal is also a site of enhanced chemical reactivity, a fact often revealed by the pattern of etch pits formed at the surface. We can often measure the number of dislocations per unit area by counting such etch pits. Densities range from 10^2 cm^{-2} in the best silver and germanium crystals (small crystals can be grown practically free of dislocations) to 10^{12} cm^{-2} in a severely deformed metal.

* J. M. Hedges and J. W. Mitchell, *Phil. Mag. 44*, 223 (1953).

† For a review of work on metals, see M. J. Whelan, *J. Inst. Metals 2*, 392 (1958). The work on talc is discussed by S. Amelinckx and P. Delavignette, *J. Appl. Phys. 32*, 34 (1961).

When a crystal is etched, the easiest place to remove an atom from the surface is at a dislocation, since here the crystal structure is not perfect. But, when a crystal grows from the vapor or melt, the easiest place to deposit each new atom or molecule is also at the site of a dislocation. We shall see later (Chapter 18) that the spontaneous nucleation of a new phase in a homogeneous system is extremely improbable, and this improbability extends also to the deposition of an atom onto a perfect crystal face. In brief, such a process is improbable because there is a loss in entropy in the condensation process, but there is no compensating decrease in energy for the first few atoms in a new layer, since they have no neighbors to welcome them. If there is an emergent screw dislocation at the surface, however, a new atom can readily deposit at the edge of this developing screw. Thus the crystal can grow in the form of a developing helix. This mechanism was suggested in 1949 by F. C Frank.* Curiously enough, pictures of helical growth of crystals had been published many years previously, but until the dislocation theory was worked out, the significance of the observation was not realized. Fig. 16.36 shows such a spiral growth from a single dislocation on a crystal of the paraffin n-$C_{36}H_{74}$.

23. IONIC CRYSTALS†

The binding in most inorganic crystals is predominantly ionic in character. Therefore, since coulombic forces are undirected, the sizes of the ions play a most important role in determining the final structure. Several attempts have been made to calculate a consistent set of ionic radii, from which the internuclear distances in ionic crystals could be estimated. The first table, given by V. M. Goldschmidt in 1926, was modified by Pauling. These radii are listed in Table 16.5.

TABLE 16.5 IONIC CRYSTAL RADII (Å)§

Li^+	0.60	Na^+	0.95	K^+	1.33	Rb^+	1.48	Cs^+	1.69
Be^{++}	0.31	Mg^{++}	0.65	Ca^{++}	0.99	Sr^{++}	1.13	Ba^{++}	1.35
B^{3+}	0.20	Al^{3+}	0.50	Sc^{3+}	0.81	Y^{3+}	0.93	La^{3+}	1.15
C^{4+}	0.15	Si^{4+}	0.41	Ti^{4+}	0.68	Zr^{4+}	0.80	Ce^{4+}	1.01
O^{--}	1.40	S^{--}	1.84	Cr^{6+}	0.52	Mo^{6+}	0.62		
F^-	1.36	Cl^-	1.81	Cu^+	0.96	Ag^+	1.26	Au^+	1.37
				Zn^{++}	0.74	Cd^{++}	0.97	Hg^{++}	1.10
				Se^{--}	1.98	Te^{--}	2.21	Tl^{3+}	0.95
				Br^-	1.95	I^-	2.16		

* F. C. Frank, *Disc. Farad. Soc. 5*, 48 (1949).

† Students who have not yet surveyed the variety of inorganic crystal structures should acquire the standard work of A. F. Wells, *Structural Inorganic Chemistry*, 3rd ed., Oxford Univ. Press (1961).

§ From L. Pauling, *The Nature of the Chemical Bond*, 3rd ed. (Ithaca: Cornell Univ. Press, 1960), p. 514.

First, let us consider ionic crystals having the general formula CA. They may be classified according to the *coordination number* of the ions; i.e., the number of ions of opposite charge surrounding a given ion. The CsCl structure, shown in Fig. 16.37, has eightfold coordination. The NaCl structure [Fig. 16.13] has sixfold coordination. Although zinc blende [Fig. 16.22] is itself covalent, there are a few ionic crystals, e.g., BeO, with this structure, which has fourfold coordination. The coordination number of a structure is determined primarily by the number of the larger ions, usually the anions, that can be packed around the smaller ion, usually the cation. It should therefore depend upon the *radius ratio*, $r(\text{cation})/r(\text{anion}) = r_C/r_A$. A critical radius ratio is obtained when the anions packed around a cation are in contact with both the cation and with one another.

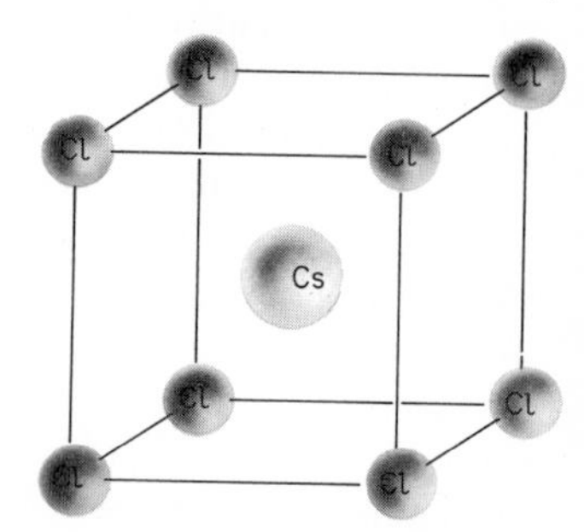

FIG. 16.37 The cesium chloride structure.

The structures of CA_2 ionic crystals are governed by the same coordination principles. Four common structures are shown in Fig. 16.38. In fluorite each Ca^{++} is surrounded by eight F^- ions at the corners of a cube, and each F^- is surrounded by four Ca^{++} at the corners of a tetrahedron. This is an example of 8 : 4 coordination. The structure of rutile illustrates a 6 : 3 coordination, and that of cristobalite a 4 : 2 type. The cadmium-iodide structure illustrates the result of a departure from typically ionic binding. The iodide ion is easily polarized, and one can distinguish definite CdI_2 groups forming a layerlike arrangement.

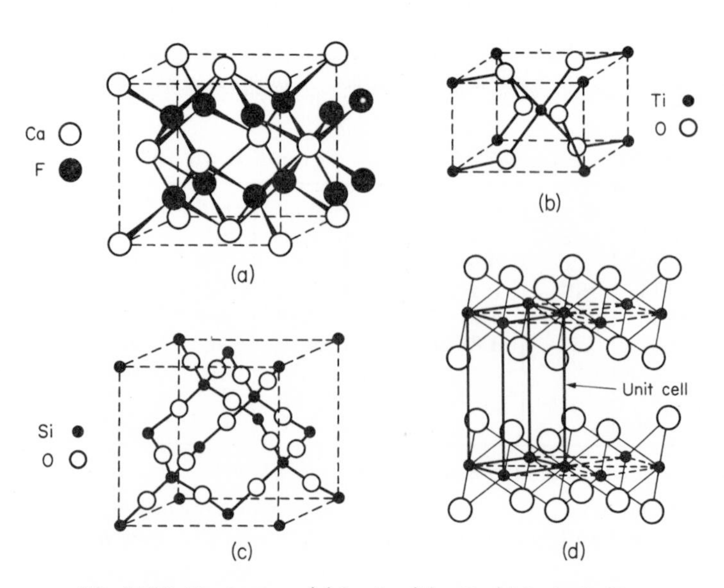

FIG. 16.38 CA_2 structures: (a) fluorite; (b) rutile; (c) β cristobalite; (d) cadmium iodide.

24. THE COHESIVE ENERGY OF IONIC CRYSTALS

In Chapter 13, we discussed the bond in a molecule such as NaCl, formed from a positive and a negative ion. We thus obtained in Eq. (13.1) an expression for the energy of interaction of the ions, which was the sum of the electrostatic attraction and the repulsion that becomes important at small separations. The energy of a crystal composed of a regular array of positive and negative ions can be calculated simply by summing the energy in Eq. (13.1) over all the ions in the array. In order to simplify the notation somewhat, we shall restrict our calculation to the case of cubic crystals in which there are two kinds of ions of equal but opposite charge. This simplified calculation illustrates all the basic features of the theory.

The *crystal energy* is then given by the summation of Eq. (13.1) as

$$U = \tfrac{1}{2} \sum_{i \neq j} \frac{Q_i Q_j}{r_{ij}} + b \sum_{i,j} exp\,(-c h_{ij}) \tag{16.10}$$

The symbol r_{ij} denotes the distance from the ion i to the ion j. The first summation can be visualized by sitting on any ion (i) in the structure and adding up the coulombic energies of its interaction with all the other ions. You must take into account the attractions between your ion and the oppositely charged ions coordinated around it, the repulsions between your ion and ions of like sign at somewhat larger separations, then attractions with unlike ions once removed, and so on. Therefore, for each ion the electrostatic interaction will be a sum of terms, alternately plus and minus, and diminishing in magnitude in accord with the r^{-1} law. For any given structure, this summation simply amounts to relating all the different interionic distances to the lattice parameter a, the length of the unit cubic cell. The repulsive forces in the second summation in Eq. (16.10) are negligible except between nearest neighbors, and thus this sum is taken only over pairs of such neighbors.

In fact, it is simpler to define a dimensionless number M, called the *Madelung number*,

$$M = \sum_i \pm \frac{1}{r_i}$$

The r_i are the distances from the origin to the points of a lattice with unit lattice parameter (e.g., a cube with unit side), and the terms are alternately + and − as given by the electrostatic law.

The cohesive energy of Eq. (16.10) then becomes

$$U = -LM\frac{e^2}{a} + A\ exp\,(-a/\rho) \tag{16.11}$$

If we calculate U per mole, L is the Avogadro number and A and ρ are constants related to those of the law of repulsion. We can eliminate one of these constants by means of an equilibrium condition and calculate the other from the compressibility of the crystal. This calculation is effective since the compressibility is mainly determined by the repulsive forces between the ions.

If a is the equilibrium lattice parameter at 0°K, the energy must be a minimum with respect to variation of a, or $dU/da = 0$. Hence from Eq. (16.11)

$$\frac{dU}{da} = \frac{LMe^2}{a^2} - \frac{A\ exp\ (-a/\rho)}{\rho} = 0$$

$$A = \rho \frac{LMe^2}{a^2}\ exp\ (a/\rho)$$

$$U = -LM\frac{e^2}{a}\left(1 - \frac{\rho}{a}\right) \tag{16.12}$$

The compressibility β is given by

$$\frac{1}{\beta} = V\frac{d^2U}{dV^2}$$

where V the volume per mole equals La^3/Z where Z is the number of molecules per unit cell. Hence, we can obtain ρ from

$$\frac{1}{\beta} = \frac{ZMe^2}{9a^4}\left(-2 + \frac{6\rho}{a}\right) \tag{16.13}$$

25. THE BORN-HABER CYCLE

The crystal energies computed from Eq. (16.12) can be compared with experimental values obtained from thermochemical data by means of the *Born-Haber cycle.* We shall consider NaCl as a typical example.

$$\begin{array}{ccccc} Na^+(g) & + & Cl^-(g) & \xrightarrow{-E_c} & NaCl(c) \\ -e\uparrow I & & +e\uparrow -A & & \downarrow -\Delta H_f \\ Na(g) & + & Cl(g) & \xleftarrow{\lambda_s + \frac{1}{2}D_0} & Na(c) + \frac{1}{2}Cl_2(g) \end{array}$$

The energetic quantities in this cycle are defined as follows, all per mole:

E_c = the crystal energy

ΔH_f = standard heat of formation of NaCl(c)

λ_s = heat of sublimation of Na(c)

D_0 = energy of dissociation of Cl_2(g) into atoms

I = ionization potential of Na

A = electron affinity of Cl

For the cycle, from the first law of thermodynamics,

$$\oint dE = 0 = -E_c - \Delta H_f + \lambda_s + \tfrac{1}{2}D_0 + I - A$$

or,

$$E_c = -\Delta H_f + \lambda_s + \tfrac{1}{2}D_0 + I - A \tag{16.14}$$

All the quantities on the right side of this equation can be evaluated, at least for alkali-halide crystals, and the value obtained for the crystal energy can be compared with that calculated from Eq. (16.12). The ionization potentials I are obtained from atomic spectra, and the dissociation energies D_0 can be accurately determined from molecular spectra. Most difficult to measure are the electron affinities A.*

A summary of the values obtained for various crystals is given in Table 16.6. When the calculated crystal energy deviates widely from that obtained through the Born-Haber cycle, nonionic contributions to the cohesive energy of the crystal are likely.

TABLE 16.6 THE BORN-HABER CYCLE
(Energy Terms in Kilocalories per Mole)

Crystal	$-\Delta H_f$	I	λ_s	D_0	A	E_c	E_c†
NaCl	99	117	26	54	88	181	190
NaBr	90	117	26	46	80	176	181
NaI	77	117	26	34	71	166	171
KCl	104	99	21	54	88	163	173
KBr	97	99	21	46	80	160	166
KI	85	99	21	34	71	151	159
RbCl	105	95	20	54	88	159	166
RbBr	99	95	20	46	80	157	161
RbI	87	95	20	34	71	148	154

† Calculated, Eq. (16.12).

26. STATISTICAL THERMODYNAMICS OF CRYSTALS: THE EINSTEIN MODEL

If we could obtain an accurate partition function for a crystal, we could then calculate immediately all its thermodynamic properties by making use of the general formulas of Chap. 15.

For one mole of a monatomic crystal, containing L atoms, there are L degrees of freedom.

We can consider that there are $3L$ vibrational degrees of freedom, since $3L - 6$ is so close to $3L$. The precise determination of $3L$ normal modes of vibration for such a system would be an impossible task, and it is fortunate that some quite simple approximations give sufficiently good answers.

* See, for example, P. P. Sutton and J. E. Mayer, *J. Chem. Phys.* *2*, 146 (1934); *3*, 20 (1935).

First of all, let us suppose that the $3L$ vibrations arise from independent oscillators, and that these are harmonic oscillators, which is a good enough approximation at low temperatures, when the amplitudes are small. The model proposed by Einstein in 1906 assigned the same frequency ν to all the oscillators.

The crystalline partition function according to the Einstein model is, from Eqs. (15.23) and (15.35),

$$Z = e^{-3L(h\nu/2kT)}(1 - e^{-h\nu/kT})^{-3L} \tag{16.15}$$

It follows immediately that,

$$E - E_0 = 3Lh\nu(e^{-h\nu/kT} - 1)^{-1} \tag{16.16}$$

$$S = 3Lk\left[\frac{h\nu/kT}{e^{h\nu/kT} - 1} - \ln\,(1 - e^{-h\nu/kT})\right] \tag{16.17}$$

$$G - E_0 = 3LkT\ln\,(1 - e^{-h\nu/kT}) \tag{16.18}$$

$$C_V = 3Lk\left(\frac{h\nu}{2kT}\operatorname{csch}\frac{h\nu}{2kT}\right)^2 \tag{16.19}$$

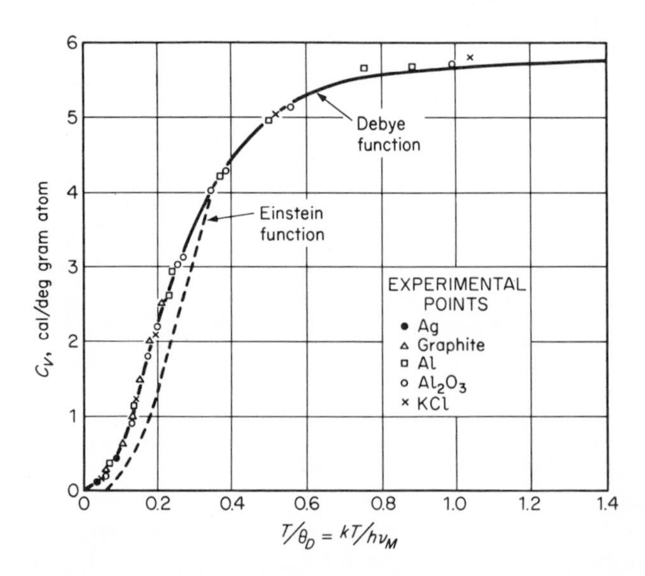

FIG. 16.39 The molar heat capacity of solids. (After F. Seitz, *The Modern Theory of Solids*, McGraw-Hill, 1940).

The predicted temperature variation of C_V is particularly interesting. We recall that Dulong and Petit, in 1819, noted that the molar heat capacities of the solid elements, especially the metals, were usually around $3R = 6$ calories per degree. Later measurements showed that this figure was merely a high-temperature limiting value, approached by different elements at different temperatures. If we expand the expression in Eq. (16.19) and simplify somewhat,* we obtain

$$C_V = \frac{3R}{1 + \frac{1}{12}(h\nu/kT)^2 + \frac{1}{360}(h\nu/kT)^4 + \ldots} \tag{16.20}$$

* Recalling that $\operatorname{csch} x = 2/(e^x - e^{-x})$, and $e^x = 1 + x + (x^2/2!) + (x^3/3!) + \ldots$

When T is large, this expression reduces to $C_V = 3R$. For smaller T's, a curve like the dotted line in Fig. 16.39 is obtained, the heat capacity being a universal function of (ν/T). The frequency ν can be determined from one experimental point at low temperatures and then the entire heat-capacity curve can be drawn for the substance. The agreement with the experimental data is good except at the lowest temperatures. It is clear that the higher the fundamental vibration frequency ν, the larger is the quantum of vibrational energy, and the higher the temperature at which C_V attains the classical value of $3R$. For example, the frequency for diamond is 2.78×10^{13} sec^{-1}, but for lead it is only 0.19×10^{13} sec^{-1}, so that C_V for diamond is only about 1.3 cal per deg per gram atom at room temperature, but C_V for lead is 6.0. The elements that follow Dulong and Petit's rule at room temperatures are those with relatively low vibration frequencies.

27. THE DEBYE MODEL

Instead of a single fundamental frequency, it would be a better model to take a spectrum of vibration frequencies for the crystal. The statistical problem then becomes somewhat more complicated. One possibility is to assume that the frequencies are distributed according to the same law as that given on p. 466 for the distribution of frequencies in black-body radiation. This problem was solved by P. Debye.

Instead of using Eq. (16.16), we must obtain the energy by averaging over all the possible vibration frequencies ν_i of the solid, from 0 to ν_M the maximum frequency. This gives

$$E - E_0 = \frac{1}{3L} \sum_{i=0}^{M} \frac{3Lh\nu_i}{e^{h\nu_i/kT} - 1} = \sum_{i=0}^{M} \frac{h\nu_i}{e^{h\nu_i/kT} - 1} \tag{16.21}$$

Since the frequencies form a virtual continuum, the summation can be replaced by an integration if we use the distribution function for the frequencies found in Eq. (12.15) (multiplied by $\frac{3}{2}$ since we now have one longitudinal and two transverse vibrations, instead of the two transverse vibrations of the radiation case). Thus,

$$dN = f(\nu)\, d\nu = 12\pi \frac{V}{c^3} \nu^2\, d\nu \tag{16.22}$$

where c is now the velocity of elastic waves in the crystal. Then Eq. (16.21) becomes

$$E - E_0 = \int_0^{\nu_M} \frac{h\nu}{e^{h\nu/kT} - 1} f(\nu)\, d\nu \tag{16.23}$$

Before substituting Eq. (16.22) in (16.23) we eliminate c by using Eq. (16.22), since when $N = 3L$, $\nu = \nu_M$, for each direction of vibration,

$$3L = \frac{4\pi}{c^3} V\nu_M^3, \qquad c^3 = \frac{4\pi}{3L} V\nu_M^3, \qquad f(\nu) = \frac{9L}{\nu_M^3} \nu^2\, d\nu$$

Then Eq. (16.23) becomes

$$E - E_0 = \frac{9Lh}{\nu_M^3} \int_0^{\nu_M} \frac{\nu^3 \, d\nu}{e^{h\nu/kT} - 1} \tag{16.24}$$

By differentiation with respect to T,

$$C_V = \frac{9Lh^2}{kT^2\nu_M^3} \int_0^{\nu_M} \frac{\nu^4 e^{h\nu/kT} \, d\nu}{(e^{h\nu/kT} - 1)^2} \tag{16.25}$$

Let us set $x = h\nu/kT$, whereupon Eq. (16.25) becomes

$$C_V = 3Lk \left(\frac{kT}{h\nu_M}\right)^3 \int_0^{h\nu_M/kT} \frac{e^x x^4 \, dx}{(e^x - 1)^2} \tag{16.26}$$

The Debye theory predicts that the heat capacity of a solid as a function of temperature should depend only on the characteristic frequency ν_M. If the heat capacities of different solids are plotted against $kT/h\nu_M$, they should fall on a single curve. Such a plot is shown in Fig. 16.39, and the confirmation of the theory appears to be very good. Debye has defined a *characteristic temperature*, $\Theta_D = h\nu_M/k$, and some of these characteristic temperatures are listed in Table 16.7 for various solids.

TABLE 16.7 Debye Characteristic Temperatures

Substance	Θ_D	Substance	Θ_D	Substance	Θ_D
Na	159	Be	1000	Al	398
K	100	Mg	290	Ti	350
Cu	315	Ca	230	Pb	88
Ag	215	Zn	235	Pt	225
Au	180	Hg	96	Fe	420
KCl	227	AgCl	183	CaF_2	474
NaCl	281	AgBr	144	FeS_2	645

The application of Eq. (16.26) to the limiting cases of high and very low temperatures is of considerable interest. When the temperature becomes large, $e^{h\nu/kT}$ becomes small, and the equation may readily be shown to reduce to simply $C_V = 3R$, the Dulong and Petit expression. When the temperature becomes low, the integral may be expanded in a power series to show that

$$C_V = aT^3 \tag{16.27}$$

This T^3 law holds below about 30°K and is of great use in extrapolating heat-capacity data to absolute zero in connection with studies based on the Third Law of Thermodynamics (cf. Sec. 6.16).

Although the specific heats calculated from the Debye model are quite good for isotropic crystals, the distribution of vibration frequencies in an actual crystal may be quite different from that employed in the model. A method based on the scattering of neutrons has led to quite exact experimental determinations of this frequency distribution.* It is possible to use such experimental frequency distributions to compute accurate thermodynamic properties of the crystals by means of the statistical formulas.

PROBLEMS

1. By means of drawings show the directions [111], [100], [100], [122] in a cubic unit cell.
2. What is the plane of closest packing in the body centered cubic structure?
3. Argon crystallizes in the ccp structure. At 20°K, $a_0 = 5.43$ Å. Calculate from this an effective diameter for the argon atom.
4. Construct a primitive square lattice and a centered square lattice. Determine the densities of points in the rows (10), (11), (21), (31), (32), (41), (42) and (43). Compare these with the distances between the rows.
5. With X rays of wavelength 1.540 Å the first reflection from a KCl crystal occurs at $\theta = 14°\ 12'$. Calculate the length of the unit cell and the density of the crystal.
6. A crystal plane intercepts the three crystallographic axes at the following multiples of the unit distances: 3/2, 2, 1. What are the Miller indices of the plane?
7. How many symmetry axes and planes are there in a simple cube? Give examples of arrangements of atoms which reduce this symmetry.
8. Show that a face-centered cubic lattice can also be represented as a rhombohedral lattice. Calculate the rhombohedral angle. [*Ans.* $\alpha = 60°$]
9. MgO has the NaCl structure and a density of 3.65 g cm^{-3}. Calculate the values of $(\sin\theta)/\lambda$ at which scattering occurs from the planes 100, 110, 111 and 210. [*Ans.* 0.238, .340, .207, .533]
10. Nickel crystallizes in the fcc structure with $a_0 = 3.52$ Å. Calculate the distance apart of nickel atoms lying in the 100, 110 and 111 planes. [*Ans.* 100 and 110: 2.47 and 3.52; 111, 2.47 Å]
11. Calculate the atomic volumes for spheres of radius 1.00 Å in cubic closest packed and hexagonal closest packed structures. Give the unit cell dimensions, a_0 for cubic, a_0 and c_0 for hexagonal. [*Ans.* 5.66 $Å^3$; for cubic $a_0 = 2\sqrt{2}$ Å; for hexagonal, $a_0 = 2$ Å, $c_0 = 4\sqrt{\frac{2}{3}}$]
12. Calculate the structure factors for planes in the diamond structure; hence explain the observed pattern of lines in an X-ray powder picture of diamond.

* A review is given by J. A. Krumhansl, *J. Appl. Physics*, *33* (Suppl. 1), 307 (1962).

13. Crystals of KNO_2 are monoclinic with $a_0 = 4.45$, $b_0 = 4.99$, $c_0 = 7.31$ Å, $\beta = 114° 50'$. There are two molecules per unit cell. Calculate the density of the crystal. With copper K_α X rays (1.539 Å) calculate the Bragg angle θ for the 101 and 110 planes.

14. Show that the void volume for spheres in both ccp and hcp is 25.9 per cent. What would be the per cent void volume in a bcc structure with corner atoms in contact with the center atom.

15. In a powder picture of lead with Cu-K_α radiation ($\lambda = 1.539$ Å) the line from the 531 planes appeared at $\sin\theta = 0.9210$. Calculate a_0 and the density of lead. [*Ans.* 4.94 Å, 11.40 g cm^{-3}]

16. The ionic (crystal) radius of Cs^+ is 1.69 Å and that of Br^- is 1.81 Å. Calculate a_0. CsBr crystallizes in the CsCl structure. Calculate $\sin\theta/\lambda$ for the line at the smallest observable scattering angle in a Debye-Scherrer diagram from CsBr crystals.

17. Calculate the number per cm^3 of (a) Frenkel (b) Schottky, defects in crystals of NaCl at 1200°K if the energies required to form the defects are 3.0 ev and 2.0 ev, respectively.

18. Discuss the possible kinds of substitutional atomic imperfections in a III-V compound (ex. InSb) using elements from groups III, IV and V. Suggest one or more rules for solubilities.

19. Calculate the critical radius ratio r_C/r_A for the CsCl type of structure (i.e. the ratio when the atms at the corners of the unit cell make contact with one another).

---

20. Show graphically that fivefold axes of symmetry are inconsistent with translations and hence cannot be elements of a space group.

21. Zinc oxide crystallizes in a hexagonal structure with $a_0 = 3.243$, $c_0 = 5.195$ Å, $Z = 2$. The atomic positions are Zn: 000, $\frac{1}{3}\,\frac{2}{3}\,\frac{1}{2}$; O: $00\frac{3}{8}$, $\frac{1}{3}\,\frac{2}{3}\,\frac{7}{8}$. Discuss two ways in which it would be possible to introduce interstitial zinc atoms into such a structure.

22. To the points in a simple orthorhombic lattice add points at $\frac{1}{2}\frac{1}{2}0$, $\frac{1}{2}0\frac{1}{2}$, i.e. at the centers of a pair of opposite faces in each cell. Prove that the resulting arrangement of points in space is not a lattice.

23. Discuss the problem of distinguishing experimentally between interstitial and substitutional solid solution.

24. A Debye-Scherrer picture of a cubic crystal with X rays of $\lambda = 1.539$Å displayed lines at the following scattering angles:

No. of line	1	2	3	4	5	6	7	8	9
θ, deg	13.70	15.89	22.75	26.91	28.25	33.15	37.00	37.60	41.95
Intensity	w	vs	s	vw	m	w	w	m	m

Index these lines. Calculate a_0 for the crystal. Identify the crystal. Explain the intensity relation between lines 5 and 4 in terms of the structure factor.

25. The Debye characteristic temperature of copper is $\Theta = 315°K$. Calculate the entropy of copper at 0°C and 1 atm assuming that $\alpha = 4.95 \times 10^{-5}$ deg^{-1}, $\beta = 7.5 \times 10^{-7}$ atm^{-1}, independent of T. [*Ans.* 7.96 cal deg^{-1} mole^{-1}].

26. The measured specific heat of copper at 253°C is $C_P = 3.1 \times 10^{-3}$ cal deg^{-1} g^{-1}. (a) Estimate C_V at 10°K and (b) the Debye characteristic temperature of copper.

27. List all the symmetry elements of each of the following molecules (assume all are isotopically pure): CHDFCl, CH_2Cl_2 (tetrahedral), OCS, trans ClBrHC—CHBrCl, $PtCl_4^=$ (nonplanar, square pyramidal), eclipsed form of ethane, boat form of cyclohexane.

28. If you assume that each copper atom contributes one free electron find the maximum kinetic energy in ev of the electrons in copper, if they act like free electrons in a box.

29. Plot the Fermi distribution function $f = \left\{\exp \frac{E - E_F}{kT} + 1\right\}^{-1}$ for a metal with the valence band filled to 5 ev and half full, for temperatures of 100°K, 1000°K and 10 000°K.

30. The diffusion coefficient D of oxygen in cuprous oxide has been measured with ^{18}O as a tracer. The $D = D_0 P_{O_2}^{1/2}$, where D_0 is the value at $P_{O_2} = 1$ atm. The concentration y of excess oxygen in cuprous oxide varies as $P_{O_2}^{1/4}$. The electrical conductivity of Cu_2O is due to positive holes and varies approximately as $P_{O_2}^{1/7}$. What can you conclude from these results about the mechanism of diffusion of oxygen and of electrical conductivity in Cu_2O.

31. The diffusion coefficient of He in aluminum is 10^{-6} cm^2 s^{-1} at 600°C. Suppose He at 1 atm is sealed into an aluminum capsule with walls 10^{-2} cm thick. Calculate the steady state rate of diffusion of He through the walls in molecules cm^{-2} s^{-1}.

32. Calculate the proton affinity of NH_3 from the following data (*i.e.*, the ΔE for reaction $NH_3 + H^+ \rightarrow NH_4^+$). NH_4F crystallizes in the ZnO type structure whose Madelung constant is 1.64. The Born repulsion exponent for NH_4F is 8, the interionic distance is 2.63 Å. The electron affinity of fluorine is 95.0 kcal. The ionization potential of hydrogen is 311.9 kcal. The heats of formation from the atoms are: $NH_3 = 279.6$; $N_2 = 225$; $H_2 = 104.1$; $F_2 = 63.5$ kcal. The heat of reaction $\frac{1}{2} N_2(g) + 2 H_2(g) + \frac{1}{2} F_2(g) = NH_4^+F^-$ (c) is 111.9 kcal. [*Ans.* 211.1 kcal]

17 THE LIQUID STATE

The gaseous and crystalline states of matter have already been surveyed. The liquid state remains to be considered. But not every substance falls neatly into one of these three classes. The variety of matter can perplex a morphologist, as he considers resins and rubbers, glasses, liquid crystals, fibers and protoplasm.

Gases, at least in the ideal approximation approached at high temperatures and low densities, are characterized by complete randomness on the molecular scale. The ideal crystal, on the other hand, is Nature's most orderly arrangement. Because the extremes of perfect chaos and perfect harmony are both relatively simple to treat mathematically, the theories of gases and of crystals are at respectably advanced stages. Liquids, however, representing a peculiar compromise between order and disorder, have so far defied a comprehensive theoretical treatment.

In an ideal gas, the molecules move independently of one another and interactions between them are neglected. The energy of the perfect gas is simply the sum of the energies of the individual molecules, their internal energies plus their translational kinetic energies; there is no intermolecular potential energy. It is therefore possible to write down a partition function such as that in Eq. (15.23), from which all the equilibrium properties of the gas are readily derived. In a crystalline solid, translational kinetic energy is usually negligible. The molecules, atoms, or ions vibrate about equilibrium positions to which they are held by strong intermolecular, interatomic, or interionic forces. In this case too, an adequate partition function, such as that in Eq. (15.23), can be obtained. In a liquid, on the other hand, the situation is much harder to define. The cohesive forces are sufficiently strong to lead to a condensed state, but not strong enough to prevent a considerable translational energy of the individual molecules. The thermal motions introduce a disorder into the liquid without completely destroying the regularity of its structure. It is therefore difficult to devise an acceptable partition function for liquids.

1. DISORDER IN THE LIQUID STATE

In studying liquids, it is often helpful to recall the relation between entropy and degree of disorder. Consider a crystal at its melting point. The crystal is energetically a more favorable structure than the liquid to which it melts. It is necessary to add energy, the latent heat of fusion, to effect the melting. The equilibrium situation, however, is determined by the difference in free energy, $\Delta G = \Delta H - T\Delta S$. The greater randomness of the liquid, and hence its greater entropy, finally makes the $T\Delta S$ term large enough to overcome the ΔH term, so that the crystal melts when the following condition is reached:

$$T(S_{\text{liq}} - S_{\text{cry}}) = H_{\text{liq}} - H_{\text{cry}}$$

The sharpness of the melting point is noteworthy: there is not a continuous gradation of properties between liquid and crystal. The sharp transition is due to the rigorous geometrical requirements that must be fulfilled by a crystal structure. It is not possible to introduce small regions of disorder into the crystal without at the same time seriously disturbing the structure over such a long range that the crystalline arrangement is destroyed. Two-dimensional models of the gaseous, liquid, and crystalline states are illustrated in Fig. 17.1. The picture of the liquid was constructed by J. D. Bernal by introducing around atom A only five other atoms, instead of its normal close-packed coordination of six. Every effort was then made to draw the rest of the circles in the most ordered arrangement possible, with the results shown. The one point of abnormal coordination among some hundred atoms sufficed to produce the long-range disorder believed to be typical of the liquid state. Thus, if there is any abnormal coordination at all, there must be quite a lot of it. This fact may help explain the sharpness of melting. When the thermal motions in one region of a crystal suffice to destroy the regular structure, the irregularity rapidly spreads throughout the entire specimen; disorder in a crystal is contagious.

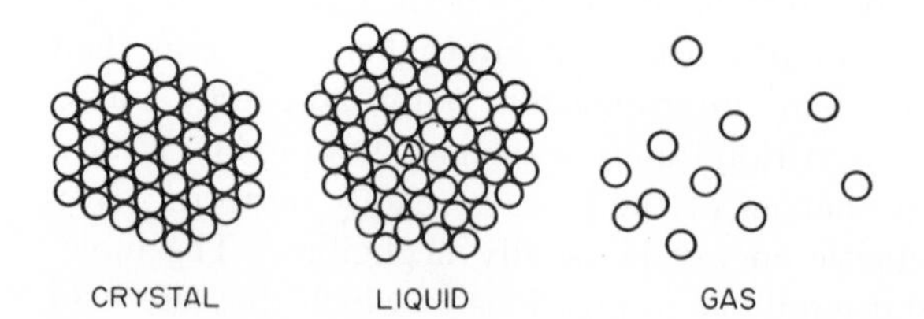

FIG. 17.1 Two-dimensional models of states of matter.

We do not mean to imply that all crystals are ideally perfect, and admit of no disorder at all. The amount of disorder allowed is usually limited. When the limit is exceeded, melting of the crystal occurs.

It is sometimes convenient to classify liquids, like crystals, from a rather chemical standpoint, according to the kind of cohesive forces that hold them together. Thus there are the ionic liquids such as molten salts, metallic liquids consisting of ions and mobile electrons, liquids such as water held together mainly by hydrogen bonds, and finally molecular liquids in which the cohesion is due to the van der Waals forces between essentially saturated molecules. Many liquids fall into this last group, and even when other forces are present, the van der Waals contribution may be large. The nature of these forces will be considered later in this chapter.

2. APPROACHES TO A THEORY FOR LIQUIDS

From these introductory remarks it may be evident that there are three possible ways of essaying a theory of the liquid state, two cautious ways and one direct way.

The cautious approaches are by way of the theory of gases and the theory of solids. The liquid may be studied as an extremely imperfect gas. This is a reasonable viewpoint, since above the critical point there is no distinction at all between liquid and gas, and the so-called *fluid state* of matter exists. On the other hand, the liquid may be considered as similar to a crystal, except that the well ordered arrangement of units extends over a short range only, five or six molecular diameters. This situation is called *short-range order and long-range disorder*. It is a reasonable model, since near the melting point the densities of crystal and liquid lie close together; the solid usually expands about 10 per cent in volume, or only about 3 per cent in intermolecular spacing, when it melts. Whatever order exists in a liquid structure is continuously changing because of thermal motions of the individual molecules; the properties of the liquid are determined by the time average of a large number of different arrangements.

The imperfect-gas theory of liquids would be suitable close to the critical point; the disordered-crystal theory would be best near the melting point. At points between, they might both fail badly. A more direct approach to liquids would abandon these flanking attacks and try to develop the theory directly from the fundamentals of intermolecular forces and statistical mechanics. This is a difficult undertaking, but a beginning has been made by Max Born, J. G. Kirkwood, H. Eyring and others.

3. X-RAY DIFFRACTION OF LIQUIDS

The study of the X-ray diffraction of liquids followed the development of the method of Debye and Scherrer for crystalline powders. As the particle size of the powder decreases, the width of the lines in the X-ray pattern increases. With particles around 100 Å in diameter, the lines have become diffuse halos, and with still further decrease in particle size the diffraction maxima become blurred out altogether.

If a liquid were completely amorphous, i.e., without any regularity of structure, it should also give a continuous scattering of X rays without maxima or minima. This was actually found not to be the case. A typical pattern, that obtained from liquid mercury, is shown in Fig. 17.2(a), as a microphotometer tracing of the photograph. This reveals the maxima and minima better than the unaided eye. One or two or sometimes more intensity maxima appear, whose positions often correspond closely to some of the larger interplanar spacings that occur in the crystalline structures. In the case of the metals, these are the close-packed structures. It is interesting that a crystal like bismuth, which has a peculiar and rather loose solid structure, is transformed on melting into a close-packed structure. We recall that bismuth is one of the few substances that contract in volume when melted.

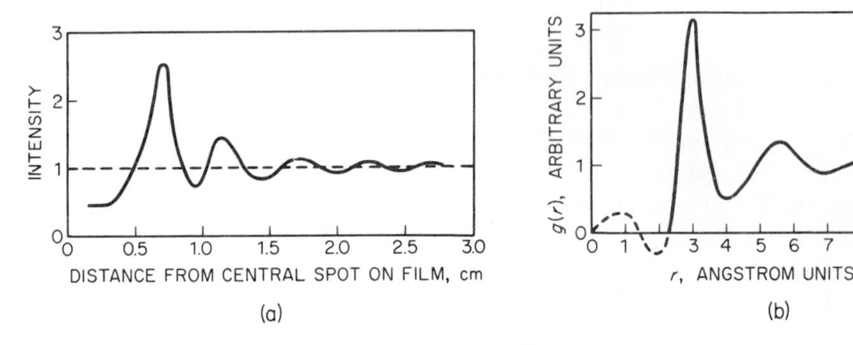

FIG. 17.2 X-ray diffraction of liquid mercury: (a) Photometric tracing of diffraction diagram; (b) radial distribution function for liquid mercury.

The fact that only a few maxima are observed in the diffraction patterns from liquids is in accord with the picture of short-range order and increasing disorder at longer range. In order to obtain the maxima corresponding to smaller interplanar spacings or higher orders of diffraction, the long-range order of the crystal must be present.

The diffraction maxima observed with crystals or liquids should be distinguished from those obtained by the X-ray or electron diffraction of gases. The latter arise from the fixed positions of the atoms within the molecules. The individual molecules are far apart and distributed at random. In deriving on p. 578 the diffraction formula for gases, we considered only a single molecule and averaged over all possible orientations in space. With solids and liquids the diffraction maxima arise from the ordered arrangement of the units (molecules or atoms) in the condensed three-dimensional structure. Thus gaseous argon, a monatomic gas, would yield no maxima due to interatomic spacings, but liquid argon displays a pattern similar to that of liquid mercury.

It is possible to analyze the X-ray diffraction data from liquids by using the Bragg relation to calculate spacings. A more instructive approach, however, is to consider a liquid specimen as a single giant molecule, and then to use the formulas, such as Eq. (14.25), derived for diffraction by single molecules. A simple theory is obtained only in the case of monatomic liquids, such as the metals and group O elements.

The arrangement of atoms in such a liquid is described by introducing the *radial distribution function* $g(r)$. Taking the center of one atom as origin, this $g(r)$ gives the probability of finding the center of another atom at the end of a vector of length r drawn from the origin. The chance of finding another atom between a distance r and $r + dr$, irrespective of angular orientation, is therefore $4\pi r^2 g(r)\, dr$ (cf. p. 492). It is now possible to obtain, for the intensity of scattered X-radiation, an expression similar to that in Eq. (14.25), except that instead of a summation over individual scattering centers, there is an integration over a continuous distribution of scattering matter, specified by $g(r)$. Thus

$$I(\theta) \propto \int_0^\infty 4\pi r^2 g(r) \frac{\sin sr}{sr}\, dr \tag{17.1}$$

As before,

$$s = (4\pi/\lambda) \sin \theta/2$$

By an application of Fourier's integral theorem, this integral can be inverted,* yielding

$$4\pi r^2 g(r) \propto \frac{2}{\lambda} \int_0^\infty I(\theta) \frac{\sin sr}{sr}\, d\theta \tag{17.2}$$

With this relationship we can calculate a radial-distribution curve, such as that plotted in Fig. 17.2(b), from an experimental scattering curve, such as that in Fig. 17.2(a). The regular coordination in the close-packed liquid-mercury structure is clearly evident, but the fact that maxima in the curve are rapidly damped out at larger interatomic distances indicates that the departure from the ordered arrangement becomes greater as one travels outward from any centrally chosen atom.

4. RESULTS OF INVESTIGATIONS OF LIQUID STRUCTURE

X-ray diffraction data from liquids are not sufficiently detailed to permit complete structure analyses like those of crystals. This situation is probably inevitable because the diffraction experiments reveal only an average or statistical structure, owing to the continual destruction and reformation of ordered arrangements by the thermal motions of the atoms or molecules in the liquid.

The results with liquid metals have already been mentioned. They appear to have approximately close-packed structures quite similar to those of the solids, with the interatomic spacings expanded by about 5 per cent. The number of nearest neighbors in a close-packed structure is twelve. In liquid sodium, each atom is found to have on the average ten nearest neighbors.

One of the most interesting liquid structures is that of water. J. Morgan and B. E. Warren† have extended and clarified an earlier discussion by Bernal

---

* See, for example, H. Bateman, *Partial Differential Equations of Mathematical Physics* (New York: Dover Publications, 1944), p. 207.

† *J. Chem. Phys. 6*, 666 (1938). This paper is recommended as a clear and excellent example of the X-ray method as applied to liquids.

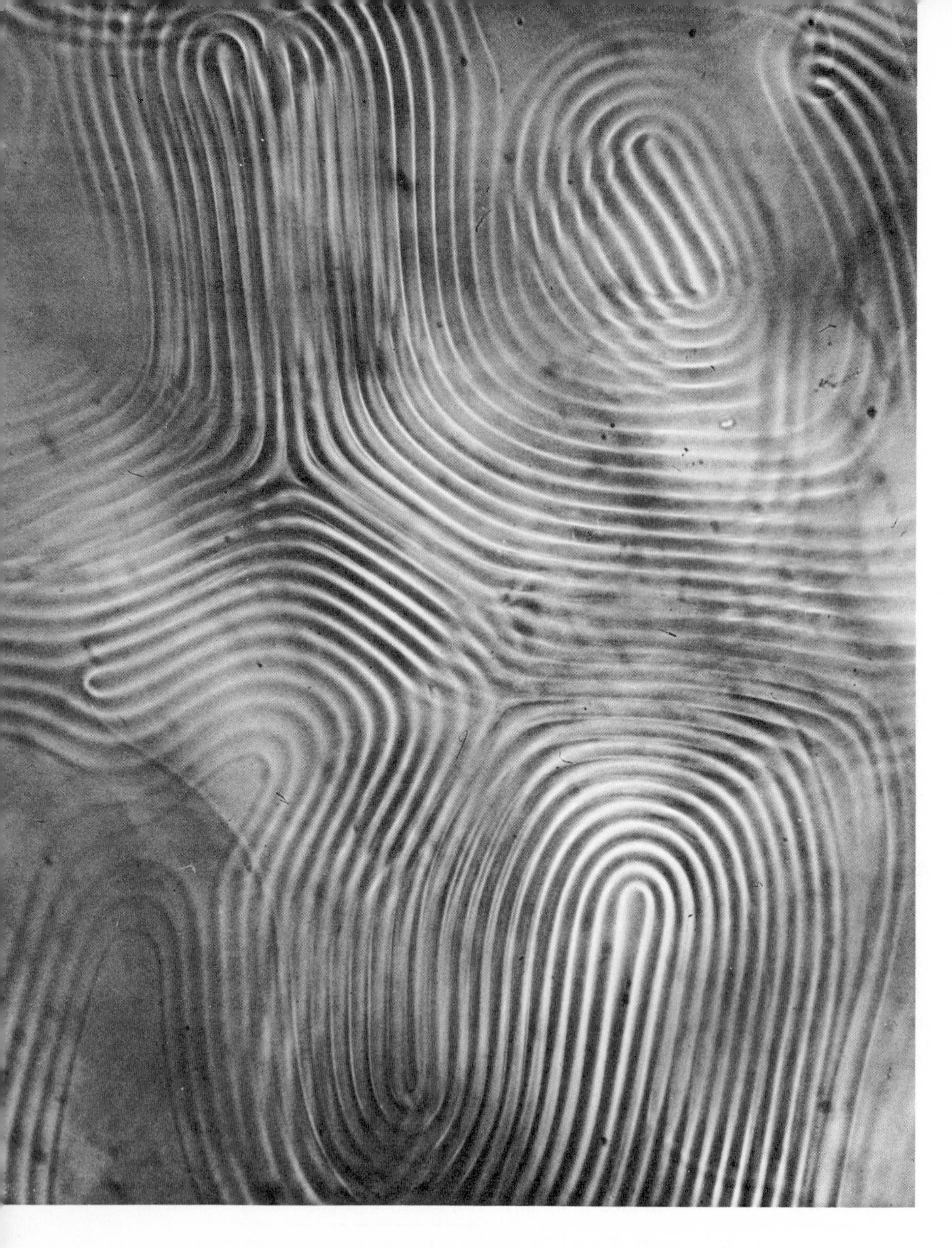

FIG. 17.3 A liquid crystalline solution of a polypeptide in dichloroacetic acid solution viewed by natural light with a low powered microscope. [C. Robinson, J. C. Ward and R. B. Beevers, Courtaulds Research Laboratory, Maidenhead, *Disc. Faraday Soc.* *25*, 29 (1958)].

and Fowler. They studied the X-ray diffraction of water over a range of temperatures, and obtained the radial distribution curves. The maximum of the large first peak occurs at a distance varying from about 2.88 Å at 1.5°C to slightly over 3.00 Å at 83°C. The closest spacing in ice is at 2.76 Å. It might at first be thought that this result is in disagreement with the fact that there is a contraction in volume of about 9 per cent when ice melts. Further analysis shows, however, that the coordination in liquid water is not exactly the same as the coordination of four nearest neighbors in ice. The number of nearest neighbors can be estimated from the area under the peaks in the radial-distribution curve, with the following results:

Temperature, °C:	1.5	13	30	63	83
Number of nearest neighbors:	4.4	4.4	4.6	4.9	4.9

Thus the tetrahedral arrangement in ice is partially broken down in water, to an extent that increases with temperature. This breakdown permits closer packing, although water is of course far from being a closest-packed structure. The combination of this effect with the usual increase of intermolecular separation with temperature explains the occurrence of the minimum in the density of water at 4°C.

Among other structures that have been investigated, those of the long-chain hydrocarbons may be mentioned. These molecules tend to pack with parallel orientations of the chains.

5. LIQUID CRYSTALS

In some substances the tendency toward an ordered arrangement is so great that the crystalline form does not melt directly to a liquid phase at all, but first passes through an intermediate stage (the *mesomorphic* or *paracrystalline* state), which at a higher temperature undergoes a transition to the liquid state. These intermediate states have been called *liquid crystals*, since they display some of the properties of each of the adjacent states. Thus some paracrystalline substances flow in a gliding stepwise fashion and form *graded droplets* having terrace-like surfaces; other varieties flow quite freely but are not isotropic, exhibiting interference figures when examined with polarized light. An example is shown in Fig. 17.3.

A compound frequently studied in its paracrystalline state is *p*-azoxyanisole,

$$CH_3O-C_6H_4-\overset{\overset{O}{\uparrow}}{N}=N-C_6H_4-OCH_3$$

The solid form melts at 84° to the liquid crystal, which is stable to 150° at which point it undergoes a transition to an isotropic liquid. The compound ethyl *p*-anisalaminocinnamate,

$$CH_3O-C_6H_4-CH=N-C_6H_4-CH=CH-COOC_2H_5$$

passes through three distinct paracrystalline phases between 83° and 139°. Cholesteryl bromide behaves rather differently.* The solid melts at 94° to an isotropic liquid, but this liquid can be supercooled to 67° where it passes over into a metastable liquid-crystalline form.

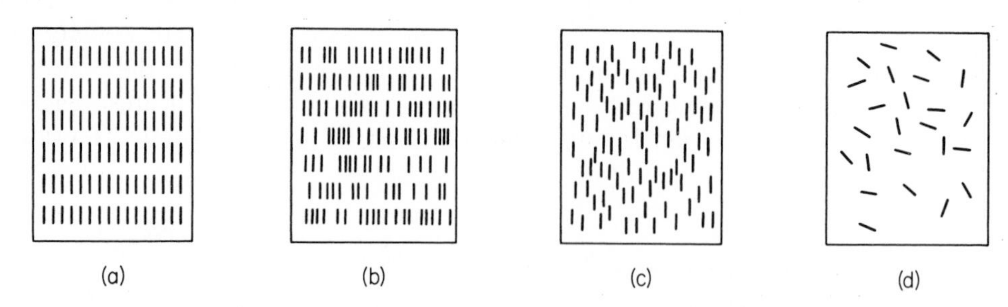

FIG. 17.4 Degrees of order: (a) crystalline — orientation and periodicity; (b) smectic — orientation and arrangement in equispaced planes, but no periodicity within planes; (c) nematic — orientation without periodicity; (d) isotropic fluid — neither orientation nor periodicity.

Liquid crystals tend to occur in compounds whose molecules are markedly unsymmetrical in shape. For example, in the crystalline state, long-chain molecules may be lined up as shown in Fig. 17.4(a). On raising the temperature, the kinetic energy may become sufficient to disrupt the binding between the ends of the molecules but insufficient to overcome the strong lateral attractions between the long chains. Two types of anisotropic melt might then be obtained, shown in Fig. 17.4(b) and (c). In the *smectic* (σμηγμα, "soap") state the molecules are oriented in well defined planes. When a stress is applied, one plane glides over another. In the *nematic* (νημα, "thread") state the planar structure is lost, but the orientation is preserved. With some substances, notably the soaps, several different phases, differentiated by optical and flow properties, can be distinguished between typical crystal and typical liquid.

Liquid crystals, it is to be noted, are not important for biology and embryology because they manifest certain properties which can be regarded as analogous to those which living systems manifest (models), but because living systems actually are *liquid crystals, or, it would be more correct to say, the paracrystalline state undoubtedly exists in living cells. The doubly refracting portions of the striated muscle fibre are, of course, the classical instance of this arrangement, but there are many other equally striking instances, such as cephalopod spermatozoa, or the axons of nerve cells, or cilia, or birefringent phases in molluscan eggs, or in nucleus and cytoplasm of echinoderm eggs.*

The paracrystalline state seems the most suited to biological functions, as it combines the fluidity and diffusibility of liquids while preserving the possibilities of internal structure characteristic of crystalline solids.†

* J. Fischer, *Zeit. physik. Chem.*, *160 A*, 110 (1932).

† Joseph Needham, *Biochemistry and Morphogenesis* (London: Cambridge, 1942), p. 661.

6. GLASSES

The glassy or vitreous state of matter is another example of a compromise between crystalline and liquid properties. The structure of a glass is essentially similar to that of an associated liquid such as water, so that there is a good deal of truth in the old description of glasses as supercooled liquids. The two-dimensional models in Fig. 17.5, given by W. H. Zachariasen, illustrate the difference between a glass and a crystal.

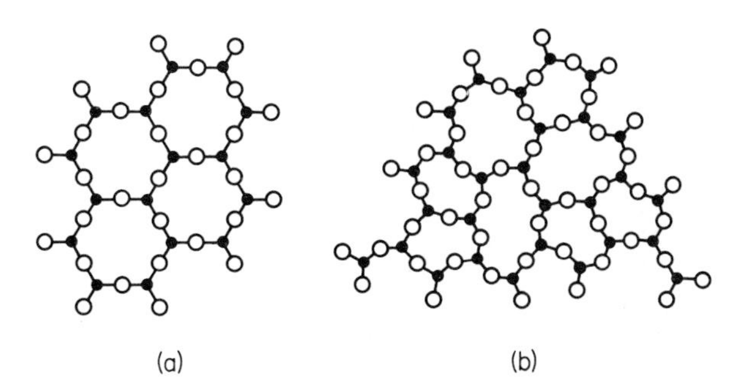

FIG. 17.5 Two-dimensional models for (a) crystal and (b) glass.

The bonds are the same in both cases, e.g., in silica the strong electrostatic Si—O bonds. Thus both quartz crystals and vitreous silica are hard and mechanically strong. The bonds in the glass differ considerably in length and therefore in strength. Thus a glass on heating softens gradually rather than melts sharply, since there is no one temperature at which all the bonds become loosened simultaneously.

The extremely low coefficient of thermal expansion of some glasses, notably vitreous silica, is explicable in terms of a structure such as that in Fig. 17.5. The structure is a very loose one, and as in the case of liquid water, increasing the temperature may allow a closer coordination. To a certain extent, therefore, the structure may "expand into itself." This effect counteracts the normal expansion in interatomic distance with temperature.

7. MELTING

In Table 17.1 are collected some data on the melting points, latent heats of fusion, latent heats of vaporization, and entropies of fusion and vaporization of a number of substances.

The heats of fusion are much less than the heats of vaporization. It requires much less energy to convert a crystal to liquid than to vaporize a liquid.

The entropies of fusion are also considerably lower than the entropies of vaporization. The latter are quite constant, around 21.6 cal deg^{-1} $mole^{-1}$ (Trouton's rule). The constancy of the former is not so marked. For some classes of substances, however, notably the close-packed metals, the entropies of fusion are remarkably constant.

TABLE 17.1 DATA ON MELTING AND VAPORIZATION

Substance	Heat of Fusion (kcal/mole)	Heat of Vaporization (kcal/mole)	Melting Point (°K)	Entropy of Fusion (cal/°)	Entropy of Vaporization (cal/°)
		Metals			
Na	0.63	24.6	371	1.70	21.1
Al	2.55	67.6	932	2.73	29.0
K	0.58	21.9	336	1.72	21.0
Fe	3.56	96.5	1802	1.97	29.5
Ag	2.70	69.4	1234	2.19	27.8
Pt	5.33	125	2028	2.63	26.7
Hg	0.58	15.5	234	2.48	24.5
		Ionic Crystals			
NaCl	7.22	183	1073	6.72	109
KCl	6.41	165	1043	6.15	93
AgCl	3.15	—	728	4.33	—
KNO_3	2.57	—	581	4.42	—
$BaCl_2$	5.75	—	1232	4.65	—
$K_2Cr_2O_7$	8.77	—	671	13.07	—
		Molecular Crystals			
H_2	0.028	0.22	14	2.0	15.8
H_2O	1.43	11.3	273	5.25	30.1
A	0.280	1.88	83	3.38	21.6
NH_3	1.84	7.14	198	9.30	29.7
C_2H_5OH	1.10	10.4	156	7.10	29.6
C_6H_6	2.35	8.3	278	8.45	23.5

8. COHESION OF LIQUIDS — THE INTERNAL PRESSURE

Whatever the model chosen for the liquid state, the cohesive forces are of primary importance. Ignoring, for the time being, the origin of these forces, we can obtain an estimate of their magnitude from thermodynamic considerations. This estimate is provided by the *internal pressure.*

We recall from Eq. (3.42) that

$$\left(\frac{\partial E}{\partial V}\right)_T = T\left(\frac{\partial P}{\partial T}\right)_V - P$$

In the case of an ideal gas, the internal pressure term $P_i = (\partial E/\partial V)_T$ is zero since intermolecular forces are absent. In the case of an imperfect gas, the $(\partial E/\partial V)_T$ term becomes appreciable, and in the case of a liquid it may become much greater than the external pressure.

The internal pressure is the resultant of the forces of attraction and the forces of repulsion between the molecules in a liquid. It therefore depends markedly on the volume V, and thus on the external pressure P. This effect is shown in the following data for diethyl ether at 25°C.

P(atm):	200	800	2000	5300	7260	9200	11 100
P_i(atm):	2790	2840	2530	2020	40	−1590	−4380

For moderate increases in P, the P_i decreases only slightly, but as P exceeds 5000 atm, the P_i begins to decrease rapidly, and goes to large negative values as the liquid is further compressed. This behavior reflects on a larger scale the law of force between individual molecules; at high compressions, the repulsive forces become predominant.

Internal pressures at 1 atm and 25°C are summarized in Table 17.2, taken from a compilation by J. H. Hildebrand. With normal aliphatic hydrocarbons there is a gradual increase in P_i with the length of the chain. Dipolar liquids

TABLE 17.2 INTERNAL PRESSURES OF LIQUIDS (25°C and 1 atm)

Compound	P_i *atm*
Diethyl ether	2370
n-Heptane	2510
n-Octane	2970
Tin tetrachloride	3240
Carbon tetrachloride	3310
Benzene	3640
Chloroform	3660
Carbon bisulfide	3670
Mercury	13 200
Water	20 000

tend to have somewhat larger values than nonpolar liquids. The effect of dipole interaction is nevertheless not predominant. As might be expected, water with its strong hydrogen bonds has an exceptionally high internal pressure.

Hildebrand was the first to point out the significance of the internal pressures of liquids in determining solubility relationships. If two liquids have about the same P_i, their solution has little tendency toward positive deviations from Raoult's Law. The solution of two liquids differing considerably in P_i will usually exhibit considerable positive deviation from ideality, i.e., a tendency toward lowered mutual solubility.

9. INTERMOLECULAR FORCES

It should be clearly understood from earlier discussions that all the forces between atoms and molecules are electrostatic in origin. They are ultimately based on Coulomb's Law of the attraction between unlike, and the repulsion between like charges. One often speaks of long-range forces and short-range forces. Thus a force that depends on r^{-2} will be effective over a longer range than one dependent on r^{-7}. All these forces may be represented as gradients of potential functions, $f = -\partial U/\partial r$, and it is often convenient to describe the potential energies rather than the forces themselves. We can then distinguish the following varieties of intermolecular and interionic potential energies:

(1) The coulombic energy of interaction between ions with net charges, leading to a long-range attraction, with $U \propto r^{-1}$.

(2) The energy of interaction between permanent dipoles, with $U \propto r^{-6}$.

(3) The energy of interaction between an ion and a dipole induced by it in another molecule, with $U \propto r^{-4}$.

(4) The energy of interaction between a permanent dipole and a dipole induced by it in another molecule with $U \propto r^{-6}$.

(5) The forces between neutral atoms or molecules, such as the inert gases, with $U \propto r^{-6}$.

(6) The overlap energy arising from the interaction of the positive nuclei and electron cloud of one molecule with those of another. The overlap leads to repulsion at very close intermolecular separations, with an r^{-9} to r^{-12} potential.

The van der Waals attractions between molecules must arise from interactions belonging to classes (2), (4), and (5).

The first attempt to explain them theoretically was by W. H. Keesom (1912), based on the interaction between permanent dipoles. Two dipoles in rapid thermal motion may sometimes be oriented so as to attract each other, sometimes so as to repel each other. On the average they are somewhat closer together in attractive configurations, and there is a net attractive energy. This energy was calculated* to be

$$U_0 = -\frac{2\mu^4}{3r^6} \cdot \frac{1}{kT} \tag{17.3}$$

where μ is the dipole moment. The observed r^{-6} dependence of the interaction energy, or r^{-7} dependence of the forces, is in agreement with deductions from experiment. This theory is of course not an adequate general explanation of van der Waals forces, since there are considerable attractive forces between molecules, such as the inert gases, with no vestige of a permanent dipole moment.

Debye, in 1920, extended the dipole theory to take into account the *induction effect*. A permanent dipole induces a dipole in another molecule and a mutual attraction results. This interaction depends on the polarizability α of the molecules, and leads to a formula,

$$U = -\frac{2\alpha\mu^2}{r^6} \tag{17.4}$$

This effect is quite small and does not help us to explain the case of the inert gases.

In 1930, F. London solved this problem by a brilliant application of quantum mechanics. Let us consider a neutral molecule, such as argon. The positive nucleus is surrounded by a "cloud" of negative charge. Although the time

* J. E. Lennard-Jones, *Proc. Phys. Soc.* (London) *43*, 461 (1931).

average of this charge distribution is spherically symmetrical, at any instant it will be somewhat distorted. We see this clearly in the case of the neutral hydrogen atom, in which the electron is sometimes on one side of the proton, sometimes on the other. Thus a snapshot taken of an argon atom would reveal a little dipole with a certain orientation. An instant later the orientation would be different, and so on, so that over any macroscopic period of time the instantaneous dipole moments would average to zero.

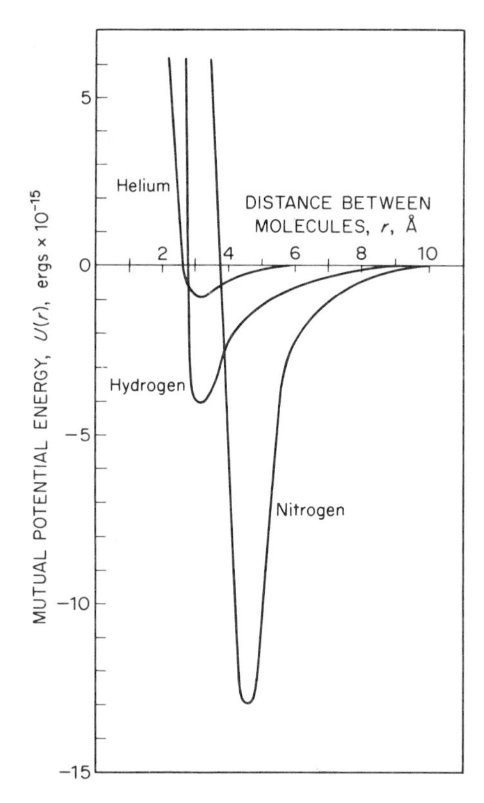

FIG. 17.6 Mutual potential energy of pairs of molecules.

We should not think that these snapshot dipoles interact with those of other molecules to produce an attractive potential. This cannot happen since there will be repulsion just as often as attraction; there is no time for the instantaneous dipoles to line up with one another. There is, however, a snapshot-dipole — polarization interaction. Each instantaneous argon dipole induces an appropriately oriented dipole moment in neighboring atoms, and these moments interact with the original to produce an instantaneous attraction. The polarizing field, traveling with the speed of light, does not take long to traverse the short distances between molecules. Calculations show that this *dispersion interaction* leads to a potential,

$$U = -\tfrac{3}{4}h\nu_0 \frac{\alpha^2}{r^6} \qquad (17.5)$$

where ν_0 is the characteristic frequency of oscillation of the charge distribution.*

It is noteworthy that all the contributions to the potential energy of intermolecular attraction display an r^{-6} dependence. The complete expression for the intermolecular energy must include also a repulsive term, the overlap energy, which becomes appreciable at very close distances. Thus we may write

$$U = -Ar^{-6} + Br^{-n} \qquad (17.6)$$

* The r^{-6} dependence of the potential can be readily derived in this case from electrostatic theory. The field due to a dipole varies as $1/r^3$, and the potential energy of an induced dipole in a field F is $\frac{1}{2}\alpha F^2$. See Harnwell, *Electricity and Magnetism*, p. 59.

For a simple quantum-mechanical derivation of Eq. (17.5), see R. H. Fowler, *Statistical Mechanics* (London: Cambridge, 1936), p. 296.

The value of the exponent n is from 9 to 12. Fig. 17.6 shows the curves for a number of gases, with $n = 12$. The constants A and B are calculated from the equations of state. The different contributions to the intermolecular interaction are shown in Table 17.3 for a number of gases.

TABLE 17.3 RELATIVE MAGNITUDES OF INTERMOLECULAR INTERACTIONS*

Molecule	Dipole Moment $\mu \times 10^{18}$ (esu cm)	Polarizability $\alpha \times 10^{24}$ (cc)	Energy $h\nu_0$ (ev)	Orientation† $\frac{2}{3}\mu^4/kT$	Induction† $2\mu^2\alpha$	Dispersion† $\frac{3}{4}\alpha^2 h\nu_0$
CO	0.12	1.99	14.3	0.0034	0.057	67.5
HI	0.38	5.4	12	0.35	1.68	382
HBr	0.78	3.58	13.3	6.2	4.05	176
HCl	1.03	2.63	13.7	18.6	5.4	105
NH_3	1.5	2.21	16	84	10	93
H_2O	1.84	1.48	18	190	10	47
He	0	0.20	24.5	0	0	1.2
A	0	1.63	15.4	0	0	52
Xe	0	4.00	11.5	0	0	217

* J. A. V. Butler, *Ann. Rep. Chem. Soc.* (London), *34*, 75 (1937).
† Units of erg $cm^6 \times 10^{-60}$.

10. EQUATION OF STATE AND INTERMOLECULAR FORCES

The calculation of the equation of state of a substance from a knowledge of the intermolecular forces is in general a problem of great complexity. The method of attack may be outlined in principle, but so far the mathematical difficulties have proved so formidable that in practice a solution has been obtained only for a few simplified cases.

We recall that the calculation of the equation of state reduces to calculating the partition function Z for the system. From Z the Helmholtz free energy A is immediately derivable, and hence the pressure, $P = -(\partial A/\partial V)_T$.

To determine the partition function, $Z = \sum e^{-E_i/kT}$, the energy levels of the system must be known. In the cases of ideal gases and crystals we can use energy levels for individual constituents of the system, such as molecules or oscillators, ignoring interactions between them. In the case of liquids, we cannot do this since it is precisely the interaction between different molecules that is responsible for the characteristic properties of a liquid. We should need to know, therefore, the energy levels of the system as a whole, for example, one mole of liquid. So far this problem has not been solved.

An indication of the difficulties of a more general theory may be obtained by a consideration of the theory of imperfect gases. In this case we consider that the total energy of the system E can be divided into two terms, the kinetic energy K, and the intermolecular potential energy U: $E = K + U$.

For a mole of gas, U is a function of the positions of all the molecules. For the L molecules in a mole there are $3L$ positional coordinates, $q_1, q_2, q_3, \ldots q_{3L}$. Therefore, $U = U(q_1, q_2, q_3 \ldots q_{3L})$.

The partition function can now be written

$$Z = \sum e^{-(K+U)/kT} = \sum e^{-K/kT} \sum e^{-U/kT} \tag{17.7}$$

It is not necessary to consider quantized energy levels, and Z may be written in terms of an integration, rather than a summation over discrete levels.

$$Z = \sum e^{-K/kT} \int \ldots \int e^{-U(q_1,q_2 \ldots q_{3L})/kT} \, dq_1, dq_2 \ldots dq_{3L} \tag{17.8}$$

The theoretical treatment of the imperfect gas reduces to the evaluation of the so-called configuration integral,

$$\beta(T) = \int \ldots \int e^{-U(q_1,q_2 \ldots q_{3L})/kT} \, dq_1, dq_2 \ldots dq_{3L} \tag{17.9}$$

Since this is a repeated integral over $3L$ coordinates, q_i, it will be easily appreciated that its general evaluation is a matter of unconscionable difficulty, so that the general theory has ended in a mathematical cul-de-sac. Physically, however, it is evident that the potential energy of interaction, even in a moderately dense gas, does not extend much beyond the nearest neighbors of any given molecule. This simplification still leaves a problem of great difficulty, which is at present the subject of active research.

The only simple approach is to consider interactions between *pairs* of molecules only. This would be a suitable approximation for a slightly imperfect gas. One lets $\phi(r_{ij})$ be the potential energy of interaction between two molecules i and j separated by a distance r_{ij}, and assumes that the total potential energy is the sum of such terms.

$$U = \sum_{ij} \phi\,(r_{ij})$$

over pairs

When this potential is substituted in Eq. (17.9), the configuration integral can be evaluated. The details of this interesting, but rather long calculation will not be given here.*

A further simplification occurs when the gas is so dilute that each molecule interacts with only one neighbor at a time. Then,

$$\beta_2(T) = \iint_V e^{-U(r_{12})/kT} \, d\tau_1 \, d\tau_2$$

where $d\tau$ is $dxdydz$ and the integral is over all the volume. We now find that the second virial coefficient $B_2(T)$ is related to β_2 by

$$B_2(T) = \tfrac{1}{2}[V - \beta_2(T)]$$

This expression can be used to fit a potential like that in Eq. (17.6) to data on the equation of state.

* See T. L. Hill, *Introduction to Statistical Mechanics* (Reading, Mass.: Addison Wesley, 1960), ch. 15.

Efforts have been made to solve the configuration integral for more exact assumptions than the interaction between pairs. These important advances toward a comprehensive theory for dense fluids are to be found in the works of J. E. Lennard-Jones, J. E. Mayer, J. G. Kirkwood, and Max Born.

11. THE VACANCY MODEL FOR A LIQUID

Since 1933 Eyring and his students have sought a simple model for the structure of liquids which would avoid the intricacies of the general statistical theory.*

They began by considering the *free volume* of the liquid, the void space which is not occupied by the molecular volumes. In a liquid at ordinary temperature

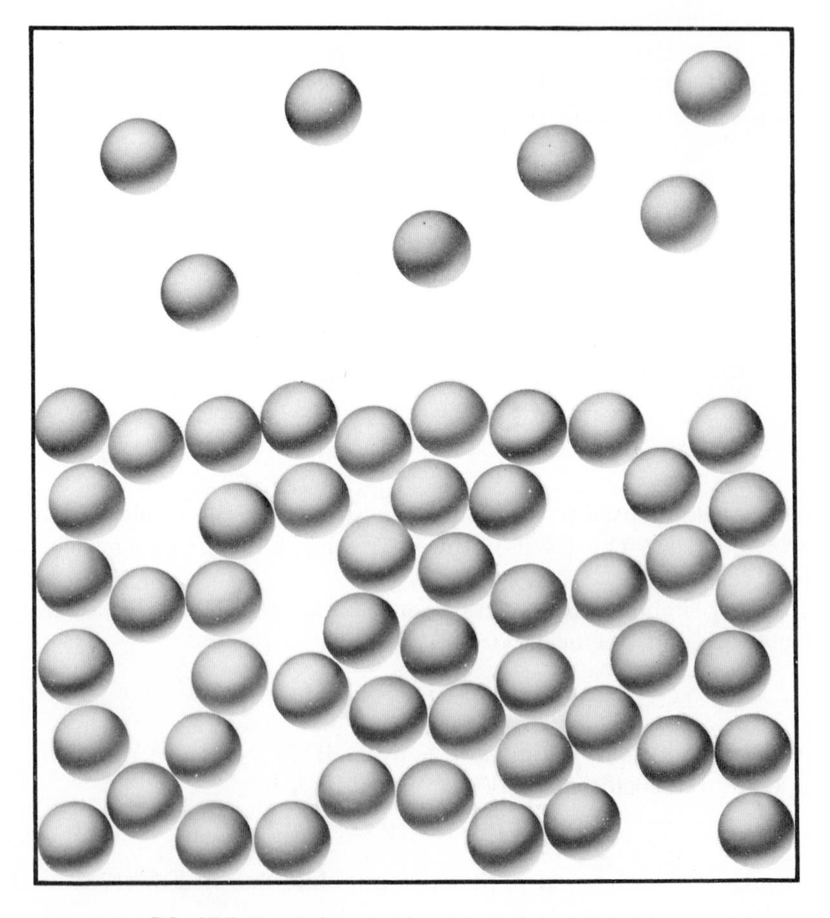

FIG. 17.7 Model of the liquid state according to H. Eyring.

* H. Eyring and T. Ree, *Proc. Nat. Acad. Sci.* (U. S.) *47*, 526 (1961) give references to recent as well as earlier work.

and pressure, about 3 per cent of the volume is free volume. We can deduce this, for example, from the studies of Bridgman on the compressibility β, which drops precipitously between 1 atm and 1000 atm. When a compression in volume of about 3 per cent is reached, β has become much smaller, so that further compression requires much larger pressure increments. It appears that the high initial β corresponds to squeezing out the free volume in the liquid.

This Eyring model for a liquid is shown in Fig. 17.7. The vapor is mostly void space with a few molecules moving at random. The liquid is mostly filled space with a few vacancies moving at random. As the temperature of a liquid is raised, the concentration of molecules in its vapor increases and the concentration of vacancies in the liquid also increases. Thus as the vapor density increases, the liquid density decreases until they become equal at the critical point.

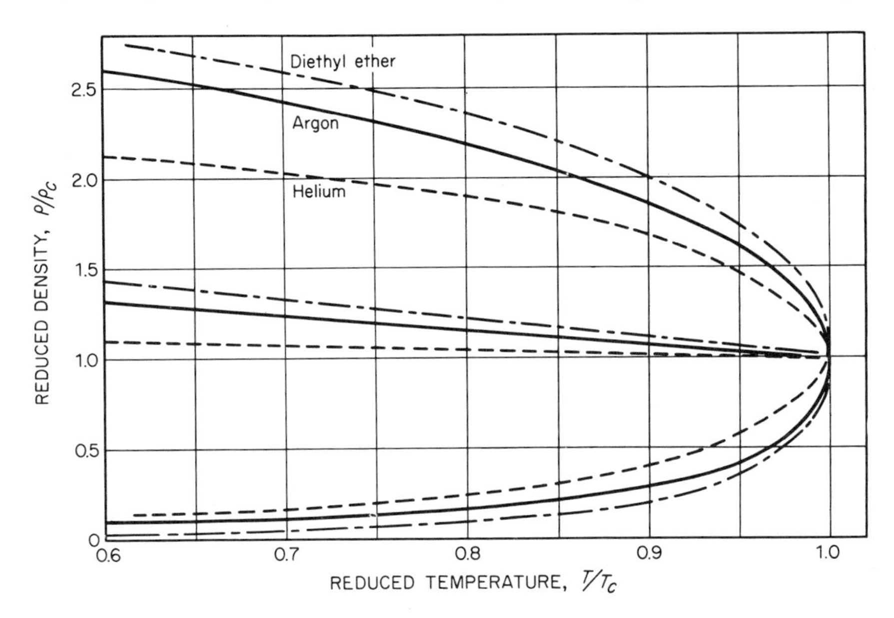

FIG. 17.8 Law of rectilinear diameters.

The average density ρ_{av} of liquid and vapor in equilibrium should remain approximately constant. Actually, there is a slight linear decrease with temperature, so that

$$\rho_{av} = \rho_0 - aT \tag{17.10}$$

where ρ_0 and a are constants characteristic of each substance. This relation was discovered by L. Cailletet and E. Mathias in 1886 and is called the *law of rectilinear diameters*. Some examples are shown in Fig. 17.8 where the data for helium, argon and ether are plotted in terms of reduced variables to bring them onto the same scale.

How is the free volume distributed throughout the liquid? Eyring suggests that the most favorable distribution is in the form of vacancies of approximately molecular size. A molecule adjacent to such a vacancy would have gas-like properties, and hence the introduction of such vacancies would give the highest increase in entropy for a given expense of energy in making free volume. A molecule not next to a vacancy would have solid-like properties.

If we neglect any increase in volume due to vacancies of other than molecular size and assume that vacancies are randomly distributed in the liquid, the mole fraction of molecules next to a vacancy is $(V - V_s)/V$, and this is the mole fraction of gas-like molecules, V and V_s being the molar volumes in liquid and solid states. The remaining mole fraction of molecules V_s/V is solid-like. Eyring and Ree thus suggest that the heat capacity of a monatomic liquid like argon should be represented by the equation

$$\bar{C}_V = \left(\frac{V_s}{V}\right) 6 + \left(\frac{V - V_s}{V}\right) 3 \tag{17.11}$$

The agreement with experiment is encouraging. Eyring and Ree now write the partition function Z of the liquid as the product of solid-like and gas-like terms.

12. FLOW PROPERTIES OF LIQUIDS

When we consider the mechanical properties of a substance, be it fluid or solid, it is convenient to divide the applied stresses into two classes, *shear stresses* and *compressive stresses*. These are shown in Fig. 17.9. A stress is a force applied to unit area of the body. A change in the dimensions of the body produced by the action of a stress is called a *strain*. The ratio of stress to strain is an *elastic modulus*.

Let us restrict our attention to isotropic bodies. A compressive stress applied uniformly over the surface of such a body (i.e., a pressure) produces a uniform compression. The bulk modulus K is defined as the ratio

$$K = \frac{\text{compressive force per unit area}}{\text{change in volume per unit volume}}$$

$$K = V(\partial P/\partial V)_T$$

The bulk modulus $K = \beta^{-1}$ where β is the compressibility.

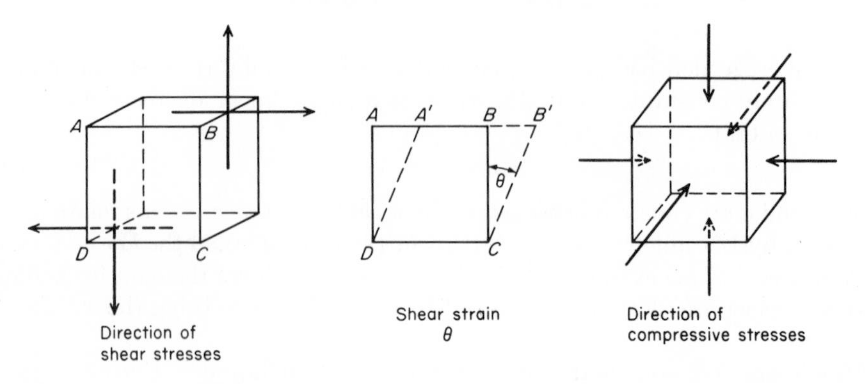

FIG. 17.9 Shear stresses and compressive stresses.

A shear stress produces an angular deformation θ, as shown in Fig. 17.9. The result of the shear is to displace a plane in the body parallel to itself relative to other parallel planes in the body. The shear stress is the force f' per unit area of the *plane displaced.* The shear strain is the ratio of the displacement between any two planes to the distance between the planes. The shear strain is measured by $\tan \theta = e/d_0 = x'$.

Perhaps the most typical property of fluids is the fact that they begin to flow appreciably as soon as a shear stress is applied. A solid, on the other hand, apparently supports a considerable shear stress, opposing to it an elastic restoring force proportional to the strain, and given by Hooke's Law, $f' = -\kappa' x'$. In fact, however, even a solid flows somewhat, but usually the stress must be maintained for a long time before the flow is noticeable. This slow flow of solids is called *creep.* Under high stresses, creep passes over into the *plastic deformation* of solids, for example, in the rolling, drawing, or forging of metals. These operations proceed by a mechanism involving the gliding of slip planes. Although creep is usually small, its occurrence suggests that the flow properties of liquids and solids differ in degree and not in kind.

The fact that liquids flow immediately under a very small shear stress does not necessarily mean that there are no elastic restoring forces within the liquid structure. These forces may exist without having a chance to be effective, owing to the rapidity of the flow process. The skipping of a thin stone on the surface of a pond demonstrates the elasticity of a liquid. An interesting silicone polymer has been exhibited under the name of "bouncing putty." This curious material is a hybrid of solid and liquid in regard to its flow properties. Rolled into a sphere and thrown at a wall, it bounces back as well as any rubber ball. Set the ball on a table and it gradually collapses into a puddle of viscous putty. Thus under long-continued stress it flows slowly like a liquid, but under a sudden sharp blow it reacts like a rubber.

It is difficult to measure the reversible or elastic properties of liquids under shear stresses, since they are usually overwhelmed by the irreversible *shear viscosity.* If η is the shear viscosity and κ' is the shear elasticity, Maxwell showed that an instantaneous shear distortion should have a *relaxation time* $\tau = \eta/\kappa'$. For ordinary light liquids, with $\kappa' \approx 10^{10}$ dyne cm^{-2} (similar to its value in a loosely bound crystal) and $\eta = 10^{-2}$ poise, $\tau \approx 10^{-12}$s. Thus the relaxation frequency (10^{12}s^{-1}) would be outside the range of measurement. With polymer solutions, however, η can be much higher, and κ' can be lower, so that the relaxation frequency may fall within the range of ultrasonic frequencies. One successful experimental method was based on the piezoelectric effect. A cylindrical crystal was suspended in the liquid and high frequency torsional vibrations were induced in the crystal by the piezoelectric excitation, so as to generate pure shearing waves in the liquid.* Fig. 17.10 shows some of the actual results. With these liquids of rather complex structures, there is evidently a considerable elasticity, which is believed to be due to coiling and uncoiling of the molecular chains.

* W. P. Mason, W. O. Baker, H. T. McSkimin and J. H. Heiss, *Phys. Rev.*, *75*, 936 (1949).

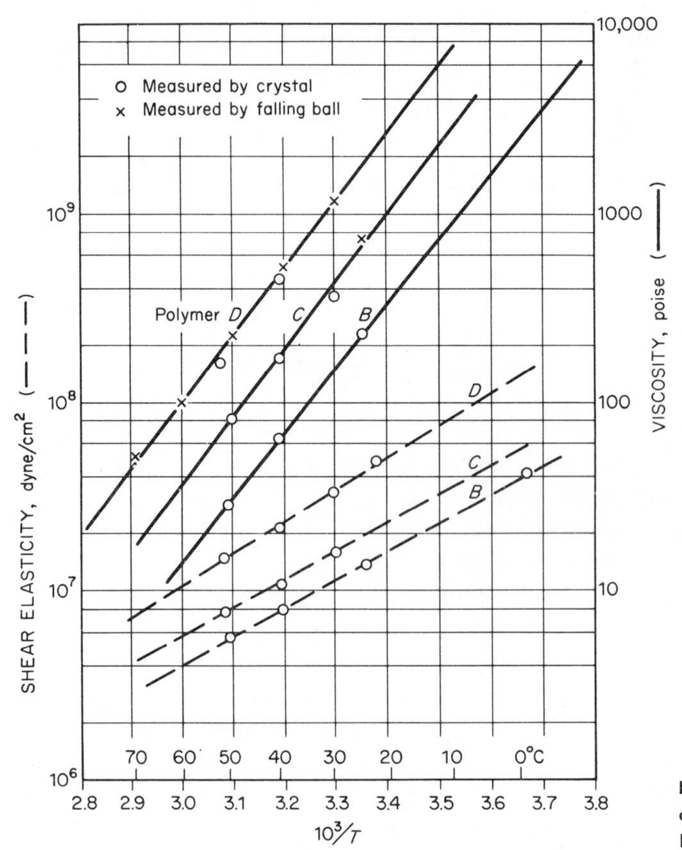

FIG. 17.10 Shear elasticities and viscosities for polyisobutylene polymer liquids.

Another interesting problem* arises when we ask whether a liquid subjected to compressive stress displays any irreversible effects due to a *volume viscosity*. In the case of compressive stresses, the elastic response or change in volume is easy to detect, but the viscous effect is transient and hard to detect. The experimental approach is to study the absorption of ultrasonic waves in liquids. The deformation caused by a sound wave is partly a change in volume and partly a shear, but it is possible to separate the contributions to the absorption coefficient due to the different mechanisms. For glycerol, a highly associated liquid, the absorption of ultrasonic waves was about twice the value calculated from shear viscosity alone, so that a large contribution was due to compressive viscosity.

13. VISCOSITY

We discussed some of the hydrodynamic theory of fluid flow in Chap. 7 in connection with the viscosity of gases. We saw how the viscosity coefficient η could

* Paraphrased from the remarks of H. S. Green, "The Structure of Liquids," *Encyclopedia of Physics* (Berlin: Springer, 1960), p. 92.

be measured from the rate of flow through cylindrical tubes. This is one of the most convenient methods for liquids as well as gases. The equation for an incompressible fluid is suitable for liquids, whereas that for a compressible fluid is used for gases. Thus, from Eq. (7.20),

$$\eta = \frac{\pi R^4 \, \Delta P}{8\, l\, (dV/dt)} \tag{17.12}$$

In the *Ostwald viscometer*, one measures the time required for a bulb of liquid to discharge through a capillary under the force of its own weight. It is usual to make relative rather than absolute measurements with these instruments, so that the dimensions of the capillary tube and volume of the bulb need not be known. The time t_0 required for a liquid of known viscosity η_0, usually water, to flow out of the bulb is noted. The time t for the unknown liquid is similarly measured. The viscosity of the unknown is

$$\eta = \frac{\rho_0}{\rho} \frac{t}{t_0} \eta_0$$

where ρ_0 and ρ are the densities of water and unknown.

Another useful viscometer is the Höppler type, based on the Stokes formula [Eq. (11.10)]:

$$\eta = \frac{f}{6\pi r v} = \frac{(m - m_0)g}{6\pi r v}$$

By measuring the rate of fall in the liquid (terminal velocity v) of metal spheres of known radius r and mass m, the viscosity can be calculated, since the force f is equal to $(m - m_0)g$, where m_0 is the mass of liquid displaced by the ball.

14. DEPENDENCE OF VISCOSITY ON TEMPERATURE

The hydrodynamic theories for the flow of liquids and gases are very similar. The kinetic-molecular mechanisms differ widely, as we might immediately suspect from the difference in the dependence of gas and liquid viscosities on temperature and pressure. In a gas, the viscosity increases with the temperature and is practically independent of the pressure. In a liquid, the viscosity increases with the pressure and decreases with increasing temperature.

The typical dependence of liquid viscosity on temperature was first pointed out by J. deGuzman Carrancio in 1913. The viscosity coefficient may be written

$$\eta = A \exp\,(\Delta E_{vis}/RT) \tag{17.13}$$

The quantity ΔE_{vis} is the energy barrier that must be overcome before the elementary flow process can occur. It is expressed per mole of liquid. The term $\exp\,(-\Delta E_{vis}/RT)$ can then be explained as a Boltzmann factor giving the fraction of the molecules having the requisite energy to surmount the barrier. Thus ΔE_{vis} is an activation energy for viscous flow.

The viscosities of several liquids as functions of temperature are plotted in Fig. 17.11 as $\log \eta$ vs T^{-1}. In most cases, a good linear relationship is found. Water is anomalous, since its hydrogen-bonded structure breaks down with increasing T. The activation energies ΔE_{vis} are usually about $\frac{1}{3}$ to $\frac{1}{4}$ the latent heats of vaporization.

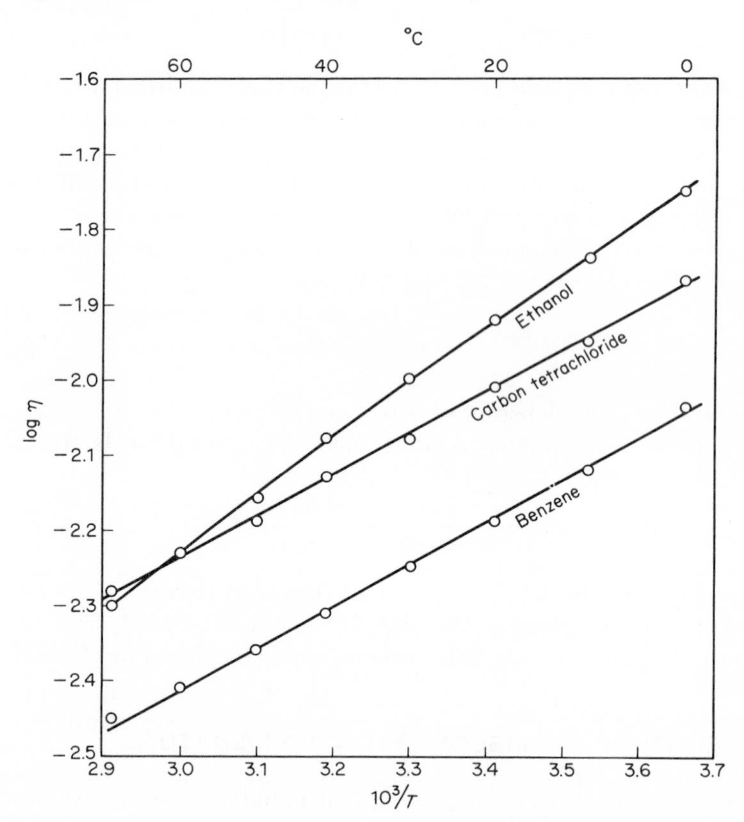

FIG. 17.11 Temperature dependence of viscosity plotted as $\log \eta$ vs. T^{-1}.

PROBLEMS

1. The thermal pressure coefficient $(\partial P/\partial T)_V$ for CCl_4 is 11.63 atm deg^{-1} at 20.4°C and 1 atm. Calculate the internal pressure. [*Ans.* 3410 atm].

2. A certain glass at 800°C has a viscosity of 10^6 poise and a density of 3.5 g cm^{-3}. How long would it take for a 5 mm diameter platinum ball to fall through 1.00 cm of the hot glass. [*Ans.* 1.13 hr]

3. The following viscosities in millipoise were measured for liquid heptane: 0°C–5.24, 20°–4.09, 40°–3.41, 70°–2.62. Plot these data and calculate ΔE_{vis}.

4. The liquid and vapor densities of ethanol in equilibrium at various temperatures are:

t, °C	100	150	200	220	240
ρ_{liq}, g/cc	0.7157	0.6489	0.5568	0.4958	0.3825
ρ_{vap}, g/cc	0.00351	0.0193	0.0508	0.0854	0.1716

The critical temperature is 243°C. What is the critical volume? [*Ans.* 167.2 cm³ mole⁻¹]

5. For the interaction of two different molecules, the London equation can be written

$$E \cong -\frac{3\,I_a\,I_b}{2(I_a + I_b)}\;\frac{\alpha_A\alpha_B}{r^6}$$

where the I's are first ionization potentials and the α's are polarizabilities. If the two molecules are identical, the equation reduces to

$$E \cong \tfrac{3}{4}\,I\alpha^2/r^6$$

The values of α for He, Ne, Ar, Kr, Xe in cm³ × 10^{-24} are 0.204, 0.392, 1.63, 2.465, and 4.008, respectively. Calculate the London interaction energy between two helium atoms, two krypton atoms, and a He with a Kr, all at a distance of 4.0 Å between centers.

6. Use the expression in Problem 5 to estimate the heat of sublimation of krypton at the melting point −169°C. Krypton crystallizes in the fcc structure with $a_0 = 5.70$ Å at the m. pt.

7. The intermolecular potential energy can be approximated by the expression in Eq. (17.6) due to Lennard-Jones. For nitrogen, with the repulsive exponent $n = 10$, $B = 3.93 \times 10^{-88}$ and $A = 18.5 \times 10^{-59}$, with energy E in ergs. Calculate the distance between the centers of two nitrogen molecules when E is a minimum.

8. From the data in Problem 7, calculate the minimum distances of approach of the centers of two nitrogen molecules in head-on collisions with relative energies equal to kT, $10kT$, $100kT$, at 100°C.

9. For a gas of rigid spheres of diameter d with an attractive energy $E(r) = -Ar^{-6}$, the pressure $P = \nu kT(1 + B'\nu)$ where ν is the concentration in molecules per cc. The coefficient

$$B' = \tfrac{2}{3}\pi d^3\left\{1 - \sum_{n=1}^{\infty}\frac{3}{n!(6n-3)}\left(\frac{A}{d^6kT}\right)^n\right\}$$

Use this expression to calculate B' for argon given that $d = 3.13$ Å and $A = 10^{-58}$. Hence calculate $z = P\overline{V}/RT$ for argon at 100 atm and 300°K.

18 PHYSICAL CHEMISTRY OF SURFACES

Looking down into the thick ice of our pond I found the imprisoned air-bubbles nothing at random but starting from centres and in particular one most beautifully regular white brush of them, each spur of it a curving string of beaded and diminishing bubbles —

GERARD M. HOPKINS (1870)

When we defined the concept of *phase* in Chapter 5 and discussed phase equilibria, we stated that the validity of the results was restricted by our neglect of any effects due to variation of the areas between the phases. A phase was defined as a part of a system which was "homogeneous throughout." Such a definition implies that matter deep in the interior of the phase is subject to exactly the same conditions as matter at the surface. But such homogeneity is clearly impossible. The atoms in the interior are surrounded by a uniform average field due to neighboring atoms, while the atoms at the surface are bounded on one side by atoms of the same substance, and on the other side by an entirely different environment.

Consider the surface of a liquid in contact with its vapor, shown in Fig. 18.1. A molecule in the interior of the liquid is in a uniform field. A molecule at the surface is subject to a net attraction toward the bulk of the liquid, which is not compensated by an equal attraction from the more dispersed vapor molecules. Thus all liquid surfaces, in the absence of other forces, tend to contract to the minimum area. For example, freely suspended volumes of liquid assume a spherical shape, since the sphere has the minimum ratio of surface to volume.

1. SURFACE TENSION

In order to extend the area of an interface like that in Fig. 18.1, i.e., to bring molecules from the interior into the surface, work must be done against the cohesive forces in the liquid. It follows that the surface portions of the liquid have a higher free energy than the bulk liquid. This extra surface free energy is more usually described by saying that there is a *surface tension*, acting parallel to the surface, which opposes any attempt to extend the interface. A tension is a negative pressure; pressure is a force per unit area, so that surface pressure is a force per unit length. If the surface tension is γ, the work done on the surface in extending its area by an amount dA is $dw = \gamma\, dA = dG$, whence

$$dG = \gamma\, dA \tag{18.1}$$

where dG is the change in free energy. The unit of surface tension in the cgs system is dyne cm^{-1}.

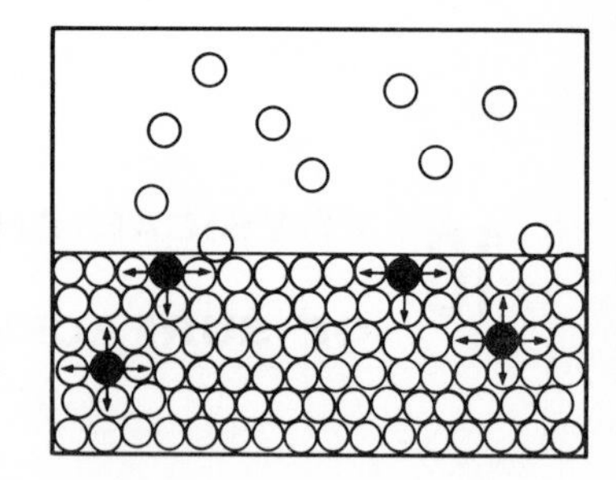

FIG. 18.1 Liquid-vapor interface.

The surface tension illustrates the new type of variable needed to describe physicochemical systems as soon as surfaces are explicitly considered. When will it be necessary to consider these surface effects? In the first place, whenever we wish deliberately to focus our attention on interfacial phenomena rather than bulk properties. Secondly, there will be instances when the interfacial phenomena must be included in order to study the system adequately. This second case will arise whenever any considerable fraction of the material in the system exists at or near interfaces.

The degree of subdivision or particle size of a substance is usually the decisive factor determining its surface-to-volume ratio. Extremely porous materials are apparently exceptional, but these materials may often be treated as loose aggregates of small particles. For example, suppose we have a gram of crystalline silica. If for simplicity we consider the crystals, with density ρ, to be small cubes, all of side l, their total surface area is

$$A = \frac{6l^2}{\rho l^3} = \frac{6}{\rho l}$$

With $\rho = 2.30$, the following results are obtained for the surface area in cm^2 per gram at various particle sizes:

l(cm)	A (cm^2/g)
10^{-1}	26.1
10^{-3}	2 610
10^{-5}	261 000
10^{-6}	2 610 000
10^{-7}	26 100 000

It is evident that the area increases enormously as the particle size decreases. The lower end of the scale, with l below about 10^{-7} cm or 10 Å, corresponds to the dimensions expected for ordinary molecules. From around 10^{-7} to 10^{-4} cm there extends the domain of *colloids*. For particles of colloidal dimensions surface phenomena are so important that much of colloidal chemistry is essentially surface chemistry.

2. PRESSURE DIFFERENCE ACROSS CURVED SURFACES

Interfaces between two liquids and between a liquid and a vapor are convenient to study because the molecules in fluids are not rigidly fixed in position. They therefore tend to adjust themselves to changes at the interface in such a way as to record automatically the surface tension. This possibility does not arise with liquid-solid or solid-gas interfaces, and measurement of the interfacial tensions in these cases is made by indirect methods.

As a direct consequence of the existence of a surface tension, it can be shown that across any curved liquid surface there must exist a difference in pressure, the pressure being greater on the concave side than on the convex side. If a curved surface is displaced parallel to itself to a new position, its area must change if its curvature is to remain the same. Work must be done against the surface tension to produce this change in area.

Figure 18.2 shows a spherical soap bubble in equilibrium at a radius R. Its total surface free energy is the surface tension γ of the film times the area $2(4\pi R^2)$ of its two sides. If the radius of the bubble were to decrease by δR, the surface free energy would decrease by $2(8\pi\gamma R\,\delta R)$. The tendency of the bubble to lower its free energy by shrinking must be counterbalanced by an excess pressure ΔP inside as compared to outside the bubble. If the radius decreased by δR, the volume $\frac{4}{3}\pi R^3$ would decrease by $4\pi R^2\,\delta R$. The increase in free energy $P\,dV$ of the gas inside the bubble would amount to $\Delta P(4\pi R^2\,\delta R)$. At equilibrium the two changes in free energy must add to zero, so that

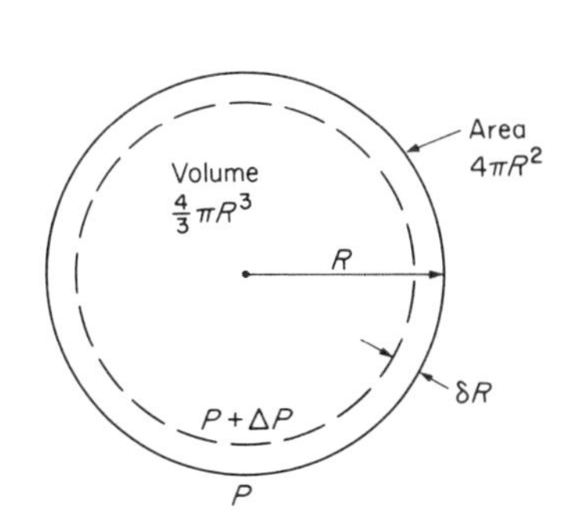

FIG. 18.2 A spherical soap bubble in air, illustrating the pressure difference across a curved surface.

$$2(8\pi\gamma R\,\delta R) = \Delta P(4\pi R^2\,\delta R)$$

$$\Delta P = \frac{2(2\gamma)}{R}$$

This is a special case of the equation of Young and Laplace for the pressure difference across curved interfaces. For interfaces with only one side (e.g., gas bubbles in water or water droplets in a gas) the extra factor of two does not appear, and we have

$$\Delta P = \frac{2\gamma}{R} \tag{18.2}$$

For example, across a bubble of 1 mm radius in water at 20°C,

$$\Delta P = 2(72.75)/10^{-1} = 1.45 \times 10^3 \text{ dyne cm}^{-2}.$$

Equation (18.2) applies to liquid-liquid as well as to gas-liquid interfaces. For a more general curved surface with radii of curvature R_1 and R_2 it becomes*

$$\Delta P = \gamma \left(\frac{1}{R_1} + \frac{1}{R_2}\right) \tag{18.3}$$

3. CAPILLARY RISE

The rise or fall of liquids in capillary tubes and its application to the measurement of surface tension may now be treated as a direct consequence of the fundamental Eq. (18.2). Whether a liquid rises in a glass capillary, like water, or is depressed, like mercury, depends on the relative magnitude of the forces of cohesion between the liquid molecules themselves, and the forces of adhesion between the liquid and the walls of the tube. These forces determine the *contact angle* θ, which the liquid makes with the tube walls (Fig. 18.3). If this angle is less than 90°, the liquid is said to *wet* the surface and a concave meniscus is formed. A contact angle of 90° corresponds to a plane meniscus; a contact angle greater than 90°, to a convex meniscus.

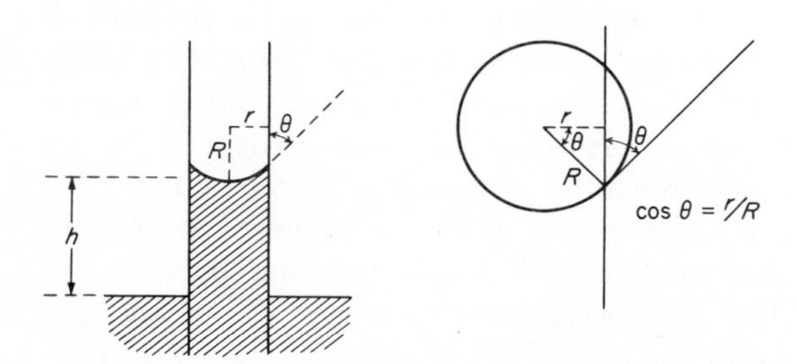

FIG. 18.3 Capillary rise of a liquid that wets the walls of a tube.

The occurrence of a concave meniscus leads to a capillary rise. The pressure under the meniscus is less than that at the plane surface of liquid outside the tube. Liquid rises in the tube until the weight of the liquid column balances the pressure difference. The liquid column acts as a manometer to register the pressure difference across the concave meniscus.

Consider in Fig. 18.3 a cylindrical tube whose radius r is sufficiently small that the surface of the meniscus can be taken as a section of a sphere with radius R. Then, since $\cos\theta = r/R$, from Eq. (18.2) $\Delta P = (2\gamma\cos\theta)/r$. If the capillary rise is h, and if ρ and ρ_0 are the densities of the liquid and the surrounding fluid, the weight of the cylindrical liquid column is $\pi r^2 gh(\rho - \rho_0)$, or the force per unit area balancing the pressure difference is $gh(\rho - \rho_0)$. Therefore,

$$\frac{2\gamma\cos\theta}{r} = gh(\rho - \rho_0), \qquad \gamma = \tfrac{1}{2}\, gh(\rho - \rho_0)\frac{r}{\cos\theta}$$

* N. K. Adam, *Physics and Chemistry of Surfaces* (New York: Oxford, 1944), p. 8.

In many cases the contact angle θ is practically zero, and if the surrounding fluid is a vapor, its density ρ_0 is negligible compared to ρ. These approximations lead to the frequently used formula:

$$\gamma = \tfrac{1}{2}\,\rho g h r \qquad (18.4)$$

4. MAXIMUM BUBBLE PRESSURE

We can also measure surface tension by blowing bubbles. Consider a bubble formed at the end of a small tube immersed in liquid (Fig. 18.4). As we begin to apply pressure, the radius of the bubble is comparatively large. As the bubble grows, the radius at first decreases until it reaches a minimum, at which point the bubble is a hemisphere with a radius equal to that of the small tube. Any further increase in pressure will lead to the loss of the bubble, which will expand and free itself from the tube.

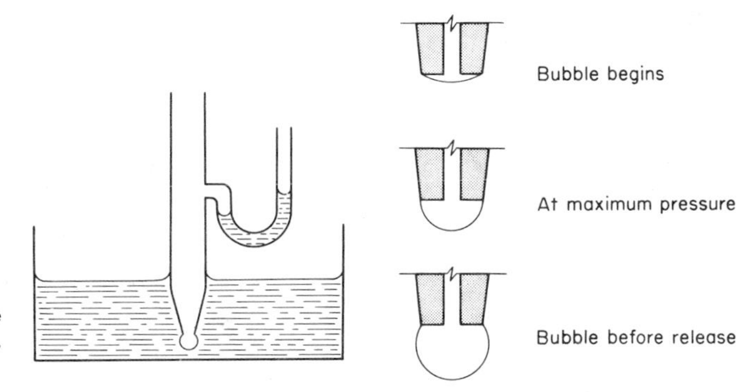

FIG. 18.4 Maximum bubble pressure method for determination of surface tension.

It is clear from Eq. (18.2) that the bubble can sustain the maximum pressure at the position of minimum radius. The applied pressure is balanced by the pressure difference across the curved surface plus a hydrostatic pressure depending on the depth h of the tube outlet under the liquid. Therefore the surface tension is determined from

$$P_{\max} = \frac{2\gamma}{r} + gh(\rho - \rho_0) \qquad (18.5)$$

5. THE DU NOÜY TENSIOMETER

A platinum ring of radius r is attached to a torsion balance, and the force required to remove the ring from the surface or interface is measured directly. The surface tension acts over the circumference of the ring and there are two sides to the new surface that is formed, so that the applied force $f = 4\pi r\gamma$. A number of correction factors are necessary for precise work.*

* P. Lecomte Du Noüy, *J. Gen. Physiol.* *1*, 521 (1918); *7*, 403 (1925).

6. SURFACE TENSION OF SOLIDS

If we take a block of a solid substance, say a NaCl crystal, and cleave it, we create new crystal-gas interfaces, and hence increase the surface free energy of the solid. The cleaved surface of the solid may not immediately achieve its equilibrium configuration. Unlike the case of the liquid, therefore, the free energy required to create such a new surface may not give a direct measure of the surface tension. Nevertheless, methods are available that do give reliable surface tensions for solids when care is taken to achieve equilibrium conditions.

One good method is to measure the rate of shrinkage of fine wires or thin foils.* In a typical experiment a fine copper wire (radius $\sim 25\ \mu$) was suspended in a furnace and loaded with a weight mg just sufficient to prevent any shrinkage in length. The surface tension acts over the circumference πd of the wire, so that $\gamma = mg/\pi d$. At 1250°C, γ = 1400 dyne cm^{-1}.

7. SURFACE-TENSION DATA

Some experimental surface tensions are collected in Table 18.1. Liquids with exceptionally high surface tensions, such as water, are those in which the cohesive forces between the molecules are large, the surface tension being a measure of the work that must be done to bring a molecule from the interior to the surface. We might expect liquids with high surface tensions to have high internal pressures, and this relationship is in general confirmed by a comparison of Table 18.1 with Table 17.2.

TABLE 18.1 SURFACE TENSION DATA

A. Surface Tensions of Pure Substances at 20°C — dyne cm^{-1}

Isopentane	13.72	Ethyl iodide	29.9
Nickel carbonyl	14.6	Benzene	28.86
Diethyl ether	17.10	Carbon tetrachloride	26.66
n-Hexane	18.43	Methylene iodide	50.76
Ethyl mercaptan	21.82	Carbon bisulfide	32.33
Ethyl bromide	24.16	Water	72.75

B. Surface Tensions of Liquid Metals and Molten Salts — dyne cm^{-1}

	°C	γ		°C	γ
Ag	970	800	AgCl	452	125.5
Au	1070	1000	NaF	1010	200
Cu	1130	1100	NaCl	1000	98
Hg	0	470	NaBr	1000	88

* H. Udin, A. J. Shaler and J. Wulff, *J. Metals 1*, 186 (1949).

8. SURFACE TENSION OF SOLUTIONS

Examples of surface tension vs. concentration curves are shown in Fig. 18.5. The surface tensions of solutions may be given a simple qualitative interpretation. Consider, for example, aqueous solutions. Substances that markedly lower the surface tension of water, such as the fatty acids, contain both a polar hydrophilic group and a nonpolar hydrophobic group. The hydrophilic group, e.g., —COOH in the fatty acids, makes the molecule reasonably soluble if the nonpolar residue is not too predominant. One may expect the hydrocarbon residues in the fatty acids to be extremely uncomfortable [in a state of high G] in the interior of an aqueous solution, and little work is required to persuade them to come from the interior to the surface. This qualitative picture leads to the conclusion that solutes lowering the surface tension of a liquid tend to accumulate preferentially at the surface. They are said to be *positively adsorbed* at the interface.

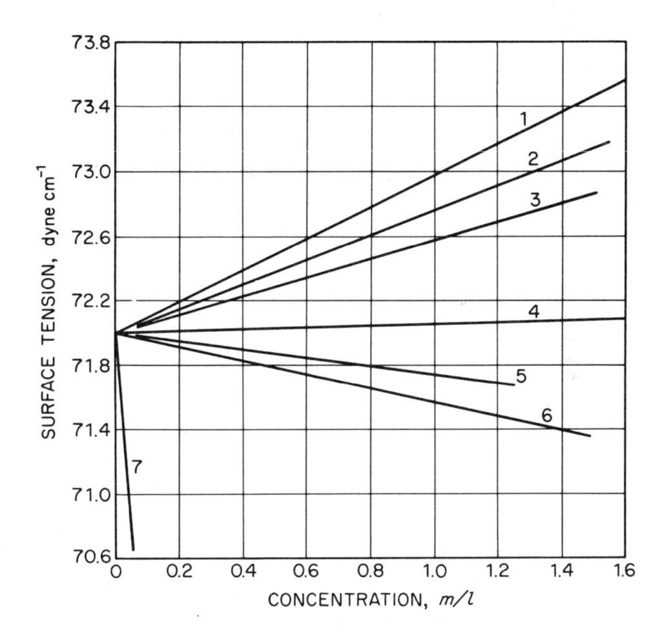

FIG. 18.5 Surface tensions at 25°C of aqueous amino acid solutions. (1) glycine; (2) β-alanine; (3) α-alanine; (4) β aminobutyric acid; (5) ϵ aminocaproic acid; (6) 1 aminobutyric acid; (7) 1 aminocaproic acid. [J. R. Pappenheimer, M. P. Lepie, and J. Wyman, *J. Am. Chem. Soc.* 58. 1851 (1936)].

On the other hand, solutes such as ionic salts usually increase the surface tension of aqueous solutions above the value for pure water, although these increases are smaller than the decreases produced by fatty acids and similar compounds. The reason for the observed increase is that the dissolved ions, by virtue of ion-dipole attractions, tend to pull the water molecules into the interior of the solution. Additional work must be done against the electrostatic forces in order to create new surface. It follows that in such solutions the surface layers are poorer in solute than is the bulk solution. The solute is said to be *negatively adsorbed* at the interface. After the thermodynamic treatment of surfaces has been discussed, we shall be able to give these conclusions a quantitative formulation.

The temperature dependence of the surface tension may often be adequately represented by an empirical equation proposed by Ramsay and Shields:

$$\gamma\left(\frac{M}{\rho}\right)^{2/3} = k'(T_c - T - 6) \tag{18.6}$$

Here M is the molecular weight, ρ the density, k' a constant, and T_c the critical temperature of the liquid. Liquids that obey Trouton's rule have values of k' that cluster around 2.1.

An alternative representation of the variation of the surface tension is the McLeod equation:

$$\gamma = C(\rho - \rho_0)^4 \tag{18.7}$$

where ρ_0 is the vapor density and C is a constant for each liquid. This equation is the basis of the *parachor*, a quantity defined by S. Sugden as

$$\mathcal{P} = MC^{1/4} = \frac{M\gamma^{1/4}}{\rho - \rho_0} \tag{18.8}$$

The parachor is essentially a molecular volume, modified to eliminate some of the influence of the cohesive forces, which vary from liquid to liquid. The parachor of a molecule can be estimated by adding terms for each of its atoms plus terms for the types of bond (double, single, etc.) that are present.*

9. THE KELVIN EQUATION

One of the most interesting consequences of surface tension is the fact that the vapor pressure of a liquid is greater when it is in the form of small droplets than when it has a plane surface. This was first deduced by Kelvin.

If a liquid distills from a plane surface to a droplet, the droplet must increase in size and therefore in surface area. The increase requires an extra surface free energy. Consider a spherical droplet whose radius grows from r to $r + dr$. The increase in surface is from $4\pi r^2$ to $4\pi(r + dr)^2$, which amounts to $8\pi r\,dr$. The corresponding increase in surface free energy is $8\pi\gamma r\,dr$. If dn moles of liquid were distilled from the plane surface whose vapor pressure is P_0 to the droplet whose pressure is P, the free energy change would be given by Eq. (3.32) as $dn\,RT \ln (P/P_0)$. Equating the free energy changes, we have

$$dn\,RT \ln \frac{P}{P_0} = 8\pi\gamma r\,dr$$

But

$$dn = 4\pi r^2\,dr\,\frac{\rho}{M}$$

* For details see O. R. Quayle, *Chem. Rev. 53*, 439 (1953).

whence

$$\ln \frac{P}{P_0} = \frac{2M\gamma}{RT\rho r} \tag{18.9}$$

The application of the equation to water droplets gives the following calculated pressure rations:

(Water at 20°C, $P_0 = 17.5$ mm)

r(cm)	10^{-4}	10^{-5}	10^{-6}	10^{-7}
P/P_0	1.001	1.011	1.114	2.95

An equation similar to that of Kelvin can be derived for the solubility of small particles, by means of the connection between vapor pressure and solubility developed in Chapter 5.

The conclusions of the Kelvin equation have been experimentally verified. Thus there can be no doubt that very small droplets of liquid have a considerably higher vapor pressure than bulk liquid, and that very small particles of solid, have a considerably greater solubility than bulk solid.

These results lead to the rather curious problem of how new phases can ever arise from old ones. For example, if a container filled with water vapor at slightly below the saturation pressure is chilled suddenly, perhaps by adiabatic expansion as in the Wilson cloud chamber, the vapor may become supersaturated with respect to liquid water. It is then in a metastable state, and we may expect condensation to take place. A reasonable molecular model of condensation would seem to be that two or three molecules of water vapor come together to form a tiny droplet, and that this *nucleus* of condensation then grows by accretion as additional vapor molecules happen to hit it. The Kelvin equation, however, indicates that a tiny droplet like this nucleus, being only a few Ångstroms in diameter, would have a vapor pressure many times that of bulk liquid. As far as tiny nuclei are concerned, the vapor would not be supersaturated at all. Such nuclei should immediately re-evaporate, and the emergence of a new phase at the equilibrium pressure, or even moderately above it should be impossible.

There are two ways of resolving this paradox. In the first place, we know the statistical basis of the Second Law of Thermodynamics. In any system at equilibrium there are always fluctuations around the equilibrium condition, and if the system contains few molecules, these fluctuations may be relatively large (cf. Sec. 7.31). There is always a chance that an appropriate fluctuation may lead to the formation of a nucleus of a new phase, even though the tiny nucleus could be called thermodynamically unstable. The chance of such a fluctuation we know to be $e^{-\Delta S/k}$ where ΔS is the deviation of the entropy from the equilibrium value.

It is unlikely, however, that new phases often arise by this fluctuation mechanism and the resultant *spontaneous nucleation.* Calculations show that the chance $e^{-\Delta S/k}$ is usually much too small. It is more likely that tiny dust particles act as nuclei in supersaturated vapors or solutions. Actually, vapors seem to be much less finicky than solutions about the sort of nuclei required. This is because a liquid will condense on almost any surface, but crystallization requires the presence of crystal faces of the proper kind.

10. THERMODYNAMICS OF SURFACES

Figure 18.6 represents two phases, α and β, separated by an interfacial region. The exact position of this region depends on how we choose to draw the boundary planes AA' and BB'. Let us place these planes so that the following condition is satisfied: there is no appreciable inhomogeneity in the properties of the bulk phase α up to the surface AA', nor in those of phase β up to the surface BB'. Within the interfacial region the properties of the system vary continuously from purely α- at AA' to purely β- at BB'. Because of the short range of intermolecular forces the interfacial region will usually be not more than a few molecular diameters in thickness.*

Any surface SS' drawn within the interfacial region parallel to the surfaces AA'' and BB' is called a *surface phase*, and is designated by a symbol σ. A surface phase defined in this way has an area but no thickness. It is a strictly two-dimensional phase. Its area will be denoted by A^σ.

The composition of the surface phase will be described in terms of quantities n_i^σ. We define n_i^σ as the number of moles of component i in the surface film region, between AA' and BB', minus the number of moles of i that would be within this region if the phases α and β both extended all the way to the surface SS' with unchanged bulk properties. It is evident according to this definition that n_i^σ may be either positive or negative. Now the *surface concentration* c_i^σ, in moles per unit area, is defined by

$$c_i^\sigma = \frac{n_i^\sigma}{A^\sigma} \qquad (18.10)$$

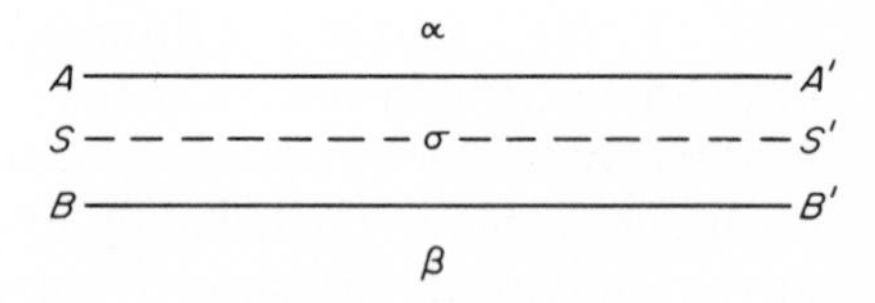

FIG. 18.6 Definition of a surface phase.

Other thermodynamic functions, such as surface energy E^σ, surface entropy S^σ, surface free energy G^σ, can be defined by exactly the same method used for the n_i^σ. They are the differences between the energy, entropy, or free energy of the actual interfacial region and the values calculated on the assumption that the phases remain uniform up to the dividing surface.

It is always possible to place the dividing surface SS' so that for one particular component (0) the surface concentration, c_0^σ, is zero; i.e., the number of moles of component (0) in the interfacial film between AA' and BB' is exactly what it would be if the bulk phases α and β both remained homogeneous right up to the

* It should be noted, however, that the attractive forces exerted by an extended surface have a much longer range than those from an isolated molecule. The latter depend on r^{-7}, and the former fall off as r^{-4}. For an extensive survey of the depth of the surface zone see J. V. Henniker, *Rev. Mod. Phys.* *21*, 322 (1949).

dividing surface SS'. When the position of the interface is chosen in this way, the surface concentrations c_i^σ of the other components are said to be the concentrations *adsorbed at the interface.* This adsorption can be either positive or negative. In the examples previously considered, solutes dissolved in water, it was found that fatty acids were positively adsorbed at the solution-vapor interface, whereas ionic salts tended to be negatively adsorbed. Now that this concept of *adsorption* has been given a precise definition, it is possible to derive a thermodynamic relation between the extent of adsorption and the change in the surface tension of the solution. This relation is the famous *Gibbs adsorption isotherm.* Its derivation is similar to that of the Gibbs-Duhem Equation (5.7).

11. THE GIBBS ADSORPTION ISOTHERM

We shall consider a system that, for simplicity, consists of two components distributed in two bulk phases with a surface phase σ. We restrict our consideration to a system at constant temperature and pressure and constant composition of the bulk phases.

From Eqs. (18.1) and (4.2), we can write for the surface phase,

$$dG^\sigma = -S^\sigma\, dT + \gamma\, dA^\sigma + \mu_1\, dn_1^\sigma + \mu_2\, dn_2^\sigma$$

At constant temperature this differential of the surface free energy becomes

$$dG^\sigma = \gamma\, dA^\sigma + \mu_1\, dn_1^\sigma + \mu_2\, dn_2^\sigma \tag{18.11}$$

Integrating this expression while holding the intensity factors constant (or using Euler's theorem), we obtain

$$G^\sigma = \gamma A^\sigma + \mu_1 n_1^\sigma + \mu_2 n_2^\sigma$$

The complete differential is therefore

$$dG^\sigma = \gamma\, dA^\sigma + A^\sigma\, d\gamma + \mu_1\, dn_1^\sigma + n_1^\sigma\, d\mu_1 + \mu_2\, dn_2^\sigma + n_2^\sigma\, d\mu_2$$

Comparison with Eq. (18.11) yields

$$A^\sigma\, d\gamma = -n_1^\sigma\, d\mu_1 - n_2^\sigma\, d\mu_2$$

Division by A^σ gives

$$d\gamma = -c_1^\sigma\, d\mu_1 - c_2^\sigma\, d\mu_2 \tag{18.12}$$

Let us now choose the dividing surface so that the excess c_1^σ of one component, which may be called the solvent, vanishes. Then

$$d\gamma = -\Gamma_2\, d\mu_2 \tag{18.13}$$

where Γ_2 is the concentration of component (2) *adsorbed* at the interface. Eq. (18.13) may be written from Eq. (6.32)

$$d\gamma = -RT\, \Gamma_2\, d \ln a_2 \tag{18.14}$$

For an ideal solution, $a_2 = X_2$, the mole fraction, so that

$$d\gamma = -RT\,\Gamma_2\,d\ln X_2$$

or

$$\Gamma_2 = -\frac{1}{RT}\cdot\frac{d\gamma}{d\ln X_2} \tag{18.15}$$

For a dilute solution, X_2 becomes proportional to c_2, the molar concentration, and

$$\Gamma_2 = -\frac{1}{RT}\cdot\frac{d\gamma}{d\ln c_2} \tag{18.16}$$

These equations are various forms of the Gibbs adsorption isotherm. The isotherm was experimentally verified by the ingenious experiments of J. W. McBain. He employed an adaptation of a swiftly moving microtome to slice off the top layer (around 0.05 mm) from a solution and scoop it into a sample tube. The composition of this layer could then be taken to determine Γ_2, and this experimental Γ_2 could be compared with that calculated, via the Gibbs isotherm, from the variation of the surface tension with the concentration of the bulk solution.

12. INSOLUBLE SURFACE FILMS — THE SURFACE BALANCE

As a result of the pioneer work of Pockels* and Rayleigh† it was discovered that in some cases a sparingly soluble substance would spread over the surface of a liquid to form a film exactly one molecule thick, a *unimolecular film*.

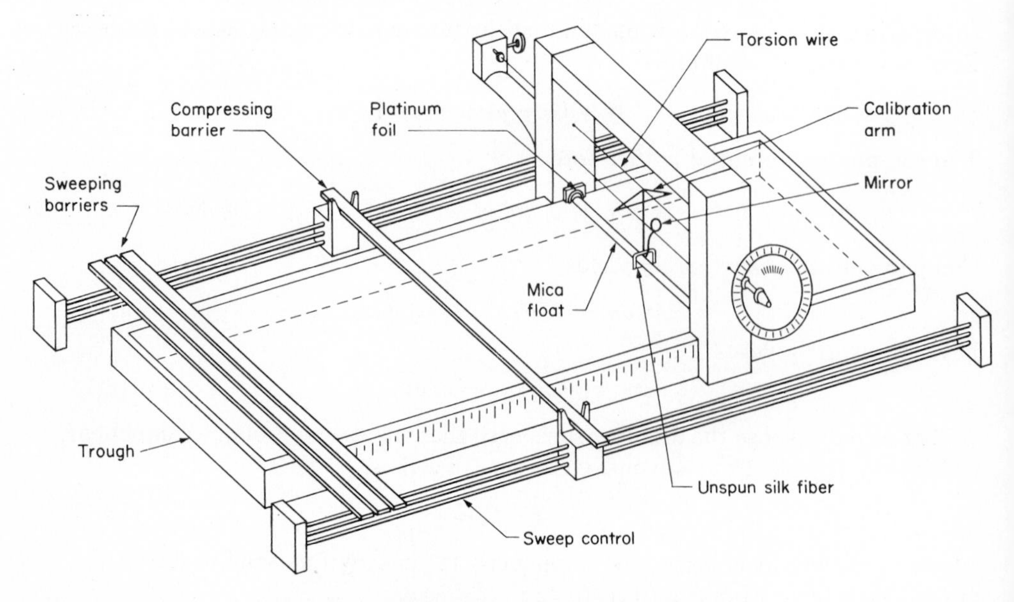

FIG. 18.7 A modern form of a Langmuir film balance.

* A. Pockels, *Nature 43*, 437 (1891).
† Rayleigh, *Proc. Roy. Soc. A 47*, 364 (1890); *Phil. Mag. 48*, 337 (1899).

In 1917, Irving Langmuir devised a method for measuring directly the *surface pressure* exerted by a film. The essential features of the instrument used, the film balance, are shown in Fig. 18.7. The so-called *fixed barrier*, which may be a strip of mica, floats on the surface of the water and is suspended from a torsion wire. At the ends of the floating barrier are attached strips of platinum foil or greased threads, which lie upon the water surface and connect the ends of the barrier to the sides of the trough. These threads prevent leakage of surface film past the float. A movable barrier rests upon the sides of the trough and is in contact with the water surface. A number of the movable barriers are provided for sweeping the surface clean.

In a typical experiment, a tiny amount of the insoluble spreading substance is introduced onto the clean water surface. For example, a dilute solution of stearic acid in benzene might be used; the benzene evaporates rapidly, leaving a film of stearic acid. Then the moving barrier is advanced toward the floating barrier. As the surface film is compressed it exerts a surface pressure on the float, pushing it backward. The torsion wire, attached to a calibrated circular scale, is twisted until the float is returned to its original position. The required force divided by the length of the float is the force per unit length or *surface pressure*.

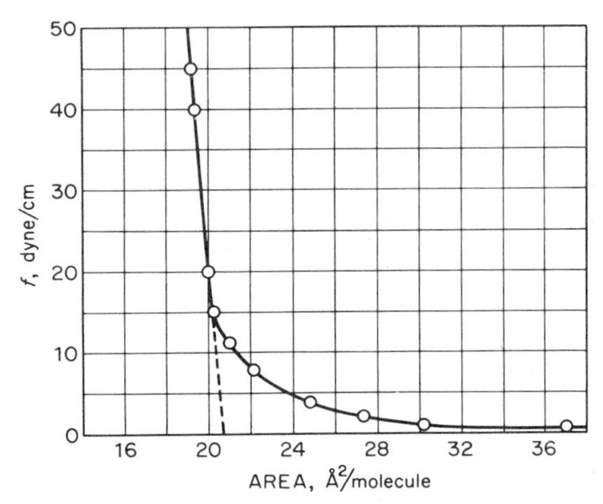

FIG. 18.8 Force-area isotherm at 20°C. Stearic acid on distilled water.

This surface pressure is simply another way of expressing the lowering of the surface tension caused by the surface film. On one side of the float is a clean water surface with tension γ_0, and on the other side a water surface covered to a certain extent with stearic acid molecules, with lowered surface tension γ. The surface pressure f is simply the negative of the change in surface tension. Thus,

$$f = -\Delta\gamma = \gamma_0 - \gamma$$

Langmuir was the first to study the surface-pressure vs. surface-area (f-A) relationships for films of the normal long-chain fatty acids, CH_3–$(CH_2)_nCOOH$. A typical f-A isotherm for stearic acid is shown in Fig. 18.8. The surface pressure in dynes per cm is plotted against the available area per molecule of stearic acid in square Ångstroms. This isotherm is a two-dimensional analog of a three-dimensional P vs. V isotherm. At large areas the pressure is small and it increases slowly with decreasing area until an area of about 20.5 Å^2 per molecule is reached. Then the pressure begins to increase rapidly with further compression of the film.

It is reasonable to believe that the long chains of stearic acid are highly oriented at the water surface, with their water-loving carboxyl groups buried in the water and their water-hating hydrocarbon chains waving above the surface.

The critical area of 20.5 Å^2 may therefore be taken as approximately equal to the cross-sectional area of the hydrocarbon chain. Any further decrease in area can be achieved only by compressing the closely packed film, and as is observed, this requires a considerable surface pressure. The molecular volume of solid stearic acid is $M/\rho L = 556$ Å^3. The length of the molecule is therefore $556/20.5 = 27.1$ Å, or about 1.50 Å per CH_2 group. This estimate agrees well with the value obtained from X-ray diffraction. The simplicity of the Langmuir method of estimating molecular dimensions is remarkable, and it has had important applications in the study of complex organic compounds such as proteins and sterols.

13. EQUATIONS OF STATE OF MONOLAYERS

Different substances in unimolecular films display a great variety of f-A isotherms. Sometimes the films behave like two-dimensional gases, sometimes like two-dimensional liquids or solids. In addition, there are other types of monolayer which have no exact analogs in the three-dimensional world. They can be recognized, however, as definite surface phases by the discontinuities in the f-A diagram which signal their occurrence.

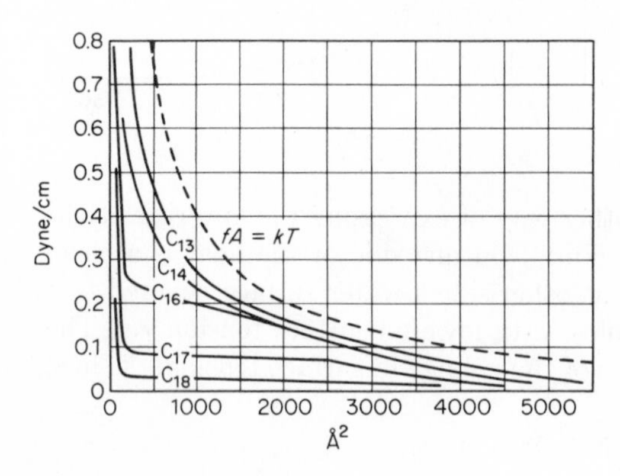

FIG. 18.9 Force-area isotherms at low film pressures for several straight chain aliphatic fatty acids on water.

In Fig. 18.9 are a series of f-A isotherms obtained for a number of the fatty acids $C_nH_{2n+1}COOH$ at 25°C. These curves resemble the P-V isotherms for a gas in the neighborhood of the critical temperature. There is a section at low

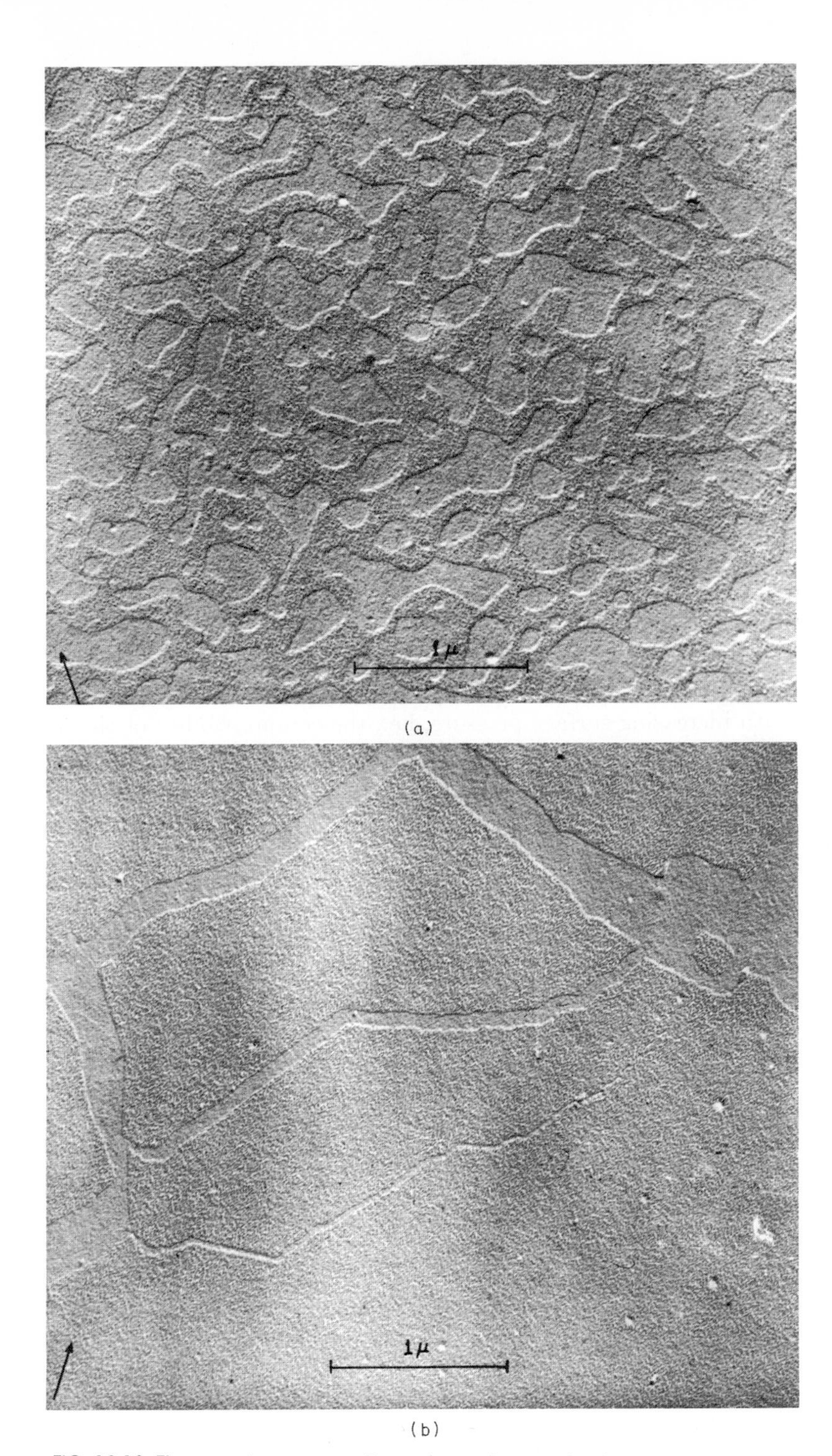

FIG. 18.10 Electron microscope replicas of monolayers of *n*-hexatriacontanoic acid spread on water. Part (a) shows the film at a surface pressure of 19 dyne cm^{-1}. In part (b) at 39 dyne cm^{-1} almost complete coverage has been reached. [Herman E. Ries, Research and Development Department, American Oil Company, Whiting, Indiana].

pressures corresponding to the high compressibility of a gas. Then there is an intermediate region where a small increase in pressure produces a large decrease in volume (the isotherm here does not seem to be absolutely flat and the analogy with the two-phase region in the P-V isotherm is imperfect). Finally there is a rapid rise in the f-A curve corresponding to the compression of a condensed phase. With decreasing molecular weight the quasi-two-phase region becomes less evident, and finally the isotherm appears to be gaseous throughout, as in the dashed curve.

If a surface film behaves as an ideal two-dimensional gas, corresponding to the three-dimensional $PV = RT$, we have*

$$fA = kT \tag{18.17}$$

The area A is usually expressed in Å^2 per molecule, and f in dynes per cm. The units of k are then (ergs $\times 10^{-16}$) per °C. For example at 300°K, $fA = 1.37 \times 10^{-16} \times 10^{+16} \times 300 = 411$.

Condensed films often follow an equation of state of the form

$$f = b - aA \tag{18.18}$$

where a and b are constants. This equation indicates that the area decreases linearly with increasing surface pressure, i.e., the compressibility of the film is a constant.

A technique has been developed† for the examination of surface films by electron microscopy. The film is taken up onto a collodion backing and shadowed by evaporation of a gold-platinum alloy at an angle of about 15°. Fig. 18.10 shows some electronmicrographs which reveal in a direct way the different surface structures that occur as a film is gradually compressed.

14. ADSORPTION OF GASES ON SOLIDS

We next consider what seems at first to be a distinctly different kind of surface phenomenon. This is adsorption onto the surface of a solid either from a vapor or from components in a liquid solution. The experimental methods used for studying these adsorptions are so different from those employed in surface-tension measurements that the fundamental similarity of the phenomena was obscured for a long time. The adsorption of vapors on solids will be considered first.

Two experimental arrangements for measuring vapor adsorption are illustrated in Fig. 18.11. One is an adsorption balance designed by McBain and Bakr. The *adsorbent* (substance on which the adsorption takes place) is contained in a light platinum bucket suspended by a spiral of quartz fiber. The *adsorbate* (substance that is adsorbed) is at the bottom of the glass tube enclosing

* This can be proved by working through the derivation on p. 213 for a two-dimensional case. We find $fA = \frac{1}{2}NmC^2 = E_K$ and $E_K = RT$.

† H. E. Ries, *Proc. 2nd Int. Congress of Surface Activity* (1957), p. 75.

the spiral and bucket. The spiral has been calibrated by hanging weights on it, so that any measured elongation, observed with a traveling microscope, corresponds to a known weight. The adsorbate is kept frozen while the tube is evacuated and sealed off. Then it is warmed by a carefully regulated oven surrounding the lower portion of the tube. The temperature of this oven controls the vapor pressure of the adsorbate. The temperature of the adsorbent is controlled by another oven encasing the upper part of the tube. The amount of gas adsorbed is then measured directly by the gain in weight of the adsorbent. The measurements are extended over a range of pressures to obtain the adsorption isotherm.

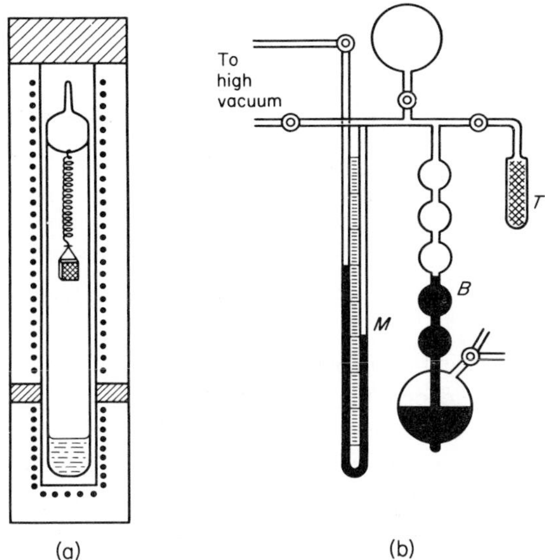

FIG. 18.11 Experimental gas adsorption methods: (a) Gravimetric — McBain balance. (b) Volumetric.

A second experimental arrangement is used in the volumetric method. The adsorbate vapor is contained in a calibrated gas buret (B), and its pressure is measured with the manometer (M). The adsorbent is contained in a thermostated sample tube (T), separated from the adsorbate by a stopcock or cutoff. All the volumes in the apparatus are calibrated. When vapor is admitted to the adsorbent sample, the amount adsorbed can be calculated from the pressure reading after equilibrium is attained. A series of measurements at different pressures determines the adsorption isotherm.

Two typical isotherms are shown in Fig. 18.12. Instead of the pressure, the *relative pressure* P/P_0 is used as a coordinate, where P_0 is the vapor pressure of the liquid adsorbate at the temperature of the isotherm. These isotherms illustrate the two distinct kinds of adsorption behavior that are usually distinguished. The case of nitrogen on silica gel at $-196°C$ is an example of *physical adsorption* or *physisorption*. The case of oxygen on charcoal at 100°C is a typical *chemical adsorption* or *chemisorption*. There are instances in which it is hard to assign the adsorption definitely to one of these types, but in most cases the decision is not difficult.

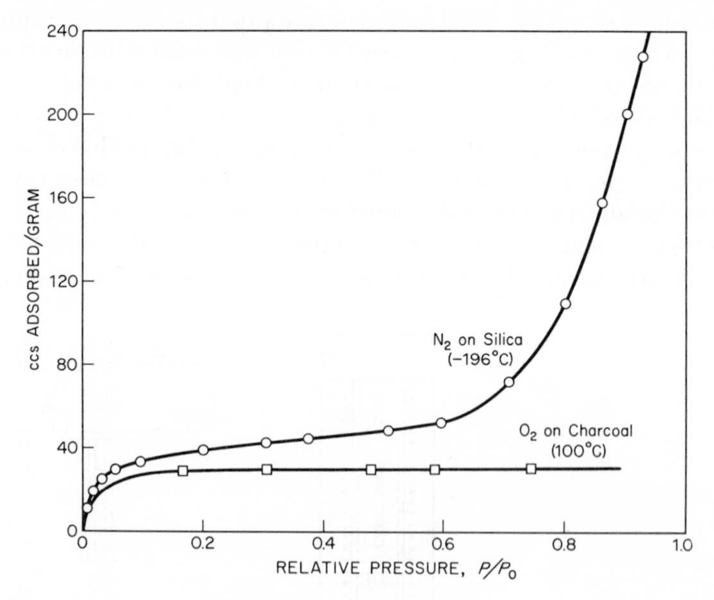

FIG. 18.12 Adsorption isotherms.

Physical adsorption is due to the operation of forces between the solid surface and the adsorbate molecules that are similar to the van der Waals forces between molecules. These forces are undirected and relatively nonspecific. They ultimately lead to the condensation of a vapor into a liquid, when P becomes equal to P_0. The energies of adsorption involved are of the order of a few hundred to a few thousand calories per mole. There will usually be little physical adsorption until the relative pressure P/P_0 reaches an appreciable value (around 0.05). The adsorption increases rapidly at high P/P_0, finally leading to condensation on the surface. Even before condensation occurs, for example at relative pressures around 0.8, there may be several superimposed layers of adsorbate on the surface. Physical adsorption is generally quite readily reversible, i.e., on decreasing the pressure the adsorbed gas is desorbed along the same isotherm curve. An exception to this rule is observed when the adsorbent contains many fine pores or capillaries.*

In contrast with physical adsorption, chemisorption is the result of much stronger binding forces, comparable with those leading to the formation of chemical compounds. The adsorption may be regarded as the formation of a sort of surface compound. The energies of adsorption range from about 10^4 to 10^5 calories per mole. Chemisorption is seldom reversible. Generally the solid must be heated to a higher temperature and pumped at a high vacuum to remove

* Just as the vapor pressure of liquids with convex surfaces (e.g., droplets) is greater than that for plane surfaces, so the vapor pressure of liquids with concave surfaces is less. The change is given by the Kelvin equation. Therefore condensation in capillaries is facilitated, whereas evaporation from capillaries is inhibited. When capillary condensation occurs, the adsorption isotherm exhibits hysteresis on desorption.

chemisorbed gas. Sometimes the gas that is desorbed is not the same as that adsorbed; for example, after oxygen is adsorbed on charcoal at 100°C, heating and pumping will cause the desorption of carbon monoxide. On the other hand, hydrogen chemisorbed on nickel, presumably with the formation of surface Ni—H bonds, can be recovered as H_2. Chemisorption is completed when a surface is covered by an adsorbed monolayer, but there is good evidence that physisorption can lead to adsorbed layers several molecules thick. Sometimes a physically adsorbed layer may form on top of an underlying chemisorbed layer.

There are cases known in which the same system exemplifies physisorption at one temperature and chemisorption at some higher temperature. Thus nitrogen is physisorbed on iron at −190°C and chemisorbed with the formation of surface iron nitride at 500°C. Chemisorption is of particular importance in contact catalysis. It often follows the Langmuir isotherm discussed in Section 8.33.

15. THERMODYNAMICS OF THE ADSORPTION ISOTHERM

A thermodynamic theory of the adsorption isotherm was developed by G. Jura and W. D. Harkins.* It was based on the important fact that adsorbed films on solid surfaces (e.g., solid-vapor interfaces) are not thermodynamically different from the films at liquid-vapor interfaces treated by the Gibbs equation (18.14).

When we are dealing with the adsorption of a gas at a solid surface, instead of the activity a of a component in the solution, we can substitute the fugacity of the gas, or as a good approximation simply the pressure. If v is the volume of gas adsorbed per gram of solid, and s is the area of the solid in cm^2 per g (specific area), then v/s is the volume of gas per cm^2 of solid. If V is the molar volume of the gas, v/sV is the number of moles of gas adsorbed per cm^2 of solid surface. But this is exactly Γ_2, so that Eq. (18.14) may be written, since the differential of surface pressure $df = -d\gamma$,

$$df = \frac{RTv}{sV}\, d\ln P \qquad (18.19)$$

Now if the two-dimensional equation of state (f-A isotherm) of the adsorbed monolayer is known, it is possible to integrate Eq. (18.19) to calculate the ordinary v-P adsorption isotherm for the vapor. Conversely one can use the observed isotherms to determine the two-dimensional equations of state. This treatment brings the adsorption of vapors on solids and the surface tension lowering by films on liquids together into a single comprehensive theory. We shall take as an example the case in which the adsorbed film is of the condensed type, following Eq. (18.18).

Since $A = (sV/Lv)$, where L is the Avogadro Number, we have from Eq. (18.18),

$$df = -a\, dA = \frac{asV}{Lv^2}\, dv$$

* *J. Am. Chem. Soc. 68*, 1941 (1946).

Substituting this in Eq. (18.19), we find

$$C\,\frac{2dv}{v^3} = d \ln P \tag{18.20}$$

where the constant $C = (aV^2s^2/2LRT)$. Integration of Eq. (18.20) yields

$$B - \frac{C}{v^2} = \ln P \tag{18.21}$$

Here B is an integration constant. If the adsorption data are plotted as $1/v^2$ vs. $\ln P$, it is found that in many cases linear graphs are obtained. These straight lines indicate that over a considerable pressure range the adsorbed films are of the condensed type.* In other cases, different two-dimensional equations of state lead to correspondingly different v-P isotherms.

16. ESTIMATION OF SURFACE AREAS

It is sometimes necessary to know the surface area of a solid adsorbent, a fine powder, or a catalytic material. If we knew the number of molecules n_A of an adsorbate necessary to form a complete adsorbed layer one molecule thick over the surface of one gram of adsorbent, we could calculate the surface area s from $s = n_A\sigma$, where σ is the area of surface occupied by a single molecule.

We may be able to estimate n_A quite well from an isotherm for physical adsorption. One useful method is based on an equation given by Brunauer, Emmett and Teller (the B.E.T. equation), which can be fitted to many adsorption isotherms.† Another method is based on the gas adsorbed at $\theta = 1$ in a chemisorption according to the Langmuir isotherm. Isotopic exchange with surface atoms may provide a suitable estimate of surface areas in some cases.

17. THE SURFACES OF SOLIDS

The study of adsorption isotherms can provide only indirect evidence about the nature of solid surfaces. We should like to be able to "really see" the surface, and then to be able to explain adsorption, contact catalysis, corrosion, electronic properties of surfaces, and the like, in terms of the actual surface structures present. Considerable progress has been made toward this goal, and we shall mention briefly here some of the methods that seem most useful.

(a) *Multiple-beam interferometry.* This technique, which has been extensively developed by Tolansky§ is a sort of three dimensional optical microscopy.

* The constant C, the negative of the slope of the linear plot, has been shown by Harkins to be simply related to the surface area of the adsorbent s. Thus $s = k_1\sqrt{C}$ where k_1 is a constant for each adsorbate at constant temperature.

† *J. Am. Chem. Soc.*, *60,* 309 (1938).

§ S. Tolansky, *Surface Microtopography,* (New York: Interscience, 1960).

An interference pattern is produced between two surfaces, by employing a succession of coherent beams of light, which all have definite relations of phase and intensity. The pattern consists of contour lines which represent changes in the elevation of the surface. The method is thus adapted to the precise determination of surface elevations. The resolution is about 10 Å, i.e., differences in elevation of this amount which extend over considerable areas of the surface will be revealed as a contour line. An example is shown in Fig. 18.13 obtained from the octahedral face of a natural diamond. The equiangular depressions on the surface are called *trigons*. It can be shown at higher resolution that the entire surface is covered with trigons. Tolansky believes that the octahedral faces of diamonds grow by addition of (111) plane sheets. Where a sheet is incomplete, a trigon occurs, since there is a threefold axis of symmetry along the [111] direction.

FIG. 18.13 Multiple beam interferometer pattern from octahedral face of diamond. [S. Tolansky, London University].

(b) *Electron microscopy.* The surfaces of solids may be studied by direct reflection electron microscopy, but better resolution has been achieved by various *replica techniques*. The surface is covered by a thin film of plastic, which is then shadowed by evaporating metal onto it. After removal from the surface the shadowed replica is examined by transmission electron microscopy. Sometimes a *direct replica* can be taken. For example platinum and carbon can be evaporated onto the surfaces of ionic crystals; when the specimen is placed in water, the surface film floats off and can be picked up on a grid for electron-microscopic examination. An interesting technique is the evaporation of small amounts of metal onto a surface. The metal atoms nucleate at dislocations, point defects and cleavage steps at the surface. Fig. 18.14 shows the result of an experiment in which gold was evaporated onto a fresh cleavage face of NaCl.* A carbon film

* C. Sella, P. Conjeaud and J. J. Trillat, *Fourth Int. Conf. Electron Microscopy* (Berlin: Springer Verlag, 1960), p. 508. This method was developed at the same time by G. A. Bassett, *Phil. Mag. 3*, 1042 (1958).

FIG. 18.14 A pattern formed by evaporation of gold on a cleavage face of rock salt. [J. J. Trillat, C. Sella and P. Conjeaud, Laboratoire de Microscopie Electronique, C.N.R.S., Bellevue].

was evaporated over the gold, and the composite floated off. The nuclei are more dense along cleavage steps than on perfect crystal planes. Steps of only one atomic height can be delineated.

(c) *Field-emission microscopy.* The field-emission microscope has given the highest resolution. In favorable cases one can apparently see individual atoms. Fig. 18.15 shows a diagram of the instrument as designed by Erwin Müller. The tip of the electrode is etched to a fine point so that the field strength at the point can reach values as high as 5×10^8 volt cm^{-1} even with potential differences of 10^4 v across the tube. In the first experiments the tips were heated and the patterns produced by thermionic electron emission were registered on the screen. In the *field-ion microscope* the tip is chilled to liquid hydrogen temperature and helium gas at low pressure is admitted to the tube. When a helium atom strikes the surface, it is ionized ($He \rightarrow He^+ + e$). The He^+ ion then travels outward to the screen in a straight line from the surface atom. Great magnification is achieved, equal to the ratio of the area of the tip to the area of the screen. Fig. 18.16 shows a He^+ ion image of a platinum crystal in the (001) position. In this picture we can "really see" the atoms of platinum. Fig. 18.17 shows an enlarged region of a platinum tip, in which we can see an *atomic vacancy* in the (102) plane. The nature of these pictures is shown by models like that in Fig. 18.18, made up of hard spheres. The large white spheres represent Xenon atoms adsorbed on the point of a tungsten emitter. The colors of the atoms indicate how many nearest neighbors each one has.

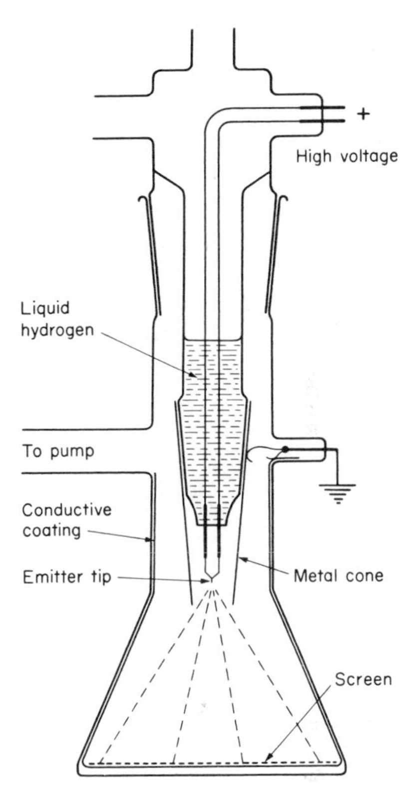

FIG. 18.15 Field Ion Microscope. [Erwin Müller, Pennsylvania State University].

(d) *Electron diffraction.* Ordinary electron diffraction studies on solids are made with fast electrons (50 to 100 kv). These penetrate several hundred atomic layers and give little information about the state of the surface itself. H. E. Farnsworth* has developed a remarkable technique which uses very slow electrons. With silver, for example, 50 per cent of the diffraction intensity from a 200 v electron beam is due to the first atomic layer, and 90 per cent to the first two layers. With carefully cleaned surfaces, it is possible to detect a single layer of adsorbed gas and to measure its location with respect to the underlying surface atoms. An atomically clean (100) single crystal face of nickel was obtained in high vacuum and then exposed to oxygen. The chemisorption first occurred in a doubly spaced face-centered crystalline lattice of oxygen atoms. With increasing oxygen pressure, a simple cubic square structure of oxygen atoms appeared; further increase in pressure led to the appearance of a nickel oxide structure.

18. ADSORPTION FROM SOLUTION

Adsorption from solution does not in general appear to lead to layers more than one molecule thick. For many cases the experimental data can be fairly well represented by an empirical isotherm proposed by Freundlich in 1909:

$$x/m = k_1 c^{1/n} \tag{18.22}$$

Here x and m are the masses of substance adsorbed and of adsorbent respectively;

* *J. Phys. Chem. Solids 9*, 48 (1958).

FIG. 18.16 Field-ion microscope picture of a platinum crystal in the (001) position. The four (111) planes are in the four corners. This is a helium-ion image at 21° K, 21800 volts. The average tip radius was 1350 Å; the image diagonal is about 2200 Å, so that the magnification of this picture is about 1 200 000X. [Erwin Müller, Pennsylvania State University].

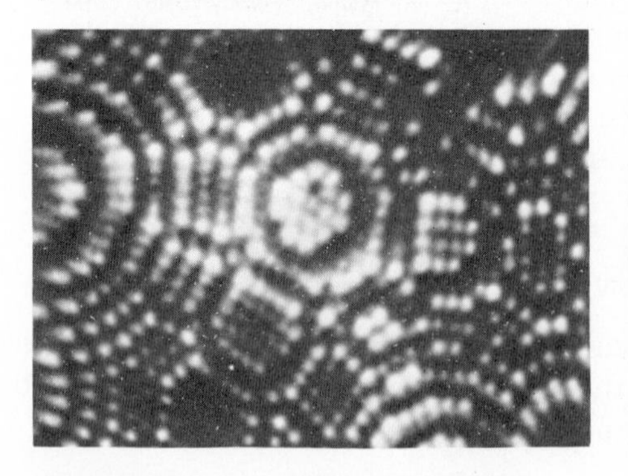

FIG. 18.17 Helium-ion image of a region of a platinum crystal showing a (102) plane in which an atomic vacancy occurs. [Erwin Müller, Pennsylvania State University].

FIG. 18.18 Hard-sphere model of the tip of a crystal as seen in the field-ion microscope. [G. Ehrlich. General Electric Research Laboratory].

c is the concentration of the solution when equilibrium is reached; and n is an empirical constant usually greater than unity. This equation implies that if $\log x/m$ is plotted against $\log c$, a straight line will be obtained with slope $1/n$.

19. ELECTRICAL PHENOMENA AT INTERFACES

Across any interface separating two phases there is in general a difference in potential, since the electrical environment of a test charge changes as it is carried from one phase to the other. We have already had occasion to mention this fact in the discussion of electrode and liquid-junction potentials.*

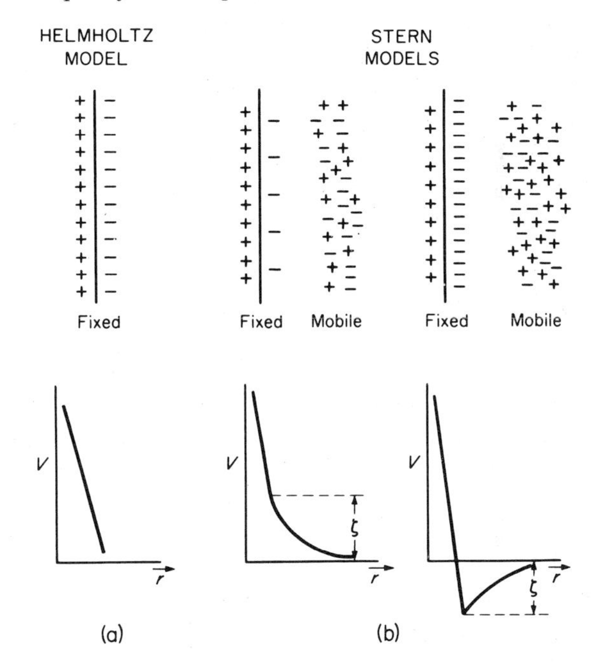

FIG. 18.19 Models for electrical double layers and the potential fall in the layers.

The potential difference across an interface, since electricity is atomic in nature, may conveniently be pictured as an *electrical double layer*. One phase acquires a net negative charge (excess of electrons), and the other acquires a net positive charge (deficiency of electrons). The first quantitative discussion of this double layer was given in 1879 by Helmholtz, who considered the case of a solid immersed in a solution. He suggested the picture shown in Fig. 18.19(a), a layer of ions at the solid surface and a rigidly held layer of oppositely charged ions in the solution. The electric potential corresponding to such a charge distribution is also shown. Such double layers are supposed to exist not only at plane surfaces, but also surrounding solid particles suspended in a liquid medium.

* Although differences in electrical potential between phases are not experimentally separable from differences in chemical potential, they have been widely used in theoretical discussions, some examples of which are given in the remainder of this chapter.

The Helmholtz double layer is equivalent to a simple parallel-plate capacitor. If l is the distance separating the oppositely charged plates and ϵ the dielectric constant of the medium, the capacitance per square centimeter of interface is $\epsilon/4\pi l$. If Q/A is the surface charge density (e.g., coulombs per cm^2) the potential difference ΔU across the double layer is

$$\Delta U = \frac{4\pi l Q}{\epsilon A} \tag{18.24}$$

The Helmholtz model of the double layer is inadequate, because the thermal motions of the liquid molecules could scarcely permit such a rigid array of charges at the interface.* The *diffuse double layer*, proposed by Stern in 1924, seems to be more realistic. This is shown in Fig. 18.19(b). The charge on the solid is rigidly fixed. Adsorbed on top of this there may be a practically immobile layer of oppositely charged molecules of the liquid. Further in the solution there is a diffuse layer of charge, which may have a sign either the same as or opposite from that of the adsorbed layer. Only this diffuse region is free to move, for example under the influence of an applied potential difference. The potential drop ζ in the diffuse layer is called the *zeta potential*.

20. ELECTROKINETIC PHENOMENA

Four interesting effects, all ascribable to the existence of a diffuse mobile double layer at phase interfaces, are grouped under the name of *electrokinetic phenomena*.

First, there is *electroösmosis*, the motion of liquid through a membrane under the influence of an applied electric field. For simplicity a single capillary tube may be considered; typical membranes may be thought of as bundles of such capillaries connected in diverse ways. At the walls of the tube there is a double layer, with zeta potential ζ. If the strength of the applied electric field is E, the force acting on a charge Q is EQ.

The treatment of viscosity on p. 223 may be consulted for the comparable case in which the force is a mechanical one, i.e., a pressure difference between the ends of the tube. Just as in that case, the force tending to move the liquid is opposed by a frictional resistance equal to $\eta v/l$ where η is the viscosity and v/l the velocity gradient. For steady flow, from Eq. (18.24), $\eta v/l = EQ/A = E\epsilon\zeta/4\pi l$, and

$$v = \frac{E\epsilon\zeta}{4\pi\eta} \tag{18.25}$$

This gives the linear velocity of flow in terms of the ζ potential and readily obtainable experimental quantities. The volume rate of flow is obtained by multiplying by the cross-sectional area of the capillary tube. It should be noted that for the ζ potential the simple formula for the potential drop in a Helmholtz double layer was used. This is actually a permissible approximation, because if we used

* See Sec. 9.22 and the discussion of the Debye-Hückel ionic atmosphere.

a diffuse double layer and integrated over each differential section of its thickness, we should find the potential proportional to l and the velocity gradient proportional to l^{-1}, so that the thickness of the double layer would drop out of the calculation in any event.*

The converse of electroösmosis is the *streaming potential.* This is the potential difference that arises across a capillary tube or membrane when a stream of liquid is forced through it. The diffuse double layer is swept along by the fluid flow, so that opposite charges are built up at opposite ends of the tube.

Electroösmosis and streaming potential are observed when we are dealing with a fixed solid surface, like the wall of a tube. If the solid surface is that of a colloidal particle, which is itself free to move through the solution, the electrokinetic effects, though arising from the same cause, the existence of a double layer at the interface, appear in a somewhat different guise. *Electrophoresis* is the name given to the migration of charged particles in an electric field. It is in fact not really different from the migration of ions, and the particles may be regarded as colloidal electrolytes. The quartet of electrokinetic phenomena is completed by the *Dorn effect.* This bears the same relation to electrophoresis as streaming potential bears to electroösmosis. It is the potential difference that is set up in a solution when particles are allowed to fall through it.

All of these electrokinetic effects have been interpreted in terms of the zeta potential in an electrical double layer. Unfortunately we have no means of measuring the zeta potential apart from the equations describing the electrokinetic phenomena. Thus the theory seems to lead us around a circle. The circle is only mildly vicious, however, because the zeta potentials calculated from measurements of different effects are often quite concordant, and this fact provides some consolation for users of the model. The calculated ζ potentials range from 1 to 50 millivolts.

PROBLEMS

1. Calculate the time necessary to cover one quarter of the sites on one square centimeter of a (100) face of nickel ($a_0 = 3.517$ Å) with CO, when the gas pressure is 10^{-7} torr and the sticking coefficient is 0.05 (fraction of molecules striking surface that are adsorbed); assume the adsorbed molecules are mobile.

2. The surface tension of liquid mercury in air at 15°C is 487 dyne cm^{-1}. Calculate the capillary depression in a tube 1.0 mm diameter.

3. How many sodium-ion sites are there in one square centimeter of crystal surface of cubic crystallites of NaCl ($a_0 = 5.629$ Å, $\rho = 2.165$ g cm^{-3}). If the crystallites are 1μ long, how many sites are there per gram? [*Ans.* 6.28×10^{14}, 17.5×10^{18}]

* For cylindrical tubes it is not quite correct to use the formula for a parallel-plate capacitor, and the constant 4π is therefore not quite correct.

4. Assume zero contact angle and estimate the height to which a column of water would rise in a glass tube 10μ diameter. [*Ans.* 297 cm]

5. What pressure would be needed to blow capillary water out of a sintered glass filter with a uniform pore width of 0.10μ. [*Ans.* 28.8 atm]

6. The surface tension of toluene at 20°C is 28.43 cyne cm^{-1} and the density is 0.86694 g cm^{-3}. Calculate the parachor. The Ramsay-Shields constant is 2.2 erg $mole^{-2/3}$ deg^{-1}. Estimate the critical temperature. [Experimental 320.6°C]

7. 20 ml of a saturated solution of $PbSO_4$ (0.0040 g l^{-1}) containing radiolead (Th-B) as a tracer with an activity of 1600 counts min^{-1} is shaken with 1.000 g precipitated $PbSO_4$. The final count in the solution is 450 cpm. If the $PbSO_4$ "molecule" has an effective area of 18.4×10^{-16} cm^2, calculate the surface area of the $PbSO_4$. [*Ans.* 1068 cm^2 g^{-1}]

8. If bubbles of air 10^{-3} mm in diameter and no other nuclei are present in water just below the boiling point, how much could the water be superheated before boiling started?

9. One milliliter of an activated charcoal has a surface area of 1000 m^2. If complete coverage is assumed, how much ammonia (cc at STP) could be adsorbed on the surface of 25 ml of the charcoal. Take the diameter of the NH_3 molecule as 3.00 Å and assume the molecules just touch each other in a plane.

10. An insoluble compound X spreads on water to give a gaseous type film at low concentrations. When 10^{-7} g of X is added to 200 cm^2 surface, the surface tension at 25°C is lowered by 0.20 dyne cm^{-1}. Calculate the molecular weight of X. [*Ans.* 61.2]

11. Calculate the surface pressure f at which the average intermolecular distance in a two-dimensional ideal gas at 0°C is equal to that in a three-dimensional ideal gas at 1 atm and 0°C. [*Ans.* 0.336 dyne cm^{-1}]

12. Polyvinyl acetate spreads on water to give an extrapolated monolayer area of 1.90 m^2 mg^{-1}. What is the area per monomer unit? What conclusion could you draw concerning the orientation of the film at the surface?

13. Under a potential gradient of 10.0 v cm^{-1}, a quartz particle 1.0 μ in diameter in water suspension migrated at a velocity of 3.00×10^{-3} cm s^{-1}. Calculate the zeta potential at the quartz-water interface. [*Ans.* 41.7 millivolt]

14. The zeta potential of water *vs.* glass is about -0.050 V. Calculate the flow of water by electroosmosis at 25°C through a glass capillary 1.0 cm long and 1.0 mm diameter when the potential difference between the ends is 40 v. [*Ans.* 0.46 ml hr^{-1}]

15. A hose carries a stream of water moving at 15 m s^{-1}. Calculate the smallest size of the droplets which could be produced isothermally by an ideal nozzle, if all the water were converted into droplets of equal size.

---

16. The surface tensions of dilute solutions of phenol in water at 30°C were:

wt % phenol	0.024	0.047	0.118	0.471
γ dyne cm^{-1}	72.6	72.2	71.3	66.5

Calculate Γ_2 from the Gibbs isotherm for a 0.1% solution.

17. Derive the v-P adsorption isotherms for the cases in which the equations of state of the surface films are (a) $fA = kT$ (b) $(f + aA^{-2})A = kT$ (inclusion of a van der Waals type molecular interaction term with constant a). [*Ans.* (a) $v = kP$ (b) $\ln P = k' \ln V - k''V$]

18. The ΔH of adsorption at constant amount of vapor adsorbed is called the *isosteric heat of adsorption*, ΔH_v. The adsorption of N_2 on charcoal amounted to 0.894 cc (STP) g^{-1} at $P = 4.6$ atm at 194°K, and at $P = 35.4$ atm at 273°K. Calculate ΔH_v and hence ΔS_v° and ΔG_v° for the adsorption process. [*Ans.* $\Delta H_v = -2715$ cal, $\Delta S_v^\circ = -17.0$ cal deg^{-1} $mole^{-1}$; $\Delta G_v^\circ = 1930$ cal $mole^{-1}$]

19. Derive an equation for the solubility of small particles from the Kelvin equation for the vapor pressure of small droplets. If the bulk solubility of dinitrobenzene in water is 10^{-3} mole $liter^{-1}$ at 25°C, estimate the solubility of crystallites 0.01μ in diameter; assume the interfacial tension γ is the same as that for liquid dinitrobenzene-water, 25.7 dyne cm^{-1}. [*Ans.* $\ln (c_r/c) = 2M\gamma/RT\rho r$, where M is the molecular weight and ρ the density]

20. Cassel and Neugebauer [*J. Phys. Chem.*, *40*, 523 (1936)] measured the lowering of the surface tension of mercury by adsorbed xenon at 0°C.

P, mm Xe	69	93	146	227	278
$\gamma_0 - \gamma_1$, dyne cm^{-1}	0.80	1.10	1.75	2.75	3.35

Calculate the number of Xe atoms adsorbed per cm^2 at $P = 278$ mm and estimate the fraction of the mercury surface that is then covered by xenon. [*Ans.* 8.91×10^{13}, 0.101]

21. Harkins and Wampler [*J. Am. Chem. Soc.*, *53*, 850 (1931)] obtained the following data for solutions of n-butanol in water at 20°C:

Molality, m	0.00329	0.00658	0.01320	0.0264	0.0536	0.1050	0.2110	0.4330
Activity, a	0.00328	0.00654	0.01304	0.0258	0.0518	0.0989	0.1928	0.3796
Surf. ten. γ	72.80	72.26	70.82	68.00	63.14	56.31	48.08	38.87

By means of the Gibbs adsorption isotherm, plot an f-A isotherm from these data. Note that in calculating the surface concentration the number of molecules already present in the surface must be considered in addition to those adsorbed at the interface.

19 HIGH POLYMERS

Just as man, under the regard of the paleontologist, merges anatomically into the mass of mammals who preceded him, so the cell, in the same descending series, both qualitatively and quantitatively merges into the world of chemical structure and visibly converges towards the molecule.

PIERRE TEILHARD DE CHARDIN (1955)

Substances with molecular weights greater than about 5000 are composed of giant molecules or *macromolecules,* which may have new and unusual properties due to their large size. Originally a *polymer* denoted a substance composed of molecules with a formula X_n, made by repetition of n identical structural units X. Combination of two structural units led to *copolymers* X_nY_m (in contrast to *homopolymers* X_n). Now we often speak also of substances such as proteins and nucleic acids as *polymers* because they contain a large number of similar structural units joined together by the same kind of linkage. The dimensions of these large molecules fall in a range from about 10 Å (readily resolved by the electron microscope) to 10 000 Å (readily resolved by a light microscope). In 1861, Thomas Graham suggested the term *colloid* for such substances (from the Greek, κoλλα, glue). Colloids were distinguished by the fact that they could not pass through membranes permeable to smaller dissolved species.

1. MOLECULAR WEIGHTS

A common polymerization mechanism begins with the introduction of a free radical $R\cdot$ into a group of unsaturated molecules M. The radical adds to the unsaturate to give a larger radical $MR\cdot$, which in turn adds to another unsaturated molecule.

$$R\cdot + M \longrightarrow MR\cdot$$
$$MR\cdot + M \longrightarrow M_2R\cdot, \text{ etc.}$$

Finally the growing radical may encounter a second radical, and the polymerization chain is broken by recombination or disproportionation.

$$M_nR\cdot + M_mR\cdot \longrightarrow M_nR{:}RM_m$$

Such a chain mechanism must lead to polymer molecules having a distribution of molecular weights, since not all the chains will break at the same stage.

If we make up a solution of styrene in benzene, all the molecules of styrene are identical and all methods of determining the molecular weight should yield the same value, within experimental uncertainties. If we dissolve polystyrene in benzene, however, the masses of the individual polymer molecules will be distributed over a range of values. As a consequence, different methods of determining the molecular weight from properties of the solution can yield different values.

Colligative properties, such as osmotic pressure, depend on the number of molecules in a solution. Thus the average molecular weight calculated from a colligative property is the *number average molecular weight*, defined by

$$\overline{M}_N = \sum N_iM_i/\sum N_i \tag{19.1}$$

To obtain $\overline{M}_N$ we add up the products of the molecular weights M_i and the number of molecules N_i having that molecular weight* and divide by the total number of molecules.

In case there is a distribution of molecular weights, the number average tends to emphasize the lower molecular weights. Suppose there were only two molecules, one with $M_1 = 100$ and one with $M_2 = 10\,000$. The number average would be $\overline{M}_N = 5050$, despite the fact that over 99% of the mass of the substance was in the heavier molecule.

Some experimental determinations of molecular weight, for example, that based on the scattering of light, depend on the masses m_i of material in the different molecular-weight fractions. These methods yield a *mass average molecular weight*, defined by

$$\overline{M}_W = \sum m_iM_i/\sum m_i \tag{19.2}$$

or,

$$\overline{M}_W = \sum N_iM_i^2/\sum N_iM_i$$

We may note also that if C is the concentration in grams per unit volume,

$$\sum m_iM_i = \sum C_iM_i/C$$

Consider a sample containing 10% by weight of polymer of $M = 10\,000$ and 90% by weight, of $M = 100\,000$. Then

$$\overline{M}_W = \frac{.1(10\,000) + .9(100\,000)}{1} = 91\,000$$

whereas,

$$\overline{M}_N = \frac{.1(10\,000) + .09(100\,000)}{.19} = 52\,500$$

* To be precise, we should not talk of the "molecular weight" of a single molecule. In terms of the masses m_i of the individual molecules, Eq. (19.1) would be $\overline{M}_N = L\sum N_im_i/\sum m_i$ where L is the Avogadro Number.

We shall now consider several methods for measuring the molecular weights, sizes and shapes of polymeric molecules in solution.

2. OSMOTIC PRESSURE

The theory of osmotic pressure, which we discussed in Sec. 5.14, applies also to solutions of polymers. Ordinary solutions follow the van't Hoff equation, $\Pi = cRT$, up to a concentration of about 1%, but serious deviations occur in polymer solutions at much lower concentrations. In 1914, Caspari reported that the osmotic pressure of a 1% solution of rubber in benzene was about twice the value calculated from the van't Hoff equation. Similar large deviations have been frequently observed.

The evaluation of data on the osmotic pressure of high-polymer solutions presents three principal problems: (1) How can we determine the molecular weight when the van't Hoff law fails? (2) Can the data on osmotic pressure be explained in terms of the sizes and shapes of the molecules of polymer? (3) Can data on osmotic pressure provide information on the interactions of polymer molecules with each other and with solvent molecules?

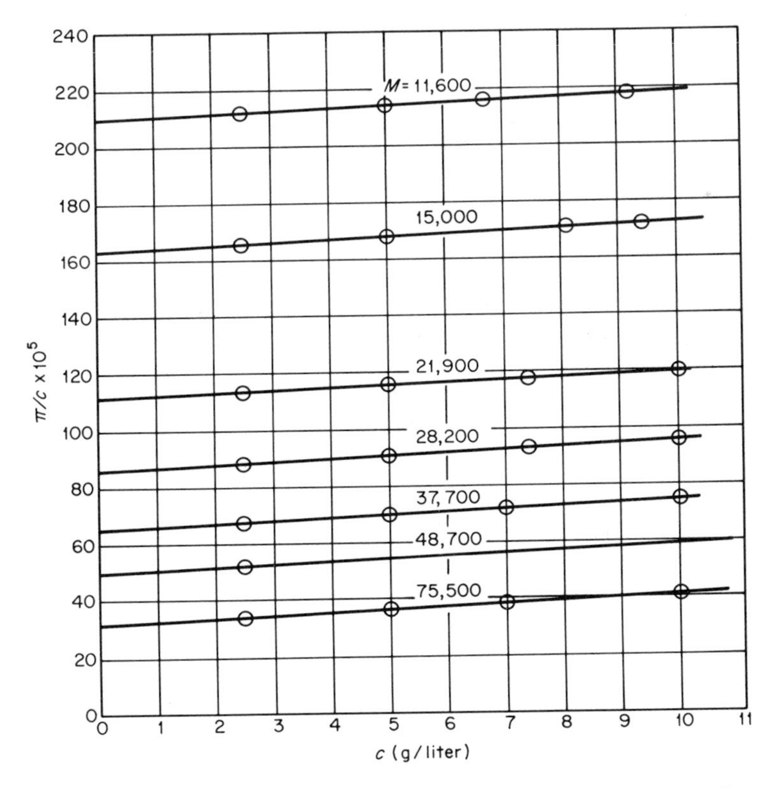

FIG. 19.1 Osmotic pressures of solutions of polypyrrolidones in water at 25°C plotted in accord with Eq. (19.4). The molecular weights are noted on the curves.

In 1945, McMillan and Mayer* showed that the osmotic pressure of non-electrolytes could be represented by a power series in the concentrations, exactly like the virial equation for a nonideal gas,

$$\Pi = (RT/\overline{M}_N)C + BC^2 + DC^3 + \dots \tag{19.3}$$

Here C is the mass concentration (e.g., g cm^{-3}). In fairly dilute solutions, the third term becomes negligible and we can write

$$\Pi/C = RT/\overline{M}_N + BC \tag{19.4}$$

Thus a plot of Π/C vs. C should give a straight line in the region of low concentration. The intercept at $C \to 0$ yields $RT/\overline{M}_N$, from which we can find the molecular weight. Fig. 19.1 shows osmotic pressures of aqueous solutions of polypyrollidones† plotted according to Eq. (19.4). The values of $\overline{M}_N$ range from 11 600 to 75 500 for different fractions.

Various designs of *osmometers* have been used for these studies. The semi-permeable membrane is usually a swollen cellulose film, which is mounted between rigid supports in such a way as to present a large area open to the solutions.

3. THE DONNAN EFFECT§

Consider in Fig. 19.2 two solutions separated by a membrane that is permeable to small ions but not to ions of high polymer (*polyelectrolyte ions*). Let us consider a system composed of solvent (component 1), high polymer (component 2), and a 1:1 neutral salt (component 3). Only one side of the membrane contains polymer ions. The condition for equilibrium is that the chemical potentials be equal on both sides of the membrane for all components which can permeate the membrane. Thus,

$$\mu_1' = \mu_1$$

$$\mu_3' = \mu_3$$

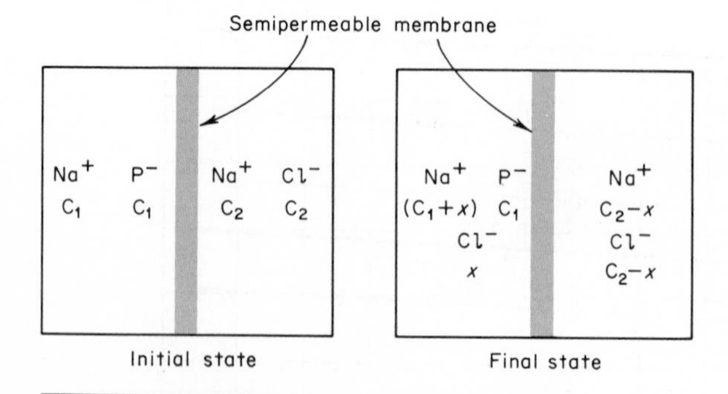

FIG. 19.2 An example of a Donnan membrane equilibrium with high polymer anions P^- and NaCl as the neutral salt.

* W. G. McMillan and J. E. Mayer, *J. Chem. Phys. 13*, 276 (1945).

† J. Hengstenberg, *Makromol. Chem. 7*, 572 (1951).

§ We follow quite closely the treatment given by Charles Tanford, *Physical Chemistry of Macromolecules* (New York: Wiley, 1961) p. 224.

In 1911, F. G. Donnan showed that this equilibrium condition may lead to an unequal distribution of diffusible ions across the membrane. Suppose that the polymer ion carries a charge z. The condition of electrical neutrality is

$$zm_p = m_- + m_+ \tag{19.5}$$

where m_p, m_-, m_+ are the molalities of polymer ions, negative, and positive salt ions, respectively. In terms of activities, the equilibrium condition for the salt (component 3) becomes

$$a'_+a'_- = a_+a_-$$

or [see Eq. (9.27)],

$$m'_+m'_-\gamma'^2_\pm = m_+m_-\gamma^2_\pm$$

When we combine this with Eq. (19.5) we find

$$\begin{aligned}(m'_+)^2 &= (\gamma_\pm/\gamma'_\pm)^2\, m_+(m_+ + zm_p)\\ (m'_-)^2 &= (\gamma_\pm/\gamma'_\pm)^2\, m_-(m_- - zm_p)\end{aligned} \tag{19.6}$$

We see, therefore, that if z is positive, $m'_+ > m_+$ and $m'_- < m_-$ (vice versa if z is negative).

These Donnan effects may be important in membrane processes in biological systems. In measurements of the osmotic pressure of high polymers, we must try to minimize Donnan effects by establishing conditions under which the charge of the polymer is minimized, or by working with a considerable excess of neutral salt.

4. LIGHT SCATTERING—THE RAYLEIGH LAW

The scattering of light by a colloidal solution was described by Tyndall in 1871. He passed a beam of white light through a gold sol, and observed bluish light scattered perpendicularly to the incident beam. A typical arrangement for the study of light scattering is shown in Fig. 19.3. The detector of scattered light is mounted so that the intensity can be measured as a function of θ, the scattering angle from the direction of the incident beam.

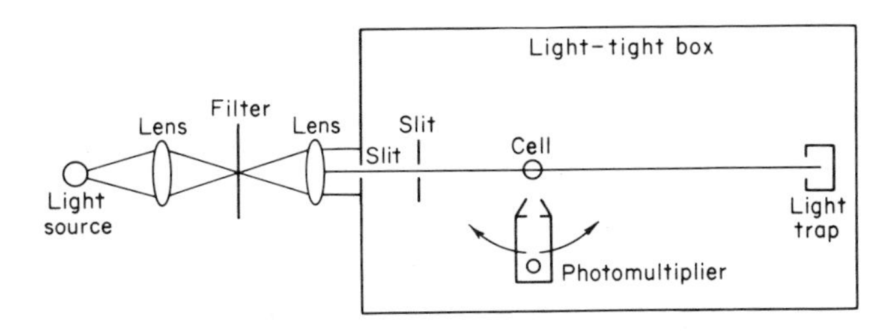

FIG. 19.3 Diagram of the basic construction of a light-scattering apparatus.

If a solution or sol is sufficiently dilute, the total scattered light is simply the sum of the light scattered from individual particles. The light scattered from a particle depends on the area that intercepts the beam, and thus upon the square of the effective "radius" of the particle, r^2.

A theory of light scattering was originally worked out by Rayleigh in 1871 for the case of isotropic particles whose dimensions were small compared to the wavelength λ of the light. The intensity of light I_θ scattered by a particle through an angle θ depends on the intensity of incident light I_0, the distance r_s from the scattering volume, and the polarizability α of the particle. For unpolarized light, the relation is*

$$R_\theta(1 + \cos^2 \theta) = \frac{I_\theta r_s^2}{I_0} = \frac{8\pi^4 \alpha^2}{\lambda^4} (1 + \cos^2 \theta)$$

The quantity $R_\theta(1 + \cos^2 \theta)$ is called the *Rayleigh ratio.*

We may note especially the strong inverse dependence of scattered intensity on wavelength. As a consequence, blue light is much more strongly scattered than red light. If we look at the sky by daylight, we see the sunlight scattered by gas molecules and dust particles through various angles θ, and the sky appears blue. At sunset, however, we look directly at the sun, and it appears red because the blue light has been selectively scattered away from the direct beams. Animal colors are often due in part to scattered light,† sometimes modified by interference phenomena.

5. LIGHT SCATTERING BY MACROMOLECULES

The total light scattered in all directions from the incident beam as it traverses a suspension is measured by the *turbidity* τ. If the intensity I_0 of an incident beam is reduced to I on passage through a distance x,

$$I/I_0 = \exp(-\tau x) \tag{19.6}$$

This expression is formally similar to the Bouguer-Lambert Law for the absorption of light. The turbidity is related to the Rayleigh ratio at $\theta = 90°$ by

$$\tau = (16\pi/3)R_{90} \tag{19.7}$$

Light scattering is not measured as a turbidity, but by an actual determination of the intensity of the light at 90° and other angles relative to the incident beam. Results, however, are often reported in terms of the τ calculated from Eq. (19.7).

When the dimensions of the scattering particle are no longer small compared to the wavelength λ, the theory of scattering becomes more complicated. We must then consider interference between light waves scattered from different parts of the same particle. The theory for such scattering was worked out by Gustav Mie in 1908 for the case of a spherical particle. In 1947, Debye extended

* A derivation is given by P. J. Flory, *Principles of Polymer Chemistry* (Ithaca: Cornell Univ. Press, 1953) p. 287.

† C. H. Greenewalt, *Hummingbirds*, (New York: Doubleday, 1960) p. 169.

the Rayleigh theory to apply to a solution of macromolecules. In a very dilute solution

$$R_\theta = \frac{2\pi^2 n_0^2[(n - n_0)/C]^2}{L\lambda^4} CM = KCM \tag{19.8}$$

In this equation n is the refractive index of the solution and n_0 that of the solvent, C is the concentration in mass per unit volume and M is the molecular weight. Thus the measurement of R_θ leads to a computation of M.

In more concentrated solutions, Eq. (19.8) can be corrected to yield

$$K\frac{C}{R_\theta} = \frac{1}{M} + \frac{2BC}{M^2} \tag{19.9}$$

This equation has the same form as Eq. (19.4) for the osmotic pressure. If a solution of polymers of differing molecular weight is studied, light scattering yields the mass average molecular weight $\overline{M}_W$,* whereas osmotic pressure data yield the number average $\overline{M}_N$. We can therefore combine data from the two methods to obtain information about the molecular weight distribution in the polymer solution.

The next extension of the theory was to take into account the sizes and shapes of the molecules. These factors are included in the *particle scattering factor* $P(\theta)$. Thus, we obtain the equation,†

$$K\frac{C}{R_\theta} = \frac{1}{MP(\theta)} + \frac{2BC}{M^2} \tag{19.10}$$

It is possible to obtain an accurate value of M from data on light scattering, by examining the solutions over a range of concentrations C and angles θ. The data are then extrapolated to zero concentration and zero angle. This graphical extrapolation is called a *Zimm plot* after its inventor. Consider the data obtained by Doty§ and his coworkers for a fraction of cellulose nitrate dissolved in acetone. In Fig. 19.4 the values of KC/R_θ are plotted against $\sin^2\theta + kC$ where k is an arbitrary constant (2000 in this case) used to spread out the data. Each set of points at constant concentration is extrapolated to zero angle and each set of points at constant angle is extrapolated to zero concentration. The two limiting sets of points are extrapolated to zero ordinate, where they should intersect at a value of $1/\overline{M}_W$ free of effects due to interaction between particles (C) or interference between different parts of the same particle (θ). In this case $\overline{M}_W = 400\,000$. The value of $\overline{M}_N$ from osmotic pressure was 234 000. The difference indicates a rather broad distribution of molecular weights in this sample.

---

* From Eq. (19.9) applied to a distribution of polymers with concentrations C_i and molecular weights M_i, the limiting value of R_θ as $C \to 0$ is $K\sum C_i M_i$. Therefore the limiting value of KC/R_θ is

$$\sum C_i / \sum C_i M_i = 1/\overline{M}_W$$

† B. H. Zimm, *J. Chem. Phys. 16*, 1093 (1948).

§ A. M. Holtzer, H. Benoit and P. Doty, *J. Phys. Chem. 58*, 624 (1954).

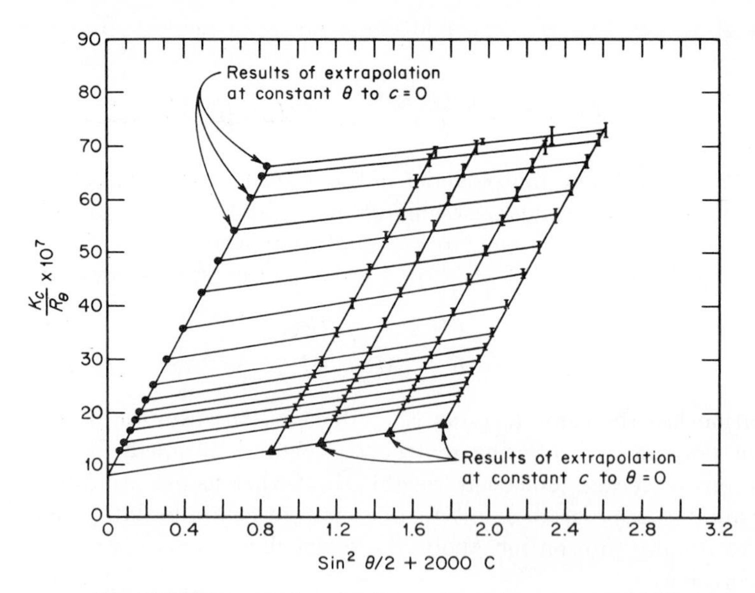

FIG. 19.4 Light scattering of cellulose nitrate in acetone at 25°C presented on a Zimm plot.

In this polymer, each monomer unit has $M = 294$ and a length of 5.15 Å. The number of units in a chain of $M = 400\,000$ would be 1350. If completely extended, this chain would be 6950 Å long. The value of the root mean square end to end distance, $(\overline{r^2})^{1/2}$, from light scattering was 1500 Å. This value is rather large for a molecule of such a short completely extended length, and suggests that this polymer is unusually stiff and extended. Most randomly coiled polymers tend to be much more tightly coiled and compact.

Figure 19.5 shows some results* of light scattering by tobacco mosaic virus, together with the theoretical curves for rods 2900 and 3200 Å long. The length of the virus appears to fit a value of 3000 ± 50 Å. The $\overline{M}_W$ is calculated to be 39.5×10^6. From the length, mass and density we can estimate an effective diameter of 150 Å. This work is a good example of the use of light scattering to characterize a macromolecule in solution.

6. SEDIMENTATION METHODS: THE ULTRACENTRIFUGE

We have already considered several instances of the distribution of particles in a gravitational field, viz., the barometric formula (p. 230) and the Millikan oil-drop experiment (p. 429). The terminal rate of fall of a particle is determined by the balance between the force of gravitation and the frictional resistance of the fluid medium to the motion of the particle. If a particle of mass m falls in a

* H. Boedtker and N. S. Simmons, *J. Am. Chem. Soc. 80*, 2550 (1958).

medium of density ρ, the gravitational force is $m(1 - \bar{v}\rho)g$, where $\bar{v}$ is the partial specific volume of the particle (i.e., $\overline{V}/L$, where $\overline{V}$ is the partial molar volume and L the Avogadro Number), and hence $\bar{v}m\rho$ is the mass of fluid displaced by the particle. If dx/dt is the velocity of sedimentation, $f(dx/dt)$ is the frictional force, where f is the frictional coefficient. Thus at terminal dx/dt,

$$f(dx/dt) = (1 - \bar{v}\rho)\, mg \tag{19.11}$$

We may note that f^{-1} is the velocity under a unit force.

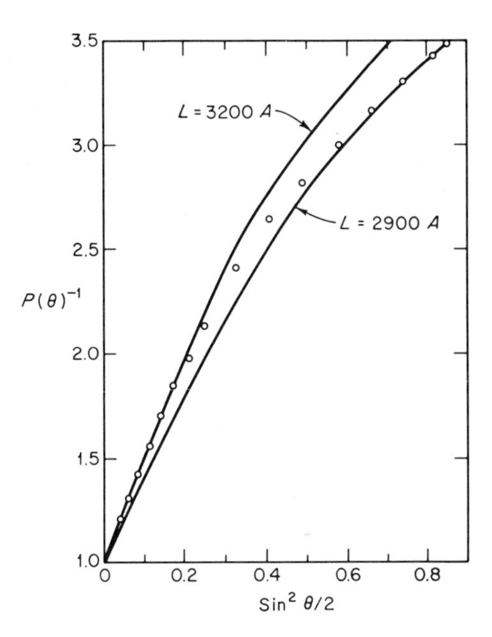

FIG. 19.5 Light scattering data from tobacco mosaic virus solution. The reciprocal of the particle scattering factor vs. $\sin^2(\theta/2)$, experimental points and theoretical scattering curves for rods of two different lengths.

Jean Perrin in 1908 studied with a microscope the sedimentation of gamboge particles in an aqueous suspension under the influence of the earth's gravitational field. The weakness of this field restricts his method to quite massive particles. The development of centrifugal techniques, capable of producing gravitational fields up to 300 000g, is due in large measure to The Svedberg of Uppsala. Beginning about 1923, he devoted great skill and genius to the problem of characterizing macromolecules, especially proteins, by means of centrifugal sedimentation. In a centrifugal field of force, we replace g in Eq. (19.11) by $\omega^2 x$, where ω is the angular velocity and x is the distance from the center of rotation. Thus

$$f(dx/dt) = (1 - \bar{v}\rho)m\omega^2 x \tag{19.12}$$

The quantity

$$s = (dx/dt)/\omega^2 x \tag{19.13}$$

is called the *sedimentation constant*. It is the sedimentation rate in a unit centrifugal field. For a given molecular species in a given solvent at a given temperature, s is a characteristic constant. It is expressed in *Svedberg units*, equal to 10^{-13} sec.

For the case of a spherical particle of radius r Stokes calculated

$$f = 6\pi\eta r$$

where η is the coefficient of viscosity of the medium. This is a special case, however, and usually we have no simple formula for f, even if we know the shape of the particle, which usually we do not.

Fortunately we can eliminate f if we can measure some other property that depends on it. For free diffusion in a dilute solution, the diffusion coefficient D is

$$D = RT/Lf = kT/f \tag{19.14}$$

This relation was derived by Einstein in 1905.* It follows directly from Eq. (9.18) if we replace u_i/Q by f^{-1}.

Assuming that the diffusional f is the same as the centrifugal f, we can eliminate it between Eqs. (19.12) and (19.14) to obtain

$$M = \frac{RTs}{D(1 - \bar{v}\rho)} \tag{19.15}$$

This equation, derived by Svedberg in 1929, has been the basis of many measurements of molecular weights from sedimentation velocities. For precise measurements, as usual, we can extrapolate s, D, and $\bar{v}$ to infinite dilution. Table 19.1 summarizes the data on some protein molecules that were studied in this way.

TABLE 19.1 CHARACTERISTIC CONSTANTS OF PROTEIN MOLECULES AT 20°C

Proteins	$\bar{v}$ (cm^3 g^{-1})	s (10^{-13} sec)	D (cm^2 sec^{-1}) $\times 10^7$	$M \times 10^{-3}$
Myoglobin (beef heart)	0.741	2.04	11.3	16.9
Hemoglobin (horse)	0.749	4.41	6.3	68
Hemoglobin (man)	0.749	4.48	6.9	63
Hemocyanin (octopus)	0.740	49.3	1.65	2800
Serumalbumin (horse)	0.748	4.46	6.1	70
Serumalbumin (man)	0.736	4.67	5.9	72
Serumglobulin (man)	0.718	7.12	4.0	153
Lysozyme (egg yellow)	(0.75)	1.9	11.2	16.4
Edestin	0.744	12.8	3.18	381
Urease (jack bean)	0.73	18.6	3.46	480
Pepsin (pig)	(0.750)	3.3	9.0	35.5
Insulin (beef)	(0.749)	3.58	7.53	46
Botulinus toxin A	0.755	17.3	2.10	810
Tobacco mosaic virus	0.73	185	0.53	31400

A second method of using the centrifuge is based on the *sedimentation equilibrium*. When equilibrium is reached, the rate at which a solute is driven out-

* A. Einstein, *Ann. Physik 17*, 549 (1905); *19*, 371 (1906).

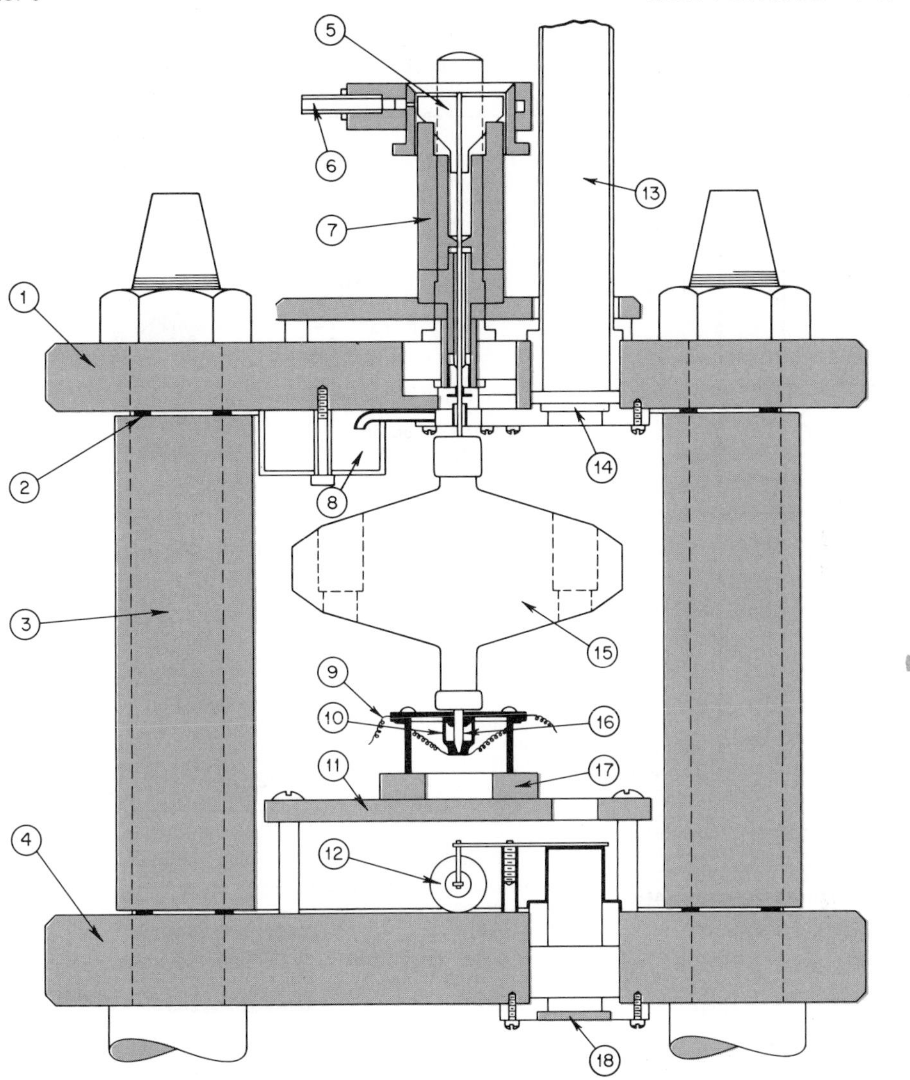

FIG. 19.6 Vertical cross-sectional view through vacuum chamber of air-driven ultracentrifuge. 1. Upper steel end plate; 2. rubber washers for vacuum seals; 3. wall of steel cylinder; 4. lower steel end plate; 5. turbine; 6. air inlet to driving jets; 7. stator; 8. oil container; 9. thermocouple lead; 10. mercury cup; 11. elevated flooring; 12. electromagnetic shutter; 13. metal sleeve connecting with camera bellows; 14. upper quartz window; 15. rotor; 16. tapered steel stem of rotor; 17. circular bakelite base; 18. lower quartz window. [T. Svedberg and K. O. Pedersen, *The Ultracentrifuge*, Oxford University Press, 1940]

wards by the centrifugal force just equals the rate at which it diffuses inwards under the influence of the concentration gradient. The sedimentation rate is

$$dn/dt = c\,dx/dt = c\omega^2 xM(1 - \mathbf{v}\rho)(1/f)$$

The diffusion rate is

$$dn/dt = -(RT/f)\,dc/dx$$

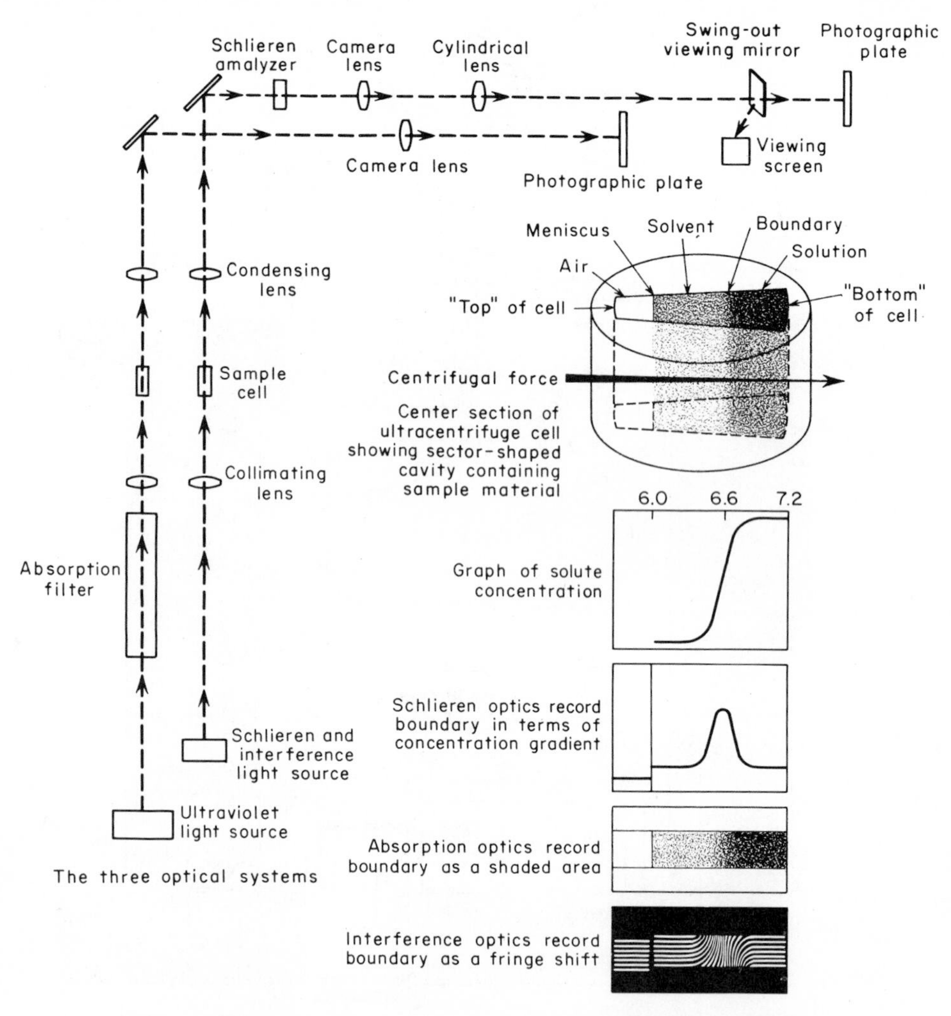

FIG. 19.7 (a) Summary of methods used for study of high polymer molecules in the analytical ultracentrifuge (Spinco).

At equilibrium, these rates are equal, and we obtain

$$dc/c = -\frac{M(1 - \bar{v}\rho)\omega^2 x\, dx}{RT}$$

Integration between x_1 and x_2 leads to

$$M = \frac{2RT \ln (c_2/c_1)}{(1 - \bar{v}\rho)\omega^2(x_2^2 - x_1^2)} \tag{19.16}$$

The molecular weight so obtained is clearly $\overline{M}_W$, the weight average.

The *sedimentation equilibrium* method does not require an independent measurement of D in order to fix the molecular weight, but the time required for

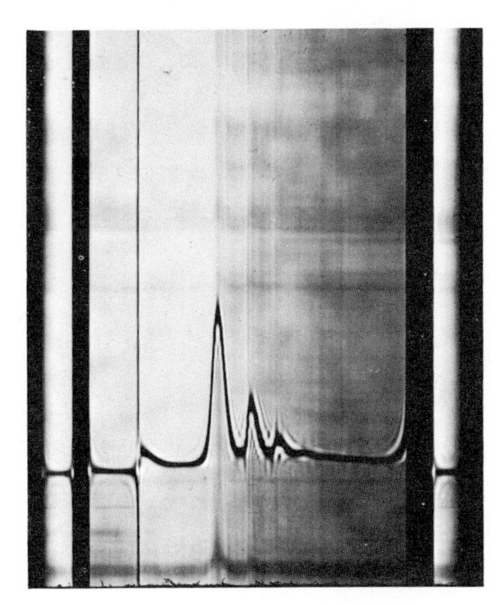

Schlieren pattern (multi-components). Preparation of ribosomes from Escherichia coli. 29,500 rpm

Ultraviolet absorption. Purified calf thymus DNA, 0.004 % in 0.2 M NaCl, pH 7.0. Speed 59,780 rpm. Photos at two minute intervols after reaching speed.

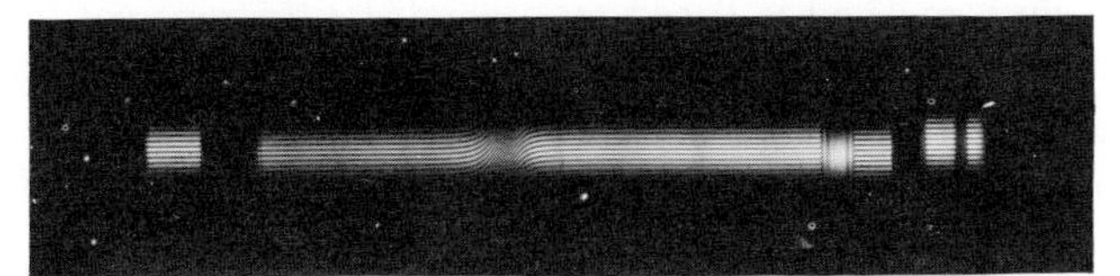

Rayleigh interference pattern. Bushy stunt virus 0.5 gm/ml in buffer at pH 4.1. Speed 14,290 rpm. Time 105 minutes.

FIG. 19.7 (b) Examples of centrifuge patterns using the three different optical systems. [Spinco Division, Beckman Instruments, Inc.]

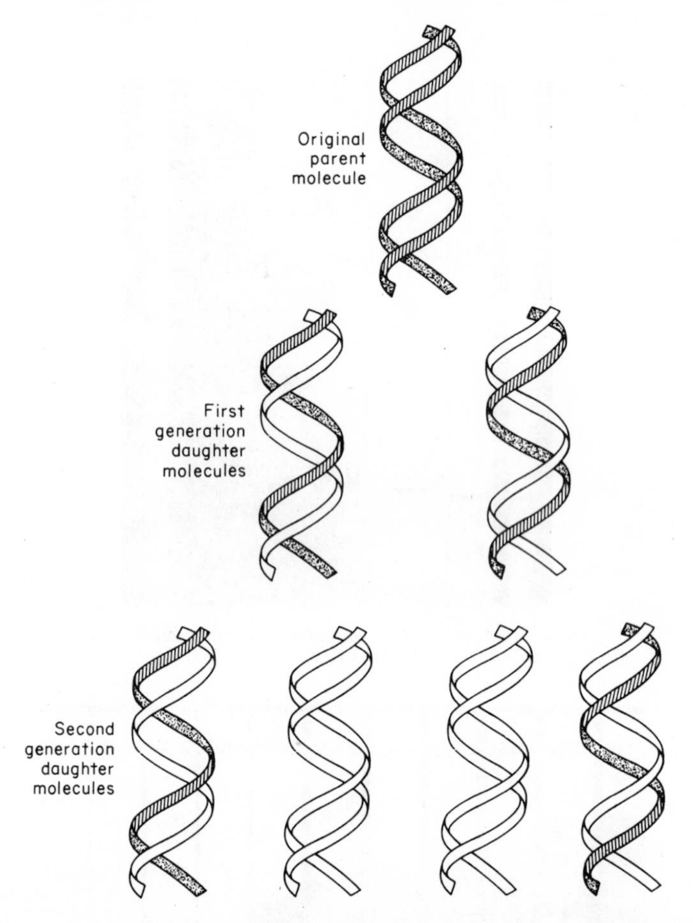

FIG. 19.8 Illustration of the mechanism of DNA duplication proposed by Watson and Crick. Each daughter molecule contains one of the parental chains (black) paired with one new chain (white). Upon continued duplication, the two original parent chains remain intact, so that there will always be found two molecules each with one parental chain. [M. S. Meselson and F. W. Stahl, California Institute of Technology].

equilibrium is so long that the method was not much used with substances having a molecular weight greater than 5000.

The equilibrium method is based on a condition of zero net flux across any plane in the solution normal to the radius of the cell. At the top meniscus and at the bottom of the cell, there can never be any net flux, so that the equilibrium condition must hold at these sections at all times.* Shortly after the centrifuge is brought to speed, therefore, a determination of the concentrations at these special planes can be used to give the equilibrium values. This modification of the equilibrium method greatly increases its useful scope.

* W. J. Archibald, *J. Phys. Chem. 51*, 1204 (1947).

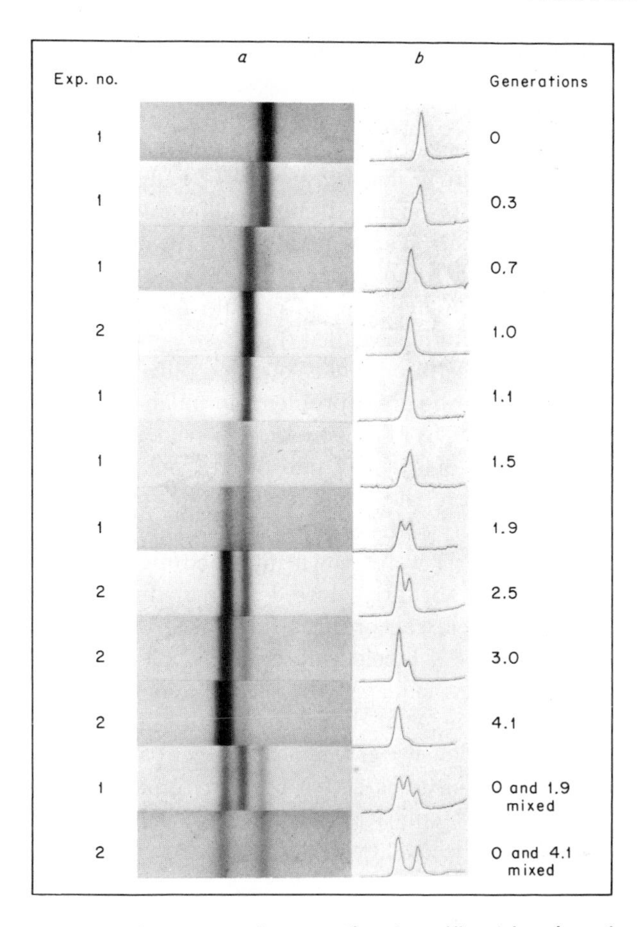

FIG. 19.9 An application of density-gradient centrifugation. Ultraviolet absorption photographs showing DNA bands resulting from density-gradient centrifugation of lysates of bacteria sampled at various times after the addition of an excess of ^{14}N substrates to a growing ^{15}N-labeled culture. Each photograph was taken after 20 hours of centrifugation at 44 770 rpm under the conditions described in the text. The density of the CsCl solution increases to the right. Regions of equal density occupy the same horizontal position on each photograph. The time of sampling is measured from the time of the addition of ^{14}N in units of the generation time. The generation times were estimated from measurements of bacterial growth. b: Microdensitometer tracings of the DNA bands shown in the adjacent photographs. The microdensitometer pen displacement above the base line is directly proportional to the concentration of DNA. The degree of labeling of a species of DNA corresponds to the relative position of its band between the bands of fully labeled and unlabeled DNA shown in the lowermost frame, which serves as a density reference. A test of the conclusion that the DNA in the band of intermediate density is just half-labeled is provided by the frame showing the mixture of generations 0 and 1.9. When allowance is made for the relative amounts of DNA in the three peaks, the peak of intermediate density is found to be centered at 50 ± 2 per cent of the distance between the N^{14} and N^{15} peaks. [M. Meselson and F. W. Stahl].

Figure 19.6 shows a centrifuge driven by an air turbine. The concentrations can be followed by various optical techniques, examples of which are shown in Fig. 19.7.

If a solution of a substance of low molecular weight is centrifuged, at equilibrium there will be a gradient in density across the cell. If we add to the cell a substance of high molecular weight, it should float in this solution of varying density at the particular position at which its buoyant density equals the density of the solution. If the macromolecular substance is made up of fractions of different molecular weights, each fraction should form a band at a particular plane in the cell. This technique is called the *density-gradient method.**

This method has been useful in studies of the replication of nucleic acids both *in vivo* and *in vitro*. One of the great problems in biochemistry is the mechanism of genetic control of heredity. The genetic material is DNA, a high polymer formed of units consisting of a sugar phosphate coupled with nitrogen bases. A model for the replication of the DNA molecule is shown in Fig. 19.8, as proposed by Watson and Crick.† The density-gradient method was applied to this problem as follows. Bacteria were grown in a medium containing heavy nitrogen ^{15}N. They were then abruptly shifted to a medium containing only ^{14}N. If the DNA molecules replicate according to the Watson-Crick model, at the end of the first generation, the ^{15}N labeled material will be depleted, and mixed ^{14}N and ^{15}N molecules will be formed. At the second generation $^{14}N^{15}N$ and $^{14}N^{14}N$ molecules should occur. Fig. 19.9 shows the results of one of the experiments. The bands observed in the density gradient in the centrifuge correspond with the predictions from the Watson-Crick structure. We must be cautious, however, in applying these results to replication of nucleic acids in the living cell, where more complex modes of replication evidently can occur.

7. VISCOSITY

We have discussed the theory of the viscosity of gases (Sec. 7.13) and of liquids (Sec. 17.13). The viscosities of solutions of high polymers depend on the sizes and shapes of the molecules in solution and thus can provide a useful method for the study of polymer configurations. The first attack on the problem was made by Einstein in 1906. For the case of rigid spherical particles in a dilute solution he derived the equation,

$$\lim_{\Phi \to 0} \left[\frac{(\eta/\eta_0) - 1}{\Phi} \right] = 2.5 \tag{19.17}$$

Here η is the viscosity of the solution and η_0 that of the pure solvent; Φ is the volume fraction of the solution occupied by solute particles. The fraction η/η_0

* M. S. Meselson, F. W. Stahl and J. Vinograd, *Proc. Nat. Acad. Sci.* *44*, 671 (1958); *43*, 581 (1957).

† F. H. C. Crick and J. D. Watson, *Proc. Roy. Soc. A* *223*, 80 (1954).

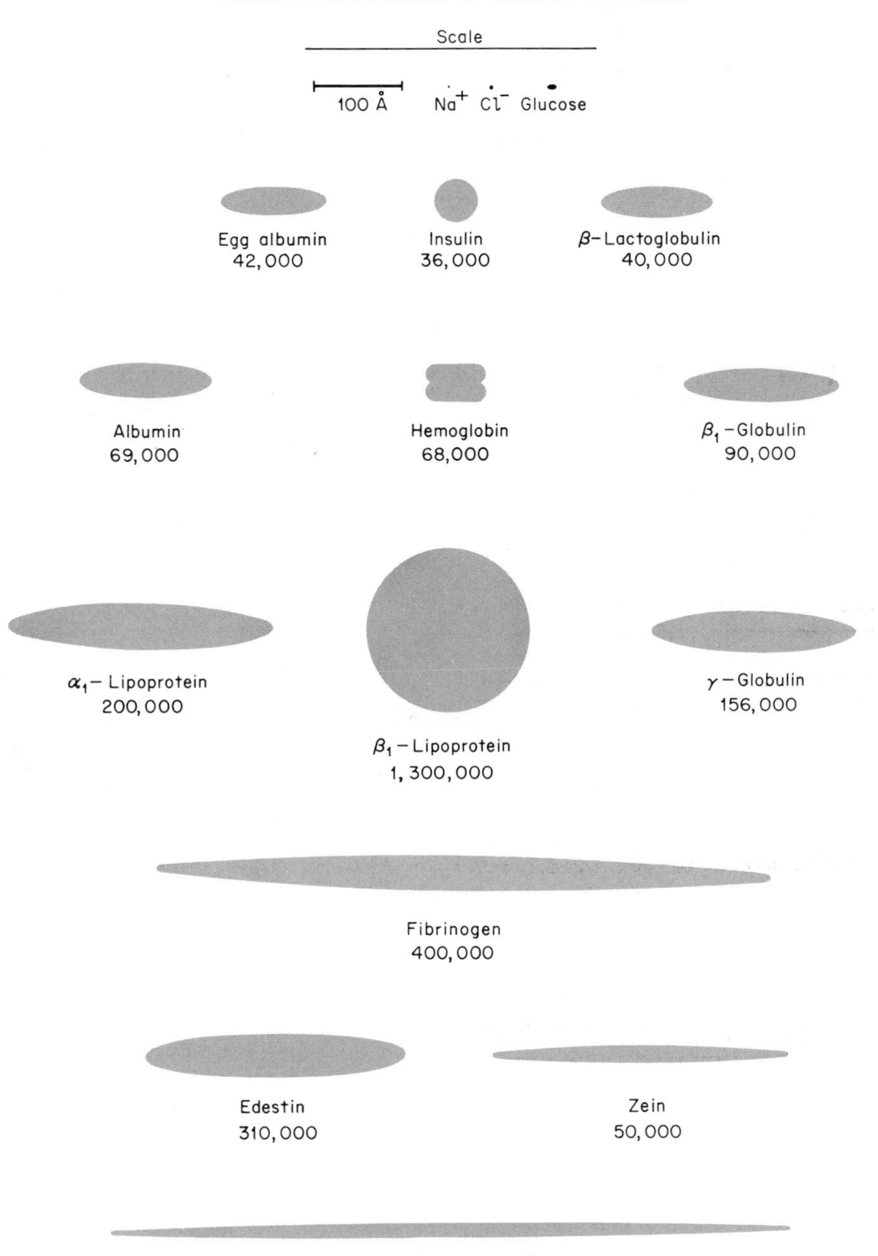

FIG. 19.10 Estimated dimensions of various protein molecules as seen in projection. Most of the proteins are represented as ellipsoids of revolution. β-lipoprotein is a sphere. [J. L. Oncley, Harvard University].

is called the *viscosity ratio* and $(\eta/\eta_0) - 1$ represents the increase in viscosity caused by the dissolved particles.

Equation (19.17) was extended by Simha to ellipsoidal particles, to give

$$\lim_{\Phi \to 0} \left[\frac{(\eta/\eta_0) - 1}{\Phi} \right] = \nu \tag{19.18}$$

where ν is related to the axial ratio of the ellipsoid.

Since it is difficult to measure Φ directly, we often use the expression

$$[\eta] = \lim_{C \to 0} \left[\frac{(\eta/\eta_0) - 1}{C} \right] \tag{19.19}$$

where C is the concentration in g ml^{-1}. The quantity $[\eta]/100$ has often been called the *intrinsic viscosity*, but the I.U.P.A.C. (1952) recommended that we use $[\eta]$ as defined by Eq. (19.19), and that we call it the *limiting viscosity number*.

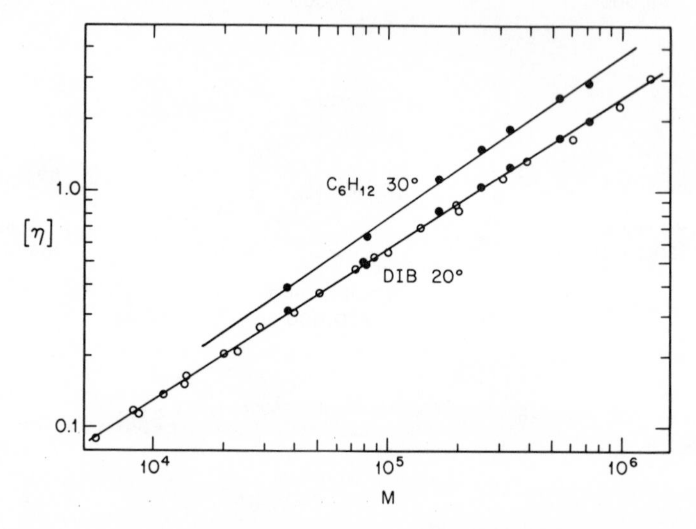

FIG. 19.11 Intrinsic viscosity — molecular weight relationship for polyisobutylene in diisobutylene (DIB) at 20°. and in cyclohexane at 30°C.

If **v** is the partial specific volume at infinite dilution (ml g^{-1}), $\Phi = C\bar{v}$, and

$$[\eta] = \nu\bar{v}$$

In the case of protein molecules, and other macromolecules hydrated in solution, we cannot take $\bar{v}$ as a true measure of the volume occupied by the dissolved molecule.*

Figure 19.10 shows our present understanding of the sizes and shapes of protein molecules in solution, as derived from the various techniques we have described.

* J. L. Oncley, *Ann. N. Y. Acad. Sci.* *41*, 121 (1941), has provided methods for treating this problem.

Molecular weights have usually been determined from viscosities on the basis of semi-empirical formulas. Thus Staudinger in 1932 proposed

$$[\eta] = KM$$

A more general relation is

$$[\eta] = KM^{\alpha} \tag{19.20}$$

This relation predicts that the logarithm of $[\eta]$ should be a linear function of the molecular weight M. Some data plotted in this way are shown in Fig. 19.11. The relation seems to hold well for a given polymer and solvent when M exceeds 30 000. For flexible coils α falls usually between 0.5 and 1.0, and for rods of constant diameter α is close to 2. Once the curve has been determined, therefore, a measurement of η can be used to determine an unknown M. In fact, if we have two well fractionated samples of polymer of known molecular weights, we can measure their viscosities and evaluate K and α for the particular polymer and solvent used. If we have a polymer with a distribution of molecular weights, the viscosity average molecular weight $\overline{M}_V$, obtained from Eq. (19.20), would be a rather complicated average falling somewhere between $\overline{M}_N$ and $\overline{M}_W$.*

For solid spheres the limiting viscosity number $[\eta]$ is independent of molecular weight, i.e., the coefficient α in Eq. (19.20) equals 0. It is found experimentally that all globular proteins, regardless of molecular weight, have essentially the same intrinsic viscosity ($\alpha = 0$). This fact is one of the best pieces of evidence that globular proteins are very compact molecules, similar to solid spheres.†

8. CONFIGURATION OF POLYMER MOLECULES

A long chain polymer molecule can often assume many different configurations in solution. Any theory of the properties of polymer solutions must begin, therefore, with a study of the statistical problem posed by the different orientations of the monomer segments of the polymer chosen. The most simple model of the polymer chain replaces the actual chemical bonds with links permitting perfectly free rotation; it also neglects the fact that no two monomer units can occupy the same location in space.

Consider in Fig. 19.12 a freely jointed polymer chain with one end fixed at the origin. What is the probability W that the other end falls in a volume element $dx\,dy\,dz$ at a distance r from the origin. The problem is like that of the free diffusion of a single molecule with a fixed jump distance a, i.e., a random walk in three dimensions. The solution is the Gaussian distribution,

$$W(x,y,z)\,dx\,dy\,dz = (\beta/\pi^{1/2})^3\, e^{-\beta^2 r^2}\,dx\,dy\,dz \tag{19.21}$$

The probability that one end of the chain lies at a distance r from the origin,

* C. Tanford, *Physical Chemistry of Macromolecules*, p. 411.

† C. Tanford, in *Symposium on Protein Structure*, ed. Neuberger (New York: Wiley, 1958).

irrespective of direction is (cf. the distribution of molecular velocities in Sec. 7.22),

$$W(r)\,dr = (\beta/\pi^{1/2})^3 e^{-\beta^2 r^2} \cdot 4\pi r^2\,dr \tag{19.22}$$

Differentiation of Eq. (19.22) shows that the maximum in $W(r)$ occurs at a value

$$r = \beta^{-1}$$

Thus β^{-1} is the most probable value of r.

If a is the length of a unit link of the chain, and n is the number of links,

$$\beta^{-1} = a(2n/3)^{1/2} \tag{19.23}$$

For a zig-zag chain of carbon atoms, with angles α and the length of the C—C bond l,

$$a = l\left(\frac{1 + \cos\alpha}{1 - \cos\alpha}\right)^{1/2}$$

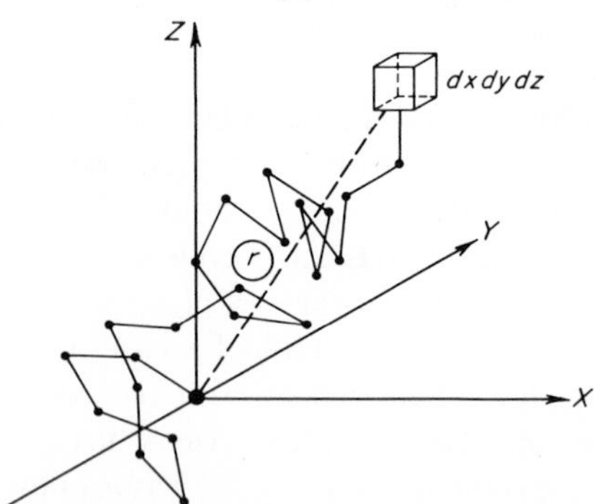

FIG. 19.12 Configuration of a freely rotating polymer chain with one end at origin and 23 links. Analog of a random walk in three dimensions.

The end to end length of the chain is important in the theory of such properties as rubber elasticity. On the other hand, properties such as light scattering and viscosity are related only to the *rms* distance of the chain segment from the center of mass.

$$(\overline{s^2})^{1/2} = (\overline{r^2})^{1/2}/6^{1/2} = \tfrac{1}{2}\beta$$

The chain with freely rotating links is really quite an unrealistic model for an actual polymer. It is necessary in further developments to consider the effect of restrictions on the bond angles, and the "free volume effect" which results from the fact that no two segments can fall at the same location. In this way, a reasonable theory for these flexible coil polymers can be developed. Such models would not apply at all, however, to proteins. As shown in Fig. 19.10, these behave more like rigid spheroids, or sometimes, as in the case of collagen,* rigid rods.

9. RUBBER ELASTICITY

The most remarkable property of a rubber is its ability to sustain a large deformation without breaking and to snap back to its original conformation when the deforming stress is removed. A rubber is like a liquid in its deformability and like a solid in its elasticity. The properties of rubbers are fundamentally related to their structures of long chainlike polymer molecules. Any long chain polymer can exhibit such properties under the right physical conditions.

* H. Boedtker and P. Doty, *J. Am. Chem. Soc. 78*, 4267 (1956).

Natural rubber is a polymerized isoprene with long hydrocarbon chains of the formula,

$$(-CH_2-C(CH_3)=CH-CH_2-)_n$$

The essential change which occurs in stretching a rubberlike polymer is shown in Fig. 19.13. In the unstretched rubber the polymer chains are coiled and twisted more or less at random. In the stretched condition, the chains uncoil to a considerable extent and tend to become oriented along the direction of elongation. Thus stretching causes the randomly oriented chains to assume a more ordered alinement. The unstretched, disordered configuration is a state of greater entropy. If the tension is released, the stretched rubber spontaneously reverts to the unstretched condition.

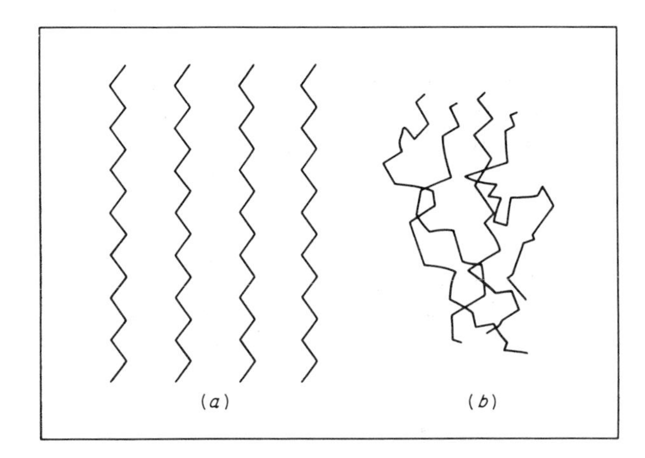

FIG. 19.13 Idealized models of chains in rubber: (a) stretched; (b) contracted.

Robert Boyle and his contemporaries used to talk about the "elasticity of a gas." Although we seldom hear this term today, we should note that the elasticity of a gas and the elasticity of a rubber band have the same thermodynamic interpretation. Consider a volume of gas compressed by a piston in a cylinder. If the pressure is released, the piston springs back as the gas expands. The expanded gas is in a state of higher entropy than the compressed gas. It is in a more disordered state because each molecule has a larger volume in which to move. A compressed gas is like a stretched rubber band. If we release the tension on the rubber, it spontaneously contracts. The contracted state of the rubber band, like the expanded state of the gas, is the state of greater disorder and hence of higher entropy.

From the relations $dA = -P\,dV - S\,dT$ and $A = E - TS$, the pressure is

$$P = -\left(\frac{\partial A}{\partial V}\right)_T = T\left(\frac{\partial S}{\partial V}\right)_T - \left(\frac{\partial E}{\partial V}\right)_T \tag{19.24}$$

For a gas the $(\partial E/\partial V)_T$ term is small and effectively, $P = T(\partial S/\partial V)_T$. The pressure is proportional to T and is determined by the change in entropy with volume. The analog of Eq. (19.24) for a rubber of length l subject to a tension K is

$$-K = T\left(\frac{\partial S}{\partial l}\right)_T - \left(\frac{\partial E}{\partial l}\right)_T$$

It is found experimentally that K is proportional to T, so that, just as in the case of the gas, the term involving the energy is relatively unimportant.

We can now use the statistical theory of polymers to calculate the probabilities of stretched and unstretched configurations, and then obtain the change in entropy from the Boltzmann relation $S = k \ln W$. For example, the probability of one particular configuration of the freely rotating chain polymer was given in Eq. (19.21). From this,

$$S = k \ln W = C - k\,\frac{x^2 + y^2 + z^2}{\frac{2}{3}na^2} \tag{19.25}$$

where C is a constant. The total entropy of all the polymer molecules is calculated by averaging over all the possible configurations, with each one weighted by its probability. Thus the total entropy per unit volume is

$$S = \int_0^\infty NSW(xyz)\,dx\,dy\,dz$$

where S is given by Eq. (19.25) and N is the concentration in molecules per unit volume. To calculate the ΔS on stretching we must consider the effect of an elongation in the x direction and consequent contraction in the y and z directions.* This method yields

$$\Delta S = -\tfrac{1}{2}Nk\left(\alpha^2 + \frac{2}{\alpha} - 3\right) \tag{19.26}$$

where $\alpha = l/l_0$ is the extension ratio.

10. CRYSTALLINITY OF POLYMERS

Although they cannot always be obtained as perfect three-dimensional crystals, high polymers often have a high degree of order in the solid state, which can be investigated by X-ray diffraction. For example, much important work has been done on X-ray diffraction by *fibers*, either natural (hair, silk, porcupine quills) or artificial (nylon, polypeptides).

In some cases, these fibers have a well defined periodicity parallel to the fiber axis, but a more random organization in other directions. The type of pattern which results can be understood from the case of diffraction by a linear array (p. 462). Consider a set of scattering centers with a repeat distance c along the c-axis. If the Bragg condition is fulfilled at angle θ,

$$c \sin \theta = l\lambda$$

* W. Kuhn and F. Grün, *J. Polymer Sci. 1*, 183 (1946).

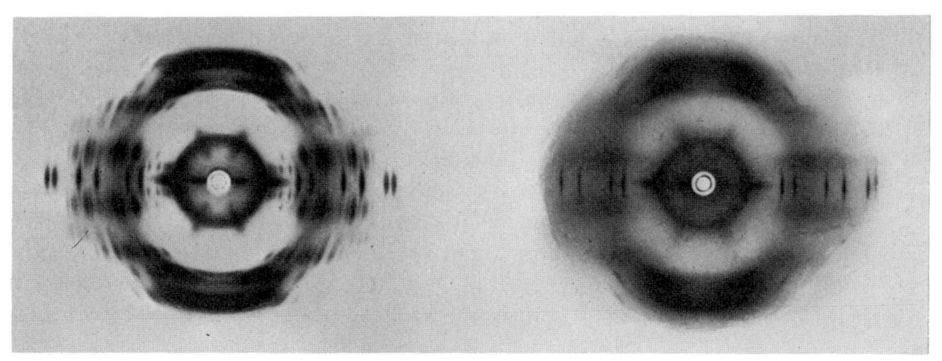

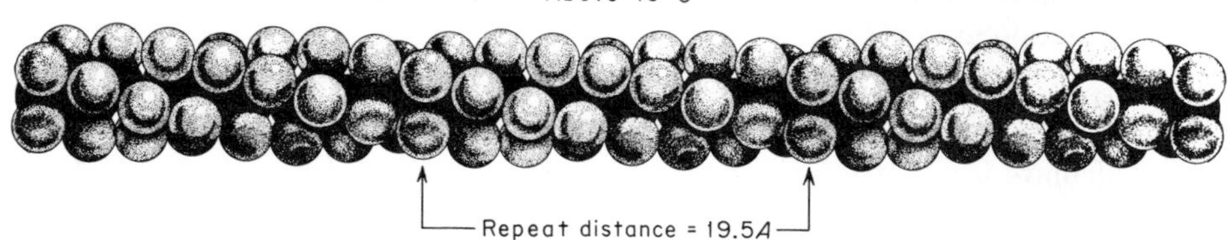

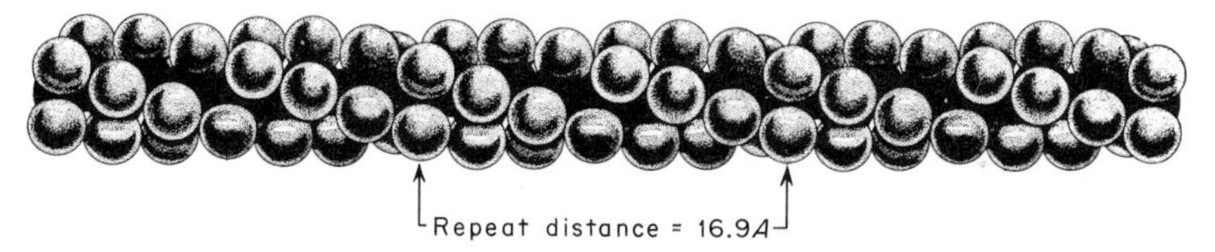

FIG. 19.14 X-ray diffraction patterns of oriented fibers of polytetrafluoroethylene above and below the transition at 19°C and models of sections of the polymer to show the transition that occurs. [C. A. Sperati and H. W. Starkweather, DuPont Experimental Station, Wilmington].

where l is an integer. The pattern on the film will consist of a set of layer lines with a spacing a, with

$$\tan \theta = a/R$$

where R is the distance between specimen and film.

Figure 19.14 shows an example of such a diagram for fibers of polytetrafluoroethylene. This polymer undergoes a transition in the crystalline state at 19°C, which is associated with an expansion of the repeat distance along the polymer chain. Such X-ray fiber diffraction diagrams have been important in elucidating the structures of proteins and nucleic acids. As shown in Chap. 16, however, complete elucidations of protein structures can be achieved by X-ray diffraction analysis of single crystals of complexes of proteins with atoms of heavy metals.

PROBLEMS

1. A suspension contains equal numbers of particles with molecular weights 10 000 and 20 000. Calculate $\overline{M}_N$ and $\overline{M}_W$. A suspension contains equal masses of particles with molecular weights 10 000 and 20 000. Calculate $\overline{M}_N$ and $\overline{M}_W$.

2. A sample of polyisobutylene in cyclohexane solution with $\overline{M}_N = 254\,000$, had a second virial coefficient from osmotic pressure data (Eq. 19.4) of $B = 6.31 \times 10^{-4}$, where π is in dyne cm^{-2} and C in g cm^{-3}. Calculate the osmotic pressure at a concentration $C = 10^{-2}$ and $t = 25°$, and compare it with the value for an ideal solution.

3. The following data were obtained for the osmotic pressures of nitrocellulose in acetone at 20°C.

C (g l^{-1}))	1.16	3.66	8.38	19.0
π (cm H_2O)	0.62	2.56	8.00	25.4

Calculate the limiting value of π/C and hence $\overline{M}_N$. [*Ans.* $M_N = 41\,400$].

4. For horse hemoglobin in water solution at 20°C, $D = 6.3 \times 10^{-7}$cm^2 sec^{-1}, $s = 4.41 \times 10^{-13}$ sec, $v = 0.749$, $\rho = 0.9982$. Calculate the molecular weight.

5. The viscosities relative to pure solvent of a fraction of polystyrene of $\overline{M}_N =$ 280 000, dissolved in tetralin at 20°C were:

conc %	0.01	0.025	0.05	0.10	0.25
η_r	1.05	1.12	1.25	1.59	2.70

Calculate the value of the constant K in the Staudinger equation. Hence estimate the relative viscosity of a 0.10 solution of polystyrene with $\overline{M}_N =$ 500 000 in the same solvent. Assume $\alpha = 1.0$.

6. The diffusion coefficient of the insulin molecule in water at 20°C is 8.2×10^{-7} cm^2 s^{-1}. Estimate the mean time required for an insulin molecule to diffuse through a distance equal to the diameter of a typical living cell, about 5μ.

7. Calculate the most probable value of the chain length of normal $C_{20}H_{42}$, given the C—C bond length of 1.54 Å and the bond angle of 109° 28′.

8. For a solution of cellulose trinitrate ($M - 140\,000$) in acetone, $dn/dc =$ 0.105 cm^3 g^{-1} and $n_0 = 1.3589$. Calculate the ratio of intensities of transmitted to incident light at wavelengths of 4000 and 7000 Å through 1.00 cm thickness of a solution of the polymer containing 2.00 g per 100 cm^3.

9. Suppose you hang a weight on a rubber band so as to keep it under constant tension. If you then heat the rubber band, will the weight rise or fall? Give a thermodynamic answer, then try it.

10. Sedimentation equilibrium in a suspension of a monodisperse polymer, congo red, was studied by Svedberg and Petersen in their ultracentrifuge. The initial concentration was 0.10 g l^{-1}, rotation speed 299.6 rps, $\bar{v} = 0.60$ and $\rho = 1.00$. At $X_2 = 5.75$ cm, $C_2 = 42.18$; at $X_1 = 5.72$ cm, $C_1 = 39.76$. Calculate the molecular weight of the congo red.

11. Estimate the diffusion coefficient in water at 20°C of a spherical molecule with a molecular weight of 10^6 and $\bar{v} = 0.75$.

12. In an experiment on light scattering by serum albumin at its isoelectric point in deionized water, the limiting value of KC/R_0 as $c \rightarrow 0$ was 1.33×10^{-5}. Calculate the molecular weight of the protein.

---

13. The molecular weight of a deoxyribonucleic acid (DNA) from calf thymus was determined as 5.00×10^6 and its sedimentation constant was 13.2×10^{-13} s. The partial specific volume was 0.530, in water at 20°C. Calculate the diffusion coefficient for this material. What would be the ratio of the concentrations at equilibrium in the earth's gravitational field at two levels 10 cm apart?
    Sedimentation equilibrium is achieved in a centrifuge at 50 000 rpm with a cell whose midpoint is 6.50 cm from the rotation axis and whose thickness is 1.00 cm. Calculate the relative concentrations of DNA at the midpoint of the cell and at a position 0.10 cm from the outer edge.

14. Prove that for a zigzag chain of identical atoms with bond distances d and bond angles α, the length of each link is $a = d[(1 + \cos \alpha)/(1 - \cos \alpha)]^{1/2}$.

15. The following particle count was obtained with the electron microscope on spherical polystyrene particles at 48 000× magnification. Diameter in mm (number of particles): 12.8(1); 12.6(1); 11.8(2); 11.6(3); 11.4(3); 11.2(15); 11.0(57); 10.8(77); 10.6(25); 10.4(12); 10.2(10); 10.0(7); 9.8(2); 9.2(1); 9.0(3); 8.8(1); 8.0(2); 7.8(3); 7.6(1); 5.4(1); 5.2(1). The density of polystyrene is 1.060 g cm^{-3}. Calculate $\overline{M}_N$ and $\overline{M}_W$ for this polymer distribution.

20 NUCLEAR CHEMISTRY AND PHYSICS

The changing of Bodies into Light, and Light into Bodies, is very conformable to the Course of Nature, which seems delighted with Transmutations.

ISAAC NEWTON, *Opticks* (1718)

The inertial properties of matter are determined by its total content of energy. If m_0 is the rest mass of a body (its mass when at rest with respect to any frame of reference) its energy content is given by

$$E_0 = c^2 m_0 \tag{20.1}$$

where c is the speed of light in a vacuum. This equation was first given by Poincaré in 1900, and derived in 1905 by Einstein as a consequence of his special theory of relativity.

If a body is moving with a speed v, its energy will be the sum of its rest energy, given by Eq. (20.1), and its kinetic energy. One of the postulates of Einstein's theory was that no body could have a speed v in excess of c. Hence as the kinetic energy increased, the inertial resistance to further acceleration must increase, so that as $v \to c$, the inertia $\to \infty$. This result can be expressed by saying that the mass increases with speed in accord with an equation given by Einstein,

$$m = m_0 \left(1 - \frac{v^2}{c^2}\right)^{-1/2} \tag{20.2}$$

We can now write the total energy of the body as

$$E = mc^2 = m_0 c^2 \left(1 - \frac{v^2}{c^2}\right)^{-1/2}$$

The kinetic energy is the total energy minus the rest energy,

$$E_K = E - E_0 = (m - m_0)c^2$$

Many exact experimental confirmations of the mass-energy relations have been obtained in nuclear reactions and particle physics.

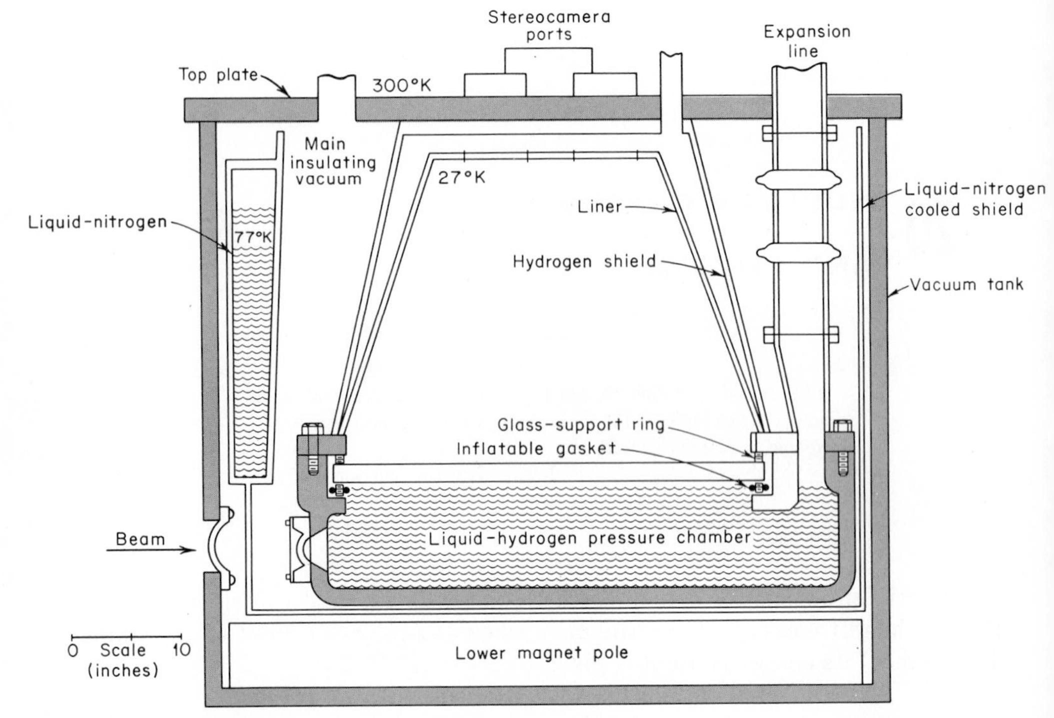

FIG. 20.1 The 180-cm liquid hydrogen bubble chamber at the Lawrence Radiation Laboratory, Berkeley, California.

1. PARTICLE TRACKING

Although we cannot see energetic particles and nuclei, we can see the tracks they leave when they pass through matter. Three important methods have been used for tracking particles.

In the *photographic method*, the tracks of particles are recorded in a sensitive emulsion. For energetic cosmic-ray particles, large stacks of emulsions are exposed at high altitudes, and the paths of the particles are followed through many layers of the developed plates.

The *cloud chamber* was invented by C. T. R. Wilson in 1912. A chamber containing water vapor is cooled by a sudden expansion so that the gas volume is supersaturated with water vapor. If an ionizing particle enters, the water vapor condenses as small droplets along its path. Thus the path is made visible and can be photographed.

The *bubble chamber* was invented by D. A. Glaser in 1952. It is the inverse of the cloud chamber. The ionizing particle passes through a chamber containing a superheated liquefied gas, and the course of the particle is made visible by the formation of gas bubbles nucleated along its path. Fig. 20.1 is a diagram of the 180-cm liquid-hydrogen bubble chamber at Berkeley.

2. ARTIFICIAL DISINTEGRATION OF ATOMIC NUCLEI

In 1919, Rutherford found that when α particles from radium-C passed through nitrogen, protons were ejected from the nitrogen nuclei. This was the first example of the disintegration of a normally stable nucleus. Other light elements were later found to emit protons when bombarded with α particles.

In 1923, P. M. S. Blackett obtained cloud-chamber photographs showing that these reactions occurred by capture of the α particle, a proton and a new nucleus being formed. For example,

$$^{14}_{7}\mathrm{N} + {}^{4}_{2}\mathrm{He} \longrightarrow ({}^{18}_{9}\mathrm{F}) \longrightarrow {}^{1}_{1}\mathrm{H} + {}^{17}_{8}\mathrm{O}$$

This type of reaction did not occur with heavy elements because of the large electrostatic repulsion between the doubly charged alpha and the high positive charge of the nucleus.

The singly charged proton $^{1}_{1}\mathrm{H}$ would clearly be a more effective nuclear projectile, but this was not available in the form of high-velocity particles from radioactive materials. J. D. Cockroft and E. T. S. Walton* therefore devised an electrostatic accelerator. This apparatus was the prototype of many more elaborate machines designed to produce high-velocity particles. Protons from the ionization of hydrogen in an electric discharge passed through slits into a tube in which they were accelerated across a high potential difference before striking a target.

One of the first reactions studied by Cockroft and Walton was

$$^{1}_{1}\mathrm{H} + {}^{7}_{3}\mathrm{Li} \longrightarrow 2\,{}^{4}_{2}\mathrm{He}$$

The bombarding protons had energies of 3×10^5 ev (0.3 mev). From the range of the emergent α particles in the cloud chamber, 8.3 cm, their energy was calculated to be 8.6 mev each, or more than 17 mev for the pair. It is evident that the bombarding proton causes a highly exothermic nuclear reaction.

The energies involved in these nuclear reactions are several million times those in the most exothermic chemical changes. Thus we can make a quantitative experimental test of the $E = c^2m$ relation. The mass-spectrographic values for the rest masses of the reacting nuclei are found to be

$$^{1}\mathrm{H} + {}^{7}\mathrm{Li} \longrightarrow 2\,{}^{4}\mathrm{He}$$
$$1.00812 + 7.01822 \longrightarrow 2 \times 4.00391$$

Thus the reaction occurs with a decrease in rest mass $-\Delta m$ of 0.01852 g per mole of lithium. This is equivalent to an energy of

$$0.01852 \times 9 \times 10^{20} = 1.664 \times 10^{19} \text{ erg per mole}$$

or

$$\frac{1.664 \times 10^{19}}{6.02 \times 10^{23}} = 2.763 \times 10^{-5} \text{ erg per lithium nucleus}$$

* *Proc. Roy. Soc. A 129*, 477 (1930); *136*, 619 (1932).

or $$2.763 \times 10^{-5} \times 6.242 \times 10^{11} = 17.25 \times 10^{6} = 17.25 \text{ mev}$$

This figure is in excellent agreement with the energy observed from the cloud-chamber experiments.

The measurement of the large amounts of energy released in nuclear reactions provides a most accurate method for determining differences in masses of nuclides. The calculation of atomic masses from the observed energies of nuclear reactions is therefore widely applied in the determination of precise atomic weights. A few of the values so obtained are collected in Table 20.1 and compared with mass-spectrographic data. The exact agreement between the two methods, within the probable error of the experiments, is a convincing proof of the equivalence of mass and energy. The starred isotopes are radioactive, and the only available mass values are those from the $E = c^2m$ relation.

TABLE 20.1 Precise Atomic Weights ($^{12}C = 12$)

Atom	*Mass Spectrometer Value*	*Mass-Energy Value*
^{1}H	1.00788	1.007820
^{2}H	2.01408	2.014092
^{3}H*	—	3.016044
^{3}He	—	3.006024
^{4}He	4.00260	4.0025988
^{6}He*	—	6.0185592
^{6}Li	6.012588	6.0149508
^{7}Li	7.015956	7.015992

3. PARTICLE ACCELERATORS

At about this point in its development nuclear physics began to outgrow the limitations of small-scale laboratory equipment. The construction of machines for the production of highly accelerated ions, capable of overcoming the repulsive forces of nuclei with large atomic numbers, demanded all the resources of large-scale engineering. Some of the basic types of accelerators are shown in Fig. 20.2.

One of the most useful of these accelerators has been the cyclotron, which was invented by E. O. Lawrence of Berkeley. The charged particles are fed into the center of the *dees* where they are accelerated by a strong electric field. The magnetic field, however, constrains them to move in a circular path. The time required to traverse a semicircle is $t = \pi R_B/v = (\pi/B)\cdot(m/Q)$ from Eq. (11.8); this is a constant for all particles having the same Q/m. The direction of the alternating electric field changes with a frequency exactly twice that of the circular motion of a charged particle. On each passage across the dees, therefore, a particle receives a new forward impulse, and describes a trajectory of ever increasing radius until it is drawn form the accelerating chamber of the cyclotron. The 470-cm machine at Berkeley produces a beam of 100 mev deuterons (nuclei of deuterium atoms) having a range in air of 45 meters.

The ionic energy that can be reached in the original type of cyclotron is limited by the relativistic increase of mass with velocity; this eventually destroys

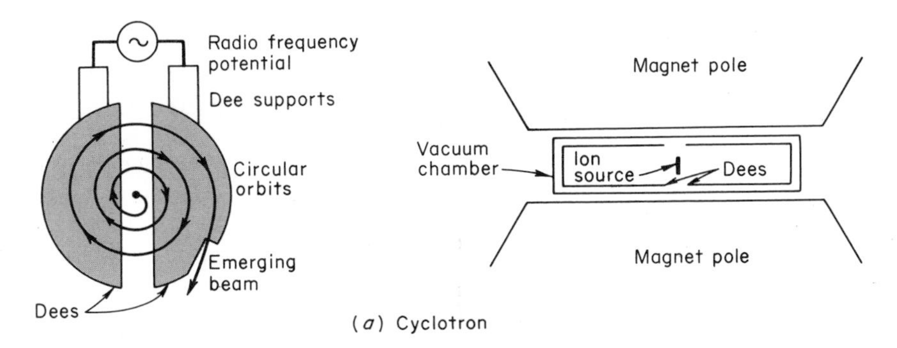

(*a*) Cyclotron

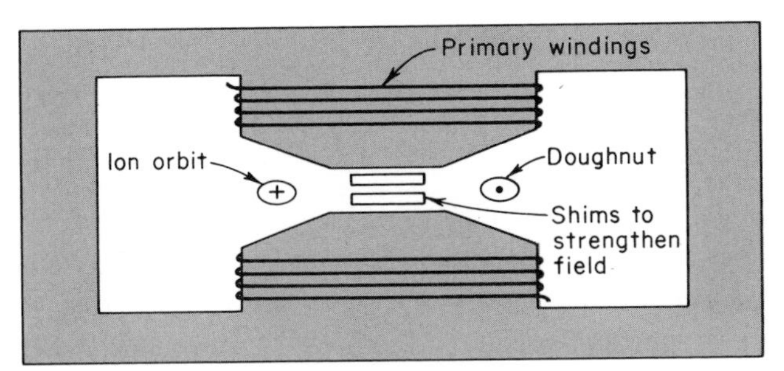

(*b*) Betatron

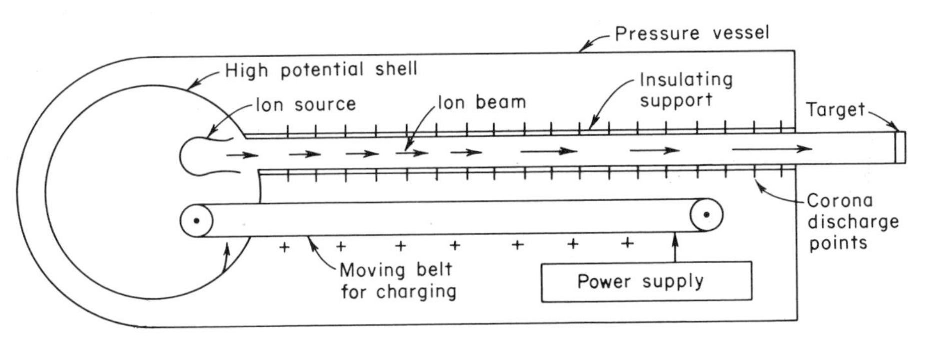

(*c*) Van de Graaff accelerator

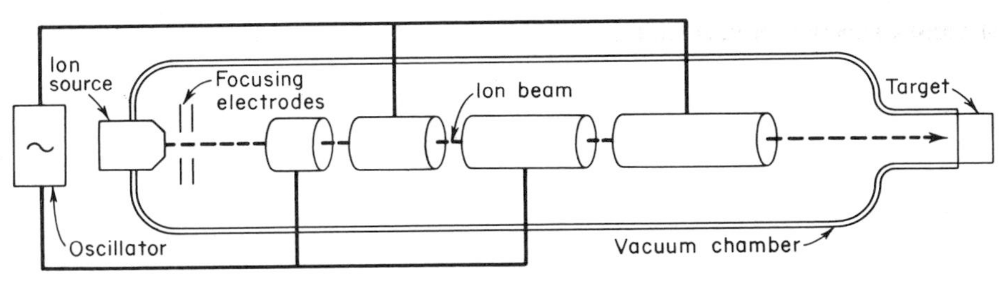

(*d*) Linear accelerator

FIG. 20.2 Basic types of accelerators [Raymond L. Murray, *Introduction to Nuclear Engineering*, 2nd edition, Prentice-Hall, Englewood Cliffs, N. J. 1961].

the synchronization in phase between the revolving ions and the accelerating field across the dees. This problem has been overcome in the synchrocyclotron, in which frequency modulation, applied to the alternating potential, compensates for the relativistic defocusing. This modification of the original design of the Berkeley instrument has more than doubled the maximum ion energies obtained. The *synchrotron* employs modulation of both the electric accelerating field and the magnetic focusing field. With this principle, it is possible to achieve the bev range for protons.

Recently linear acceleration has again become important. A linear accelerator under construction at Stanford is to be 3.3 km long and to produce a beam of electrons at 45×10^9 ev (45 bev).

Cosmic rays often contain particles far more energetic than those from the biggest accelerators. Cosmic ray energies of 10^6 bev are not uncommon.

4. THE NEUTRON

In 1930, W. Bothe and H. Becker discovered that a very penetrating secondary radiation was produced when α particles from polonium impinged on light elements such as beryllium, boron, or lithium. No tracks were made in a cloud chamber, and therefore charged particles were not being formed. In 1932, Frederic and Irene Curie-Joliot found that the new radiation had a much greater ionizing power after it had passed through paraffin, or some other substance having a high hydrogen content, and during its passage protons were emitted from these hydrogen-rich materials.

James Chadwick* solved the problem, by proposing a particle of a new kind, having a mass comparable to that of the proton but bearing no electric charge. This particle he called the *neutron*. Because it is electrically neutral the neutron exerts an appreciable force on other particles only at very close distances. The neutron, therefore, loses energy slowly as it passes through matter; in other words, it has a great penetrating power. Because it can approach close to an atomic nucleus without being electrostatically repelled, the neutron is an extraordinarily potent reactant in nuclear processes. The hydrogen nucleus is most effective in slowing a neutron, since energy exchange is a maximum between particles of like mass.

The reaction producing the neutron can now be written

$$^4_2\text{He} + ^9_4\text{Be} \longrightarrow ^{12}_6\text{C} + ^1_0n$$

Neutrons can be produced by similar reactions of other light elements with high energy α particles, protons, deuterons, or even γ rays, for example,

$$^2_1\text{H} + h\nu \longrightarrow ^1_1\text{H} + ^1_0n$$

$$^1_1\text{H} + ^7_3\text{Li} \longrightarrow ^7_4\text{Be} + ^1_0n$$

* *Proc. Roy. Soc. A 136*, 692 (1932).

Beams of neutrons can be formed by means of long pinholes or slits in thick blocks of paraffin, and methods are available for producing beams of uniform energy.*

The neutron is an unstable particle with a half life $\tau = 7651$ sec. It decays into a proton and an electron:†

$$n \longrightarrow p + e^- + 0.783 \text{ mev}$$

5. POSITRON AND MESONS

In 1932, Carl D. Anderson at Caltech discovered the positive electron or *positron* in cloud-chamber tracks from cosmic rays. It had previously been predicted by the theoretical work of Dirac. In 1933, the Curie-Joliots found that a shower of positrons was emitted when α rays from polonium impinged on a beryllium target. When targets of boron, magnesium, or aluminum were used, the emission of positrons was observed to continue for some time after the particle bombardment was stopped. This was the first demonstration of *artificial radioactivity*.§ A typical reaction sequence is the following:

$$^{10}_{5}\text{B} + {}^{4}_{2}\text{He} \longrightarrow {}^{1}_{0}n \longrightarrow {}^{13}_{7}\text{N}; \qquad {}^{13}_{7}\text{N} \longrightarrow {}^{13}_{6}\text{C} + e^+$$

More than a thousand artificial radioactive isotopes are now known, produced in a variety of nuclear reactions.‡

The positron escaped detection for a long time, because it can exist only until it happens to meet an electron. Then a reaction occurs, which annihilates both of them to produce at least two γ-ray photons:

$$e^+ + e^- \longrightarrow h\nu + h\nu'$$

The energy equivalent to the rest mass of an electron of either sign is

$$\epsilon = mc^2 = 9.11 \times 10^{-28} \times (3.00 \times 10^{10})^2 = 8.20 \times 10^{-7} \text{ erg}$$

If this is converted into two identical γ-ray photons, the wavelength will be

$$\lambda = \frac{h}{mc} = \frac{6.62 \times 10^{-27}}{9.11 \times 10^{-28} \times 3.00 \times 10^{10}} = 2.42 \times 10^{-10} \text{ cm} = 0.0242 \text{ Å}$$

The reverse process, the production of an electron-positron pair from a pair of energetic photons, has also been observed.

In 1935, H. Yukawa proposed for the structure of the nucleus a theory that postulated the existence of a hitherto unknown kind of particle, which would be unstable and have a mass of about 150 (electron = 1). From 1936 to 1938 Anderson's work at Pasadena revealed the existence of particles, produced by

* E. Fermi, J. Marshall and L. Marshall, *Phys. Rev. 72*, 193 (1947); W. Zinn, *ibid, 71*, 757 (1947).

† Plus an *antineutrino*, see Sec. 7.

§ *C. R. Acad. Sci.* (Paris) *198*, 254, 599 (1934).

‡ G. Seaborg and I. Perlman, *Rev. Mod. Phys. 20*, 585 (1948).

cosmic rays, which seemed to have many of the properties predicted by Yukawa. These particles are the *μ-mesons* or *muons* which may be charged plus or minus, have a mass of 209 ± 2, and a half life of 2.2×10^{-6} sec. The particles required by the theory, however, resemble more closely the *π-mesons* or *pions*, discovered in 1947 by the Bristol cosmic-ray group headed by C. F. Powell. These have a mass of 275, and decay to μ-mesons, with a half life of 2.0×10^{-8} sec.

Fig. 20.3 shows the production of positive and negative pions in a cosmic-ray event in a bubble chamber.

6. ELEMENTARY PARTICLES

From the times of Democritus and Leucippus, through those of Dalton, Boltzmann, J. J. Thomson and Fermi, men have tried to see the world as a structure of elementary particles. The search for these ultimate and indivisible units of structure led from atoms to protons, neutrons, electrons and mesons. Table 20.2 summarizes our current knowledge of "elementary" particles. Have we reached the ultimate particles at last? Probably not — some "elementary particles" are beginning to reveal that they must themselves have a "structure."

TABLE 20.2 ELEMENTARY PARTICLES

The particles are tabulated on the left. The "reflections" on the right are the corresponding antiparticles. The stable particles are circled. [J. Orear, *Fundamental Physics* (New York: John Wiley, 1961).]

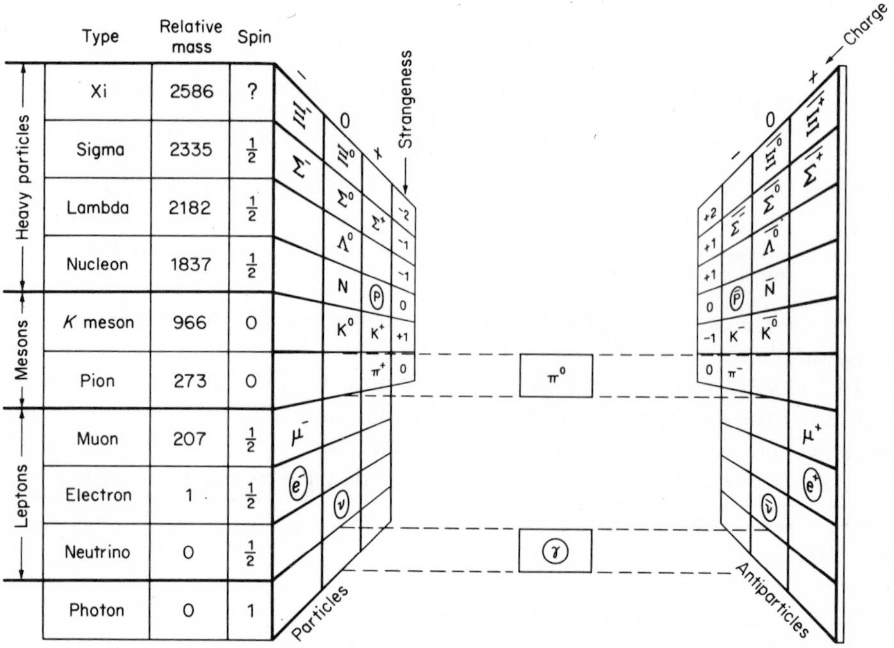

	Type	Relative mass	Spin	Particles: charge −	Particles: charge 0	Particles: charge +	Strangeness		Strangeness	Antiparticles: charge −	Antiparticles: charge 0	Antiparticles: charge +
Heavy particles	Xi	2586	?	Ξ^-	Ξ^0		−2		+2		$\bar{\Xi}^0$	$\bar{\Xi}^+$
	Sigma	2335	$\frac{1}{2}$	Σ^-	Σ^0	Σ^+	−1		+1	$\bar{\Sigma}^-$	$\bar{\Sigma}^0$	$\bar{\Sigma}^+$
	Lambda	2182	$\frac{1}{2}$		Λ^0		−1		+1		$\bar{\Lambda}^0$	
	Nucleon	1837	$\frac{1}{2}$		N	(P)	0		0	($\bar{P}$)	$\bar{N}$	
Mesons	K meson	966	0		K^0	K^+	+1		−1	K^-	$\bar{K}^0$	
	Pion	273	0			π^+	0	π^0	0	π^-		
Leptons	Muon	207	$\frac{1}{2}$	μ^-								μ^+
	Electron	1	$\frac{1}{2}$	(e^-)								(e^+)
	Neutrino	0	$\frac{1}{2}$		(ν)						($\bar{\nu}$)	
	Photon	0	1					(γ)				

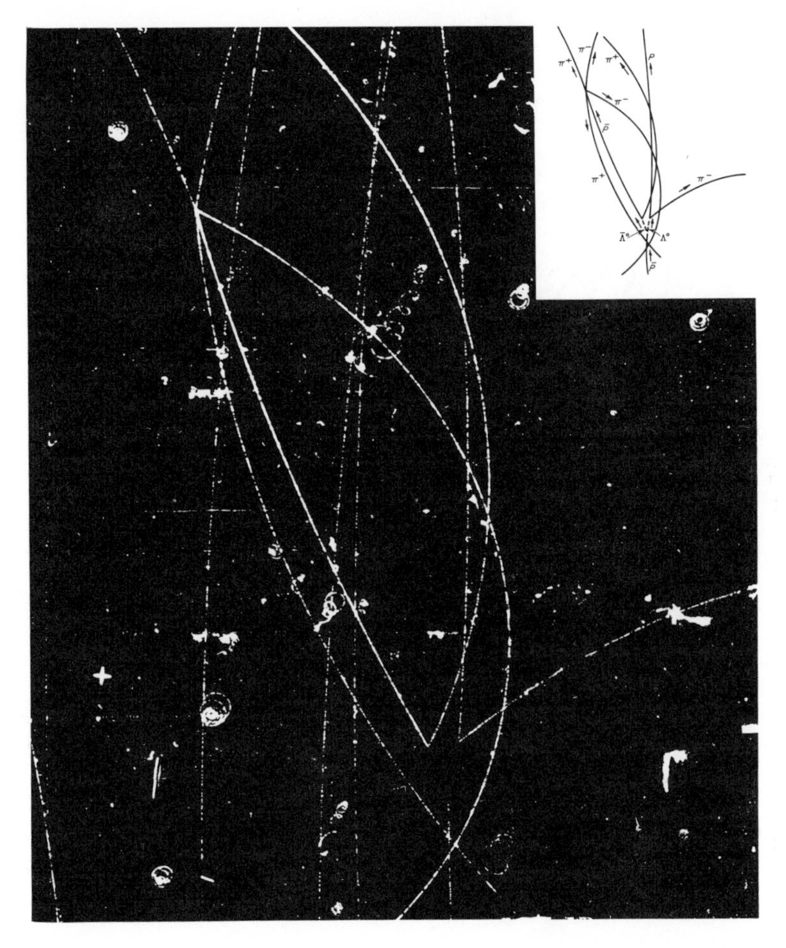

FIG. 20.3 A cosmic ray event in a bubble chamber: Production and decay of neutral lambda and anti-lambda hyperons. Note the production of positive and negative pions, a proton and anti-proton. [Lawrence Radiation Laboratory—University of California.]

The interactions which are studied in physics may be arranged in a sort of hierarchy. The *strong interactions* are those which occur between nucleons and are responsible for the forces which hold together the nucleus. *Electromagnetic interactions* are those between positive and negative charges, between the magnetic fields of spinning particles, and in the magnetic fields caused by moving charges. We can think of the particles associated with such fields (photons) as being normal modes of the vibrating fields. There are also, however, much weaker interactions, called simply *weak interactions*, which are responsible for important nuclear processes, such as the decay of the neutron. Among the elementary particles only the protons, the electrons, the neutrinos and the

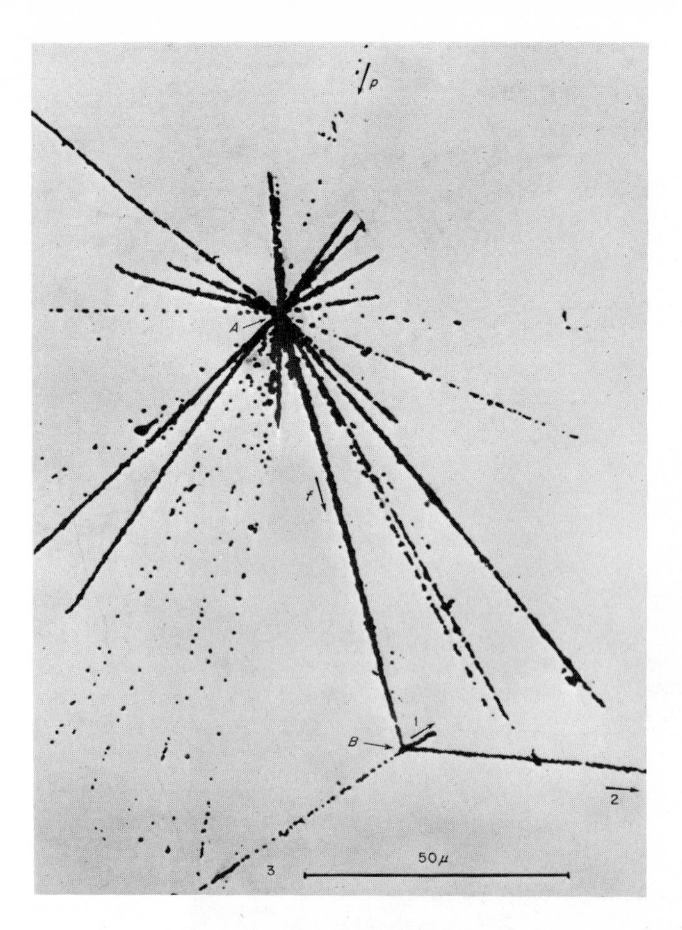

FIG. 20.4 A nuclear reaction observed in a photographic emulsion.

photons are stable against these weak interactions. Even weaker than the weak interactions is the interaction responsible for gravitation.

In 1947 a strange heavy neutral particle Λ° was revealed in a cloud chamber photograph of cosmic rays by the sudden appearance of a proton and a negative pion.

$$\Lambda^\circ \longrightarrow p^+ + \pi^-$$

This was the first to be discovered of several such *hyperons.* They are particles unstable against weak interaction.

If a proton has an excited state, it must have some internal structure. Such structure is revealed by the use of probes of high energy. Energies up to 10^6 bev have been observed in cosmic ray particles. Fig. 20.4 shows an interesting nuclear reaction,* the delayed disintegration of an excited nucleus at the end of its range in an emulsion. An incoming cosmic ray particle (p) strikes a nucleus in the emulsion at A and produces a disintegration. One outgoing particle f with a charge of about $5e$ reaches the end of its range at B and disintegrates into three fast charged particles.

The inner structure of the nucleons can be revealed by how they scatter electron beams of high energy. Fig. 20.5 shows the results of such experiments

* Danysz and Pniewski, *Phil. Mag.* *44*, 348 (1953).

made with 1.3 bev electron beams.* The distribution of charge is shown as a function of the distance r from the center in units of 10^{-16} cm (fermi). The proton and the neutron both have positive cores containing about half the total charge. Then there is a more diffuse region, which is positive in the proton but negative in the neutron. The neutron also has an outer shell containing a small net positive charge.

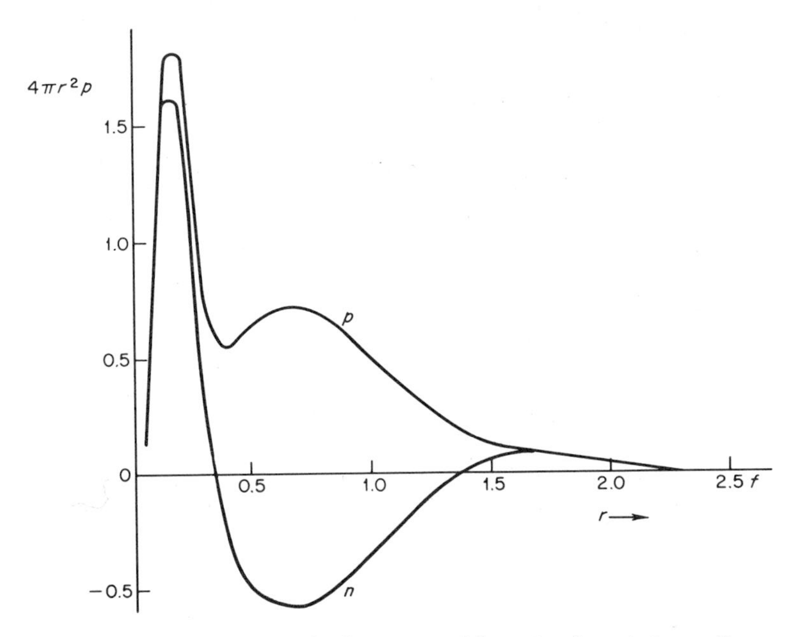

Fig. 20.5 Charge distribution for the proton and the neutron from electron scattering experiments.

The positron is the *antiparticle* of the electron. According to Dirac's theory, some other elementary particles should also have *antiparticles*. For example, there should be an *antiproton* $\overline{p}$, with the mass of the proton but a negative charge. By 1959, the Berkeley bevatron had been developed and tested, and one of the first experiments with it led to the discovery of the *antiproton*. Fig. 20.6 shows a bubble-chamber photograph in which a proton strikes an antiproton and charge exchange occurs to form a neutron and an antineutron,

$$p + \overline{p} \longrightarrow n + \overline{n}$$

The antineutron is not at home in our world. When the one in the picture vanishes, it produces an *annihilation star* of four particles at the end of its life.

Does there exist somewhere an antiworld, with antihydrogen formed of positrons and antiprotons, and hence a complete set of antielements, anticompounds, and antibeasts? There is no reason against it, but we could not detect such a world by astronomical means, because these all depend on electro-

* D. N. Olson, H. F. Schopper and R. R. Wilson, *Phys. Rev. Letters* 6, 286 (1961).

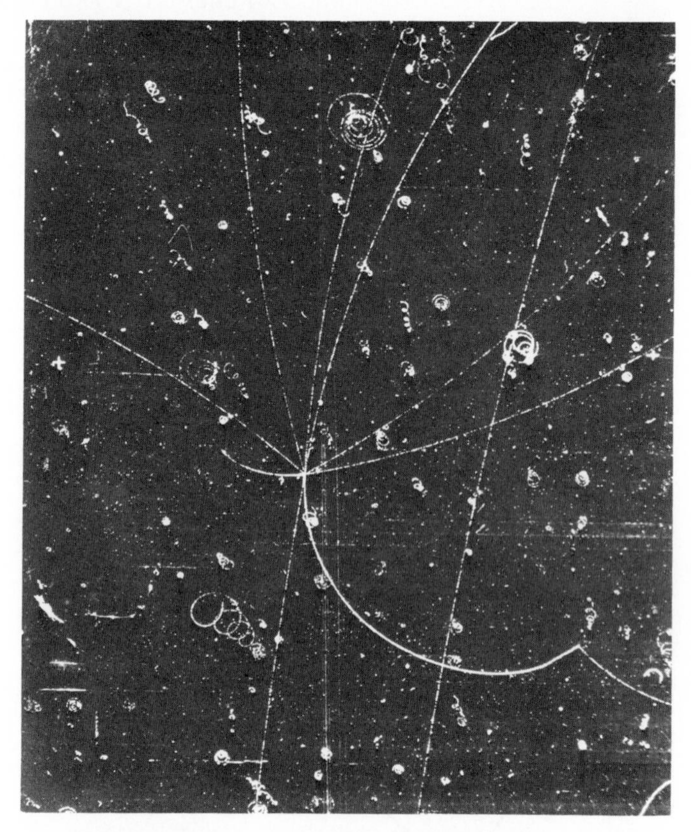

FIG. 20.6 A proton annihilates an antiproton and produces multiple pions. The $\bar{p}$ enters from bottom of picture. [180-cm bubble chamber — Lawrence Radiation Laboratory].

magnetic phenomena, such as spectra, which are invariant under charge exchange (For example, the spectrum of antihydrogen would be identical in every respect with that of hydrogen.) Yet, in principle, a means does exist for detecting antimatter because the invariance rule fails in certain weak interactions, such as beta decay.

7. BETA DECAY AND THE NEUTRINO

Fig. 11.9 showed the energy E of the β particles in a typical radioactive decay. In α decay, all the particles emitted have the same energy, and the same is true of the photons emitted as γ-rays. The wide distribution of the energies of the β-particles presented a difficult problem. Presumably the nucleus emits a β as it falls from a state of higher energy to a state of lower energy. These two states are sharply defined. In the decay process, a neutron in the nucleus is converted to a proton and an electron is emitted,

$$n \longrightarrow p + e^-$$

What has happened, therefore, to the extra energy in cases when the E of the β is less than E_{max}?

Pauli suggested that the conservation of energy could be saved if the β were accompanied by an electrically neutral particle with a rest mass much less ($\sim 1/2000$) than that of the neutron. Fermi called this particle the *neutrino*, the little neutral one. The neutrino has a spin of $\frac{1}{2}$ which might be either in the direction of its motion or opposite. It turns out that neutrinos must spin oppositely to their direction of motion. All neutrinos are therefore said to be left-handed. Antineutrinos are right-handed: their spin is in the direction of their motion. Actually β^- decays give antineutrinos $\bar{\nu}$, while β^+ decays give neutrinos ν.

The interaction cross section of the neutrino* is $\sim 10^{-44}$ cm^2 and a neutrino would travel on the average 5×10^6 km in air before reacting with a nucleus. The detection of neutrinos thus presents some difficulties. In 1956, Cowan and Reines succeeded in detecting antineutrinos in a beautiful experiment. A nuclear reactor is a strong source of $\bar{\nu}$ from beta decays, in which a neutron *within the nucleus* transforms to a proton: $n \rightarrow p + e^- + \bar{\nu}$. The $\bar{\nu}$ can be detected from the reaction of inverse beta decay, $\bar{\nu} + p \rightarrow n + e^+$. The "$\bar{\nu}$" were passed through large tanks of water containing cadmium. The e^+ is annihilated at once to produce two γ rays and the n is captured by Cd, with the emission of other γ rays. The expected time sequence between these two events was known, so that the passage of an antineutrino through the tank could be detected by the occurrence of two γ-ray events of the right energy at exactly the proper interval.

8. NUCLEAR FORCES

The discovery of the neutron led to an important revision in the previously accepted picture of nuclear structure. The electron as such does not exist in the nucleus. Protons and neutrons are the true building units. These are therefore called *nucleons*.

Each nucleus contains a number of protons equal to its atomic number Z, plus a number of neutrons N, sufficient to make up the observed mass number A. Thus, $A = N + Z$. A nuclear species characterized by its values of A and Z is called a *nuclide*.

The *binding energy* E of the nucleus is the sum of the masses of the nucleons minus the actual nuclear mass M. Thus,

$$E = Zm_p + (A - Z)m_n - M \tag{20.3}$$

The proton mass $m_p = 1.008142$, the neutron mass $m_n = 1.008983$ in atomic mass units. To convert this energy from grams per mole to mev per nucleon, it must be multiplied by

$$\frac{c^2}{L \times 10^6 \times 1.602 \times 10^{-12}} = 934$$

* Neutrinos of bev energy, however, have much larger cross sections.

Figure 20.7 shows the binding energy per nucleon as a function of the mass number. Only stable nuclides lie on this reasonably smooth curve. Natural or artificial radioactive elements fall below the curve by an amount that is a measure of their instability relative to a stable isotope of the same mass number.

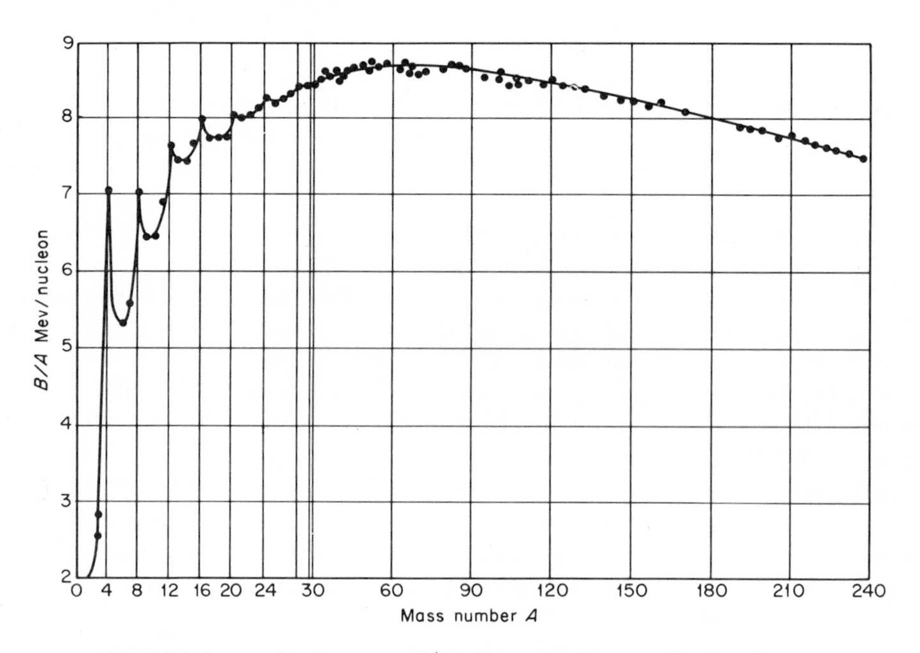

FIG. 20.7 Average binding energy E/A in Mev per nucleon as a function of mass number A, for the naturally occurring nuclides (and Be). Note the change of magnification in the A scale at $A = 30$. The Pauli four-shells in the lightest nuclei are evident.

The successive maxima in the early part of the curve occur at the following nuclei: ^{4}He, ^{8}Be,* ^{12}C, ^{16}O, ^{20}Ne. These are all nuclei containing an equal number of protons and neutrons, and in fact they are all polymers of ^{4}He. It is possible to say, therefore, that the forces between nucleons become saturated, like valence bonds between atoms. The unit ^{4}He, two protons and two neutrons, appears to be one of exceptional stability. Just as is the case for electrons in an atom, there are certain allowed energy levels for nucleons in a nucleus. In accord with the Pauli principle, each level can hold two neutrons and two protons. Of all the stable nuclei, 152 have both N and Z even; 52 have Z odd, N even; 55, Z even, N odd; and only 4 have both N and Z odd. The four odd-odd nuclei are ^{2}H, ^{6}Li, ^{10}B, ^{14}N. Not only are the even-even nuclei the most frequent, they also usually have the greatest relative abundance. It can be concluded that filled nuclear energy levels confer exceptional stability.

We do not yet understand completely the forces between nucleons. The nuclear diameter is approximately $d = 1.4 \times 10^{-13} A^{1/3}$ cm. The density of

* ^{8}Be is unstable and breaks into two ^{4}He with a $\tau < 4 \times 10^{-15}$s.

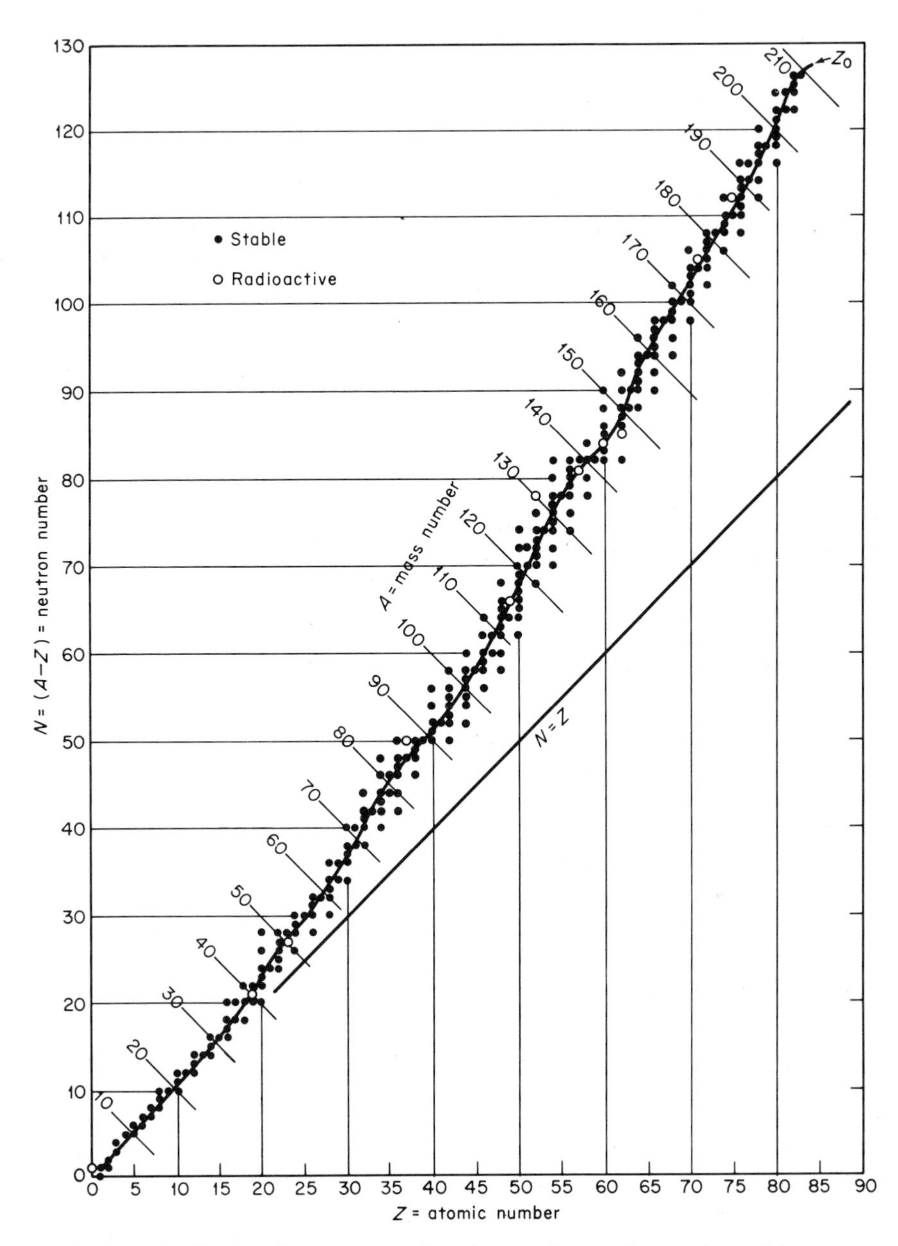

FIG. 20.8 Number of neutrons vs. number of protons in naturally occurring nuclides with $Z \leq 83$. [Robley D. Evans, *The Atomic Nucleus,* (New York: McGraw Hill, 1955)].

nuclear material is about 10^{14} g cm^{-3}; a drop big enough to see would weigh 10^{10} kg. The forces therefore must be extremely short-range, unlike electrostatic or gravitational forces. There is an electrostatic repulsion between two protons, but this longer-range (inverse square) force is outweighed by the short-range attraction, so that at separations around 10^{-13} cm the attraction between two protons is about the same as that between two neutrons, or between a neutron and a proton. According to the Yukawa theory, the attractive forces between nucleons are due to a new type of radiation field, in which the mesons play a role like that of photons in the ordinary electromagnetic field.

A further insight into nuclear forces can be obtained by examining the composition of the stable (nonradioactive) nuclei. In Fig. 20.8 the number of neutrons in a nucleus is plotted against the number of protons. The line has an initial slope of unity, corresponding to a one-to-one ratio, but it curves upward at higher atomic numbers. The electrostatic repulsion of the protons increases as the nucleus becomes larger, since it is a longer-range force than the attraction between protons. To compensate for this repulsion, more neutrons are necessary. The nucleons (protons and neutrons) are particles that must obey the Pauli exclusion principle, hence as more neutrons (or protons) are added, they must enter higher energy levels. Thus there is a limit to the number of extra neutrons that can cause a net increase in the stability. Consequently, heavier nuclei become relatively less stable, and the N vs. Z plot curves upward as shown.

9. NEUTRONS AND NUCLEI

Since the neutron is an uncharged particle, it is not repelled as it approaches a nucleus, even if its energy is very low. We often distinguish fast neutrons, with a kinetic energy > 100 ev, and slow neutrons, with energies from 0.01 to 10 ev. If the energies have the same magnitude as those of ordinary gas molecules (kT), the neutrons are called *thermal neutrons*. At 300°K, $kT = 0.026$ ev.

The interaction of a neutron and a nucleus can be represented by the intermediate formation of a *compound nucleus* which may then react in several ways. If the neutron is released again, with the reformation of the original nucleus, the process is called *scattering*. If the neutron is retained for some time, even though there may be a subsequent decomposition of the compound nucleus into new products by beta decay or the like, the process is called *capture* or *absorption*. There may also be processes such as (n,α), $(n,2n)$ [*cf.* Sec. 12].

The yield of a nuclear reaction is expressed by its *effective cross section* which has the dimensions of an area. Let us consider, for example, a beam of particles (protons, neutrons, etc.) which traverses a layer of matter. For a given reaction and for a given energy of the bombarding particles, we can consider that every incident particle will cause a reaction in the target nucleus if the distance between their centers is less than a critical value d. Thus if we send a projectile particle onto 1 cm^2 of a layer of matter which contains N nuclei per cm^3, the probability that there is a reaction is $N\sigma$, where $\sigma = \pi d^2$ is the area of the little disk that we can associate with each target nucleus. The effective cross section σ is therefore the stopping area which the nucleus opposes to the incident particles. As the diameter of heavier nuclei is of the order of 10^{-12} cm, effective cross sections are often of the order of 10^{-24} cm^2. Whimsical physicists have called this unit the *barn*.

The concept of effective cross section is not restricted to nuclear reactions. It can be applied to any process of interaction, such as scattering or ionization. The different effective nuclear cross sections vary from fractions of a microbarn to a few thousand barns, depending on the target nuclei and the type of interaction considered. They depend also on the speed of the incident particles. The relation between σ and the kinetic energy of the particle gives important information about the energy levels in the nucleus. For instance, when the kinetic energy of a neutron matches an energy level in the nucleus (above the ground state), a resonance effect can occur which greatly augments the capture cross section of the neutron. Thus cadmium possesses a large effective cross section for *thermal neutrons*, so that a cadmium foil a few mm thick is practically opaque to such neutrons.

Let us consider a beam of neutrons of initial intensity I_0, which traverses a layer of material in which the effective cross section is σ. Let I be the intensity of the beam at any depth in the layer. If $-dI$ is the decrease in intensity in traversing a thickness dx,

$$-dI = I\sigma N\, dx \tag{20.4}$$

For a layer of thickness x, integration yields

$$I = I_0\, e^{-N\sigma x} \tag{20.5}$$

As an example, σ for thermal neutrons in arsenic is 4.6 barn, $N = 3.77 \times 10^{22}$ atoms cm^{-3}, so that $\sigma N = 0.17$ cm^{-1}. Then $I/I_0 = e^{-0.17x} \simeq 1 - 0.17x$ in the case of very small x. We see that a plate of arsenic 1 cm thick would attenuate the beam of neutrons by about 17%.

In order to slow or *moderate* fast neutrons, we need a material that can effectively take up the energy of the fast light neutrons. Energy transfer is most effective between particles of like mass: when a moving billiard ball strikes a stationary ball, it loses a fair share of its energy, but when the moving ball strikes the cushion, it loses very little energy.* Both ^{1}H and ^{2}H would be effective in slowing neutrons, but in the case of ^{1}H many of the thermal neutrons produced are lost by the capture reaction

$${}^1_1\text{H} + {}^1_0n \longrightarrow {}^2_1\text{H}$$

For this reason, light water is a less useful neutron moderator than heavy water. In H_2O, a thermal neutron would average 240 collisions before capture; in D_2O, 10^4; in pure graphite, 10^3.

The cross section for silver is shown in Fig. 20.9 as a function of neutron energy. The peaks in the curve correspond to definite energy levels for neutrons in the nucleus. The energy levels of electrons in atoms were explained by the Bohr theory and quantum mechanics. The task of the nuclear physicist is to explain the levels in the nucleus in a similar way.

* If the kinetic energy of a moving particle of mass M_1 is E, the *maximum energy* which it can impart to a particle of mass M_2 in a collision is $E_m = [4M_1M_2/(M_1 + M_2)^2]E$. (Derive this equation from the laws of conservation of energy and momentum.)

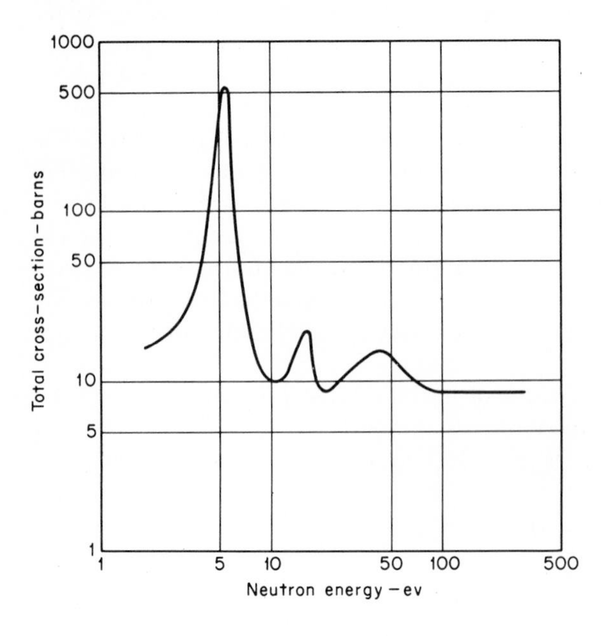

FIG. 20.9 Nuclear cross-section of silver. [Rainwater, Havens, Wu, and Dunning, *Phys. Rev. 71*, 65 (1947)].

10. NUCLEAR DECAY SCHEMES

In the emission of a γ-ray a nucleus falls from an excited state to some lower stationary state. The γ-ray emission of the nucleus is analogous to the emission of light when an atom falls from an excited state to a lower state. In both cases, $h\nu = E_2 - E_1$. When a nucleus emits a β particle, the daughter nucleus is usually in an excited state and can reach a more stable state by emission of a γ-ray photon. Examples of decay schemes are shown in Fig. 20.10.

Consider, for instance, the decay of ^{60}Co in (d). In almost every case it emits a 0.312 mev β^- to yield ^{60}Ni in an excited state. This ^{60}Ni passes almost instantaneously to the ground state by emission of two successive α-ray photons. About one in 10^4 times, however, the ^{60}Co emits a 1.478 mev β^-.

11. THE STRUCTURE OF THE NUCLEUS

Every student of mechanics knows that it is not possible to obtain an analytic solution of the *three-body problem*, i.e., the motions of three masses under the influence of their mutual gravitational interactions. As the number of interacting bodies increases, so does the mathematical difficulty, so that many-body problems must be attacked by approximation methods. Also, in the nuclear case, the law of force between the nucleons is not well understood. Thus we do not have any exact theory of the structure of a nucleus composed of Z protons and N neutrons interacting together with attractive exchange forces as well as electrostatic repulsions between the protons. The best we can do is to work with simplified models. Two such models have been used with success, the *shell model* and the *collective model.*

The shell model was suggested by analogy with the shell model of the electronic structure of atoms. The very stable *magic-number nuclei* were reminiscent of the closed electron shells of the inert gases. The nuclear model is more complicated since there is no central field of force, and two kinds of nucleon must be accommodated.

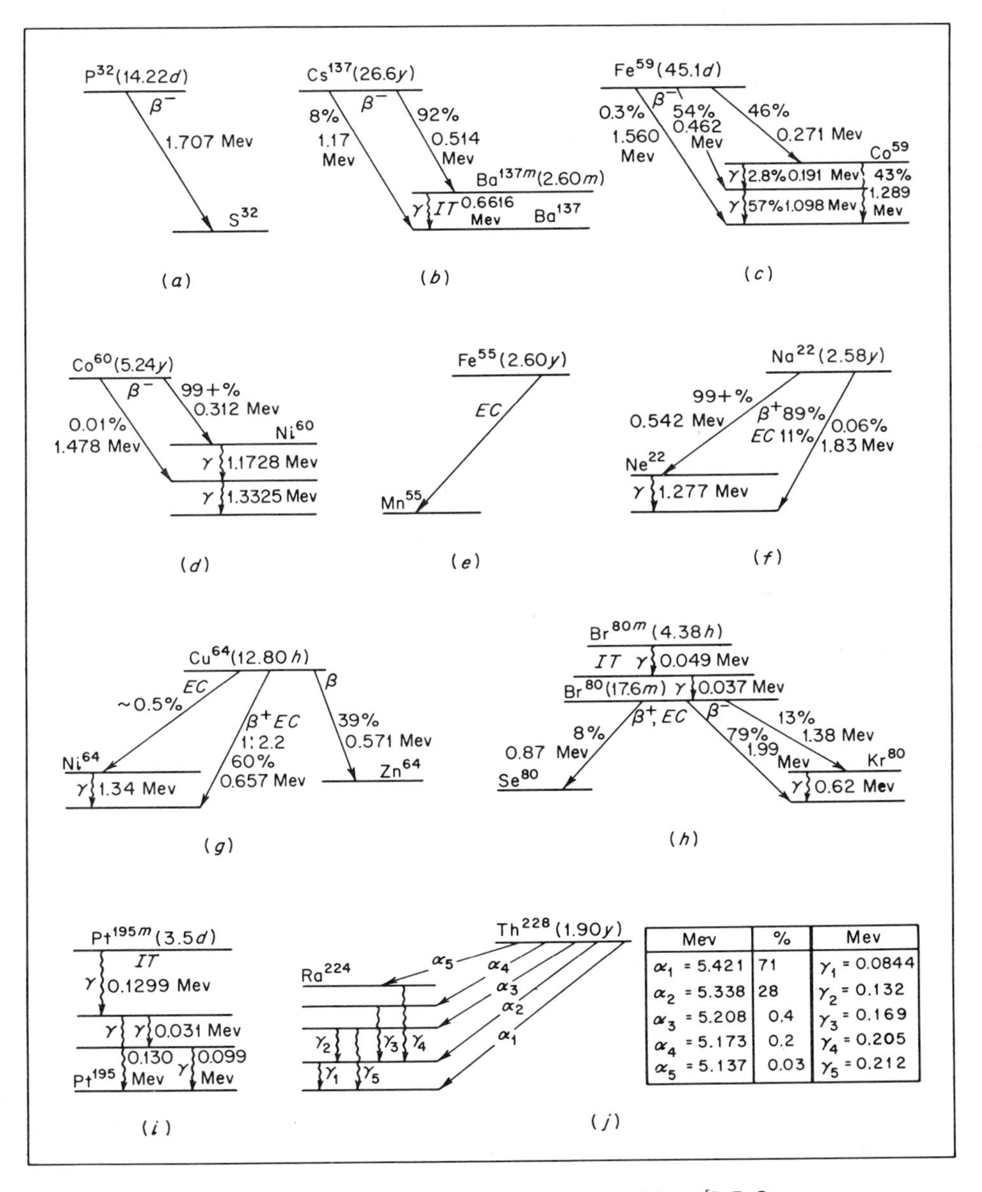

Mev	%	Mev
α_1 = 5.421	71	γ_1 = 0.0844
α_2 = 5.338	28	γ_2 = 0.132
α_3 = 5.208	0.4	γ_3 = 0.169
α_4 = 5.173	0.2	γ_4 = 0.205
α_5 = 5.137	0.03	γ_5 = 0.212

FIG. 20.10 Examples of decay schemes of radioactive nuclides. [R. T. Overman and H. M. Clark, *Radioisotope Techniques* (New York: McGraw Hill, 1960)].

A section through the potential field experienced by a nucleon is shown in Fig. 20.11. As a nucleon approaches the nucleus, it feels the attraction of the other nucleons and the potential becomes negative. Once the nucleon is fairly well below the surface, however, the potential is effectively constant, since the forces between nucleons are of such short range. The energy levels of the nucleons in such a field will be specified by two quantum numbers n and l. These energy levels are shown in Fig. 20.12. If we fill these levels with nucleons, the Pauli exclusion principle applies, but each level can contain $2l + 1$ protons and $2l + 1$ neutrons, since the presence of a proton does not exclude the presence of a neutron in the same level. Thus the lowest magic numbers 2, 8 and 20 are explained.

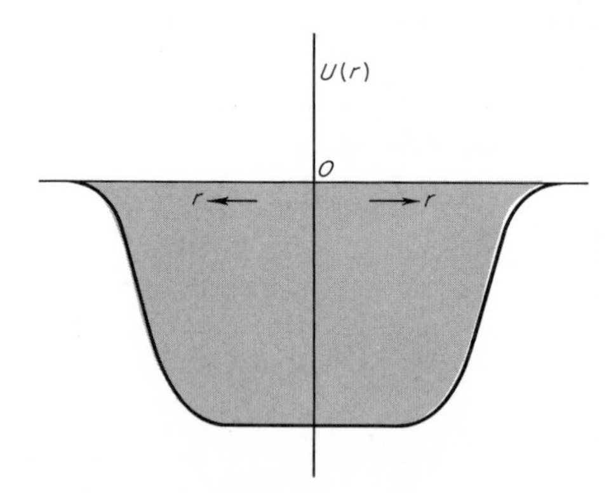

FIG. 20.11 Potential energy $U(r)$ of a nucleon as a function of distance from center of nucleus.

In 1948, Maria Mayer and J. H. Jensen explained the shell structure of the heavier nuclei. The nucleon experiences a strong spin-orbit interaction, so that its spin s and angular momentum l couple to give a total angular momentum j. States of different j are split in energy. Since the spin is $\frac{1}{2}$, the j values are $l + \frac{1}{2}$ and $l - \frac{1}{2}$. The resultant energy levels are shown at the right of Fig. 20.12. The magic numbers occur just before each energy gap, hence their relatively great stability.

The other simple model of the nucleus is the collective model. It was originally suggested by John Wheeler and Niels Bohr. Recent developments have been due principally to Aage Bohr (son of Niels). The nucleus is considered as a rotating and vibrating drop of fluid. Their quadrupole moments indicate that many nuclei are ellipsoids (often with a ratio of major to minor axis as high as 1.25). An ellipsoidal nucleus behaves like a diatomic rotating molecule. For an even-even nucleus, the energy levels are given by

$$E_J = \frac{J(J + 1)h^2}{8\pi^2 I} \tag{20.6}$$

where I is the moment of inertia of the nucleus and J can have values 0, 2, 4, 6. Fig. 20.13 shows the observed and calculated energy levels for the nucleus ^{180}Hf. The capture of a neutron by ^{179}Hf may result in the formation of an isomeric state in ^{180}Hf with an energy of 1143 kev and a lifetime of 5.5 hr. This state decays by emission of a 57 kev γ ray to an excited rotational state with $J = 8$ of ^{180}Hf. A series of γ-ray emissions occur leading to the ground state $J = 0$. The γ-ray energies agree closely with those calculated on the simple collective model.

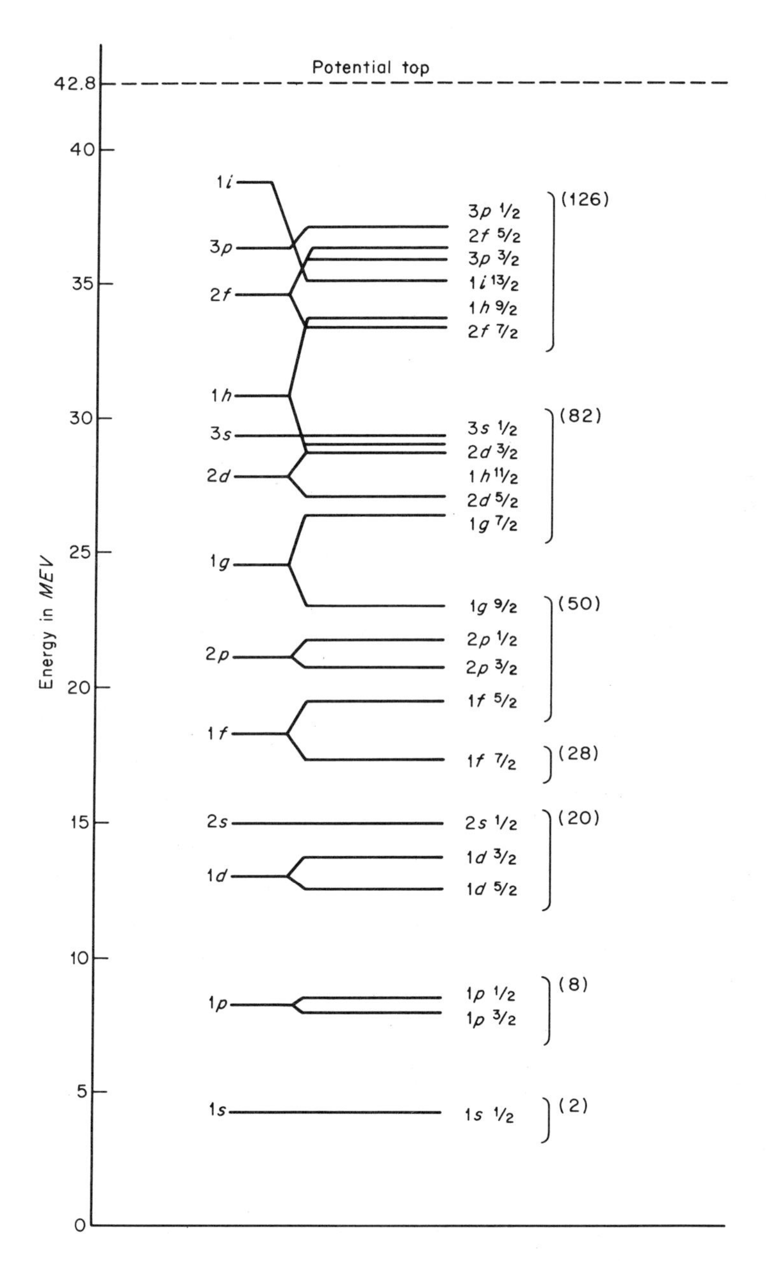

FIG. 20.12 Energy levels in a potential well of the type shown in FIG. 20.11. The notation used is as follows: States with $1 = 0,1,2,3,\ldots$, etc. are denoted by the letters $s,p,d,f,g,\ldots$, etc. The number to the left of each letter is the value of n and to the right, the value of j. Each level can hold $2j + 1$ nucleons. On the extreme right of the diagram are the magic numbers representing the number of nucleons that completely fill all the preceding levels.

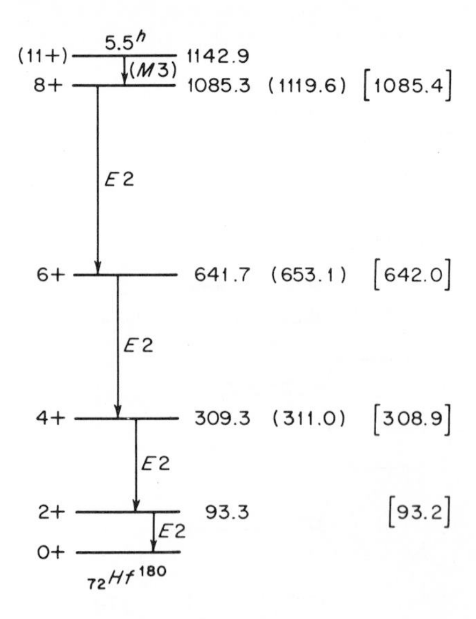

FIG. 20.13 Rotation spectrum of Hf^{180}. The capture of a neutron by Hf^{179} may result in the formation of an isomeric state in Hf^{180} with an energy of 1143 kev and a lifetime of 5½ hr. This state, whose spin quantum number has the very high value of about 11 units, decays by emission of a γ ray of 57 kev to a rotational level (having a large rotational quantum number, $J = 8$) of the ground state of Hf^{180}. The original rotational level decays to lower rotational levels by emission of a series of γ rays. The numbers immediately to the right of the rotational states give their energies in kev. In the round parentheses are given the energies calculated from Eq. (6) when the moment of inertia is determined from the energy of the lowest rotational level ($J = 2$). The measured energies are, especially for the higher states, a little less than the calculated ones. This can be explained on the basis that the eccentricity of the nucleus (and therewith the moment of inertia) increases with increasing rotational velocity because of a centrifugal effect. Including such a term, one can account for the measured energies with accuracy as can be seen from the numbers in the square parentheses of Fig. 20.13. [Aage Bohr, *Am. Journ. Physics*, 25, 547, (1957)].

Thus the shell model and the collective model have each had their successes. But failures also occur, and much work remains before we shall have a satisfactory understanding of nuclear structure.

12. NUCLEAR REACTIONS

The different types of nuclear reactions are conveniently designated by an abbreviated notation, which shows the reactant particle and the particle emitted. Thus an (n,p) reaction is one in which a neutron reacts with a nucleus to yield a new nucleus and a proton, e.g., ${}^{14}_{7}N + {}^{1}_{0}n \rightarrow {}^{14}_{6}C + {}^{1}_{1}H$ would be written ${}^{14}_{7}H$ (n,p) ${}^{14}_{6}C$.

Table 20.3 summarizes various types of nuclear reactions. The table is divided into sections according to the energy of the incident particle, the identity

TABLE 20.3 NUCLEAR REACTIONS

Incident Particle	Intermediate Nuclei ($30 < A < 90$)				Heavy Nuclei ($A > 90$)			
Energy of Incident Particle	n	p	α	d	n	p	α	d
Low 0–1 kev	n(el) γ (res)	no appreciable reaction	no appreciable reaction	no appreciable reaction	γ n(el) (res)	no appreciable reaction	no appreciable reaction	no appreciable reaction
Intermediate 1–500 kev	n(el) γ (res)	n γ α (res)	n γ p (res)	p n	n(el) γ (res)	Very small reaction cross-section	Very small reaction cross-section	Small reaction cross-section
High 0.5–10 Mev	n(el) n(inel) p α (res for lower energies)	n p(inel) α (res for lower energies)	n p α(inel) (res for lower energies)	p n pn $2n$	n(el) n(inel) p γ	n p(inel) γ	n p γ	p n pn $2n$
Very high 10–50 Mev	$2n$ n(inel) n(el) p np $2p$ α three or more particles	$2n$ n p(inel) np $2p$ α three or more particles	$2n$ n p np $2p$ α(inel) three or more particles	p $2n$ pn $3n$ d(inel) tritons three or more particles	$2n$ n(inel) n(el) p pn $2p$ α three or more particles	$2n$ n p(inel) np $2p$ α three or more particles	$2n$ n p np $2p$ α(inel) three or more particles	p $2n$ np $3n$ d(inel) tritons three or more particles

*[L. Eisenbud and E. P. Wigner, *Nuclear Structure* (Princeton University Press, 1958)].

of the incident particle, and the mass number of the target. The reaction product is then entered in the table, in the order of decreasing cross sections. Observation of resonance levels is indicated, and occurrence of elastic and inelastic scattering.

13. NUCLEAR FISSION

Perusal of the binding-energy curve in Fig. 20.7 reveals that a large number of highly exothermic nuclear reactions are possible, since the heavy nuclei toward the end of the periodic table are all unstable relative to the nuclei lying near the minimum of the curve.

In the January, 1939 number of *Naturwissenschaften*, the chemists Otto Hahn and S. Strassmann reported that when the uranium nucleus is bombarded with neutrons it may split into fragments, one of which they identified as an isotope of barium. About 200 mev of energy is released at each fission.

It was immediately evident that secondary neutrons could be emitted in the uranium fission, making a chain reaction possible. Consider the fission of a $^{235}_{92}U$ nucleus to yield, typically, a $^{139}_{56}Ba$ as one of the products plus two neutrons. If balance is to be achieved between the numbers of protons and neutrons before and after fission, the other product would have to be $^{94}_{36}Kr$. This product would be far heavier than any previously known krypton isotope, the heaviest of which was $^{87}_{36}Kr$, a β^- emitter of 4 hours half life. Now the hypothetical $^{96}_{36}Kr$ can get back to the proton-neutron curve of Fig. 20.8 by a series of β^- emissions, and in fact a large number of new β^- emitters have been identified among the fission products.

The fission process in uranium usually consists, therefore, of a disintegration into two lighter nuclei, one of mass number from 82 to 100, and the other, from 128 to 150, plus about three rapidly moving neutrons. In only about one case in a thousand does symmetrical fission occur into two nuclei of approximately equal mass.

To determine which isotope of uranium was principally responsible for fission, A. O. Nier and his coworkers separated small samples of ^{235}U (0.7 per cent abundance) from ^{238}U (99.3 per cent) with a mass spectrometer. It was found that ^{235}U undergoes fission even when it captures a slow thermal neutron, but ^{238}U is split only by fast neutrons with energies greater than 1 mev. As usual, the capture cross section for slow neutrons is much greater than that for fast neutrons, so that ^{235}U fission is a much more likely process than that of ^{238}U.

The process of fission can be visualized by considering the nucleus as a drop of liquid. When a neutron hits it, oscillations are set up. The positive charges of the protons acquire an unsymmetrical distribution, and the resulting repulsion can lead to splitting of the nuclear drop. Since ^{235}U contains an odd number of neutrons, considerable energy is set free when it gains a neutron. This kinetic energy starts the disturbance within the nucleus that leads to fission. The isotope ^{238}U already contains an even number of neutrons, and the capture process is not so markedly exothermic. In this case only a fast neutron can initiate fission, by bringing considerable kinetic energy into the nucleus. Fission of stable heavy elements, such as lead, has been produced by bombardment with 200 mev deuterons. Fission can also be induced by γ rays with energies greater than about 5 mev (*photofission*).

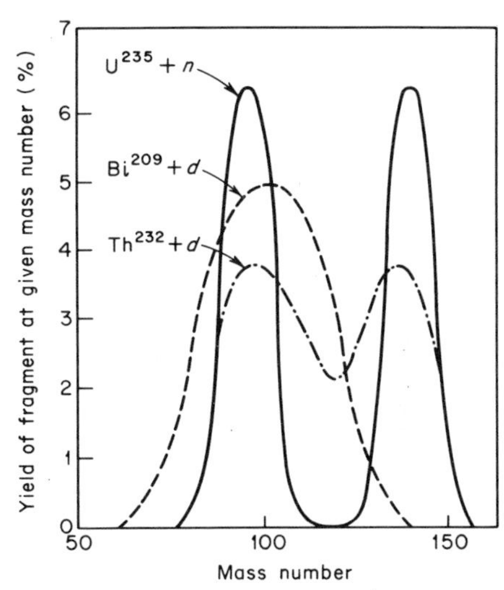

FIG. 20.14 Mass distribution of products in three different fission reactions. The energies of the particles initiating the fission are: *n*, thermal; α, 38 mev; *d*, 200 mev. Note how the distribution becomes more symmetrical as the energy of the incident particle increases. [From P. Morrison, "A Survey of Nuclear Reactions" in *Experimental Nuclear Physics*, ed. E. Segre (New York: John Wiley, 1953)].

Figure 20.14 shows the mass distributions of the fission products in three different cases that have been carefully studied. When fission is produced by highly energetic particles, the distribution of masses is quite symmetrical, and the most probable split is one that yields two nuclei of equal mass. This is the result that would be expected from the liquid-drop model. The unsymmetrical splitting that follows capture of slower particles is related to the detailed shell structure inside the nucleus.

14. THE TRANSURANIUM ELEMENTS

In 1940, E. McMillan and P. H. Abelson* found that when ^{238}U is irradiated with neutrons, a resonance capture can occur that leads eventually to the formation of two new transuranium elements.

$$^{238}_{92}U + ^{1}_{0}n \longrightarrow ^{239}_{92}U$$

$$^{239}_{92}U \xrightarrow{23\text{ min}} ^{239}_{93}Np + \beta$$

$$^{239}_{92}Np \xrightarrow{2.3\text{ day}} ^{239}_{94}Pu + \beta$$

The $^{239}_{94}Pu$ is a weakly radioactive α emitter ($\tau = 2.4 \times 10^4$ yr). Its most important property is that, like $^{235}_{92}U$, it undergoes fission by slow neutrons.

* *Phys. Rev. 57*, 1185 (1940).

It was shown by G. T. Seaborg* and his coworkers that bombardment of $^{238}_{92}U$ with α particles leads by an (α,n) reaction to $^{241}_{94}Pu$. This is a β emitter which decays to give $^{241}_{95}Am$, an isotope of americium which is α-radioactive with $\tau = 500$ yr.

By 1961, elements up to 103 had been prepared. The preparation of new elements has been facilitated by the technique of using heavy ions accelerated in the cyclotron. Thus high energy beams of carbon ions $(^{12}_{6}C)^{6+}$ can increase the atomic number of a target nucleus by six units in one step. For example, isotopes of californium have been synthesized as follows:†

$$^{238}_{92}U + ^{12}_{6}C \longrightarrow ^{246}_{98}Cf + 4\,^{1}_{0}n$$

$$^{238}_{92}U + ^{12}_{6}C \longrightarrow ^{244}_{98}Cf + 6\,^{1}_{0}n$$

Fermium was made by

$$^{238}_{92}U + ^{16}_{8}O \longrightarrow ^{250}_{100}Fm + 4\,^{1}_{0}n$$

15. NUCLEAR CHAIN REACTIONS

Since absorption of one neutron can initiate fission, and more than one neutron is produced at each fission, a branching chain can occur in a mass of fissionable material. The rate of escape of neutrons from a mass of ^{235}U, for example, depends on the area of the mass, whereas the rate of production of neutrons depends on its volume. As the volume is increased, therefore, a critical point is finally reached at which neutrons are being produced more rapidly than they are being lost. If two masses of ^{235}U of subcritical mass are suddenly brought together, a nuclear explosion can take place.

For the continuous production of power, a *nuclear reactor* is used. The fissionable material is mixed with a moderator such as graphite or heavy water, which slows the neutrons. The rate of fission is controlled by introducing rods of a material such as cadmium, which absorb the thermal neutrons. The depth to which the cadmium rods are pushed into the reactor controls the rate of fission.

A reactor can provide a source of intense beams of neutrons. These beams can be either fast neutrons from the center of the reactor, or thermal neutrons drawn out through a layer of moderator. Figure 20.15 shows a diagram of the research reactor at the Argonne National Laboratory.

16. STELLAR ENERGY

Exothermic nuclear reactions are the source of the energy of the stars. At the temperatures prevailing in stellar interiors ($\sim 10^7$ °K in the case of our sun) the nuclei have been stripped of electrons and their thermal velocities have reached

---

* *Science, 104,* 379 (1946); *Chem. Eng. News 25,* 358 (1947).

† A. Ghiorso, S. G. Thompson, K. Street, and G. T. Seaborg, *Phys. Rev. 81,* 1954 (1951).

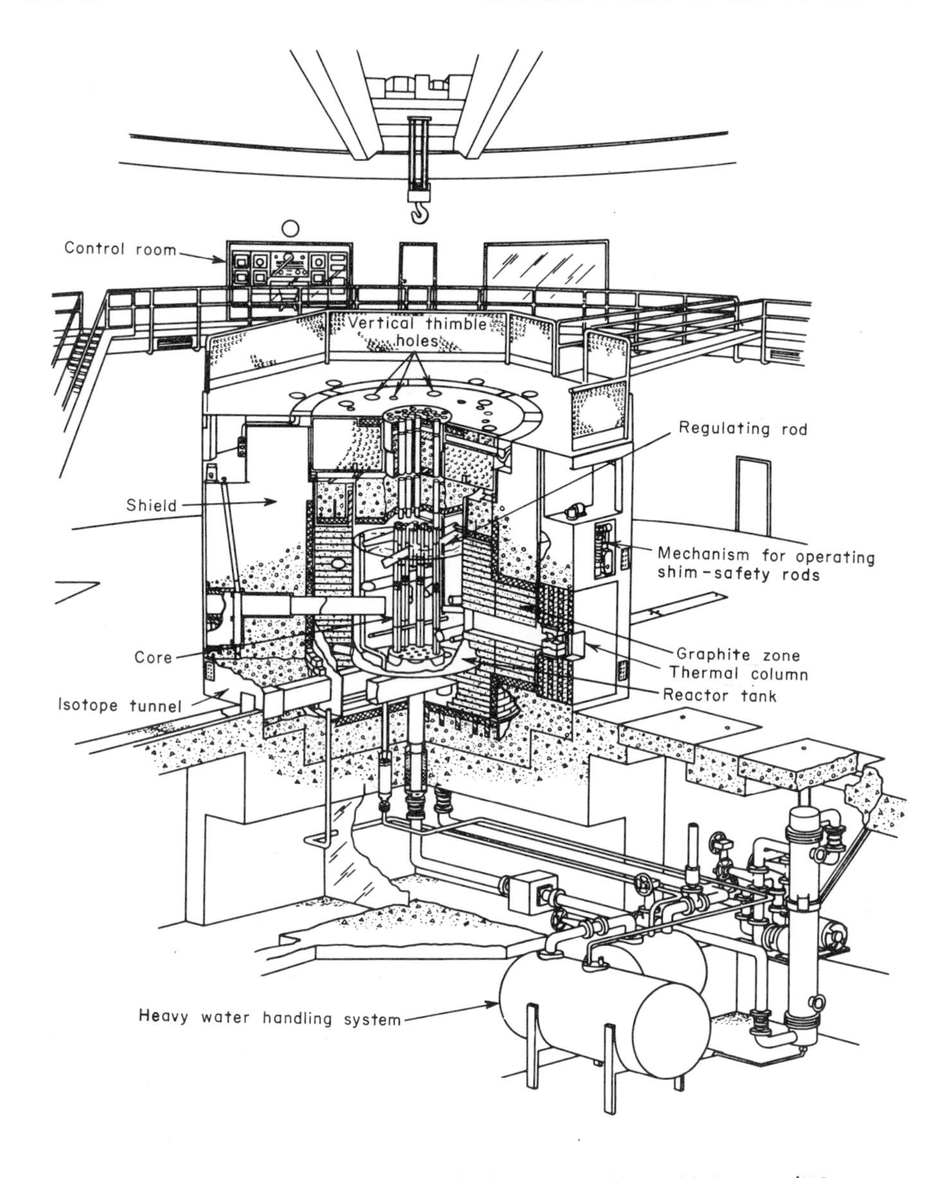

FIG. 20.15 The research reactor CP-5 of the Argonne National Laboratory (U.S. Atomic Energy Commission). The reactor uses uranium enriched in ^{235}U as a fuel. The moderator is D_2O, with a graphite reflector. Thermal neutron fluxes of up to 10^{15} cm^{-2} sec^{-1} are achieved.

high values. Thus the mean thermal kinetic energy of an α particle at room temperature is of the order of .03 ev, but at the temperature of the sun it has become 10^4 ev. In other words, nuclei at stellar temperatures attain energies which begin to approach those produced in cyclotrons or other accelerators.

As is the case with molecules at ordinary temperatures (Sec. 7.23), a few of the nuclei possess exceptionally high energies. These may be able to overcome the electrostatic repulsion between their positive charges and approach close enough to one another to initiate nuclear reactions. Such *thermonuclear reactions* account for the energy production of the stars.

In 1938, Carl von Weizsäcker and Hans Bethe independently proposed a mechanism for production of stellar energy. This is a cyclic process:

$$^{12}C + {}^{1}H \longrightarrow {}^{13}N + h\nu$$
$$^{13}N \longrightarrow {}^{13}C + e^{+} + \nu$$
$$^{13}C + {}^{1}H \longrightarrow {}^{14}N + h\nu$$
$$^{14}N + {}^{1}H \longrightarrow {}^{15}O + h\nu$$
$$^{15}O \longrightarrow {}^{15}N + e^{+} + \nu$$
$$^{15}N + {}^{1}H \longrightarrow {}^{12}C + {}^{4}He$$

The net result is the conversion of four H nuclei into one He nucleus through the mediation of ^{12}C and ^{14}N as "catalysts" for the nuclear reaction; 30 mev are liberated in each cycle. This carbon cycle appears to be the principal source of energy in very hot stars ($T > 5 \times 10^{8}$ °K).

The stars should be good sources of neutrinos, but present methods are not sensitive enough to detect these.

The energy of somewhat cooler stars, like our sun ($T \sim 10^{7}$ °K), appears to be generated by the proton-proton cycle:

$$^{1}_{1}H + {}^{1}_{1}H \longrightarrow {}^{2}_{1}H + e^{+} + \nu + 0.42 \text{ mev}$$
$$^{1}_{1}H + {}^{2}_{1}H \longrightarrow {}^{3}_{2}He + \gamma + 5.5 \text{ mev}$$
$$^{3}_{2}He + {}^{3}_{2}He \longrightarrow {}^{4}_{2}He + 2\,{}^{1}_{1}H + 12.8 \text{ mev}$$

The net result is the conversion of 4 protons to one helium nucleus, with the liberation of 24.6 mev plus the annihilation energy of the positrons.

17. CONTROLLED NUCLEAR FUSION

Reactions of nuclear fusion have been achieved in hydrogen bombs, and considerable research is devoted to methods for carrying out the reactions under controlled conditions. The principal reactions of interest are those that use deuterium as a fuel (D,D reactions).

$$^{2}_{1}H + {}^{2}_{1}H \begin{cases} \nearrow {}^{3}_{2}He + {}^{0}_{1}n + 3.2 \text{ mev} \\ \searrow {}^{3}_{1}H + {}^{1}_{1}H + 4.0 \text{ mev} \end{cases}$$

The barrier of activation energy due to internuclear repulsion amounts to about 0.1 mev in these reactions. In principle, therefore, we need only heat deuterium gas to a sufficiently high temperature to start the reactions. At such temperatures, the gas atoms are completely ionized, $H \rightarrow H^+ + e$, to form a hot mixture of positive ions and electrons, called a *plasma*.

As the plasma is heated, it radiates an increasing amount of energy. In order for a fusion reaction to be self sustaining, therefore, the rate of generation of energy must exceed the rate of loss of energy by radiation. The critical temperatures for a self-sustaining fusion reaction are about 400×10^6 °K for the D-D reaction and 45×10^6 °K for the D-T reaction.

The problem is to create and to confine a plasma at such densities and temperatures. Since no material walls could withstand the temperature, magnetic fields are used to confine the plasma. Many ingenious devices have been used to apply this principle. Like Aladdin's Djinn the hot plasma bitterly resents confinement in a bottle. Thus difficult problems of stability arise and research on the fusion process has not yet yielded a practical solution.*

18. SYNTHESIS OF ELEMENTS IN STARS†

In addition to generating energy by fusion reactions, the stars synthesize heavier elements from hydrogen. Hydrogen is by far the most abundant element, contributing 93% of the total number of atoms or 76% of the mass of the universe. Helium makes up 7% of the atoms and 23% of the mass. All the elements beyond helium together amount to only a little more than 1% of the mass of the universe. Fig. 20.16 shows the relative abundances of the elements.§

Our understanding of how the heavy elements are synthesized from hydrogen and helium is now quite advanced. There is no stable nuclide of mass 5 and a major problem was how to surmount this gap in the sequence of elements. In a hot gas of helium at about 10^8 °K, two He nuclei may combine in a rare event to form ^8Be: ${}^4_2He + {}^4_2He \rightarrow {}^8_4Be$. The ${}^8_4Be$ is extremely unstable, but it may sometimes exist long enough to capture another He: ${}^8_4Be + {}^4_2He \rightarrow {}^{12}_6C$. Once ${}^{12}_6C$ is produced it may build up by successive captures of He nuclei to ${}^{16}_8O$, ${}^{20}_{10}Ne$ and ${}^{24}_{12}Mg$. These processes are called *helium burning*. Helium burning is believed to occur at a late stage in the evolution of red giant stars. The hydrogen in the central core has all been burned, and gravitational contraction has raised the temperature to $\sim 10^8$ °K and the density to $\sim 10^5$ g cm^{-3}. The elements Li, Be, B are believed to be made by chipping fragments from heavier nuclei.

As the He is used up, the star contracts and becomes hotter. At around 5×10^8 °K other fusion reactions produce the members of the silicon group of elements. Finally the fusion processes come to a halt with the production of the most stable elements, iron and its neighbors at about $A = 56$. Any nuclear reaction involving the iron group is endothermic and thus these elements cannot

* A. S. Bishop, *Project Sherwood — The U. S. Program in Controlled Fusion* (New York: Anchor Books, 1960).

† E. M. Burbidge, G. R. Burbidge, W. A. Fowler and F. Hoyle, *Rev. Mod. Phys. 29*, 4 (1957). This comprehensive article is a landmark in the development of the subject.

§ Based on the data of H. E. Suess and H. C. Urey, *Rev. Mod. Phys. 28*, 53 (1956).

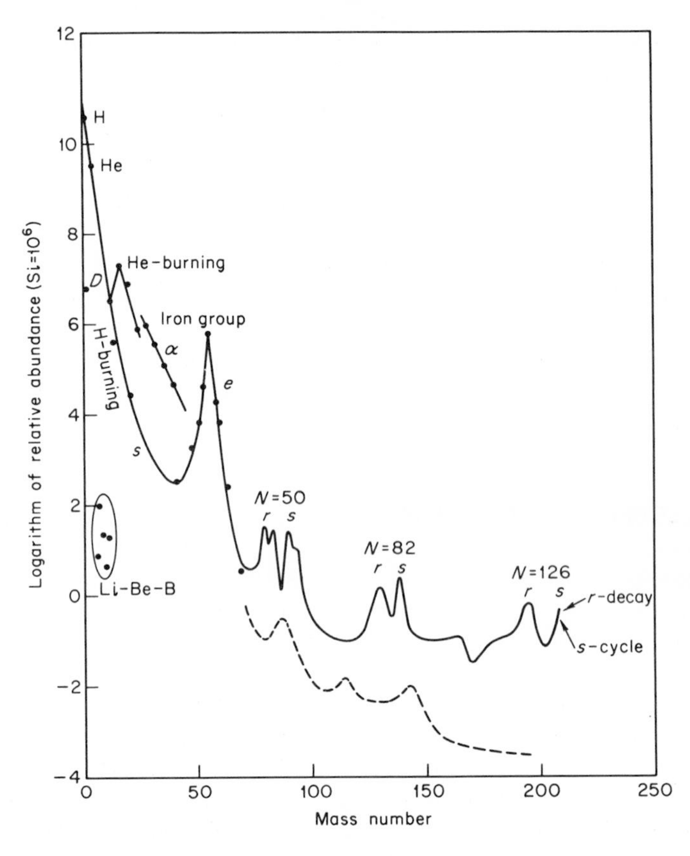

FIG. 20.16 Atomic abundances as a function of atomic weight based on the data of Suess and Urey. Note the overabundances relative to their neighbors of the alpha-particle nuclei $A = 16, 20, \ldots 40$, the peak at the iron group nuclei, and the twin peaks at $A = 80$ and 90, at 130 and 138, and at 194 and 208.

serve as fuel for fusion reactions. The synthesis of the elements is outlined in Fig. 20.17.

Sometimes stars explode as novae and their matter is dispersed. New stars may be formed by condensation of interstellar matter. Such a new star would be called a *second generation* star. In addition to hydrogen and helium, it would contain small amounts of ^{12}C and Fe. The H in the core would again be converted into He, but now, because ^{12}C is present as a catalyst, the Bethe-Weiszsäcker cycle would be followed. Reactions of proton capture would yield ^{13}C, ^{17}O and ^{21}Ne. These nuclides react with ^{4}He to emit neutrons,

$$^{4}_{2}\mathrm{He} + {}^{13}_{6}\mathrm{C} \longrightarrow {}^{1}_{0}n + {}^{16}_{8}\mathrm{O}, \text{ etc.}$$

Thus in a second generation star there is a steady supply of neutrons in the core. The heavy elements beyond Fe can be built up readily by successive captures of slow neutrons, at least as far as Bi. Still heavier elements can be formed by neutron capture during stellar explosions.

Good evidence that stars do synthesize heavy elements was the observation that *technetium* occurs in certain giant stars. The longest lived isotope of Tc has a half life of only 2.16×10^5 yr, far less than the age of the star where it is found. It must therefore have been synthesized long after the birth of the star.

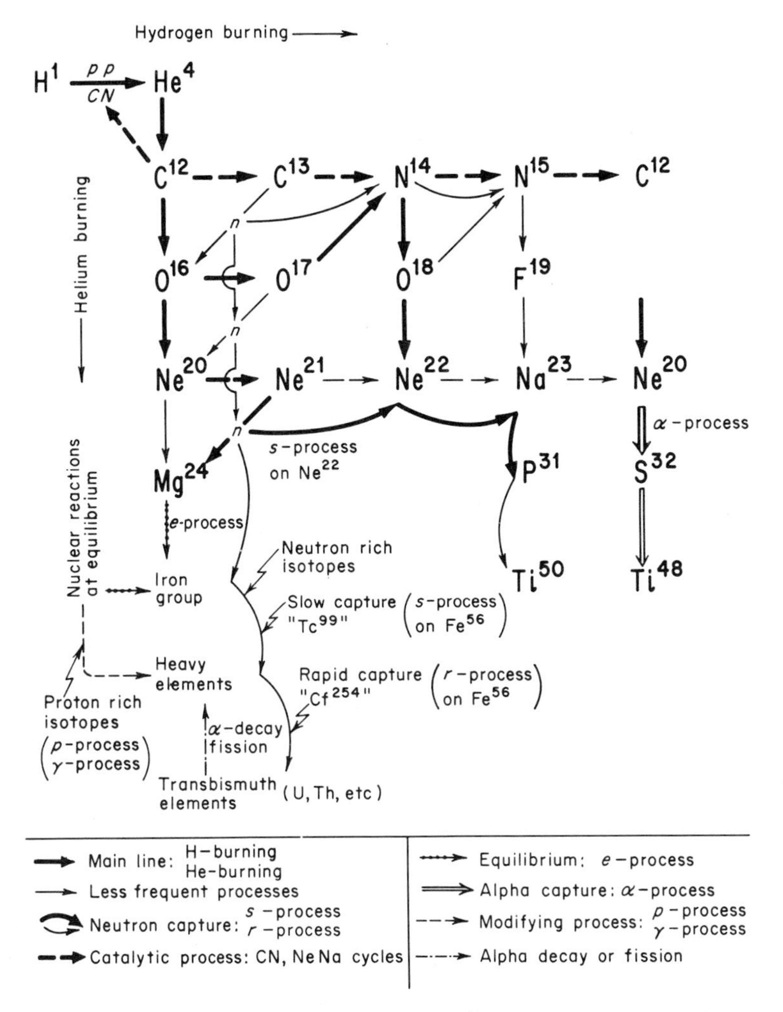

FIG. 20.17 The synthesis of the elements in the stars [E. M. Burbidge, G. R. Burbidge, W. A. Fowler and F. Hoyle].

19. LIGHTER RADIOACTIVE NUCLIDES

Radioactive isotopes of the lighter elements are obtained from three principal sources: (1) irradiation of stable nuclides with beams of ions or electrons obtained from accelerators such as cyclotrons, betatrons, etc. (2) irradiation of stable nuclides with neutrons from a reactor or other source (3) fission products. In addition, a number of naturally occurring radioactive nuclides have been found among the lighter elements. A list of some naturally occurring radionuclides with $Z < 82$ is given in Table 20.4.

TABLE 20.4 ARTIFICIAL RADIOACTIVE ELEMENTS

Nucleus	*Activity*	*Half Life*
^{11}C	β^+, γ	21 min
^{14}C	β^-	5700 yr
^{13}N	β^+, γ	9.9 min
^{15}O	β^+	125 sec
^{22}Na	β^+, γ	3.0 yr
^{24}Na	β^-, γ	14.8 hr
^{32}P	β^-	14.3 days
^{35}S	β^-	87.1 days
^{45}Ca	β^-	152 days
^{59}Fe	β^-, γ	46 days
^{60}Co	β^-, γ	5.3 yr
^{64}Cu	β^+, β^-	12.8 hr

Cosmic rays striking the atmosphere and the surface of the earth are continuously producing a number of radioactive species. For example,

$$^{14}N + n \longrightarrow {}^{12}C + {}^{3}H$$

$$^{14}N + n \longrightarrow {}^{14}C + {}^{1}H$$

Both tritium and ^{14}C are β emitters, with half lives of 12.4 and 5568 years, respectively.

Whereas the heavy nuclides often decay by alpha emission, the lighter radioactive nuclides usually decay by emission of a positron or electron. If the nuclide is unstable owing to an excess of neutrons, the decay process can be considered as an internal conversion of a neutron to a proton with the emission of a β^-. For example,

$$^{87}_{36}Kr \xrightarrow[\text{min}]{78} {}^{87}_{37}Rb + {}^{0}_{-1}e$$

If the nuclide is unstable owing to an excess of protons, the decay process can be considered as an internal conversion of a proton to a neutron with the emission of a β^+. For example,

$$^{81}_{38}Sr \xrightarrow[\text{min}]{29} {}^{81}_{37}Rb + {}^{0}_{+1}e$$

Instead of emitting a positron, the unstable nucleus may capture an electron from one of the atomic orbitals, usually one of the K electrons. This reaction is called *K-capture.* Usually K-capture and positron emission both occur for the same nuclide, but sometimes only one process occurs. For example,

$$^{81}_{37}Rb \xrightarrow{4.7\text{ hr}} {}^{81}_{36}Kr + {}^{0}_{+1}e$$

$$^{0}_{-1}e(K) + {}^{81}_{37}Rb \xrightarrow{4.7\text{ hr}} {}^{81}_{36}Kr + \gamma$$

Examples of these processes were shown in Fig. 20.10.

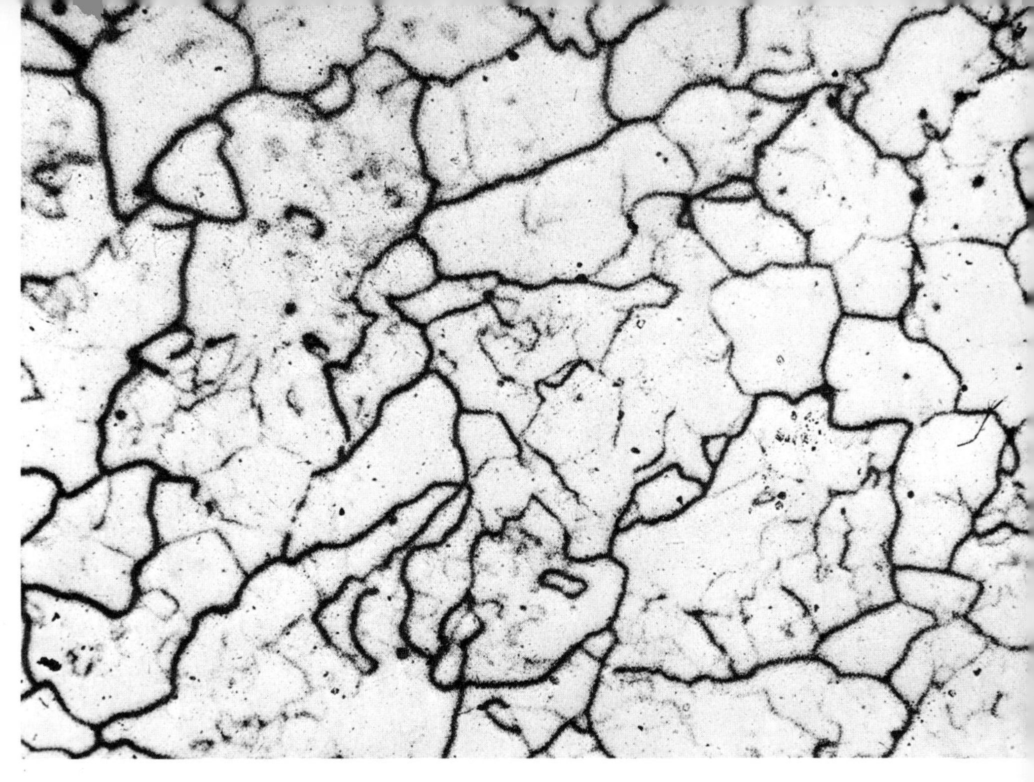

FIG. 20.18 Example of an autoradiograph — the preferential diffusion of the radioactive tracer ^{59}Fe along grain boundaries in a specimen of polycrystalline iron. [P. Lacombe, University of Paris].

20. TRACERS

The great variety of radioactive isotopes has made possible many applications in *tracer experiments,* in which a given type of atom can be followed through a sequence of chemical or physical changes. Stable isotopes can also be used as tracers, but they are not so easily followed and are available for fewer elements. The development of tracer techniques was originated by G. von Hevesy and F. Paneth.

One of the earliest studies with radioactive tracers used radioactive lead to follow the diffusion of lead ions in solid metals and salts. For example, a thin coating of radiolead can be plated onto the surface of a sample of metallic lead. After this is maintained at constant temperature for a definite time, thin slices are cut off and their radioactivity measured with a Geiger counter. The self-diffusion constant of Pb in the metal can readily be calculated from the observed distribution of activity. Many such diffusion studies have now been made in metals and in solid compounds. The results obtained are of fundamental importance in theories of the nature and properties of the solid state. Fig. 20.18 shows the diffusion of ^{59}Fe, a γ emitter, in a polycrystalline specimen of iron. After the diffusion, the specimen was sectioned and an *autoradiograph* made by placing the face in contact with a photographic film. In this way a detailed picture is obtained of the preferential distribution of the diffusing tracer along the intercrystalline boundaries of the metal. Diffusion in liquids, as well as the permeability of natural and synthetic membranes, can also be conveniently followed by radioactive tracer methods.

A useful tracer method is *isotopic dilution analysis.* An example is the determination of amino acids in the products of protein hydrolysis. The conventional method would require the complete isolation of each amino acid in pure form. Suppose, however, a known amount of an amino acid labeled with deuterium or carbon-14 is added to the hydrolysate. After thorough mixing, a small amount of the given acid is isolated and its activity measured. From the decrease in activity, the total concentration of the acid in the hydrolysate can be calculated.

Tracers are used to elucidate reaction mechanisms. One interesting problem was the mechanism of ester hydrolysis. Oxygen does not have a radioactive isotope of long enough half life to be a useful tracer, but the stable ^{18}O can be used. By using water enriched with heavy oxygen ($O^{\star}$) the reaction was shown to proceed as follows:

$$R{-}C({=}O)(OR') + HO^{\star}H \longrightarrow R{\cdot}C({=}O)(O^{\star}H) + R'OH$$

The tagged oxygen appeared only in the acid, showing that the OR group is substituted by $-O^{\star}H$ in the hydrolysis.*

An application of tracer techniques to elucidate a reaction mechanism was made in the photolysis of $^{15}N^{14}NO$ by light of 1236 Å wavelength.† The products included $^{29}N_2$, ^{15}NO, ^{14}NO and small amounts of $^{30}N_2$. The occurrence of the $^{30}N_2$ indicated that sometimes the primary photolytic steps must occur as

$$^{15}N^{14}NO \xrightarrow{h\nu} {}^{15}N + {}^{14}NO$$

although usually the process would be

$$^{15}N^{14}NO \xrightarrow{h\nu} {}^{15}N^{14}N + O$$

There would appear to be no possible way of getting $^{30}N_2$ that did not involve formation of an atom of ^{15}N. As in this example, the evidence provided by tracer experiments is usually very clear cut and decisive.

PROBLEMS

1. From the atomic weights in Table 20.1, calculate the ΔE in kcal per mole for the following reactions:

$$^1_1H + {}^1_0n \longrightarrow {}^2_1H, \quad {}^2_1H + {}^1_0n \longrightarrow {}^3_1H, \quad {}^1_1H + e \longrightarrow {}^1_0n, \quad 2\,{}^2_1H \longrightarrow {}^4_2He$$

* M. Polanyi and A. L. Szabo, *Trans. Farad. Soc. 30*, 508 (1934).

† J. P. Doering and B. H. Mahan, *J. Chem. Phys. 34*, 1617 (1961).

2. Calculate the mass of an electron accelerated through a potential of 2×10^8 volts. [*Ans.* 3.56×10^{-25} g]

3. The π-meson has a mass about 285 times that of the electron; the μ-meson has a mass about 215 times that of the electron. The π-meson decays into a μ-meson plus a neutrino. Estimate ΔE for the reaction in ev. [*Ans.* 35.9 ev]

4. Calculate the energy necessary to create a pair of light mesons.

5. The scattering cross section, σ, of lead is 5 barns for fast neutrons. How great a thickness of lead is required to reduce the intensity of a neutron beam to 5 per cent of its initial value? How great a thickness of magnesium with $\sigma = 2$ barns? [*Ans.* 18.1, 34.7 cm]

6. A normal male subject weighing 70.8 kg was injected with 5.09 ml of water containing tritium (9×10^9 cpm). Equilibrium with body water was reached after 3 hr when a 1-ml sample of plasma water from the subject had an activity of 1.8×10^5 cpm. Estimate the weight per cent of water in the human body. [*Ans.* 70.6 per cent]

7. The isotope $^{225}_{89}Ac$ has $\tau = 10$ days and emits an α with energy of 5.80 mev. Calculate the power generation in watts per 100 mg of the isotope. [*Ans.* 199]

8. According to W. F. Libby [*Science, 109,* 227 (1949)] it is probable that radioactive carbon-14 ($\tau = 5720$ years) is produced in the upper atmosphere by the action of cosmic-ray neutrons on ^{14}N, being thereby maintained at an approximately constant concentration of 12.5 cpm per g of carbon. A sample of wood from an ancient Egyptian tomb gave an activity of 7.04 cpm per g C. Estimate the age of the wood. [*Ans.* 5160 yr]

9. To a hydrolysate from 10 g of protein is added 100 mg of pure CD_3CHNH_2COOH (deuterium-substituted alanine). After thorough mixing, 100 mg of crystalline alanine is isolated which has a deuterium content of 1.03 per cent by weight. Calculate the per cent alanine in the protein. [*Ans.* 53.4 per cent]

10. A 10-g sample of iodobenzene is shaken with 100 ml of molar KI solution containing 2500 counts per min radio-iodine. The activity of the iodobenzene layer at the end of 2 hours is 250 cpm. What per cent of the iodine atoms in the iodobenzene have exchanged with the iodide ions in solution? [*Ans.* 30.4 per cent]

11. A gamma ray of 1.66 mev is emitted from a ^{60}Co nucleus. Calculate the recoil velocity of the nucleus. Suppose the ^{60}Co atom is in a definite crystal structure, CoO for example. How could this situation affect the recoil velocity?

12. When $^{88}_{38}Sr$ is bombarded with deuterons, $^{89}_{38}Sr$ is formed. The cross section for the reaction is 0.1 barn. A $SrSO_4$ target 1.0 mm thick is exposed to a deuteron beam current of 100 microamperes. If scattering of deuterons is neglected, compute the number of Sr atoms transmuted in 1.0 hr. The ^{88}Sr is 82.6 per cent of Sr, and ^{89}Sr is a β-emitter of 53-day half life. Compute the curies of ^{89}Sr produced. [*Ans.* 2.38×10^{14}; 9.73×10^{-4} curie]

13. When $^{197}_{79}Au$ (capture cross section $\sigma_c = 10^{-22}$ cm²) is irradiated with slow neutrons it is converted into $^{198}_{79}Au$ ($\tau = 2.8$ days). Show that in general the number of unstable nuclei present after irradiation for a time t is

$$n = \frac{\sigma n_0 \phi}{\lambda} (1 - e^{-\lambda t})$$

Here n_0 is the number of target atoms and ϕ is the slow neutron flux. For the case in question, calculate the activity in microcuries of a 100-mg gold sample exposed to a neutron flux of 200 per cm² sec for 2 days. [*Ans.* $dn/dt = -\lambda n + \sigma n_0 \Phi$, hence, $\ln (\sigma n_0 \Phi - \lambda n) = -\lambda t +$ const. At $t = 0$, $n = 0$. Hence, const $= \ln \sigma n_0 \Phi$, and $n = [(\sigma n_0 \Phi)/\lambda](1 - e^{-\lambda t})$. 6.4×10^{-5} μC]

14. The conventional unit of quantity of X radiation is the roentgen, r. It is the quantity of radiation that produces 1 esu of ions in 1 cc of air at STP (1 esu $= 3.3 \times 10^{-10}$ coulomb). If 32.5 eV are required to produce a single ion pair in air, calculate the energy absorbed in 1 liter of air per roentgen.

15. Suppose a γ-ray photon of energy $h\nu$ strikes an electron at rest. Let $h\nu'$ be the energy of the scattered photon and v the velocity of the electron (Compton effect). From the conservation of energy and of the x and y components of momentum, show that the change in frequency $\Delta\nu = \nu - \nu' = (h\nu^2/mc^2)(1 - \cos \alpha)$ where α is the angle between the original and scattered directions of the photon.

16. A deuteron beam of 20 μA strikes a carbon target 2.5×10^{-3} cm thick having an area of 3.0 cm². The reaction $^{12}_{6}C(d, n)^{13}_{7}N$ occurs and the rate of formation of $^{13}_{7}N$ nuclei is 3.0×10^8/sec. The density of the carbon is 1.88 g cm⁻³. Calculate the cross section of the nuclear reaction.

17. The earth receives 327 calories per sec of solar radiation on each square meter normal to the radiation. The distance from the earth to the sun is 1.49×10^{11} m. Calculate the radiation loss in mass of the sun in one year.

18. The dosage rate at a distance of 1 m from a source of ^{54}Mn is 50 mr per hr. This nuclide decays by emission of a 0.85 mev γ. Estimate the strength of the source in millicuries.

21 PHOTOCHEMISTRY AND RADIATION CHEMISTRY

In Chapter 8 on chemical kinetics we considered only thermal reactions. In these the energy for the climb to the activated state comes from the random energies of the reacting molecules and their neighbors. Another way to provide the activation energy is to bring the reactant molecule into collision with quanta of electromagnetic energy (photons), with high-velocity electrons (β rays), or with other corpuscular beams, such as neutrons, protons, or α-particles, obtained from nuclear reactors or from accelerators. The study of reactions caused by any of these methods is the field called *radiation chemistry*. The name arose from the historical fact that the emissions from radioactive elements were called *rays*.

The older field called *photochemistry* would logically appear to be a subdivision of radiation chemistry. It is the science of the chemical effects of light, where *light* includes the infrared and ultraviolet, as well as the visible regions of the spectrum, i.e., the range of wavelengths from about 1000 to 10 000 Å. The energies of quanta in this range vary from about 1 to 10 ev, or 23 to 230 kcal per mole. These energies are comparable with the strengths of chemical bonds. Thus, if a molecule absorbs a photon of visible light, definite chemical effects may be expected, yet the collision is still a rather gentle one, and the effects usually follow paths made familiar from spectroscopic studies. In particular, there is almost never enough energy in a single quantum to activate more than one molecule in the primary step.

On the other hand, if a 1 000 000 ev γ-ray photon traverses a medium, thousands of molecules may become activated along its trajectory. As we shall see, these activations often result in ionization of the molecules, whereas in the photochemical region, ionization would be a rare occurrence. Radiations like α, β, γ rays, neutrons, and cyclotron beams, are therefore called *ionizing radiations*. Usually, when we speak of radiation chemistry we mean the science of the chemical effects of such highly energetic, ionizing rays. We tend, therefore, to divide the whole subject, on energetic grounds, into *photochemistry* and *radiation chemistry*.

1. LIGHT ABSORPTION

Light incident upon a system can be transmitted, refracted and scattered, or absorbed. The fraction of incident light absorbed depends on the thickness of the medium that is traversed. The law of absorption, originally stated in 1729 in a memoir by P. Bouguer, was later rediscovered by Lambert. It can be expressed as

$$-dI/I = a\,dx \tag{21.1}$$

where I is the intensity of light at a distance x from its entry into the medium, and a is called the *absorption coefficient* or *extinction coefficient*. On integration with the boundary condition $I = I_0$ at $x = 0$, we obtain

$$I = I_0\,e^{-ax} \tag{21.2}$$

In 1852, Beer showed, for many solutions of absorbing compounds in practically transparent solvents, that the coefficient a was proportional to the concentration of solute c. Thus Beer's law is

$$I = I_0\,e^{-\epsilon' cx} \tag{21.3}$$

If c is the molar concentration, ϵ' is called the *molar extinction coefficient*. The light absorbed is

$$I_a = I_0 - I = I_0(1 - e^{-\epsilon' cx})$$

These absorption laws are the bases for various spectrophotometric methods of analysis.* They are obeyed strictly only for monochromatic light.

A device that measures the total amount of incident radiation is called an *actinometer*. This measurement, *actinometry*, is a necessary part of any quantitative study of photochemical reactions.

An important type of actinometer is the *thermopile*. This consists of a number of thermocouples connected in series, with their hot junctions imbedded at a blackened surface which absorbs almost all the incident light and converts it into heat. Calibrated lamps of known energy output are available from the National Bureau of Standards. The emf developed by the thermopile is measured first with the standard lamp and then with the source of radiation of unknown intensity. The reaction vessel is mounted between the thermopile and the light, and the radiation absorbed by the reacting system is measured by the difference between readings with the vessel filled and empty.

2. SOME PHOTOCHEMICAL PRINCIPLES†

In 1818 Grotthuss and Draper stated a principle which we may call the *principle of photochemical activation*: *Only the light that is absorbed by a substance is effective*

* See, for example, the complete account given by M. G. Mellon, *Analytical Absorption Spectroscopy* (New York: Wiley, 1950).

† We follow closely a systematic discussion given by Michael Kasha.

in producing a photochemical change. In earlier days the distinction between scattering processes and quantum transitions was not understood, so that this activation principle was helpful. It now appears to be an almost self evident starting point for any discussion of photochemical reactions.

Stark in 1908 and Einstein in 1912 applied the concept of the quantum of energy to photochemical reactions of molecules. They stated a principle which we may call the *principle of quantum activation*: *Each quantum of radiation absorbed by a molecule activates one molecule in the primary step of a photochemical process.* It is essential to distinguish clearly between the primary step of light absorption and the subsequent processes of chemical reaction. An activated molecule does not necessarily undergo reaction; on the other hand, in some cases one activated molecule through a chain mechanism may cause the reaction of many other molecules. Thus the principle of quantum activation should *never* be interpreted to mean that one molecule *reacts* for each quantum absorbed.

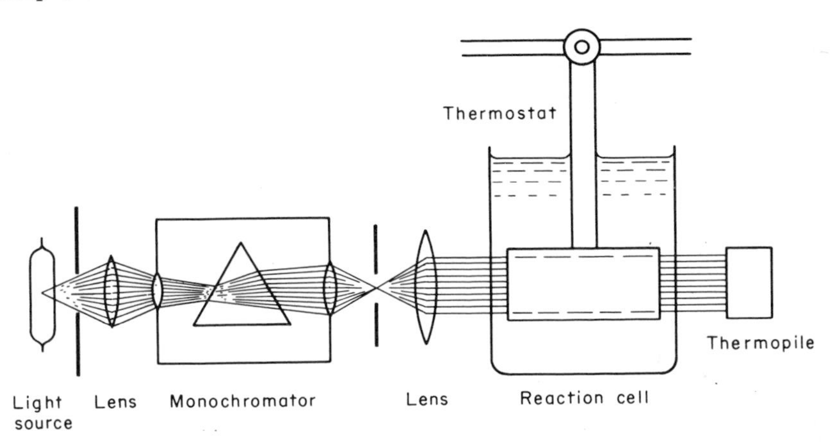

FIG. 21.1 Arrangement for photochemical investigation.

The energy $E_E = Lh\nu$, where L is the Avogadro Number is called *one einstein.* The value of the einstein depends on the wavelength. For orange light with $\lambda = 6000$ Å, it has a value in kilocalories of

$$E_E = \frac{6.02 \times 10^{23} \times 6.62 \times 10^{-27} \times 3.0 \times 10^{10}}{6 \times 10^3 \times 10^{-8} \times 4.184 \times 10^7 \times 10^3} = 45 \text{ kcal}$$

This is enough energy to break certain rather weak covalent bonds, but for C—C bonds and others with strengths higher than 72 kcal, radiation in the ultraviolet region is required. The *quantum yield* of a photochemical reaction is the number of molecules of reactant consumed or product formed per quantum of light absorbed. When we consider in more detail the mechanisms of photochemical activation, we shall need to define other more specialized *quantum yields.*

An experimental arrangement for a photochemical study is shown in Fig. 21.1. The light from the source passes through a monochromator which yields a narrow band of wavelengths in the desired region. The monochromatic light passes through the reaction cell, and the part that is not absorbed strikes an actinometer such as a thermopile.

Consider, for example, an experiment on the photolysis of gaseous HI with light of 2537 Å.

$$2\,HI \longrightarrow H_2 + I_2$$

It was found that absorption of 3.07×10^9 ergs of energy decomposed 1.30×10^{-3} moles of HI. The energy of the 2537 Å quantum is $h\nu = (6.62 \times 10^{-27})(3.0 \times 10^{10}/2.537 \times 10^{-5}) = 7.84 \times 10^{-12}$ erg. The HI has therefore absorbed $3.07 \times 10^9/7.84 \times 10^{-12} = 3.92 \times 10^{20}$ quanta. An *einstein* has $L = 6.02 \times 10^{23}$ quanta, so that $3.92 \times 10^{20}/6.02 \times 10^{23} = 6.52 \times 10^{-4}$ einstein were absorbed. The quantum yield Φ is the number of moles reacted per einstein absorbed. Hence, $\Phi = 1.30/.652 = 1.99$ for the photolysis of the HI.

One of the most reproducible reactions is the decomposition of oxalic acid *photosensitized* by uranyl salts. The uranyl ion UO_2^{++} absorbs radiation from 2500 to 4500 Å, becoming an excited ion $(UO_2^{++})^\star$ which decomposes the oxalic acid. This reaction has a quantum yield of 0.50.

$$UO_2^{++} + h\nu \longrightarrow (UO_2^{++})^\star$$

$$(UO_2^{++})^\star + (COOH)_2 \longrightarrow UO_2^{++} + CO_2 + CO + H_2O$$

The oxalic acid concentration is easily followed by titration with permanganate. A quartz vessel filled with the uranyl oxalate mixture can be used like a thermopile to measure light absorbed, from the oxalic acid decomposed and the known quantum yield. Another reaction sometimes used as an actinometer is the photochemical hydrolysis of chloroacetic acid, $ClCH_2COOH + H_2O + h\nu \rightarrow CH_2OHCOOH + HCl$. This reaction has a quantum yield of 1.0.

3. PRIMARY PROCESSES IN PHOTOCHEMISTRY

Absorption by an atom in the line-spectrum region leads to an excited atom; in the region of continuous absorption, to an ion plus an electron.

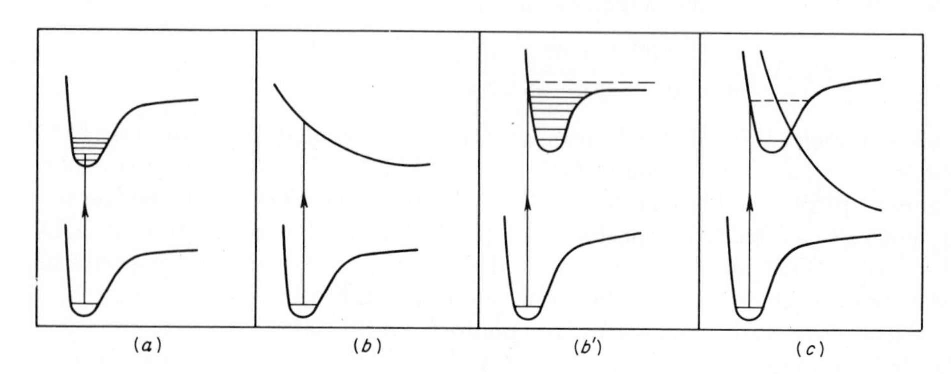

FIG. 21.2 Primary photochemical processes.

Absorption by molecules can lead to the different results shown in Fig. 21.2 In (a) the transition is from a stable ground state to a stable excited state. The corresponding spectrum consists of discontinuous bands with a fine structure of closely packed lines. In (b) the transition is to an unstable state, which immediately undergoes dissociation. Absorption of a quantum in case (b′) also leads to dissociation, because the energy level reached lies above the binding energy of the excited state. Both (b) and (b′) correspond to continuous absorption spectra, without bands. A third and less usual result is shown in (c). The initial transition is from one stable state to another, but the upper state is "intersected" by the potential-energy surface of an unstable state, and the excited molecule can switch over to this after one or more vibrations. The resultant spectra are quite diffuse but not completely continuous. This phenomenon was named *predissociation* by V. Henri.

It should be noted that all the transitions in Fig. 21.2 are depicted as vertical jumps on the potential-energy diagrams. This picture is in accord with the Franck-Condon principle that electronic transitions occur without influencing the positions of the nuclei.

4. THE BIPARTITION OF MOLECULAR EXCITATION

In Sec. 14.28 we described the different kinds of states which can occur in electronic excitation of a molecule. In most molecules the absorption of a quantum leads to a transition from a singlet ground state to a singlet excited state. There will usually be an excited triplet state somewhat below this excited singlet. A typical situation is shown in Fig. 21.3. We can interpret the initial processes in photochemical activation in terms of this pattern of states.

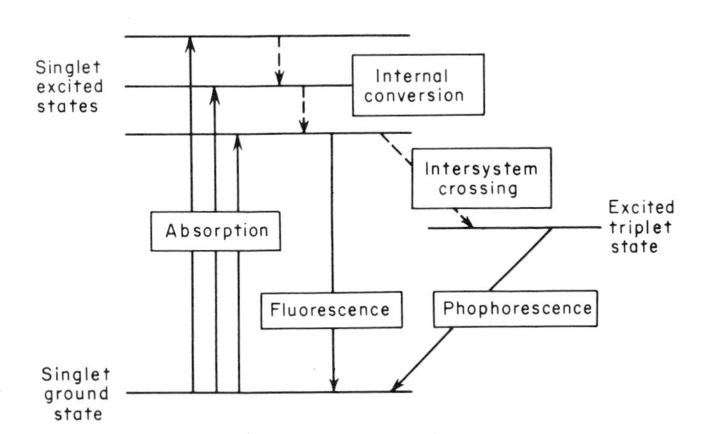

FIG. 21.3 Molecular energy levels concerned in photochemical processes.

Immediately after the primary quantum jump, a series of extremely rapid events takes place, *before* any photochemical reaction or emission of luminescent radiation can occur. First, there is *internal conversion*: no matter which upper singlet state has been reached in the primary quantum jump, there is a rapid radiationless transfer of energy to the lowest excited singlet state. Second, there is *intersystem crossing:* there is a competition between the lowest excited singlet and triplet states, and some of the energy is transferred to the triplet by a radiationless process. *Each quantum of radiation absorbed by a normal polyatomic molecule has a probability of bipartition between the lowest excited singlet and triplet states of the molecule.*

The basic model for excitation in a polyatomic molecule therefore involves three important states: the ground singlet, the first excited singlet, and the first excited triplet. We can therefore define two quantum yields in terms of this model.

The *two-state quantum yield* is the number of molecules emitting or reacting from a particular excited state divided by the number of quanta absorbed in going from the ground state to that particular excited state.

The *three-state quantum yield* is defined as the number of molecules emitting or reacting from a particular excited state divided by the number of quanta absorbed in going from the ground state to some other excited state, above the excited state in question. In particular, the quantum yield of reaction or emission of a molecule in a triplet state will almost always be a three-state quantum yield.

5. SECONDARY PHOTOCHEMICAL PROCESSES: FLUORESCENCE

If the light absorption lies in the banded region of the spectrum, there are several careers open to the excited molecule formed in the primary step. (1) It may re-emit a quantum of either the same or a different frequency. This emission is called *fluorescence* or *phosphorescence.** (2) It may collide with other molecules and pass on to them some or all of its excitation energy. This energy either can cause reaction in the other molecule, or can gradually be degraded into heat. (3) It may collide with another molecule and react with it. (4) It may spontaneously decompose if the excitation energy reaches a bond that can be broken (predissociation).

Fluorescence is the emission of light which has been absorbed by the molecule. It should not be confused with the *scattering* of light which has not been absorbed, i.e., the *Rayleigh scattering* without change in wavelength, and the *Raman scattering* with change in wavelength. The natural life time of an excited state in a molecule undisturbed by collisions is about 10^{-8} sec. At a pressure of one atmosphere, a molecule experiences about 100 collisions in 10^{-8} sec. As a consequence, excited molecules in most gaseous systems at ordinary pressures usually lose their energies by collision before they have a chance to fluoresce. The fluorescence is said to be *quenched*. In some such systems, fluorescence can be observed if the pressure is sufficiently reduced. An example is the fluorescence of NO_2 excited by light of wavelength $\lambda = 4000$ Å. In Fig. 21.4 the relative

* The distinction between these two processes was defined in Sec. 14.29.

quantum yield for the fluorescence is plotted against the pressure, and the increased quenching at higher pressures is evident. Actually, this case is rather unusual since the life time of the excited state is 10^{-5} sec, instead of about 10^{-8}.

A kinetic expression for the quenching of fluorescence is obtained by considering the two parallel processes for an excited atom or molecule $M^\star$:

$$\text{Fluorescence} \qquad M^\star \xrightarrow{k_1} M + h\nu$$

$$\text{Quenching} \qquad M^\star + Q \xrightarrow{k_2} M + Q + \text{kinetic energy}$$

The total rate of deactivation is

$$\frac{-d[M^\star]}{dt} = k_1[M^\star] + k_2[M^\star][Q]$$

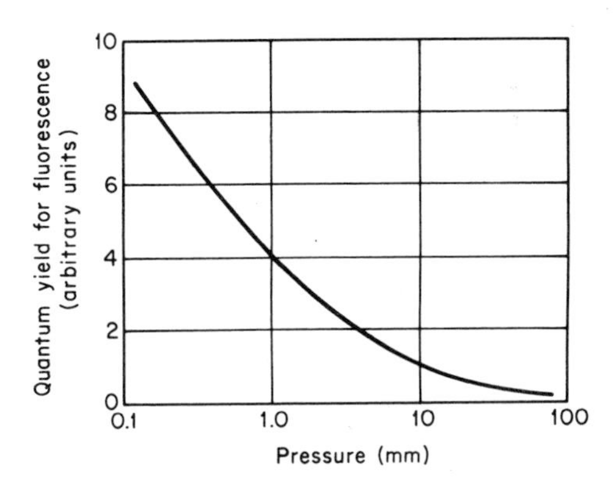

FIG. 21.4 Relative quantum yield for fluorescence of NO_2.

If the intensity of absorbed light is I_0, and the fluorescent intensity is I, the fraction of excited molecules that fluoresce is the fluorescence yield y_f,

$$y_f = \frac{I}{I_0} = \frac{k_1[M^\star]}{k_1[M^\star] + k_2[M^\star][Q]} = \frac{1}{1 + (k_2/k_1)[Q]} \tag{21.4}$$

If k_1 is known from an independent determination of the life time τ of the excited state in the absence of quencher Q ($k_1 = \tau^{-1}$), we can evaluate k_2, the specific rate of the quenching process. It is usual to express the results in terms of a *quenching cross section* σ_Q. This is calculated from Eq. (8.20) for the number of binary collisions Z_{12} in a gas. It is the value that must be taken for the cross section $\pi d_{12}^2/4$ in order that the value of k_2 calculated by simple collision theory should exactly equal the experimental value. From Eq. (8.21) with $E = 0$ since there is no activation energy for the process of energy transfer, we therefore obtain

$$\sigma_Q = \frac{10^3}{4L}\left(\frac{\pi\mu}{8kT}\right)^{1/2} k_2 \tag{21.5}$$

where k_2 is the usual units of liter mole^{-1} sec^{-1}.

An example of the results obtained is shown in Table 21.1, which deals with the quenching of mercury resonance radiation ($^3P_1 \rightarrow {}^1S_0$) by added gases. The great effectiveness of hydrogen and some of the hydrocarbons is due to dissociative reactions like

$$Hg^{\star} + H_2 \longrightarrow HgH + H, \qquad Hg^{\star} + RH \longrightarrow HgH + R$$

TABLE 21.1 EFFECTIVE CROSS SECTIONS FOR QUENCHING MERCURY FLUORESCENCE

Gas	$10^{16}\ \sigma_Q$ – cm^2	Gas	$10^{16}\ \sigma_Q$ – cm^2
O_2	13.9	CO_2	2.48
H_2	6.07	PH_3	26.2
CO	4.07	CH_4	0.06
NH_3	2.94	n-C_7H_{16}	24.0

6. LUMINESCENCE IN SOLIDS

The phenomena of excitation followed by re-emission or deactivation are basically the same in solid, liquid, and gaseous systems. In solids, the processes of energy transfer do not, of course, involve collisions, but the degradation of the electronic energy of excitation into the thermal vibrational energy of the crystal provides an analogous mechanism of quenching. Luminescent solids have been classified as (1) pure (2) impurity activated.

Examples of type (1) are certain inorganic salts such as those of the uranyl ion UO_2^{+2}. Light absorption by these ions is followed by fluorescence both in the crystalline state and in solution, and it is evident that quenching is not efficient. The reason seems to be that electronic excitation occurs in inner orbitals, which are effectively shielded from interaction with vibrational levels of neighboring ions or molecules. Another example of a pure luminescent solid is anthracene, which displays a pale violet fluorescence in the purest samples ever obtained.

If an anthracene crystal contains as little as 0.01 per cent of naphthacene, the characteristic green fluorescence of naphthacene appears and the violet anthracene fluorescence is suppressed. When such a crystal is heated, the green fluorescence disappears at the instant of melting, and the violet anthracene fluorescence reappears. The explanation of these remarkable events seems to be the following. When the anthracene crystal absorbs a photon and one of its π electrons is excited to an upper band, a hole is left behind in the lower band. The hole, being a location of missing negative charge, has an effective positive charge, and hence attracts the electron, somewhat in the way that an H^+ nucleus attracts its planetary electron. Such an association between an excited electron and a positive hole is called an *exciton*. Now the exciton hops about through the crystal until it happens to hit a naphthacene molecule, which traps it long enough for the fluorescent emission to take place. Thus, although the photon is almost always absorbed in an anthracene molecule, it is almost always emitted from a naphthacene molecule. The example of naphthacene in anthracene is midway between the pure luminescent crystal and the typical case of impurity activated crystals.

The example of zinc sulfide may be considered as typical of impurity activation. Pure ZnS of stoichiometric composition displays practically no luminescence. If this material is heated at 500–1000°C it dissociates slightly to form ZnS with excess Zn interstitially dissolved: $ZnS(c) \rightarrow Zn_i$ (in ZnS) $+ \frac{1}{2}S_2$. The excess Zn atoms form impurity centers of the type shown in Fig. 16.29(d). When illuminated with light of about 3400 Å, the heat-treated ZnS displays phosphorescence. The ZnS on illumination also becomes a better conductor of electricity; this phenomenon is called *photoconductivity*.

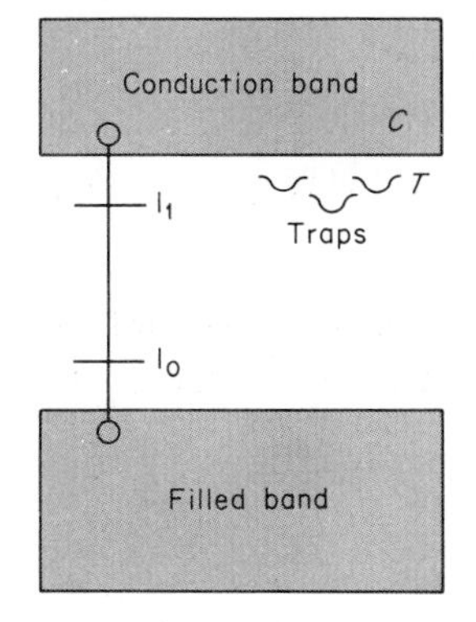

FIG. 21.5 Band model for an impurity-activated phosphor.

An oversimplified model to account for these observations is shown in Fig. 21.5. The levels I_0 and I_1 represent a ground state and an excited stage for an impurity center, e.g., an interstitial zinc atom. If a quantum of radiation of sufficient energy is absorbed by the crystal, an electron may be driven from the filled band to the empty conduction band, and a hole is left in the filled band. If the hole and the electron remained associated, the result would be an *exciton*, similar to that found in anthracene. In pure ZnS, the electron and the positive hole will recombine without the emission of light, the energy being dissipated as heat. The impurity centers, such as excess Zn, provide a mechanism by which the excitation energy can be re-emitted as light.

Both pure ZnS and impurity activated ZnS contain *traps* for electrons, metastable levels from which transition to the ground state is forbidden. These traps may be dislocations, grain boundaries, or other impurities in the crystals. Only by thermal excitation back to the conduction band can an electron escape from its trap and eventually emit the phosphorescent radiation. For such a thermal excitation from T to C, the probability p per unit time has the simple form of a first order rate constant $p = ae^{-E/RT}$, where E is the energy gap between T and C. If n is the number of electrons trapped at any instant, the phosphorescent intensity is proportional to their rate of escape,

$$I = \frac{-dn}{dt} = pn = nae^{-E/RT} \tag{21.6}$$

For a fixed temperature, integration of this equation gives the decay of phosphorescence with time. For the typical example of a thallium activated KCl phosphor, the constants are $a = 3 \times 10^9$ sec^{-1}, and $E = 15.5$ kcal per mole.

7. SECONDARY PHOTOCHEMICAL PROCESSES: DISSOCIATION

As an example of an interesting photochemical system, we shall describe the reactions of Victoria Blue R leuconitrile when irradiated with ultraviolet light.* This substance is one of a group of compounds which produce a visual image

* A. H. Sporer, *Trans. Faraday Soc.* *57*, 983 (1961).

immediately on irradiation with no subsequent development being required. The reaction is shown in Fig. 21.6. The leuconitrile is colorless; on irradiation it loses a CN^- ion and the remaining triacylmethyl ion is a deep blue. In addition, there is occasionally a splitting of the molecule to yield a CH_3 radical. Fig. 21.6 shows in one model both these reaction paths. The light at 2620 Å is absorbed in the dimethylaniline groups. The activation can then follow three different paths:

(1) Transfer to the C—C bond with photoionization to yield the dye.

(2) Transfer to the N—C bond with dissociation of a methyl radical.

(3) Transfer to the N-phenyl-1-naphthylamine group, where it is emitted as fluorescence.

In this particular compound, at room temperature most of the absorbed light is re-emitted as fluorescence. By changing the substituent groups, however, the quantum yields for the different paths can be varied. For the malachite green leuconitrile ($R_3 = C_6H_5$) a quantum yield of unity was found for the dye formation in a solvent of high dielectric constant.

8. SECONDARY PHOTOCHEMICAL PROCESSES: CHAIN REACTIONS

If a molecule is dissociated as a consequence of absorbing a quantum of radiation, extensive secondary reactions may occur, since the fragments are often highly reactive atoms or radicals. Sometimes, also, the products of the primary fission process are still in excited states, as so-called *hot atoms* or *hot radicals*.

For example, if a mixture of chlorine and hydrogen is exposed to light in the continuous region of the absorption spectrum of chlorine ($\lambda < 4800$ Å) a fast reaction to hydrogen chloride ensues. The quantum yield Φ is 10^4 to 10^6. Bodenstein was the first to explain the high value of Φ in terms of a long reaction chain. The first step is dissociation of the chlorine molecule,

$$\text{(1)} \qquad Cl_2 + h\nu \longrightarrow 2\,Cl \qquad \Phi_1 I_a$$

This is followed by

$$\text{(2)} \qquad Cl + H_2 \longrightarrow HCl + H \qquad k_2$$

$$\text{(3)} \qquad H + Cl_2 \longrightarrow HCl + Cl \qquad k_3$$

$$\text{(4)} \qquad Cl \longrightarrow \tfrac{1}{2}\,Cl_2 \text{ (on wall)} \qquad k_4$$

If we set up the steady-state expressions for [Cl] and [H] in the usual way (p. 284), we obtain for the rate of HCl production,

$$\frac{d[HCl]}{dt} = k_2[Cl][H_2] + k_3[H][Cl_2]$$

$$= \frac{2k_2\Phi_1 I_a}{k_4}[H_2]$$

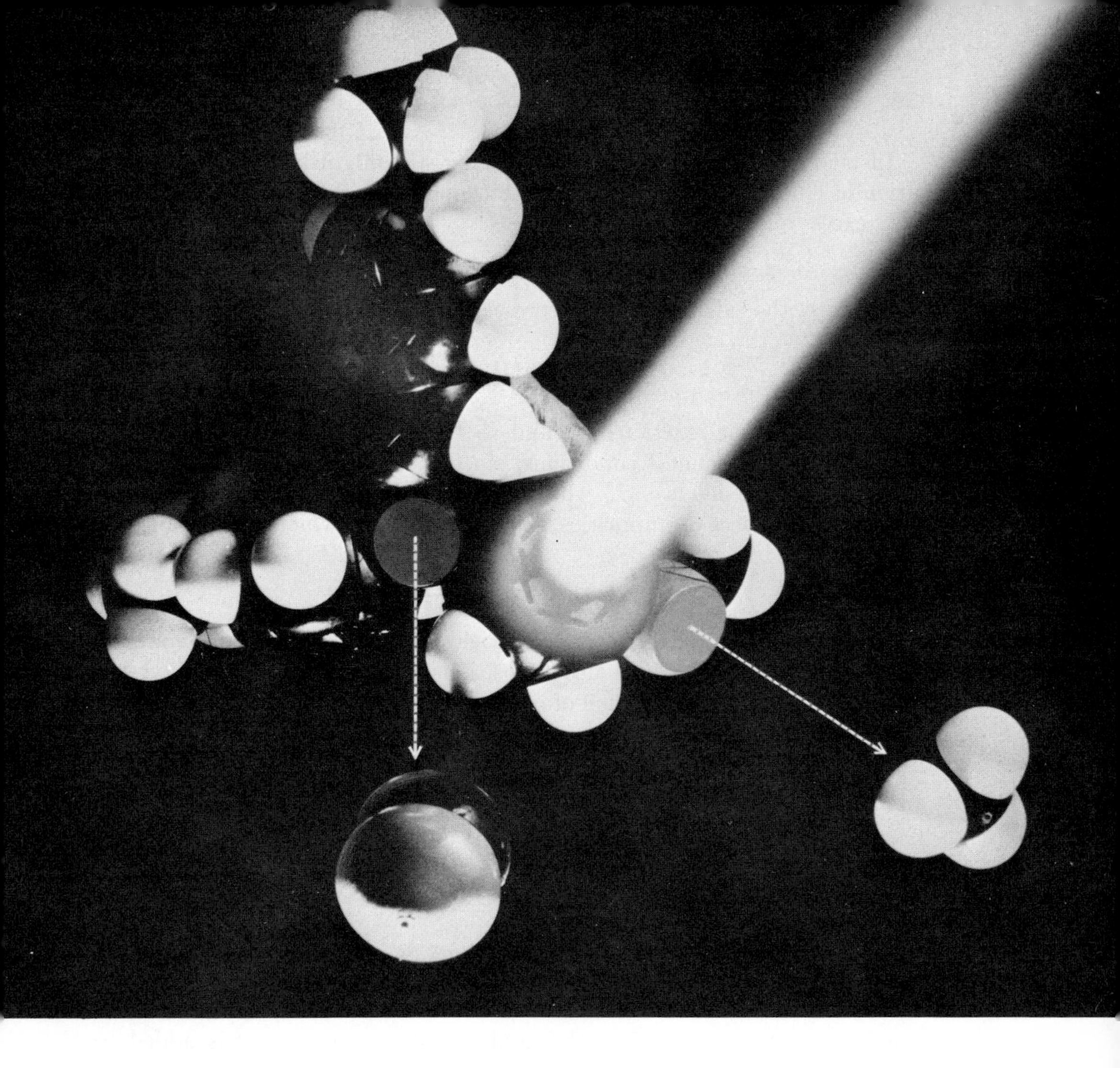

Leuconitrile $\xrightarrow{h\nu}$ $[\text{Dye}]^+ + CN^-$

$R_1 = R_2 = CH_3$; $R_3 = C_6H_5$: malachite green — I

$R_1 = R_2 = CH_3$; $R_3 = C_6H_4N(CH_3)_2$: crystal violet — II

$R_1 = H$; $R_2 = CH_2CH_2OH$; $R_3 = C_6H_4N(H)CH_2CH_2OH$: hydroxyethylated pararosaniline — III

$R_1 = R_2 = CH_3$; R_3 = (naphthyl–NH–phenyl) : Victoria blue B — IV

FIG. 21.6 The photoionization of triaryl methyl leuconitriles. (The model shows the Victoria blue R molecule). [A. H. Sporer, I.B.M. Research Laboratory, San Jose, Cal.].

Instead of reaction (4), the chain-ending step might be a gas-phase recombination of chlorine atoms, perhaps with cooperation of a third body M to carry away excess energy.

(5) $$Cl + Cl(+M) \longrightarrow Cl_2(+M) \qquad k_5$$

In this case, the calculated rate expression would be

$$\frac{d[HCl]}{dt} = k_2[H_2]\left[\frac{\Phi_1 I_a}{k_5}[M]\right]^{1/2}$$

It is likely that reactions (4) and (5) both contribute to the chain ending under most experimental conditions, since in most experiments with pure H_2 and Cl_2 the rate depends on I_a^n, with n somewhere between $\frac{1}{2}$ and 1. The reaction is sensitive to traces of impurities, especially oxygen, which acts as an inhibitor by removing H atoms:

$$H + O_2(+M) \longrightarrow HO_2(+M)$$

In contrast with the high quantum yield of the $H_2 + Cl_2$ reaction are the low yields in the photochemical decompositions (*photolyses*) of the alkyl iodides. These compounds have a region of continuous absorption in the near ultraviolet, at 2300 to 2500 Å, which leads to a break into free alkyl radicals and iodine atoms. For example,

$$CH_3I + h\nu \longrightarrow CH_3 + I$$

The quantum yield of the photolysis is only about 10^{-2}. The reason for the low Φ is that the most likely secondary reaction is a recombination,

$$CH_3 + I \longrightarrow CH_3I$$

Only a few radicals react with more alkyl iodide,

$$CH_3 + CH_3I \longrightarrow CH_4 + CH_2I$$

The final products are CH_4, CH_2I_2 and I_2. If mercury vapor is added to the system, the quantum yield is much increased. The mercury acts by removing iodine atoms, preventing their recombination with alkyl radicals.

A reaction that has been carefully studied is the photolysis of acetone; more than fifty papers have been devoted to it during the past 25 years.

$$(CH_3)_2CO + h\nu \longrightarrow C_2H_6 + CO$$

Small amounts of methane and biacetyl are also formed. Acetone absorbs ultraviolet light, with a banded spectrum from 3300 to 2950 Å merging into a continuous absorption that extends to 2200 Å. Electronic excitation in the carbonyl group is responsible for this absorption, but the C=O bond is strong and energy must flow into the weaker C—C bonds before dissociation can occur.

In an investigation by Farrington Daniels and G. H. Damon,* acetone vapor contained in a quartz vessel was irradiated with virtually monochromatic light obtained from a high-pressure mercury-vapor lamp with a quartz monochromator. In a typical experiment, radiation at $\lambda = 3130$ Å was used. Measure-

* *J. Am. Chem. Soc.* *55*, 2362 (1933).

ment with a thermopile gave an absorption rate of 85 200 erg per sec over a period of 23 000 sec. The volume of the vessel was 60.3 cc, the thermostat temperature 56°C, and the pressure increased from 760 to 790.4 mm or $\Delta P = 30.4$ mm.

Apart from minor subsidiary reactions, two moles of product appeared for each mole of acetone decomposed. The number of molecules decomposed was therefore

$$N = \frac{30.4}{760} \cdot \frac{273}{329} \frac{6.03}{22\,414} \times 6.02 \times 10^{23} = 5.23 \times 10^{19}$$

The number of quanta absorbed was

$$q = \frac{85\,200 \times 23\,000 \times 3.13 \times 10^{-5}}{6.62 \times 10^{-27} \times 3.0 \times 10^{10}} = 3.08 \times 10^{20}$$

The quantum yield was therefore $\Phi = N/q = 0.17$. It is evident that of the quanta absorbed, less than one in five leads to reaction.

When acetone vapor is irradiated with ultraviolet light there is an intense and beautiful green fluorescence, and it was thought at first that the light that did not cause reaction was emitted in fluorescence. Daniels measured the fluorescent intensity and found that it actually accounted for less than 3 per cent of the light absorbed. Thus about 80 per cent of the radiation absorbed is degraded into heat. It was later shown that the fluorescence was due to biacetyl.

The products from acetone photolysis in a flow system remove lead mirrors, forming $Pb(CH_3)_4$.* This result, as well as other evidence, indicates that methyl radicals are formed. The most likely mechanism for the photolysis appears to be†

$$(CH_3)_2CO + h\nu \longrightarrow CH_3 + CH_3CO$$
$$CH_3 + CH_3 \longrightarrow C_2H_6$$
$$CH_3CO + CH_3CO \longrightarrow (CH_3CO)_2$$
$$CH_3CO \longrightarrow CH_3 + CO$$
$$CH_3 + CH_3CO \longrightarrow (CH_3)_2CO$$

The recombination reaction accounts for the low quantum yield, and, as would be expected, the yield therefore increases as the pressure is lowered.

9. PHOTOLYSIS IN LIQUIDS

When a molecule in a gas absorbs a quantum and splits into two radicals, there is little chance that these two radicals will recombine with each other. By the time they are separated by one mean free path, the chance that any particular

* T. G. Pearson, *J. Chem. Soc. 1934*, 1718; T. G. Pearson and R. H. Purcell, *ibid. 1935*, 1151.

† A complete discussion of the evidence for the mechanism and a solution of the steady-state rate equation are given by W. Davis, *Chem. Rev. 40*, 201 (1947).

pair will meet again is negligible. In a liquid, on the other hand, radicals formed in a dissociation reaction are surrounded by a cage of closely packed molecules. In many cases the radicals will recombine within a time which is not much greater than 10^{-13} s, a typical vibration period. The radicals may diffuse away from each other but even then the chance is high that the same pair soon meet again and recombine. For example, Richard Noyes* has estimated that for dissociation of iodine in hexane solution, the probability that the original pair recombines is about 0.5. This kind of recombination of a pair which came originally from the same parent molecule is called *geminate recombination.*

The course of the reaction can be influenced by the addition to the solution of a *scavenger* or radical trap, that is, a substance that combines readily with free radicals. Scavengers frequently used have been iodine, vinyl monomers and diphenylpicrylhydrazyl (DPPH).

The typical mechanism for a photolysis in a liquid in the presence of a scavenger S can thus be written as follows:

(1)	$AB + h\nu \longrightarrow (A + B)$	dissociation
(2)	$(A + B) \longrightarrow AB$	geminate recombination
(3)	$(A + B) \longrightarrow A + B$	separation by diffusion
(4)	$A + S \longrightarrow AS$ $B + S \longrightarrow BS$	scavenging of radicals
(5)	$A + B \longrightarrow AB,\ 2A \longrightarrow A_2$	recombination
(6)	$A + X \longrightarrow$ product, $2B \longrightarrow B_2$ $B + X \longrightarrow$ product	reaction of radicals

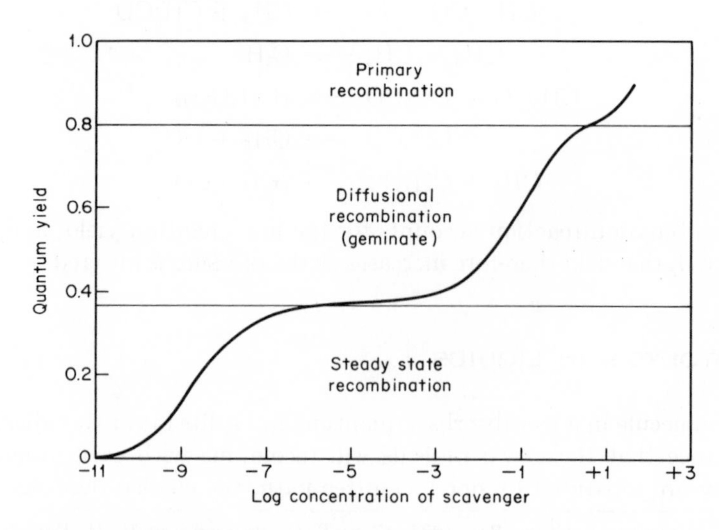

FIG. 21.7 Quantum yield for photolysis in liquid solution in the presence of a scavenger for radicals or atoms.

* R. Noyes, *J. Am. Chem. Soc. 18*, 999 (1950).

Figure 21.7 shows values of the quantum yield Φ calculated by Noyes as a function of the scavenger concentrations.

Although radical formation seems to be more common, sometimes excited states do decompose by a mechanism of molecular detachment. For example, radiation of ethylene at 1470 Å causes photolysis by two different mechanisms, having approximately equal quantum yields:

$$C_2H_4^{\star} \longrightarrow C_2H_2 + H_2$$

$$C_2H_4^{\star\star} \longrightarrow C_2H_2 + 2\,H$$

10. FLASH PHOTOLYSIS

The technique called *flash photolysis* is especially useful in the study of atoms and radicals that have only a short lifetime before reacting.* A powerful flash of light, with energy up to 10^5 joules and a duration of about 10^{-4} sec, is obtained by discharging a bank of capacitors through an inert gas such as argon or krypton. The reactants are in a vessel alined parallel with the lamp, and at the instant of the flash, an extensive photolysis of the absorbing gas occurs in the reaction vessel. Thus the primary products of photolysis, usually radicals and atoms,

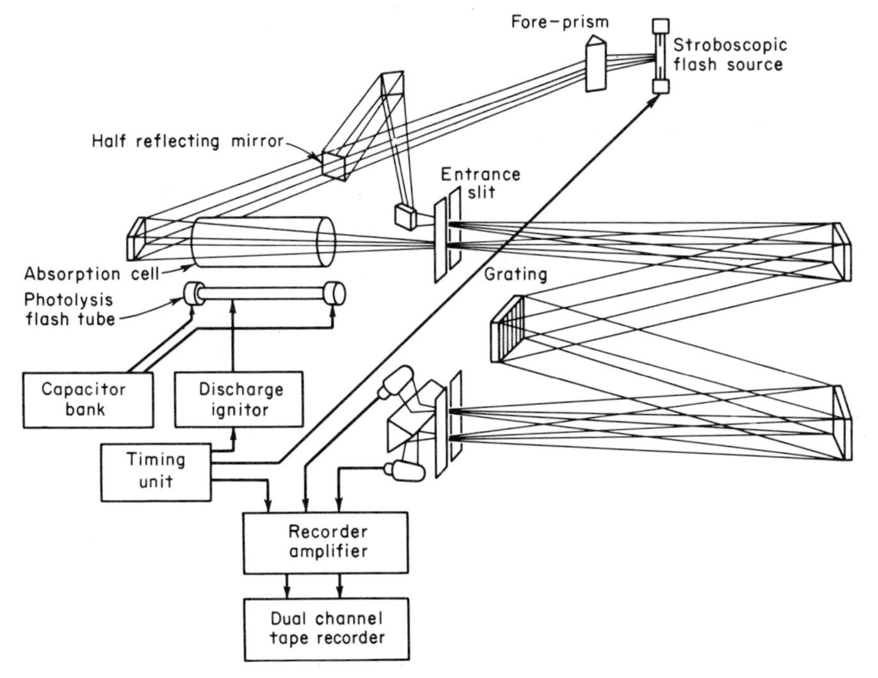

FIG. 21.8 High resolution kinetic spectroscopy by a multiple flash technique. [E. J. Bair, Indiana University].

* R. G. W. Norrish and G. Porter, *Nature 164*, 685 (1950); G. Porter, *Proc. Roy. Soc. A 200*, 284 (1950); O. Oldenburg, *J. Chem. Phys. 3*, 266 (1935).

are produced at much higher concentrations than in the usual experiment with continuous illumination at low intensities. A good method for following the subsequent reactions of the radicals is to make a continuous record of their absorption spectra.

The apparatus designed by Bair† for high resolution kinetic spectroscopy is shown in schematic form in Fig. 21.8. The concentrations of species in the reaction mixture can be followed by double-beam absorption measurements made at high spectral resolution at an accurate sequence of time intervals as short as 200 μs. The apparatus was tested by a study of the kinetics of recombination of iodine atoms in the presence of argon. The concentration of iodine molecules was studied by measuring an absorption line of highest extinction. This was found to be a band head at 19 192.2 cm^{-1}. The band arises from the vibrational transition $v'' = 0$ to $v' = 39$ of the $^3\Pi \leftarrow {}^1\Sigma$ electronic transition in molecular iodine.

The iodine atoms recombine by a three body process, with either argon or I_2 as the third body. Thus,

$$d[I_2]/dt = k_A[I]^2[Ar] + k_{I_2}[I]^2[I_2]$$

This can be rewritten as

$$\frac{1}{[I]^2[Ar]}\frac{d[I_2]}{dt} = k_A + k_{I_2}\frac{[I_2]}{[Ar]}$$

The left-hand expression was plotted against the ratio $[I_2]/[Ar]$ and extrapolated to zero to obtain $k_A = 1.6 \times 10^9\ l^2\ mole^{-2} s^{-1}$ at 25°C.

11. EFFECTS OF INTERMITTENT LIGHT

In the flash-photolysis experiment, a high initial concentration is formed of reactive intermediates, which gradually disappear by various reactions during the dark period. In the usual photochemical experiment, a steady intensity of light is used, so that intermediates build up to a steady-state concentration, which is maintained during the course of the run. Let us consider now a situation in which there is a regular sequence of light and dark periods. A convenient way to achieve such an intermittent illumination is to place between the light source and the reaction vessel a rotating circular disk from which sectors have been cut. If four sectors, for example, have angles of $22\frac{1}{2}°$ and are evenly spaced, the light and dark periods in the vessel will be in the ratio 1:3, and the flashing rate will be four times the rotation speed of the disk.

The use of the method can be illustrated in terms of a simple schematic reaction mechanism:

(1) $$A_2 + h\nu \longrightarrow 2\,A$$

(2) $$A + B \longrightarrow C + A$$

(3) $$2\,A \longrightarrow \text{stable product}$$

† H. H. Kramer, M. H. Hanes, E. J. Bair, *J. Opt. Soc. Am.* *51*, 775 (1961).

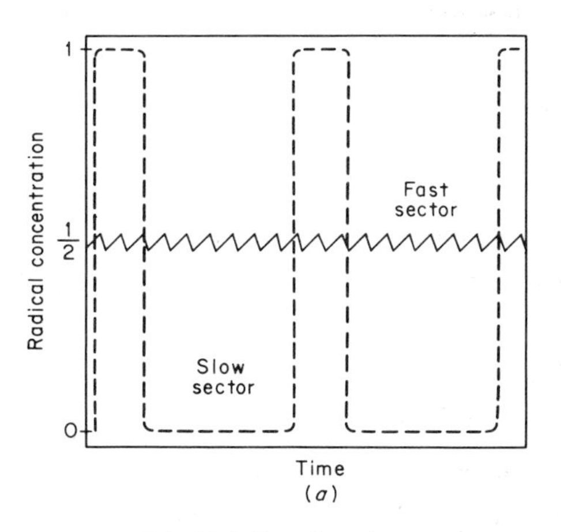

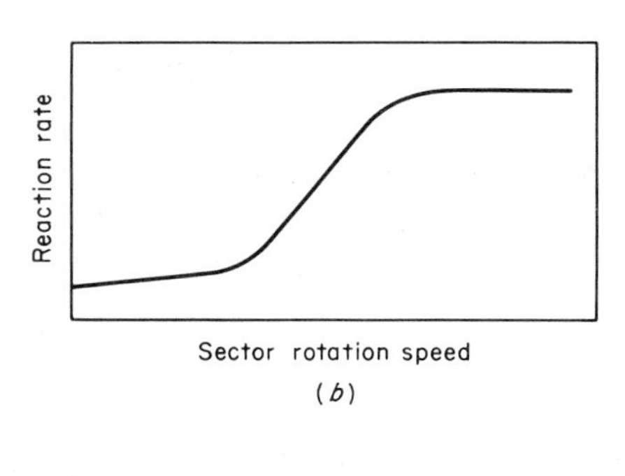

FIG. 21.9 The effect of intermittent light on (a) radical concentration; (b) reaction rate, for a case in which rate depends on $I_a^{1/2}$.

The steady-state concentration of the radicals A is $[A] = (\Phi I_a/2k_3)^{1/2}$. If the sector wheel with one-quarter open area is rotated very rapidly (and by "rapidly" we mean with a period much less than the half life for disappearance of radicals A in the dark), the net result is the same as if the intensity of a steady illumination was reduced to one-quarter. Thus the steady state concentration of A, and hence the rate of reaction, is reduced by a factor of $(\frac{1}{4})^{1/2} = \frac{1}{2}$. On the other hand, suppose that the period of rotation of the sector is long compared to the half life of A. In this case, the concentration of A during each dark period will fall far below the steady-state value. The net result will be the same as if the time of reaction is reduced to one-quarter with the light intensity unchanged. Thus the rate of reaction would be reduced by a factor of $\frac{1}{4}$. Fig. 21.9(a) shows how the concentration of radicals varies during the two experiments, and (b) shows how the reaction rate varies with sector speed.

The transition region between reaction rates for slow rotation and those for fast rotation will occur when the sector period is about equal to the half life of the reactive intermediate. Thus the experiments with intermittent illumination provide a method for measuring short half lives of intermediates, which would be difficult to study by other methods. It must be noted, however, that the method cannot be used if the overall rate is proportional to I_a, the first power of the light intensity.

A typical sector study* was that of the photochemical formation of phosgene, which follows a mechanism proposed by Bodenstein:

$$\begin{array}{rcll} Cl_2 + h\nu & \longrightarrow & Cl + Cl & \Phi I_a \\ Cl + CO & \longrightarrow & COCl & k_2 \\ COCl & \longrightarrow & Cl + CO & k_3 \\ COCl + Cl_2 & \longrightarrow & COCl_2 + Cl & k_4 \\ COCl + Cl & \longrightarrow & CO + Cl_2 & k_5 \end{array}$$

* W. G. Burns and F. S. Dainton, *Trans. Faraday Soc. 48*, 39 (1952).

The observed rate law is

$$\frac{d[COCl_2]}{dt} = k'(\Phi I_a)^{1/2}[CO]^{1/2}[Cl_2]$$

From the Bodenstein mechanism, $k' = k_4(k_1k_3/k_2k_5)^{1/2}$. The application of the sector technique made it possible to evaluate each of the rate constants. For example, in liter mole^{-1} sec^{-1}.

$$k_4 = 2.5 \times 10^9 \exp(-2960/RT)$$

$$k_5 = 4.0 \times 10^{11} \exp(-830/RT)$$

Reaction (5) goes at almost every collision, with a small energy barrier. In reaction (4) the activation energy is only 5 per cent of the energy of the Cl—Cl bond that is broken, whereas the frequency factor is only one per cent of the collision frequency. The low frequency factor indicates a loss of freedom and decrease in entropy when the activated complex is formed.

12. PRIMARY PROCESSES WITH HIGH-ENERGY RADIATIONS

When we compare the effects of high-energy radiation with those of light, we find a number of similarities but also a number of important differences. Table 21.2 summarizes information on the sources of high-energy radiations.

Table 21.2 RADIATIONS EMPLOYED IN RADIATION CHEMISTRY

Source	Radiation Particle	Typical Maximum Energy, mev
X-ray tube	Photon	0.6
Van de Graaf generator	Electron	10
	Proton	10
Cyclotron	Proton	40
	Deuteron	20
	Alpha	10
	Neutron	40
Betatron	Electron	20
	Photon	
Nuclear reactor (pile)	Photon	Dependent on conditions
	Neutron	
	Fission recoil	
Natural or artificial radioactive isotope	Photon	Dependent on isotope
	Electron	
	Alpha	
	Atom recoil	

With such radiations the yield is usually computed in terms of the *G-value*, the number of molecules of a given product formed or reactant converted for each 100 ev of energy absorbed. The high-energy radiations all produce ionization in the matter through which they pass. Thus, while the typical photochemical activation would be written

$$\mathrm{M} \xrightarrow{h\nu} \mathrm{M}^{\star} \text{ (singlet)}$$

the typical activation in radiation chemistry would be*

$$\mathrm{M} \longrightarrow \mathrm{M}^{+} + e$$

The Einstein principle of quantum activation has its counterpart in the principle that the amount of chemical reaction is proportional to the number of ion pairs produced in the reaction medium by an ionizing radiation. This principle harks back to a calculation made by W. H. Bragg in 1907, which indicated that the number of molecules of water decomposed by radon was equal to the number of ions that the same amount of radon would have produced in air. Bragg, however, was evidently not impressed by this agreement, which he noted as "a curious parallelism in numbers." In 1908, W. Duane demonstrated that the chemical effects of α particles were due to the ionization they caused, and in 1910, Marie Curie clearly stated the law of equivalence for α particles in water. From about 1911 onwards, S. C. Lind made use of ion-pair yields in an extensive series of experiments. He found that for some reactions the quantum yield with light and the ion-pair yield with α-particles were nearly identical, but in other cases they might differ by a factor of two or three.

The details of the ionization process depend somewhat on the particle concerned. When an X ray or γ ray interacts with a molecule, the most frequent result is the ejection of an electron by the Compton effect, i.e., the process is a collision between a photon and an electron, in which the electron is driven out of its molecule, and the photon is deflected with altered energy and momentum. The formation of a photoelectron by a process of absorption of the photon, which is the usual event with low-energy quanta, is much less likely at high energies. For example, with 100 kv X rays, only 3 per cent of the electrons are photoelectrons, and 97 per cent are Compton electrons. At 1 mev, almost all the electrons ejected are Comptons, which have an average energy of 440 kv. As a 440-kv electron is slowed to room temperature ($\sim$0.02 ev) it ionizes or excites many molecules as it passes near them. One ion pair is produced for about each 30 ev, so that the 440-kv electron produces about 15 000 ion pairs, and two or three times that many excited molecules. The effect of the single ion formed in the first ionization will obviously be negligible compared with that of the numerous secondary ions and excited molecules.

The difference between effects of electrons and those of ions is due mainly to the slower speed of the latter. A proton travels one-fortieth as fast as an electron of the same energy. Thus, for a given path distance, the slowly moving ion produces many more ionizations than the swift electron. For example, per micron of path in water, a 440-kv electron would cause about two ionizations, but a proton of the same energy would cause about 2000 ionizations. The effec-

* The symbol $\longrightarrow$ indicates a reaction caused by high energy radiation.

FIG. 21.10 Electrical Discharge in Irradiated Glass. A piece of lead-cerium silicate glass (2.5 × 2.5 × 1.0 cm) was irradiated with 10 microamp of electrons from a 1.5 mev van de Graaf accelerator. The beam was normal to the plane of the paper and the electrons penetrated to a depth of about 1 mm. The discharge occurred at this depth and parallel to the surface of the glass when the top edge was struck with a sharp point. [P. S. Rudolph, Chemistry Division, Oak Ridge National Laboratory, Oak Ridge, Tennessee].

tiveness in causing ionization simply depends on the length of time that the moving particle remains in the immediate neighborhood of the molecule.

The primary effects of fast neutrons differ somewhat from those of the charged particles, since a neutron can penetrate the electron cloud around an atomic nucleus without electrostatic repulsion. A neutron can thus literally knock the nucleus out of an atom, and usually the nucleus is knocked out so vigorously that some of the electrons are left behind and ionization results. The ejected nuclei may produce further secondary displacements and ionizations. Energetic ions can also knock out nuclei in this way, but they are much less effective than neutrons. For example, in aluminum, a 2-mev neutron will produce about 6000 primary displacements, but a 20-mev proton will produce only about 80. Available sources of radiation are intense enough to produce extensive displacements in solids. For example, in a layer 1 mm deep exposed to a cyclotron beam of 20 mev protons, about 10 per cent of the nuclei would be displaced after an irradiation of 1 coulomb per cm^2. A solid in which the atoms have been displaced in this way is said to be *discomposed*. The phenomenon of *discomposition* was first described by E. Wigner during the development of nuclear reactors.

When insulating solids are irradiated with charged particles, they may trap a large number of charges and hence build up a high electric potential. Fig. (21.10) shows the result of such an experiment. A piece of glass was irradiated with electrons, which accumulated in and near a layer below the surface. When the edge of the glass was struck with a sharp metal point, an electrical discharge occurred which was photographed by its own light. Many research problems remain to be solved in connection with the mechanisms of such electrical discharges and their physicochemical effects.

13. TRACK EFFECTS

In photochemical reactions each quantum activates one molecule, so that the activated molecules are quite uniformly distributed throughout the reaction volume. In a reaction caused by ionizing radiation, however, the path of each particle creates a track of ionized and activated molecules. The nature of the track depends on the kind of particle. For example, a 1-mev electron ionizes about one molecule in every 5000 along its track, whereas a 1-mev α particle ionizes every molecule it traverses. From these primary ionization tracks there often extend *spurs*, caused by ionization due to secondary electrons. An average spur would contain three ions and five excited molecules. The active species at once begin to diffuse outward from the track. These diffusional processes

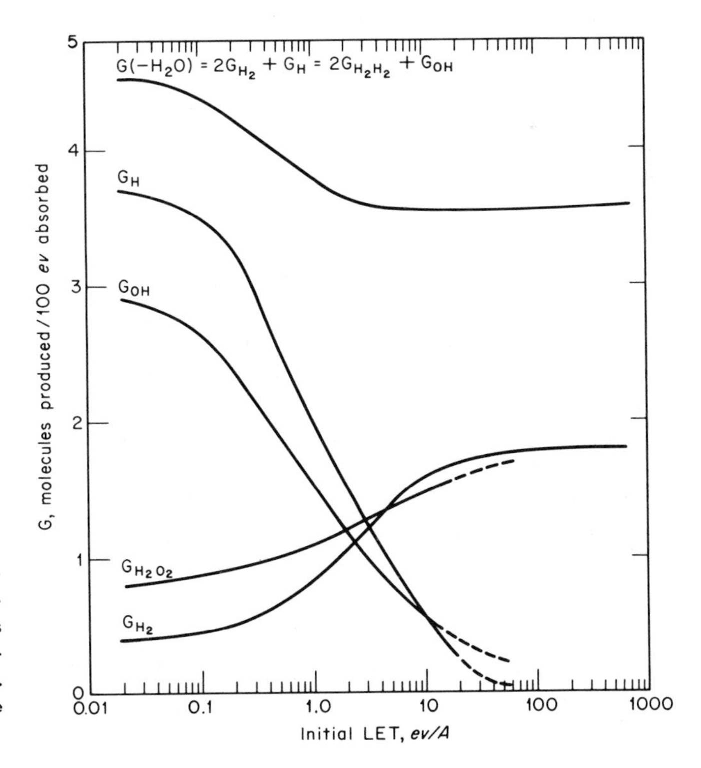

FIG. 21.11 Yields of the secondary products in the decomposition of water by various ionizing radiations as functions of linear energy transfer. [C. J. Hochanadel, Oak Ridge National Laboratory].

may be important in determining the yield of a given product in the wake of the ionizing particle.

The loss in energy, $-dE/dx$, as the energetic particle traverses a distance dx in the medium, is called the *linear energy transfer* (L.E.T.). Some typical results for protons passing through water are shown in Fig. 21.11. According to the *Bragg rule*, the stopping powers of atoms in a molecule are additive and independent of the state of aggregation. Deviations from this rule become appreciable at lower energies. The *Bethe formula* for the stopping power or L.E.T. is

$$-dE/dx = \frac{4\pi z^2 e^4}{mv^2} NZ \ln \frac{2mv^2}{I} \tag{21.7}$$

Here ze and v are the charge and speed of the incident particle, m is the mass of the electron, N is molecules per cm^3, Z is the number of electrons per molecule, and I is an average ionization potential.

14. SECONDARY PROCESSES IN RADIATION CHEMISTRY

As radiation passes through a reaction medium, several excited molecules are formed for each ion formed. The excited molecules are even more important than this fact would indicate, however, since one of the most probable secondary reactions of an ion is its neutralization to yield an excited molecule.* A schematic reaction sequence is as follows.

$$A \longrightarrow A^\star$$

$$A \longrightarrow A^+ + e$$

$$A^+ + e \longrightarrow A^\star$$

$$A^\star \longrightarrow \text{break into radicals}$$

$$A^\star \longrightarrow \text{rearrangement to molecules}$$

It should be noted that any one of these steps may involve reactions more complicated than the simple ones written. For example, the ionization step may occur with a rupture of bonds, as $A \longrightarrow A^\star \rightarrow B^+ + C + e$. The large number of excited molecules formed in irradiated systems explains the parallelism frequently observed between photochemical and radiochemical reactions.

Examples of many typical reactions are provided by the results observed on irradiation of water. Aqueous systems have been most intensively studied because of their great importance in radiobiology. In pure water, the first steps, regardless of the source of radiation, appear to be

$$H_2O \longrightarrow H_2O^+ + e$$

$$H_2O^+ + H_2O \longrightarrow H_3O^+ + OH$$

The fate of the OH radicals seems to depend on the type of radiation. With

* H. Eyring, J. Hirschfelder, and H. S. Taylor, *J. Chem. Phys.* *4*, 479, 570 (1936).

slow moving particles (α's) many OH radicals may be produced close together, and a likely subsequent step is radical combination,

$$2\,OH \longrightarrow H_2O_2$$

With fast particles (β, γ) the OH radical concentration along the paths is much lower, and removal of radicals by the following sequence appears reasonable:

$$e + H_2O \longrightarrow OH + H + e'$$
$$H + H \longrightarrow H_2$$
$$H + OH \longrightarrow H_2O$$

The dependence of intermediate concentrations on the path of radiation through the system, and the diffusion of intermediates away from the tracks of the radiation particles are typical features of this field of chemical kinetics.*

15. DOSIMETRY IN AQUEOUS SOLUTIONS

When water is decomposed by ionizing radiation, we need to distinguish a variety of reactions, all taking place soon after the initial ionization and excitation. We may summarize these as:

$$H_2O \longrightarrow H + OH,\ H_2,\ H_2O_2,\ HO_2$$

We should like to know the G values for each of these reactions separately. Much useful data can be obtained if we irradiate not pure water, but a solution of $FeSO_4$ in 0.8 N H_2SO_4, first proposed by Fricke as a chemical dosimeter for radiations.

If air is present, the reactions are

$$H + O_2 \longrightarrow HO_2$$
$$HO_2 + Fe^{2+} \longrightarrow HO_2^- + Fe^{3+}$$
$$H_2O_2 + Fe^{2+} \longrightarrow OH + OH^- + Fe^{3+}$$
$$OH + Fe^{2+} \longrightarrow OH^- + Fe^{3+}$$

Thus all the reactive products are consumed. We can say that the G for oxidation of Fe^{2+} to Fe^{3+} is fixed by the G's for formation of active products.

$$G(Fe^{2+} \rightarrow Fe^{3+}) = 3G(H) + 2G(H_2O_2) + G(OH)$$

For ^{60}Co-γ radiation (1.17,1.33 mev) this sum of G's = 15.6. In a deäerated system, we have

$$H + H^+ + Fe^{2+} \longrightarrow H_2 + Fe^{3+}$$

so that

$$G'(Fe^{2+} \rightarrow Fe^{3+}) = G(H) + 2G(H_2O_2) + G(OH)$$

For ^{60}Co- γ, $G' = 8.2$. Hence, $G(H) = 3.7$.

---

* A good discussion is given by Aron Kuppermann, *Action chimique et biologique des Radiations*, (ed. M. Haissinsky), Vol. 5 (Paris: Masson, 1960).

We can get further information by measuring the G value of the *ceric dosimeter*. The reactions are:

$$H + Ce^{4+} \longrightarrow H^+ + Ce^{3+}$$
$$HO_2 + Ce^{4+} \longrightarrow H^+ + O_2 + Ce^{3+}$$
$$H_2O_2 + 2\,Ce^{4+} \longrightarrow 2\,H^+ + O_2 + 2\,Ce^{3+}$$
$$OH + Ce^{3+} \longrightarrow OH^- + Ce^{4+}$$

Thus $G''(Ce^{4+} \rightarrow Ce^{3+}) = G(H) + 2G(H_2O_2) - G(OH)$.

It is found for ^{60}Co-γ that $G'' = 2.4$. Thus, from the Fricke dosimeter results,

$$G(OH) = 2.9$$

Different kinds of radiation produce different yields of products, determined mainly by differences in the L.E.T. Radiations for which the L.E.T. is low will produce ions and spurs at relatively large separations, so that diffusional effects will become more important. Fig. 21.11 shows how the yields of various products from water depend on the L.E.T. for the radiation used.

16. CHEMICAL EFFECTS OF NUCLEAR RECOIL

When a nucleus emits an α, β, or γ particle, conservation of momentum requires that the product nucleus recoil in a direction opposite to that of the emitted particle. An important effect of such recoil was discovered by Szilard and Chalmers in 1934. They irradiated ethyl iodide ($C_2H_5{}^{127}I$) with neutrons: $^{127}I\ (n, \gamma)^{128}I$. The ^{128}I is a β emitter of 25 min half life. The ethyl iodide, after irradiation, was shaken with a dilute aqueous solution of ordinary iodine, in which it is not appreciably soluble; much of the radioactive ^{128}I was then found in the aqueous layer. Exchange between iodine in ethyl iodide and that in aqueous solution is known to be very slow. It appears, therefore, that the recoil of the iodine nucleus on emission of the γ particle is sufficiently energetic to break the C—I bond in C_2H_5I, thereby converting the iodine into a water-soluble form.

The Szilard-Chalmers effect has since been observed in many n, γ reactions. Besides its intrinsic interest as a new kind of chemical reaction, the effect has practical value in that it provides a method of preparing highly concentrated radioactive elements.

PROBLEMS

1. What is the energy in kcal/mole of one einstein of 2537 Å light, a wavelength much used in photobiological work?

2. When propionaldehyde is irradiated at 200 torr and 30°C with light of wavelength 3020 Å, the quantum yield for CO production is found to be 0.54.

If the incident light intensity is 15 000 erg per sec, calculate the rate of CO formation. What is the light intensity in einsteins per sec? [*Ans.* 2.04 $\times$ 10^{-9} mole sec^{-1}; 3.78 $\times$ 10^{-9}]

3. In a study of the quenching of sodium resonance radiation at 200°C, it is found that 1.6 torr of N_2 reduces the fluorescence intensity to 50 per cent of the value in the absence of added gas. If the natural lifetime of the excited Na atom is 10^{-7} sec, calculate the quenching cross section for N_2. [*Ans.* 8.64 sq. Å.]

4. A photographic film is exposed for 10^{-3} sec to a 100-watt incandescent light at a distance of 10 meters. If 5 per cent of the power is emitted as visible light to which the film is sensitive, estimate the number of silver atoms that will be produced in a AgBr grain 10 microns in diameter. [*Ans.* 3800, if effective wavelength is taken to be 6000 Å]

---

5. When uridine-2′-phosphate is irradiated with 2537 Å, there is a first order reaction with a quantum yield of 0.0216 mole/einstein, as HOH is added to a double bond. The reaction is reversible in the dark and the reverse reaction is also first order. A solution initially 0.02 molar in the parent compound is irradiated at one einstein/hour, until a steady-state concentration of 0.018 molar of product is reached. What is the rate constant of the reverse reaction?

6. The quantum yield for inactivation of the T1 phage at 2600 Å is 3 $\times$ 10^{-4}. If the molecular weight of this species is 10^7, estimate the target cross section of the segment of the phage at which absorption of a quantum has a lethal effect.

7. The kinetics of recombination of bromine atoms was measured following flash photolysis of gaseous Br_2. [*J. Chem. Phys.* *26*, 1287 (1957)] For Br atoms in argon, the rate followed the equation $d[Br_2]/dt = k_3[Br]^2[Ar]$. The values of k_3 were: 27°C, 3.7 $\pm$ 0.2; 60°C, 2.7 $\pm$ .1; 75°C, 2.3 $\pm$ 0.2. Estimate the activation energy for this reaction and discuss possible interpretations of the value obtained.
   In a typical run at 25°C, the reaction cell was filled to a concentration of 2.37 $\times$ 10^{-4} mole/l Br_2 and 3.84 $\times$ 10^{-2} mole/l argon. The cells were cylindrical, 10 cm long and 25 mm I.D. with flat parallel faces of pyrex glass. If the Br_2 was 80 per cent dissociated by the flash, what would be the half life of the recombination reaction in this experiment?

8. Garvin [*J. Chem. Phys.* *32*, 880 (1960)] has studied the emission spectrum of the flame produced by the reaction of ozone and atomic hydrogen. He finds that a major portion of the emission is due to OH radicals in excited vibrational states of the electronic ground state. Emission is observed from all vibrational levels up to and including $v = 9$. A significant change in the intensity pattern occurs between $v = 4$ and $v = 5$, emission from the $v = 4$ level being more intense. Explain the nature and energetics of the flame

process. $\Delta H_f = 0.00$ (O_2); $+31.5$ (O_3); $+58.6$ (O); $+3.5$ (OH); $+51.6$ (H). The following electronic excited states exist: OH $^3\Pi i$, 32 682 cm^{-1}; O_2, $^1\Sigma_g^+$ 13 195 cm^{-1}. The vibrational constants for the OH ground state are $\omega_e = 3739$ cm^{-1} and $\omega_e x_e = 85.5$ cm^{-1} where the vibrational energy is given by $G = (v + \frac{1}{2})\ \omega_e - (v + \frac{1}{2})^2\ \omega_e x_e$. [*Ans.* $v_9 - v_0 = 28\,860 - 1850 = 27\,010$ cm^{-1}; $v_{10} - v_0 = 29\,900 - 1850 = 28\,150$ cm^{-1}; $\Delta H(O_3 + H \rightarrow O_2 + OH) = 27\,900$ cm^{-1}. The energy of the reaction is sufficient to excite the $v = 9$ vibrational level of the OH but not the $v = 10$ level. $\Delta H - (v_5 - v_0) = 27\,900 - 18\,000 + 1850 = 11\,750$ cm^{-1}; $\Delta H - (v_4 - v_0) = 27\,900 - 15\,070 + 1850 = 13\,780$ cm^{-1}. Encounters which leave OH in the fourth vibrational level also leave O_2 in the excited electronic state. The reaction produces either oxygen in the electronic ground state plus OH in additional states greater than $v = 4$ or oxygen in the $^1\Sigma_g^+$ state and OH in levels $v = 4$ or smaller.]

9. The photochemical chlorination of chloroform ($CHCl_3 + Cl_2 \rightarrow HCl + CCl_4$) follows the rate equation $d[CCl_4]/dt = k' I_a^{1/2}[Cl_2]^{1/2}[CHCl_3]$ where I_a is the intensity of light absorbed. Devise a reaction scheme to explain this kinetics.

10. Show that when a γ ray of energy E_γ in ev, is ejected from a nucleus of mass m atomic weight units, the recoil kinetic energy of the nucleus in ev is $E_a = 5.33 \times 10^{-10} E_\gamma^2/m$. Calculate the recoil energy of ^{65}Zn on emission of a 1.1 mev γ ray.

APPENDIX

PHYSICAL CONSTANTS*

electronic charge	e	4.8029×10^{-10} statcoulomb (esu) 1.6021×10^{-19} coulomb
Planck constant	h	6.6252×10^{-27} ergs
speed of light	c	2.997930×10^{10} cm s^{-1}
electron rest mass	m_e	9.1090×10^{-28} g
proton rest mass	m_p	1.67239×10^{-24} g
neutron rest mass	m_n	1.67470×10^{-24} g
Avogadro number	L	6.0226×10^{23} mole^{-1}
Faraday constant	F	9.6491×10^{4} coulomb mole^{-1}
gas constant	R	8.31432 joule °K^{-1}
Boltzmann constant	k	1.3805×10^{-16} erg °K^{-1}
First Bohr radius	a_0	5.2917×10^{-9} cm
Bohr magneton	μ_B	9.2731×10^{-24} amp m^2 9.2731×10^{-21} erg gauss^{-1}
nuclear magneton	μ_n	5.0504×10^{-27} amp m^2 5.0504×10^{-24} erg gauss^{-1}

* For estimates of errors and references see *Rev. Mod. Phys.* *27*, 363 (1955).

CONVERSION FACTORS AND DEFINED CONSTANTS

1 bar $= 10^6$ dyne cm^{-2}

1 atm $= 1.01325$ bar $= 1.0332 \times 10^4$ kg m^{-2} $= 760$ torr

1 erg $= 10^{-7}$ joule $= 2.3901 \times 10^{-8}$ defined calorie

1 defined calorie $= 4.18400$ joule

1 BTU $= 1055$ joule

1 electron volt $= 1.60209 \times 10^{-12}$ erg $= 23.053$ kcal mole^{-1}

wavelength corresponding to 1 ev $= 1.23980 \times 10^{-4}$ cm

1 kw $= 1.341$ horsepower $= 239$ cal s^{-1} $= 2545$ BTU hr^{-1}

1 coulomb $= \frac{1}{10}$ emu $= (c/10)$ esu

1 weber m^{-2} $= 10^4$ gauss

1 gauss $= c^{-2}$ esu

standard gravitational constant, $g = 980.665$ cm s^{-2}

INDEX OF NAMES

INDEX OF SUBJECTS